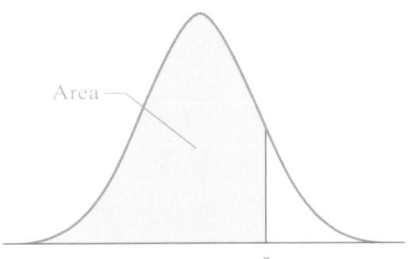

TABLE II (continued)

Standard Normal Distribution

z	.00	.01	.02	.03	.04	.05	.06	.07	.08	.09
0.0	0.5000	0.5040	0.5080	0.5120	0.5160	0.5199	0.5239	0.5279	0.5319	0.5359
0.1	0.5398	0.5438	0.5478	0.5517	0.5557	0.5596	0.5636	0.5675	0.5714	0.5753
0.2	0.5793	0.5832	0.5871	0.5910	0.5948	0.5987	0.6026	0.6064	0.6103	0.6141
0.3	0.6179	0.6217	0.6255	0.6293	0.6331	0.6368	0.6406	0.6443	0.6480	0.6517
0.4	0.6554	0.6591	0.6628	0.6664	0.6700	0.6736	0.6772	0.6808	0.6844	0.6879
0.5	0.6915	0.6950	0.6985	0.7019	0.7054	0.7088	0.7123	0.7157	0.7190	0.7224
0.6	0.7257	0.7291	0.7324	0.7357	0.7389	0.7422	0.7454	0.7486	0.7517	0.7549
0.7	0.7580	0.7611	0.7642	0.7673	0.7704	0.7734	0.7764	0.7794	0.7823	0.7852
0.8	0.7881	0.7910	0.7939	0.7967	0.7995	0.8023	0.8051	0.8078	0.8106	0.8133
0.9	0.8159	0.8186	0.8212	0.8238	0.8264	0.8289	0.8315	0.8340	0.8365	0.8389
1.0	0.8413	0.8438	0.8461	0.8485	0.8508	0.8531	0.8554	0.8577	0.8599	0.8621
1.1	0.8643	0.8665	0.8686	0.8708	0.8729	0.8749	0.8770	0.8790	0.8810	0.8830
1.2	0.8849	0.8869	0.8888	0.8907	0.8925	0.8944	0.8962	0.8980	0.8997	0.9015
1.3	0.9032	0.9049	0.9066	0.9082	0.9099	0.9115	0.9131	0.9147	0.9162	0.9177
1.4	0.9192	0.9207	0.9222	0.9236	0.9251	0.9265	0.9279	0.9292	0.9306	0.9319
1.5	0.9332	0.9345	0.9357	0.9370	0.9382	0.9394	0.9406	0.9418	0.9429	0.9441
1.6	0.9452	0.9463	0.9474	0.9484	0.9495	0.9505	0.9515	0.9525	0.9535	0.9545
1.7	0.9554	0.9564	0.9573	0.9582	0.9591	0.9599	0.9608	0.9616	0.9625	0.9633
1.8	0.9641	0.9649	0.9656	0.9664	0.9671	0.9678	0.9686	0.9693	0.9699	0.9706
1.9	0.9713	0.9719	0.9726	0.9732	0.9738	0.9744	0.9750	0.9756	0.9761	0.9767
2.0	0.9772	0.9778	0.9783	0.9788	0.9793	0.9798	0.9803	0.9808	0.9812	0.9817
2.1	0.9821	0.9826	0.9830	0.9834	0.9838	0.9842	0.9846	0.9850	0.9854	0.9857
2.2	0.9861	0.9864	0.9868	0.9871	0.9875	0.9878	0.9881	0.9884	0.9887	0.9890
2.3	0.9893	0.9896	0.9898	0.9901	0.9904	0.9906	0.9909	0.9911	0.9913	0.9916
2.4	0.9918	0.9920	0.9922	0.9925	0.9927	0.9929	0.9931	0.9932	0.9934	0.9936
2.5	0.9938	0.9940	0.9941	0.9943	0.9945	0.9946	0.9948	0.9949	0.9951	0.9952
2.6	0.9953	0.9955	0.9956	0.9957	0.9959	0.9960	0.9961	0.9962	0.9963	0.9964
2.7	0.9965	0.9966	0.9967	0.9968	0.9969	0.9970	0.9971	0.9972	0.9973	0.9974
2.8	0.9974	0.9975	0.9976	0.9977	0.9977	0.9978	0.9979	0.9979	0.9980	0.9981
2.9	0.9981	0.9982	0.9982	0.9983	0.9984	0.9984	0.9985	0.9985	0.9986	0.9986
3.0	0.9987	0.9987	0.9987	0.9988	0.9988	0.9989	0.9989	0.9989	0.9990	0.9990
3.1	0.9990	0.9991	0.9991	0.9991	0.9992	0.9992	0.9992	0.9992	0.9993	0.9993
3.2	0.9993	0.9993	0.9994	0.9994	0.9994	0.9994	0.9994	0.9995	0.9995	0.9995
3.3	0.9995	0.9995	0.9995	0.9996	0.9996	0.9996	0.9996	0.9996	0.9996	0.9997
3.4	0.9997	0.9997	0.9997	0.9997	0.9997	0.9997	0.9997	0.9997	0.9997	0.9998

Statistics

INFORMED DECISIONS USING DATA

Annotated Instructor's Edition

Statistics

Informed Decisions Using Data

Michael Sullivan, III

Joliet Junior College

Prentice Hall

PEARSON EDUCATION, INC.
Upper Saddle River, New Jersey 07458

Editor in Chief/Acquisitions Editor: Sally Yagan
Assistant Editor: Vince Jansen
Associate Editor: Dawn Murrin
Project Manager: Jacquelyn Riotto
Vice President/Director of Production and Manufacturing:
  David W. Riccardi
Executive Managing Editor: Kathleen Schiaparelli
Senior Managing Editor: Linda Mihatov Behrens
Production Editor: Barbara Mack
Assistant Managing Editor, Math Media Production: John Matthews
Media Production Editor: Donna Crilly
Manufacturing Buyer: Michael Bell
Manufacturing Manager: Trudy Pisciotti
Marketing Manager: Krista M. Bettino
Marketing Assistant: Christine Bayeux
Development Editors: Anne Scanlan-Rohrer and Frank Purcell
Editor in Chief, Development: Carol Trueheart
Editorial Assistant/Print Supplements Editor: Joanne Wendelken
Art Director: Jonathan Boylan
Interior Designers: Judy Matz-Coniglio, Joseph Sengotta, and
  Geoffrey Cassar
Cover Designer: John Christiana
Art Editor: Thomas Benfatti
Creative Director: Carole Anson

Director of Creative Services: Paul Belfanti
Manager of Formatting: Jim Sullivan
Electronic Production Specialist: Joanne Del Ben
Electronic Page Makeup: Joanne Del Ben, Donna Marie Paukovits,
  Jackie Ambrosius
Director, Image Resource Center: Melinda Reo
Manager, Rights and Permissions: Zina Arabia
Interior Image Specialist: Beth Boyd-Brenzel
Cover Image Specialist: Karen Sanatar
Image Permission Coordinator: Michelina Viscusi
Photo Researcher: Melinda Alexander
Cover Photos: (From top to bottom) Antonio Mo/Getty Images,
  Inc.; Yellow Dog Productions/Getty Images, Inc.; Photodisc/
  Getty Images, Inc.; Michael Rosenfeld/Getty Images, Inc.
Art Studio: Artworks
  Senior Manager: Patricia Burns
  Production Manager: Ronda Whitson
  Manager, Production Technologies: Matt Haas
  Project Coordinator: Jessica Einsig
  Illustrators: Jackie Ambrosius, Kathryn Anderson, Christopher
    Kayes, Mark Landis, Bill Neff, Audrey Simonetti, Stacy Smith
  Quality Assurance: Pamela Taylor, Kenneth Mooney,
    Timothy Nguyen

Printed in the United States of America
10 9 8 7 6 5 4 3 2

ISBN 0-13-046489-9
ISBN 0-13-061864-0 (Student Edition)

Pearson Education LTD., London
Pearson Education Australia PTY, Limited, Sydney
Pearson Education Singapore, Pte. Ltd
Pearson Education North Asia Ltd, Hong Kong
Pearson Education Canada, Ltd., Toronto
Pearson Educación de Mexico, S.A. de C.V.
Pearson Education—Japan, Tokyo
Pearson Education Malaysia, Pte. Ltd

To My Wife
Yolanda

and

My Children
Michael, Kevin, and Marissa

CONTENTS

Chapter 1

Chapter 2

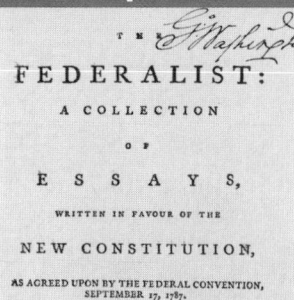

Chapter 3

vii

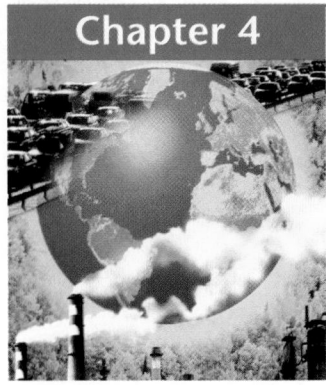

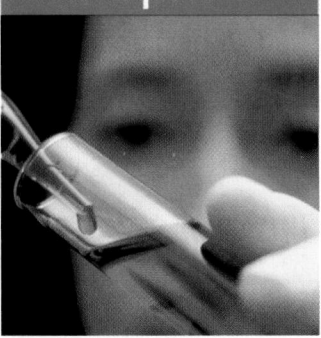

Chapter 8	

Confidence Intervals about a Single Parameter 454

Chapter 9	

Hypothesis Testing 516

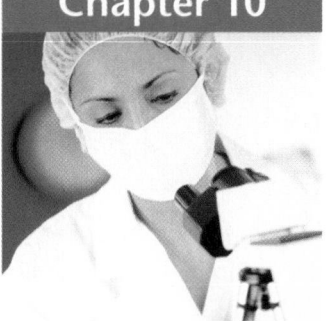

Chapter 10	

Inferences on Two Samples 592

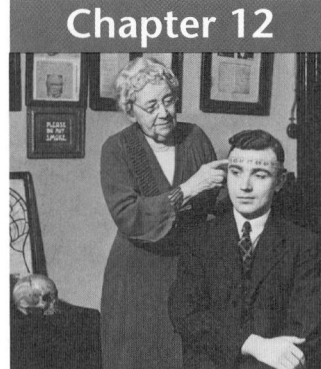

Having taught introductory statistics for the past 10 years at both 2-year and 4-year institutions has brought to my attention some basic needs and issues of the Introductory Statistics course. The diversity of both the students taking the course and the instructors teaching the course drives many of the challenges in presenting statistics at this level. Statistics is a powerful subject and one that I hold great passion for. It is the coupling of my passion for the subject with the desire for a text that would work for me, my students, and my school that led me to decide to pursue writing this textbook.

Before getting started on this text, I spent many hours reflecting on the goals of the project. Overall, I wanted a textbook that instilled in students my enthusiasm and appreciation for the subject and supported the variety of approaches to teaching the subject. In particular, the following were my goals for the text:

- Students see and appreciate the usefulness of the subject
- Students can be more successful in the course
- Students are provided ample practice
- Instructors can present the material using multiple philosophies

Keeping the Students' Interest

An immediate challenge for any instructor teaching this course is the motivation of the students. I always ask my students to pass in their class notes at the end of the semester. By studying these notes, I have been able to determine areas where my students lost interest and where they became excited about the subject. In addition, I was able to determine topics where the concept was lost and topics where the concept was completely understood. I also noticed that my students appreciated when I took a formal definition or theorem and expressed it in everyday language that they could understand. This view into how students read texts, attend lectures, and take notes was invaluable to me in writing this text.

Today's students demand that the material they study have relevance in their everyday lives. One of the joys of teaching a statistics course is that the question, "When will I ever use this stuff?" rarely comes up. However, students still say, "Okay, I can see the usefulness of this if I was a medical researcher, but that is not my goal in life!" Introductory statistics texts need to have interesting, real data sets that students can relate to. They need to see themselves analyzing the data and using the conclusions to make informed decisions that impact their lives. For example, what type of car should I buy? Where should I invest my retirement money? Where should I live? What major should I choose?

Student Success

It is absolutely true that if students experience success early in a course, they will be inclined to work harder as the course progresses. However, if students struggle early, it will lead to disenchanted students who are more willing to "give up" when a difficult concept is introduced.

How can success be experienced while still maintaining the integrity of the course? After all, statistics is a discipline whose theory is deep and mathematically intensive. In addition, understanding the concepts of statistics can be elusive. This does not mean, however, that an introductory textbook should "spare students details" of statistical thought. It is possible, and indeed, desirable, to expose students to the intricacies of statistics. This can be done without delving deep into mathematical thought and losing most of your students.

The text has been written using a conversational tone that "speaks" to the student. This is accomplished through explanations that don't overly complicate the material. Because the text was written using the class notes obtained from my students, the presentation flows like a lecture. The pedagogy that is found in the text mirrors the presentation that I use in my lectures. When my lecture begins, I tie concepts learned earlier in the course to concepts that I am about to present. This is the "Putting It All Together" feature found at the beginning of each chapter. Before tackling a new section, I review topics that are going to be needed in order to succeed in the section. This is the "Preparing for This Section" feature. I then list the objectives that we are going to cover within the section. As I present the material, I provide students with statistically accurate definitions/theorems. I then restate the definitions/theorems using everyday language that doesn't compromise the definition or theorem. This is the "In Your Own Words" feature. I also mention some of the pitfalls in statistical analysis. These pitfalls are displayed in the "Caution" feature. After going over an example in class, I like to have my students attempt to solve a similar problem in class so that I am confident that they understand the concept before continuing. This is the "Now Work Problem xx" feature.

In addition, the text has been written to appeal to a variety of learning styles. There are many, many graphs and figures that allow students to visualize results. For students who learn best through discovery, there are Explorations that guide students through a series of questions that develop statistical concepts. For auditory learners there is a lecture series in which I present all the examples in the text on compact disk or video.

Practice, Practice, Practice

The only way that students will learn statistics is by doing statistics. The exercise sets of a strong statistics text will help develop a student's confidence in, and understanding of, the material. This is accomplished in a twofold manner: (1) through graduated exercise sets, and (2) through problems that ask the student to think about concepts and encourage statistical thinking.

All the exercise sets begin with Concepts and Vocabulary, which are open-ended questions that ask students to define words and explain concepts using their own words. The next portion of the exercise sets is Skill Building. These are drill and practice type problems that develop computational skills that increase student understanding of formulas and concepts. These problems also serve as confidence building problems so that students experience early success. Finally, the Applying the Concepts problems are real data-based problems that ask a variety of questions that help develop solid statistical analysis. Not only do these problems ask the standard questions such as find the mean or compute a 95% confidence interval, they also ask for students to explain the results. In addition, there are questions that ask students to consider some additional questions. For example, what is the impact of an outlier on the arithmetic mean? Is the linear correlation coefficient resistant? What happens if we have outliers when constructing confidence intervals from small data sets? How do I know that the relation between two variables really is linear? These "higher level of thinking" problems truly develop a student's understanding of statistical thinking.

Flexibility

Just as there are many different learning styles, there are many different teaching styles. One of the challenges in writing a text is to create a product that "appeals to the masses." As I survey the halls of the Mathematics Department at Joliet Junior College, I see many high-quality instructors who present the same material in many different ways. Some like to incorporate as much technology as possible into their classroom, some prefer to minimize the technology. Some instructors prefer to use collaborative learning in order to present material, while others utilize lecture. For the Introductory Statistics course, some of the instructors are trained in the discipline of statistics, while others are trained in mathematics, but teach statistics. With these varied backgrounds, it is clear that a text needs to meet the needs of all these backgrounds and teaching philosophies.

Let's consider how technology is presented in the course. Every example in the text is presented using the "by hand" approach. The reason for this is twofold. First, and probably most importantly, by presenting a solution by hand, the student's ability to understand the concept is enhanced. How else can a student understand the concept of linear correlation, except by seeing the product of z-scores? Second, it allows for flexibility in philosophies. If your particular philosophy is to present statistics by utilizing "by hand" solutions, it is there for you. If you are more apt to use technology, then you can utilize the "Using Technology" feature. Following virtually every example is a gray "Using Technology" screen, which provides the output from a TI83+, Minitab, or Excel. In addition, problems that have 15 or more observations in the data set have a CD icon, which indicates to the instructor that the data set is available on the data CD.

Using the Text Efficiently with Your Syllabus

To meet the varied needs of diverse syllabi, this book has been organized with flexibility of use in mind. When structuring your syllabus, notice the topics listed in the "Preparing for This Section" material at the beginning of the section, which will tip you off to dependencies within the course.

The two most common variations within an Introductory Statistics course are the treatment of Regression Analysis and the treatment of Probability.

- **Coverage of Correlation and Regression** The text was written with the descriptive portion of bivariate data (Chapter 4) presented after the descriptive portion of univariate data (Chapter 3). For instructors who prefer to postpone the discussion of bivariate data until later in the course, simply skip Chapter 4 and return to it prior to covering Sections 12.1 and 12.2. Within Chapter 4, an instructor may skip Sections 4.3 and/or 4.4 without loss of continuity.

- **Coverage of Probability** The text allows for a course to present an extensive introduction to probability or light coverage of probability. For instructors wishing to present light coverage of probability, they may cover Section 5.1 and skip the remaining sections. A word of caution is in order, however. Instructors who will be covering the Chi-Square Test for Independence will want to cover Sections 5.1 through 5.3. In addition, any instructor who will be covering Binomial Probabilities will want to cover Independence in Section 5.3 and Combinations in Section 5.5.

Chapter by Chapter Content

Chapter 1 Data Collection

This chapter deals with the methods of obtaining data. There is a detailed presentation of the various sampling techniques along with circumstances under which each is used. In addition, there is an entire section dedicated to nonsampling errors and how to control them. The chapter ends with a detailed discussion of experimental design.

Chapter 2 Organizing and Summarizing Data

This chapter addresses methods for summarizing qualitative data (Section 2.1) and quantitative data (Sections 2.2 and 2.3). For instructors who do not wish to cover topics such as frequency polygons and ogives, Section 2.3 can be skipped without loss of continuity. The chapter ends with a discussion of graphical misrepresentations of data. This section can be covered as a reading assignment.

Chapter 3 Numerically Summarizing Data

Sections 3.1 and 3.2 present numerical measures of central tendency and dispersion. Section 3.3 is optional and can be skipped without loss of continuity. However, if it is skipped and Section 6.1 is covered, proceed slowly through the mean and standard deviation of a discrete random variable. Section 3.4 discusses measures of position including the z-score, percentiles, and outliers. Section 3.5 presents exploratory data analysis.

Chapter 4 Describing the Relation between Two Variables

Section 4.1 introduces scatter diagrams and correlation. Section 4.2 presents the least-squares regression line. Section 4.3 presents the coefficient of determination, residual analysis, and influential observations. This section is particularly important because it allows students to graphically assess whether the data they are analyzing are, in fact, linearly related. Section 4.4 presents methods for using least-squares to fit data to exponential and power models. It is optional and can be skipped without loss of continuity. In addition, the material in this chapter can be postponed until after Chapter 11.

Chapter 5 Probability

Section 5.1 introduces the basic concepts of probability and unusual events. Section 5.2 presents the Addition Rule. Section 5.3 presents the Multiplication Rule. Section 5.4 presents Conditional Probability and can be skipped without loss of continuity. Section 5.5 presents Counting Techniques and can be skipped without loss of continuity with the exception of Combinations.

Chapter 6 Discrete Probability Distributions

The entire chapter is optional. Section 6.1 introduces the concept of a random variable and discrete probability distributions along with expected value. Section 6.2 presents the binomial probability formula and an introduction to inference using binomial probabilities. If you intend to cover Section 6.2, then it is a good idea to also cover Section 5.3. Section 6.3 presents the Poisson probability distribution.

Chapter 7 The Normal Probability Distribution

Sections 7.1 through 7.3 introduce the normal probability distribution. Section 7.4 presents normal probability plots as a means for assessing normality and is required in order to cover topics presented in Chapters 8–13. Section 7.4 does not require the use of technology because the output generated by technology is presented. This section is necessary in order to help students see that verifying normality is necessary before proceeding with inference for small samples. Section 7.5 introduces sampling distributions. Section 7.6 discusses the normal approximation to the binomial and is optional.

Chapter 8 Confidence Intervals about a Single Parameter

Section 8.1 introduces the construction of a confidence interval when the population standard deviation is known, while Section 8.2 constructs confidence intervals when the population standard deviation is unknown. This approach is different from that in some other texts, but it is logical. It's as simple as "σ known, use z; σ unknown, use t." In both cases, small samples require that the population from which the sample was drawn must be normal–we check this requirement with a normal probability plot. Section 8.3 covers confidence intervals about a population proportion, while Section 8.4 covers confidence intervals about a population standard deviation. Section 8.4 is optional and can be skipped without loss of continuity.

Chapter 9 Hypothesis Testing

Section 9.1 provides an introduction to the language of hypothesis testing. Sections 9.2 and 9.3 test hypotheses regarding a population mean, again segmented by "σ known, use z; σ unknown, use t." Section 9.4 presents hypothesis testing about a population proportion. An interesting feature in this section is that it includes how to use the binomial probability distribution to compute exact P-values. This is especially important if the requirement for using the normal approximation to the binomial is not satisfied. Section 9.5 discusses hypothesis testing about a population standard deviation, while Section 9.6 discusses the power of the test and probability of Type II errors. Both Sections 9.5 and 9.6 are optional.

Chapter 10 Inferences on Two Samples

Section 10.1 presents the analysis required for matched-pairs design. Section 10.2 presents the analysis for comparing two means from independent samples. Notice that the discussion regarding pooled estimates of σ is absent. This is because the pooled estimate approach requires that the two populations have a common variance and this is an extremely difficult requirement to test. Because "pooling" versus "not pooling" often provide the same results, it is not necessary at this level to cloud the students' thought process any further. Section 10.3 discusses comparing two population proportions. Section 10.4 presents the comparison of two variances and is optional.

Chapter 11 Chi-Square Procedures

Section 11.1 presents the chi-square goodness of fit. It presents a discussion of the chi-square distribution for those who skipped Sections 8.4 and 9.5. If you did skip these sections, be sure to introduce students to the chi-square table. Section 11.2 presents contingency tables, marginal distributions, and conditional distributions. If you skipped Section 5.4, you may want to proceed at a slower pace. Section 11.3 discusses chi-square tests for independence and homogeneity. Again, if Sections 5.3 and/or 5.4 were skipped, proceed slowly.

Chapter 12 Inference on the Least-Squares Regression Model; ANOVA

Sections 12.1 and 12.2 are independent of Section 12.3. Sections 12.1 and 12.2 require that Sections 4.1 and 4.2 were covered. Section 12.3 is simply a continuation of the discussion in Section 10.2.

Chapter 13 Nonparametric Statistics

Section 13.2 is on the runs test for randomness and can be covered any time after Section 9.1. Section 13.3 can be presented right after Section 9.3. Section 13.4 can be covered after Section 10.1. Section 13.5 can be covered after Section 10.2. Section 13.6 can be covered after Section 12.2. Section 13.7 can be covered after Section 12.3.

Acknowledgments

Textbooks evolve into their final form through the efforts and contributions of many people. First and foremost, I would like to thank my family, whose dedication to this project was just as much as mine: my wife, Yolanda, whose words of encouragement and support were unabashed, and my children, Michael, Kevin, and Marissa, who would come and greet me every morning with smiles that only children can deliver. I owe each of them my sincerest gratitude.

I would also like to thank the entire Mathematics Department at Joliet Junior College, who provided support, ideas, and encouragement to help me complete this project.

Countless ideas were bounced off of each of them and their responses are present throughout the text. Special thanks also go to the Joliet Junior College community, who also supported this project.

I sincerely appreciate the comments and suggestions of Erica Egizio, who had the courage to use the text in its nascent stages. Her comments and suggestions have proven to be invaluable. Erica is also to be commended for her "Note to the Instructor" annotations. Special thanks to Michael McCraith, who helped locate interesting data and also made the PowerPoint presentations friendly for both PCs and Macs. Thank you to Faye Dang and Priscilla Gathoni for checking all the answers. Thank you to Elena Catoiu, Kathleen Miranda, and Gigi Williams for proofreading the text to help ensure its accuracy. Thanks to Lindsay Packer, who took on the daunting task of writing the solutions manuals; and to Beverly J. Dretzke, Kate McLaughlin, and Dorothy Wakefield, who wrote the technology guides; and David Lane, who wrote the applets workbook. I would also like to thank Max Linn, who wrote the Case Studies at the end of each chapter. A big thank you to the development editors: Frank Purcell of Twin Prime Editorial and Anne Scanlan-Rohrer. I would also like to thank my father, who has taught me the ropes. It is always nice to learn from the best.

There are many colleagues I would like to thank for their input. I owe each of them my sincerest thanks. I apologize for any omissions.

Fusan Akman, *Coastal Carolina Community College*

Grant Alexander, *Joliet Junior College*

Randall Allbritton, *Daytona Beach Community College*

Anthony Aquirre, Consumers Union, *Manager, Customer Relations*

Margaret M. Balachowski, *Michigan Technological University*

Charles Biles, *Humboldt College*

Joanne Brunner, *Joliet Junior College*

Jim Butterbach, *Joliet Junior College*

Roxanne Byrne, *University of Colorado–Denver*

Elena Catoiu, *Joliet Junior College*

Pinyuen Chen, *Syracuse University*

Faye Dang, *Joliet Junior College*

Erica Egizio, *Joliet Junior College*

Richard Einsporn, *The University of Akron*

Franco Fedele, *University of West Florida*

Joe Gallegos, *Salt Lake City Community College*

Frieda Ganter, *California State University–Fresno*

Richard Handel, *Consumers Union, Assistant Project Leader*

Kim Jones, *Virginia Commonwealth University*

Maryann E. Justinger, *Erie Community College–South Campus*

Iraj Kalantari, *Western Illinois University*

Donna Katula, *Joliet Junior College*

Mohammad Kazemi, *University of North Carolina–Charlotte*

Edward Kippel, Consumers Union, Program Leader

Melody Lee, *Joliet Junior College*

Mike Mays, *West Virginia University*

Jean McArthur, *Joliet Junior College*

Marilyn McCollum, *North Carolina State University*

Michael McCraith, *Joliet Junior College*

Jill McGowan, *Howard University*

Judy Meckley, *Joliet Junior College*

Kathleen Miranda, *SUNY at Old Westbury*

Lindsay Packer, *College of Charleston*

Linda Padilla, *Joliet Junior College*

Ingrid Peterson, *University of Kansas*

Nancy Pevey, *Pellissippi State Technical Community College*

Philip Pina, *Florida Atlantic University*

David Ray, *University of Tennessee–Martin*

Martin E. Romm, *Consumers Union, Senior Statistician*

Eric Rosenberg, *Consumers Union, Statistician*

Mike Rosenthal, *Florida International University*

Michael S. Saccucci, *Consumers Union, Director of Statistics & Quality Management*

Robert Sackett, *Erie Community College–North Campus*

Karen Spike, *University of North Carolina–Wilmington*

Timothy D. Stebbins, *Kalamazoo Valley Community College*

Patrick Stevens, *Joliet Junior College*

Keith Newsom–Stewart, Consumers Union, Senior Statistician

Sharon Stokero, *Michigan Technological University*

Cathleen M. Zucco Teveloff, *Trinity College*

Kirk Trigsted, *University of Idaho*

Robert Tuskey, *Joliet Junior College*

Farroll Tim Wright, *University of Missouri–Columbia*

Recognition and thanks are due particularly to the following individuals for their valuable assistance in the preparation of this text: Sally Yagan for her support, interest, and friendship; Patrice Jones for his sage advice and marketing skills; Krista M. Bettino for her innovative marketing efforts; Barbara Mack for her organizational skills as a production supervisor; and the entire Prentice Hall sales staff for their confidence.

Michael Sullivan, III

As you begin your study of statistics, you may feel overwhelmed with the number of theorems, definitions, and formulas that confront you. Many students enter their first statistics course with a sense of anxiety. While these feelings are normal, I want to reassure you that statistics is an exciting discipline that can be learned, appreciated, and most importantly, applied, so that you can make informed decisions throughout your life.

My goal in writing this text was to provide students with a "how to" manual for studying and learning statistics. I have written the textbook using clear, uncomplicated language. In fact, the first draft of the text was written using my students' class notes. There are many learning aids included in the text to help make your study of the material easier and more rewarding. In addition, there are many supplements that accompany the text, including: a student solutions manual that presents completely worked out solutions to all the odd-numbered exercises; a CD lecture series that presents worked out solutions to all the examples in the text; and tutorial software (SullivanTutor) that will generate and grade as many problems as you like along with hints and worked out solutions. The questions are based on the objectives presented in the text. The goal is to minimize the number of frustrating experiences that inevitably come up in the learning process.

To help make your study of statistics more enjoyable and rewarding, I have included a list of time-tested "study tips" that promote successful learning. This list is a sequence of events that should occur prior to, during, and after each class meeting. While this list may seem overwhelming, personal experience indicates that it works.

Before Class Begins

1. Read the section(s) to be covered in the upcoming class meeting.
2. Prepare a list of questions that you have based upon your reading. In many cases, your questions will be answered through the lecture. Those that are not answered completely can then be asked.

During Class

1. Arrive early enough to prepare your mind and material for the lecture.
2. Stay alert. Do not doze off or daydream during class. It will be very difficult to understand the lecture when you "return to the class."
3. Take thorough notes. It is normal that certain topics will not be completely understood during the lecture. However, this does not mean that you throw your hands up in despair. Rather, continue to write your class notes. You can ask questions when appropriate. In my personal experience, I was amazed how often my confusion during class was alleviated after studying the in-class notes later when I had more time for reflection.

After Class

1. Reread (and possibly rewrite) your class notes.
2. Reread the section.
3. Do your homework. Homework is not optional. There is an old Chinese proverb that says:

> I hear ... and I forget
> I see ... and I remember
> I do ... and I understand

This proverb applies to anything where one wants to succeed. Would a pianist expect to be the best if she didn't practice? The only way you are going to learn statistics is by doing statistics. When you get problems wrong, ask for help.

4. If you have questions, visit your professor during office hours.

Just like your previous mathematics courses, statistics is a building process. This means the material is used throughout the course. If a topic is not understood, then this lack of understanding could come back to haunt you later in the class. This is the source of a lot of frustration in learning statistics or mathematics. You need to build a strong foundation before you continue to build the house.

How to Use This Book Effectively and Efficiently

First, and foremost, this text was written to be read. You will find that the text has additional explanations and examples that will help you. As mentioned previously, be sure to read the text before attending class.

Many sections begin with "Preparing for This Section," a list of concepts that will be used in the section. Take the short amount of time required to refresh your memory. This will make the section easier to understand and will actually save you time and effort. Each section that has the "Preparing for This Section" feature will have a "Preparing for This Section" quiz on the companion Web site (www.prenhall.com/sullivanstats). The quiz asks questions related to the concepts that are listed. Objectives are provided at the beginning of each section. Read them. They will help you recognize the important ideas and skills developed in the section.

After a concept has been introduced and an example given, you will see **NW** *Now Work Problem xx.* Go to the exercises at the end of the section, work the problem cited, and check your answer in the back of the book. If you get it right, you can be confident in continuing on in the section. If you don't get it right, go back over the explanations and examples to see what you might have missed. Then rework the problem. Ask for help if you miss it again.

I have included an "In Your Own Words" feature that explains definitions, theorems, and concepts using everyday language. This is meant to help you understand the concepts presented in the text. There are also "Caution" statements. These are meant to make you aware of common errors that occur in statistics, so that you don't make these mistakes.

The chapter review contains a list of formulas and vocabulary introduced in the chapter. Be sure you understand how to use the formulas and that you know the definitions of the vocabulary. There is also a list of objectives along with review problems that correspond to the objective. If you can't do the problems listed for a particular objective, go back to the page indicated and review the material.

Please do not hesitate to contact me, through Prentice Hall, with any suggestions or comments that would improve the text. I look forward to hearing from you.

Michael Sullivan, III

From left to right, Michael IV, Michael III, Marissa, Yolanda, and Kevin

Utilizing the features found throughout this text will help you learn and study the content for this course. Many of these features were developed by the author's students for students.

Putting It All Together

In Chapter 1, we learned that statistics is a process. The process begins with asking a research question. In order to determine the answer to the question, information (data) must be collected. The information is obtained from a census, existing data sources, surveys or designed experiments. When data are collected from a survey or designed experiment, they must be organized into a manageable form. Data that are not organized are referred to as **raw data**.

Methods for organizing raw data include the creation of tables or graphs, which allow for a quick overview of the information collected. The organization of data is the third step in the statistical process. The procedures used in organizing data into tables and graphs depend upon whether the data are qualitative, discrete, or continuous.

Putting It All Together

Each chapter opens with a discussion of topics that were covered and how they relate to topics that are about to be discussed. This allows students to see the "big picture" of how the topics relate to each other.

Companion Web Site

Many additional free resources for this text can be found at:
www.prenhall.com/sullivanstats

CHAPTER

2

Organizing and Summarizing Data

Outline

 For additional study help, go to
www.prenhall.com/sullivanstats

   Materials include

   • Self-Graded Quizzes
   • "Preparing for This Section" Quizzes
   • STATLETs
   • PowerPoint Downloads
   • Step-by-Step Technology Guide
   • Graphing Calculator Help

Preparing for This Section

Most sections open with a referenced list (by section and page number) of key items to review in preparation for the section ahead. This provides a just-in-time review for the students.

Objectives

A numbered list of key objectives appears in the beginning of each section. As the topic corresponding to the objective is addressed, the number appears in the column.

2.1 Organizing Qualitative Data

Preparing for This Section   Before getting started, review the following:

✓ Qualitative data (Section 1.1, p. 6)

Objectives ① Construct frequency and relative frequency distributions from qualitative data
② Construct bar graphs
③ Construct pie charts

In this section we will concentrate on tabular and graphical summaries of qualitative data. Sections 2.2 and 2.3 discuss methods for summarizing quantitative data.

① **Organizing Qualitative Data**

Recall that qualitative data provide nonnumerical measures that categorize or classify an individual. When qualitative data are collected, we are often interested in determining the number of individuals that occur within each category.

Definition   A **frequency distribution** lists the number of occurrences for each category of data.

PAGE 52

In Your Own Words

When a definition or concept is presented, the "In Your Own Words" feature presents the definition or concept using everyday language while maintaining accuracy.

Definition

In Your Own Words
A frequency distribution shows how often each category occurs. A relative frequency distribution shows the percent of the observations that belong in each category.

The **relative frequency** is the proportion or percent of observations within a category and is found using the formula

$$\text{Relative frequency} = \frac{\text{frequency}}{\text{sum of all frequencies}} \qquad (1)$$

A **relative frequency distribution** lists the relative frequency of each category of data.

*History considers Cleveland to be two different presidents, even though he is the same individual, because he was not elected to two consecutive terms.

PAGE 53

---

② **Bar Graphs**

One of the most common devices for graphically representing qualitative data is a bar graph.

Definition   A **bar graph** is constructed by labeling each category of data on a horizontal axis and the frequency or relative frequency of the category on the vertical axis. A rectangle of equal width is drawn for each category. The height of the rectangle is equal to the category's frequency or relative frequency.

▶ **EXAMPLE 3**   **Constructing a Frequency and Relative Frequency Bar Graph**

Problem: Use the data summarized in Table 3 to construct (a) a frequency bar graph and (b) a relative frequency bar graph.

Approach: A horizontal axis is used to indicate the category of the data (states, in this case), and a vertical axis is used to represent the frequency or relative frequency (in this case, number of presidential births). Draw bars, or rectangles of equal width for each category whose height is the frequency or relative frequency. The bars do not touch each other.

Solution:

(a) Figure 1 shows the frequency bar graph.

Figure 1   **The U.S. Presidents' Birthplaces**

Caution

This alerts students to some of the pitfalls in statistical analysis.

Caution
Whenever constructing bar graphs, be sure to include labels for the axes as well as a title for the graph!

PAGE 55

xxi

Historical Notes

For many of the concepts introduced, a short historical note regarding the individual responsible is presented. These historical notes are meant to "humanize" famous statisticians.

TABLE 13			
Class (Three-Year Rate of Return)	Tally	Frequency	Relative Frequency
10.0–14.9	||| ||	7	7/40 = 0.175
15.0–19.9	|||| ||||		11	11/40 = 0.275
20.0–24.9	|||| |||	8	8/40 = 0.2
25.0–29.9	||||		6	0.15
30.0–34.9	|||	3	0.075
35.0–39.9	|||	3	0.075
40.0–44.9		0	0
45.0–49.9	||	2	0.05

Historical Note

Florence Nightingale was born in Italy on May 12, 1820. She was named after the city of her birth. Florence was educated by her father, who attended Cambridge University. Between 1849 and 1851, Florence studied nursing throughout Europe. In 1854, she was asked to oversee the introduction of female nurses into the military hospitals in Turkey. While there, she greatly improved the mortality rate of wounded soldiers. She collected data and invented graphs (the polar area diagram), tables, and charts to show that improving sanitary conditions would lead to decreased mortality rates. In 1869, Florence founded the Nightingale School Home for Nurses. Florence died on August 13, 1910.

Only 5% of the mutual funds had a three-year rate of return between 45.0% and 49.9%. We might conclude that mutual funds with a rate of return at this level outperform their peers and consider them worthy of our investment. This type of information would be difficult to obtain from the raw data. ◄◄

Notice that the choice of the lower class limit of the first class and the class width was rather arbitrary. While formulas and procedures do exist for creating frequency distributions from raw data, they do not necessarily provide "better" summaries. It is incorrect to say that one particular frequency distribution is the correct one. Constructing frequency distributions is somewhat of an art form in which the distribution that seems to provide the best overall summary of the data should be used.

Consider the frequency distribution in Table 14, which also summarizes the three-year rate of return data discussed in Example 3. Here, the lower class limit of the first class is 10.0 and the class width is 8.0. Do you think Table 13 or Table 14 provides a better summary of the distribution of three-year rates of return? In forming your opinion, consider the following: Too few classes will cause a "bunching" effect. Too many classes will spread the data out, thereby not revealing any pattern.

The goal in constructing a frequency distribution is to reveal interesting features of the data. With that said, when constructing frequency distributions, we typically want the number of classes to be between 5 and 20. When the data set is small, we want fewer classes; when the data set is large, we want more classes. Why do you think this is reasonable?

In Your Own Words

Creating the classes for summarizing continuous data is an art form. There is no such thing as the correct frequency distribution. However, there can be incorrect frequency distributions. The larger the class width, the fewer classes a frequency distribution will have.

TABLE 14		
Class	Tally	Frequency
10.0–17.9	|||| ||||		11
18.0–25.9	|||| |||| ||||		16
26.0–33.9	|||| |||	8
34.0–41.9	|||	3
42.0–49.9	||	2

NW *Now Work Problems 19(a) and (b).*

Examples

Examples are set up in "Problem," "Approach," and "Solution" structure. The "Problem" explains the situation and the question that is being asked. The "Approach" walks through the steps of how to analyze the information. Finally, the "Solution" applies the "Approach" and solves the "Problem."

▶ EXAMPLE 5   Constructing a Pie Chart

Problem: The data presented in Table 6 represent the educational attainment of residents of the United States 25 years or older, based upon data obtained from the 2000 United States Census. Construct a pie chart of the data.

TABLE 6	
Educational Attainment	**2000**
Less than 9th grade	12,327,601
9th–12th grade, no diploma	20,343,848
High school diploma	52,395,507
Some college, no degree	36,453,108
Associate's degree	11,487,194
Bachelor's degree	28,603,014
Graduate/professional degree	15,930,061
Totals	**177,540,333**

Approach: The pie chart will have seven parts, or sectors, corresponding to the seven categories of data. The area of each sector is proportional to the frequency of each category. For example,

$$\frac{12,327,601}{177,540,333} = 0.0694 = 6.94\%$$

of all U.S. residents 25 years or older have less than a 9th-grade education. The category "less than 9th grade" will make up 6.94% of the pie chart. Since a circle has 360°, the degree measure of the sector for the category "less than 9th-grade education" will be $(0.0694)360° \approx 25.0°$. Use a protractor to measure each angle.

Solution: We follow the approach presented for the remaining categories of data to obtain Table 7.

TABLE 7			
Education	Frequency	Relative Frequency	Degree Measure of Each Sector
Less than 9th grade	12,327,601	0.0694	25.0
9th to 12th grade, no diploma	20,343,848	0.1146	41.3
High school diploma	52,395,507	0.2951	106.2
Some college, no degree	36,453,108	0.2053	73.9
Associate's degree	11,487,194	0.0647	23.3
Bachelor's degree	28,603,014	0.1611	58.0
Graduate/professional degree	15,930,061	0.0897	32.3

Figure 6

Educational Attainment, 2000

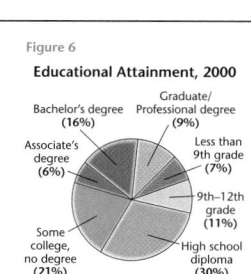

To construct a pie chart by hand, we use a protractor to approximate the angles for each sector. See Figure 6. ◀◀

Using Technology: Certain statistical spreadsheets have the ability to draw pie charts. Figure 7 shows the pie chart of the data in Table 6, using Minitab.

Figure 7

Educational Attainment, 2000

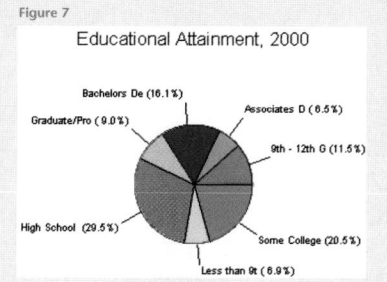

Pie charts can be created only if all the categories of the variable under consideration are represented. In other words, we could create a bar chart that lists the proportion of presidents born in the states of Virginia, Texas, and New York, but it would not make sense to construct a pie chart for this situation. Do you see why? Only 34.88% of the pie would be accounted for.

NW *Now Work Problem 19(e).*

Using Technology

Immediately following an example whenever appropriate, the output from a TI-83 Plus, MINITAB, or Excel is presented.

Now Work Problem xxx

A NW icon **NW** along with a corresponding problem to be solved appears after a concept has been introduced. This directs the student to a problem in the exercises that tests the concept, ensuring that the concept has been mastered before moving on. The Now Work problems are identified in the exercises using orange numbers and a NW icon.

4.4 Assess Your Understanding

Concepts and Vocabulary

1. State the definition of a logarithm.
2. What is a common logarithm?
3. What is the linear form of $y = ab^x$?

4. Suppose data are known to be related through the equation $y = ax^b$. What variables need to be transformed in order to use linear least squares to estimate a and b?

Exercises

- **Skill Building**

In Problems 1–8, change each exponential expression to an equivalent expression involving a logarithm.

1. $4^2 = 16$
2. $2^5 = 32$
3. $x^5 = 18$
4. $c^3 = 21$

5. $7^x = 15$
6. $12^x = 43$
7. $5^3 = y$
8. $6^{1.5} = y$

35. **The United States Population** The following data, obtained from the U.S. Census Bureau, represent the population of the United States. An ecologist is interested in finding an equation that describes the population of the United States over time. She is convinced that the population is growing exponentially.

Year, x	Population, y
1900	76,212,168
1910	92,228,496
1920	106,021,537
1930	123,202,624
1940	132,164,569
1950	151,325,798
1960	179,323,175
1970	203,302,031
1980	226,542,203
1990	248,709,873
2000	281,421,906

Source: United States Census Bureau

(a) Draw a scatter diagram treating time as the predictor variable.
(b) Determine the logarithm of the y-values so that $Y = \log y$. Draw a scatter diagram of the transformed data.
(c) Find the least-squares regression line for the transformed data.
(d) Find the exponential equation of best fit.
(e) Use the exponential equation of best fit to predict the population of the United States in 2010, the year of the next census.
(f) Do you think your prediction will overestimate or underestimate the actual population in 2005? Why?
(g) Compare your prediction with that provided by the U.S. Census Bureau. Is your prediction higher or lower than the Census Bureau's prediction?

36. **Finance** The following data, represent the amount of money an investor has in an investment account each year for the last six years. The theory of finance states that account values grow exponentially over time.

(a) Draw a scatter diagram treating time as the predictor variable.
(b) Determine the logarithm of the y-values so that $Y = \log y$. Draw a scatter diagram of the transformed data.
(c) Find the least-squares regression line for the transformed data.
(d) Find the exponential equation of best fit.
(e) Use the exponential equation of best fit to predict the value of the account after 30 years.
(f) If we subtract 1 from the base, b, in the exponential equation of best fit, we obtain the average annual rate of return on the investment. What was the average rate of return on this investment over the past seven years?

37. **Kepler's Law of Planetary Motion** The time it takes for a planet to complete its orbit around the sun is called the planet's sidereal year. In 1618, Johann Kepler discovered that the sidereal year of a planet is related to the distance of the planet from the sun through a power equation. The following data, show the distances that the planets are from the sun and their sidereal years.

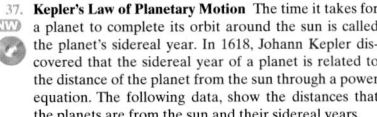

Planet	Distance from Sun, x (millions of miles)	Sidereal Year, y
Mercury	36	0.24
Venus	67	0.62
Earth	93	1.00
Mars	142	1.88
Jupiter	483	11.9
Saturn	887	29.5
Uranus	1,785	84.0
Neptune	2,797	165.0
Pluto	3,675	248.0

(a) Draw a scatter diagram treating distance from the sun as the predictor variable.
(b) Determine the logarithm of both the x- and y-values so that $X = \log x$ and $Y = \log y$. Draw a scatter diagram of the transformed data.
(c) Find the least-squares regression line for the transformed data.

Problems

A problem with 15 or more observations in the data set is marked with a CD icon. 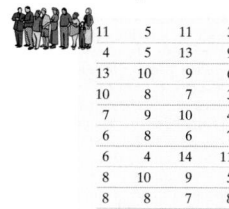 This indicates that the data set can be found on the CD packaged with the text.

These problems can be solved using "by hand" methods or technology. The idea is to give an instructor flexibility that allows for solving the problem using the approach that he or she desires.

---

17. Waiting The following data represent the number of customers waiting for a table at 6:00 P.M. on Saturday for 40 consecutive Saturdays at Bobak's Restaurant:

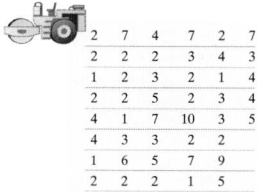

11	5	11	3
4	5	13	9
13	10	9	6
10	8	7	3
7	9	10	4
6	8	6	7
6	4	14	11
8	10	9	5
8	8	7	8
8	6	11	8

(a) Construct a frequency distribution of the data.
(b) Construct a relative frequency distribution of the data.
(c) What percentage of the Saturdays had 10 or more customers waiting for a table at 6:00 P.M.?
(d) What percentage of the Saturdays had 5 or fewer customers waiting for a table at 6:00 P.M.?
(e) Construct a frequency histogram of the data.
(f) Construct a relative frequency histogram of the data.
(g) Describe the shape of the distribution.

18. Highway Repair The following data represent the number of potholes on 50 randomly selected 1-mile stretches of highway in the city of Chicago.

2	7	4	7	2	7
2	2	2	3	4	3
1	2	3	2	1	4
2	2	5	2	3	4
4	1	7	10	3	5
4	3	3	2	2	
1	6	5	7	9	
2	2	2	1	5	
3	5	1	3	5	

(a) Construct a frequency distribution of the data.
(b) Construct a relative frequency distribution of the data.
(c) What percentage of the 1-mile stretches of highway had seven or more potholes?

19. Tensile Strength Tensile strength is the maximum stress at which one can be reasonably certain that failure will not occur. The following data represent the tensile strength (in thousands of pounds per square inch) of a composite material to be used in an aircraft.

203.41	185.97	184.41	160.44	174.63
209.58	190.67	200.73	180.95	185.34
213.35	207.88	206.51	201.95	205.59
218.56	210.80	209.84	204.60	212.00
242.76	231.46	212.15	219.51	225.25

Source: Vangel, Mark G., "New Methods for One-sided Tolerance Limits for a One-way Balanced Random-Effects ANOVA Model," *Technometrics* 34 (May, 1992) no. 2, 176-185

With the first class having a lower class limit of 160 and a class width of 10,

(a) Construct a frequency distribution.
(b) Construct a relative frequency distribution.
(c) Construct a frequency histogram of the data.
(d) Construct a relative frequency histogram of the data.
(e) Describe the shape of the distribution.
(f) Repeat parts (a)–(e), using a class width of 15. Which frequency distribution seems to provide a better summary of the data?

20. Miles on a Cavalier A random sample of 36 three-year-old Chevy Cavaliers was obtained in the Miami, Florida area, and the number of miles on each car was recorded. The results are shown in the table below.

34,122	17,685	15,499	26,455	30,500	41,194
39,416	29,307	26,051	27,368	35,936	29,289
28,281	34,511	32,305	37,904	44,448	31,883
37,021	34,500	39,884	23,221	41,043	32,923
30,747	41,620	17,595	38,041	30,739	40,614
35,439	30,283	44,224	35,295	38,995	42,398

Source: cars.com

With the first class having a lower class limit of 15,000 and a class width of 4,000,

(a) Construct a frequency distribution.
(b) Construct a relative frequency distribution.
(c) Construct a frequency histogram of the data.
(d) Construct a relative frequency histogram of the data.

PAGE 80

Technology Step-by-Step
Drawing Histograms and Stem-and-Leaf Plots

TI-83 Plus Histograms

Step 1: Enter the raw data in L1 by pressing STAT and selecting 1:Edit.
Step 2: Press 2nd Y = to access the StatPlot menu. Select 1:Plot1.
Step 3: Place the cursor on "On" and press ENTER.
Step 4: Highlight the histogram icon.
Step 5: Press ZOOM and select 9:ZoomStat.

MINITAB Histograms

Step 1: Enter the raw data in C1.
Step 2: Select the **Graph** menu and highlight **Histogram**.
Step 3: Select the data in C1 and press OK.

Stem-and-Leaf Plot

Step 1: With the raw data entered in C1, select the **Graph** menu and highlight **Stem-and-Leaf** ...
Step 2: Select the data in C1 and press OK.

Excel Histograms

Step 1: Enter the raw data in column A.
Step 2: Select **Tools** and **Data Analysis** ...
Step 3: Select Histogram from the list.
Step 4: With the cursor in the Input Range cell, use the mouse to highlight the raw data. Select the Chart Output box and press OK.
Step 5: Double-click on one of the bars in the histogram. Select the Options tab from the menu that appears. Reduce the gap width to zero.

Excel does not draw stem-and-leaf plots.

Technology Step-by-Step

Brief step-by-step instructions for using the TI-83 Plus, MINITAB, and Excel follow each exercise set. This is meant as a supplement to the technology guides.

Summary

In this chapter, we introduced techniques that allow us to describe the relation between two quantitative variables. The first step in identifying the type of relation that might exist is to draw a scatter diagram. The predictor variable is plotted on the horizontal axis, the corresponding response variable on the vertical axis. The scatter diagram can be used to discover whether the relation between the predictor and the response variable is linear. In addition, for linear relations, we can judge whether the linear relation shows positive or negative association.

A numerical measure for the strength of linear relation between two variables is the linear correlation coefficient. It is a number between -1 and 1, inclusive. Values of the correlation coefficient near -1 are indicative of a negative linear relation between the two variables; values of the correlation coefficient near $+1$ indicate a positive linear relation between the two variables. If the correlation coefficient is near 0, then there is little *linear* relation between the two variables.

Once a linear relation between the two variables has been discovered, we describe the relation by finding the least-squares regression line. This line best describes the linear relation between the predictor and the response variables. We can

use the least-squares regression line to predict a value of the response variable for a given value of the predictor variable.

The coefficient of determination, R^2, measures the percent of variation in the response variable that is explained by the least-squares regression line. It is a measure between 0 and 1 inclusive. The closer R^2 is to 1, the more explanatory value the line has. Whenever a least-squares regression line is obtained, certain diagnostics must be performed. These include verifying that the residuals have constant variance, verifying that the linear model is appropriate, and checking for outliers and influential observations.

In Section 4.4, we introduced methods that can be used to discover exponential equations and power equations of best fit. This method requires that we transform the data via logarithmic transformations.

One item worth mentioning again is that a researcher should never claim causation between two variables in a study unless the data are experimental. Observational data allow us to say that two variables might be associated, but we cannot claim causation.

Formulas

Correlation Coefficient

$$r = \frac{\sum\left(\dfrac{x_i - \bar{x}}{s_x}\right)\left(\dfrac{y_i - \bar{y}}{s_y}\right)}{n - 1}$$

Equation of the Least-Squares Regression Line
The equation of the least-squares regression line is given by
$$\hat{y} = b_1 x + b_0$$
where

$\hat{y}$ is the predicted value of the response variable,

$b_1 = r \cdot \dfrac{s_y}{s_x}$ is the slope of the least-squares regression

line, and

$b_0 = \bar{y} - b_1\bar{x}$ is the intercept of the least-squares regression line.

Coefficient of Determination, R^2

$$R^2 = \frac{\text{variation explained by predictor variable}}{\text{total variation}}$$

$$= 1 - \frac{\text{unexplained variation}}{\text{total variation}}$$

$$= r^2 \text{ for the least-squares regression model } \hat{y} = b_0 + b_1 x$$

Vocabulary

Bivariate data (p. 190)	Negatively associated (p. 194)	Total deviation (p. 222)
Response variable (p. 192)	Linear correlation coefficient (p. 195)	Explained deviation (p. 222)
Predictor variable (p. 192)	Residuals (p. 209)	Unexplained deviation (p. 222)
Lurking variable (p. 192)	Least-squares regression line (p. 209)	Influential observation (p. 229)
Scatter diagram (p. 192)	Outside the scope of the model (p. 213)	Logarithm (p. 237)
Positively associated (p. 194)	Coefficient of determination (p. 222)	Common logarithm (p. 238)

Objectives

Section	You should be able to . . .	Review Exercises
4.1	1 Draw scatter diagrams (p. 192)	1–4, 9, 10, 20, 33–35(a)
	2 Interpret scatter diagrams (p. 194)	1–4(c)
	3 Understand the properties of the linear correlation coefficient (p. 194)	36
	4 Compute and interpret the linear correlation coefficient (p. 197)	1–4(c), 9(d), 10(d)
4.2	1 Find the least-squares regression line (p. 209)	5–8(a), 19(a), 20(b)
	2 Interpret the slope and y-intercept of the least-squares regression line (p. 211)	5–8(c)
	3 Predict the value of the response variable, based upon the least-squares regression line (p. 211)	5–8(d)
	4 Determine residuals, based upon the least-squares regression line (p. 212)	5–8(e)
	5 Compute the sum of squared residuals (p. 214)	9, 10 (f) and (g)
4.3	1 Compute and interpret the coefficient of determination (p. 221)	13–16(a)
	2 Perform residual analysis on a regression model (p. 225)	9–12; 13–16(b),(c); 17(c), (d)
	3 Identify influential observations (p. 229)	13(d), (e); 14–16(d); 17(b)
4.4	1 Change exponential expressions to logarithmic expressions and logarithmic expressions to exponential expressions (p. 237)	19–28
	2 Simplify expressions containing logarithms (p. 238)	29–32
	3 Use logarithmic transformations to linearize exponential relations (p. 239)	33
	4 Use logarithmic transformations to linearize power relations (p. 242)	34

Review Exercises

1. **Engine Displacement versus Fuel Economy** The following data represent the size of a car's engine (in liters) versus its miles per gallon in the city for various 2001 domestic automobiles.
   (a) Draw a scatter diagram treating engine displacement as the predictor variable and miles per gallon as the response variable.
   (b) Compute the linear correlation coefficient between engine displacement and miles per gallon.
   (c) Based upon the scatter diagram and the linear correlation coefficient, comment on the type of relation that appears to exist between the two variables.

Car	Engine Displacement (in liters)	City Miles per Gallon
Buick Century	3.1	20
Buick LeSabre	3.8	19
Cadillac DeVille	4.6	16
Chevrolet Camaro	3.8	19
Chevrolet Cavalier	2.2	24
Chevrolet Malibu	3.1	23
Chrysler LHS	3.5	18
Dodge Intrepid	2.7	19
Ford Crown Victoria	4.6	17
Ford Focus	2.0	28
Ford Mustang	3.8	20
Oldsmobile Aurora	3.5	19
Pontiac Grand Am	2.4	22
Pontiac Sunfire	2.2	23
Saturn Coupe	1.9	28

Source: Road and Track magazine

Chapter Review

The extensive review provides a list of important formulas and vocabulary and a list of objectives along with the corresponding Review Exercises that test the student's understanding of the objective.

The Day the Sky Roared

Shortly after daybreak on April 3, 1974, thunder began to rumble through the dark skies that covered much of the midwestern United States. Lightning struck areas from the Gulf Coast states to the Canadian border. By the predawn hours of the next day, the affected region of around 490,000 acres was devastated by over 100 tornadoes. This "super outbreak" was responsible for the deaths of over 300 people in 11 states. More than 6100 people were injured by the storms, with approximately 27,500 families suffering some kind of loss. The total cost attributed to the disaster was more than $600 million. Amazingly, the storm resulted in six Category 5 tornadoes with wind speeds exceeding 261 miles per hour. To put this figure in perspective, the region endured about one decade's worth of Category 5 tornadoes in a single 24-hour period!

Fujita Wind Damage Scale

Number	Wind Speed	Damage
F-0	Up to 72 mph	Light
F-1	73 to 112 mph	Moderate
F-2	113 to 157 mph	Considerable
F-3	158 to 206 mph	Severe
F-4	207 to 260 mph	Devastating
F-5	Above 260 mph	Incredible

Structural engineers and meteorologists are interested in understanding catastrophic events such as this tornado outbreak. Variables such as tornado intensity (as described by the F-Scale), tornado duration (time spent by the tornado in contact with the ground), and death demographics can provide insights into these events and their impact upon the human population. The following data list the duration time and F-Scale for each tornado in the April 1974 Super Outbreak:

Tornado Duration Times for Outbreak of April 3–4, 1974

F-Scale	Tornado Duration (minutes)
F-0	1,1,5,1,1,6,4,10,5,4,1,1,1,1,1,1,1,1,30,1,9
F-1	16,13,9,8,13,10,15,1,17,23,10,8,12,5,20,31,12,5,30,13,7,1,5,13,1,2,5,10,1,20,5
F-2	7,15,2,10,23,10,7,12,8,1,8,19,5,10,15,20,10,13,20,15,13,14,1,4,2,15,30,91,11,5
F-3	9,20,8,16,26,36,10,20,50,17,26,31,21,30,23,28,23,18,35,35,15,25,30,15,22,18,58,19,23,31,13,26,40,14,11
F-4	120,23,23,42,47,25,22,22,34,50,38,28,39,29,28,25,34,16,40,55,124,30,30,31
F-5	37,69,23,52,61,122

The following tables present the number of deaths as a function of F-Scale and community size:

Deaths as a Function of F-Scale for April 3–4, 1974, Tornadoes

F-Scale	Deaths
F-0	0
F-1	0
F-2	14
F-3	32
F-4	129
F-5	130

Deaths as a Function of Community Size for Tornado Super Outbreak of April 3–4, 1974

Community Size	Deaths
Rural areas	99
Small communities	77
Small cities	63
Medium cities	56
Large cities	10

Create a report that graphically displays and discusses the tornado-related data. Your report should include the following:

1. A bar graph or pie chart (or both) that depicts the number of tornadoes by F-Scale. Generally, only a little more than 1 percent of all tornadoes exceed F-3 on the Fujita Wind Damage Scale. How does the frequency of the most severe tornadoes of the April 3–4, 1974, outbreak compare with normal tornado formation?
2. A single histogram that displays the distribution of tornado duration for all of the tornadoes.
3. Six histograms displaying tornado duration for each of the F-Scale categories. Does there appear to be a relationship between duration and intensity? If so, describe this relationship.
4. A bar chart that shows the relationship between the number of deaths and tornado intensity. Ordinarily, the most severe tornadoes (F-4 and F-5) account for more than 70 percent of deaths. Is the death distribution of this outbreak consistent with this observation?
5. A bar chart that shows the relationship between the number of deaths and community size. Include a discussion describing the number of deaths as a function of community size.
6. A general summary of your findings and conclusions.

Data Source: Abbey, Robert F. and T. Theodore Fujita. "Tornadoes: The Tornado Outbreak of 3–4 April 1974." In *The Thunderstorm in Human Affairs*, 2nd ed, edited by Edwin Kessler, 37–66. Norman, OK: University of Oklahoma Press, 1983. The death figures presented in this case study are based on approximations made from charts by Abbey and Fujita. Additional descriptions of events and normal tornado statistics are derived from Jack Williams's *The Weather Book*. (New York: Vintage Books, 1992.)

PAGES 106 & 107

Case Studies

Each chapter ends with a case study that requires the student to use skills learned within the section to perform statistical analysis.

Tables or Graphs?

Suppose that you work for the school newspaper. Your editor approaches you with a special reporting assignment. Your task is to write an article that describes the "typical" student at your school, complete with supporting information. In order to write this article, you have to survey at least 40 students and ask them to respond to a questionnaire. The editor would like to have at least two qualitative and two quantitative variables that describe the typical student. The results of the survey will be presented in your article, but you are unsure whether you should present tabular or graphical summaries, so you decide to perform the following "experiment."

1. Develop a questionnaire that results in obtaining the values of 2 qualitative and 2 quantitative variables. Administer the questionnaire to at least 40 students on your campus.
2. Summarize the data in both tabular and graphical form.
3. Select 20 individuals. (They don't have to be students at your school.) Give the tabular summaries to 10 of the individuals and the graphical summaries to the other 10. Ask each individual to study each table or graph for 5 seconds. After 1 minute, give a questionnaire that asks various questions regarding the information contained in the table or graph. For example, if you had age data summarized, ask the individual which age group had the highest frequency. Record the number of correct answers for each individual. Which summary results in a higher percentage of correct answers, the tables or the graphs? Write a report that discusses your findings.
4. Now use the data collected from the questionnaire to create a couple of misleading graphs. Again, select 20 individuals. Give 10 of the individuals the misleading graphs and 10 of the individuals the correct graphs. Ask each of the individuals to study each graph for 5 seconds. After 1 minute has elapsed, give a questionnaire that asks various questions regarding the information contained in the graphs. Record the number of correct answers for each individual. Did the misleading graphs mislead? Write a report that discusses your findings.

Decisions

Also a chapter-ending project, the student is required to conduct statistical analysis in order to help make an informed decision.

PAGE 108

Consumer Reports Rates Treadmills

Consumer Reports

A study that compared exercisers who worked out equally hard for the same time on several different types of machines found that they generally burned the most calories on treadmills. Our own research has shown that treadmills are less likely than other machines to sit unused. So it should come as no surprise that treadmills are the best-selling home exercise machine in the U.S.

In a recent study by Consumer Reports (March 2002), we tested 11 best-selling brands of treadmills ranging in price from $500 to $3000. The treadmills were rated on ease of use, ergonomics, exercise factors, construction, and durability. Ease of use is based on how straightforward the treadmill is to use. Ergonomics, including safety factors, belt size, and handrail placement, indicates how well the treadmill fits people of different sizes. Exercise includes evaluations of the minimum incline level, speed control, and heart-rate monitoring. Construction covers factors like the motor's continuous-duty horsepower rating and weld quality.

In order to help compare the treadmills, the individual attribute scores were combined into an overall score. The figure shown below is a ratings chart for the 11 treadmills based on our test results. In addition to the performance ratings, other useful information, such as the models' price and belt size, is included.

(a) What type of graph is illustrated to display overall score in the figure?

(b) Which model has the highest construction score? Which models have the lowest ease of use score?

(c) For ease of use, how many treadmills rated excellent? Very good? Good? Fair? Poor?

(d) Draw a frequency bar graph for each rating category. In other words, draw a bar graph for ease of use, ergonomics, and so on.

(e) Does there appear to be a relationship between price and overall score? Explain your opinion.

Note to Readers: In many cases, our test protocol and analytical methods are more complicated than described in these examples. The data and discussions have been modified to make the material more appropriate for the audience.

Ratings Chart for Treadmills

KEY NO.	BRAND & MODEL; SIMILAR MODELS IN SMALL TYPE	PRICE	OVERALL SCORE	BELT (IN.)	EASE	ERGONOMICS	EXERCISE	CONSTRUCTION	FOLDS
1	**Life Fitness** T3 T3i	$2,200		19x52	◉	◉	◉	◓	
2	**Reebok** ACD4	1,850		19x61	◓	◉	◉	◓	✓
3	**Precor** M9.33 M9.35	3,000		20x59	○	◉	◉	◉	
4	**Star Trac** TR901	2,500		19x50	◓	◓	◉	◓	
5	**Image** 10.60L	1,500		20x61	◓	◓	◉	○	✓
6	**HealthRider** S500xi	1,100		19x54	◓	○	◉	○	✓
7	**Tunturi** J6F J6	2,100		18x55	◒	◓	◓	◓	✓
8	**Trimline** 2610	1,200		18x48	◓	○	◓	◓	
9	**ProForm** 785SS	750		20x55	◓	◓	◒	◒	✓
10	**NordicTrack** EXP 1000i	800		20x55	◓	◓	◒	◒	✓
11	**ProForm** 525E	500		18x52	◒	○	◒	◒	✓

Overall Ratings — In performance order

Overall score scale: 0 — P F G VG E — 100

Excellent ◉ Very good ◓ Good ○ Fair ◒ Poor ●

109

Consumer Reports

Each chapter contains a Consumer Reports Project that requires students to go through the same type of analysis that was used by researchers at Consumer Reports to help form the basis for product ratings.

Supplements

For the Student—**Available via your bookstore**

Student's Solutions Manual (0-13-046492-9)
- Contains solutions to the odd-numbered exercises in the textbook. Written by: Lindsay Packer, College of Charleston.

Excel Guide (0-13-046495-3)
- Contains PHStat with Data Files CD. Presents instructions on how to use Microsoft Excel to carry out selected examples and exercises. Written by: Beverly Dretzke, University of Wisconsin, Eau Claire.

TI-83 Guide (0-13-046496-1)
- Provides hands-on technology assistance and detailed instructions for working selected examples and exercises utilizing both the TI-83 and the TI-83+. Written by: Kathleen McLaughlin and Dorothy Wakefield, University of Connecticut and Manchester Community College.

Minitab Guide (0-13-046497-X)
- Provides hands-on technology assistance and detailed instructions for working selected examples and exercises with Minitab. Written by: Dorothy Wakefield and Kathleen McLaughlin, University of Connecticut and Manchester Community College.

Lab Manual (0-13-009482-X)
- Utilizing Java applets written for the introductory statistics market, this lab manual provides explanations of how to work the applets as well as full discovery labs on the concepts. Written by David Lane, Rice University.

Companion Web Site
- *www.prenhall.com/sullivanstats*
- Includes materials for each chapter and section–including Preparing for This Section tests, reading comprehension quizzes, STATLETs™, PowerPoint slides, data files, graphing calculator help, and more. Written by numerous authors.

Sullivan Videos on CD
- The author presents full lectures over the entire text, keyed to each chapter and section. A collection of CDs. Written and presented by Michael Sullivan, III, Joliet Junior College.

For the Instructor—**Available via your Prentice Hall representative**

Annotated Instructor's Edition with Instructor's Resource CD (0-13-046489-9)
- Contains helpful teaching tips and answers to all the exercises throughout the text at appropriate moments. Written by: Erica Lynn Kwiatkowski-Egizio at Joliet Junior College.
- Also contains the Instructor's Resource CD containing TestGen-EQ, Instructor's Solutions Manual, Test Item File, PowerPoint files, and other resources for the instructor. The ISM and TIF are password protected with your district manager's territory code.

Instructor's Solutions Manual (0-13-046480-5)
- Contains the full set of both odd- and even-numbered solutions to the exercises within the text along with suggestions for the end-of-chapter materials. Written by: Lindsay Packer, College of Charleston.

Test Bank (0-13-046493-7)
- Printed test questions derived from the algorithmic testing software TestGen. Questions selected and edited by: Elena Catoiu and Yen-Phi Dang.

TestGen-EQ (0-13-046503-8)
- Test generator allows for easy creation of tests. Fully editable and allows authoring of new questions. Algorithmic functionality allows for the creation of unlimited versions of a single test. Quiz Master feature allows for online delivery. Questions selected and edited by: Elena Catoiu and Yen-Phi Dang.

VHS Lecture Videos (0-13-046494-5)
- The author presents full lectures over the entire text, keyed to each chapter and section. VHS tape format. Written and presented by Michael Sullivan, III, Joliet Junior College.

LIST OF APPLICATIONS

PHOTO AND ILLUSTRATION CREDITS

Statistics

INFORMED DECISIONS USING DATA

Statistics is a discipline that plays a major role in many different areas. For example, it is used in sports to help a coach or manager make informed decisions about his/her competition. It is used to predict the outcome of elections and to help determine governmental policies. Statistics assists in determining the effectiveness of new medications. Statistics can be used to discover unlikely occurrences. In fact, statistics was used by the Democratic National Committee to determine that voters in Palm Beach County, Florida likely voted for Pat Buchanan incorrectly instead of their desired candidate, Al Gore. This statistical evidence led the Democrats to demand a recount of the ballots within that county and other counties in Florida.

Used appropriately, statistics can provide an understanding of the world around us. Used inappropriately, it can lend support to inaccurate beliefs. Understanding the methodologies of statistics will provide you with the ability to analyze and critique studies and experiments. With this ability, you will be an informed consumer of information, which will enable you to distinguish solid statistical analyses from the bogus presentation of numerical "facts."

Note to Instructor
Due to the tremendous number of terms in this chapter, you may want students to create a list of terms, definitions, and their own examples of each term. This will allow students to make a personal connection to the concepts, and it will lead to a greater understanding of the vocabulary. Remind students that many of the terms presented in this chapter will be presented again in upcoming chapters, so they should not feel overwhelmed by the number of definitions.

CHAPTER 1

Data Collection

Outline

 For additional study help, go to
www.prenhall.com/sullivanstats

Materials include

- Self-Graded Quizzes
- "Preparing for This Section" Quizzes
- STATLETS
- PowerPoint Downloads
- Step-by-Step Technology Guide
- Graphing Calculator Help

1.1   Introduction to the Practice of Statistics

Objectives Define statistics
 Understand the process of statistics
 Distinguish between qualitative and quantitative variables
 Distinguish between discrete and continuous variables

 What is statistics? When asked this question, many people respond that statistics is numbers. This response is only partially correct.

Definition   **Statistics** is the science of collecting, organizing, summarizing and analyzing information in order to draw conclusions.

It is helpful to consider this definition in three parts. The first part of the definition states that statistics is the collection of information. The second part refers to the organization and summarization of information. Finally, the third part states that the information is analyzed in order to draw conclusions.

 The definition implies that the methods of statistics follow a process.

The Process of Statistics

1. *Identify the research objective*. A researcher must determine the question(s) he or she wants answered. The question(s) must be detailed so that it identifies a group that is to be studied and the questions that are to be answered. The group that is to be studied is called the **population**. An **individual** is a person or object that is a member of the population being studied. For example, a researcher may want to study the population of all 2002 model-year automobiles. The individuals in this study would be the cars.

2. *Collect the information needed to answer the questions posed in (1)*. Gaining access to an entire population is often difficult and expensive. In conducting research, we typically look at a subset of the population, called a **sample**. For example, the United States population of people 18 years or older is about 210 million. Many national studies consist of samples of size 1100. The "collection of information" step is vital to the statistical process because if the information is not collected correctly, the conclusions drawn are meaningless. Do not overlook the importance of appropriate data collection processes.

3. *Organize and summarize the information*. This step in the process is referred to as *descriptive statistics*.

> ⚫
> ⚫   **Caution**
> ⚫
> Many nonscientific studies are
> based on *convenience samples*, such
> as Internet surveys or phone-in
> polls. The results of any study
> performed using this type of
> sampling method are not reliable.

Definition   **Descriptive statistics** consists of organizing and summarizing the information collected.

Descriptive statistics describes the information collected through numerical measurements, charts, graphs and tables. The main purpose of descriptive statistics is to provide an overview of the information collected.

4. *Draw conclusions from the information*. This is the step in which the information collected from the sample is generalized to the population.

Definition   **Inferential statistics** uses methods that generalize results obtained from a sample to the population and measure their reliability.

For example, if a researcher is conducting a study based on the population of Americans aged 18 years or older, she might obtain a sample of 1,100 Americans aged 18 years or older. The results obtained from the sample would be generalized to the population. There is always uncertainty when using samples to draw conclusions regarding a population because we can't learn everything about a population by looking at a sample. Therefore, statisticians will report a level of confidence in their conclusions. This level of confidence is a way of representing the reliability of results. If the entire population is studied, then inferential statistics is not necessary because descriptive statistics would provide all the information that we need regarding the population.

The following example is a medical study to determine the effectiveness (medical researchers use the word "efficacy") of a drug. It will help illustrate the process of a statistical study.

▶ **EXAMPLE 1**   **Effectiveness of a Drug Treatment on the Common Cold**

According to researchers, little information exists on the cause and treatment of pain, pressure, and other discomfort attributed to the common cold.* Researchers Steven J. Sperber, MD, and his associates wanted to determine the effectiveness of a new drug combination** on symptoms of the common cold. The following procedures allowed the researchers to measure effectiveness of these drugs:

1. *Identify the research objective.* Researchers wished to determine the effectiveness of a new drug combination on the symptoms associated with the common cold.

2. *Collect the information needed to answer the questions.* The researchers divided 430 subjects with cold symptoms into two groups. The first group (Group 1) had 216 subjects and the second group (Group 2) had 214 subjects. The Group 1 subjects were given two daily doses of the new drug combination. The Group 2 subjects were given two daily doses of a *placebo*. A **placebo** is an innocuous drug such as sugar water. Group 1 is called the **experimental group** and the drug is called the **treatment**. Group 2 is called the **control group**. Neither the doctor administering the drug nor the patient knew whether he or she was in the experimental or control group. This is referred to as a **double-blind** experiment. Prior to the first dose and after the second dose, the patients reported symptoms on a scale from 0 to 4 with 0 reflecting the absence of pain and 4 reflecting severe pain.

3. *Organize and summarize the information.* The results of the experiment indicated that both the experimental and control group had similar levels of pain prior to the administering of the drugs. However, after the second dose was administered, the reported pain of the experimental group decreased by 1.30 while the control group reported a decrease of 0.93.

*The discussion is based upon a study done by Steven J. Sperber, Ronald B. Turner, James V. Sorrentino, Robert R. O'Connor, James Rogers, and Jack M. Gwaltney that is published in the Archives of Family Medicine, 2000; 9:979–985.
**The combination of pseudoephedrine hydrochloride with acetaminophen.

4. *Draw conclusions from the data.* We wish to extend the results obtained from the sample of 430 subjects to all individuals that have a common cold. That is, the new drug combination is effective in relieving the symptoms attributable to the common cold.   ◄◄

NW *Now Work Problem 25.*

Types of Data

Once a research objective is stated, a list of the type of information the researcher desires about the individual must be created. **Variables** are the characteristics of the individuals within the population. For example, this past spring my son and I planted a tomato plant in our backyard. We decided to collect some information about the tomatoes harvested from the plant. The individuals we studied were the tomatoes. The variable that interested us was the weight of the tomatoes. My son noted that the tomatoes had different weights even though they all came from the same plant. He discovered that variables vary. If variables did not vary, they would be constants and statistical inference would not be necessary. Think about it this way: If all the tomatoes had the same weight, then knowing the weight of one tomato would be sufficient in determining the weight of all tomatoes. However, the weights of tomatoes vary from one tomato to the next. One of the goals of research is to learn the causes of the variability so that we could learn to grow plants that yield the best tomatoes.

 Variables can be classified into two groups.

Definition

> **Qualitative or Categorical variables** allow for classification of individuals based on some attribute or characteristic.
>
> **Quantitative variables** provide numerical measures of individuals. Arithmetic operations such as addition and subtraction can be performed on the values of a quantitative variable and provide meaningful results.

Many examples in this text will include a suggested **approach**, or a way to look at and organize a problem so that it can be solved. The approach will be a suggested method of "attack" toward solving the problem. This does not mean that the approach given is the only way to solve the problem because many problems have more than one approach leading to a correct solution. For example, if you turn the key on your car's ignition and it doesn't start, one approach would be to look under the hood and try to determine what is wrong. (Of course, this approach would work only if you know how to fix cars.) A second, equally valid approach would be to call an automobile mechanic to service the car.

In Your Own Words

Typically, there is more than one correct approach to solving a problem.

► EXAMPLE 2 **Distinguishing between Qualitative and Quantitative Variables**

Problem: Determine whether the following variables are qualitative or quantitative.

(a) Gender
(b) Temperature
(c) Number of days during the past week a college student aged 21 years or older has had at least one drink
(d) Zip code

Approach: Quantitative variables are numerical measures such that arithmetic operations can be performed on the values of the variable, while qualitative variables describe an attribute or characteristic of the individual that allow researchers to categorize the individual.

Solution:

(a) Gender is a qualitative variable because it allows a researcher to categorize the individual as male or female. Notice that arithmetic operations cannot be performed on the attributes "male" and "female."

(b) Temperature is a quantitative variable because it is numeric and operations such as addition and subtraction provide meaningful results. For example, 70°F is 10°F warmer than 60°F.

(c) Number of days during the past week that a college student aged 21 years or older had at least one drink is a quantitative variable because it is numeric and operations such as addition and subtraction provide meaningful results.

(d) Zip code is a qualitative variable because it categorizes a location. Notice that the addition or subtraction of zip codes does not provide meaningful results. ◀◀

On the basis of the result of Example 2(d), we conclude that a variable may be qualitative while having values that are numeric. Just because a variable is numeric does not mean that the variable is quantitative.

NW *Now Work Problem 3.*

We can further classify quantitative variables into two types.

Definition

In Your Own Words

Anytime that you count to get the value of a variable, it is discrete. If you measure to get the value of the variable, it is continuous. When deciding whether a variable is discrete or continuous, ask yourself if it is counted or measured.

A **discrete variable** is a quantitative variable that has either a finite number of possible values or a countable number of possible values. The term "countable" means that the values result from counting such as 0, 1, 2, 3, and so on.

A **continuous variable** is a quantitative variable that has an infinite number of possible values that are not countable.

Figure 1 illustrates the relationship among qualitative, quantitative, discrete, and continuous variables.

Figure 1

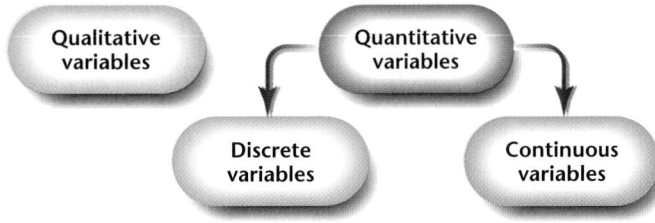

Recognizing the type of variable being studied is important because it dictates the type of analysis that can be performed.

An example should help to clarify the definitions.

▶ **EXAMPLE 3** **Distinguishing between Discrete and Continuous Variables**

Problem: Determine whether the following quantitative variables are discrete or continuous.

(a) The number of heads obtained after flipping a coin five times.
(b) The number of cars that arrive at McDonald's drive-through between 12:00 pm and 1:00 pm.
(c) The distance a 1995 Pontiac Bonneville can travel in city driving conditions with a full tank of gas.

Approach: A variable is discrete if its value results from counting. A variable is continuous if its value is measured.

Solution:

(a) The number of heads obtained by flipping a coin five times would be a discrete variable because we would count the number of heads obtained. The possible values of the discrete variable are {0, 1, 2, 3, 4, 5}.
(b) The number of cars that arrive at McDonalds drive-through between 12:00 pm and 1:00 pm is a discrete variable because its value would result from counting the cars. The possible values of the discrete variable are 0, 1, 2, 3, 4, and so on. Notice that there is no predetermined upper limit to the number of cars that may arrive.
(c) The distance traveled is a continuous variable because we measure the distance. ◀◀

Continuous variables are often rounded. For example, when the miles per gallon of gasoline for a certain make of car is given as 24 miles per gallon, it really means that the miles per gallon is greater than or equal to 23.5 and less than 24.5, or 23.5 ≤ miles per gallon < 24.5.

NW *Now Work Problem 13.*

The list of observations a variable assumes is called **data**. While gender is a variable, the observations, male or female, are data. **Qualitative data** are observations corresponding to a qualitative variable. **Quantitative data** are observations corresponding to a quantitative variable. **Discrete data** are observations corresponding to a discrete variable and **continuous data** are observations corresponding to a continuous variable.

▶ **EXAMPLE 4** **Distinguishing between Variables and Data**

Problem: Table 1 represents a group of selected countries and information regarding these countries as of December 15, 2001. Identify the individuals, variables, and data in Table 1.

Approach: An individual is an object or person that we wish to obtain data for. The variables are the characteristics of the individuals and the data are the specific values of the variables.

Solution: The individuals in the study are the countries: Australia, Canada, and so on (in red ink). The variables measured for each country are "government type," "life expectancy," and "birth rate" (in blue ink). The variable "government type" is qualitative because it categorizes the individual. The quantitative variables are "life expectancy" and "birth rate." Further, both

TABLE 1			
Country	Government Type	Life Expectancy (years)	Birth Rate per 1000 People
Australia	Democratic	79.87	12.86
Canada	Confederation	79.56	11.21
France	Republic	78.9	12.1
Morocco	Constitutional Monarchy	69.43	24.16
Poland	Republic	73.42	10.2
Sri Lanka	Republic	72.09	16.58
United States	Federal Republic	77.26	14.2

Source: CIA World Factbook

quantitative variables are continuous because they are measured. The observations are the data (in green ink). For example, the data corresponding to the variable "life expectancy" are 79.87, 79.56, 78.9, 69.43, 73.42, 72.09, and 77.26. The following data correspond to the individual Poland: a republic government with residents whose life expectancy is 73.42 years and a birth rate of 10.2 per 1,000 people. "Republic" is qualitative data that results from observing the value of the qualitative variable "government type." The life expectancy of 73.42 years is quantitative data that results from observing the value of the quantitative variable "life expectancy." ◄◄

NW *Now Work Problem 31.*

1.1 Assess Your Understanding

Concepts and Vocabulary

1. Define statistics and list the requirements of the statistical process.
2. Explain the difference between a population and a sample.
3. Explain the difference between descriptive statistics and inferential statistics.
4. What does it mean when an experiment is double blind?
5. Define qualitative variable. Provide some examples. Define quantitative variable. Provide some examples.
6. Discuss the difference between discrete and continuous variables.

Exercises

1. Qualitative   2. Quantitative   3. Quantitative   4. Qualitative
5. Quantitative   6. Quantitative   7. Quantitative   8. Quantitative

• **Skill Building**

In Problems 1–10, classify the variable as qualitative or quantitative.

1. Hair color
2. Salary
   NW 3. Weight of cars
4. Religious affiliation
5. ACT score
6. Grams of fat in a cheeseburger
7. Number of customers served at Wendy's during lunch
8. Number of times "3" is observed after rolling a die 10 times

9. Types of surgical procedures offered at General Hospital Qualitative

10. Amount of rainfall in Topeka, Kansas, during the summer of 2001 Quantitative

In Problems 11–20, determine whether the quantitative variable is discrete or continuous.

11. Home runs hit by Barry Bonds this season Discrete

12. Time spent studying for your first statistics exam

13. Strength of concrete in pounds per square inch
NW

14. Number of typos in a 500-page novel Discrete

15. Height of a tree Continuous

16. Number of people in a poll of 500 who believe Albert Einstein was the greatest scientist of the twentieth century Discrete

17. Number of flips of a coin needed until the first tail is observed Discrete

18. Speed of a car on the highway Continuous

19. Serum HDL cholesterol of a 32-year-old male Continuous

20. Annual income of a 45-year-old female executive

12. Continuous   13. Continuous   20. Continuous

In Problems 21–24, a research objective is presented. For each research objective, identify the population and sample in the study.

21. The Gallup Organization contacts 1019 adult residents of the United States aged 18 years or older and asks whether the events of September 11, 2001 were a life-altering experience.

22. A quality control manager randomly selects 50 bottles of Coca-Cola that were filled on October 15 in order to assess the calibration of the filling machine.

23. A farmer wanted to learn about the weight of his soybean crop. He randomly sampled 100 plants and measured the weight of the soybeans on the plant.

24. Every year the United States Census Bureau releases the Current Population Report based on a survey of 50,000 households. The goal of this report is to learn demographic characteristics of all households within the United States such as income.

• Applying the Concepts

For the studies given in Problems 25–30, (a) identify the research objective, (b) identify the sample, (c) list the descriptive statistics, and (d) state the conclusions made in the study.

25. **Is Brain Volume Associated with Schizophrenia?** A
NW study conducted by researchers was designed "to determine the genetic and nongenetic factors to structural brain abnormalities on schizophrenia." The researchers determined the brain volumes of 29 twins who were patients diagnosed with schizophrenia and compared them to the brain volumes of 29 healthy twins. Based upon a high-resolution MRI, it was determined the whole-brain volumes were 2.2% smaller in the schizophrenic patients. The researchers concluded that an increased genetic risk to develop schizophrenia is related to reduced brain growth early in life.

Source: "Volumes of Brain Structures in Twins Discordant for Schizophrenia," William F.C. Baare, et al.; *Archives of General Psychiatry* 58 (2000): 33–40.

26. **Blood Pressure and Diet** A study was conducted by researchers to determine "if blood pressure level is associated with dietary micronutrients in adolescents at risk for hypertension." The researchers randomly selected adolescents aged 14 to 16 years that had high blood pressure. They measured the folic acid intake of the adolescents. The high-folate group had folic acid intake greater than the recommended daily allowance while the low-folate group had intake less than the recommended daily allowance. It was determined that the average diastolic blood pressure for the low-folate group was substantially higher than in the high-folate group. For boys it was 72 versus 67 mm Hg and for girls it was 76 versus 73 mm Hg. It was determined that for adolescents who are at risk for high blood pressure, the benefits of a diet rich in folic acid (such as fruit, vegetables, and low-fat dairy products) could contribute to the prevention of hypertension (high blood pressure) when instituted at an early age.

Source: "Dietary Nutrients and Blood Pressure in Urban Minority Adolescents at Risk for Hypertension," Bonita Falkner, et al.; *Archives of Pediatrics and Adolescent Medicine* 154 (2000): 918–922.

27. **The Mozart Effect** Researchers at the University of California, Irvine, wished to determine whether "music cognition and cognitions pertaining to abstract operations such as mathematical or spatial reasoning" were related. To test the research question, 36 college students listened to Mozart's sonata for two pianos in D major, K488, for 10 minutes and then were administered a spatial reasoning test using the Stanford-Binet intelligence scale. The same students were also administered the test after sitting in a room for 10 minutes in complete silence. The mean score on the test following the Mozart piece was 119, while the mean test score following the silence was 110. The researchers concluded that

subjects performed better on abstract/spatial reasoning tests after listening to Mozart.

Source: "Music and spatial performance," Frances H. Rauscher, et al.; *Nature* 365 (14 October 1993): 611.

28. **Propecia** Merck Pharmaceutical Company manufactures Propecia, a drug that claims to treat male pattern hair loss on the vertex (top of the head) and anterior midscalp area in men. For 12 months, doctors studied over 1800 men aged 18 to 41 with mild to moderate amounts of ongoing hair loss. All men, whether receiving Propecia or placebo (a pill containing no medication), were given a medicated shampoo. In general, men who took Propecia maintained or increased the number of visible scalp hairs and noticed improvement in their hair in the first year, with the effect maintained in the second year. Hair counts in men who did not take Propecia continued to decrease. Merck concluded that Propecia is effective in maintaining or increasing the amount of hair on the vertex and anterior midscalp area.

Source: www.merck.com

29. **Victims of Crime** Gallup News Service conducted a survey of 1012 adults aged 18 years old or older, August 29–September 5, 2000. The respondents were asked, "Has anyone in your household been the victim of a crime in the past 12 months?" Of the 1012 adults surveyed, 24% said they or someone in the household had experienced some type of crime during the preceding year. Gallup News Service concluded that 24% of all households had been victimized by crime during the past year.

30. **Global Warming** Gallup News Service conducted a survey of 1004 adults 18 years and older, April 3–9, 2000. The respondents were asked, "Do you have a great deal of concern regarding global warming (the greenhouse effect)?" Of the 1004 adults surveyed, 40% said they worried about global warming a great deal. Gallup News Service concluded that 40% of all Americans worry about global warming a great deal.

In Problems 31–34, identify the individuals, variables, and data corresponding to the variables. Determine whether each variable is qualitative, continuous, or discrete.

31. **Survey of Students in Sullivan's Business Calculus Course** Michael Sullivan surveyed five students in his business calculus course and obtained the following information:

Student	Gender	Age	Number of Siblings
Neta Van Duyne	F	19	1
Dave Ebert	M	19	1
Kristin Bols	F	19	2
Michael Wirth	M	19	1
Jinita Desai	F	20	1

32. **BMW Cars** The following information relates to the entire product line of BMW automobiles:

Model	Body Style	Weight (pounds)	Number of Seats
M/Z3 Coupe	Coupe	2945	2
M/Z3 Roadster	Convertible	2690	2
3 Series	Coupe	2780	5
5 Series	Sedan	3450	5
7 Series	Sedan	4255	5
Z8	Convertible	3600	2

Source: Car and Driver magazine

33. **Driver's License Laws** The following data represent driver's license laws for various states.

State	Age for Driver's License	Blood Alcohol Concentration Limit	Mandatory Belt-use Law Seating Positions	Maximum Allowable Speed Limit, 1999
Alabama	16	0.08	Front	70
Illinois	18	0.08	Front	65
Montana	18	0.10	All	75
New York	17	0.10	Front	65
Texas	18	0.10	Front	70

Source: Time Almanac, 2000

34. NCAA Division I Women Basketball Players The following data represent the leading scorers in NCAA Division I Women's Basketball during the 1998/1999 season.

Player	College	Number of Games	Points Scored
Tamika Whitmore	Memphis	32	843
Jackie Stiles	SW Missouri State	32	823
Kim Knuth	Toledo	31	788
Kristina Behnfeldt	Marshall	26	621
Jamie Cassidy	Maine	31	738

Source: *Time Almanac,* 2000

35. Read a newspaper, magazine, or journal that contains a research study and identify (a) the research question the study addresses, (b) the population, (c) the sample, (d) any descriptive statistics, and (e) the inferences of the study.

1.2   Observational Studies; Simple Random Sampling

Objectives   **1**   Distinguish between an observational study and an experiment

          2   Obtain a simple random sample

We are now familiar with some of the terminology used in describing data. Now, we need to determine how to obtain data. When we defined the word statistics, we said it is a science that involves the collection of data. Data can be obtained from four sources:

1. A census
2. Existing sources
3. Survey sampling
4. Designed experiments

We start by defining a census.

Definition   A **census** is a list of all individuals in a population along with certain characteristics of each individual.

The United States conducts a census every 10 years in order to learn the demographic make-up of the United States. Everyone whose usual residence is within the United States borders must fill out a questionnaire packet. The cost of obtaining the census in 2000 was approximately $6 billion. The census data provide information such as the number of members in a household, number of years at present address, household income, and more. Because of the cost of obtaining census data, most researchers obtain data through existing sources, survey samples, or designed experiments.

Have you ever heard the phrase, "There is no point in reinventing the wheel?" Well, there is no point in spending energy obtaining data that already exist either. If a researcher wishes to conduct a study, and a data set exists that can be used to answer the researcher's questions, then it would be silly to collect the data from scratch. For example, in the August 22, 2001 issue of the *Journal of the American Medical Association* ["Physical Activity, Obesity, Height, and the Risk of Pancreatic Cancer," Dominique S. Michaud, ScD, et al. Volume 286, No. 8], researchers did a study in which they attempted to identify factors that increase the likelihood of an individual getting pancreatic cancer. Rather than conducting their own survey, they used data from two existing surveys: the Health Professionals Follow-up Study and the Nurses' Health Study. By doing this, they saved time and money. The moral of the story: **Don't collect data that have already been collected!**

Survey sampling is used in research where there is no attempt to influence the value of the variable of interest. For example, we may want to identify the "normal" systolic blood pressure of American men aged 40–44. The researcher would obtain a sample of men aged 40–44 and determine their systolic blood pressure. No attempt is made to influence the systolic blood pressure of the men surveyed. Polling data is another example of data obtained from a survey sample because the respondent is simply asked his or her opinion. No attempt is made to influence this opinion. Data obtained from a survey sample lead to an *observational study*.

Definition | An **observational study** measures the characteristics of a population by studying individuals in a sample, but does not attempt to manipulate or influence the variable(s) of interest. Observational studies are sometimes referred to as *ex post facto* (after-the-fact) studies because the value of the variable of interest has already been established.

We distinguish an observational study with a *designed experiment*.

Definition | A **designed experiment** applies a treatment to individuals (referred to as **experimental units**) and attempts to isolate the effects of the treatment on a **response variable**.

In Your Own Words

In observational studies, there is no control, while designed experiments try to maintain control.

Data obtained through experimentation will be thoroughly discussed in Section 1.5, but the main idea is that the researcher is able to control factors that influence the individuals. For example, suppose my son has two types of fertilizer and wants to determine which one is better. He might conduct an experiment in which he divides his garden into two plots. Plot 1 might receive the recommended amount of the first fertilizer and Plot 2 might receive the recommended amount of the second fertilizer. All other factors that affect plant growth (amount of sunlight, water, soil condition, and so on) would be the same for the two plots. The type of fertilizer is the treatment and the tomatoes are the experimental units. The weight of the tomatoes would be the response variable.

An example should clarify the difference between an observational study and a designed experiment.

▶ **EXAMPLE 1** **Observational Study versus Designed Experiment**

In most types of research, the goal is to determine the relation, if any, that may exist between two or more variables. For example, a researcher may want to determine whether there is a connection between smoking and lung

Note to Instructor
Have students brainstorm advantages and disadvantages of an observational study. What are some advantages and disadvantages of an experiment?

Caution

Beware of observational studies that claim causation!

cancer.* This type of study would be performed using an observational study because it is *ex post facto* (after-the-fact) research. The individuals in the study are examined after they have been smoking for some period of time. The individuals are not controlled in terms of the number of cigarettes smoked per day, eating habits, and so on. A researcher simply interviews a sample of smokers and monitors their rate of cancer as it compares with a sample of nonsmokers. The nonsmokers serve as a *control group*; that is, the nonsmokers serve as the benchmark upon which the smokers' rate of cancer is judged. The hope is that nonsmokers and smokers are alike in all of their traits, such as diet and exercise, except for smoking. Then, if a significant difference between the two groups' rates of cancer exists, the researcher might claim smoking *causes* cancer.

In actuality, the researcher determined that smoking is *associated* with cancer. It may be that the population of smokers has a higher rate of cancer, but this higher incidence rate is not necessarily a direct result of the smoking. It is possible that smokers have some characteristic that differs from the nonsmoking group, other than smoking, that is the *cause* of cancer. The characteristics that may be related to cancer, but that have not been identified in the study, are referred to as **lurking variables**. For example, a lurking variable might be the amount of exercise. Maybe smokers generally exercise less than nonsmokers and the lack of exercise is the cause of cancer. In this observational study we might be able to state that smokers have a higher rate of cancer than nonsmokers and that smoking is *associated* with cancer, but we would not be able to definitively state that smoking causes cancer.

Obtaining this type of data through experimentation would require randomly dividing a sample of people into two groups. We would then require one of the groups to smoke a pack of cigarettes each day for the next 20 years (the treatment) to determine whether it has a higher incidence rate of lung cancer (the response variable) than the nonsmoking (control) group! By approaching the study in this way, we would be able to control many of the factors that were beyond our control in the observational study. For example, we could make sure each group had the same diet and exercise regiment. This would allow us to determine whether smoking is a cause of cancer. Of course, there are moral issues to consider in conducting this type of experiment. ◄◄

It is vital that we understand that observational studies do not allow a researcher to claim causation, only association.

Observational studies are very useful tools for determining whether there is a relation between two variables, but it requires a designed experiment to isolate the cause of the relation.

Many observational studies are set up to learn characteristics of a population, such as polls. For example, the Gallup Organization routinely surveys Americans in an attempt to identify opinion.

Observational studies are performed for two reasons:

1. To learn characteristics of a population;
2. To determine whether there is an association between two or more variables where the values of the variables have already been determined. (Again, this is often referred to as *ex post facto* research.)

*The interested reader may wish to read Chapter 18, "Does Smoking Cause Cancer?" in David Salsburg's book *The Lady Tasting Tea*. W. H. Freeman and Co., 2001.

Ex post facto research is common in research where control of certain variables is impossible or unethical. For example, economists often perform research using observational studies because they do not have the ability to control many of the factors that affect our purchasing decisions. Some medical research requires that observational studies be conducted because of the risks thought to be associated with experimental study, such as the perceived link between smoking and lung cancer.

Experiments, on the other hand, are used whenever control of certain variables is desired. This type of research allows the researcher to identify certain cause and effect relationships among the variables in the study.

The bottom line to consider is control. If control is possible, an experiment should be performed. However, if control is not possible or necessary, then observational studies are appropriate.

 Now Work Problem 5.

Sampling

The goal in sampling is to obtain individuals that will participate in a study so that accurate information about the population can be obtained. For example, the Gallup Organization typically will poll a sample of about 1,000 adults aged 18 years or older from the population of adults aged 18 years or older. We want the sample to provide as much information as possible, but each additional piece of information has a price. So the question becomes "How can the researcher obtain accurate information about the population through the sample while minimizing the costs in terms of money, time, personnel, and so on?" There is a balance between information and cost. An appropriate sample design can maximize the amount of information obtained about the population for a given cost.

We will discuss four basic sampling techniques: simple random sampling, stratified sampling, systematic sampling, and cluster sampling. These sampling methods are based on planned randomness. Planned randomness means that the individuals selected for the study are chosen on the basis of some predetermined method, so that any biases that may be introduced (knowingly and unknowingly) by the surveyor during the selection process are eliminated. In other words, the surveyor does not have a choice as to who is in the study. We discuss simple random sampling now and discuss the remaining three types of sampling in the next section.

② Simple Random Sampling

The most basic sample survey design is **simple random sampling**, which is often abbreviated as **random sampling**.

Definition

In Your Own Words

Simple random sampling is like selecting names from a hat.

> A sample of size *n* from a population of size *N* is obtained through **simple random sampling** if every possible sample of size *n* has an equally likely chance of occurring. The sample is then called a **simple random sample**.

The sample is always a subset of the population with $n < N$. Let's look at an example.

▶ **EXAMPLE 2**   Illustrating Simple Random Sampling

Problem: Sophia has four tickets to a concert. Six of her friends, Yolanda, Michael, Kevin, Marissa, Annie, and Katie, have all expressed an interest in going to the concert. Sophia decides to randomly select three of the six.

Note to Instructor
In class discussion: What is meant by sampling "with replacement"? What is meant by sampling "without replacement"?

(a) List all possible samples of size $n = 3$ (without replacement) from the population of size $N = 6$.

(b) Comment on the likelihood of the sample containing Michael, Kevin, and Marissa.

Approach: We list all possible combinations of three people chosen from the six. Remember, in simple random sampling, each sample of size three is equally likely to occur.

Solution:

(a) The possible samples of size three are listed in Table 2.

TABLE 2			
Yolanda, Michael, Kevin	Yolanda, Michael, Marissa	Yolanda, Michael, Annie	Yolanda, Michael, Katie
Yolanda, Kevin, Marissa	Yolanda, Kevin, Annie	Yolanda, Kevin, Katie	Yolanda, Marissa, Annie
Yolanda, Marissa, Katie	Yolanda, Annie, Katie	Michael, Kevin, Marissa	Michael, Kevin, Annie
Michael, Kevin, Katie	Michael, Marissa, Annie	Michael, Marissa, Katie	Michael, Annie, Katie
Kevin, Marissa, Annie	Kevin, Marissa, Katie	Kevin, Annie, Katie	Marissa, Annie, Katie

From Table 2, we see that there are 20 possible samples of size three from the population of size six. We use the term "sample" to mean the individuals in the sample.

(b) There is 1 sample that contains Michael, Kevin, and Marissa and 20 possible samples, so there is a 1 in 20 chance that the simple random sample would contain Michael, Kevin, and Marissa. In fact, all the samples of size three have a 1 in 20 chance of occurring. ◄◄

NW *Now Work Problem 13.*

Obtaining a Simple Random Sample   The results of Example 2 leave one question unanswered: How do we actually select the individuals in a simple random sample? Simple random sampling is just like drawing names out of a hat. To obtain a simple random sample of size three from the population in Example 2, we could write the names of the six people in the population on different sheets of paper and then select three names from the hat. Simple random sampling is that easy!

Often, however, the size of the population is so large that performing simple random sampling in this fashion is not practical. Typically, random numbers are used by assigning each individual in the population a unique number between 1 and N, where N is the size of the population. Then, n random numbers from this list are selected. Because we must number the individuals in the population, we must have a list of all the individuals within the population, called a **frame**.

In Your Own Words

A frame lists all the individuals in a population. For example, a list of registered voters might be a frame.

► **EXAMPLE 3**   **Obtaining a Simple Random Sample**

Problem: The Village of Lemont wants to learn the opinion of its residents regarding the construction of a new shopping mall. The mayor wishes to obtain a simple random sample of size 10 from the 8791 residents of Lemont.

Approach: The mayor must first obtain a list of all residents in the village, the frame, and assign the residents numbers from 1–8791. Finally, the mayor will randomly select 10 residents to be in the sample. Once an individual is selected to be in the sample, he or she cannot be selected again. This is called **sampling without replacement**. We sample without replacement so that we don't select the same individual twice.

Solution: A table of random numbers is used to select the individuals to be in the sample. See Table 3.* We select a starting place in the table of random numbers. This can be done by closing our eyes and placing a finger on the table. That may sound haphazard, but it accomplishes our goal of being completely random. Suppose we start in column 9, row 13. Since our data have four digits, we select four-digit numbers from the table.

Column 9

TABLE 3										
	Number Column									
Row Number	**01–05**	**06–10**	**11–15**	**16–20**	**21–25**	**26–30**	**31–35**	**36–40**	**41–45**	**46–50**
01	89392	23212	74**483**	36590	25956	36544	68518	40805	09980	00467
02	61458	17639	96**252**	95649	73727	33912	72896	66218	52341	97141
03	11452	74197	81**962**	48433	90360	26480	73231	37740	26628	44690
04	27575	04429	31**308**	02241	01698	19191	18948	78871	36030	23980
05	36829	59109	88**976**	46845	28329	47460	88944	08264	00843	84592
06	81902	93458	42**161**	26099	09419	89073	82849	09160	61845	40906
07	59761	55212	33360	68751	86737	79743	85262	31887	37879	17525
08	46827	25906	64708	20307	78423	15910	86548	08763	47050	18513
09	24040	66449	32353	83668	13874	86741	81312	54185	78824	00718
10	98144	96372	50277	15571	82261	66628	31457	00377	63423	55141
11	14228	17930	30118	00438	49666	65189	62869	31304	17117	71489
12	55366	51057	90065	14791	62426	02957	85518	28822	30588	32798
13	96101	30**646**	**35**526	90389	73634	79304	96635	6626	94683	16696
14	38152	55**474**	**30**153	26525	83647	31988	82182	98377	33802	80471
15	85007	18**416**	**24**661	95581	45868	15662	28906	36392	07617	50248
16	85544	15**890**	**80**011	18160	33468	84106	40603	01315	74664	20553
17	10446	20**699**	**98**370	17684	16932	80449	92654	02084	19985	59321
18	67237	45**509**	**17**638	65115	29757	80705	82686	48565	72612	61760
19	23026	89**817**	**05**403	82209	30573	47501	00135	33955	50250	72592
20	67411	58**542**	**18**678	46491	13219	84084	27783	34508	55158	78742

Row 13 — (pointer to row 13)

We skip 9080 because it is larger than 8791

Note to Instructor
Concept check: How do you know how many digits to look at when selecting a simple random sample from a table of random digits?

So, we start our sample by surveying individual 4635. We then proceed downward. The next individual in the sample would be 7430. If a number is repeated, we do not count it twice, since we are sampling without replacement. Because our population has individuals numbered from 1 to 8791, anytime we

*Each digit is in its own column. The digits are displayed in groups of five for ease of reading. The digits in row 1 are 893922321274483 and so on. The first digit, 8, is in column 1; the second digit, 9, is in column 2; the ninth digit, 1, is in column 9.

encounter 0 or a number larger than 8791, we skip it and continue. Continuing in this fashion, we have the following individuals in our sample:

4635, 7430, 1624, 0917, 1705, 4218, 4833, 2529, 3080, 1612

Each of the individuals selected in the sample is set in bold face type in Table 3 to help understand where the numbers came from. So the Village of Lemont would interview the residents corresponding to these numbers.   ◄◄

> **Using Technology:** In practice, a random-number table is not used to obtain simple random samples. This is because many calculators and computers have random-number generators that use programs to obtain random numbers.

▶ **EXAMPLE 4**

Using a Graphing Calculator to Generate a Simple Random Sample

Problem: Use a graphing calculator to find a simple random sample of 10 residents for the Village of Lemont presented in Example 3.

Approach: The approach will be the same as that presented in Example 3. We number the residents 1–8791 and randomly select 10 residents to be in the sample, again without replacement.

The Solution: First, we must set the *seed*. The **seed** in a random-number generator provides an initial point for the calculator to start generating numbers. It is just like selecting the initial point in the table of random numbers from Example 3. The seed can be any nonzero number. See Figure 2(a). We are now ready to obtain the individuals in our simple random sample. Using the `randInt(` feature, we obtain the first individual in the random sample shown in Figure 2(b).

Figure 2

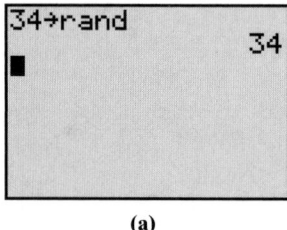 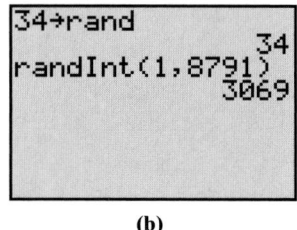

(a)   (b)

The first person in our sample will be 3069. Continue pressing ENTER until we obtain our sample of size 10. The following people will be in our sample:

3069, 885, 5822, 8385, 3055, 7802, 6349, 1274, 2861, 8775

There is a very important consequence in comparing the individuals in the samples from Example 3 and Example 4. Notice that while both samples were constructed in a similar fashion, they resulted in different individuals in the sample! For this reason, each sample will likely result in different descriptive statistics. Any inference based on each sample may result in different conclusions regarding the population. Therein lies the nature of statistics. Inferences based upon samples will vary because the individuals in two different samples vary.

Caution

Random-number generators are not truly random, because they are programs and programs do not act "randomly." The seed dictates the "random numbers" that are generated.

NW *Now Work Problem 15.*

Note to Instructor
In class discussion: If different samples result in different individuals being in the sample, how can any valid conclusions be made regarding the population being studied?

1.2 Assess Your Understanding

Concepts and Vocabulary

1. Explain the difference between an observational study and an experiment. In your explanation, be sure to discuss the circumstances in which each is appropriate.
2. Explain why a frame is necessary to obtain a simple random sample.
3. Discuss why sampling is used in statistics.
4. What does it mean when sampling is done without replacement?

Exercises

2. Experiment   4. Observational study   7. Observational study
8. Observational study   9. Experiment   10. Experiment
11. Observational study   12. Observational study

• Applying the Concepts

In Problems 1–12, determine whether the study depicts an observational study or an experiment.

1. A study to determine whether there is a relation between the rate of cancer and an individual's proximity to high-tension wires. *Observational study*
2. Rats with cancer are divided into two groups. One group receives 5 mg of an experimental drug that is thought to fight cancer, and the other receives 10 mg. After two years, the spread of the cancer is measured.
3. Seventh-grade students are randomly divided into two groups. One group is taught math using traditional techniques while the other is taught math using a reform method. After one year, each group is given an achievement test to compare its proficiency with that of the other group. *Experiment*
4. A poll is conducted in which 500 people are asked whom they plan to vote for in the upcoming election.

5. **(NW)** A survey is conducted asking 400 people, "Do you prefer Coke or Pepsi?" *Observational study*
6. While shopping, 200 people are asked to perform a taste test in which they drink from two unmarked cups. They are then asked which drink they prefer. *Experiment*
7. The article cited in Problem 25 from Section 1.1.
8. The article cited in Problem 26 from Section 1.1.
9. The article cited in Problem 27 from Section 1.1.
10. The article cited in Problem 28 from Section 1.1.
11. The article cited in Problem 29 from Section 1.1.
12. The article cited in Problem 30 from Section 1.1.

13. **(NW)** **Listing Possible Simple Random Samples** The United States Senate finance committee has a subcommittee on long-term growth and debt reduction. As of 12/2001 the members of this subcommittee were Bob Graham, Frank Murkowski, Jon Kyl, Max Baucus, and Kent Conrad. Suppose two randomly selected committee members are asked to investigate the impact of a tax reduction bill on the federal deficit.
    (a) List all possible simple random samples of size two.
    (b) Comment on the likelihood that the two individuals selected are Bob Graham and Max Baucus.

14. **Listing Possible Simple Random Samples** During the presidency of Andrew Jackson, there were six cabinet positions: secretary of state, secretary of the treasury, secretary of war, attorney general, postmaster general, and secretary of the Navy. Suppose the president needs to send two members of the cabinet to represent the United States at a foreign dignitary's funeral.
    (a) List all possible simple random samples of size two.
    (b) Comment on the likelihood that the secretary of state and attorney general attend the funeral.

(NW) 15. Obtaining a Simple Random Sample The following table lists the 50 states:

1	Alabama	11	Hawaii	21	Massachusetts	31	New Mexico	41	South Dakota
2	Alaska	12	Idaho	22	Michigan	32	New York	42	Tennessee
3	Arizona	13	Illinois	23	Minnesota	33	North Carolina	43	Texas
4	Arkansas	14	Indiana	24	Mississippi	34	North Dakota	44	Utah
5	California	15	Iowa	25	Missouri	35	Ohio	45	Vermont
6	Colorado	16	Kansas	26	Montana	36	Oklahoma	46	Virginia
7	Connecticut	17	Kentucky	27	Nebraska	37	Oregon	47	Washington
8	Delaware	18	Louisiana	28	Nevada	38	Pennsylvania	48	West Virginia
9	Florida	19	Maine	29	New Hampshire	39	Rhode Island	49	Wisconsin
10	Georgia	20	Maryland	30	New Jersey	40	South Carolina	50	Wyoming

(a) Obtain a simple random sample of size 10 using Table I in Appendix A, a graphing calculator, or computer software.

(b) Obtain a second simple random sample of size 10 using Table I in Appendix A, a graphing calculator, or computer software.

16. **Obtaining a Simple Random Sample** The following table lists the 43 presidents of the United States.

(a) Obtain a simple random sample of size eight using Table I in Appendix A, a graphing calculator, or computer software.

(b) Obtain a second simple random sample of size eight using Table I in Appendix A, a graphing calculator, or computer software.

1	Washington	10	Tyler	19	Hayes	28	Wilson	37	Nixon
2	J. Adams	11	Polk	20	Garfield	29	Harding	38	Ford
3	Jefferson	12	Taylor	21	Arthur	30	Coolidge	39	Carter
4	Madison	13	Fillmore	22	Cleveland	31	Hoover	40	Reagan
5	Monroe	14	Pierce	23	B. Harrison	32	F.D. Roosevelt	41	George H. Bush
6	J.Q. Adams	15	Buchanan	24	Cleveland	33	Truman	42	Clinton
7	Jackson	16	Lincoln	25	McKinley	34	Eisenhower	43	George W. Bush
8	Van Buren	17	A. Johnson	26	T. Roosevelt	35	Kennedy		
9	W.H. Harrison	18	Grant	27	Taft	36	L.B. Johnson		

17. **Obtaining a Simple Random Sample** Suppose you are the president of the student government. You wish to conduct a survey in order to determine the student body's opinion regarding student services. The administration provides you with a list that contains the names and phone numbers of the 19,935 registered students.

(a) Discuss the procedure you would follow in order to obtain a simple random sample of 25 students.

(b) Obtain this sample.

18. **Obtaining a Simple Random Sample** Suppose the mayor of Justice, Illinois, asks you to poll the residents of the village. The mayor provides you with a list that contains the names and phone numbers of the 5832 residents of the village.

(a) Discuss the procedure you would follow in order to obtain a simple random sample of 20 residents.

(b) Obtain this sample.

Technology Step-by-Step
Obtaining a Simple Random Sample

TI-83 Plus

Step 1: Enter any nonzero number on the HOME screen.

Step 2: Press the STO $\Rightarrow$ button.

Step 3: Press the MATH button.

Step 4: Highlight the PRB menu and select 1: rand.

Step 5: From the HOME screen press ENTER.

Step 6: Press the MATH button. Highlight PRB menu and select 5: randInt(.

Step 7: With randInt(on the HOME screen enter 1 , N where N is the population size. For example, if $N = 500$, enter the following:

randInt(1,500)

Press ENTER to obtain the first individual in the sample. Continue pressing ENTER until the desired sample size is obtained.

MINITAB

Step 1: Select the **Calc** menu and highlight **Set Base** ....

Step 2: Enter any seed number you desire. Note that it is not necessary to set the seed, because MINITAB uses the time of day in seconds to set the seed.

Step 3: Select the **Calc** menu and highlight **Random Data** and select **Integer** ...

Step 4: Fill in the window shown below with the appropriate values. To obtain a simple random sample for the situation in Example 3, we would fill in the following:

Integer Distribution	☒

Generate [15]   rows of data

Store in column[s]:

[c1]

Minimum value: [1]
Maximum value: [8791]

[Select]

[Help]   [OK]   [Cancel]

The reason we generate 15 rows of data (instead of 10) is in case any of the random numbers repeat. Select OK, and the random numbers will appear in column 1 (C1) in the spreadsheet.

Excel   *Step 1:* Be sure the Data Analysis Tool Pak is activated. This is done by selecting the **Tools** menu and highlighting **Add – Ins** ... Check the box for the Analysis ToolPak and select OK.

Step 2: Select **Tools** and highlight **Data Analysis** ... Highlight **Random Number Generation** and select OK.

Step 3: Fill in the window with the appropriate values. To obtain a simple random sample for the situation in Example 3, we would fill in the following:

Random Number Generation	? ☒

Number of Variables: [1]   [OK]

Number of Random Numbers: [15]   [Cancel]

Distribution: [Uniform ▼]   [Help]

Parameters

Between   [1]   and   [8792]

Random Seed: [34]

Output options

○ Output Range: [▦]
◉ New Worksheet Ply: [   ]
○ New Workbook

The reason we generate 15 rows of data (instead of 10) is in case any of the random numbers repeat. Notice also that the parameter is between 1 and 8792 so that any value less than or equal to that number is possible. In the unlikely event that 8792 appears, simply ignore it. Select OK, and the random numbers will appear in column 1 (A1) in the spreadsheet. Ignore any values to the right of the decimal place.

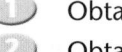

Other Types of Sampling

Objectives Obtain a stratified sample

Obtain a systematic sample

Obtain a cluster sample

One of the goals of sampling is to obtain as much information as possible about the population at the least cost. Remember, we are using the word cost in a general sense. Cost includes monetary outlays, time, and other resources. With this goal in mind, we may find it advantageous to use sampling techniques other than simple random sampling.

Stratified Sampling

Under certain circumstances, *stratified sampling* provides more information about the population for less cost than simple random sampling.

Definition   A **stratified sample** is obtained by separating the population into nonoverlapping groups called *strata* and then obtaining a simple random sample from each stratum. The individuals within each stratum should be homogeneous (or similar) in some way.

In Your Own Words

"Stratum" is singular while "strata" is plural. The word "strata" means division. So a stratified sample is a simple random sample of different divisions of the population.

For example, suppose Congress was considering a bill that abolishes estate taxes. In an effort to determine the opinion of her constituency, a senator asks a pollster to conduct a survey within her district. The pollster may divide the population of registered voters within the district into three strata: Republican, Democrat, and Independent. This is because the members within the three party affiliations may have the same opinion regarding estate taxes. The main criterion in performing a stratified sample is that each group (stratum) must have a common attribute that results in the individuals being similar within the stratum.

An advantage of stratified sampling over simple random sampling is that it may allow fewer individuals to be surveyed while obtaining the same or more information. This result occurs because individuals within each subgroup have similar characteristics, so opinions within the group do not vary much from one individual to the next.

▶ EXAMPLE 1   **Obtaining a Stratified Sample**

Problem: The president of DePaul University wants to conduct a survey in order to determine the community's opinion regarding campus safety. The president feels the DePaul community can be divided into three groups—resident students, nonresident (commuting) students, and staff (including faculty)—and so will obtain a stratified sample. Suppose there are 6204 resident students, 13,304 nonresident students, and 2401 staff, for a total of 21,909 individuals in the population. The president wants to obtain a sample of size 100, with the number of individuals selected from each stratum weighted by the population size. So resident students will make up $6204/21,909 = 28\%$ of the sample, nonresident students account for 61% of the sample, and staff will constitute 11% of the sample. To obtain a sample of size 100, the president will obtain a stratified sample of $0.28(100) = 28$ resident students, $0.61(100) = 61$ nonresident students, and $0.11(100) = 11$ staff.

Approach: To obtain the stratified sample, conduct a simple random sample within each group. That is, obtain a simple random sample of 28 resident students (from the 6204 resident students), a simple random sample of 61 nonresident students and a simple random sample of 11 staff.

Solution: Using Minitab, with the seed set to 4032 and the values shown in Figure 3, we obtain the following sample of staff:

240, 630, 847, 190, 2096, 705, 2320, 323, 701, 471, 744

Figure 3

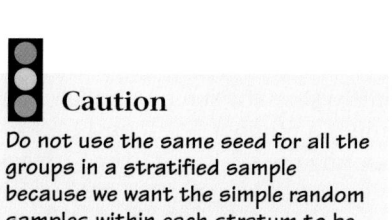

Caution

Do not use the same seed for all the groups in a stratified sample because we want the simple random samples within each stratum to be independent of each other.

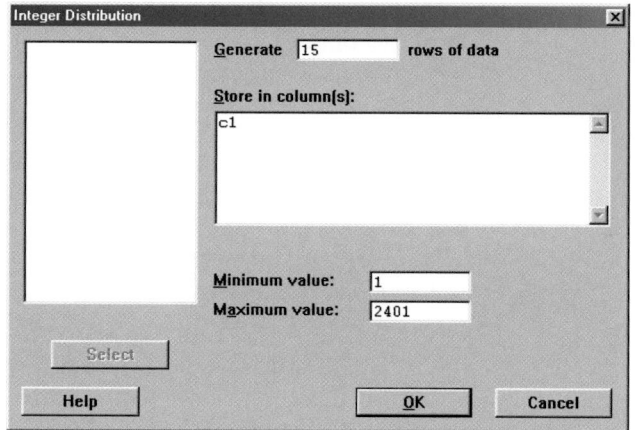

Repeat this procedure for the resident and nonresident students. ◄◄

An advantage of stratified sampling over simple random sampling is that it allows the researcher to determine characteristics within each stratum. This allows analysis to be performed on each subgroup to see if any significant differences between the groups exist. For example, we could analyze the data obtained in Example 1 to see if there is a difference in the opinions of students versus faculty.

② Systematic Sampling

In both simple random sampling and stratified sampling, it is necessary that a list of the individuals in the population being studied (the frame) exists. Therefore, these sampling techniques require some preliminary work before the sample is obtained. A sampling technique that does not require a frame is *systematic sampling.*

Definition

A **systematic sample** is obtained by selecting every kth individual from the population. The first individual selected is a random number between 1 and k.

 In Your Own Words

Systematic sampling is like selecting every fifth person out of a line.

Because systematic sampling does not require a frame, it is a useful technique to employ when you can't obtain a list of the individuals in the population that you wish to study.

The idea behind obtaining a systematic sample is relatively simple: select a number k, randomly select a number between 1 and k and survey that individual, and then survey every kth individual thereafter. For example, we might decide to survey every $k = 8$th individual. We randomly select a number between 1 and 8 such as 5. This means we survey the 5th, $5 + 8 = 13$th, $13 + 8 = 21$st, $21 + 8 = 29$th, and so on, individual until we reach the desired sample size.

▶ **EXAMPLE 2** **Obtaining a Systematic Sample Without a Frame**

Problem: The manager of Jewel Food Stores wants to measure the satisfaction of the store's customers. Design a sampling technique that can be used to obtain a sample of 40 customers.

Approach: A frame of Jewel customers would be difficult, if not impossible, to obtain because it is unlikely that Jewel can maintain a list of all its customers. Therefore, it is reasonable to use systematic sampling by surveying every kth customer that leaves the store.

Solution: The manager decides to obtain a systematic sample by surveying every 7th customer. He randomly determines a number between 1 and 7—say, 5. He then surveys the 5th customer exiting the store and every 7th customer thereafter, until a sample of 40 customers exists. The survey will include customers 5, 12, 19, ..., 278.* ◀◀

But how do we select the value of k? If the size of the population is unknown, there is no mathematical way to determine k. It must be chosen simply by determining a value of k that is not so large that we are unable to achieve our desired sample size, but is not so small that we do not obtain a sample size that is representative of the population.

To clarify this point, let's revisit Example 2. Suppose we chose a value of k that was too large—say, 30. This means that we will survey every 30th shopper, starting with the 5th. To obtain a sample of size 40 would require that 1175 shoppers visit Jewel on that day. If Jewel does not have 1175 shoppers, the desired sample size will not be achieved. On the other hand, if k is too small—say, 4—we would survey the 5th, 9th, ..., 161st shopper. It may be that the 161st shopper exits the store at 3 P.M., which means our survey did not include any of the evening shoppers. Certainly, this sample is not representative of *all* Jewel patrons! An estimate of the size of the population would certainly help determine an appropriate value for k.

To determine the value of k when the size of the population, N, is known is relatively straightforward. Suppose we wish to survey a population whose size is known to be $N = 20{,}325$. We desire a sample of size $n = 100$. To guarantee that individuals are selected evenly from the beginning as well as the end of the population (such as early and late shoppers), we compute N/n and round down to the nearest integer. For example, $20{,}325/100 = 203.25$, so $k = 203$. Then we randomly select a number between 1 and 203 and select every 203rd individual thereafter. So, if we randomly selected 90 as our starting point, we would survey the 90th, 293rd, 496th, ..., 20,187th individuals.

---

*Because we are surveying 40 customers, the first individual surveyed is the 5th, the second is the $5 + 7 = 12$th, the third is the $5 + 2(7) = 19$th, and so on, until we reach the 40th, which is the $5 + 39(7) = 278$th shopper.

We summarize the procedure as follows:

Steps in Systematic Sampling, Population Size Known

Step 1: Determine the population size, N.

Step 2: Determine the sample size desired, n.

Step 3: Compute N/n and round down to the nearest integer. This value is k.

Step 4: Randomly select a number between 1 and k. Call this number p.

Step 5: The sample will consist of the following individuals:

$$p, \ p + k, \ p + 2k, \ldots, \ p + (n - 1)k$$

Because systematic sampling does not require that the size of the population be known, it typically provides more information for a given cost than does simple random sampling. In addition, systematic sampling is easier to employ, so there is less possibility of interviewer error occurring, such as selecting the wrong individual to be surveyed.

NW *Now Work Problem 17.*

③ Cluster Sampling

A fourth sampling method is called *cluster sampling*. The previous three sampling methods discussed have benefits under certain circumstances; so does cluster sampling.

Definition

A **cluster sample** is obtained by selecting all individuals within a randomly selected collection or group of individuals.

In Your Own Words

Imagine a mall parking lot. Each subsection of the lot could be a cluster (Section F-4 for example).

Consider a quality control engineer who wants to verify that a certain machine is filling bottles with 16 ounces of liquid detergent. To obtain a sample of bottles from the machine, the engineer could use systematic sampling by sampling every kth bottle from the machine; however, it would be time consuming waiting next to the filling machine for the bottles to come off the line. Suppose that, as the bottles come off the line, they are placed into cartons of 12 bottles each. An alternative sampling method would be to randomly select a few cartons and measure the contents of all 12 bottles. This would be an example of cluster sampling. It is a good sampling method in this situation because it would speed up the data collection process.

▶ **EXAMPLE 3**   **Obtaining a Cluster Sample**

Problem: A sociologist wants to gather data regarding the household income within the City of Chicago. Obtain a sample using cluster sampling.

Approach: The City of Chicago can easily be set up so that each city block is a cluster. Once the city blocks have been identified, we obtain a simple random sample of the city blocks and survey all households on the blocks selected.

Solution: Suppose there are 10,493 city blocks in Chicago. First, we must number the blocks from 1 to 10,493. Suppose the sociologist has enough time and money to survey 20 clusters (city blocks). Therefore, the sociologist should obtain a simple random sample of 20 numbers between 1 and 10,493 and survey all households from those clusters selected. Cluster sampling is a good choice in this example because it reduces the travel time to households that is likely to occur with both simple random sampling and stratified sampling. In addition, there is no need to obtain a detailed frame with cluster sampling. The only frame needed is one that provides information regarding city blocks.　◄◄

Note to Instructor
In-Class Activity: Compare and contrast each of the sampling techniques. Discuss a research situation in which each type of sampling would be the most appropriate.

Recall that in systematic sampling we had to determine an appropriate value for k, the number of individuals to skip between individuals selected to be in the sample. We have a similar problem in cluster sampling. The following are a few of the questions that arise:

- How do I cluster the population?
- How many clusters do I sample?
- How many individuals should be in each cluster?

First, it must be determined whether the individuals within the proposed cluster are homogeneous (similar individuals) or heterogeneous (dissimilar individuals). Consider the results of Example 3. City blocks tend to have similar households. Surveying one house on a city block is likely to result in similar responses from another house on the same block. This results in duplicate information. We conclude the following: If the clusters have homogeneous individuals, it is better to have more clusters with fewer individuals in each cluster.

What if the cluster is heterogeneous? Under this circumstance, the heterogeneity of the cluster likely resembles the heterogeneity of the population. In other words, each cluster is a scaled-down representation of the overall population. For example, a quality control manager might use shipping boxes that contain 100 light bulbs as a cluster, since the rate of defects within the cluster would closely mimic the rate of defects in the population. Thus, when each of the clusters is heterogeneous, fewer clusters with more individuals in each cluster is appropriate.

The four sampling techniques just presented are sampling techniques in which the individuals are selected randomly. Often, however, sampling methods are used in which the individuals are not randomly selected, such as *convenience sampling*.

Convenience Sampling

Convenience sampling is probably the easiest sampling method.

Definition　　A **convenience sample** is a sample in which the individuals are easily obtained.

Caution

Studies that use convenience sampling generally have results that are suspect. The results should be looked upon with extreme skepticism.

There are many types of convenience samples, but probably the most popular are those in which the individuals in the sample are **self-selected** (i.e., the individuals themselves decide to participate in a survey). Examples of self-selected sampling include phone-in polling where a radio personality will ask his or her listeners to phone the station to submit their opinions. Another example is the use of the Internet to conduct surveys. For example, *Dateline* will present a story regarding a certain topic and ask its viewers to "tell us what you think" by completing a questionnaire online or phoning in an opinion. Both of these samples are poor designs because the individuals who decide to be in the sample generally have strong opinions about the topic. Additionally, a typical individual in the population will not bother phoning or logging on to their computer to complete a survey. Any inference made regarding the population from this type of sample should be made with extreme caution.

Multistage Sampling

In practice, most large-scale surveys obtain samples using a combination of the techniques just presented.

As an example of multistage sampling, consider Nielsen Media Research. This company measures the number of households watching TV programs. Nielsen randomly selects households and monitors the programs these households are watching through a "People Meter." The meter is an electronic box placed on each TV within the household. The "People Meter" measures what program is being watched and who is watching it. Nielsen selects the households with the use of a two-stage sampling process.

Stage 1: Using U.S. Census data, Nielsen divides the country into geographic areas (strata). The strata are typically city blocks in urban areas and geographic regions in rural areas. About 6000 strata are randomly selected.

Stage 2: Nielsen sends representatives to the selected strata and lists the households within the strata. The households are then randomly selected through a simple random sample.

As another example of multistage sampling, consider the sample conducted by the Census Bureau used for the Current Population Survey. This survey requires five stages of sampling:

Stage 1: Stratified sample
Stage 2: Cluster sample
Stage 3: Stratified sample
Stage 4: Cluster sample
Stage 5: Systematic sample

This survey is very important because it is used to obtain demographic estimates of the United States in noncensus years. A detailed presentation of the sampling method used by the Census Bureau can be found in *The Current Population Survey: Design and Methodology*, Technical Paper No. 40.

Sample Size Considerations

Throughout the discussion of sampling, we did not mention how to determine the sample size. Determining the sample size is key in the overall statistical process. In other words, the researcher must ask the following question: "How many individuals must I survey in order to draw conclusions about the population within some predetermined margin of error?" The researcher must find the correct balance between the reliability of the results and the cost of obtaining those results. The bottom line is that time and money determine the level of confidence a researcher will place in the conclusions drawn from the sample data. The more time and money the researcher has available, the more accurate will be the results of the statistical inference.

Figure 4

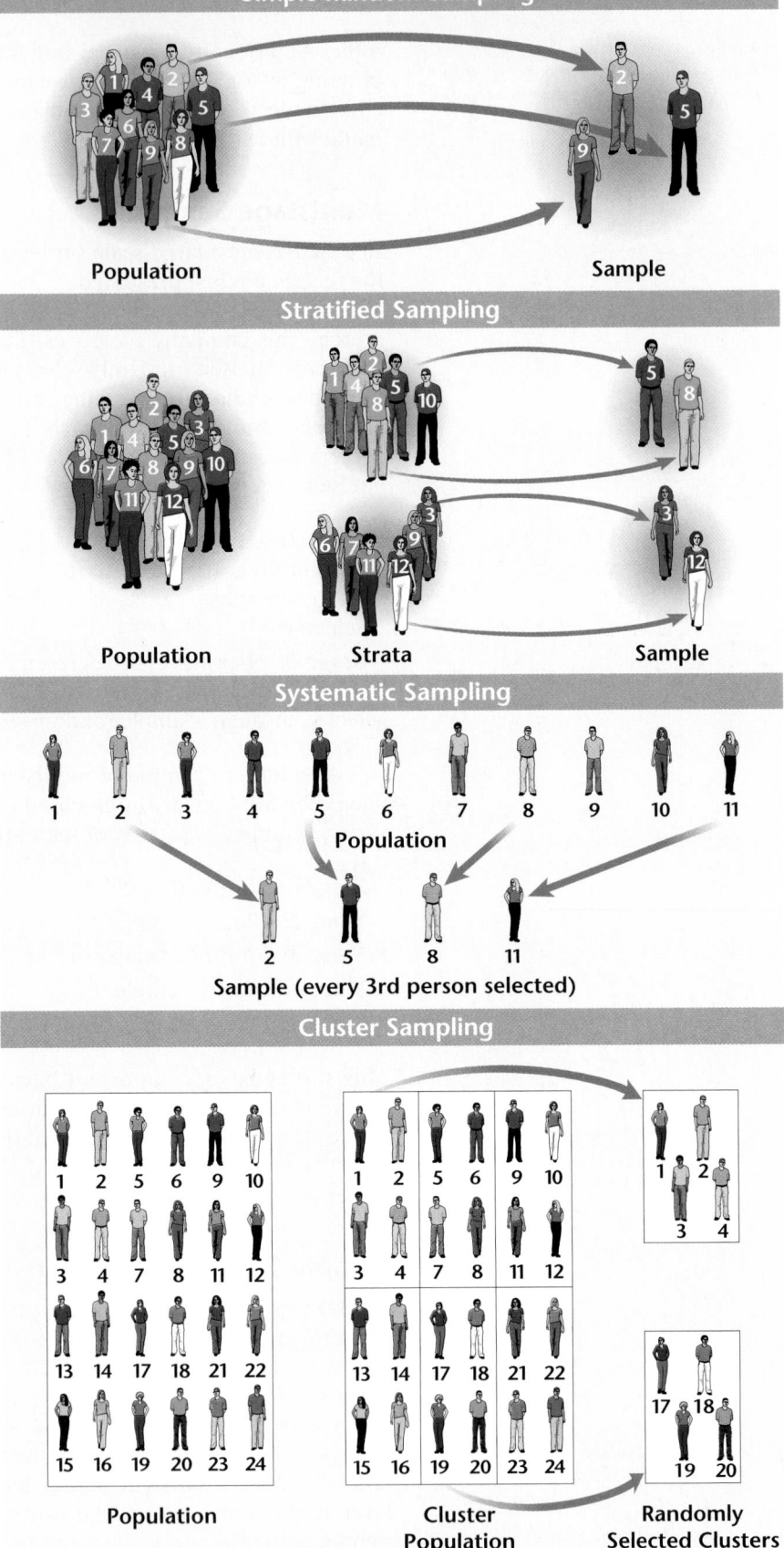

Nonetheless, techniques do exist for determining the sample size required in order to estimate characteristics regarding the population within some margin of error. We will consider some of these techniques in Sections 8.1 and 8.3. (For a detailed discussion of sample size considerations, consult a text on sampling techniques such as *Elements of Sampling Theory and Methods* by Z. Govindarajulu, Prentice Hall, 1999.)

Summary

Figure 4 provides a summary of the four sampling techniques presented.

1.3 Assess Your Understanding

Concepts and Vocabulary

1. Describe a circumstance in which stratified sampling would be an appropriate sampling method.

2. Which sampling method does not require a frame?

3. Why are convenience samples ill advised?

Exercises

• Skill Building

10. Systematic

In Problems 1–10, identify the type of sampling used.

1. In order to estimate the percentage of defects in a recent manufacturing batch, a quality control manager at Intel selects every 8th chip that comes off the assembly line starting with the 3rd, until she obtains a sample of 140 chips. Systematic

2. In order to determine the average IQ of ninth-grade students, a school psychologist obtains a list of all high schools in the local public school system. She randomly selects five of these schools and administers an IQ test to all ninth-grade students at the selected schools. Cluster

3. In an effort to determine customer satisfaction, United Airlines randomly selects 50 flights during a certain week and surveys all passengers on the flights. Cluster

4. A member of Congress wishes to determine her constituency's opinion regarding estate taxes. She divides her constituency into three income classes: low-income households, middle-income households, and upper-income households. She then takes a random sample of households from each income class. Stratified

5. In an effort to identify whether an advertising campaign has been effective, a marketing firm conducts a nation-wide poll by randomly selecting individuals from a list of known users of the product. Simple random

6. A radio station asks its listeners to call in their opinion regarding the use of American forces in peacekeeping missions. Convenience

7. A farmer divides his orchard into 50 subsections, randomly selects 4 and samples all of the trees within the 4 subsections in order to approximate the yield of his orchard. Cluster

8. A school official divides the student population into five classes: freshman, sophomore, junior, senior, graduate student. The official takes a random sample from each class and asks the members' opinions regarding student services. Stratified

9. A survey regarding download time on a certain Web site is administered on the Internet by a market research firm to anyone who would like to take it. Convenience

10. A lobby has a list of the 100 senators of the United States. In order to determine the Senate's position regarding farm subsidies, they decide to talk with every seventh senator on the list starting with the third.

• Applying the Concepts

11. **Sample Design** The city of Naperville is considering the construction of a new commuter rail station. The city wishes to survey the residents of the city to obtain their opinion regarding the use of tax dollars for this purpose. Design a sampling method to obtain the individuals in the sample. Be sure to support your choice.

12. **Sample Design** A school board at a local community college is considering raising the student services fees.

The board wants to obtain the opinion of the student body before proceeding. Design a sampling method to obtain the individuals in the sample. Be sure to support your choice.

13. **Sample Design** Target wants to open a new store in the village of Lockport. Before construction, they want to obtain some demographic information regarding the area under consideration. Design a sampling method to

obtain the individuals in the sample. Be sure to support your choice.

14. **Sample Design** The county sheriff wishes to determine whether a certain highway has a high proportion of speeders traveling on it. Design a sampling method to obtain the individuals in the sample. Be sure to support your choice.

15. **Sample Design** A pharmaceutical company wants to conduct a survey of 30 individuals who have high cholesterol. The company has a list of 6,600 individuals who are known to have high cholesterol that they obtained from doctors throughout the country. Design a sampling method to obtain the individuals in the sample. Be sure to support your choice.

16. **Sample Design** A marketing executive for Coca Cola, Inc., wants to identify television shows that people in the Boston area who typically drink Coke are watching. The executive has a list of all households in the Boston area. Design a sampling method to obtain the individuals in the sample. Be sure to support your choice.

17. **Systematic Sample** The human resource department at a certain company wants to conduct a survey regarding worker morale. The department has an alphabetical list of all 4502 employees at the company and wants to conduct a systematic sample.
(a) Determine k if the sample size is 50.
(b) Determine the individuals who will be administered the survey. More than one answer is possible.

18. **Systematic Sample** In order to predict the outcome of a county election, a newspaper obtains a list of all 945,035 registered voters in the county and wants to conduct a systematic sample.
(a) Determine k if the sample size is 130.
(b) Determine the individuals who will be administered the survey. More than one answer is possible.

19. Research the sampling methods used by a market research firm in your neighborhood. Report your findings to the class. The report should include the types of sampling methods used, number of stages, and sample size.

1.4   Sources of Errors in Sampling

Objective ①   Understand the sources of error in sampling

① Thus far, we have discussed *how* to obtain samples but have neglected to look at any of the pitfalls that inevitably arise in sampling. In this section we look at problems that can occur in sampling. Some of these problems can be remedied; some, however, have no solution. Collectively, these errors are called *nonsampling errors*.

Definition   **Nonsampling errors** are errors that result from the survey process. They are due to the nonresponse of individuals selected to be in the survey, to inaccurate responses, to poorly worded questions, to bias in the selection of individuals to be given the survey, and so on.

We contrast nonsampling errors with *sampling errors*.

Definition   **Sampling error** is the error that results from using sampling to estimate information regarding a population. This type of error occurs because a sample gives incomplete information about the population.

In Your Own Words

We can think of sampling error as error that results from using a subset of the population to describe characteristics of the population. Nonsampling error is error that results from obtaining and recording information collected.

By incomplete information, we mean that the individuals in the sample cannot reveal all the information about the population because individuals are unique. Consider the following: Suppose the average age of 4 randomly selected students from a class of 30 is found to be 23.4 years. Further, assume that no students lied about their age, nobody misunderstood the question being asked, and the sampling was done appropriately. If the average age of all 30 students (the population) is 22.9 years old, then the sampling error is 23.4–22.9 = 0.5 year. Suppose now that the same survey is conducted, but this time one of the individuals in the survey lied about his age. Then the results of the survey will have nonsampling error.

Fortunately, we can control the amount of sampling error through an appropriately designed survey or experiment. Nonsampling error, on the other hand, can be more difficult to control.

When a sampling design is done poorly, the descriptive statistics computed from the data obtained in the sample may not be close to the values that would be obtained if the entire population were surveyed. For example, the *Literary Digest* predicted that Alfred M. Landon would defeat Franklin D. Roosevelt in the 1936 presidential election. The *Literary Digest* conducted a poll by mailing questionnaires based upon a list of its subscribers, telephone directories, and automobile owners. On the basis of the results, the *Literary Digest* predicted that Landon would win with 57% of the popular vote. However, Roosevelt won the election with about 62% of the popular vote. The incorrect prediction by the *Literary Digest* was the result of a poor sample design. In 1936, most of the subscribers to the magazine, households with telephones and automobile owners, were Republican, the party of Landon. Therefore, the choice of the frame that was used to conduct the survey led to an incorrect prediction. This is an example of nonsampling error.

We now list the various sources of nonsampling error. These sources include the frame, nonresponse, data entry error, and poorly worded questions.

The Frame

Recall that the frame is the list of all individuals in the population under study. For example, in a study regarding voter preference in an upcoming election, the frame would be a list of all registered voters. Sometimes, obtaining the frame would seem to be a relatively easy task, such as obtaining the list of all registered voters. Even under this circumstance, however, the frame may be incomplete. People who recently registered to vote may not be on the published list of registered voters.

Often, it is difficult to gain access to a *complete* list of individuals in a population. For example, in general public opinion polls, random telephone surveys are frequently conducted, which implies that the frame is all households with telephones. This method of sampling will exclude any household that does not have a telephone as well as all homeless people. In such a situation, certain segments of the population are *underrepresented*.

In designing any sample, the hope is that the frame used is as complete as possible so that any results inferred regarding the population have as little error as possible.

Nonresponse

Nonresponse means that an individual selected for the sample does not respond to the survey. Nonresponse can occur because individuals selected for the sample do not wish to respond or because the interviewer was unable to contact them.

This type of error can be controlled using callbacks. The type of callback employed typically will depend upon the type of survey initially used. For example, if nonresponse occurs because a mailed questionnaire was not returned, a callback might mean phoning the individual in order to conduct the survey. If nonresponse occurs because an individual was not at home, then a callback might mean returning to the home at other times in the day or other days of the week.

Another method that can be used to improve nonresponse is using rewards and incentives. Rewards may include cash payments for completing a questionnaire, made only upon receipt of the completed questionnaire. Incentives might also include a cover letter that states that the responses to the questionnaire will dictate future policy. For example, a village may send out questionnaires to households and state in a cover letter that the responses to the questionnaire will be used to decide pending issues within the village.

Interviewers

A trained interviewer is essential in order to obtain accurate information from a survey. A good interviewer will have the skill necessary to elicit responses from individuals within a sample and be able to make the interviewee feel comfortable enough to give truthful responses. For example, a good interviewer should be able to obtain truthful answers to questions as sensitive as, say, "Have you ever cheated on your taxes?"

Data Checks

Once data are collected, the results typically must be entered into a computer. Data entry inevitably results in input errors. It is imperative that data be checked for accuracy at every stage of the statistical analysis. In this text, we present some methodology that can be used to check for data entry errors.

Questionnaire Design

Appropriate questionnaire design is critical in minimizing the amount of nonsampling error. We will concentrate on the main aspects in the design of a good questionnaire.

One of the first considerations in designing a question is determining whether the question should be open or closed.

An **open question** is one in which the respondent is free to choose his or her response. For example:

What is the most important problem facing America's youth today?

A **closed question** is one in which the respondent must choose from a list of predetermined responses.

What is the most important problem facing America's youth today?
- **(a)** Drugs
- **(b)** Violence
- **(c)** Single parent homes
- **(d)** Promiscuity
- **(e)** Peer pressure

Note to Instructor
Have students discuss some problems in coding responses to open questions.

When designing an open question, be sure to phrase the question so that the responses are similar. (You don't want a wide variety of responses.) This allows for easy analysis of the responses. The benefit of closed questions is that they limit the number of respondent choices, and therefore, the results are much easier to analyze. However, this limits the choices and does not always allow the respondent to respond the way he or she might want to respond. If the desired answer is not provided as a choice, the respondent will be forced to choose a secondary answer.

Survey designers recommend conducting pretest surveys with open questions and then using the most popular answers as the choices on closed question surveys. Another issue to consider in the closed question design is the number of responses the respondent may choose from. It is recommended that the option "no opinion" be omitted, because this option does not allow for meaningful analysis. The bottom line is to try and limit the number of choices in a closed question format without forcing respondents to choose an option they otherwise would not.

Wording of Questions

⊘ **Caution**

The wording of questions can significantly affect the responses and, therefore, the validity of a study.

The wording of a survey question is vital in order to obtain data that are not misrepresentative. Questions must always be asked in balanced form. For example, the "yes/no" question

Do you oppose the reduction of estate taxes?

should be written

Do you favor or oppose the reduction of estate taxes?

The second question is balanced. Do you see the difference? Consider the following report based on studies from Schuman and Presser (*Questions and Answers in Attitude Surveys*, 1981, p. 277), who asked the following two questions:

(A) Do you think the United States should forbid public speeches against democracy?

(B) Do you think the United States should allow public speeches against democracy?

For those respondents presented with question A, 21.4% gave "yes" responses, while for those given question B, 47.8% gave "no" responses. The conclusion you may arrive at is that most people are not necessarily willing to forbid something, but more people are willing not to allow something. These results imply that the wording of the question can alter the outcome of a survey.

Another consideration in wording a question is not to be vague. For example, the question, "How much do you study?" is too vague. Does the researcher mean how much do I study for all my classes or just for statistics? Does the researcher mean per day or per week? The question should be written, "How many hours do you study statistics each week?"

The Order of the Questions, Words, and Responses

Many surveys will rearrange the order of the questions within a questionnaire so that responses are not affected by prior questions. Consider the following example from Schuman and Presser in which the following two questions were asked:

(A) Do you think the United States should let Communist newspaper reporters from other countries come in here and send back to their papers the news as they see it?

(B) Do you think a Communist country such as Russia should let American newspaper reporters come in and send back to America the news as they see it?

For surveys conducted in 1980 in which the questions appeared in the order (A, B), 54.7% of respondents answered yes to A and 63.7% answered yes to B. If the questions were ordered (B, A), then 74.6% answered yes to A and 81.9% answered yes to B. When Americans are asked if U.S. reporters should be allowed to report Russian news first, they are more likely to agree that Russians should be allowed to report American news. Questions should be rearranged as much as possible to help reduce the effects of this type.

Pollsters will also rearrange words within a question. For example, the Gallup Organization asked the following question of 1017 adults aged 18 years or older:

> **"Do you consider the first six months of the Bush administration to be a [rotated: success (or a) failure]?"**

Notice how the words "success" and "failure" were rotated. The purpose of this is to remove the effect that may occur by writing the word "success" first in the question.

Not only should the order of the questions and or certain words within the question be rearranged, but, in closed questions, the possible responses should also be rearranged. The reason for this is that respondents are likely to choose early choices in a list rather than later choices.

1.4 Assess Your Understanding

Concepts and Vocabulary

1. Why is it rare for frames to be completely accurate?
2. What are some solutions to nonresponse?
3. What is a closed question? What is an open question?
4. Discuss methods that can be used to improve response rate.
5. Discuss the benefits of having trained interviewers.
6. What are the advantages of having a pretest when constructing a questionnaire that has closed questions?
7. Discuss the pros and cons of telephone interviews that take place during the typical dinner hour.
8. Why is a high response rate desired? How would a low response rate affect survey results?
9. Discuss the advantages and disadvantages of open versus closed questions.

Exercises

1. Flawed sampling method   2.Flawed sampling method   4. Poorly worded question

- **Skill Building**

In Problems 1–8, the survey design is flawed. (a) Determine whether the sampling method or the survey itself is flawed. For flawed surveys, identify the cause of the error (wording of question, nonresponse, etc.). (b) Suggest a remedy to the problem.

1. A college vice president wants to conduct a study regarding student achievement of undergraduate students. He selects the first 50 students who enter the building on a given day and administers his survey.

2. The Village of Oak Lawn wishes to conduct a study regarding the income level of households within the village. The village manager selects 10 homes in the southwest corner of the village and sends an interviewer to the homes to ascertain the household income.

3. An antigun advocate wants to estimate the percentage of people who favor stricter gun laws. He conducts a nationwide survey of 1203 randomly selected adults 18 years old and older. The interviewer asks the respondents, "Do you favor harsher penalties for individuals who sell guns illegally?" *Poorly worded question*

4. A magazine is conducting a study on the effects of infidelity in a marriage. The editors randomly select 400 women whose husbands were unfaithful and ask, "Do you believe a marriage can survive when the husband destroys the trust that must exist between husband and wife?"

5. A polling organization is going to conduct a study to estimate the percentage of households that speak a foreign language as the primary language. It mails a questionnaire to 1023 randomly selected households throughout the United States and asks the head of household if a foreign language is the primary language

spoken in the home. Of the 1023 households selected, 12 responded. *Nonresponse*

6. Petland is considering opening a new store in Orland Park. Prior to opening the store, the company would like to know the percentage of households in Orland Park that own a pet. The market researcher obtains a list of households in Orland Park and randomly selects 100 of them. She mails a questionnaire that asks questions regarding pets in the house to the 100 households. Of the 100 questionnaires sent out, she receives 3 in return. *Nonresponse*

7. Suppose you are conducting a survey regarding illicit drug use among teenagers in the Baltimore School District. You obtain a cluster sample of 12 schools within the district and sample all sophomore students in the randomly selected schools. The survey is administered by the teachers. *Untrustworthy interviewer*

8. Suppose you are conducting a survey regarding students' study habits. You obtain a list of full-time registered students and obtain a simple random sample of 90 students. One of the survey questions is "How many hours do you study?" *Poorly worded question*

• **Applying the Concepts**

9. Consider the following two questions.

A. *Suppose for a moment that a rape is committed in which the woman becomes pregnant. Do you think the criminal should or should not face additional charges if the woman becomes pregnant?*

B. *Do you think abortions should be legal under any circumstances, legal under certain circumstances, or illegal in all circumstances?*

Do you think the order in which the questions are asked will affect the survey results? If so, what can the pollster do to alleviate this response bias?

10. Consider the following question from a recent Gallup poll:

Thinking about how the abortion issue might affect your vote for major offices, would you vote only for a candidate who shares your views on abortion or consider a candidate's position on abortion as just one of many important factors? [rotated]

Why is it important to rotate the two choices presented in the question?

11. Write a survey question that contains strong wording and a survey question that contains tempered wording. Present the strongly worded question to 10 randomly selected people and the tempered question to 10 different randomly selected people. How does the wording affect the response?

12. Write two questions that could have different responses, depending upon the order in which the questions are presented. Randomly select 20 people and present the questions in one order to 10 of the people and in the opposite order to the other 10 people. Did the results differ?

13. Plan your own survey. Start with your objective and take the survey all the way to the data collection step. Comment on the difficulties encountered.

14. Research a survey method used by a company or government branch. Present the methods used to your class. Your report should include sampling methods used, sample size, method of collection, and the frame used.

1.5   The Design of Experiments

Objectives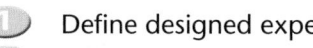

1 Define designed experiment
2 Understand the steps in designing an experiment
3 Understand the completely randomized design
4 Understand the randomized block design
5 Understand the matched-pairs design

One of the major themes of this chapter has been data collection. Sections 1.2–1.4 discussed techniques for obtaining data through surveys. Obtaining data through an experiment is discussed in this section.

1   When people hear the word "experiment," they typically think of a laboratory with a controlled environment. Statisticians have control when they perform experiments as well.

Definition

A **designed experiment** is a controlled study in which one or more treatments are applied to *experimental units*. The experimenter then observes the effect of varying these *treatments* on a response variable. Control, manipulation, randomization, and replication are the key ingredients of a well-designed experiment.

The **experimental unit** (or **subject**) is a person, object, or some other well-defined item upon which a *treatment* is applied. The experimental unit is analogous to the individual in a survey. The **treatment** is a condition applied to the experimental unit. A **response variable** is a quantitative or qualitative variable that represents our variable of interest.

The goal in an experiment is to determine the effect the treatment has on the response variable. For example, a researcher may want to measure the effect of sleep deprivation on a person's fine-motor skills. The researcher might take a group of 100 individuals and randomly divide them into four groups. The first group might sleep eight hours a night for four nights, the second will sleep six hours per night for four nights, the third will sleep four hours per night for four nights, while the fourth group will sleep two hours per night for four nights. The experimental unit is the person, the treatment is the amount of sleep and the response variable might be the reaction time of the person to some stimulus.

Many designed experiments are **double blind**. This means that neither the experimental unit nor the experimenter knows what treatment is being administered to the experimental unit. For example, in clinical studies of the cholesterol-lowering drug Lipitor, researchers administered either 10 mg, 20 mg, 40 mg, 80 mg, or a **placebo**, an innocuous medication such as a sugar tablet, to patients with high cholesterol. Because the experiment was double blind, neither the patients nor the researchers knew which medication was being administered. It is important that double-blind methods be used in this case so that the patients and researchers do not behave in such a way as to affect the results. For example, the researcher might not give as much time to a patient receiving the placebo.

The process of conducting an experiment requires a series of steps.

Steps in Conducting an Experiment

Step 1: *Identify the problem to be solved.* The statement of the problem should be as explicit as possible. The statement should provide the experimenter with direction. In addition, the statement must identify the response variable and the population to be studied. Often, the statement is referred to as the **claim**.

Step 2: *Determine the factors that affect the response variable.* The factors that affect the response variable are referred to as **predictor variables**. These factors are usually identified by an expert in the field of study. In identifying the factors, we must ask, "What things affect the value of the response variable?" Once the factors (predictor variables) are identified, it must be determined which factors will be fixed at some predetermined level (the controls), which factors will be manipulated, and which factors will be uncontrolled.

Step 3: *Determine the number of experimental units.* As a general rule of thumb, choose as many experimental units as time and money will allow.

Note to Instructor
How are lurking variables related to predictor variables?

Techniques do exist for determining sample size provided certain information is available.

Step 4: *Determine the level of the predictor variables.* There are three ways to deal with the predictor variables:

1. Control their levels so they remain fixed throughout the experiment. These are variables whose effect on the response variable is not of interest.
2. Manipulate or set them at predetermined levels. These are the variables whose effect on the response variable interests us. These variables constitute the treatment in the experiment.
3. Randomize so that the effects of variables whose level cannot be controlled is minimized. The idea is that randomization "averages out" the effects of uncontrolled predictor variables.

Step 5: *Collect and process the data.* This is the replication mentioned in the definition. In this step, we perform the experiment on each of the experimental units. The researcher then measures the value of the response variable and organizes the results. The idea is that any difference in the value of the response variable can be attributed to differences in the level of the treatment.

Step 6: *Test the claim.* This is the subject of inferential statistics. **Inferential statistics** is a process in which generalizations about a population are made on the basis of results obtained from a sample. In addition, a statement regarding our level of confidence in our generalization is provided. We study methods of inferential statistics in Chapters 8–13.

An example will help clarify the process of experimental design.

▶ **EXAMPLE 1**   **Designing an Experiment**

Problem: A farmer wishes to determine the optimal level of a new fertilizer on his soybean crop. Design an experiment that will assist him.

Approach: We perform the previously listed steps.

Solution:

Step 1: The farmer wants to identify the optimal level of fertilizer in growing soybeans. We define "optimal" as the level that maximizes yield. Therefore, the response variable will be crop yield.

Step 2: Some of the factors that affect crop yield are fertilizer, precipitation, sunlight, method of tilling the soil, type of soil, seed, and temperature.

Step 3: In this experiment, we will divide one acre of land into three equal sized plots of land. On each plot, we will plant 500 soybean plants (experimental units).

Step 4: We list the variables and their levels.

- **Fertilizer.** We manipulate the level of this variable. We wish to measure the effect of varying the level of this variable on the response variable, yield. We will set the level of fertilizer (the treatment) as follows:

   Plot 1 receives no fertilizer.

   Plot 2 receives two teaspoons per gallon of water every two weeks.

   Plot 3 receives four teaspoons per gallon of water every two weeks.

- **Precipitation.** Although we cannot control the amount of rainfall, we can control the amount of watering we do. This variable will be controlled so that each plot receives the same amount of water.
- **Sunlight.** This is an uncontrollable variable, but it will be the same for each plot.
- **Method of tilling.** We can control this variable. We agree to use the round-up ready method of tilling for each plot.
- **Type of soil.** We can control certain aspects of the soil such as level of acidity. In addition, because each plot is within a one-acre area, it is reasonable to assume that the soil conditions of each plot are equivalent.
- **Plant.** There may be variation from plant to plant. To account for this, we randomly assign the plants to a plot.
- **Temperature.** This variable is not within our control, but will be the same for each plot.

Step 5: Till the soil, plant the soybean plants, and fertilize according to the schedule prescribed. At the end of the growing season, determine the crop yield for each plot.

Step 6: Determine whether any differences in yield exist between the three plots. ◀◀

Figure 5 illustrates the experimental design presented in Example 1.

Figure 5

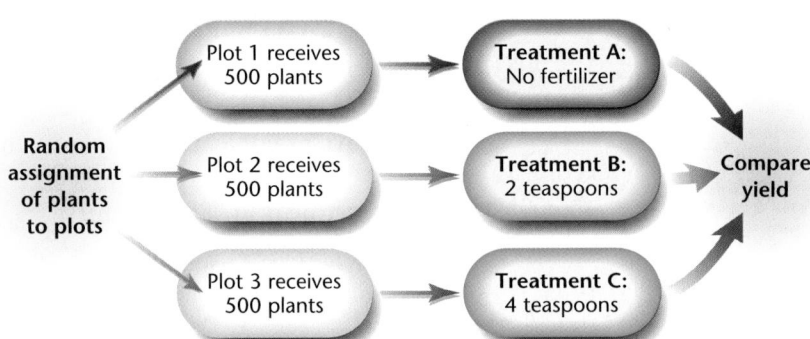

Example 1 presents an example of an experiment that is referred to as a **completely randomized design** because the experimental units (the plants) were randomly assigned the treatment. It is the most popular experimental design because of its simplicity, but it is not always the best. We discuss inferential procedures for the completely randomized design in which there are two treatments in Section 10.2. We discuss inferential procedures for the completely randomized design in which there are three or more treatments in Section 12.3.

 Now Work Problem 1.

④ Randomized Block Design

Let's revisit our crop yield experiment from Example 1. In this example, we assumed that the soil conditions for each plot were the same, but this is not necessarily the case. For example, suppose Figure 6 represents the plots as laid out in Example 1. Plot 1 might be the plot that received no fertilizer (treatment *A*), Plot 2 the plot that received two teaspoons (treatment *B*),

Figure 6

and Plot 3 the plot that received 4 teaspoons (treatment *C*). It may be that Plot 1 has different soil conditions than Plots 2 or 3. If this were the case, then we would not know whether to attribute the different crop yields to the level of fertilizer or to the soil conditions. This effect is known as *confounding*. **Confounding** occurs when the effect of two predictor variables on the response variable cannot be distinguished.

To resolve issues of this type, Sir Ronald A. Fisher developed a new experimental design called *randomized block design*. We discuss this design in the next example.

▶ **EXAMPLE 2**   **Illustrating the Randomized Block Design**

Historical Note

Sir Ronald Fisher, often called the "Father of Modern Statistics," was born in England on February 17, 1890. He received a B.A. in astronomy from Cambridge University in 1912. In 1914, he took a position teaching mathematics and physics at a high school. He did this to help serve his country during World War I. (He was rejected by the army because of his poor eyesight.) In 1919, Fisher took a job as a statistician at Rothamsted Experimental Station, where he was involved in agricultural research. In 1933, Fisher became Galton Professor of Eugenics at Cambridge University, where he studied Rh blood groups. In 1943 he was appointed to the Balfour Chair of Genetics at Cambridge. He was knighted by Queen Elizabeth in 1952. Fisher retired in 1957 and died in Adelaide, Australia, on July 29, 1962. One of his famous quotations is "To call in the statistician after the experiment is done may be no more than asking him to perform a postmortem examination: he may be able to say what the experiment died of."

Problem: Suppose the soil in plots 1, 2, and 3 were analyzed and it was determined the soil conditions in the three plots differed and that the difference in soil conditions might affect the yield within each plot. Design an experiment that could be used to measure the effect of fertilizer while taking into account the difference in soil conditions.

Approach: One way to take into account the fact that the soil conditions in each plot are different is to divide each plot into three subplots. In this way, we divide Plot 1 into three parts and randomly assign no fertilizer to one part (treatment A), two teaspoons to one of the remaining two parts (treatment B) and four teaspoons to the third part (treatment C). A similar situation occurs in plots 2 and 3.

Solution: In a randomized block design, the field would be divided up into smaller plots (called **blocks**) as shown in Figure 7(a).

Figure 7

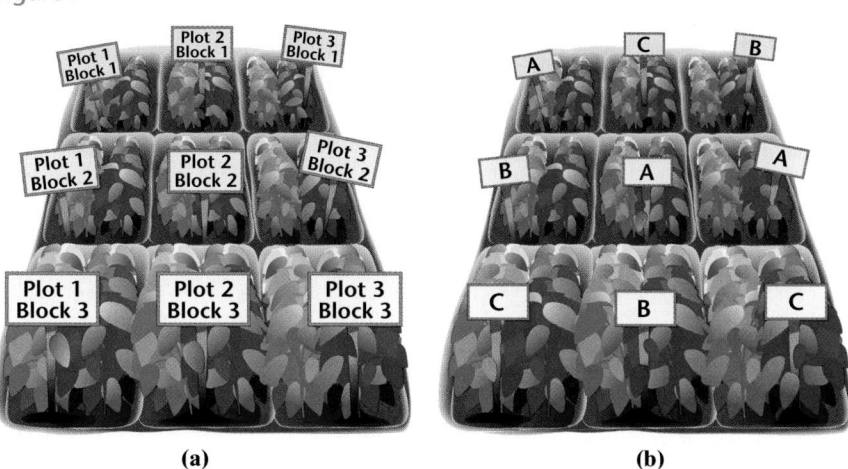

(a)   (b)

Within each of the smaller plots, we randomly assign a treatment (*A*, *B*, or *C*). The idea is that each of the smaller plots (blocks) will have uniform soil so that the factor "soil type" does not affect the value of the response variable within each block. A design that requires each fertilizer to be used in each plot is a **randomized block design**. In the design presented in Figure 8 the arrangement of the fertilizer within each plot is random, but each plot gets all three fertilizers. This way we can measure the effect of the level of fertilizer because all three levels of fertilizer are included in each plot.

Figure 8

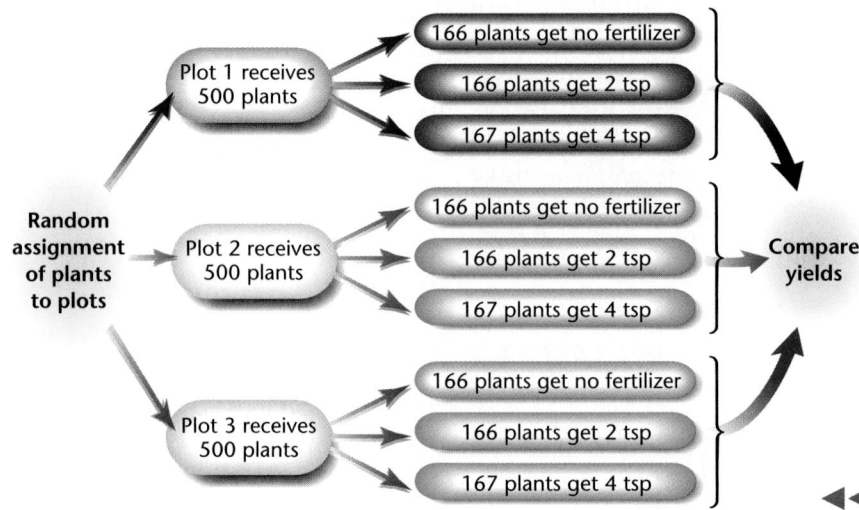

NW *Now Work Problem 3.*

In a randomized block design, we analyze not only the effect of the various levels of fertilizer, but also the effect of the various soil conditions (the plots). This will allow us to test whether there is plot-to-plot variation.

A specific type of randomized block design is called a *matched-pairs design*. A **matched-pairs design** is a randomized block design in which the experimental units are somehow related (that is, the same person before and after a treatment, twins, husband and wife, same geographical location, and so on). There are only two treatments in a matched-pairs design. The matching serves as a method of blocking. In matched-pairs design, one of the matched individuals will receive one treatment and the matched individual receives the second treatment. We then look at the difference in the results of each matched-pair. One common type of matched-pairs design is to measure a response variable on an experimental unit before a treatment is applied and then measure the response variable on the same experimental unit after the treatment is applied. In this way, the individual is matched against itself. These experiments are sometimes called before–after or pretest–posttest experiments.

Note to Instructor
Have a class discussion in which students compare and contrast the completely randomized design, the randomized block design, and the matched pairs design.

▶ **EXAMPLE 3**   **A Matched-Pairs Design**

Problem: An employee of Joliet Junior College's health and fitness center wondered what effect exercise has on systolic blood pressure. Design an experiment that will determine this effect.

Approach: The design will be a matched-pairs design because we are measuring the response variable, systolic blood pressure (the blood pressure of an individual while the heart contracts), on the same experimental unit before and after a treatment.

Solution: This experiment will require that we measure the systolic blood pressure for each participant in the study before the exercise program and at the completion of the exercise program. We would then compare the difference in systolic blood pressures. Figure 9 shows a diagram illustrating the design.

Figure 9

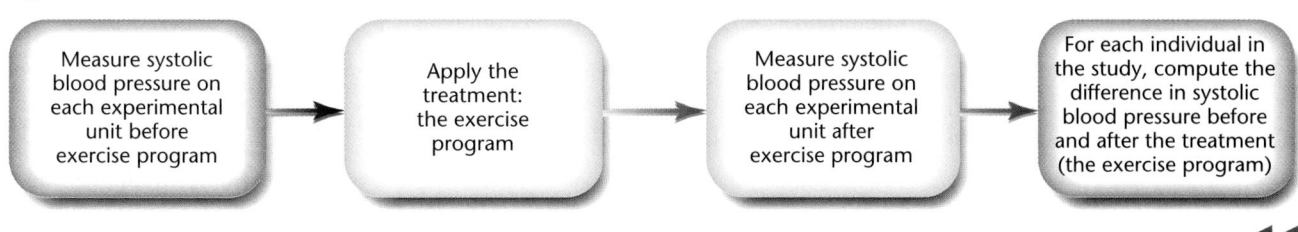

| Measure systolic blood pressure on each experimental unit before exercise program | → | Apply the treatment: the exercise program | → | Measure systolic blood pressure on each experimental unit after exercise program | → | For each individual in the study, compute the difference in systolic blood pressure before and after the treatment (the exercise program) |

◄◄

We discuss the statistical inference of matched pairs design in Section 10.1.

NW *Now Work Problem 7.*

1.5 Assess Your Understanding

Concepts and Vocabulary

1. Define the following:
(a) experimental unit
(b) treatment
(c) response variable
(d) predictor variable
(e) double blind
(f) placebo
(g) confounding

2. Describe the difference between an observational study and an experiment.

Exercises

(1a) Achievement test score
(1c) Grade, teacher, school district
(1e) Completely randomized

(2a) Percentage with cold
(2c) Gender, age, location
(2e) Completely randomized

(3a) Sales
(3d) Randomized block design

• Applying the Concepts

1. School Psychology A school psychologist wants to test
NW the effectiveness of a new method for teaching reading. She selects five hundred first grade students in District 203 and randomly divides them into two groups. Group 1 is taught by means of the new method, while Group 2 is taught via traditional methods. The same teacher is assigned to teach both groups. At the end of the year, an achievement test is administered and the results of the two groups compared.

(a) What is the response variable in this experiment?
(b) What is the treatment? How many levels does the treatment have? *Method of teaching; 2*
(c) Are any of the predictor variables controlled?
(d) How does the researcher's design handle students from different socioeconomic levels? *Same district*
(e) What type of experimental design is this?
(f) Identify the experimental units. *500 students*
(g) Draw a diagram similar to Figure 5, Figure 8, or Figure 9 to illustrate the design.

2. Pharmacy A pharmaceutical company has developed an experimental drug meant to relieve symptoms associated with the common cold. The company found 300 adult males in Chicago aged 25–29 years old and randomly divided them into two groups. Group 1 is given the experimental drug, while Group 2 is given a placebo. After one week of treatment, the percentage of each group that still has cold symptoms is compared.

(a) What is the response variable in this experiment?
(b) What is the treatment? How many levels does the treatment have? *Drug; 2*
(c) Are any of the predictor variables controlled?
(d) How does the researcher handle people from different parts of the country? *Same city*
(e) What type of experimental design is this?
(f) Identify the experimental units. *300 males*
(g) Draw a diagram similar to Figure 5, Figure 8, or Figure 9 to illustrate the design.

3. Marketing A marketing research firm wishes to deter-
NW mine the effects of its new advertising campaign. They divide the country into four geographical regions. Each region is then divided into three subregions and randomly assigned a level of advertising to each subregion. Subregion 1 has no advertising dollars spent, Subregion 2 has $100,000 dollars spent per week, and Subregion 3 has $250,000 spent per week. After three months, the sales of the product over the course of the three months are measured.

(a) What is the response variable in this experiment?
(b) What is the treatment? How many levels does the treatment have? *Advertising; 3*
(c) Are any of the predictor variables controlled? Which ones? *Region of country*
(d) What type of experimental design is this?
(e) Draw a diagram similar to Figure 5, Figure 8, or Figure 9 to illustrate the design.

4. **Agriculture** A farmer wishes to determine the optimal tilling method to use. He divides his farm into three regions. The three plots are divided into four subplots and randomly assigned a tilling method: no tilling, fall plowed, chisele plowed, and round-up ready. At the end of the season, the farmer compares the yield.
   (a) What is the response variable in this experiment? Yield
   (b) What is the treatment? How many levels does it have? Tilling method; 4
   (c) Can any of the predictor variables be controlled?
   (d) What type of experimental design is this? How can it be improved upon?
   (e) Draw a diagram similar to Figure 5, Figure 8, or Figure 9 to illustrate the design.

5. **Diet** In a study to determine the benefits of tomatoes, a researcher randomly selects 600 adult males 30 years of age. She randomly divides the males into three groups of 200 each. Group 1 eats one serving of tomatoes per week, Group 2 eats three servings of tomatoes per week, and Group 3 receives five servings of tomatoes per week. The proportion of males in each group who contract prostate cancer is determined after 40 years.
   (a) What is the response variable in this experiment?
   (b) What is the treatment? How many levels does it have? Servings of tomatoes; 3
   (c) Are any of the predictor variables controlled? Which ones? Tomatoes, age, exercise, eating habits
   (d) What type of experimental design is this?
   (e) Identify the experimental units. 600 males
   (f) Draw a diagram similar to Figure 5, Figure 8, or Figure 9 to illustrate the design.

6. **Social Work** A social worker wants to examine methodologies that can be used to improve truancy. She randomly samples 300 chronically truant students from District 103. The students are randomly divided into three groups. The students in Group 1 receive no intervention; the students in Group 2 are treated with positive reinforcement in which each day the student is not truant he or she receives a star that can be traded in for rewards; and the students in Group 3 are treated with negative reinforcement such that each truancy results in a one-hour detention. However, the hours of detention are cumulative, meaning that the first truancy results in one hour of detention, the second truancy results in two hours, and so on. After a full school year, the aggregate numbers of truancies are compared.
   (a) What is the response variable in this experiment?
   (b) What is the treatment? How many levels does it have? Method of intervention; 3
   (c) Are any of the predictor variables controlled?
   (d) Can you think of any predictor variables that should be controlled? Age, gender, guardianship
   (e) What type of experimental design is this?

   (f) Identify the experimental units. 300 students
   (g) Draw a diagram similar to Figure 5, Figure 8, or Figure 9 to illustrate the design.

7. **Rats in Space** NASA conducted an experiment entitled "Regulation of Erythropoiesis during Spaceflight." Rats were placed in an Animal Enclosure Module 28 days prior to the flight. Two days prior to the flight, the weights of the rats were obtained. Upon return, the weights of the rats were again obtained. The difference in before-flight and after-flight weights was recorded to determine the effect of spaceflight on weight.
   (a) What is the response variable in this experiment?
   (b) What is the treatment? Spaceflight
   (c) What type of experimental design is this?
   (d) Draw a diagram similar to Figures 5, Figure 8, or Figure 9 to illustrate the design.

8. For the experiment of Problem 27 in Section 1.1,
   (a) What is the response variable in this experiment?
   (b) What is the treatment? Music
   (c) What type of experimental design is this?
   (d) Draw a diagram similar to Figure 5, Figure 8, or Figure 9 to illustrate the design.

9. For the experiment of Problem 28 in Section 1.1,
   (a) What is the response variable in this experiment?
   (b) What is the treatment? How many levels does it have? Drug; 2
   (c) What type of experimental design is this?
   (d) Draw a diagram similar to Figure 5, Figure 8, or Figure 9 to illustrate the design.

10. **Designing an Experiment** Suppose you are interested in comparing Benjamin Moore's MoorLife Latex house paint with Sherwin Williams' LowTemp 35 Exterior Latex paint. Design an experiment that will answer the question, "Which paint is better for painting the wood siding on the exterior of a home?" In your design, be sure to identify the type of experimental design, population, experimental unit, response variable, treatment, factors, and their levels.

11. **Designing an Experiment** Suppose you are interested in determining the effectiveness of a new workout regimen. In particular, you want to know whether the new workout helps to increase lung capacity. Design an experiment that will answer the question, "Does this workout regimen increase lung capacity?" In your design, be sure to identify the type of experimental design, population, experimental unit, response variable, treatment, factors, and their levels.

12. **Completely Randomized Design** A pharmaceutical company wants to test the effectiveness of an experimental drug meant to reduce high cholesterol. The researcher at the pharmaceutical company has decided to test the effectiveness of the drug through a completely

(4c) Fertilizer, acidity of soil, tilling method (4d) Randomized block design (5a) Proportion of cancer cases (5d) Completely randomized (6a) Number of truancies (6c) School district (6e) Completely randomized (7a) Difference in weight (7c) Matched-pairs (8a) Test score (8c) Matched-pairs (9a) Hair counts (9c) Completely randomized

randomized design. She has obtained 20 volunteers with high cholesterol:

Ann, John, Michael, Kevin, Marissa, Christina, Eddie, Shannon, Julia, Randy, Sue, Tom, Wanda, Roger, Laurie, Rick, Kim, Joe, Colleen, and Bill.

Number the volunteers from 1–20. Use a random-number generator to randomly assign 10 of the volunteers to the experimental group. The remaining volunteers will go into the control group. List the individuals in each group.

13. **Effects of Alcohol** A researcher has recruited 20 volunteers to participate in a study. The researcher wishes to measure the effect of alcohol on an individual's reaction time. The 20 volunteers are randomly divided into two groups. Group 1 will serve as a control group in which participants drink four one-ounce cups of a liquid that looks, smells, and tastes like alcohol in 15-minute increments. Group 2 will serve as an experimental group in which participants drink four one-ounce cups of 80-

proof alcohol in 15-minute increments. After drinking the last one-ounce cup, the participants sit for 20 minutes. After the 20-minute resting period, the reaction time to a stimulus is measured. *Completely randomized*

(a) What type of experimental design is this?
(b) Use Table I in Appendix A or a random-number generator to divide the 20 volunteers into Group 1 and Group 2 by assigning the volunteers a number between 1 and 20. Then randomly select 10 numbers between 1 and 20. The individuals corresponding to these numbers will go into Group 1.

14. Search a newspaper, a magazine, or some other periodical that describes an experiment. Identify the population, experimental unit, response variable, treatment, factors, and their levels.

15. Research the "placebo effect" and "Hawthorne effect." Write a paragraph that describes how each affects the outcome of an experiment.

CHAPTER 1 REVIEW

Summary

We defined statistics as a science in which data are collected, organized, summarized, and analyzed in order to infer characteristics regarding a population. Descriptive statistics consists of organizing and summarizing information, while inferential statistics consists of drawing conclusions about a population, based on results obtained from a sample. The population is a collection of individuals upon which the study is made, and the sample is a subset of the population.

Data are the observations of a variable. Data can be either qualitative or quantitative. Quantitative data are either discrete or continuous.

Data can be obtained from four sources: a census, existing sources, survey sampling, or a designed experiment. A census will list all the individuals in the population, along

with certain characteristics. Due to the cost of obtaining a census, most researchers opt for obtaining a sample. In observational studies, the variable of interest has already been established. For this reason, they are often referred to as *ex post facto* studies. Designed experiments are used when control of the individuals in the study is desired in order to isolate the effect of a certain treatment on a response variable.

We introduced five sampling methods: simple random sampling, stratified sampling, systematic sampling, cluster sampling, and convenience sampling. All of the sampling methods, except for convenience sampling, are based on planned randomness, which allows for unbiased statistical inference to be made. Convenience sampling typically leads to an unrepresentative sample and biased results.

Vocabulary

Be sure you can define the following . . .

Statistics (p. 4)	Data (p. 8)	Cluster sampling (p. 25)
Population (p. 4)	Qualitative data (p. 8)	Convenience sampling (p. 26)
Sample (p. 4)	Quantitative data (p. 8)	Sampling error (p. 30)
Descriptive statistics (p. 4)	Continuous data (p. 8)	Nonsampling error (p. 30)
Inferential statistics (p. 5)	Discrete data (p. 8)	Open question (p. 32)
Treatment (pp. 5, 36)	Census (p. 12)	Closed question (p. 32)
Placebo (pp. 5, 36)	Observational study (p. 13)	Experimental unit (p. 36)
Double blind (pp. 5, 36)	Designed experiment (pp. 13, 36)	Response variable (p. 36)
Variable (p. 6)	Lurking variable (p. 14)	Predictor variable (p. 36)
Qualitative variable (p. 6)	Simple random sampling (p. 15)	Completely randomized design (p. 38)
Quantitative variable (p. 6)	Frame (p. 16)	Confounding (p. 39)
Continuous variable (p. 7)	Stratified sampling (p. 22)	Randomized block design (p. 39)
Discrete variable (p. 7)	Systematic sampling (p. 23)	Matched-pairs design (p. 40)

Objectives

Section	You should be able to ...	Review Exercises
1.1	1 Define statistics (p. 4)	1
	2 Understand the process of statistics (p. 4)	6
	3 Distinguish between qualitative and quantitative variables (p. 6)	9–14
	4 Distinguish between discrete and continuous variables (p. 7)	9–14
1.2	1 Distinguish between and observational study and an experiment (p. 13)	15–18
	2 Obtain a simple random sample (p. 15)	23
1.3	1 Obtain a stratified sample (p. 22)	24
	2 Obtain a systematic sample (p. 23)	25
	3 Obtain a cluster sample (p. 25)	26
1.4	1 Understand the sources of error in sampling (p. 30)	7
1.5	1 Define designed experiment (p. 35)	5
	2 Understand the steps in designing an experiment (p. 36)	8
	3 Understand the completely randomized design (p. 37)	27, 28, 30, 31
	4 Understand the randomized block design (p. 38)	30
	5 Understand the matched-pairs design (p. 40)	29, 31

Review Exercises

In Problems 1–5, provide a definition using your own words.

1. Statistics

2. Population

3. Sample

4. Observational study

5. Designed experiment

6. What is meant by "the process of statistics"?

7. State some sources of error in sampling. Provide some methods for correcting these errors. Distinguish sampling and nonsampling error.

8. Describe the components in an appropriately designed experiment.

In Problems 9–14, classify the variable as qualitative or quantitative. If the variable is quantitative, state whether it is discrete or continuous.

9. State in which a person resides. Qualitative

10. Marital status. Qualitative

11. Amount of water consumed per day in ounces.

12. Total number of people in a household.

13. Frequency with which the word "statistics" appears in this text. Quantitative; discrete

14. Number of people who visit the emergency room on Saturday. Quantitative; discrete

11. Quantitative; continuous   12. Quantitative; discrete

In Problems 15–18, determine whether the study depicts an observational study or a designed experiment.

15. A poll of residents of the Village of Orland Park to obtain their opinion on a new bond issue. Observational study

16. A study in which 1000 randomly selected arthritis patients are divided into two groups. One receives a placebo while the other receives an experimental drug. The patients from the two groups are then compared after six months. Designed experiment

17. A study in which the rates of cancer in people living near high-tension wires is compared with the general public's cancer rate to see if there are any differences between the two groups. Observational study

18. A study in which 500 households in the Houston metropolitan area are randomly selected. The head of household is asked to disclose the household income. The average household income in the Houston metropolitan area is compared with the average household income in the United States to determine whether there is any difference. Observational study

In Problems 19–22, determine the type of sampling used.

19. An interviewer in a mall is told to survey every fifth shopper, starting with the second. Systematic

20. A researcher randomly selects 5 of the 70 hospitals in a metropolitan area and then surveys all of the surgical doctors in each hospital. Cluster

21. A researcher segments the population of car owners into four groups: Ford, General Motors, Chrysler, and foreign. She obtains a random sample from each group and conducts a survey. Stratified

22. A list of students in elementary statistics is obtained in which the individuals are numbered 1 to 540. A professor randomly selects 30 of the students. Simple random

23. **Obtaining a Simple Random Sample** A credit card company wants to perform a study on the outstanding balances of its 1,403,032 cardholders. Obtain a simple random sample of 15 cardholders.

24. **Obtaining a Stratified Sample** A congresswoman wants to survey her constituency regarding public policy. She asks one of her staff members to obtain a sample of residents of the district. The frame she has available lists 9012 Democrats, 8302 Republicans, and 3012 Independents. Obtain a stratified random sample of eight Democrats, seven Republicans, and three Independents.

25. **Obtaining a Systematic Sample** A quality control engineer wants to be sure that bolts coming off an assembly line are within prescribed tolerance levels. He wants to conduct a systematic sample by selecting every 9th bolt to come off the assembly line. The machine produces 30,000 bolts per day and the engineer wants a sample of 32 bolts. Which bolts will be sampled?

26. **Obtaining a Cluster Sample** A farmer has a 500-acre orchard in Florida. Each acre is subdivided into blocks of five. So altogether, there are 2500 blocks of trees on the farm. After a frost, he wants to get an idea of the extent of the damage. Obtain a sample of 10 blocks of trees, using a cluster sample.

27. **Postpartum Depression** A total of 120 postpartum women meeting DSM-IV criteria for major depression were selected and randomly assigned 12 weeks of interpersonal psychotherapy or to a waiting-list condition-control group. The Hamilton Rating Scale for Depression scores of the women in each group were measured.

(a) What is the response variable in this experiment?
(b) What is the treatment? How many levels does it have? Group; 2
(c) Create a list of predictor variables. Are any of them controlled? Age, gender, geography, income
(d) What type of experimental design is this?
(e) Identify the experimental units. 120 women
(f) Draw a diagram similar to Figure 5, Figure 8, or Figure 9 to illustrate the design.

28. **Acute Bipolar Mania** A total of 115 patients with a DSM-IV diagnosis of bipolar disorder was randomly divided into two groups. The 55 individuals in Group 1 received 5 to 20 mg/d of olanzapine and the 60 individuals in Group 2 received a placebo in this double-blind experiment. The effect of the drug was measured on the Young-Mania Rating Scale total score.

(a) What is the response variable in this experiment?
(b) What is the treatment? How many levels does it have? drug; 2
(c) What type of experimental design is this?
(d) Identify the experimental units. 115 patients
(e) What does "double blind" mean in the context of this experiment?
(f) Draw a diagram similar to Figure 5, Figure 8, or Figure 9 to illustrate the design.

29. **Skylab** The four members of Skylab had their lymphocyte count per cubic millimeter measured one day before liftoff and measured again upon their return to Earth.

(a) What is the response variable in this experiment?
(b) What is the treatment? spaceflight
(c) What type of experimental design is this?
(d) Identify the experimental units. 4 members
(e) Draw a diagram similar to Figure 5, Figure 8, or Figure 9 to illustrate the design.

30. Describe what is meant by an experiment that is a completely randomized design. Contrast this experimental design with a randomized block design.

31. Describe what is meant by a matched-pairs design. Contrast this experimental design with a completely randomized design.

(27a) Hamilton Rating Scale score
(27d) Completely randomized
(28a) Young-Mania Rating Scale score
(28c) Completely randomized
(29a) lymphocyte count
(29c) Matched-pairs

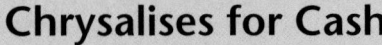

The colorful butterfly symbolizes the notion of personal change. Increasingly, people are turning to butterflies to consecrate meaningful events such as birthdays, weddings, and funerals. To fill this need, a new industry was hatched.

Suppliers of butterflies are closely monitored by governmental agencies to ensure that local environments are not subjected to the introduction of invasive species. In addition to following these regulations, butterfly suppliers need to ensure the quality and quantity of their product, while maintaining a profit. To that end, an individual supplier may hire a number of smaller independent contractors to hatch the varieties needed. These entrepreneurs are paid a small fee for each chrysalis delivered, with a 50 percent bonus added for each hatched healthy butterfly. This fee structure provides little room for profit. Therefore, it is important that these small contractors deliver a high proportion of healthy butterflies that hatch at a fairly predictable rate.

In Florida, one such entrepreneur specializes in harvesting the black swallowtail butterfly. In the southern United States, the black swallowtail has at least three broods annually. The female flutters through open fields seeking plants of the Apiaceae family, such as carrot and parsley, upon which to lay her eggs. The resulting larvae are dark brown with a small white saddle mark. As the larvae consume the leaves of their host plant, they increase in size, changing color to a vibrant green with intermittent stripes of yellow and black. Once a larva has eaten enough, it secures itself and sheds its skin, revealing an emerald chrysalis. During this resting phase, environmental factors such as temperature and humidity may affect the transformation process. Typically, the black swallowtail takes about a week to complete its metamorphosis and emerge from its cocoon. The transformation occasionally results in a deformed butterfly. Deformities range from wings that will not fully open to missing limbs.

The Florida contractor believes that there are differences in quality and hatch time among his broods. Not having taken a scientific approach to the problem, he relies on his memory of seasons past. It seems to him that late season butterflies hatch sooner and with a greater number of deformities than their early season counterparts. Additionally, he speculates that the type and nutritional value of the food consumed by the larva might contribute to any observed differences. This year he is committed to a more formal approach to his butterfly harvest.

Since it takes two days to deliver the chrysalises from the contractor to the supplier, it is important that the butterflies do not emerge prematurely. It is equally important that the number of defective butterflies be minimized. With these two goals in mind, the contractor seeks the best combination of food source, fertilizer, and brood season to maximize his profits. In order to examine the effects of these variables on hatch time and number of deformed butterflies, the entrepreneur designed the following experiment:

Eight identical pots were filled with equal amounts of a particular soil mixture. The watering of all the pots and the plants contained within them was carefully monitored for consistency. Four pots were set outside during the early part of the brood season. Of these, two contained carrot plants, while the remaining pair grew parsley. For the carrot pair, one pot was fed a fixed amount of liquid fertilizer, while the other pot was fed a nutritionally similar amount of solid fertilizer. The two pots containing parsley were similarly fertilized. All four pots were placed next to each other to ensure similar exposures to environmental conditions such as temperature and solar radiation. Five black swallowtail larvae of similar age were placed into each container. The larvae were allowed to mature and form a chrysalis. The time from chrysalis formation until emergence was reported to the nearest day. The occurrence of any defects was also noted. The same procedure was followed with the four pots that were placed outdoors during the late brood season.

Write a report describing the experimental goals and design for the entrepreneur's experiment. Follow the procedure outlined in the section titled Steps in Conducting an Experiment (pp. 36–37). The fifth step (*collect and process the data*) of this procedure is provided in the following table and should be included in your report.

| | Florida Black Swallowtail Chrysalis Experiment Data | | | |
Season	Food	Fertilizer	Number Deformed	Hatch Time (Days)
Early	Parsley	Solid	0	6,6,7,7,7
Early	Parsley	Liquid	0	6,7,7,8,8
Early	Carrot	Solid	1	3,6,6,7,8
Early	Carrot	Liquid	0	6,6,7,8,8
Late	Parsley	Solid	2	2,3,4,4,5
Late	Parsley	Liquid	1	2,3,4,5,5
Late	Carrot	Solid	2	3,3,3,4,5
Late	Carrot	Liquid	0	2,4,4,4,5

In your report, provide a general descriptive analysis of these data. Be sure to include recommendation for the combination of season, food source, and type of fertilizer that results in the least amount of deformed butterflies while achieving a lengthy hatch time.

Conclude your report with recommendations for further experiments. For each proposed experiment, be sure to

1. State the problem to be solved and define the response variables.
2. Define the predictor variables that affect the response variables.
3. State the number of experimental units.
4. State the level of each predictor variable.

What Movie Should I Go To?

One of the most difficult tasks of surveying is phrasing questions so that they are not misunderstood. In addition, they must be phrased so that the researcher obtains answers that allow for meaningful analysis. The purpose of this exercise is to create a questionnaire that can be used to make an informed decision about whether to attend a certain movie. Select a movie that you wish to see. If the movie is still in theaters, make sure that it has been released for at least a couple of weeks so that it is likely that a number of people have seen it. Design a questionnaire that would be filled out by the individuals that have seen the movie. You may wish to include questions regarding demographics of the respondents first (such as age, gender, level of education, and so on). Ask as many questions as you feel would be necessary to obtain an opinion regarding the movie. The questions can be open or closed. Administer the survey to at least 20 randomly selected people who have seen the movie. While administering the survey, keep track of those individuals who have not seen the movie. In particular, keep track of their demographic information. After administering the survey, summarize your findings. On the basis of the survey results, do you think that you will enjoy the movie? Why? Now see the movie. Did you like it? Did the survey accurately predict whether you would enjoy the movie? Now answer the following questions:

(a) What sampling method did you use? Why? Did you have a frame for the population?

(b) Did you have any problems with respondents misinterpreting your questions? How could this issue have been resolved?

(c) What role did the demographics of the respondent have in forming your opinion? Why?

(d) Did the demographics of individuals who did not see the movie play a role while you were forming your opinion regarding the movie?

(e) Look up a review of the movie by a professional movie critic. Did the movie critic's opinion agree with yours? What might account for the similarities or differences in your opinions?

(f) Describe the problems that you had in administering the survey. If you had to do this survey over again, would you change anything? Why?

Americans have a long history of altering their moods—with chemicals ranging from alcohol and illicit drugs to prescription medications, such as diazepam (Valium) for anxiety and fluoxetine (Prozac) for depression. Today there's a new trend: the over-the-counter availability of apparently effective mood modifiers in the form of herbs and other so-called dietary supplements.

One problem is that many people who are treating themselves with these remedies may be sufficiently anxious or depressed to require professional care and monitoring. Self-treatment can be dangerous, particularly with depression, which causes some 20,000 reported suicides a year in the United States. Another major pitfall is that dietary supplements are largely unregulated by the government, so consumers have almost no protection against substandard preparations.

To help consumers and doctors, Consumer Reports tested the amounts of key ingredients in representative brands of several major mood-changing pills (December 2000). To avoid potential bias, we tested samples from different lots of the pills using a randomized statistical design. The following table contains a subset of the data from this study:

Each of these pills has a label claim of 200 mg of SAM-E. The column labeled "Random Code" contains a set of 3-digit random codes that were used so that the laboratory did not know which manufacturer was being tested. The column labeled "Mg SAM-E" contains the amount of SAM-E measured by the laboratory.

(a) Why is it important to label the pills with random codes?

(b) Why is it important to randomize the order in which the pills are tested instead of testing all of brand A first, followed by all of brand B, and so on?

(c) Sort the data by brand. Does it appear as if each of the brands are meeting their label claims?

(d) Design an experiment that follows the steps presented in order to conduct an experiment to answer the following research question: "Is there a difference in the amount of SAM-E contained in brands A, B, C, and D?"

Note to Readers: In many cases, our test protocol and analytical methods are more complicated than described in these examples. The data and discussions have been modified to make the material more appropriate for the audience.

Run Order	Brand	Random Code	Mg SAM-E
1	B	461	238.9
2	D	992	219.2
3	C	962	227.1
4	A	305	231.2
5	B	835	263.7
6	D	717	251.1
7	A	206	232.9
8	D	649	192.8
9	C	132	213.4
10	B	923	224.6
11	A	823	261.1
12	C	515	207.8

Putting It All Together

In Chapter 1, we learned that statistics is a process. The process begins with asking a research question. In order to determine the answer to the question, information (data) must be collected. The information is obtained from a census, existing data sources, surveys or designed experiments. When data are collected from a survey or designed experiment, they must be organized into a manageable form. Data that are not organized are referred to as **raw data**.

Methods for organizing raw data include the creation of tables or graphs, which allow for a quick overview of the information collected. The organization of data is the third step in the statistical process. The procedures used in organizing data into tables and graphs depend upon whether the data are qualitative, discrete, or continuous.

CHAPTER 2

Organizing and Summarizing Data

Outline

 For additional study help, go to
www.prenhall.com/sullivanstats

Materials include

● Self-Graded Quizzes

● "Preparing for This Section" Quizzes

● STATLETs

● PowerPoint Downloads

● Step-by-Step Technology Guide

● Graphing Calculator Help

2.1 Organizing Qualitative Data

Preparing for This Section   Before getting started, review the following:

✓ Qualitative data (Section 1.1, p. 6)

Objectives   ①   Construct frequency and relative frequency distributions from qualitative data

②   Construct bar graphs

③   Construct pie charts

In this section we will concentrate on tabular and graphical summaries of qualitative data. Sections 2.2 and 2.3 discuss methods for summarizing quantitative data.

①   **Organizing Qualitative Data**

Recall that qualitative data provide nonnumerical measures that categorize or classify an individual. When qualitative data are collected, we are often interested in determining the number of individuals that occur within each category.

Definition   A **frequency distribution** lists the number of occurrences for each category of data.

▶ **EXAMPLE 1**   **Organizing Qualitative Data into a Frequency Distribution**

Problem: Table 1 lists the presidents of the United States, along with their state of birth. Construct a frequency distribution of the state of birth.

TABLE 1

Birthplace of U.S. President

President	State of Birth	President	State of Birth	President	State of Birth
Washington	Virginia	Lincoln	Kentucky	Coolidge	Vermont
J. Adams	Massachusetts	A. Johnson	North Carolina	Hoover	Iowa
Jefferson	Virginia	Grant	Ohio	F.D. Roosevelt	New York
Madison	Virginia	Hayes	Ohio	Truman	Missouri
Monroe	Virginia	Garfield	Ohio	Eisenhower	Texas
J.Q. Adams	Massachusetts	Arthur	Vermont	Kennedy	Massachusetts
Jackson	South Carolina	Cleveland	New Jersey	L.B. Johnson	Texas
Van Buren	New York	B. Harrison	Ohio	Nixon	California
W.H. Harrison	Virginia	Cleveland	New Jersey	Ford	Nebraska
Tyler	Virginia	McKinley	Ohio	Carter	Georgia
Polk	North Carolina	T. Roosevelt	New York	Reagan	Illinois
Taylor	Virginia	Taft	Ohio	George H. Bush	Massachusetts
Fillmore	New York	Wilson	Virginia	Clinton	Arkansas
Pierce	New Hampshire	Harding	Ohio	George W. Bush	Connecticut
Buchanan	Pennsylvania				

Approach: To construct a frequency distribution, we create a list of the states (categories) and tally each occurrence. Finally, we add up the number of tallies to determine the frequency.

Solution: See Table 2. From the table, we can see that Virginia is the state in which most presidents were born—a total of eight.*

TABLE 2		
State	**Tally**	**Frequency**
Virginia	ⅢⅢ III	8
Massachusetts	IIII	4
South Carolina	I	1
New York	IIII	4
North Carolina	II	2
New Hampshire	I	1
Pennsylvania	I	1
Kentucky	I	1
Ohio	ⅢⅢ II	7
Vermont	II	2
New Jersey	II	2
Iowa	I	1
Missouri	I	1
Texas	II	2
California	I	1
Nebraska	I	1
Georgia	I	1
Illinois	I	1
Arkansas	I	1
Connecticut	I	1

◄◄

With frequency distributions, it is a good idea to add up the frequency column to make sure that it adds up to the correct number of observations. In the case of the data in Example 1, the frequency column adds up to 43, as it should.

Often, rather than being concerned with the frequency with which categories of data occur, we would like to know the relative frequency of the categories.

Definition

✍ In Your Own Words

A frequency distribution shows how often each category occurs. A relative frequency distribution shows the percent of the observations that belong in each category.

The **relative frequency** is the proportion or percent of observations within a category and is found using the formula

$$\text{Relative frequency} = \frac{\text{frequency}}{\text{sum of all frequencies}} \qquad (1)$$

A **relative frequency distribution** lists the relative frequency of each category of data.

*History considers Cleveland to be two different presidents, even though he is the same individual, because he was not elected to two consecutive terms.

▶ **EXAMPLE 2** **Constructing a Relative Frequency Distribution of Qualitative Data**

Problem: Using the data in Table 2 on page 53, construct a relative frequency distribution.

Approach: Add all the frequencies, and then use Formula (1) to compute the relative frequency of each category of data.

Solution: We add the values in the frequency column from Table 2:

$$\text{Sum of all frequencies} = 8 + 4 + 1 + \ldots + 1 + 1 = 43$$

Note to Instructor
Discuss situations in which the frequency distribution might be preferred over the relative frequency distribution and vice versa.

This result shouldn't be surprising, since there have been 43 presidents of the United States! We now compute the relative frequency of each category. For example, the relative frequency of the category "Virginia" is $8/43 \approx 0.1860$. After computing the relative frequency of the remaining categories, we obtain the relative frequency distribution shown in Table 3.

TABLE 3		
State	**Frequency**	**Relative Frequency**
Virginia	8	$8/43 \approx 0.1860$
Massachusetts	4	$4/43 \approx 0.0930$
South Carolina	1	$1/43 \approx 0.0233$
New York	4	0.0930
North Carolina	2	0.0465
New Hampshire	1	0.0233
Pennsylvania	1	0.0233
Kentucky	1	0.0233
Ohio	7	0.1628
Vermont	2	0.0465
New Jersey	2	0.0465
Iowa	1	0.0233
Missouri	1	0.0233
Texas	2	0.0465
California	1	0.0233
Nebraska	1	0.0233
Georgia	1	0.0233
Illinois	1	0.0233
Arkansas	1	0.0233
Connecticut	1	0.0233

So 18.60% of all United States presidents were born in Virginia. ◀◀

We would expect the relative frequency column in Table 3 to add to 1. However, the column adds up to 1.0004. The discrepancy is simply due to rounding error. Nonetheless, it is a good idea to add up the relative frequency column to verify your results.

NW *Now Work Problems 19(a) and (b).*

Once raw data are organized in a table, we can create graphs. This allows us to "see" the data and therefore get a sense as to what the data are saying regarding the individuals in the study. In general, pictures of data result in a more powerful message than tables. Try the following exercise for yourself: Open a newspaper and look at a table and graph. Study each. Now put the paper away and close your eyes. What do you see in your mind's eye? Can you recall information obtained from the table or the graph? In general, people are more likely to recall information obtained from a graph than they are from a table.

❷ Bar Graphs

One of the most common devices for graphically representing qualitative data is a bar graph.

Definition

A **bar graph** is constructed by labeling each category of data on a horizontal axis and the frequency or relative frequency of the category on the vertical axis. A rectangle of equal width is drawn for each category. The height of the rectangle is equal to the category's frequency or relative frequency.

▶ **EXAMPLE 3**   **Constructing a Frequency and Relative Frequency Bar Graph**

Problem: Use the data summarized in Table 3 to construct (a) a frequency bar graph and (b) a relative frequency bar graph.

Approach: A horizontal axis is used to indicate the category of the data (states, in this case), and a vertical axis is used to represent the frequency or relative frequency (in this case, number of presidential births). Draw bars or rectangles of equal width for each category whose height is the frequency or relative frequency. The bars do not touch each other.

Solution:

(a) Figure 1 shows the frequency bar graph.

Figure 1

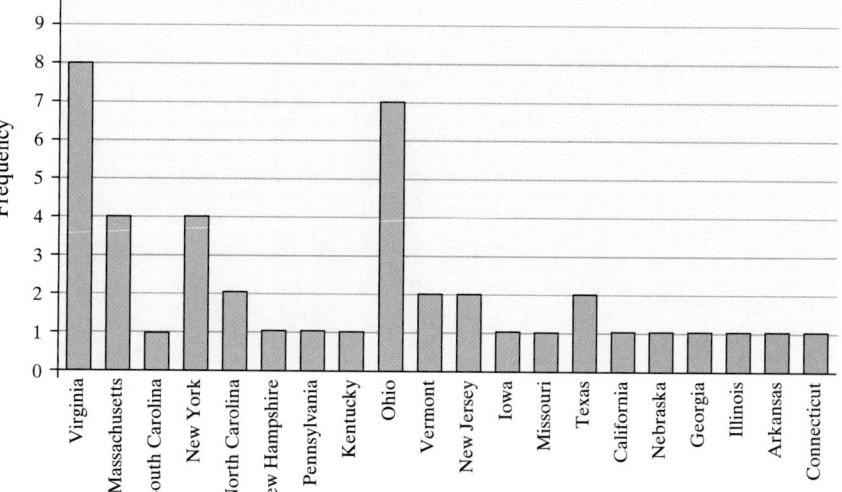

The U.S. Presidents' Birthplaces

🚦 **Caution**

Whenever constructing bar graphs, be sure to include labels for the axes as well as a title for the graph!

(b) Figure 2 shows the relative frequency bar graph.

Figure 2

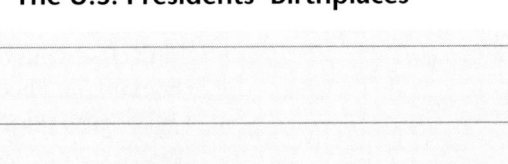

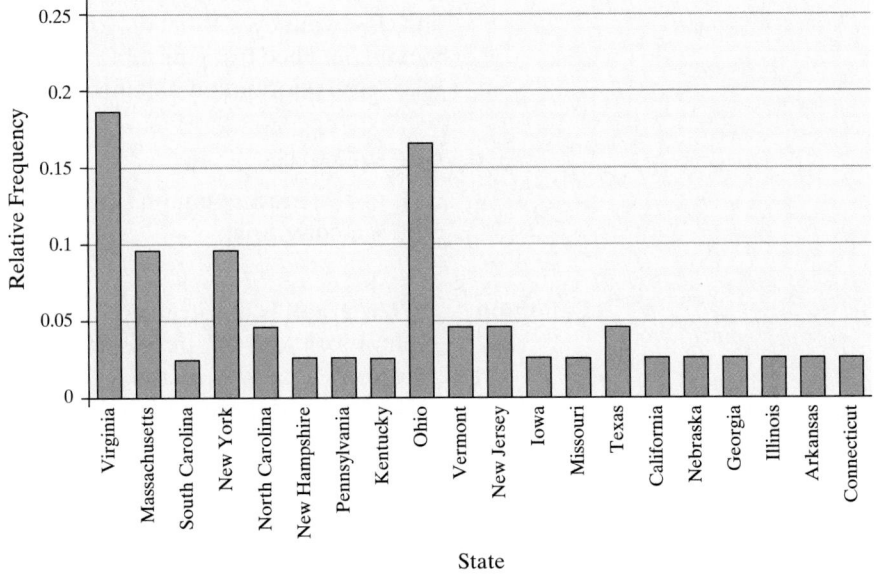

The U.S. Presidents' Birthplaces

◄◄

Caution

Watch out for graphs that start the scale at some value other than 0, have bars with unequal widths, or have bars with different colors, because they can misrepresent the data.

Notice that the frequency and relative frequency bar charts presented in Figures 1 and 2 look the same, except for the scale on the vertical axis.

Some statisticians prefer to create bar graphs with the categories arranged in decreasing order of frequency.

Definition   A **Pareto chart** is a bar graph whose bars are drawn in decreasing order of frequency or relative frequency.

Figure 3 illustrates a relative frequency Pareto chart for the data in Table 3.

Figure 3

The U.S. Presidents' Birthplaces

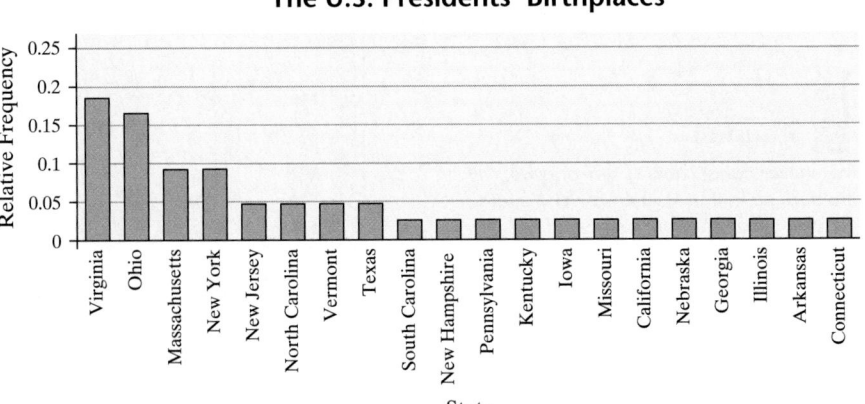

Using Technology: Statistical spreadsheets such as Excel have the ability to draw bar charts and Pareto charts. Figure 4 shows the relative frequency bar chart of the data in Table 3, drawn with Excel.

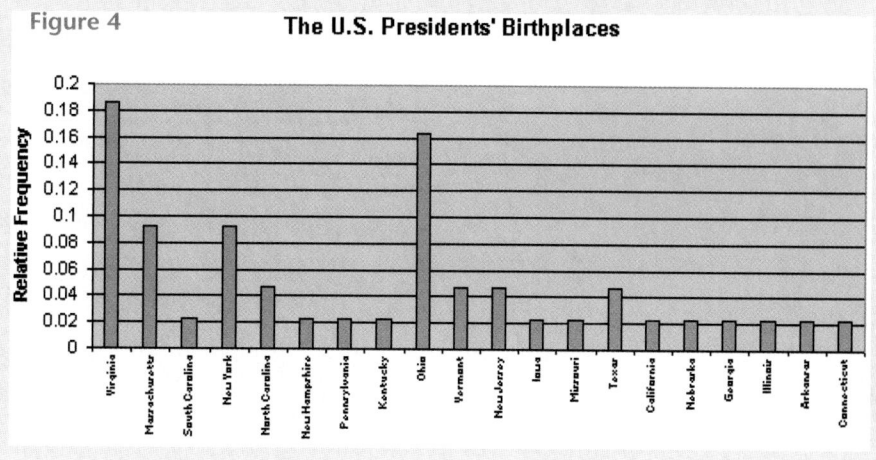

Figure 4

The U.S. Presidents' Birthplaces

NW

Now Work
Problems 19(c) and (d).

Side-by-Side Bar Graphs

Graphics provide insight when comparing two sets of data. For example, suppose we wanted to know if more people are finishing college today than in 1990. We could draw a **side-by-side bar graph** to compare the two data sets. Data sets should always be compared by using relative frequencies, because different sample or population sizes make comparisons using frequencies difficult.

> **Caution**
>
> When comparing two or more data sets, use relative frequencies!

▶ **EXAMPLE 4**   Comparing Two Data Sets

Problem: The data in Table 4 represent the educational attainment in 1990 and 2000 of adults 25 years and older who are residents of the United States.

(a) Draw a side-by-side relative frequency bar graph of the data.

(b) Are Americans becoming more educated?

TABLE 4		
Educational Attainment	**1990**	**2000**
Less than 9th grade	16,502,211	12,327,601
9th–12th grade, no diploma	22,841,507	20,343,848
High school diploma	47,642,763	52,395,507
Some college, no degree	29,779,777	36,453,108
Associate's degree	9,791,925	11,487,194
Bachelor's degree	20,832,567	28,603,014
Graduate/professional degree	11,477,686	15,930,061
Totals	**158,868,436**	**177,540,333**

Source: United States Census Bureau

Approach: First, we determine the relative frequencies of each category for each year. To construct the side-by-side bar graphs, we draw two bars for each category of data. One of the bars will represent 1990 and the other will represent 2000.

Solution: Table 5 shows the relative frequency for each category.

TABLE 5		
Educational Attainment	**1990**	**2000**
Less than 9th grade	0.1039	0.0694
9th–12th grade, no diploma	0.1438	0.1146
High school diploma	0.2999	0.2951
Some college, no degree	0.1874	0.2053
Associate's degree	0.0616	0.0647
Bachelor's degree	0.1311	0.1611
Graduate/professional degree	0.0722	0.0897

(a) The side-by-side bar graph is shown in Figure 5.

Figure 5 **Educational Attainment in 1990 versus 2000**

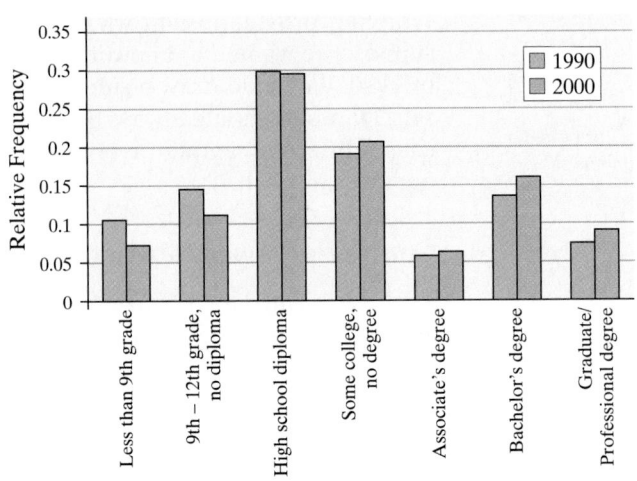

(b) From the graph, we can see that the proportion of Americans 25 years and older who are earning at least a bachelor's degree is increasing. This information is not clear from the frequency table, because the sizes of the populations are different, so that increases in the number of Americans who earned a bachelor's degree are due partly to the increases in the sizes of the populations. ◄◄

NW *Now Work Problem 15.*

3 Pie Charts

Pie charts are typically used to present the relative frequency of qualitative data.

Definition

A **pie chart** is a circle divided into sectors. Each sector represents a category of data. The area of each sector is proportional to the frequency of the category.

▶ **EXAMPLE 5**   **Constructing a Pie Chart**

Problem: The data presented in Table 6 represent the educational attainment of residents of the United States 25 years or older, based upon data obtained from the 2000 United States Census. Construct a pie chart of the data.

TABLE 6	
Educational Attainment	**2000**
Less than 9th grade	12,327,601
9th–12th grade, no diploma	20,343,848
High school diploma	52,395,507
Some college, no degree	36,453,108
Associate's degree	11,487,194
Bachelor's degree	28,603,014
Graduate/professional degree	15,930,061
Totals	**177,540,333**

Approach: The pie chart will have seven parts, or sectors, corresponding to the seven categories of data. The area of each sector is proportional to the frequency of each category. For example,

$$\frac{12,327,601}{177,540,333} = 0.0694 = 6.94\%$$

of all U.S. residents 25 years or older have less than a 9th-grade education. The category "less than 9th grade" will make up 6.94% of the pie chart. Since a circle has 360°, the degree measure of the sector for the category "less than 9th-grade education" will be $(0.0694)360° \approx 25.0°$. Use a protractor to measure each angle.

Solution: We follow the approach presented for the remaining categories of data to obtain Table 7.

TABLE 7			
Education	**Frequency**	**Relative Frequency**	**Degree Measure of Each Sector**
Less than 9th grade	12,327,601	0.0694	25.0
9th to 12th grade, no diploma	20,343,848	0.1146	41.3
High school diploma	52,395,507	0.2951	106.2
Some college, no degree	36,453,108	0.2053	73.9
Associate's degree	11,487,194	0.0647	23.3
Bachelor's degree	28,603,014	0.1611	58.0
Graduate/professional degree	15,930,061	0.0897	32.3

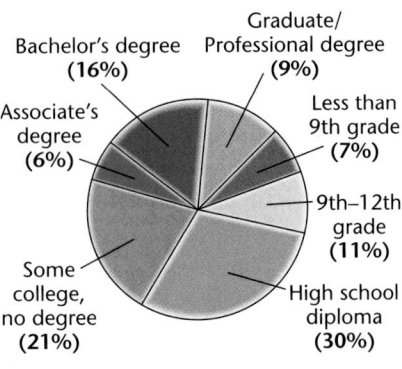

Figure 6

Educational Attainment, 2000

To construct a pie chart by hand, we use a protractor to approximate the angles for each sector. See Figure 6. ◀◀

Using Technology: Certain statistical spreadsheets have the ability to draw pie charts. Figure 7 shows the pie chart of the data in Table 6, using Minitab.

Figure 7

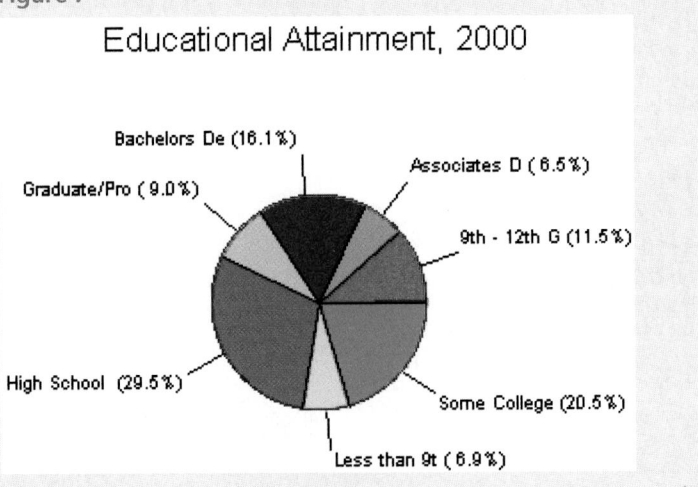

Pie charts can be created only if all the categories of the variable under consideration are represented. In other words, we could create a bar chart that lists the proportion of presidents born in the states of Virginia, Texas, and New York, but it would not make sense to construct a pie chart for this situation. Do you see why? Only 34.88% of the pie would be accounted for.

 Now Work Problem 19(e).

2.1 Assess Your Understanding

Concepts and Vocabulary

1. What are raw data?
2. What is the relative frequency of a category of data?
3. What is a Pareto chart?

4. Why should relative frequencies be used in comparing two data sets?
5. Explain why Pareto charts might be preferred over bar graphs.

Exercises

• **Basic Skills**

In Problems 1–8, answer the questions on the basis of the graph.

1. **Mutual Fund Owners** The pie chart on the right depicts the percent of people within each age group who own mutual funds.
   (a) Which age group has the highest percentage of ownership? 34–52
   (b) Which age group has the lowest percentage of ownership? 18–33
   (c) What percentage of people 53 or older own mutual funds? 27%

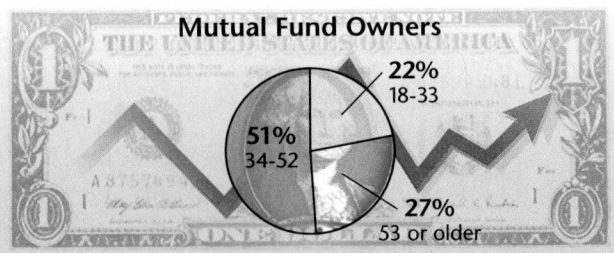

Source: *USA Today* Snapshot; Investment Company Institute, Summer 1999

2. Golf Driving Range The following pie chart depicts the bucket size golfers choose while at the driving range.

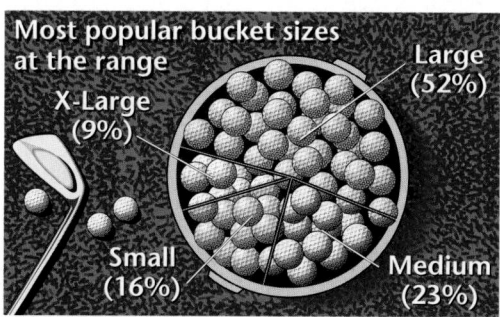

Source: USA Today Snapshot and the National Golf Foundation

(a) What is the most popular size? What percentage of golfers choose this size? Large; 52%
(b) What is the least popular size? What percentage of golfers choose this size? X-Large; 9%
(c) What percent of golfers choose a medium-sized bucket? 23%

3. Internet Users The following bar graph represents the top eight countries in Internet users as of December 31, 2000, based on information provided by the Internet Industry Almanac. (a) United States

Top 8 Users of Internet

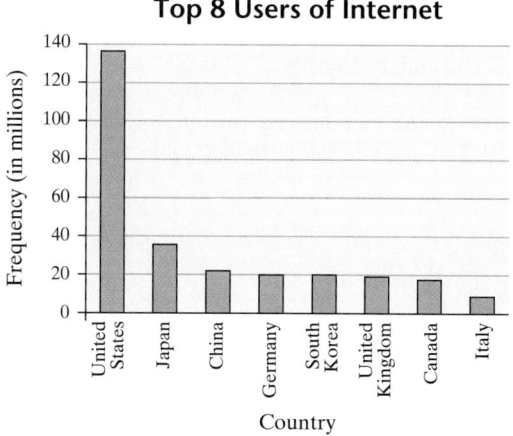

(a) Which country has the highest Internet usage?
(b) Approximately what is the Internet usage in Canada? 18 million

4. Poverty Every year the United States Census Bureau counts the number of people living in poverty. The Bureau uses money income thresholds as its definition of poverty, so that noncash benefits such as Medicaid and food stamps do not count toward poverty thresholds.

For example, in 1999, the poverty threshold for two adults and one child was $13,410. The bar chart below represents the number of people living in poverty in the United States in 1999, by ethnicity:

Number in Poverty

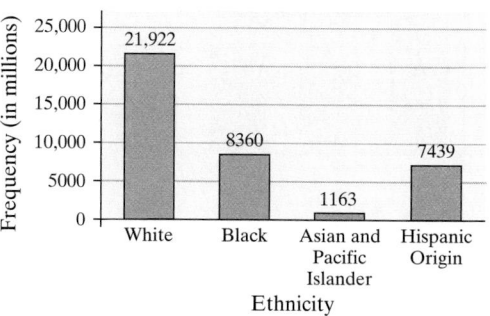

(a) 21,922
(a) How many whites were living in poverty in 1999?
(b) Of the impoverished, what percent are of Hispanic origin? 19.1%
(c) Why might this graph be misleading?

5. 2000 Presidential Election The following bar chart represents the number of voters who cast votes for the top six vote-getters in the 2000 presidential election. The number of votes received for each candidate appears above the bar.

Votes in 2000 Presidential Election

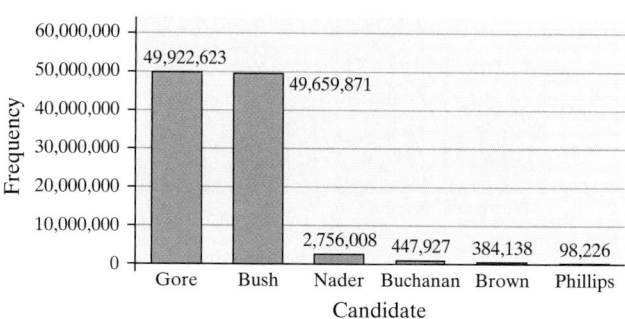

Source: cbsnews.com

(a) 447,927
(a) How many votes were cast for Pat Buchanan?
(b) What percent of the votes were cast for Al Gore? George W. Bush? 48.3%; 48.1%
(c) In order to receive presidential election funds, a candidate must garner at least 5% of the vote. Will Ralph Nader receive presidential election funds? No

6. Birth Characteristics The bar chart on page 62 represents the percentage of women who gave birth to a child in 1998, by educational attainment.

Educational Attainment of Women Having a Child in 1998

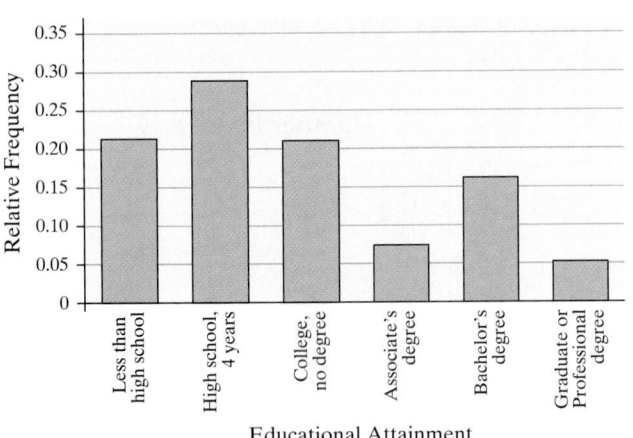

Source: U.S. Census Bureau, Current Population Reports

(a) What percentage of women who had a child in 1998 had four years of high school education? ≈ 28%
(b) If 60,519,000 women gave birth to a child in 1998, how many had four years of high school education?
(b) ≈ 16,945,320

7. Home Heating Fuel The following side-by-side bar graph represents the percentage of households with the indicated source of home heating fuel for the years 1978, 1987, and 1997.

Home Heating Fuel

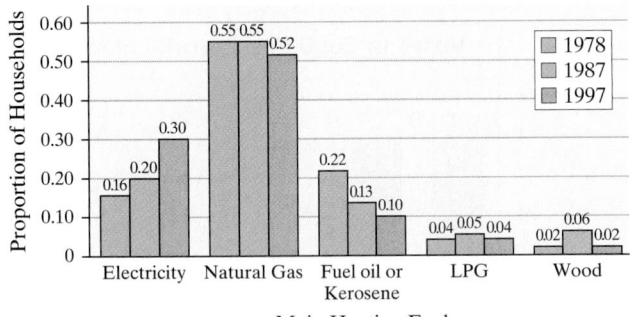

Source: Energy Information Administration, Residential Energy Consumption Survey, 1978, 1987, and 1997

(a) What percentage of households used electricity as their main source of home heating fuel in 1978? 16%
(b) What was the most popular source of home heating fuel in 1987? Natural gas
(c) What was the least popular source of home heating fuel in 1987? LPG
(d) What might account for the rise in homes that use electricity as the main source of home heating fuel?
(e) What might account for the decline in homes that use fuel oil or kerosene as the main source of home heating fuel?

8. Bigger Houses The following side-by-side bar graph represents the percentage of households that have the indicated number of rooms in their homes for the years 1978, 1987, and 1997. (a) 23%

Number of Rooms in House, 1978, 1987, 1997

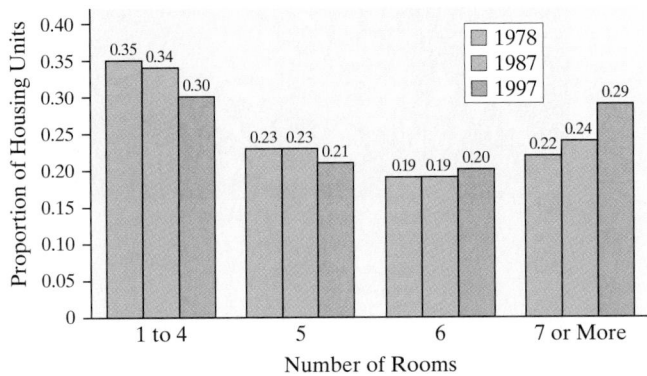

Source: Energy Information Administration, Residential Energy Consumption Survey, 1978, 1987, and 1997.

(a) What percentage of homes had five rooms in 1987?
(b) What percentage of homes had seven or more rooms in 1997? 29%
(c) What was the most common home size in all three years of the survey? 1 to 4
(d) What might account for the fact that the percentage of homes with seven or more rooms has increased over the three years of the survey?

• Applying the Concepts

9. Government Income For fiscal year 2000 (October 1999–September 2000), the federal government collected $2,046.9 billion. The various sources of income are broken down in the following table.

Source of Income	Amount (in billions of dollars)
Individual Income Tax and Tax Withholdings	1,009.5
Corporate Income Taxes	234.7
Social Insurance and Retirement Receipts	691.5
Excise, Estate and Gift Taxes, Customs, and Miscellaneous Receipts	111.2

Source: Budget of the United States

(a) Construct a relative frequency distribution.
(b) What percentage of total income is attributable to individual income taxes? 49.3%
(c) Construct a frequency bar graph.

(d) Construct a relative frequency bar graph.
(e) Construct a pie chart.
(f) In your opinion, which graph appears to place more emphasis on social insurance and retirement receipts as a source of income, the relative frequency bar graph or the pie chart? Why?

10. **Government Expenditures** For fiscal year 2000 (October 1999–September 2000), the federal government spent $1,998.8 billion. The breakdown of expenditures is given in the following table.

Category	Expenditure (in billions of dollars)
National Defense and Foreign Affairs	397.3
Human Resources	1,119.7
Physical Resources	121.0
Net Interest on the Debt	230.2
Other Functions	130.6

Source: Budget of the United States

(a) Construct a relative frequency distribution of the data shown.
(b) What percentage of total expenditures is attributable to net interest? 11.5%
(c) Construct a frequency bar graph.
(d) Construct a relative frequency bar graph.
(e) Construct a pie chart.
(f) In your opinion, which graph appears to place more emphasis on net interest on the debt, the relative frequency bar graph or the pie chart? Why?

11. **College Survey** In a national survey conducted by the Centers for Disease Control in order to determine health-risk behaviors among college students, college students were asked, "How often do you wear a seat belt when riding in a car driven by someone else?" The frequencies are displayed below.

Response	Frequency
Never	125
Rarely	324
Sometimes	552
Most of the time	1257
Always	2518

(a) Construct a relative frequency distribution.
(b) What percentage of respondents answered "Always"? 52.7%
(c) What percentage of respondents answered "Never" or "Rarely"? 9.4%

(d) Construct a frequency bar graph.
(e) Construct a relative frequency bar graph.
(f) Construct a pie chart.

12. **College Survey** In a national survey conducted by the Centers for Disease Control in order to determine health-risk behaviors among college students, college students were asked, "How often do you wear a seat belt when driving a car?" The frequencies are displayed below.

Response	Frequency
I do not drive a car	249
Never	118
Rarely	249
Sometimes	345
Most of the time	716
Always	3093

(a) Construct a relative frequency distribution.
(b) What percentage of respondents answered "Always"? 64.8%
(c) What percentage of respondents answered "Never" or "Rarely"? 7.7%
(d) Construct a frequency bar graph.
(e) Construct a relative frequency bar graph.
(f) Construct a pie chart.
(g) Compare the relative frequencies of "Never," "Rarely," "Sometimes," "Most of the time," and "Always" with those in Problem 11. What might you conclude?

13. **Foreign-Born Population** The following data represent the region of birth of foreign-born residents of the United States in 2000.

Region	Number (thousands)
Europe	4772
Asia	8364
Africa	840
Oceania	180
Latin America	15,472
North America	836

Source: U.S. Bureau of the Census

(a) Construct a relative frequency distribution.
(b) What percentage of foreign-born residents were born in Africa? 2.8%
(c) Construct a frequency bar graph.
(d) Construct a relative frequency bar graph.
(e) Construct a pie chart.

14. **Robbery** The following data represent the number of robberies in 1998. (b) 2.6%

Type of Crime	Number of Offenses (in thousands)
Street or highway	219
Commercial house	61
Gas station	10
Convenience store	26
Residence	54
Bank	9

Source: U.S. Federal Bureau of Investigation

(a) Construct a relative frequency distribution.
(b) What percentage of robberies were of a gas station?
(c) Construct a frequency bar graph.
(d) Construct a relative frequency bar graph.
(e) Construct a pie chart.

15. **Educational Attainment** On the basis of the 1999 Current Population Survey, there were 100.0 million males and 100.1 million females aged 25 years old or older in the United States. The educational attainment of males and females is listed below.

Educational Attainment	Males (millions)	Females (millions)
Not a high school graduate	16.6	16.6
High school graduate	31.8	34.8
Some college, but no degree	17.1	17.5
Associate's degree	7.0	8.0
Bachelor's degree	17.9	16.2
Advanced degree	9.6	7.0

(a) Construct a relative frequency distribution for males.
(b) Construct a relative frequency distribution for females.
(c) Construct a side-by-side relative frequency bar graph.
(d) Compare each gender's educational attainment. Make a conjecture about the reasons for the differences.

16. **Internet Access** The following data represent the number of people that had Internet access in the years 1997 and 2000, by level of education. Data are in thousands of U.S. residents.
(a) Construct a relative frequency distribution for each year.
(b) Draw a side-by-side relative frequency bar graph.
(c) Compare the access for the two years. Conjecture some reasons for the differences and similarities.

Educational Attainment	1997	2000
No college	7427	24,662
Some college	9742	31,462
Graduated college	10,367	34,379

Source: United States Statistical Abstract, 2000

17. **Space Launches** The following data represent the number of successful space launches in 1995 and 1998. A successful space launch is a launch in which the craft attains the Earth's orbit or escapes Earth.

Country	Number of Launches, 1995	Number of Launches, 1998
Soviet Union/ Commonwealth of Independent States	32	24
United States	27	34
Japan	2	2
European Space Agency	11	11
China	2	6
Israel	1	0

(a) Construct a relative frequency distribution for each year.
(b) Draw a side-by-side relative frequency bar graph.
(c) Compare space launches for the two years. Make a conjecture about the reasons for the differences.

18. **Transplants** The following data represent the number of transplants performed in 1990 and 1998.

Transplant	1990	1998
Heart	2108	2345
Liver	2690	4487
Kidney	9877	13,139
Heart–lung	52	47
Lung	203	862
Pancreas/islet cell	528	1221
Intestine	5	69

Source: U.S. Department of Health and Human Services

(a) Construct a relative frequency distribution for the years 1990 and 1998.
(b) What percentage of transplants in 1990 were heart transplants? What percentage of transplants in 1998 were heart transplants? What might account for the difference? 13.6%; 10.6%

(c) Construct a side-by-side relative frequency bar graph.

(d) Compare the relative frequencies of each type of transplant for the two years. Make a conjecture about the reasons for the differences.

19. **2000 Presidential Election** An exit poll was conducted in Palm Beach County, Florida, in which a random sample of 40 voters revealed whom they voted for in the presidential election. The results of the survey are listed below.

Bush	Bush	Gore	Bush	Gore	Gore	Gore
Gore	Gore	Gore	Gore	Bush	Gore	Gore
Bush	Bush	Gore	Nader	Gore	Gore	Gore
Bush	Bush	Gore	Gore	Bush	Gore	Bush
Gore	Gore	Bush	Gore	Gore	Bush	Gore
Bush	Gore	Gore	Gore	Bush		

(a) Construct a frequency distribution.
(b) Construct a relative frequency distribution.
(c) Construct a frequency bar graph.
(d) Construct a relative frequency bar graph.
(e) Construct a pie chart.
(f) On the basis of the data, make a conjecture about which candidate will win Palm Beach County. If George W. Bush wins Palm Beach County, what conclusions might be drawn, assuming that the sample was conducted appropriately? Would you be confident in making this prediction with a sample of size 40? If the sample consisted of 100 voters, would your confidence increase? Why?

20. **Hospital Admissions** The following data represent the diagnoses of a random sample of 20 patients admitted to a hospital.   *(c) Gun shot wound*

Cancer	Motor Vehicle Accident	Congestive Heart Failure
Gun Shot Wound	Fall	Gun Shot Wound
Gun Shot Wound	Motor Vehicle Accident	Gun Shot Wound
Assault	Motor Vehicle Accident	Gun Shot Wound
Motor Vehicle Accident	Motor Vehicle Accident	Gun Shot Wound
Motor Vehicle Accident	Gun Shot Wound	Motor Vehicle Accident
Fall	Gun Shot Wound	

Source: Tamela Ohm, Student at Joliet Junior College

(a) Construct a frequency distribution.
(b) Construct a relative frequency distribution.
(c) Which diagnosis has the most admissions?
(d) What percentage of diagnoses are motor vehicle accidents? 35%
(e) Construct a frequency bar graph.
(f) Construct a relative frequency bar graph.
(g) Construct a pie chart.

21. **Which Position in Baseball Is the Highest Paying?** You are a prospective baseball agent and are in search of some clients. You would like to recruit the highest paid players as clients, so you perform a study in which you identify the 36 top-paid players as of February 2000 and their positions. The table below shows the results of your study.   *(c) Pitcher*

Player	Position	Player	Position	Player	Position
Kevin Brown	Pitcher	Derek Jeter	Shortstop	John Smoltz	Pitcher
Randy Johnson	Pitcher	Raul Mondesi	Right Field	Jim Thome	First Base
Albert Belle	Right Field	Gary Sheffield	Right Field	Todd Stottlemyre	Pitcher
Bernie Williams	Center Field	Tom Glavine	Pitcher	Robin Ventura	Third Base
Mike Piazza	Catcher	Shawn Green	Right Field	Chuck Finley	Pitcher
Larry Walker	First Base	Ken Griffey, Jr.	Center Field	Al Leiter	Pitcher
David Cone	Pitcher	Mark McGwire	First Base	Brian Jordan	Center Field
Pedro Martínez	Pitcher	Wilson Alvarez	Pitcher	Ray Lankford	Center Field
Mo Vaughn	First Base	Rafael Palmeiro	First Base	Juan González	First Base
Greg Maddux	Pitcher	Iván Rodriguez	Catcher	Kenny Rogers	Pitcher
Sammy Sosa	Right Field	Matt Williams	Third Base	Kenny Lofton	Center Field
Barry Bonds	Right Field	Andrés Gallarraga	First Base	Alex Rodríguez	Shortstop

Source: SLAM! Baseball

(a) Construct a frequency distribution.
(b) Construct a relative frequency distribution.
(c) Which position appears to be the most lucrative? For which position would you recruit?
(d) Are there any positions for which you would avoid recruiting? Why? *Second base, left field*
(e) Draw a frequency bar graph.
(f) Draw a relative frequency bar graph.
(g) Draw a pie chart.

22. Blood Type A phlebotomist draws the blood of a random sample of 50 patients and determines their blood types as shown at right.

(a) Construct a frequency distribution.
(b) Construct a relative frequency distribution.
(c) According to the data, which blood type is most common? *O*
(d) According to the data, which blood type is least common? *AB*
(e) Use the results of the sample to conjecture the percentage of the population that is blood type O. Is this statistic descriptive or inferential? *44%; inferential*

(f) Contact a local hospital and ask them the percentage of the population that is blood type O. Why might the results differ?
(g) Draw a frequency bar graph.
(h) Draw a relative frequency bar graph.
(i) Draw a pie chart.

O	O	A	A	O
B	O	B	A	O
AB	B	A	B	AB
O	O	A	A	O
AB	O	A	B	A
O	A	A	O	A
O	A	O	AB	A
O	B	A	A	O
O	O	O	A	O
O	A	O	A	O

Technology Step-by-Step
Drawing Bar Graphs and Pie Charts

TI-83 Plus   The TI-83 Plus does not have the ability to draw bar graphs or pie charts.

MINITAB   **Bar Graphs**

Step 1: Enter the categories in C1 and the frequency or relative frequency in C2.

Step 2: Select the **Graph** menu and highlight **Chart**.

Step 3: Fill in the window with the appropriate values. In the Function cell, select Sum. In the "Y" cell, select the column containing the frequency or relative frequency. In the "X" cell, select the column containing the categories. The Display cell should be selected as "Bar." Click OK to obtain the bar graph.

Pie Charts

Step 1: With the categories entered in C1 and the frequencies entered in C2, select the **Graph** menu and highlight **Pie Chart** ...

Step 2: Fill in the window as shown on the left to obtain the pie chart of Example 5. Click OK.

Excel   **Bar Graphs**

Step 1: Enter the categories in column A and the frequency or relative frequency in column B.

Step 2: Select the chart wizard icon. Click the "column" chart type. Select the chart type in the upper left-hand corner and hit "Next."

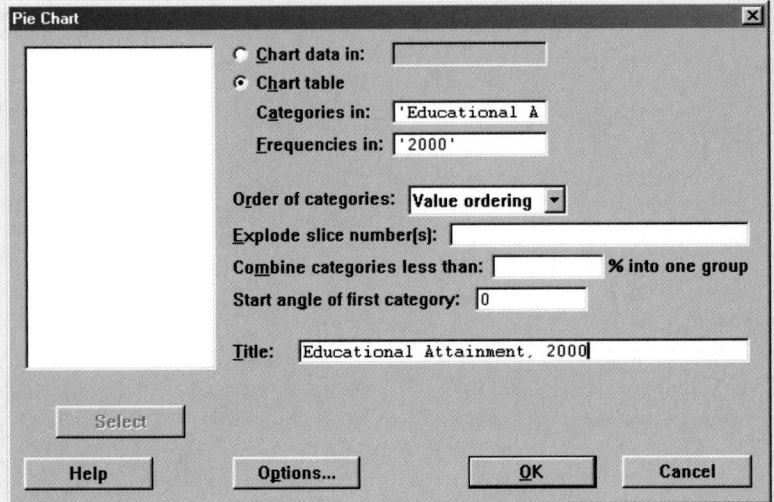

Step 3: Click inside the data range cell. Use the mouse to highlight the data to be graphed. Click "Next."

Step 4: Click the "Titles" tab to enter *x*-axis, *y*-axis, and chart titles. Click "Finish."

Pie Charts

Step 1: Enter the categories in column A and the frequencies in column B. Select the chart wizard icon and click the "pie" chart type. Select the pie chart in the upper left-hand corner.

Step 2: Click inside the data range cell. Use the mouse to highlight the data to be graphed. Click "Next."

Step 3: Click the "Titles" tab to the chart title. Click the "Data Labels" tab and select "Show label and percent." Click "Finish."

2.2 Organizing Quantitative Data I

Preparing for This Section   Before getting started, review the following:

   ✓ Quantitative data (Section 1.1, p. 8)

   ✓ Continuous data (Section 1.1, p. 8)

   ✓ Discrete data (Section 1.1, p. 8)

Objectives 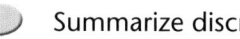 Summarize discrete data in tables

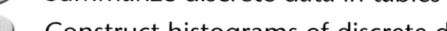 Construct histograms of discrete data

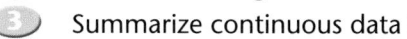 Summarize continuous data in tables

 Construct histograms of continuous data

    Draw stem-and-leaf plots

    Identify the shape of a distribution

Note to Instructor
Remind students of the differences
between discrete and continuous data.

The first step in summarizing quantitative data is to determine whether the data are discrete or continuous. If the data are discrete, the categories of data will be the observations (as in qualitative data); however, if the data are continuous, the categories of data (called *classes*) must be created using intervals of numbers. We will first present the techniques required to summarize discrete quantitative data and then proceed to summarizing continuous quantitative data.

Summarizing Discrete Data in Tables

The values of a discrete variable are used to create the categories of data.

▶ EXAMPLE 1   **Constructing Frequency and Relative Frequency Distributions from Discrete Data**

Problem: The manager of a Wendy's fast-food restaurant is interested in studying the typical number of customers who arrive during the lunch hour. The data in Table 8 represent the number of customers who arrive at Wendy's for 40 randomly selected 15-minute intervals of time during lunch.

TABLE 8				
Number of Arrivals at Wendy's				
7	6	6	6	4
5	6	6	11	4
2	7	1	2	4
6	5	5	3	7
2	2	9	7	5
6	2	6	5	7
6	8	2	6	5
4	6	9	8	5

For example, during one 15-minute interval, seven customers arrived. Construct a frequency and relative frequency distribution.

Approach: The number of people arriving could be 0, 1, 2, 3, …. From Table 8, we see that there are 11 categories of data from this study: 1, 2, 3, …, 11. We tally the number of observations for each category, add up each tally, and create the frequency and relative frequency distributions.

Solution: The frequency and relative frequency distributions are shown in Table 9.

TABLE 9			
Number of Customers	Tally	Frequency	Relative Frequency
1	I	1	$\frac{1}{40} = 0.025$
2	⫿⫿⫿⫿ I	6	0.15
3	I	1	0.025
4	IIII	4	0.1
5	⫿⫿⫿⫿ II	7	0.175
6	⫿⫿⫿⫿ ⫿⫿⫿⫿ I	11	0.275
7	⫿⫿⫿⫿	5	0.125
8	II	2	0.05
9	II	2	0.05
10		0	0.0
11	I	1	0.025

On the basis of the relative frequencies, 27.5% of the 15-minute intervals had six customers arrive at Wendy's during the lunch hour. ◀◀

 Now Work Problems 17(a)–(d).

② Histograms of Discrete Data

As with qualitative data, quantitative data may also be represented graphically. We begin our discussion with a graph called the *histogram*, which is similar to the bar graph drawn for qualitative data.

Definition

A **histogram** is constructed by drawing rectangles for each class of data. The height of each rectangle is the frequency or relative frequency of the class. The width of each rectangle should be the same and the rectangles should touch each other.

▶ EXAMPLE 2   Drawing a Histogram for Discrete Data

Problem: Construct a frequency histogram and a relative frequency histogram using the data summarized in Table 9.

Approach: On the horizontal axis, we place the value of each category of data (number of customers). The vertical axis will be the frequency or rela-

Caution

The rectangles in histograms touch, while the rectangles in bar graphs do not touch.

tive frequency of each category. Rectangles of equal width are drawn, with the center of each rectangle located at the value of each category. For example, the first rectangle is centered at 1. For the frequency histogram, the height of the rectangle will be the frequency of the category. For the relative frequency histogram, the height of the rectangle will be the relative frequency of the category. Remember, the rectangles touch for histograms.

Solution: Figure 8(a) shows the frequency histogram. Figure 8(b) shows the relative frequency histogram.

Figure 8

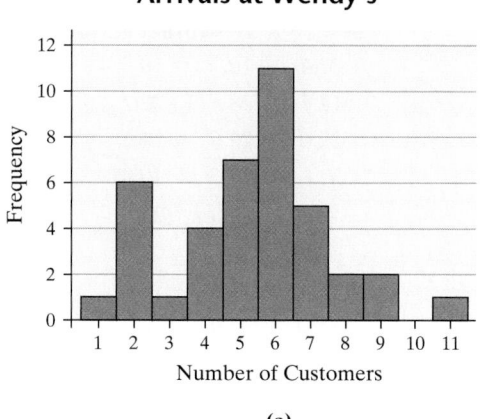

(a)

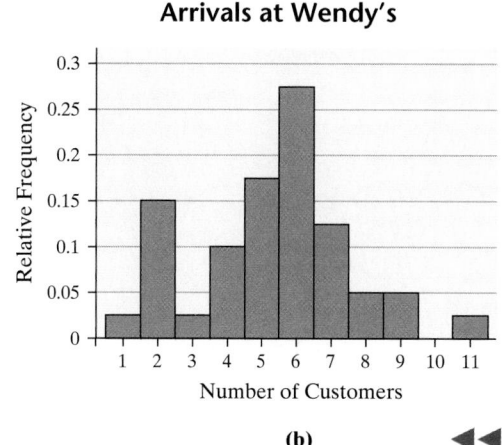

(b)

 Now Work Problems 17(e) and (f).

③ Summarizing Continuous Data in Tables

Raw continuous data do not have any predetermined categories that can be used to construct a frequency distribution; therefore, the categories must be created. Categories of data are created by using intervals of numbers called **classes**.

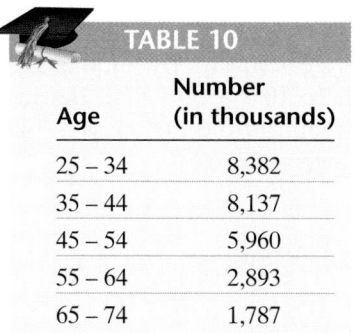

TABLE 10

Age	Number (in thousands)
25 – 34	8,382
35 – 44	8,137
45 – 54	5,960
55 – 64	2,893
65 – 74	1,787

TABLE 11

Age	Number
20 – 29	765
30 – 39	1,301
40 – 49	971
50 – 59	394
60 and older	80

Source: United States Justice Department

Table 10 is a typical frequency distribution created from continuous data. The data represent the number of United States residents between the ages of 25 and 74 that have earned a bachelor's degree. The data are based on the Current Population Survey conducted in 1998.

In the table, we notice that the data are categorized, or grouped, by intervals of numbers. Each interval represents a class. For example, the first class is 25–34-year-old residents of the United States who have a bachelor's degree. There are five classes in the table, each with a lower bound and an upper bound. The **lower class limit** of a class is the smallest value within the class, while the **upper class limit** of a class is the largest value within the class. The lower class limit for the first class in Table 10 is 25, while the upper class limit is 34. The **class width** is the difference between consecutive lower class limits. The class width for the data in Table 10 is $35 - 25 = 10$.

The classes in Table 10 do not overlap, so there is no confusion as to which class a data value belongs. Notice that the class widths are equal for all classes. One exception to this requirement is in open-ended tables. A table is **open ended** if the last class does not have an upper class limit. The data in Table 11 represent the number of persons under sentence of death as of December 31, 1999, in the United States. The last class in the table, "60 and older," is open ended.

▶ **EXAMPLE 3** **Organizing Continuous Data into a Frequency and Relative Frequency Distribution**

Problem: Suppose you are considering investing in a Roth IRA. You collect the data in Table 12, which represent the three-year rate of return (in percent) for a simple random sample of 40 small capitalization growth mutual funds. Construct a frequency and relative frequency distribution of the data.

TABLE 12				
Three-Year Rate of Return of Mutual Funds				
27.4	16.7	10.8	24.1	35.9
12.7	28.5	22.2	18.4	17.4
22.6	29.6	11.6	45.9	16.6
32.1	47.7	10.9	18.4	23.3
18.2	32.0	25.5	23.7	38.1
23.7	14.7	12.8	31.1	21.9
18.4	21.3	27.0	19.6	15.8
14.7	37.0	19.2	18.5	29.1

Source: Morningstar.com

Approach: In order to construct a frequency distribution, we first create classes of equal width. There are 40 observations in Table 12, and they range from 10.8 to 47.7, so we decide to create the classes such that the lower class limit of the first class is 10.0 (a little smaller than the smallest data value) and the class width is 5. There is nothing magical about the choice of 5 as a class width. We could have selected a class width of 8 (or any other class width, as well). We simply choose a class width that we think will nicely summarize the data. If our choice doesn't accomplish this, we can always try another one. The lower class limit of the second class will be $10.0 + 5 = 15.0$. Because the classes must not overlap, the upper class limit of the first class is 14.9. Continuing in this fashion, we obtain the following classes:

$$10.0 - 14.9$$
$$15.0 - 19.9$$
$$\vdots$$
$$45.0 - 49.9$$

This gives us eight classes. We tally the number of observations in each class, add up the tallies, and create the frequency distribution. The relative frequency distribution would be created by dividing each class's frequency by 40, the number of observations.

Solution: We tally the data as shown in the second column of Table 13. The third column in the table shows the frequency of each class. From the frequency distribution, we conclude that a three-year rate of return between 15.0% and 19.9% occurs with the most frequency. The fourth column in the table shows the relative frequency of each class. So, 27.5% of the small-capitalization growth mutual funds had a three-year rate of return between 15.0% and 19.9%.

Historical Note

Florence Nightingale was born in Italy on May 12, 1820. She was named after the city of her birth. Florence was educated by her father, who attended Cambridge University. Between 1849 and 1851, Florence studied nursing throughout Europe. In 1854, she was asked to oversee the introduction of female nurses into the military hospitals in Turkey. While there, she greatly improved the mortality rate of wounded soldiers. She collected data and invented graphs (the polar area diagram), tables, and charts to show that improving sanitary conditions would lead to decreased mortality rates. In 1869, Florence founded the Nightingale School Home for Nurses. Florence died on August 13, 1910.

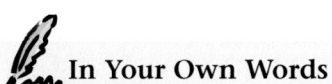

In Your Own Words

Creating the classes for summarizing continuous data is an art form. There is no such thing as the correct frequency distribution. However, there can be incorrect frequency distributions. The larger the class width, the fewer classes a frequency distribution will have.

TABLE 13			
Class (Three-Year Rate of Return)	Tally	Frequency	Relative Frequency
10.0–14.9	ⵉⵉⵉⵉ ⵉⵉ	7	7/40 = 0.175
15.0–19.9	ⵉⵉⵉⵉ ⵉⵉⵉⵉ ⵉ	11	11/40 = 0.275
20.0–24.9	ⵉⵉⵉⵉ ⵉⵉⵉ	8	8/40 = 0.2
25.0–29.9	ⵉⵉⵉⵉ ⵉ	6	0.15
30.0–34.9	ⵉⵉⵉ	3	0.075
35.0–39.9	ⵉⵉⵉ	3	0.075
40.0–44.9		0	0
45.0–49.9	ⵉⵉ	2	0.05

Only 5% of the mutual funds had a three-year rate of return between 45.0% and 49.9%. We might conclude that mutual funds with a rate of return at this level outperform their peers and consider them worthy of our investment. This type of information would be difficult to obtain from the raw data.   ◀◀

Notice that the choice of the lower class limit of the first class and the class width was rather arbitrary. While formulas and procedures do exist for creating frequency distributions from raw data, they do not necessarily provide "better" summaries. It is incorrect to say that one particular frequency distribution is the correct one. Constructing frequency distributions is somewhat of an art form in which the distribution that seems to provide the best overall summary of the data should be used.

Consider the frequency distribution in Table 14, which also summarizes the three-year rate of return data discussed in Example 3. Here, the lower class limit of the first class is 10.0 and the class width is 8.0. Do you think Table 13 or Table 14 provides a better summary of the distribution of three-year rates of return? In forming your opinion, consider the following: Too few classes will cause a "bunching" effect. Too many classes will spread the data out, thereby not revealing any pattern.

The goal in constructing a frequency distribution is to reveal interesting features of the data. With that said, when constructing frequency distributions, we typically want the number of classes to be between 5 and 20. When the data set is small, we want fewer classes; when the data set is large, we want more classes. Why do you think this is reasonable?

TABLE 14		
Class	Tally	Frequency
10.0–17.9	ⵉⵉⵉⵉ ⵉⵉⵉⵉ ⵉ	11
18.0–25.9	ⵉⵉⵉⵉ ⵉⵉⵉⵉ ⵉⵉⵉⵉ ⵉ	16
26.0–33.9	ⵉⵉⵉⵉ ⵉⵉⵉ	8
34.0–41.9	ⵉⵉⵉ	3
42.0–49.9	ⵉⵉ	2

NW   *Now Work Problems 19(a) and (b).*

Histograms of Continuous Data

We're now ready to draw histograms of continuous data.

▶ **EXAMPLE 4** **Drawing a Histogram for Continuous Data**

Problem: Construct a frequency and relative frequency histogram of the three-year rate of return data discussed in Example 3.

Approach: To draw the frequency histogram, we will use the frequency distribution in Table 13. We label the lower class limits of each class on the horizontal axis. Then, for each class, we draw a rectangle whose width is the class width and whose height is the frequency. To construct the relative frequency histogram, we let the height of the rectangle be the relative frequency instead of the frequency.

Solution: Figure 9(a)* represents the frequency histogram, and Figure 9(b) represents the relative frequency histogram.

Note to Instructor
Have students think about the factors to consider in determining an appropriate class width. Are there any ways that a histogram can be used to "distort" the data?

Figure 9
Frequency and Relative
Frequency Histograms

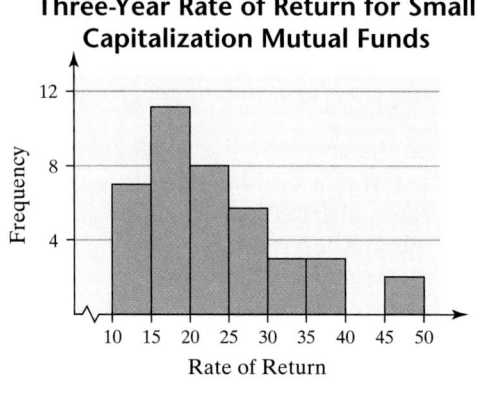

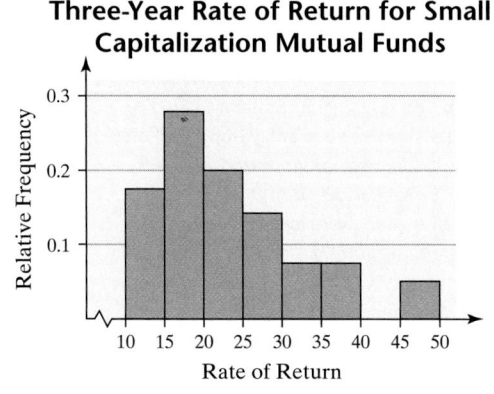

(a)

(b)

 *Now Work Problems 19(c) and (d).*

◀◀

Using Technology: Statistical software and certain graphing calculators have the ability to draw histograms from raw data. Figure 10 shows the frequency histogram for the raw data in Table 12, using Minitab.

Figure 10

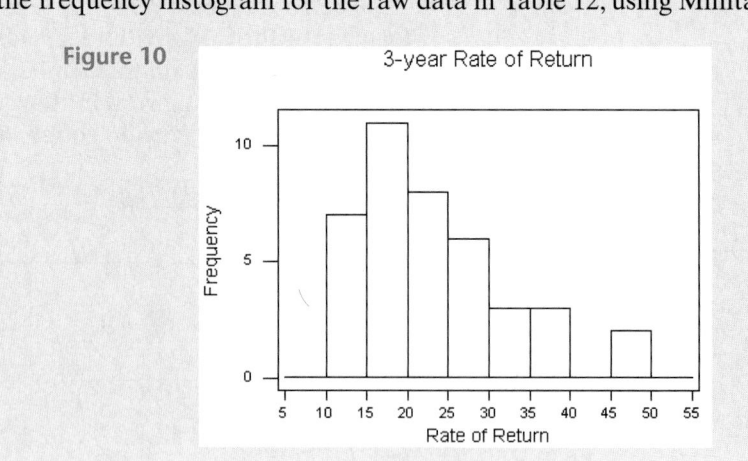

*The ∧ symbol on the horizontal axis indicates that part of the graph has been "cut out." This is done to avoid a lot of white space in the graph.

⑤ Stem-and-Leaf Plots

A **stem-and-leaf plot** is another way to represent quantitative data graphically. As we shall see, stem-and-leaf plots have some advantages over histograms. Use the following steps to construct a stem-and-leaf plot:

Construction of a Stem-and-Leaf Plot

Step 1: The **stem** of the graph will consist of the digits to the left of the rightmost digit. The **leaf** of the graph will be the rightmost digit. Sometimes it is necessary to modify the method of choosing the stem if a different class width is desired.

Step 2: Write the stems in a vertical column in increasing order. Draw a vertical line to the right of the stems.

Step 3: Write each leaf corresponding to the stems to the right of the vertical line. The leaves must be written in ascending order.

▶ **EXAMPLE 5**   **Constructing a Stem-and-Leaf Plot**

Problem: The data in Table 15 represent the percentage of persons in poverty, by state, in 1997. Draw a stem-and-leaf plot of the data.

Approach:

Note to Instructor
Spend some time discussing how the stems are chosen.

Step 1: We will treat the integer portion of the number as the stem and the decimal portion as the leaf. For example, the stem of Alabama will be 14 and the leaf will be 8. The stem of 14 will include all data from 14.0 to 14.9.

TABLE 15					
Percent of Persons Living in Poverty					
State	**Percent**	**State**	**Percent**	**State**	**Percent**
Alabama	14.8	Kentucky	16.4	North Dakota	12.3
Alaska	8.5	Louisiana	18.4	Ohio	11.8
Arizona	18.8	Maine	10.7	Oklahoma	15.2
Arkansas	18.4	Maryland	9.3	Oregon	11.7
California	16.8	Massachusetts	11.2	Pennsylvania	11.4
Colorado	9.4	Michigan	10.7	Rhode Island	11.9
Connecticut	10.1	Minnesota	9.7	South Carolina	13.1
Delaware	9.1	Mississippi	18.6	South Dakota	14.1
D.C.	23.0	Missouri	10.6	Tennessee	15.1
Florida	14.3	Montana	16.3	Texas	16.7
Georgia	14.7	Nebraska	10.0	Utah	8.3
Hawaii	13.0	Nevada	9.6	Vermont	10.9
Idaho	13.3	New Hampshire	7.7	Virginia	12.5
Illinois	11.6	New Jersey	9.2	Washington	10.5
Indiana	8.2	New Mexico	23.4	West Virginia	17.5
Iowa	9.6	New York	16.6	Wisconsin	8.5
Kansas	10.4	North Carolina	11.8	Wyoming	12.7

Source: Poverty in the United States, 1997 Current Population Reports

Figure 11

```
 7 | 7
 8 | 2 3 5 5
 9 | 1 2 3 4 6 6 7
10 | 0 1 4 5 6 7 7 9
11 | 2 4 6 7 8 8 9
12 | 3 5 7
13 | 0 1 3
14 | 1 3 7 8
15 | 1 2
16 | 3 4 6 7 8
17 | 5
18 | 4 4 6 8
19 |
20 |
21 |
22 |
23 | 0 4
```

In Your Own Words

The choice of the stem in the construction of a stem-and-leaf diagram is also an art form. It acts just like the class width. For example, the stem of 7 in Figure 11 represents the class 7.0–7.9. The stem of 8 represents the class 8.0–8.9. Notice that the class width is 1.0. The number of leaves is the frequency of each category.

Step 2: Write the stems vertically in ascending order, and then draw a vertical line to the right of the stems.
Step 3: Write the leaves corresponding to the stem in ascending order.

Solution:

Step 1: The stem from Alabama is 14 while the corresponding leaf is 8. The stem from Alaska is 8 and its leaf is 5, and so on.
Step 2: We write the stems vertically in Figure 11, along with a vertical line to the right of the stem.
Step 3: We write the leaves corresponding to each stem in ascending order. Figure 11 shows the stem-and-leaf diagram. ◀◀

If you look at the stem-and-leaf plot carefully, you'll notice that it is essentially a histogram turned on its side. The stem serves as the class. For example, the stem 15 contains all data from 15.0–15.9. The leaf serves as the frequency (height of the rectangle). Therefore, it is important to space the leaves equally when drawing a stem-and-leaf plot.

One of the advantages of the stem-and-leaf plot over frequency distributions and histograms is that the raw data can be retrieved from the stem-and-leaf plot.

Once a frequency distribution or histogram of continuous data is created, the raw data are lost (unless reported with the frequency distribution); however, the raw data can be retrieved from the stem-and-leaf plot.

The steps listed for creating stem-and-leaf plots sometimes must be modified in order to meet the needs of the data. Consider the next example.

▶ **EXAMPLE 6**   **Constructing a Stem-and-Leaf Plot**

Problem: Construct a stem-and-leaf plot of the three-year rate of return data in Table 12 on page 70.

Approach:

Step 1: If we use the approach from Example 5, the stems will be 10, 11, 12, ..., 47. However, this will not provide a very good visual display of the data (it will be too spread out). Using these stems would be like choosing a class width of 1. To address this problem, the data can be rounded. For example, we might round the data in Table 12 to the nearest integer. The stem can be the tens digits and the leaf can be the ones digits.
Step 2: We create a vertical column of the tens digits.
Step 3: The leaves will be the ones digits.

Solution:

Step 1: We round the data to the nearest integer as shown in Table 16.
Step 2: We use the tens digit for the stem as shown:

```
1 |
2 |
3 |
4 |
```

Note to Instructor
Discuss the similarities and differences
of histograms and stem-and-leaf
diagrams. Remind students that they
can determine the shape of the
distribution just as they did with
histograms by turning the stem-and-
leaf plot on its side.

TABLE 16				
27	17	11	24	36
13	29	22	18	17
23	30	12	46	17
32	48	11	18	23
18	32	26	24	38
24	15	13	31	22
18	21	27	20	16
15	37	19	19	29

Source: Morningstar.com

Step 3: Fill in the leaves in ascending order as shown in Figure 12. ◀◀

Looking at the stem-and-leaf plot in Figure 12, we notice that the data are bunched. To resolve this problem, we can use **split stems**. For example, rather than using one stem for mutual funds earning 10–19 percent, we could use two stems, one for the 10–14 interval and the second for the 15–19 interval. We do this in Figure 13.

The stem-and-leaf plot shown in Figure 13 reveals the distribution of the data better. As with the construction of class intervals in the creation of frequency histograms, judgment plays a major role. There is no such thing as a correct stem-and-leaf plot. However, a quick comparison of Figures 12 and 13 shows that some are better than others.

One final note regarding stem-and-leaf plots: They are best used when the data set is small.

Figure 12

```
1 | 1 1 2 3 3 5 5 6 7 7 7 8 8 8 8 9 9
2 | 0 1 2 2 3 3 4 4 4 6 7 7 9 9
3 | 0 1 2 2 6 7 8
4 | 6 8
```

Figure 13

```
1 | 1 1 2 3 3
1 | 5 5 6 7 7 7 8 8 8 8 9 9
2 | 0 1 2 2 3 3 4 4 4
2 | 6 7 7 9 9
3 | 0 1 2 2
3 | 6 7 8
4 |
4 | 6 8
```

Using Technology: Certain statistical software packages, such as Minitab, will draw stem-and-leaf plots. Figure 14 illustrates a stem-and-leaf plot for the data in Table 12.

Minitab truncated the data values (i.e., 10.8 is represented as 10) instead of rounding. The stem is found in the second column. The value (8) in the left column indicates that there are eight observations in the class containing the middle value (called the *median*). The values in the left column above the (8) represent the number of observations less than or equal to the upper class limit of the class. For example, 18 observations have a three-year rate of return of 19% or less. The values in the left column below the (8) indicate the number of observations greater than or equal to the lower class limit of the class. For example, 5 observations have a three-year rate of return of 35% or higher.

Figure 14

```
  7    1  0 0 1 2 2 4 4
 18    1  5 6 6 7 8 8 8 8 8 9 9
 (8)   2  1 1 2 2 3 3 3 4
 14    2  5 7 7 8 9 9
  8    3  1 2 2
  5    3  5 7 8
  2    4
  2    4  5 7
```

✍ **In Your Own Words**

Using split stems is like adding
more classes to a frequency
distribution.

NW *Now Work Problem 25.*

Distribution Shapes

One of the ways that a variable is described is through the shape of its distribution. Distribution shapes are typically classified as symmetric, skewed left, or skewed right. Figure 15 displays various histograms and the shape of the distribution.

Figure 15

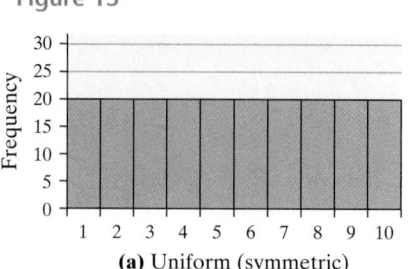

(a) Uniform (symmetric)

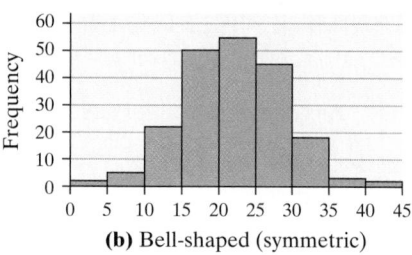

(b) Bell-shaped (symmetric)

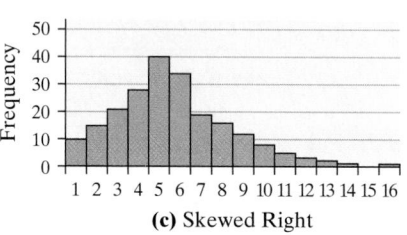

(c) Skewed Right

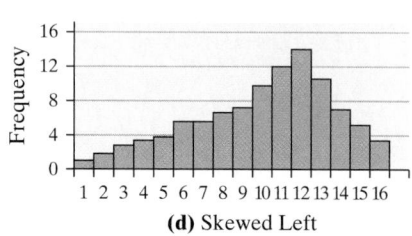

(d) Skewed Left

Note to Instructor
Give examples of data sets that may be uniform, bell shaped, skewed right, and skewed left—for example, IQ scores, income, rolling a single die, and so on.

Figures 15(a) and (b) display symmetric distributions. These distributions are symmetric because, if we split the histogram down the middle, the right and left sides of the histograms are mirror images of each other. Figure 15(a) is a **uniform distribution**, because the frequency of each value of the variable is evenly spread out across the values of the variable. Figure 15(b) displays a **bell-shaped distribution**, because the highest frequency occurs in the middle and frequencies tail off to the left and right of the middle. Figure 15(c) illustrates a distribution that is **skewed right**. Notice that the tail to the right of the peak is longer than the tail to the left of the peak. Finally, Figure 15(d) illustrates a distribution that is **skewed left**, because the tail to the left of the peak is longer than the tail to the right of the peak.

▶ **EXAMPLE 7**   **Identifying the Shape of a Distribution**

Problem: Figure 16 displays the histogram obtained for the three-year rates of return for small capitalization stocks. Describe the shape of the distribution.

Approach: We will compare the shape of the distribution displayed in Figure 16 with those in Figure 15.

Solution: Since the tail to the right of the peak is longer than the tail to the left of the peak, the distribution is skewed right.

Figure 16

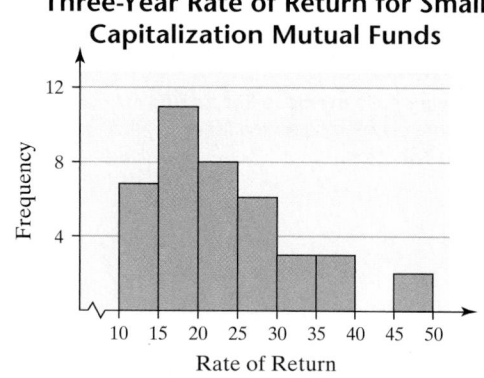

Three-Year Rate of Return for Small Capitalization Mutual Funds

NW *Now Work Problem 19(e).*

2.2 Assess Your Understanding

Concepts and Vocabulary

1. Discuss circumstances under which it is preferable to use relative frequency distributions, instead of frequency distributions, as a tabular summary.
2. Why shouldn't classes overlap when one summarizes continuous data?
3. The histogram at the right represents the total rainfall for each time it rained in Chicago during the month of August since 1871. The histogram was taken from the *Chicago Tribune* on August 14, 2001. What is wrong with the histogram?
4. State the advantages and disadvantages of histograms versus stem-and-leaf plots.

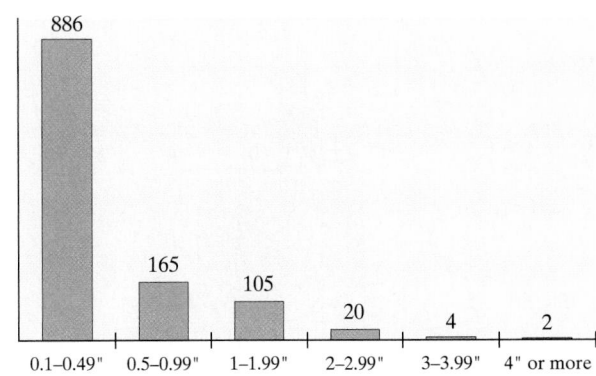

Total August Rain Events Since 1871 in Chicago

Exercises

• Basic Skills

1. **Rolling the Dice** An experiment was conducted in which two fair dice were thrown 100 times. The sum of the dice was then recorded. The following frequency histogram gives the results.

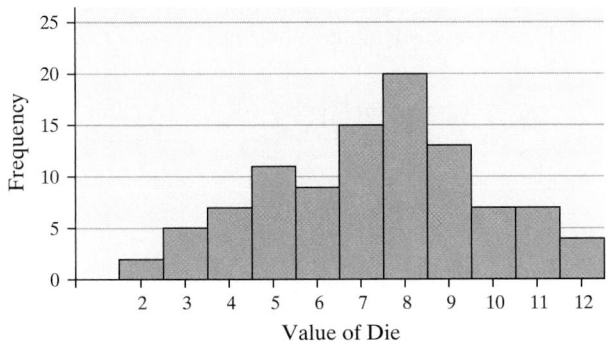

Sum of Two Dice

(a) What was the most frequent outcome of the experiment? 8
(b) What was the least frequent? 2
(c) How many times did we observe a seven? 15
(d) Determine the percentage of time a seven was observed. 15%
(e) Describe the shape of the distribution. Bell shaped

2. **Car Sales** A car salesman records the number of cars he sold each week for the past year. The following frequency histogram shows the results.

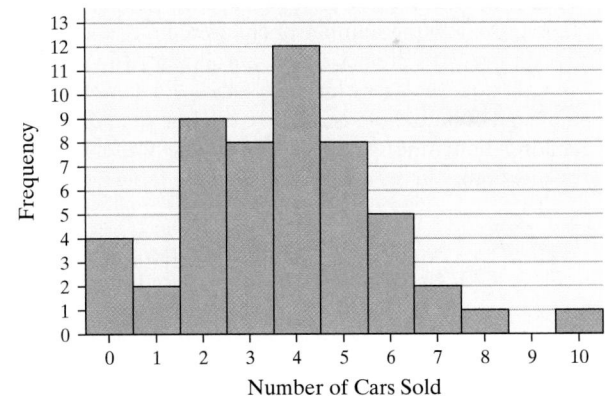

Cars Sold Per Week

(a) What is the most frequent number of cars sold in a week? 4
(b) How many weeks were two cars sold? 9
(c) Determine the percentage of time two cars were sold. 17.3%
(d) Describe the shape of the distribution. Skewed right

3. **IQ Scores** The following frequency histogram represents the IQ scores of a random sample of seventh grade students. IQs are measured to the nearest whole number. The frequency of each class is labeled above each rectangle.

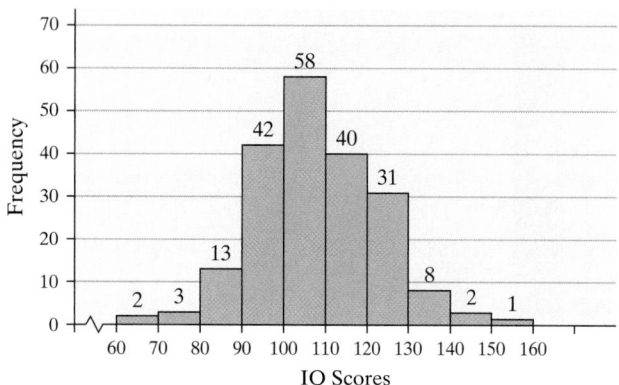

IQs of 7th Grade Students

(a) How many students were sampled? 200
(b) Determine the class width. 10
(c) Identify the classes and their frequency.
(d) Which class has the highest frequency? 100–109
(e) Which class has the lowest frequency? 150–159

(f) What is the relative frequency of an IQ between 120 and 129? 0.155
(g) Describe the shape of the distribution. Bell-shaped

4. **Number of Licensed Drivers** The following frequency histogram represents the number of licensed drivers in the United States in 1997, by age.

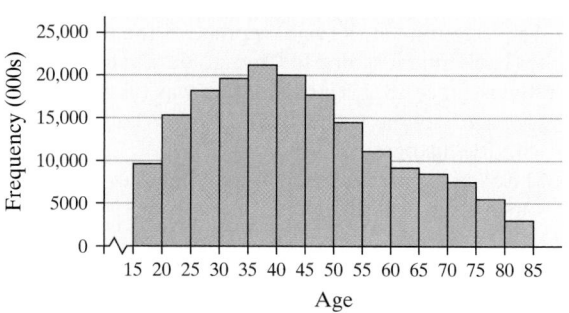

Number of Licensed Drivers by Age

(a) Determine the class width. 5
(b) Identify the classes.
(c) Which class has the highest frequency? 35–39
(d) Which class has the lowest frequency? 80–84
(e) Describe the shape of the distribution. Why do you think the distribution has this shape? Skewed right

---

• **Applying the Concepts**

5. **Predicting School Enrollment** A local school district wants to know the number of children under the age of five in order to predict future enrollment. Toward that end, 50 households within the district are sampled, and the head of household is asked to disclose the number of children under the age of five living in the household. The results of the survey are presented in the table below.

Number of Children Under Five	Number of Households
0	16
1	18
2	12
3	3
4	1

(a) Construct a relative frequency distribution of the data.
(b) What percentage of households have two children under the age of five? 24%
(c) What percentage of households have one or two children under the age of five? 60%

6. **Free Throws** A basketball player habitually makes 70% of her free throws. In an experiment, a researcher asks this basketball player to record the number of free throws

she shoots until she misses. The experiment is repeated 50 times. The table below lists the distribution of the number of free throws attempted until a miss is recorded.

Number of Free Throws Until a Miss	Frequency
1	16
2	11
3	9
4	7
5	2
6	3
7	0
8	1
9	0
10	1

(a) Construct a relative frequency distribution of the data.
(b) What percentage of the time did she miss on her 4th free throw? 14%
(c) What percentage of the time did she make 9 in a row and then miss the 10th free throw? 2%
(d) What percentage of the time did she make at least 5 in a row? 10%

In Problems 7 and 8, determine the original set of data. The stem represents the tens digit and the leaf represents the ones digit.

7.

```
1 | 0   1   4
2 | 1   4   4   7   9
3 | 3   5   5   5   7   7   8
4 | 0   0   1   2   6   6   8   9   9
5 | 3   3   5   8
6 | 1   2
```

8.

```
4 | 0   4   7
5 | 2   2   3   9   9
6 | 3   4   5   8   8   9
7 | 0   1   1   3   6   6
8 | 2   3   8
```

In Problems 9–12, find (a) the number of classes (b) the class limits of each class, and (c) the class width.

9. Health Insurance The following data represent the number of people aged 25–64 covered by health insurance in 1998.

Age	Number (in millions)
25–34	29.3
35–44	37.0
45–54	30.4
55–64	19.5

Source: *Current Population Reports*

(a) 4 (b) Lower class limits: 25, 35, 45, 55;
Upper class limits: 34, 44, 54, 64 (c) 10

10. Earthquakes The following data represent the number of earthquakes worldwide whose magnitude was less than 8.0 in 1998. (a) 8 (c) 1.0

Magnitude	Number
0–0.9	2389
1.0–1.9	752
2.0–2.9	3851
3.0–3.9	5639
4.0–4.9	6943
5.0–5.9	832
6.0–6.9	113
7.0–7.9	10

Source: National Earthquake Information Center

11. Meteorology The following data represent the high-temperature distribution in August in Chicago since 1872. (a) 6 (c) 10

Temperature	Days
50–59°	1
60–69°	308
70–79°	1519
80–89°	1626
90–99°	503
100–109°	11

Source: NOAA

12. Multiple Births The following data represent the number of live multiple delivery births (three or more babies) in 1999 for women 15–44 years old.

Age	Number of Multiple Births
15–19	66
20–24	411
25–29	1653
30–34	2926
35–39	1813
40–44	956

Source: *National Vital Statistics Report* 49, (1): April 17, 2001

In Problems 13–16 construct (a) a relative frequency distribution, (b) a frequency histogram, and (c) a relative frequency histogram for the data in the problem listed. Then answer the questions that follow.

13. (Problem 9). Of the people covered by health insurance, what percentage are 25–34 years old? Of the people covered by health insurance, what percentage are 44 years or younger? 25.2%, 57.1%

14. (Problem 10). What percentage of earthquakes registered 4.0–4.9? What percentage of earthquakes registered 4.9 or less? 33.8%, 95.3%

15. (Problem 11). What percentage of the days had a temperature of 70–79°? What percentage of the days was it 79° or less? 38.3%, 46.1%

16. (Problem 12). What percentage of multiple births were to women 40–44 years old? What percentage of multiple births were to women 24 years old or younger?

17. Waiting The following data represent the number of customers waiting for a table at 6:00 P.M. on Saturday for 40 consecutive Saturdays at Bobak's Restaurant:

11	5	11	3
4	5	13	9
13	10	9	6
10	8	7	3
7	9	10	4
6	8	6	7
6	4	14	11
8	10	9	5
8	8	7	8
8	6	11	8

(a) Construct a frequency distribution of the data.
(b) Construct a relative frequency distribution of the data.
(c) What percentage of the Saturdays had 10 or more customers waiting for a table at 6:00 P.M.? 27.5%
(d) What percentage of the Saturdays had 5 or fewer customers waiting for a table at 6:00 P.M.? 20%
(e) Construct a frequency histogram of the data.
(f) Construct a relative frequency histogram of the data.
(g) Describe the shape of the distribution. Symmetric

18. Highway Repair The following data represent the number of potholes on 50 randomly selected 1-mile stretches of highway in the city of Chicago.

2	7	4	7	2	7
2	2	2	3	4	3
1	2	3	2	1	4
2	2	5	2	3	4
4	1	7	10	3	5
4	3	3	2	2	
1	6	5	7	9	
2	2	2	1	5	
3	5	1	3	5	

(a) Construct a frequency distribution of the data.
(b) Construct a relative frequency distribution of the data.
(c) What percentage of the 1-mile stretches of highway had seven or more potholes? 14%

(d) What percentage of the 1-mile stretches of highway had two or fewer potholes? 32%
(e) Construct a frequency histogram of the data.
(f) Construct a relative frequency histogram of the data.
(g) Describe the shape of the distribution. Skewed right

19. Tensile Strength Tensile strength is the maximum stress at which one can be reasonably certain that failure will not occur. The following data represent the tensile strength (in thousands of pounds per square inch) of a composite material to be used in an aircraft.

203.41	185.97	184.41	160.44	174.63
209.58	190.67	200.73	180.95	185.34
213.35	207.88	206.51	201.95	205.59
218.56	210.80	209.84	204.60	212.00
242.76	231.46	212.15	219.51	225.25

Source: Vangel, Mark G., "New Methods for One-sided Tolerance Limits for a One-way Balanced Random-Effects ANOVA Model," *Technometrics* 34 (May, 1992) no. 2, 176-185

With the first class having a lower class limit of 160 and a class width of 10,

(a) Construct a frequency distribution.
(b) Construct a relative frequency distribution.
(c) Construct a frequency histogram of the data.
(d) Construct a relative frequency histogram of the data.
(e) Describe the shape of the distribution. Symmetric
(f) Repeat parts (a)–(e), using a class width of 15. Which frequency distribution seems to provide a better summary of the data?

20. Miles on a Cavalier A random sample of 36 three-year-old Chevy Cavaliers was obtained in the Miami, Florida area, and the number of miles on each car was recorded. The results are shown in the table below.

34,122	17,685	15,499	26,455	30,500	41,194
39,416	29,307	26,051	27,368	35,936	29,289
28,281	34,511	32,305	37,904	44,448	31,883
37,021	34,500	39,884	23,221	41,043	32,923
30,747	41,620	17,595	38,041	30,739	40,614
35,439	30,283	44,224	35,295	38,995	42,398

Source: cars.com

With the first class having a lower class limit of 15,000 and a class width of 4,000,

(a) Construct a frequency distribution.
(b) Construct a relative frequency distribution.
(c) Construct a frequency histogram of the data.
(d) Construct a relative frequency histogram of the data.

(e) Describe the shape of the distribution. *(e) Symmetric*

(f) Repeat parts (a)–(e), using a class width of 6000. Which class width seems to provide a better summary of the data?

21. Serum HDL Dr. Paul Oswiecmiski randomly selects 40 of his 20–29-year-old patients and obtains the following data regarding their serum HDL cholesterol:

70	56	48	48	53	52	66	48
36	49	28	35	58	62	45	60
38	73	45	51	56	51	46	39
56	32	44	60	51	44	63	50
46	69	53	70	33	54	55	52

With the first class having a lower class limit of 20 and a class width of 10,

(a) Construct a frequency distribution.
(b) Construct a relative frequency distribution.
(c) Construct a frequency histogram of the data.
(d) Construct a relative frequency histogram of the data.
(e) Describe the shape of the distribution. *Bell-shaped*
(f) Repeat parts (a)–(e), using a class width of 5. Which frequency distribution seems to provide a better summary of the data?

22. Volume of Philip Morris Stock The daily volume of a stock is the number of shares of the stock traded in a day. The following data represent a random sample of volume (in millions of shares) of Philip Morris stock traded for 35 days in 2001:

3.98	8.90	10.40	7.52	13.84
14.04	9.14	7.96	11.40	13.30
5.29	9.69	8.94	12.10	13.25
4.62	10.85	24.52	14.62	16.10
4.24	8.54	11.59	6.75	27.54
16.06	17.62	7.17	6.13	25.32
7.71	10.14	4.28	7.24	10.88

Source: http://finance.yahoo.com

With the first class having a lower class limit of 3 and a class width of 4,

(a) Construct a frequency distribution.
(b) Construct a relative frequency distribution.
(c) Construct a frequency histogram of the data.
(d) Construct a relative frequency histogram of the data.
(e) Describe the shape of the distribution. *Skewed right*
(f) Repeat parts (a)–(e), using a class width of 6. Which frequency distribution seems to provide a better summary of the data?

23. M&Ms The following data represent the weights (in grams) of a simple random sample of 50 M&M plain candies.

0.87	0.88	0.91	0.92	0.86
0.91	0.90	0.94	0.82	0.89
0.89	0.88	0.91	0.86	0.84
0.83	0.88	0.88	0.86	0.85
0.91	0.94	0.88	0.87	0.90
0.86	0.93	0.91	0.84	0.83
0.87	0.79	0.87	0.88	0.90
0.93	0.90	0.82	0.88	0.86
0.89	0.86	0.76	0.85	0.84
0.79	0.93	0.84	0.93	0.87

With the first class having a lower class limit of 0.76 and a class width of 0.02,

(a) Construct a frequency distribution.
(b) Construct a relative frequency distribution.
(c) Construct a frequency histogram of the data.
(d) Construct a relative frequency histogram of the data.
(e) Describe the shape of the distribution. *Symmetric*
(f) Repeat parts (a)–(e), using a class width of 0.04. Which frequency distribution seems to provide a better summary of the data?

24. Old Faithful The following data represent the length of eruption (in seconds) for a random sample of eruptions of "Old Faithful," a geyser in California.

108	113	102	106	107
102	100	100	109	105
103	108	116	105	90
110	99	101	103	111
110	103	120	110	101
102	104	103	101	108
105	101	92	104	94
110	106	103	90	110
104	109	99	95	

Source: Ladonna Hansen, park curator

With the first class having a lower class limit of 90 and a class width of 5,

(a) Construct a frequency distribution.
(b) Construct a relative frequency distribution.
(c) Construct a frequency histogram of the data.
(d) Construct a relative frequency histogram of the data.
(e) Describe the shape of the distribution. *Symmetric*
(f) Repeat parts (a)–(e), using a class width of 10. Which frequency distribution seems to provide a better summary of the data?

In Problems 25–28, construct stem-and-leaf diagrams.

25. Age at Inauguration The following data represent the age of United States presidents on inauguration day.

57	61	57	57	58
54	68	51	49	64
65	52	56	46	54
47	55	55	54	42
55	51	54	51	60
55	56	61	52	69
57	50	49	51	62
61	48	50	56	43
64	46	54		

26. Divorce Rate The following data represent the percentage of divorces (as a percentage of marriages in 1996) for selected countries. (*Note:* The U.S. figure is 49%. The highest is Belarus, at 68%, and the lowest is Macedonia, at 5%.

68	65	64	63	63
56	55	53	52	49
43	43	41	41	40
38	35	34	28	26
24	21	19	18	18
15	15	13	13	12
61	46	39	26	18
56	45	39	25	17
7	6	5	12	12

Source: Time Almanac, 2000

27. Grams of Fat in McDonald's Breakfast The following data represent the number of grams of fat in breakfast meals offered at McDonald's.

12	23	28	2	31	37
15	23	38	31	16	11
8	17	20	34	8	

Source: McDonald's Corporation

28. Miles per Gallon The following data represent the number of miles per gallon achieved on the highway, for domestic cars for the 2001 model year.

30	30	30	29	24	27	26
26	30	34	28	32	32	32
37	28	26	26	27	26	28
35	20	25	38	38	30	28
28	25	25	34	24	28	32
28	28	35	23	29	30	30
29	33	40	33	40		

Source: Road and Track Magazine

*In Problems 29 and 30, we compare data sets. Relative frequencies are more appropriate than frequencies when comparing data sets because relative frequencies compare the proportion of total individuals that belong to a certain class, rather than the total number of individuals, which can be misleading if one data set is larger than the other. A great way to compare two data sets is through **back-to-back histograms**. The figure on page 83 is a back-to-back histogram that represents the distribution of homicides for males and females 20–75 years old murdered in 1998, by age.*

Homicides by Age and Gender

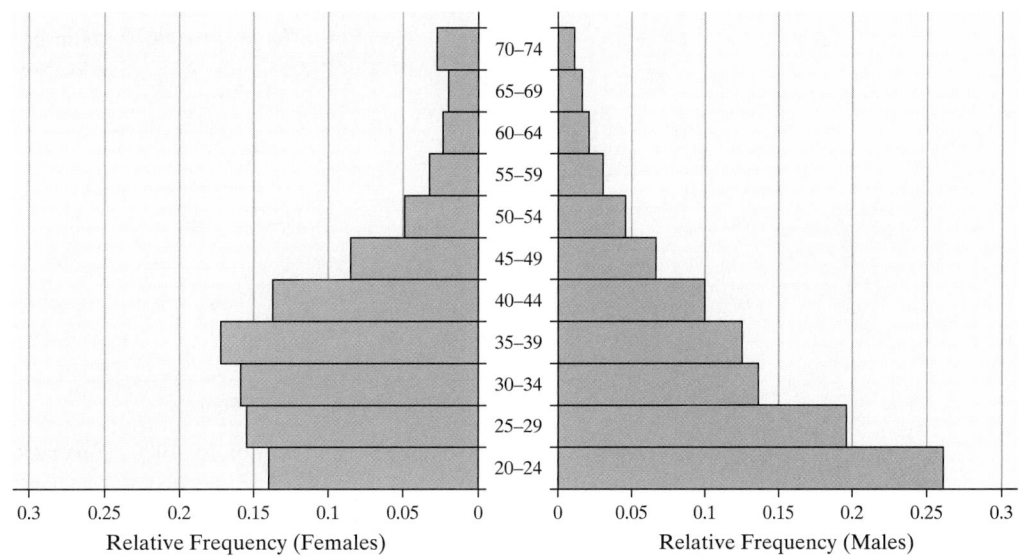

29. Population The following data represent the male and female population of the United States, by age, for residents under 100 years old in 1999.

Age	Male Resident Population (in thousands)	Female Resident Population (in thousands)
0–9	19,881	18,994
10–19	20,174	19,143
20–29	18,264	18,038
30–39	21,001	21,305
40–49	20,550	21,091
50–59	14,187	15,148
60–69	9312	10,669
70–79	6926	9191
80–89	2664	4788
90–99	384	1112

Source: U.S. Census Bureau

(a) Construct a relative frequency distribution for males. Construct a relative frequency distribution for females.
(b) Which group has the higher percentage in the 20–29 age bracket? Which group has the higher percentage in the 90–99 age bracket? Male; Female
(c) Draw back-to-back relative frequency histograms.
(d) Compare the two populations. What can you conclude from the back-to-back histograms?

30. Age of Mother The following data represent the age of a mother at childbirth in 1980 and 1997.

Age of Mother	Number of Births in 1980 (in thousands)	Number of Births in 1997 (in thousands)
10–14	1.1	1.2
15–19	53.0	52.9
20–24	115.1	110.9
25–29	112.9	114.3
30–34	61.9	85.4
35–39	19.8	36.0
40–44	3.9	6.9
45–49	0.2	0.3

Source: U.S. National Center for Health Statistics

(a) Construct a relative frequency distribution for 1980. Construct a relative frequency distribution for 1997.
(b) For what percentage of births was the age of the mother 25–29 in 1980? For what percentage of births was the age of the mother 25–29 in 1997? *30.7%; 28.0%*
(c) Draw back-to-back relative frequency histograms.
(d) Compare the two populations. What can you conclude from the back-to-back histograms?

Technology Step-by-Step
Drawing Histograms and Stem-and-Leaf Plots

TI-83 Plus　**Histograms**

Step 1: Enter the raw data in L1 by pressing STAT and selecting 1:Edit.

Step 2: Press 2nd Y = to access the StatPlot menu. Select 1:Plot1.

Step 3: Place the cursor on "On" and press ENTER.

Step 4: Place the cursor on the histogram icon (see the figure) and press ENTER.

Step 5: Press ZOOM and select 9:ZoomStat.

MINITAB　**Histograms**

Step 1: Enter the raw data in C1.

Step 2: Select the **Graph** menu and highlight **Histogram**.

Step 3: Select the data in C1 and press OK.

Stem-and-Leaf Plot

Step 1: With the raw data entered in C1, select the **Graph** menu and highlight **Stem-and-Leaf**...

Step 2: Select the data in C1 and press OK.

Excel　**Histograms**

Step 1: Enter the raw data in column A.

Step 2: Select **Tools** and **Data Analysis**...

Step 3: Select Histogram from the list.

Step 4: With the cursor in the Input Range cell, use the mouse to highlight the raw data. Select the Chart Output box and press OK.

Step 5: Double-click on one of the bars in the histogram. Select the Options tab from the menu that appears. Reduce the gap width to zero.

Excel does not draw stem-and-leaf plots.

2.3   Organizing Quantitative Data II

Objectives

1. Construct frequency polygons
2. Create cumulative frequency and relative frequency tables
3. Construct frequency and relative frequency ogives
4. Draw time series graphs

Note to Instructor
The material in this section may be omitted without loss of continuity, depending on the time constraints. One suggestion is to have students read the section on their own.

In this section, we continue to organize and summarize quantitative data.

Frequency Polygons

Another way of graphically representing quantitative data sets is through frequency *polygons*. They provide the same information as histograms. Before we can provide a method for constructing frequency polygons, we must learn how to obtain the class midpoint of a class.

Definition

The **class midpoint** is found by adding the lower class limit and upper class limit of a class and dividing the result by 2. That is,

$$\text{Class midpoint} = \frac{\text{Lower class limit} + \text{Upper Class limit}}{2}$$

The class midpoint is used to draw frequency polygons.

Definition

A **frequency polygon** is drawn by plotting a point above each class midpoint on a horizontal axis at a height equal to the frequency of the class. After the points for each class are plotted, straight lines are drawn between consecutive points.

Suppose we wish to construct a frequency polygon of the data summarized in Table 13 on page 71 from Section 2.2. First, we need to determine the class midpoints of each class, as shown in Table 17 on page 86.

We then plot points whose *x*-coordinate is the class midpoint and *y*-coordinate is the frequency. Finally, we connect the points with straight lines and obtain Figure 17 on page 86.

Using Technology: Statistical spreadsheets and certain graphing calculators have the ability to create frequency polygons.

NW *Now Work Problem 9(c)*

Cumulative Frequency and Relative Frequency Tables

Since quantitative data can be ordered (that is, written in ascending or descending order), they can be summarized in a cumulative frequency distribution and a cumulative relative frequency distribution.

	TABLE 17		
Class (three-year rate of return)	Class Midpoint	Frequency	Relative Frequency
10.0–14.9	$\dfrac{10.0 + 14.9}{2} = 12.45$	7	0.175
15.0–19.9	17.45	11	0.275
20.0–24.9	22.45	8	0.2
25.0–29.9	27.45	6	0.15
30.0–34.9	32.45	3	0.075
35.0–39.9	37.45	3	0.075
40.0–44.9	42.45	0	0
45.0–49.9	47.45	2	0.05

Figure 17

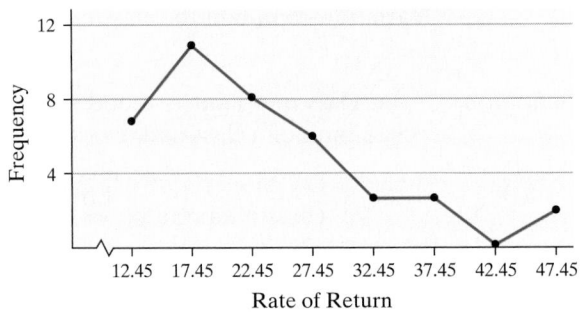

Three-Year Rate of Return

Definitions

A **cumulative frequency distribution** displays the aggregate frequency of the category. In other words, for discrete data, it displays the total number of observations less than or equal to the category. For continuous data, it displays the total number of observations less than or equal to the upper class limit of a class.

A **cumulative relative frequency distribution** displays the proportion (or percentage) of observations less than or equal to the category for discrete data and the proportion (or percentage) of observations less than or equal to the upper class limit for continuous data.

Note to Instructor
The cumulative relative frequency distribution foreshadows the concept of a percentile.

The cumulative frequency for a class is obtained by adding the frequencies of the classes less than or equal to the upper class limit of the class. For example, the cumulative frequency for the second class would be the sum of the frequencies of classes one and two, the cumulative frequency for the third class would be the sum of the frequencies of classes one, two, and three, and so on.

The cumulative relative frequency for continuous data is obtained using the same procedures that were used in creating the cumulative frequency distribution, except that we would use the relative frequencies instead of the frequencies.

Table 18 displays the cumulative frequency and cumulative relative frequency of the data summarized in Table 13 in Section 2.2. From the table, we see that 26 of the 40 mutual funds had three-year rates of return of 24.9% or less. The cumulative relative frequency distribution is shown in

TABLE 18				
Class (three-year rate of return)	Frequency	Relative Frequency	Cumulative Frequency	Cumulative Relative Frequency
10.0–14.9	7	0.175	7	0.175
15.0–19.9	11	0.275	7 + 11 = 18	0.175 + 0.275 = 0.45
20.0–24.9	8	0.2	18 + 8 = 26	0.45 + 0.2 = 0.65
25.0–29.9	6	0.15	32	0.8
30.0–34.9	3	0.075	35	0.875
35.0–39.9	3	0.075	38	0.95
40.0–44.9	0	0	38	0.95
45.0–49.9	2	0.05	40	1

the fifth column of the table. We see that 65% of the mutual funds had a three-year rate of return of 24.9% or less. We can also see that a mutual fund with a three-year rate of return of 45.0% or higher is outperforming 95% of its peers.

 *Now Work Problems 9(a) and (b).*

③ Ogives

Recall that the cumulative frequency of a class is the aggregate frequency less than or equal to the upper class limit.

Definition

> An **ogive** (read as "oh jive") is a graph that represents the cumulative frequency or cumulative relative frequency for the class. It is constructed by plotting points whose *x*-coordinates are the upper class limits and whose *y*-coordinates are the cumulative frequencies or cumulative relative frequencies. After the points for each class are plotted, straight lines are drawn between consecutive points.

We can construct a relative frequency ogive using the data in Table 18 by plotting points whose *x*-coordinate is the class's upper class limit and whose *y*-coordinate is the cumulative relative frequency of the class. We would then connect the points with straight lines. (See Figure 18.)

Figure 18

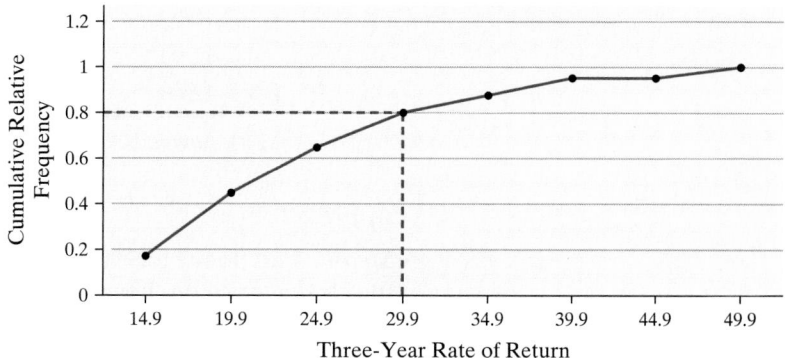

Cumulative Relative Frequency Ogive

From Figure 18 we can see that 80% of the mutual funds had a three-year rate of return less than or equal to 29.9%.

Using Technology: Statistical spreadsheets and certain graphing calculators have the ability to draw ogives.

NW *Now Work Problems 9(d) and (e).*

④ Time Series Plots

If the value of a variable is measured at different points in time, the data are referred to as **time series data**. The closing price of Cisco Systems stock each month for the past two years is an example of time series data.

Definition A **time series plot** is obtained by plotting the time in which a variable is measured on the horizontal axis and the corresponding value of the variable on the vertical axis. Lines are then drawn connecting the points.

Time series plots are very useful in identifying trends in the data.

▶ **EXAMPLE 1** A Time Series Plot

Problem: The data in Table 19 represent the closing price of Cisco Systems stock at the end of each month from January 2000 through November 2001, adjusted for stock splits. Construct a time series plot of the data.

TABLE 19			
Date	**Closing Price**	**Date**	**Closing Price**
1/00	54.75	1/01	37.4375
2/00	66.0938	2/01	23.6875
3/00	77.3125	3/01	15.8125
4/00	69.3281	4/01	16.98
5/00	56.9375	5/01	19.26
6/00	63.5625	6/01	18.20
7/00	65.4375	7/01	19.22
8/00	68.625	8/01	16.33
9/00	55.25	9/01	12.18
10/00	53.875	10/01	16.92
11/00	47.875	11/01	20.44
12/00	38.25		

Source: NASDAQ

Approach:

Step 1: Plot points for each month, with the date on the horizontal axis and the closing price on the vertical axis.
Step 2: Connect the points with straight lines.

Solution: Figure 19 shows the graph of the time series plot. The trend does not bode well for investors of Cisco Systems stock.

Figure 19

Cisco Systems Closing Price

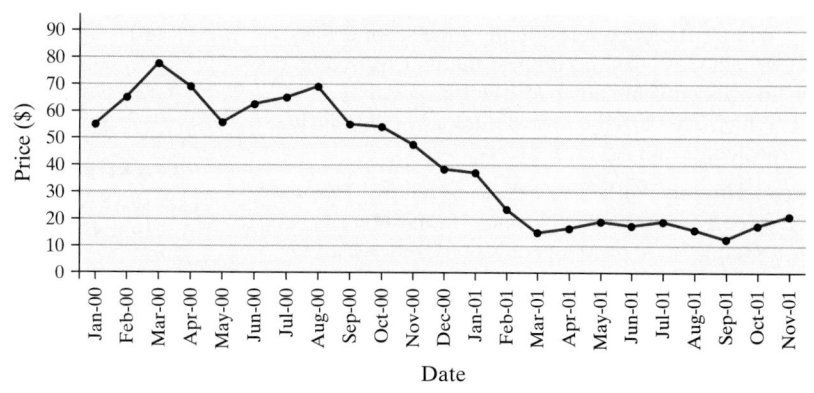

Date

Using Technology: Statistical spreadsheets, such as Excel or Minitab, and certain graphing calculators, such as the TI-83, have the ability to create time series graphs.

NW *Now Work Problem 11.*

2.3 Assess Your Understanding

Concepts and Vocabulary

1. Which do you prefer, histograms, stem-and-leaf plots, or frequency polygons? Be sure to support your opinion. Are there circumstances in which one might be preferred over another?

2. The cumulative relative frequency for the last class must always be 1. Why?

3. What is an ogive?

4. What are time series data?

Exercises

• **Basic Skills**

1. Marital Status of Women The following relative frequency polygon shows the proportion of women age 20 to 54 who were divorced after their first marriage. The data are based upon the Current Population Survey of 1997.

Proportion of Women Divorced After First Marriage

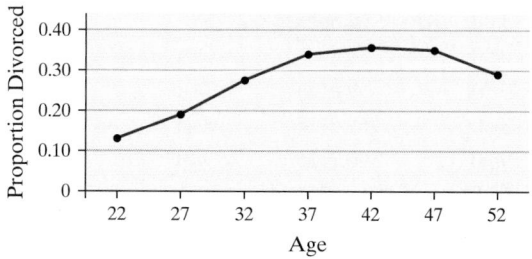

Age

(a) What is the class width? 5
(b) What is the lower class limit of the first class? 20
(c) What is the upper class limit of the first class? 24

(d) 40–44   *(e)* 20–24

(d) Which class has the highest proportion of divorce?
(e) Which class has the lowest proportion of divorce?

2. Cause of Death The following frequency polygon represents the number of deaths due to accidents and adverse effects in 1996 for people 0 to 84 years old. The figure is based upon data from the U.S. National Center for Health Statistics.

Number of Deaths Due to Accidents and Adverse Effects

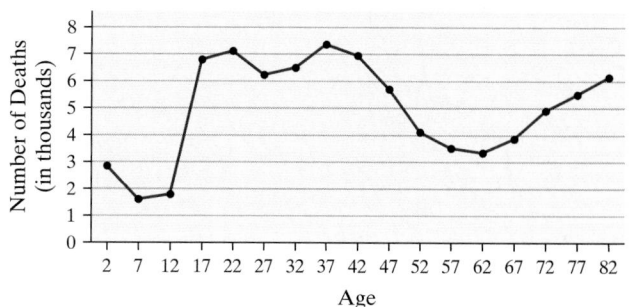

Age

(a) What is the class width? 5
(b) What is the lower class limit of the second class? 5
(c) What is the upper class limit of the second class? 9
(d) Which class has the highest number of deaths due to accidents and adverse effects? 35–39
(e) Which class has the lowest number of deaths due to accidents and adverse effects? 5–9

3. **Travel Time to Work** The following relative frequency ogive represents the travel times (in minutes) to work for a sample of 50 residents of Morris, Illinois.

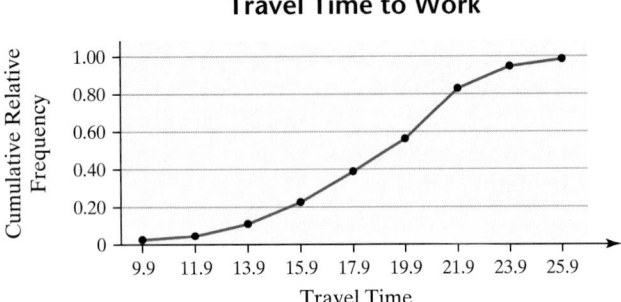

Travel Time to Work

(a) What is the class width? 2
(b) What is the upper class limit of the second class? 11.9

(c) Approximately what percent of commuters have a commute of 17.9 minutes or less? 40%
(d) Approximately what percent of commuters have a commute of more than 17.9 minutes? 60%
(e) Approximately 10% of commuters have a travel time less than how many minutes? 13.9

4. **SAT Scores** The following frequency ogive represents the SAT verbal scores of 120 randomly selected college-bound students.

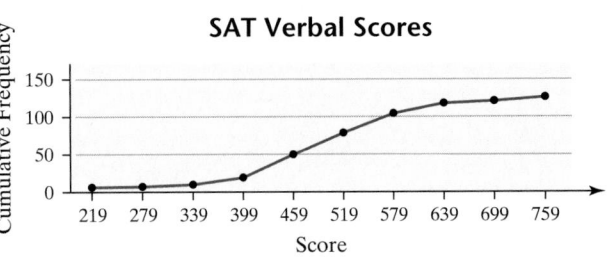

SAT Verbal Scores

(a) What is the class width? 60
(b) What is the upper class limit of the second class? 279
(c) Approximately how many students scored 459 or less? 579 or less? 50; 105

• **Applying the Concepts**

In Problems 5–10, use the frequency distributions in the problem indicated from Section 2.2 to do the following:

(a) *Construct a cumulative frequency distribution.*
(b) *Construct a cumulative relative frequency distribution.*
(c) *Draw a frequency polygon.*
(d) *Draw a frequency ogive.*
(e) *Draw a relative frequency ogive.*

5. Problem 9   6. Problem 10   7. Problem 11
8. Problem 12   9. Problem 19   10. Problem 20

---

11. **Microsoft Corporation** The following data represent the stock price for Microsoft Corporation at the end of each month, adjusted for stock splits, from January 2000 to November 2001. Construct a time series plot of the data. Comment on the trend.

Date	Closing Price	Date	Closing Price
1/00	97.875	1/01	61.0625
2/00	89.375	2/01	59
3/00	106.25	3/01	54.6875
4/00	69.75	4/01	67.75
5/00	62.5625	5/01	69.18
6/00	80	6/01	73
7/00	69.8125	7/01	66.19
8/00	69.8125	8/01	57.05
9/00	60.3125	9/01	51.17
10/00	68.875	10/01	58.15
11/00	57.375	11/01	64.21
12/00	43.375		

Source: NASDAQ

12. Walt Disney Corporation The following data represent the stock price for Walt Disney Corporation at the end of each month from January 2000 to November 2001. Construct a time series plot of the data. Comment on the trend.

Date	Closing Price	Date	Closing Price
1/00	35.6853	1/01	30.1303
2/00	33.4128	2/01	30.625
3/00	40.5376	3/01	28.2997
4/00	42.8715	4/01	29.9324
5/00	41.4589	5/01	31.288
6/00	38.1422	6/01	28.5867
7/00	37.8965	7/01	26.0733
8/00	38.2804	8/01	25.163
9/00	37.5894	9/01	18.4245
10/00	35.194	10/01	18.3948
11/00	28.4377	11/01	20.2551
12/00	28.6337		

Source: NYSE

13. College Enrollment The following data represent the percentage of recent high school graduates (graduated within 12 months prior to the given year-end) who enroll in college. Construct a time series plot of the data.

Year	Percent Enrolled	Year	Percent Enrolled
1985	57.7	1992	61.7
1986	53.8	1993	62.6
1987	56.8	1994	61.9
1988	58.9	1995	61.9
1989	59.6	1996	65.0
1990	59.9	1997	67.0
1991	62.4		

Source: U.S. Center for Education Statistics

14. IRS Audits The following data represent the percentage of tax returns audited by the Internal Revenue Service. Construct a time series plot of the data.

Year	Percent Audited	Year	Percent Audited
1988	1.57	1993	0.92
1989	1.29	1994	1.08
1990	1.04	1995	1.67
1991	1.17	1996	1.67
1992	1.06		

Source: Internal Revenue Service

15. Rates of Return of Stocks Stocks may be categorized by industry. The following data represent the five-year rates of return for a simple random sample of financial stocks and energy stocks ending December 28, 2001.

Financial Stocks				
16.12	18.61	4.04	13.93	17.85
3.34	8.39	21.32	34.22	16.56
28.51	13.29	11.03	14.61	6.67
2.98	14.06	28.90	11.26	9.24
10.97	7.13	5.32	0.63	13.43
17.10	22.21	6.18	5.80	1.39
0.83	5.63	8.39	8.02	1.23
3.32	9.42	2.98	13.62	6.36

Energy Stocks				
2.49	9.70	21.67	8.31	5.07
7.70	23.72	5.59	6.09	9.69
1.82	12.68	6.07	11.09	6.35
2.00	14.22	13.17	6.29	6.25
7.39	9.09	30.39	11.25	7.17
9.48	9.23	9.70	5.41	10.29
6.11	7.38	11.60	12.10	13.38

Source: Morningstar.com

(a) Construct a frequency distribution for each industry. In order to make an easy comparison, create each frequency distribution so that the lower class limit of the first class is 0.00 and the class width is 5.00.

(b) Construct a relative frequency distribution for financial stocks. Construct a relative frequency distribution for energy stocks.

(c) On the same graph, construct a relative frequency polygon for the two industries.

(d) On the same graph, construct a relative frequency ogive for the two industries.

(e) Which stock industry appears to have better performance for the five-year period? Support your opinion.

16. American League versus National League The following data represent the earned run average of the top 37 pitchers in both the American League and National League in 2001.

(a) Why would it be appropriate to use frequencies to compare the two leagues? Why?

(b) Construct a frequency distribution for each league. In order to make an easy comparison, create each frequency distribution so that the lower class limit of the first class is 2.40 and the class width is 0.40.

(c) On the same graph, construct a frequency polygon for the American and National Leagues.

(d) On the same graph, construct a frequency ogive for the American and National Leagues.

(e) Which league appears to have better pitchers? Support your opinion. (*Note*: Be sure to take into account the fact that the National League does not have a designated hitter.)

American League				
3.05	3.15	3.16	3.29	3.37
3.43	3.45	3.49	3.51	3.59
3.60	3.65	3.77	3.90	3.94
3.99	4.05	4.08	4.09	4.09
4.09	4.25	4.32	4.36	4.37
4.39	4.42	4.45	4.45	4.50
4.76	4.93	5.02	5.08	5.17
5.54	5.82			

National League				
2.49	2.98	3.04	3.05	3.09
3.16	3.29	3.31	3.36	3.40
3.42	3.50	3.57	3.57	3.69
3.70	3.80	4.03	4.05	4.05
4.19	4.31	4.33	4.34	4.42
4.42	4.45	4.46	4.46	4.47
4.48	4.49	4.63	4.79	4.81
4.85	4.90			

Technology
Drawing Frequency Polygons, Ogives, and Time Series Plots

TI-83 Plus   The TI-83 Plus is capable of drawing all three of these graphs.

MINITAB   Minitab is capable of drawing all three of these graphs.

Excel   Excel is capable of drawing all three of these graphs.

2.4   Graphical Misrepresentations of Data

Objective   Understand the origins of misleading or deceptive graphs

Note to Instructor
The material in this section can be omitted without loss of continuity. For those instructors who are pressed for time, it can be assigned for reading.

Often, statistics gets a bad rap for having the ability to manipulate data in order to support any position desired. One popular method of distorting the truth is through graphics. Sometimes graphics *mislead*, while other times they *deceive*. We will call graphs misleading if they unintentionally create an incorrect impression. We consider graphs deceptive if they purposely create an incorrect impression. We have already discussed the power that graphical representations of data can have, so it is important to be able to recognize misleading and deceptive graphs. The most common graphical misrepresentation of data is typically accomplished through the manipulation of the scale of the graph.

▶ **EXAMPLE 1**   **Misrepresentation of Data**

Problem: The bar graph in Figure 20 is from a *USA Today* "Snapshot." A survey was conducted by Impulse Research for Quilted Northern Confidential in which individuals were asked how they would flush a toilet when the facilities are not sanitary. What's wrong with the graphic?

Figure 20

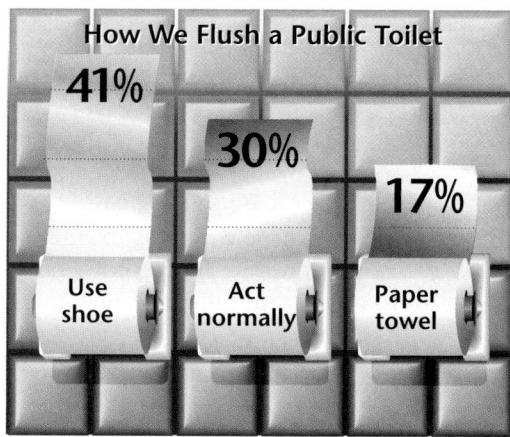

Approach: We need to compare the vertical scales of each bar to see if they accurately depict the percentages given.

Solution: First, it is unclear whether the bars include the roll of toilet paper or not. In either case, the roll corresponding to "use shoe" should be 2.4(=41/17) times longer than the roll corresponding to "paper towel." If we include the roll of toilet paper, then the bar corresponding to "use shoe" is less than double the length of "paper towel." If we do not include the roll of toilet paper, then the bar corresponding to "use shoe" is almost exactly double the length of the bar corresponding to "paper towel." The vertical scaling is incorrect. ◄◄

▶ **EXAMPLE 2** **Misrepresentation of Data by Manipulating the Vertical Scale**

Problem: The bar graph shown in Figure 21 depicts the average SAT Math scores of college-bound seniors for the years 1989–1999, based on data from the College Board. Determine why this graph might be considered misrepresentative.

Figure 21

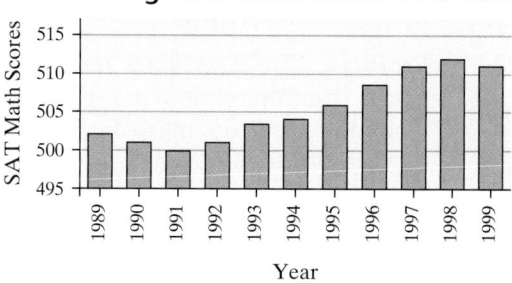

Approach: We need to look at the graph for any characteristics that may mislead a reader, such as manipulation of the vertical scale.

Solution: The graph in the figure may lead a reader to believe that SAT math scores have increased substantially between 1989 and 1999. While SAT math scores have increased between 1989 and 1999, they have not doubled or tripled, as may be inferred from the graph (since the bar for 1997 is three times as high as the bar for 1991). We notice in the figure that the vertical axis begins its labeling at 495 instead of 0. This type of scaling is common when the smallest observed data value is a rather large number. It is not necessarily done purposely to confuse or mislead the reader. Often, the main purpose in graphs is to discover a trend rather than the actual differences in the data. The trend is clearer in Figure 21 than in Figure 22, where the vertical axis begins at 0.

Often, instead of beginning the axis of a graph at 0 as in Figure 22, the graph is begun at a value slightly less than the smallest value in the data set. However, special care must be taken to make the reader aware of the vertical-axis scaling. Figure 23 shows the proper construction of the graph of the SAT scores, with the graph beginning at 495. The symbol ⚡ is used to signify that the graph has a "gap" in it.

Figure 22

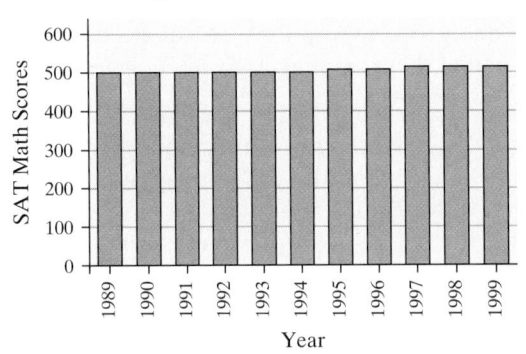

Figure 23

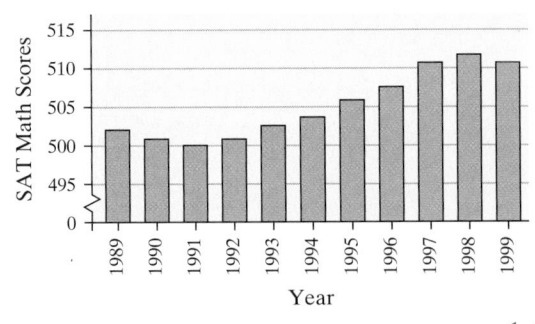

 Now Work Problem 5.

In addition to vertical-axis scaling, figures can be misleading through pictures. Consider the next example.

▶ **EXAMPLE 3** **Misleading Graphs**

Figure 24

February 8, 1996   May 3, 1999

Problem: The Dow Jones Industrial Average (DJIA) is a collection of 30 stocks from the stock market that are thought to be representative of the United States economy. It includes companies such as Intel, Wal-Mart, and General Motors. Had you invested $10,000 in the DJIA on February 8, 1996, it would have been worth $20,000 May 3, 1999. To illustrate this investment, a brokerage firm might create the graphic shown in Figure 24. Describe how this graph is misleading.

Approach: Again, we look for characteristics of the graph that seem to manipulate the facts, such as an incorrect depiction of the size of the graphics.

Solution: The graphic on the right of the figure has been doubled in length, width, and height, causing an eight-fold increase in the size, thereby misleading the reader into thinking that the size of the investment increased by eight times instead of by two times. ◀◀

NW *Now Work Problem 13.*

Note to Instructor
Class Project: Have student collect graphs from newspapers, magazines, and so on that are misleading or incorrect. Create a binder of these graphs for the class to refer to and explore.

There are many ways to create graphs that mislead. Two popular texts written about ways that graphs mislead or deceive are *How to Lie with Statistics* (W. W. Norton & Company, Inc., 1982), by Darrell Huff, and *The Visual Display of Quantitative Information* (Graphics Press, 2001), by Edward Tufte.

We conclude this section with some guidelines for constructing good graphics.

Characteristics of Good Graphics

- Label the graphic clearly and provide explanations if needed.
- Avoid distortion. Don't lie about the data.
- Avoid three dimensions. Three-dimensional charts may look nice, but they distract the reader and often result in misinterpretation of the graphic.
- Do not use more than one design in the same graphic. Sometimes graphs use a different design in a portion of the graphic in order to draw attention to this area. Don't use this technique. Let the numbers speak for themselves.

2.4 Assess Your Understanding

Exercises

1. The following graphic was taken from a *USA Today* "Snapshot." Explain how it is misleading.

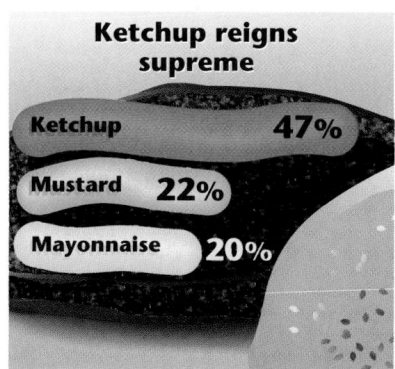

2. The following graphic was taken from the *Chicago Tribune* on Sunday, August 12, 2001. What is wrong with the pie chart on the right?

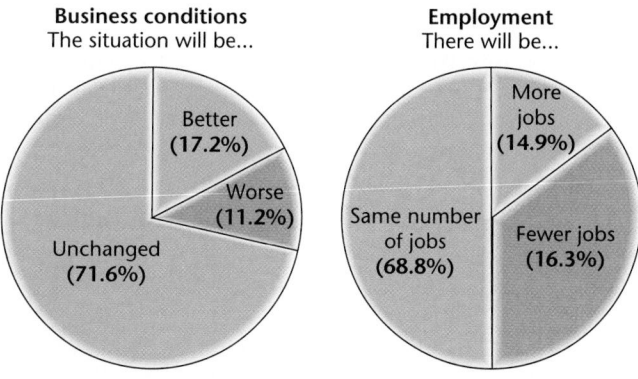

3. The following graphic was taken from http://www.unilever.com. Explain how it is misleading.

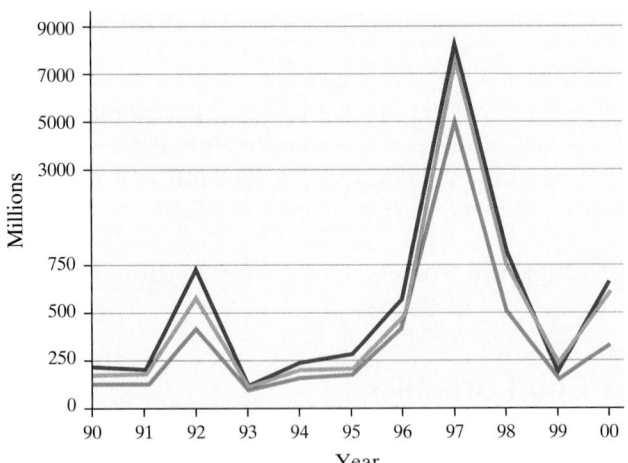

4. **Health Insurance** The following relative frequency histogram represents the percentage of people aged 25–64 years old covered by health insurance:

Proportion Covered by Health Insurance

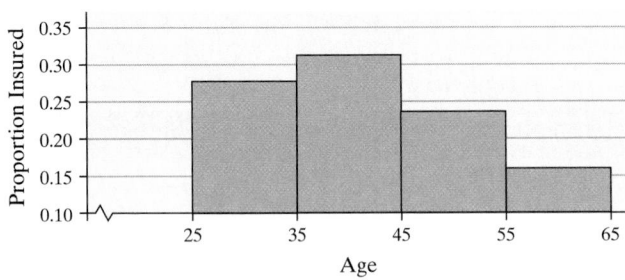

(a) Describe how this graph is misleading. What might a reader conclude from the graph?
(b) Redraw the histogram in two ways so that it is not misleading.

5. **Persons with Work Disability** The following frequency histogram represents the number of persons with work disability in 1998, based upon data from the U.S. Census Bureau.

Number of People with Work Disability

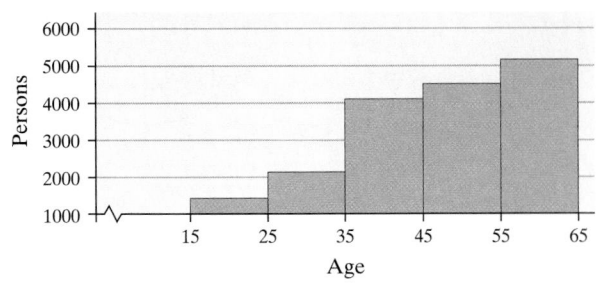

(a) Describe how this graph is misleading. What might a reader conclude from the graph?
(b) Redraw the histogram in two ways so that it is not misleading.

6. **Movie Production** The following time series plot shows the average production costs for making a movie in the years 1985–1997, based on data obtained from the Motion Picture Association of America:

Average Cost for Making a Movie

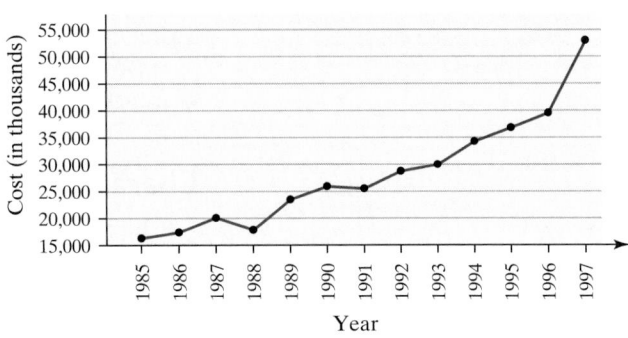

(a) Describe how this graph is misleading.
(b) What impression is the graph trying to convey?

7. **Health Care** The following time series plot displays health-care expenditures per person in the United States.

Health-Care Expenditures per Person

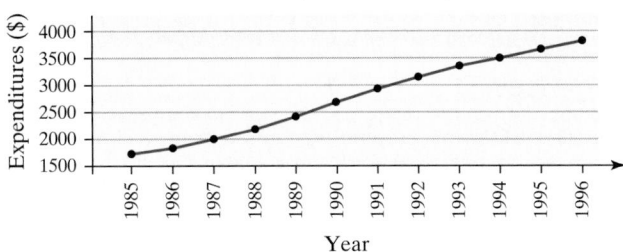

(a) Describe how this graph is misleading.
(b) What impression is the graph trying to convey?

8. **National Debt** The following graphic is from the *USA Today* "Snapshot."

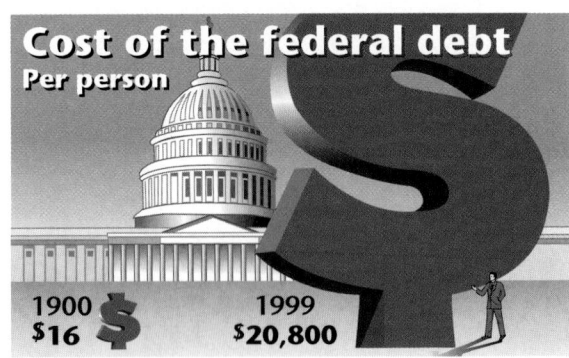

How many times larger should the graphic for 1999 be than the 1900 graphic? *1300 times*

9. Cost of Kids The following graphic is from a *USA Today* "Snapshot" based on data from the Agriculture Department. It represents the percentage of income a middle-income family will spend on their children.

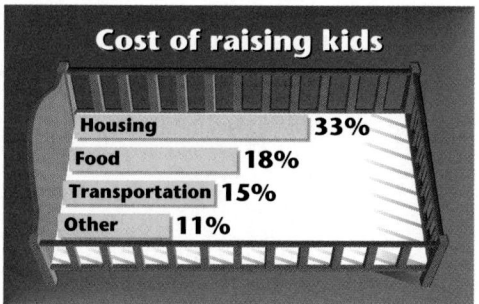

(a) How is the graphic misleading?
(b) What could be done to improve the graphic?

10. Health-Care Expenditures The following data represent health-care expenditures as a percentage of gross domestic product (GDP) from 1989–1996. Gross domestic product is the total value of all goods and services created during the course of the year.

Year	Health Care as a Percent of GDP
1989	11.4
1990	12.2
1991	13.0
1992	13.4
1993	13.6
1994	13.6
1995	13.6
1996	13.6

Source: U.S. Health Care Financing Administration

(a) Construct a time series plot that a politician would create to support the position that health-care expenditures, as a percentage of GDP, are increasing and must be slowed.
(b) Construct a time series plot that the health-care industry would create to refute the opinion of the politician.
(c) Construct a time series plot that is not misleading.

11. Landfill Utilization The following data represent the number of pounds of solid waste generated per person per day that went into landfills in the United States from 1990–1997.

Year	Waste Generated
1990	3.1
1991	2.9
1992	2.9
1993	2.9
1994	2.8
1995	2.5
1996	2.4
1997	2.4

Source: U.S. Environmental Protection Agency

(a) Construct a time series plot that supports the opinion that the amount of solid waste per person that goes into landfills is declining substantially.
(b) Construct a time series plot that supports the opinion that the amount of solid waste per person that goes into landfills is declining, but not substantially.
(c) Construct a time series plot that is not misleading.

12. Population Growth Between 1940 and 1998, the United States population nearly doubled.

(a) Construct a graphic that is not misleading to depict this situation.
(b) Construct a graphic that is misleading to depict this situation.

13. Chlorofluorocarbons The amount of chlorofluorocarbons (CFCs) emissions in 1990 was 193 metric tons, or approximately three times as much as the amount in 1997.

(a) Construct a graphic that is not misleading to depict this situation.
(b) Construct a graphic that is misleading to depict this situation.

CHAPTER 2 REVIEW

Summary

Raw data are first organized into tables. Data are organized by creating classes into which they fall. Qualitative data and discrete data have values that provide clear-cut categories of data. However, with continuous data, the categories, called classes, must be created. Typically, the first table created is a frequency distribution, which lists the frequency with which each class of data occurs. Other types of distributions include the relative frequency distribution and the cumulative frequency distribution.

Once data are organized into a table, graphs are created. For data that are qualitative, we can create bar charts and pie charts. For data that are quantitative, we can create histograms, stem-and-leaf plots, frequency polygons, and ogives.

In creating graphs, care must be taken not to draw a graph that misleads or deceives the reader. If a graph's vertical axis does not begin at zero, the symbol ⚡ should be used to indicate the "gap" that exists in the graph.

Vocabulary

Raw data (p. 50)
Frequency distribution (p. 52)
Relative frequency distribution (p. 53)
Bar graph (p. 55)
Pareto chart (p. 56)
Side-by-side bar graph (p. 57)
Pie chart (p. 59)
Histogram (p. 68)

Class (p. 69)
Lower and upper class limit (p. 69)
Class width (p. 69)
Stem-and-leaf plot (p. 73)
Uniform distribution (p. 76)
Bell-shaped distribution (p. 76)
Skewed right (p. 76)
Skewed left (p. 76)

Class midpoint (p. 85)
Frequency polygon (p. 85)
Cumulative frequency distribution (p. 86)
Ogive (p. 87)
Time series plot (p. 88)

Objectives

Section	You should be able to . . .	Review Exercises
2.1	1 Construct frequency and relative frequency distributions from qualitative data. (p. 52)	3(a), 4(a), 7(a),(b), 8(a),(b)
	2 Construct bar graphs (p. 55)	3(c) and (d), 4(c) and (d), 7(c), 8(c)
	3 Construct pie charts (p. 58)	3(e), 4(e), 7(d), 8(d)
2.2	1 Summarize discrete data in tables (p. 67)	9(a) and (b), 10(a) and (b)
	2 Construct histograms of discrete data (p. 68)	9(e) and (f), 10(e) and (f)
	3 Summarize continuous data in tables (p. 69)	11(a) and (b), 12(a) and (b), 13(a) and (b), 14(a) and (b)
	4 Construct histograms of continuous data (p. 72)	11(e) and (f), 12(e) and (f); 13(c) and (d), 14(c) and (d)
	5 Draw stem-and-leaf plots (p. 73)	15 and 16
	6 Identify the shape of a distribution (p. 75)	11(e), 12 (e), 13(c), 14(c); 15, 16
2.3	1 Construct frequency polygons (p. 85)	5(f), 6(f)
	2 Create cumulative frequency and relative frequency tables (p. 85)	5(b), 5(c), 6(b), 6(c)
	3 Construct frequency and relative frequency ogives (p. 87)	5(h), 5(i), 6(h), 6(i)
	4 Draw time series graphs (p. 88)	17, 18
2.4	1 Understand the origins of misleading or deceptive graphs (p. 92)	19, 20, 21

Review Exercises

1. Energy Consumption The following bar chart represents the energy consumption of the United States (in quadrillion Btus) in 1999.

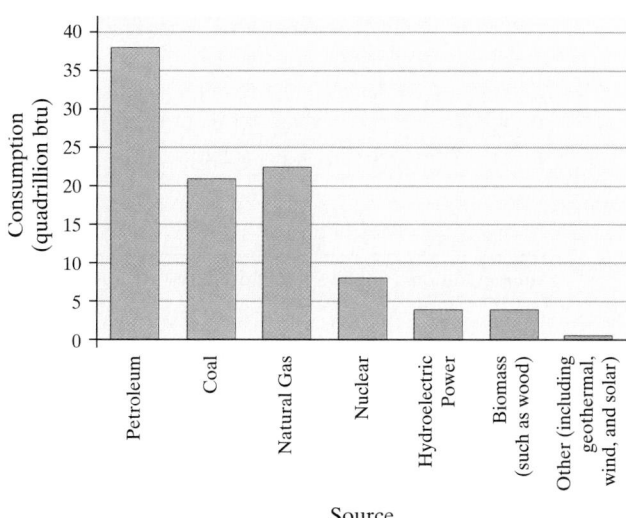

Energy Consumption

(a) 22 quadrillion btus

(a) Approximately how much energy did the United States consume through natural gas?
(b) Approximately how much energy did the United States consume through biomass? 4 quadrillion btus
(c) Approximate the total energy consumption of the United States in 1999. ≈ 95 quadrillion btus

2. Taxi Time The following histogram represents the taxi time (in minutes) on November 21, 2001, for Southwest Airlines at Nashville International Airport.

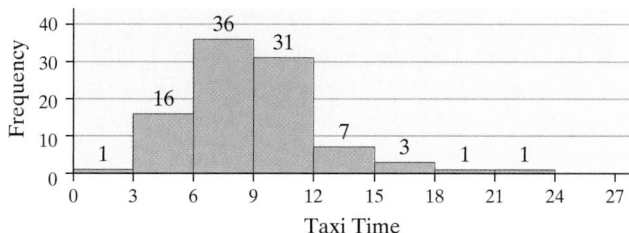

Taxi Time Nashville Airport Southwest Airlines

(a) How many Southwest flights departed from Nashville on November 21, 2001? 96
(b) Determine the class width. 3

(c) Identify the classes and their frequency.
(d) Which class has the highest frequency? 6–8.9
(e) What is the relative frequency of taxi time between 3 and 5.9 minutes? 0.167
(f) Describe the shape of the distribution. Skewed right

3. Weapons Used in Homicide The following frequency distribution represents the cause of death in homicides for the year 1998.

Cause of Death	Frequency
Gun	9222
Cutting/stabbing	1890
Blunt object	753
Personal weapons (hands, fists, etc.)	952
Strangulation	313
Other	1080

Source: U.S. Federal Bureau of Investigation

(a) Construct a relative frequency distribution.
(b) What percentage of homicides were committed using a blunt object? 5.3%
(c) Construct a frequency bar graph.
(d) Construct a relative frequency bar graph.
(e) Construct a pie chart.

4. U.S. Greenhouse Gas Emissions The following frequency distribution represents the total emissions in millions of metric tons of carbon equivalent in 1997 in the United States.

Gas	Emissions
Carbon dioxide	1487.9
Methane	179.6
Nitrous oxide	109.0
Hydrofluorocarbons, perfluorocarbons, and sulfur hexafluoride	37.1

Source: *Time Almanac,* 2000

(b) 82.0%

(a) Construct a relative frequency distribution.
(b) What percent of emissions is due to carbon dioxide?
(c) Construct a frequency bar graph.
(d) Construct a relative frequency bar graph.
(e) Construct a pie chart.

5. Vehicle Fatalities The following frequency distribution represents the number of drivers in fatal crashes in 1999, by age, for males aged 20 to 84 years.

Age	Number of Drivers	Age	Number of Drivers
20–24	8067	55–59	2332
25–29	6195	60–64	1606
30–34	6274	65–69	1341
35–39	5130	70–74	1273
40–44	4631	75–79	1179
45–49	3636	80–84	902
50–54	3021		

Source: National Highway Traffic Safety Administration

(a) Construct a relative frequency distribution.
(b) Construct a cumulative frequency distribution.
(c) Construct a cumulative relative frequency distribution.
(d) Construct a frequency histogram. Describe the shape of the distribution.
(e) Construct a relative frequency histogram.
(f) Construct a frequency polygon.
(g) Construct a relative frequency polygon.
(h) Construct a frequency ogive.
(i) Construct a relative frequency ogive.
(j) What percentage of males aged 20 to 84 involved in fatal crashes were 20–24? 17.7%
(k) What percentage of males aged 20 to 84 involved in fatal crashes were less than 29 years old? 31.3%
(l) Compare the relative frequencies in Problem 29 from Section 2.2 with the relative frequencies in this problem. Is there a higher percentage of fatal accidents involving 20–29-year-old males than there are 20–29-year-old males in the population? How might an insurance company use this information?

6. Vehicle Fatalities The following frequency distribution represents the number of drivers in fatal crashes in 1999, by age, for females aged 20 to 84 years old.   (k) 25.7%

Age	Number of Drivers	Age	Number of Drivers
20–24	3190	55–59	1236
25–29	2446	60–64	956
30–34	2366	65–69	1015
35–39	2396	70–74	1050
40–44	2204	75–79	978
45–49	1813	80–84	779
50–54	1480		

Source: National Highway Traffic Safety Administration

(a) Construct a relative frequency distribution.
(b) Construct a cumulative frequency distribution.
(c) Construct a cumulative relative frequency distribution.
(d) Construct a frequency histogram. Describe the shape of the distribution.
(e) Construct a relative frequency histogram.
(f) Construct a frequency polygon.
(g) Construct a relative frequency polygon.
(h) Construct a frequency ogive.
(i) Construct a relative frequency ogive.
(j) What percentage of females aged 20 to 84 involved in fatal crashes were 20–24? 14.6%
(k) What percentage of females aged 20 to 84 involved in fatal crashes were less than 29 years old? 25.7%
(l) Compare the relative frequencies in Problem 29 from Section 2.2 with the relative frequencies in this problem. Is there a higher percentage of fatal accidents involving 20–29-year-old females than there are 20–29-year-old females in the population? How might an insurance company use this information?

7. Political Affiliation A survey of 100 randomly selected registered voters in the city of Naperville were asked their political affiliation—Democrat (D), Republican (R), or Independent (I). The results of the survey are as follows:

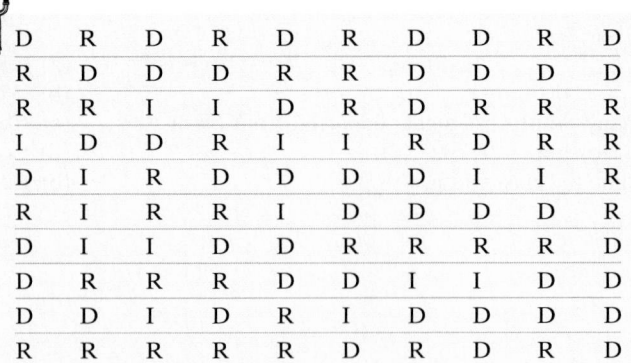

D	R	D	R	D	R	D	D	R	D
R	D	D	D	R	R	D	D	D	D
R	R	I	I	D	R	D	R	R	R
I	D	D	R	I	I	R	D	R	R
D	I	R	D	D	D	D	I	I	R
R	I	R	R	I	D	D	D	D	R
D	I	I	D	D	R	R	R	R	D
D	R	R	R	D	D	I	I	D	D
D	D	I	D	R	I	D	D	D	D
R	R	R	R	R	D	R	D	R	D

(a) Construct a frequency distribution of the data.
(b) Construct a relative frequency distribution of the data.
(c) Construct a relative frequency bar graph of the data.
(d) Construct a pie chart of the data.
(e) What appears to be the most common political affiliation in Naperville? Democrat

8. **Educational Attainment** The Metra Train Company was interested in knowing the educational background of its customers. The company contracted a marketing firm to conduct a survey with a random sample of 50 commuters at the train station. In the survey, commuters were asked to disclose their educational attainment. The following results were obtained:

No high school degree	Some college	Advanced degree	High school graduate	Advanced degree
High school graduate	High school graduate	High school graduate	High school graduate	No high school degree
Some college	High school graduate	Bachelor's degree	Associate's degree	High school graduate
No high school degree	Bachelor's degree	Some college	High school graduate	No high school degree
Associate's degree	High school graduate	High school graduate	No high school degree	Some college
Bachelor's degree	Bachelor's degree	Some college	High school graduate	Some college
Bachelor's degree	Advanced degree	No high school degree	Advanced degree	No high school degree
High school graduate	Bachelor's degree	No high school degree	High school graduate	No high school degree
Associate's degree	Bachelor's degree	High school graduate	Bachelor's degree	Some college
Some college	Associate's degree	High school graduate	Some college	High school graduate

(a) Construct a frequency distribution of the data.
(b) Construct a relative frequency distribution of the data.
(c) Construct a relative frequency bar graph of the data.
(d) Construct a pie chart of the data.
(e) What is the most common educational level of a commuter? High school graduate

9. **Family Size** A random sample of 60 couples married for seven years were asked the number of children they have. The results of the survey are as follows:

0	0	3	1	2	3
3	4	3	3	0	3
1	2	1	3	0	3
4	2	3	2	2	4
2	1	3	4	1	3
0	3	3	3	2	1
2	0	3	1	2	3
4	3	3	5	2	0
4	2	2	2	3	3
2	4	2	2	2	2

(a) Construct a frequency distribution of the data.
(b) Construct a relative frequency distribution of the data.
(c) Construct a cumulative frequency distribution of the data.
(d) Construct a cumulative relative frequency distribution of the data.
(e) Construct a frequency histogram of the data. Describe the shape of the distribution.
(f) Construct a relative frequency histogram of the data.
(g) What percentage of couples married seven years have two children? 30%
(h) What percentage of couples married seven years have at least two children? 76.7%

10. **Waiting in Line** The following data represent the number of cars that arrive at McDonald's drive-through between 11:50 A.M. and 12:00 noon each Wednesday for the past 50 weeks:

1	7	3	8	2	3	8	2	6	3
6	5	6	4	3	4	3	8	1	2
5	3	6	3	3	4	3	2	1	2
4	4	9	3	5	2	3	5	5	5
2	5	6	1	7	1	5	3	8	4

(a) Construct a frequency distribution of the data.
(b) Construct a relative frequency distribution of the data.
(c) Construct a cumulative frequency distribution of the data.
(d) Construct a cumulative relative frequency distribution of the data.
(e) Construct a frequency histogram of the data. Describe the shape of the distribution.
(f) Construct a relative frequency histogram of the data.
(g) What percentage of the time did exactly three cars arrive between 11:50 A.M. and 12:00 noon? 24%
(h) What percentage of the time did three or more cars arrive between 11:50 A.M. and 12:00 noon? 76%

11. Crime Rates by State The following data represent the crime rate (crimes per 100,000 population) for each state in 1998.

State	Crime Rate	State	Crime Rate	State	Crime Rate
Alabama	4597	Kentucky	4859	North Dakota	2681
Alaska	4777	Louisiana	2889	Ohio	4328
Arizona	6575	Maine	6098	Oklahoma	5004
Arkansas	4283	Maryland	3041	Oregon	5647
California	4343	Massachusetts	5366	Pennsylvania	3273
Colorado	4488	Michigan	3436	Rhode Island	3518
Connecticut	3787	Minnesota	4683	South Carolina	5777
Delaware	5363	Mississippi	4047	South Dakota	2624
D.C.	8836	Missouri	4384	Tennessee	5034
Florida	6886	Montana	4826	Texas	5112
Georgia	5463	Nebraska	4071	Utah	5506
Hawaii	5333	Nevada	4405	Vermont	3139
Idaho	3715	New Hampshire	5281	Virginia	3660
Illinois	4873	New Jersey	2420	Washington	5867
Indiana	4169	New Mexico	3654	West Virginia	2547
Iowa	3501	New York	6719	Wisconsin	3543
Kansas	4859	North Carolina	3589	Wyoming	3808

Source: U.S. Census Bureau

In (a)–(f), start the first class at a lower class limit of 2000, and maintain a class width of 500:
(a) Construct a frequency distribution.
(b) Construct a relative frequency distribution.
(c) Construct a cumulative frequency distribution.
(d) Construct a cumulative relative frequency distribution.
(e) Construct a frequency histogram. Describe the shape of the distribution.
(f) Construct a relative frequency histogram.
(g) Repeat (a)–(f), using a class width of 1000. In your opinion, which class width provides the better summary of the data? Why?

12. Disposable Income by State The disposable personal income of individuals is their income after paying taxes. The data on page 103 represent the average disposable personal income (in dollars) for each state in the United States in 1999.

In (a)–(f), start the first class at a lower class limit of 18,000, and maintain a class width of 1000:
(a) Construct a frequency distribution.
(b) Construct a relative frequency distribution.
(c) Construct a cumulative frequency distribution.
(d) Construct a cumulative relative frequency distribution.
(e) Construct a frequency histogram. Describe the shape of the distribution.
(f) Construct a relative frequency histogram.
(g) Repeat (a)–(f), using a class width of 2000. In your opinion, which class width provides the better summary of the data? Why?

State	Average Income	State	Average Income	State	Average Income
Alabama	20,068	Kentucky	19,930	North Dakota	20,842
Alaska	24,978	Louisiana	20,016	Ohio	23,018
Arizona	21,855	Maine	21,530	Oklahoma	19,800
Arkansas	19,412	Maryland	26,686	Oregon	22,964
California	25,100	Massachusetts	29,589	Pennsylvania	24,498
Colorado	26,801	Michigan	23,684	Rhode Island	25,686
Connecticut	31,797	Minnesota	26,003	South Carolina	20,491
Delaware	25,714	Mississippi	18,241	South Dakota	22,443
D.C.	31,457	Missouri	22,469	Tennessee	22,626
Florida	24,201	Montana	19,590	Texas	23,223
Georgia	23,225	Nebraska	23,805	Utah	20,013
Hawaii	24,305	Nevada	26,205	Vermont	22,308
Idaho	20,419	New Hampshire	26,732	Virginia	25,010
Illinois	26,519	New Jersey	30,251	Washington	26,203
Indiana	22,223	New Mexico	19,396	West Virginia	18,337
Iowa	22,252	New York	28,072	Wisconsin	22,213
Kansas	22,880	North Carolina	22,424	Wyoming	22,244

Source: U.S. Bureau of Economic Analysis

13. Towing Capacity The following data represent the towing capacity (in pounds) for 2001 sport utility vehicles.

SUV	Towing Capacity	SUV	Towing Capacity	SUV	Towing Capacity
Acura MDX	4500	GMC Yukon	8700	Land Rover Range Rover	7700
BMW X5	6000	GMC Yukon XL	12000	Lincoln Navigator	8800
Buick Rendezvous	3500	Honda Passport	4500	Mitsubishi Montero	5000
Chevrolet Blazer	5600	Hummer	8300	Nissan Pathfinder	5000
Chevrolet Suburban	12000	Infiniti QX4	5000	Pontiac Aztek	3500
Chevrolet Tahoe	8700	Isuzu Axiom	4500	Suzuki XL-7	3000
Dodge Durango	7650	Isuzu Rodeo	4500	Toyota 4Runner	5000
Ford Escape	3500	Jeep Cherokee	5000	Toyota Highlander	3500
Ford Expedition	8100	Jeep Grand Cherokee	6500	Toyota Land Cruiser	6500
Ford Excursion	10000	Jeep Liberty	5000		
GMC Jimmy	5900	Land Rover Discovery	7700		

Source: Manufacturers

Start the first class at a lower class limit of 3000, and maintain a class width of 1000:
(a) Construct a frequency distribution.
(b) Construct a relative frequency distribution.
(c) Construct a frequency histogram. Describe the shape of the distribution.
(d) Construct a relative frequency histogram.

14. **Home Sales** The data to the right represent the closing price (in U.S. dollars) of homes sold in Joliet, Illinois, in December, 1999.

Start the first class at a lower class limit of 85,000, and maintain a class width of 10,000
(a) Construct a frequency distribution.
(b) Construct a relative frequency distribution.
(c) Construct a frequency histogram. Describe the shape of the distribution.
(d) Construct a relative frequency histogram.

138,820	149,143	99,000	115,000	157,216
169,541	140,794	136,924	124,757	149,380
135,512	153,146	136,833	128,429	136,529
147,500	120,936	95,491	115,744	119,900
89,900	102,696	149,634	123,103	126,630
140,269	183,000	133,646	121,225	121,524
146,439	182,000	110,128	109,520	104,640
124,760	134,305	111,220	121,795	170,072
136,550	115,595	155,507	152,600	130,000
152,537	163,165			

Source: Transamerica Intellitech

15. **Air-traffic Control Errors** An air-traffic control error is said to occur when planes come too close to one another. The following data represent the number of air-traffic control errors in various regions around the United States for fiscal year 2000. Construct a stem-and-leaf diagram and comment on the shape of the distribution.

Center	Errors, 2000	Center	Errors, 2000	Center	Errors, 2000
Washington	102	Oakland	17	Kansas City, MO	28
New York ARTCC	71	Chicago TRACON	14	Albuquerque	25
Indianapolis	54	Oakland Bay	8	Boston	21
Memphis	38	Washington Dulles	7	Houston	18
Los Angeles	33	Cleveland	74	Minneapolis	15
Jacksonville, FL	30	Chicago ARTCC	70	Salt Lake City	12
New York TRACON	27	Atlanta	40	Miami	8
Miami	21	Dallas-Ft. Worth	34		
Northern California	18	Denver	33		

Source: Associated Press

16. **Eat Your Vegetables!** The following data represent the number of servings of vegetables per day that a random sample of forty 20–39-year-old females consumes:

1.7	2.7	0.3	3.5	0.7	1.4	5.1	3.9
0.2	2.1	4.1	5.8	3.8	0.4	6.1	0.7
2.4	11.1	3.5	6.7	2.3	4.9	5.9	0.4
3.3	0.8	7.6	10.2	5.8	2.6	0.6	3.2
0.5	2.4	4.9	2.3	8.3	6.0	5.3	3.5

The data are based on a survey conducted by the United States Department of Agriculture. Construct a stem-and-leaf diagram of the data and comment on the shape of the distribution.

17. **Federal Minimum Wage Rates** The data to the right represent the value of the minimum wage for the years 1980–1997.

Year	Minimum Wage	Year	Minimum Wage
1980	3.10	1989	3.35
1981	3.35	1990	3.80
1982	3.35	1991	4.25
1983	3.35	1992	4.25
1984	3.35	1993	4.25
1985	3.35	1994	4.25
1986	3.35	1995	4.25
1987	3.35	1996	4.75
1988	3.35	1997	5.15

Source: U.S. Employment Standards Administration

(a) Construct a time series plot of the data.
(b) Comment on the apparent trend.

18. Federal Minimum Wage The following data represent the federal minimum wage for 1980–1997 in constant 1996 dollars. Constant dollars are dollars adjusted for inflation.

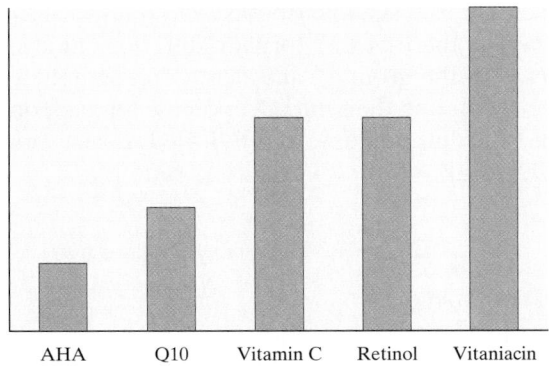

Year	Minimum Wage	Year	Minimum Wage
1980	5.90	1989	4.24
1981	5.78	1990	4.56
1982	5.45	1991	4.90
1983	5.28	1992	4.75
1984	5.06	1993	4.61
1985	4.88	1994	4.50
1986	4.80	1995	4.38
1987	4.63	1996	4.75
1988	4.44	1997	5.03

Source: U.S. Employment Standards Administration

(a) Construct a time series plot of the data.
(b) Comment on the apparent trend.
(c) Compare the time series plot in Problem 17 with that in this problem. Which graph is misleading? Why?

19. Misleading Graphs The following graph was found in a magazine advertisement for skin cream:

Skin Health
(Moisture Retention)

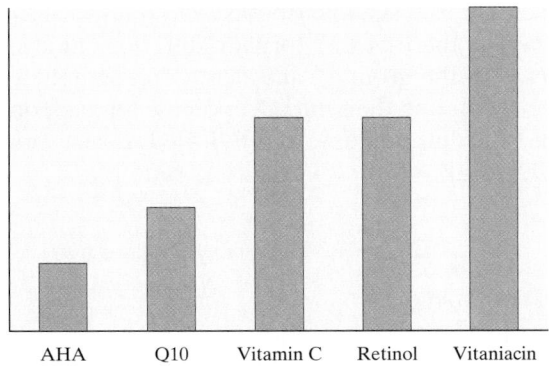

AHA   Q10   Vitamin C   Retinol   Vitaniacin

How is this graph misleading?

20. Misleading Graphs The following graphic is from a *USA Today* "Snapshot:"

Do you think the graph is misleading? Why? If you think it is misleading, what might be done to improve the graph?

21. Misleading Graphs In 1998, the average earnings of a high school graduate were $22,895. At $40,478, the average earnings of a recipient of a bachelor's degree were about 75% higher.
(a) Construct a graph that a college recruiter might create in order to convince high school students that they should attend college.
(b) Construct a graph that does not mislead.

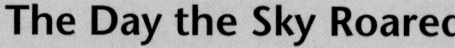

The Day the Sky Roared

Shortly after daybreak on April 3, 1974, thunder began to rumble through the dark skies that covered much of the midwestern United States. Lightning struck areas from the Gulf Coast states to the Canadian border. By the predawn hours of the next day, the affected region of around 490,000 acres was devastated by over 100 tornadoes. This "super outbreak" was responsible for the deaths of over 300 people in 11 states. More than 6100 people were injured by the storms, with approximately 27,500 families suffering some kind of loss. The total cost attributed to the disaster was more than $600 million. Amazingly, the storm resulted in six Category 5 tornadoes with wind speeds exceeding 261 miles per hour. To put this figure in perspective, the region endured about one decade's worth of Category 5 tornadoes in a single 24-hour period!

Fujita Wind Damage Scale		
F-Scale	**Wind Speed**	**Damage**
F-0	Up to 72 mph	Light
F-1	73 to 112 mph	Moderate
F-2	113 to 157 mph	Considerable
F-3	158 to 206 mph	Severe
F-4	207 to 260 mph	Devastating
F-5	Above 260 mph	Incredible

Structural engineers and meteorologists are interested in understanding catastrophic events such as this tornado outbreak. Variables such as tornado intensity (as described by the F-Scale), tornado duration (time spent by the tornado in contact with the ground), and death demographics can provide insights into these events and their impact upon the human population. The following data list the duration time and F-Scale for each tornado in the April 1974 Super Outbreak:

Tornado Duration Times for Outbreak of April 3–4, 1974	
F-Scale	**Tornado Duration (minutes)**
F-0	1,1,5,1,1,6,4,10,5,4,1,1,1,1,1,1,1,1,1,1,30,1,9
F-1	16,13,9,8,13,10,15,1,17,23,10,8,12,5,20,31,12,5,30,13,7,1,5,13,1,2,5,10,1,20,5
F-2	7,15,2,10,23,10,7,12,8,1,8,19,5,10,15,20,10,13,20,15,13,14,1,4,2,15,30,91,11,5
F-3	9,20,8,16,26,36,10,20,50,17,26,31,21,30,23,28,23,18,35,35,15,25,30,15,22,18,58,19,23,31,13,26,40,14,11
F-4	120,23,23,42,47,25,22,22,34,50,38,28,39,29,28,25,34,16,40,55,124,30,30,31
F-5	37,69,23,52,61,122

The following tables present the number of deaths as a function of F-Scale and community size:

Deaths as a Function of F-Scale for April 3–4, 1974, Tornadoes	
F-Scale	**Deaths**
F-0	0
F-1	0
F-2	14
F-3	32
F-4	129
F-5	130

Deaths as a Function of Community Size for Tornado Super Outbreak of April 3–4, 1974	
Community Size	**Deaths**
Rural areas	99
Small communities	77
Small cities	63
Medium cities	56
Large cities	10

Create a report that graphically displays and discusses the tornado-related data. Your report should include the following:

1. A bar graph or pie chart (or both) that depicts the number of tornadoes by F-Scale. Generally, only a little more than 1 percent of all tornadoes exceed F-3 on the Fujita Wind Damage Scale. How does the frequency of the most severe tornadoes of the April 3–4, 1974, outbreak compare with normal tornado formation?

2. A single histogram that displays the distribution of tornado duration for all of the tornadoes.

3. Six histograms displaying tornado duration for each of the F-Scale categories. Does there appear to be a relationship between duration and intensity? If so, describe this relationship.

4. A bar chart that shows the relationship between the number of deaths and tornado intensity. Ordinarily, the most severe tornadoes (F-4 and F-5) account for more than 70 percent of deaths. Is the death distribution of this outbreak consistent with this observation?

5. A bar chart that shows the relationship between the number of deaths and community size. Include a discussion describing the number of deaths as a function of community size.

6. A general summary of your findings and conclusions.

Data Source: Abbey, Robert F. and T. Theodore Fujita. "Tornadoes: The Tornado Outbreak of 3–4 April 1974." In *The Thunderstorm in Human Affairs*, 2nd ed, edited by Edwin Kessler, 37–66. Norman, OK: University of Oklahoma Press, 1983. The death figures presented in this case study are based on approximations made from charts by Abbey and Fujita. Additional descriptions of events and normal tornado statistics are derived from Jack Williams's *The Weather Book*. (New York: Vintage Books, 1992.)

Suppose that you work for the school newspaper. Your editor approaches you with a special reporting assignment. Your task is to write an article that describes the "typical" student at your school, complete with supporting information. In order to write this article, you have to survey at least 40 students and ask them to respond to a questionnaire. The editor would like to have at least two qualitative and two quantitative variables that describe the typical student. The results of the survey will be presented in your article, but you are unsure whether you should present tabular or graphical summaries, so you decide to perform the following "experiment."

1. Develop a questionnaire that results in obtaining the values of 2 qualitative and 2 quantitative variables. Administer the questionnaire to at least 40 students on your campus.

2. Summarize the data in both tabular and graphical form.

3. Select 20 individuals. (They don't have to be students at your school.) Give the tabular summaries to 10 of the individuals and the graphical summaries to the other 10. Ask each individual to study each table or graph for 5 seconds. After 1 minute, give a questionnaire that asks various questions regarding the information contained in the table or graph. For example, if you had age data summarized, ask the individual which age group had the highest frequency. Record the number of correct answers for each individual. Which summary results in a higher percentage of correct answers, the tables or the graphs? Write a report that discusses your findings.

4. Now use the data collected from the questionnaire to create a couple of misleading graphs. Again, select 20 individuals. Give 10 of the individuals the misleading graphs and 10 of the individuals the correct graphs. Ask each of the individuals to study each graph for 5 seconds. After 1 minute has elapsed, give a questionnaire that asks various questions regarding the information contained in the graphs. Record the number of correct answers for each individual. Did the misleading graphs mislead? Write a report that discusses your findings.

DECISIONS

Consumer Reports

A study that compared exercisers who worked out equally hard for the same time on several different types of machines found that they generally burned the most calories on treadmills. Our own research has shown that treadmills are less likely than other machines to sit unused. So it should come as no surprise that treadmills are the best-selling home exercise machine in the U.S.

In a recent study by Consumer Reports (March 2002), we tested 11 best-selling brands of treadmills ranging in price from $500 to $3000. The treadmills were rated on ease of use, ergonomics, exercise factors, construction, and durability. Ease of use is based on how straightforward the treadmill is to use. Ergonomics, including safety factors, belt size, and handrail placement, indicates how well the treadmill fits people of different sizes. Exercise includes evaluations of the minimum incline level, speed control, and heart-rate monitoring. Construction covers factors like the motor's continuous-duty horsepower rating and weld quality.

In order to help compare the treadmills, the individual attribute scores were combined into an overall score. The figure shown below is a ratings chart for the 11 treadmills based on our test results. In addition to the performance ratings, other useful information, such as the models' price and belt size, is included.

(a) What type of graph is illustrated to display overall score in the figure?

(b) Which model has the highest construction score? Which models have the lowest ease of use score?

(c) For ease of use, how many treadmills rated excellent? Very good? Good? Fair? Poor?

(d) Draw a frequency bar graph for each rating category. In other words, draw a bar graph for ease of use, ergonomics, and so on.

(e) Does there appear to be a relationship between price and overall score? Explain your opinion.

Note to Readers: In many cases, our test protocol and analytical methods are more complicated than described in these examples. The data and discussions have been modified to make the material more appropriate for the audience.

Ratings Chart for Treadmills

Overall Ratings — In performance order

Excellent ● / Very good ◒ / Good ○ / Fair ◒ / Poor ●

KEY NO.	BRAND & MODEL; SIMILAR MODELS IN SMALL TYPE	PRICE	OVERALL SCORE	BELT (IN.)	EASE	ERGONOMICS	EXERCISE	CONSTRUCTION	FOLDS
1	**Life Fitness** T3 T3i	$2,200		19x52	●	●	●	◒	
2	**Reebok** ACD4	1,850		19x61	◒	●	●	◒	✔
3	**Precor** M9.33 M9.35	3,000		20x59	○	●	●	●	
4	**Star Trac** TR901	2,500		19x50	◒	◒	◒	◒	
5	**Image** 10.60L	1,500		20x61	◒	◒	●	○	✔
6	**HealthRider** S500xi	1,100		19x54	◒	○	●	○	✔
7	**Tunturi** J6F J6	2,100		18x55	◒	◒	◒	◒	✔
8	**Trimline** 2610	1,200		18x48	◒	○	◒	◒	
9	**ProForm** 785SS	750		20x55	◒	◒	◒	◒	✔
10	**NordicTrack** EXP 1000i	800		20x55	◒	◒	◒	◒	✔
11	**ProForm** 525E	500		18x52	◒	○	◒	◒	✔

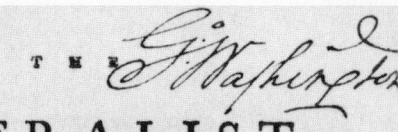

T H E

FEDERALIST:

A COLLECTION

O F

E S S A Y S,

WRITTEN IN FAVOUR OF THE

NEW CONSTITUTION,

AS AGREED UPON BY THE FEDERAL CONVENTION,
SEPTEMBER 17, 1787.

IN TWO VOLUMES.

VOL. II.

N E W - Y O R K:

PRINTED AND SOLD BY J. AND A. M'LEAN,
No. 41, HANOVER-SQUARE.
M, DCC, LXXXVIII.

The distribution of data refers to three characteristics of the data: its shape, its center, and its spread. In the last chapter, we discussed methods for organizing raw data into tables and graphs. These graphs (such as the histogram) allow us to identify the shape of the distribution. Recall that we describe the shape of a distribution as symmetric (in particular, bell-shaped or uniform), skewed right, or skewed left.

The center and spread are numerical summaries of the data. The center of a data set is commonly called the average. There are many ways to describe the "average" value of a distribution. In addition, there are many ways to measure the spread of a distribution. The most appropriate measure of center and spread to use depends upon the shape of the distribution.

Once these three characteristics of the distribution are known, we can analyze the data for interesting features, such as unusual data values, called *outliers*.

Numerically Summarizing Data

Outline

 For additional study help, go to
www.prenhall.com/sullivanstats

Materials include

• Self-Graded Quizzes

• "Preparing for This Section" Quizzes

• STATLETs

• PowerPoint Downloads

• Step-by-Step Technology Guide

• Graphing Calculator Help

3.1 Measures of Central Tendency

Preparing for This Section Before getting started, review the following:

✓ Quantitative data (Section 1.1, p. 6)

✓ Qualitative data (Section 1.1, p. 6)

✓ Population versus sample (Section 1.1, p. 4)

✓ Simple random sampling (Section 1.2, p. 15–18)

Objectives Determine the arithmetic mean of a variable from raw data

 Determine the median of a variable from raw data

 Determine the mode of a variable from raw data

Use the mean and the median to help identify the shape of a distribution

Note to Instructor
Discuss with students that we describe distributions using three characteristics: shape, center, and spread. Shape can be determined from pictures of data, like the histogram. Center is discussed in this section, and spread is discussed in Section 3.2.

We will first consider measures of central tendency. By this, we mean to numerically describe the average or typical data value. We hear the word "average" in the news all the time:

Caution

Whenever you hear the word "average" used, be aware that there are many types of averages out there. One average could be used to support one position, while another average could be used to support a different position.

- The average miles per gallon of gasoline of the 2000 Chevrolet Camaro in city driving is 19 miles.
- According to the United States Census Bureau, the average commute time to work in 2000 was 24.3 minutes.
- According to the United States Census Bureau, the average household income in 2000 was $41,349.
- The average American woman is 5′4″ tall and weighs 142 pounds.

In this chapter, we discuss three averages: the *mean*, the *median*, and the *mode*. While other measures of central tendency exist, these three are the most widely used. When the word "average" is used in the media (newspapers, reporters, and so on) it usually refers to the mean. But beware! An average can be the mean, median or mode, and as we shall see, these three measures of central tendency can give very different results!

Before we discuss measures of central tendency, we must consider whether we are computing a measure of central tendency that describes a population or a sample.

Definitions

A **parameter** is a descriptive measure of a population.

A **statistic** is a descriptive measure of a sample.

In Your Own Words

To help you remember the difference between a parameter and a statistic, think of the following:
p = parameter = population;
s = statistic = sample

For example, if we determined the average test score for *all* the students in a statistics class, the average would be a parameter. If we computed the average based upon a random sample of five of the students, the average would be a statistic.

To obtain the value of a parameter we need a census. Recall that a census is a list of all the individuals in the population along with the values of the variables that we wish to study. Samples are used to compute statistics, which serve as estimates of the parameter.

① The Arithmetic Mean

When used in everyday language, the word "average" often stands for the arithmetic mean. To compute the arithmetic mean of a set of data, the data must be quantitative.

Definitions

The **arithmetic mean** of a variable is computed by determining the sum of all the values of the variable in the data set, divided by the number of observations. The **population arithmetic mean**, μ (read "mew"), is computed using all the individuals in a population. The population mean is a parameter. The **sample arithmetic mean**, $\bar{x}$ (read "x-bar"), is computed using sample data. The sample mean is a statistic.

While other types of means exist (see Problems 36, 37, 38, and 39), the arithmetic mean is generally referred to as the **mean**. We will follow this practice for the remainder of the text.

In statistics, Greek letters are used to represent parameters while Roman letters are used to represent statistics. Statisticians use mathematical expressions instead of words to describe the method for computing means.

Definitions

If $x_1, x_2, \ldots, x_N$ are the N observations of a variable from a population, then the population arithmetic mean, μ, is

$$\mu = \frac{x_1 + x_2 + \cdots + x_N}{N} = \frac{\sum x_i}{N} \qquad (1)$$

If $x_1, x_2, \ldots, x_n$ are n observations of a variable from a sample, then the sample arithmetic mean, $\bar{x}$, is

$$\bar{x} = \frac{x_1 + x_2 + \cdots + x_n}{n} = \frac{\sum x_i}{n} \qquad (2)$$

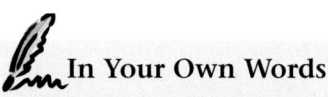
In Your Own Words

To find the mean of a set of data, simply add up all the observations and divide by the number of observations.

Note that N represents the size of the population while n represents the size of the sample. The symbol Σ (the Greek letter capital sigma) means the terms are to be added up. The subscript i is used to make the various values distinct and does not serve as any mathematical operation. For example, x_1 is the first data value, x_2 is the second, and so on.

Let's look at an example to help distinguish the population mean and sample mean.

▶ **EXAMPLE 1**   Computing a Population Mean and Sample Mean

Problem: The data in Table 1 represent the number of home runs hit by all teams in the American League in 2001.

(a) Compute the population mean.
(b) Find a simple random sample of size $n = 5$.
(c) Compute the sample mean of the sample obtained in part (b).

TABLE 1

Team	Home Runs	Team	Home Runs
1. Anaheim Angels	158	8. Minnesota Twins	164
2. Baltimore Orioles	136	9. New York Yankees	203
3. Boston Red Sox	198	10. Oakland Athletics	199
4. Chicago White Sox	214	11. Seattle Mariners	169
5. Cleveland Indians	212	12. Tampa Bay Devil Rays	121
6. Detroit Tigers	139	13. Texas Rangers	246
7. Kansas City Royals	152	14. Toronto Blue Jays	195

Source: Major League Baseball

Approach:

(a) To compute the population mean, we add up all the data values and then divide by the number of individuals in the population.

(b) Recall from Section 1.2 that we can use either Table I in Appendix A, a calculator with a random number generator, or computer software to obtain simple random samples. We will use a TI-83 Plus graphing calculator.

(c) The sample mean is found by adding the data values that correspond to the individuals selected in the sample and then dividing by $n = 5$, the sample size.

Note to Instructor
A nice in-class activity is to have students determine their own pulse. Treat the students as a population and compute the population mean pulse. Now obtain a simple random sample of students and determine the sample mean. Determine a second sample mean. This helps to introduce the students to the fact that the sample mean is a random variable.

Solution:

(a) We compute the population mean by adding the number of home runs hit by all 14 American League teams:

$$\Sigma x_i = 158 + 136 + 198 + \ldots + 195 = 2{,}506$$

We now take this result and divide by 14, the number of teams in the league:

$$\mu = \frac{\Sigma x_i}{N} = \frac{2{,}506}{14} = 179$$

(b) To find a simple random sample of size $n = 5$ from a population whose size is $N = 14$, we will use the TI-83 plus random number generator with a seed of 55. (Recall that this is the starting point that the calculator uses to generate the list of "random" numbers.) Figure 1 shows the teams in the sample.

The Anaheim Angels (158 home runs), Baltimore Orioles (136 home runs), Detroit Tigers (139 home runs), Tampa Bay Devil Rays (121 home runs), and Seattle Mariners (169 home runs) are in our sample.

(c) We compute the sample mean of this sample by first adding the number of home runs hit by each of the teams in the sample:

$$\Sigma x_i = 158 + 136 + 139 + 121 + 169 = 723$$

Figure 1

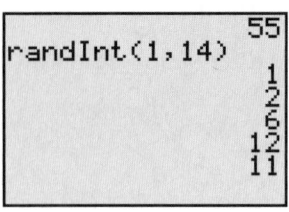

We now take this result and divide by 5, the number of observations in the sample:

$$\overline{x} = \frac{\sum x_i}{n} = \frac{723}{5} = 144.6*$$ ◄◄

Notice from Example 1 that the mean does not necessarily have to equal the value of one of the actual observations. In addition, a sample mean will not necessarily equal the population mean.

EXPLORATION   Using the data from Example 1, find two additional simple random samples of size $n = 5$ and compute the sample mean corresponding to these samples. Conclude that different samples lead to different sample means. ◄◄

NW *Now Work Problem 11.*

It is helpful to think of the mean of a data set as the "center of gravity". In other words, the mean is the value such that a histogram of the data would be perfectly balanced with equal weight on each side of the mean. Figure 2 shows the histogram of the data in Table 1 with the mean labeled. The histogram balances at $\mu = 179$.

Figure 2

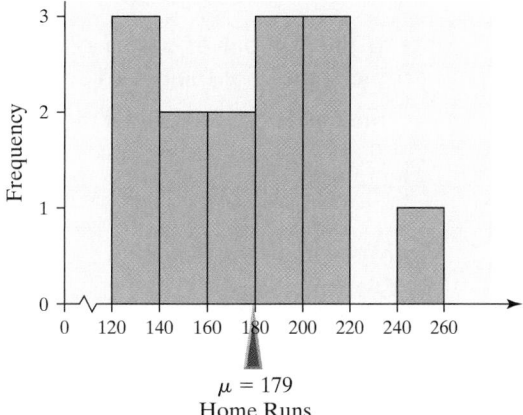

$\mu = 179$
Home Runs

EXPLORATION   Find a yardstick, a fulcrum, and three objects of equal weight (maybe obtain 1-kilogram weights from the physics department). Place the fulcrum at 18 inches so that the yardstick balances like a teeter-totter. Now place one weight on top of the yardstick at 12 inches, another at 15 inches and the third at 27 inches. See Figure 3.

Figure 3

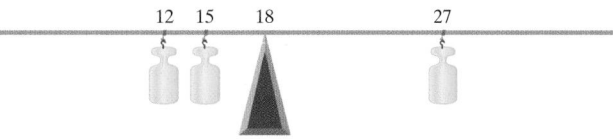

Does the yardstick balance? Now compute the arithmetic mean of the location of the three weights. Compare this result with the location of the fulcrum. Conclude that the arithmetic mean is the center of gravity of the data set. ◄◄

*When necessary, round to one more decimal place than that in the raw data.

The Median

A second measure of central tendency is the median. To compute the median of a set of data, the data must be quantitative.

Definition

In Your Own Words

To help remember the idea behind the median, think of the median of a highway; it divides the highway in half.

Note to Instructor
Suppose that a data set has 10 observations. In class, have students explain in their own words how to find the median. What if the data set has 11 observations?

The **median** of a variable is the value that lies in the middle of the data when arranged in ascending order. That is, half the data are below the median and half the data are above the median. We use M to represent the median.

To compute the median of a set of data, we use the following steps:

Steps in Computing the Median of a Data Set

Step 1: Arrange the data in ascending order.
Step 2: Determine the number of observations, n.
Step 3: Determine the observation in the middle of the data set.

- If the number of observations is odd, then the median is the data value that is exactly in the middle of the data set. That is, the median is the observation that lies in the $\frac{n+1}{2}$ position.

- If the number of observations is even, then the median is the arithmetic mean of the two middle observations in the data set. That is, the median is the arithmetic mean of the data values that lie in the $\frac{n}{2}$ and $\frac{n}{2}+1$ positions.

▶ **EXAMPLE 2** **Computing the Median of a Data Set with an Even Number of Observations**

Problem: Find the median of the population data listed in Table 1 on page 114.

Approach: We will follow the steps listed above.

Solution:

Step 1: Arrange the data in ascending order:

121, 136, 139, 152, 158, 164, 169, 195, 198, 199, 203, 212, 214, 246

Step 2: There are $n = 14$ observations.
Step 3: Because there are 14 observations (an even number), we compute the median, M, by determining the mean of the $\frac{n}{2} = \frac{14}{2} = 7$th observation and $\frac{n}{2} + 1 = \frac{14}{2} + 1 = 8$th observation. So the median is the mean of 169 and 195:

$$M = \frac{169 + 195}{2} = 182$$

121, 136, 139, 152, 158, 164, 169, 195, 198, 199, 203, 212, 214, 246

$$\boxed{M = 182}$$

Notice that there are seven observations to the left and seven observations to the right of the median. We conclude that 50% of American League teams hit fewer than 182 home runs and 50% hit more than 182 home runs.   ◄◄

▶ **EXAMPLE 3**   **Computing the Median of a Data Set with an Odd Number of Observations**

Problem: The data in Table 2 represent the length (in seconds) of a random sample of songs released in the 70's.

TABLE 2			
Song Name	**Length**	**Song Name**	**Length**
"Sister Golden Hair"	201	"Stayin' Alive"	222
"Black Water"	257	"We Are Family"	217
"Free Bird"	284	"Heart of Glass"	206
"The Hustle"	208	"My Sharona"	240
"Southern Nights"	179		

Approach: We will follow the steps listed on page 116.

Solution:

Step 1: Arrange the data in ascending order:

$$179, 201, 206, 208, 217, 222, 240, 257, 284$$

Step 2: There are $n = 9$ observations.

Step 3: Since there are an odd number of observations, the median will be the observation exactly in the middle of the data set. The median, M, is 217 seconds (the $\frac{n+1}{2} = \frac{9+1}{2} = 5$th data value). We list the data in ascending order, with the median in blue.

$$179, 201, 206, 208, 217, 222, 240, 257, 284$$

Notice there are four observations to the left and four observations to the right of the median. So 50% of the songs of the 70's have lengths less than 217 seconds and 50% have lengths more than 217 seconds.   ◄◄

NW   *Now compute the median of the data in Problem 3.*

Using Technology: Statistical spreadsheets and most calculators will compute the mean and median. Figure 4 shows the results of Example 1(a) and (2), using Excel.

Figure 4

American League Home Runs	
Mean	179
Standard error	9.58019936
Median	182
Mode	#N/A

The Mode

A third measure of central tendency is the mode. The mode can be computed for either quantitative or qualitative data.

Definition

> The **mode** of a variable is the most frequent observation of the variable that occurs in the data set.

To compute the mode, tally the number of observations that occur for each data value. The data value that occurs most often is the mode. A set of data can have no mode, one mode or more than one mode. If there is no observation that occurs with the most frequency, we say the data has **no mode**.

▶ **EXAMPLE 4** **Finding the Mode of Quantitative Data**

Problem: The following data represent the number of children of the members of the Joliet Junior College mathematics department:

$$0, 0, 0, 0, 0, 0, 1, 1, 2, 2, 2, 3, 3, 3, 4$$

Find the mode number of children.

Approach: We tally the number of times we observe each data value. The data value with the highest frequency is the mode.

Solution: The mode is 0 because it occurs most frequently (six times).
◀◀

▶ **EXAMPLE 5** **Finding the Mode of Quantitative Data**

Problem: Find the mode of the data listed in Table 1 on page 114.

Approach: Tally the number of times we observe each data value. The data value with the highest frequency is the mode. Although not necessary, it is helpful to find the mode of quantitative data by arranging the data in ascending order.

Solution: We arrange the data in ascending order:

$$121, 136, 139, 152, 158, 164, 169, 195, 198, 199, 203, 212, 214, 246$$

Since each data value occurs an equal number of times (once), there is no mode.
◀◀

Notice that the output in Figure 4 on page 117 provided by Excel for this data set includes the mode. Why do you think the output for the mode is #N/A?

 Now compute the mode of the data in Problem 3.

A data set can have more than one mode. For example, the Boston Red Sox and New York Yankees played only 161 of the 162 scheduled games in 2001. Suppose Boston hit 1 home run and New York hit 9 home runs (the Yankees were feeling especially strong that day!) in the makeup game. Then Boston would have 199 home runs and New York would have 212 home runs, and the set of data in Table 1 would have two modes: 199 and 212. In this case, we say the data are **bimodal**. If a data set has three or more data values that occur with the highest frequency, the data set is

multimodal. Typically, the mode is not reported for multimodal data because it is not representative of a central tendency or typical value. Data that has more than one mode might be an indication of some underlying relationship. For example, a histogram of heights in which the data set contained both males and females might show two modes. The two modes occur because of the variable gender. See Figure 5.

Figure 5
A bimodal distribution

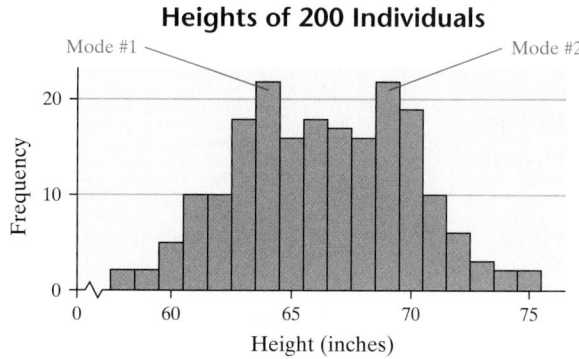

Heights of 200 Individuals

▶ **EXAMPLE 6**   **Determining the Mode of Qualitative Data**

Problem: Find the mode of the data listed in Table 1 in Section 2.1 on page 53, which lists the states in which the 43 presidents of the United States were born.

Approach: We look at the table to determine the state that has the highest frequency.

Solution: The state of Virginia occurs with the highest frequency, eight. The mode is therefore Virginia.   ◀◀

④ The Shape of the Distribution and the Mean and the Median

Often, the mean and the median provide different values. Table 3 shows the mean and median number of home runs hit by American League teams in 2001.

TABLE 3	
Mean	179
Median	182

Notice that the median and the mean are close in value. Suppose the number of home runs hit by the Texas Rangers was 500 instead of 246. The median would not change, but the mean would increase from 179 to 197.1. In other words, the arithmetic mean is sensitive to extreme (very large or small) values in the data set, while the median is not. We say that the median is **resistant** to extreme values, but the arithmetic mean is not resistant. Therefore, when data sets have unusually large or small values relative to the entire set of data or when the distribution of the data is skewed, the median is the preferred measure of central tendency over the arithmetic mean because it is more representative of the typical observation.

In fact, the arithmetic mean and the median can be useful in determining the shape of a distribution. It can be shown that if a distribution is perfectly symmetric, then the median will equal the arithmetic mean (and the mode). So symmetric distributions will have a median and an arithmetic mean that are close in value. If the arithmetic mean is substantially larger than the median, the distribution will be skewed right. Do you know why? In distributions that are skewed right, there are a few data values substantially larger than the others. These larger data values cause the mean to be inflated

Note to Instructor
In-class concept check: Ask students to discuss how extreme observations affect the mean and median. Which measure of center is "best" when extreme values exist? Which is a better measure of central tendency for the following variables: income, price of housing, height, or IQ?

Caution

Because the mean is not resistant, it should not be reported as a measure of central tendency when the distribution of data is highly skewed.

while having little, if any, effect on the median. Similarly, distributions that are skewed left will have a mean that is substantially smaller than the median. We summarize these ideas in Table 4 and Figure 6.

TABLE 4	
Relation Between the Mean, Median, and Distribution Shape	
Distribution Shape	**Mean versus Median**
Skewed Left	Mean < Median
Symmetric	Mean = Median
Skewed Right	Mean > Median

Figure 6 Mean/median versus skewness

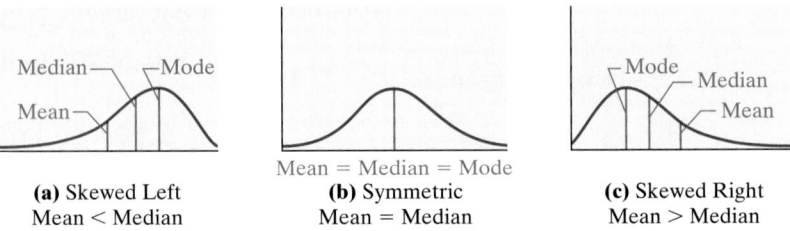

(a) Skewed Left	**(b)** Symmetric	**(c)** Skewed Right
Mean < Median	Mean = Median	Mean > Median

▶ **EXAMPLE 7**   **Using the Mean and the Median to Identify Distribution Shape**

Problem: The data in Table 5 represent the annual salary for players on the Los Angeles Lakers for the 2000–2001 season. The data are in thousands of dollars. For example, Shaquille O'Neal earned $19,290,000 during the 2000–2001 season.

TABLE 5			
Player	**Salary (thousands of dollars)**	**Player**	**Salary (thousands of dollars)**
Shaquille O'Neal	$19,290	Chuck Person	$1,200
Kobe Bryant	$10,130	Tyronn Lue	$870
Horace Grant	$6,500	Devean George	$850
Robert Horry	$4,800	Mark Madsen	$710
Rick Fox	$3,400	Isaiah Ryder	$550
Derek Fisher	$3,380	Mike Penberthy	$320
Brian Shaw	$2,250	Stanislav Medvedenko	$320
Ron Harper	$2,200	Sam Jacobson	$270
Greg Foster	$1,760		

Source: bskball.com

(a) Find the mean and the median.
(b) Describe the shape of the distribution.
(c) Which measure of central tendency better describes the average salary of a player on the Los Angeles Lakers?

Approach:

(a) We will use statistical software to determine the mean and the median.
(b) We can identify the shape of the distribution using the frequency histogram and the relation between the mean and the median. (Refer to Figure 15 in Section 2.2 for identifying distribution shapes from histograms.)
(c) If the data are roughly symmetric, then the mean is a good measure of central tendency; if the data are skewed, then the median is a good measure of central tendency.

Solution:

(a) Using Minitab, we find $\mu = 3459$ and $M = 1760$. See Figure 7.

Figure 7 **Descriptive statistics**

Variable SE Means	N	Mean	Median	TrMean	StDev	SE Mean
Salaries	17	3459	1760	2616	4852	1177

Variable	Minimum	Maximum	Q1	Q3
Salaries	270	19290	630	4100

The mean is much larger than the median; we conclude that the data are skewed right.

(b) Figure 8 shows a frequency histogram of the data. The shape of the histogram is skewed right.

Figure 8

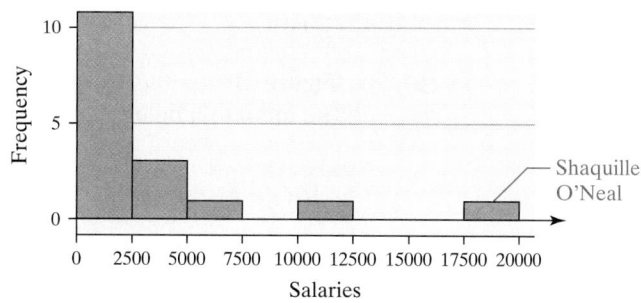

Histogram of Salaries

(c) Notice that only four players on the Lakers earned more than the mean salary of $3,459,000, while half the players earned less than the median of $1,760,000 and half earned more than the median. Therefore, the median better describes the typical salary on the Lakers. ◄◄

▶ **EXAMPLE 8   Comparing the Mean and the Median**

Problem: The data in Table 6 represent the birth weights (in pounds) of 50 randomly sampled babies.

TABLE 6								
5.8	7.4	9.2	7.0	8.5	7.6	7.3	7.1	7.6
7.9	7.8	7.9	7.7	9.0	7.1	6.9	7.0	6.7
8.7	7.2	6.1	7.2	7.1	7.2	6.9	7.0	
7.9	5.9	7.0	7.8	7.2	7.5	6.4	7.4	
7.3	6.4	7.4	8.2	9.1	7.3	7.8	8.2	
9.4	6.8	7.0	8.1	8.0	7.5	8.7	7.2	

(a) Find the mean and the median.

(b) Describe the shape of the distribution.

(c) Which measure of central tendency better describes the average birth weight?

Approach:

(a) Use a TI-83 Plus to compute the mean and the median.

(b) The histogram, along with the mean and the median, are used to identify the shape of the distribution.

(c) If the data are roughly symmetric, then the mean is a good measure of central tendency; if the data are skewed, then the median is a good measure of central tendency.

Solution:

(a) Using a TI-83 Plus, we find $\bar{x} = 7.49$ and $M = 7.35$. See Figure 9.

Figure 9

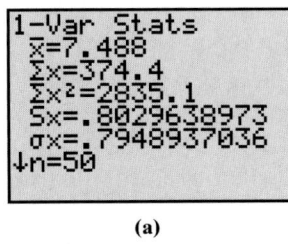
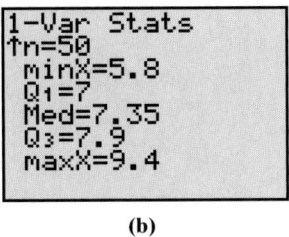

(a) (b)

(b) See Figure 10 for the frequency histogram with the arithmetic mean and the median labeled.

Figure 10
Birth weights of 50 randomly selected babies

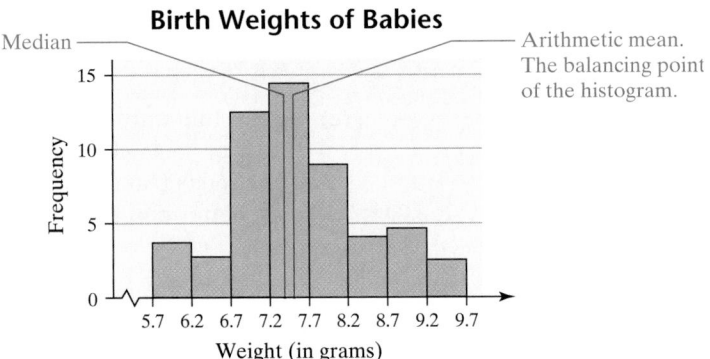

The distribution is bell shaped. We have further evidence of the shape because the arithmetic mean and the median are close to each other.

(c) Because the mean and the median are close in value, we use the mean as the measure of central tendency. ◄◄

NW *Now Work Problem 19.*

A question you may be asking yourself is "Why would I ever compute the mean?" After all, the mean and median are close in value for symmetric data and the median is the better measure of central tendency for skewed data. The reason we compute the mean is that much of the statistical inference that we perform is based upon the mean. We will have more to say about this in Chapter 7.

We conclude this section with the following chart, which addresses the circumstances under which each measure of central tendency should be used:

Measure of Central Tendency	Computation	Interpretation	When to Use
Mean	Population Mean: $\mu = \dfrac{\Sigma x_i}{N}$ Sample Mean: $\bar{x} = \dfrac{\Sigma x_i}{n}$	Center of gravity	When data are quantitative and the frequency distribution is roughly symmetric
Median	Arrange data in ascending order and divide the data set in half	Divides the bottom 50% of the data from the top 50% of the data	When the data are quantitative and the frequency distribution is skewed left or skewed right
Mode		Most frequent observation	When most frequent observation is desired measure of central tendency or the data are qualitative

3.1 Assess Your Understanding

Concepts and Vocabulary

1. What does it mean if a statistic is resistant? Why is the median resistant, but the mean is not?
2. Describe how the mean and the median can be used to determine the shape of a distribution.
3. In the 2000 Census conducted by the United States Census Bureau there were two average household incomes reported: $41,349 and $55,263. One of these averages is the mean and the other is the median. Which is the mean? Support your answer.
4. The United States Department of Housing and Urban Development (HUD) uses the median to report the average price of a home in the United States. Why do you think they use the median?
5. A histogram of a set of data indicates that the distribution of the data is skewed right. Which measure of central tendency will be larger, the mean or the median? Why?

Exercises

- **Skill Building** $381.75; $414.50; None

1. **Crash Test Results** The Insurance Institute for Highway Safety crashed the 2001 Honda Civic four times at five miles per hour. The cost of repair for each of the four crashes is listed on the following line:

   $420, $462, $409, $236

   Compute the mean, median, and mode cost of repair.

2. **Cell Phone Usage** The following data represent the monthly cell phone bill for my wife's phone for six randomly selected months.

   $35.34, $42.09, $39.43, $38.93, $43.39, $49.26

   Compute the mean, median, and mode phone bill. $41.41; $40.76; None

3. **Concrete Mix** A certain type of concrete mix is designed to withstand 3000 pounds per square inch (psi) of pressure. The strength of concrete is measured by pouring the mix into casting cylinders 6 inches in diameter and 12 inches tall. The cylinder is allowed to "set up" for 28 days. The cylinders are then stacked upon one another until the cylinders are crushed. The following data represent the strength of nine randomly selected casts.

   3960, 4080, 3200, 3100, 2940, 3830, 4090, 4040, 3780

   Compute the mean, median, and mode strength of the concrete (in pounds per square inch). 3668.9; 3830; None

4. **Flight Time** The following data represent the flight time (in minutes) of a random sample of seven flights from Las Vegas, NV, to Newark, NJ, on Continental Airlines.

282, 270, 260, 266, 257, 260, 267

Compute the mean, median, and mode flight time.

266; 266; 260

• Applying the Concepts

5. **Corn Production** The following data represent the number of corn plants in randomly sampled rows (a 17-foot-by-5-inch strip) for various plot types. Compute the mean, median, and mode for each plot type. Which plot type appears to yield the most crops?

Plot Type	Number of Plants
Sludge Plot	25 27 33 30 28 27
Spring Disk	32 30 33 35 34 34
No Till	30 26 29 32 25 29
Spring Chisele	30 32 26 28 31 29
Great Lakes Bt	28 32 27 30 29 27

Source: Andrew Dieter and Brad Schmidgall, Joliet Junior College

6. **Soybean Yield** The following data represent the number of pods on a random sample of soybean plants for various plot types. Compute the mean, median, and mode for each plot type. Which plot type appears to yield the most pods per plant?

Plot Type	Pods
Liberty	32 31 36 35 41 34 39 37 38
Fall Plowed	29 31 33 22 7 19 30 36 30
No Till	34 30 31 27 40 33 37 42 39
Chisele Plowed	34 37 24 23 32 33 27 34 30
Round-up Ready	49 27 34 46 32 35 20 29 35

Source: Andrew Dieter and Brad Schmidgall, Joliet Junior College

7. **Day of Birth** A researcher wanted to know whether more births occur on Mondays than on Saturdays. She collects the following data that represent the number of live births on Mondays and Saturdays for the first 6 weeks in 1997, from the National Center for Health Statistics. Compute the mean, median, and mode number of births for each day. Does there appear to be a difference in the number of births on Monday versus Saturday? What might account for any difference?

Births on Monday		Births on Saturday	
10,456	10,527	8,617	8,634
10,267	10,596	8,368	8,488
10,444	10,778	8,340	8,411

Source: National Center for Health Statistics

8. **Month of Birth** A researcher wanted to know whether more births occur in September than in March. She randomly selects seven weekdays in September, 1997 and seven weekdays in March, 1997, and records the number of births on these days. Compute the mean, median, and mode number of births for each month. Does there appear to be a difference in the number of births in March versus the number in September? What might account for any difference?

Births in March		Births in September	
11,726	11,571	11,307	11,453
11,944	11,523	12,462	12,132
11,570	10,283	12,891	12,457
10,903		12,372	

Source: National Center for Health Statistics

9. **Rats in Space** In the experiment "Regulation of Erythropoiesis During Spaceflight," led by NASA scientist Dr. Robert D. Lange, rats were sent to space on Spacelab Life Sciences I to measure the effect of space travel on weight. The following data represent the weights (in grams) of rats in an Animal Enclosure Module (AEM) on the flight return day for both a control (ground) group and experimental (flight) group. Compute the mean, median, and mode weights for both the control and experimental groups. Does there appear to be a difference in the weights? What might account for any difference?

Control Group		Flight Group	
305	330	330	320
320	316	310	326
345		383	

Source: NASA Life Sciences Data Archive

7. Monday: 10,511.3; 10,491.5; None; Saturday: 8476.3; 8449.5; None
8. March: 11,360; 11,570; None; September: 12,153.4; 12,372; None
9. Control: 323.2; 320; None; Flight: 333.8; 326; None

10. Reaction Time In an experiment conducted on-line at the University of Mississippi, study participants are asked to react to a stimulus. In one experiment, the participant must press a key upon seeing a blue screen. The time (in seconds) to press the key is measured. The same person is then asked to press a key upon seeing a red screen, again with the time to react measured. The results for six study participants are listed below. Compute the mean, median, and mode reaction time for both blue and red. Does there appear to be a difference in the reaction time? What might account for any difference? How might this information be used?

Blue: 0.551; 0.5315; None; Red: 0.458; 0.432; None

Participant Number	Reaction Time to Blue	Reaction Time to Red
1	0.582	0.408
2	0.481	0.407
3	0.841	0.542
4	0.267	0.402
5	0.685	0.456
6	0.45	0.533

Source: PsychExperiments at the University of Mississippi (http://www.olemiss.edu/psychexps/)

11. Pulse Rates The following data represent the pulse rates (beats per minute) of the nine students enrolled in a section of Sullivan's Introductory Statistics course. Treat the nine students as a population.

Student	Pulse
Perpectual Bempah	76
Megan Brooks	60
Jeff Honeycutt	60
Clarice Jefferson	81
Crystal Kurtenbach	72
Janette Lantka	80
Kevin McCarthy	80
Tammy Ohm	68
Kathy Wojdyla	73

(a) Compute the population mean pulse. *72.2*
(b) Determine two simple random samples of size three and compute the sample mean pulse of each sample.
(c) Which samples result in a sample mean that overestimates the population mean? Which samples result in a sample mean that underestimates the population mean? Do any samples lead to a sample mean that equals the population mean?

12. Travel Time The following data represent the travel time (in minutes) to school for the nine students en-

rolled in Sullivan's College Algebra course. Treat the nine students as a population.

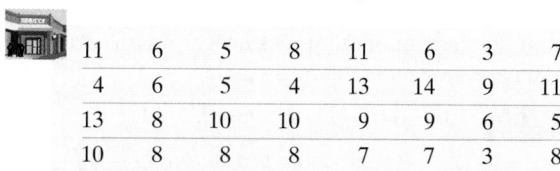

Student	Travel Time	Student	Travel Time
Amanda	39	Scot	45
Amber	21	Erica	11
Tim	9	Tiffany	12
Mike	32	Glenn	39
Nicole	30		

(a) Compute the population mean travel time. *26.4*
(b) Determine three simple random samples of size four and compute the sample mean travel time of each sample.
(c) Which samples result in a sample mean that overestimates the population mean? Which samples result in a sample mean that underestimates the population mean? Do any samples lead to a sample mean that equals the population mean?

13. Waiting for a Table The following data represent the number of customers waiting for a table at 6:00 P.M. on Saturday for 40 consecutive Saturdays at Bobak's Restaurant:

11	6	5	8	11	6	3	7
4	6	5	4	13	14	9	11
13	8	10	10	9	9	6	5
10	8	8	8	7	7	3	8
7	8	9	6	10	11	4	8

(a) Compute the mean and the median number of customers waiting. *7.875; 8*
(b) Identify the shape of the distribution based on the histogram drawn in Problem 17 in Section 2.2, the arithmetic mean, and the median. *Symmetric*

14. Highway Repair The following data represent the number of potholes on 50 randomly selected 1-mile stretches of highway in the city of Chicago:

2	7	4	7	2	7
2	2	2	3	4	3
1	2	3	2	1	4
2	2	5	2	3	4
4	1	7	10	3	5
4	3	3	2	2	
1	6	5	7	9	
2	2	2	1	5	
3	5	1	3	5	

(a) Compute the mean and the median number of potholes. *3.5, 3*
(b) Identify the shape of the distribution based on the histogram drawn in Problem 18 in Section 2.2, the arithmetic mean, and the median. *Skewed right*

15. **Tensile Strength** Tensile strength is the maximum stress at which one can be reasonably certain failure will not occur. The following data represent tensile strength (in thousands of pounds per square inch) of a composite material to be used in an aircraft. (a) 203.934, 206.51

203.41	185.97	184.41	160.44	174.63
209.58	190.67	200.73	180.95	185.34
213.35	207.88	206.51	201.95	205.59
218.56	210.80	209.84	204.60	212.00
242.76	231.46	212.15	219.51	225.25

Source: Vangel, Mark G., "New Methods for One-sided Tolerance Limits for a One-way Balanced Random-Effects ANOVA Model," *Technometrics*; May, 1992, Vol. 34, Issue 2, pp. 176–185.

(a) Compute the mean and median tensile strength.
(b) Identify the shape of the distribution based on the histogram drawn in Problem 19 in Section 2.2 and the relationship between the arithmetic mean and the median. Symmetric

16. **Miles on a Cavalier** A random sample of 36 three-year-old Chevy Cavaliers was obtained in the Miami, FL area and the number of miles on each car was recorded. The data are shown the following table.
(a) 33,242.7; 34,311

34,122	34,511	17,595	30,500	31,883
39,416	34,500	44,224	35,936	32,923
28,281	41,620	26,455	44,448	40,614
37,021	30,283	27,368	41,043	42,398
30,747	15,499	37,904	30,739	
35,439	26,051	23,221	38,995	
17,685	32,305	38,041	41,194	
29,307	39,884	35,295	29,289	

Source: cars.com

(a) Compute the mean and median miles.
(b) Identify the shape of the distribution based on the histogram drawn in Problem 20 in Section 2.2 and the relationship between the arithmetic mean and, the median. Symmetric

17. **Serum HDL** Dr. Paul Oswiecmiski randomly selects forty of his 20–29-year-old patients and obtains the following data regarding their serum HDL cholesterol:
(a) 51.1, 51

70	56	48	48	53	52	66	48
36	49	28	35	58	62	45	60
38	73	45	51	56	51	46	39
56	32	44	60	51	44	63	50
46	69	53	70	33	54	55	52

(a) Compute the mean and the median serum HDL.
(b) Identify the shape of the distribution based on the histogram drawn in Problem 21 in Section 2.2 and the relationship between the arithmetic mean and the median. Symmetric

18. **Volume of Philip Morris Stock** The volume of a stock is the number of shares traded on a given day. The following data, in millions, so that 3.98 represents 3,980,000 shares traded, represent the volume of Philip Morris stock traded for a random sample of 35 trading days in 2000:

3.98	8.90	10.40	7.52	13.84
14.04	9.14	7.96	11.40	13.30
5.29	9.69	8.94	12.10	13.25
4.62	10.85	24.52	14.62	16.10
4.24	8.54	11.59	6.75	27.54
16.06	17.62	7.17	6.13	25.32
7.71	10.14	4.28	7.24	10.88

Source: http://finance.yahoo.com

(a) Compute the mean and the median number of shares traded. 11.191, 10.14
(b) Identify the shape of the distribution based on the histogram drawn in Problem 22 in Section 2.2 and the relationship between the arithmetic mean and the median. Skewed right

19. **M&Ms** The following data represent the weights (in grams) of a simple random sample of 50 M&M plain candies. (a) 0.874; 0.88

0.87	0.88	0.82	0.90	0.90	0.84	0.84
0.91	0.94	0.86	0.86	0.86	0.88	0.87
0.89	0.91	0.86	0.87	0.93	0.88	
0.83	0.94	0.87	0.93	0.91	0.85	
0.91	0.91	0.86	0.89	0.87	0.93	
0.88	0.88	0.89	0.79	0.82	0.83	
0.90	0.88	0.84	0.93	0.76	0.90	
0.88	0.92	0.85	0.79	0.84	0.86	

Source: Michael Sullivan

(a) Compute the mean and the median weight.
(b) Identify the shape of the distribution based on the histogram drawn in Problem 23 in Section 2.2 and the relationship between the arithmetic mean and the median. Symmetric

20. Old Faithful The following data represent the length of eruption (in seconds) for a random sample of eruptions of the Old Faithful Geyser in California. (a) 104.1; 104

108	108	99	105	103	103	94
102	99	106	90	104	110	110
103	109	109	111	101	101	
110	102	105	110	106	104	
104	100	103	102	120	90	
113	116	95	105	103	101	
100	101	107	110	92	108	

Source: Ladonna Hansen, Park Curator

(a) Compute the mean and the median length of eruption.
(b) Identify the shape of the distribution based on the histogram drawn in Problem 24 in Section 2.2 and the relationship between the arithmetic mean and the median. Symmetric

21. Foreign-born Population The following data represent the region of birth of foreign-born residents of the United States in 2000. Determine the mode region of birth.

Latin America

Region	Number (thousands)
Europe	4,772
Asia	8,364
Africa	840
Oceania	180
Latin America	15,472
North America	836

Source: United States Census Bureau

22. Robbery The following data represent the number of offenses for various robberies in 1998. Determine the mode offense. Street or highway

Type of Crime	Number of Offenses (in thousands)
Street or Highway	219
Commercial house	61
Gas Station	10
Convenience Store	26
Residence	54
Bank	9

Source: U.S. Federal Bureau of Investigation

23. 2000 Presidential Election An exit poll was conducted in Palm Beach County, Florida, in which a random sample of 40 voters revealed whom they voted for in the presidential election. The results of the survey are as follows:

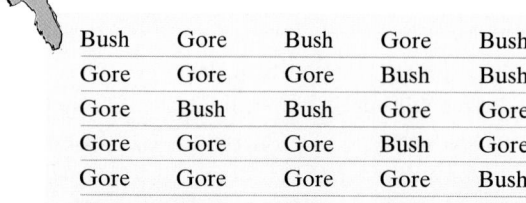

Bush	Gore	Bush	Gore	Bush
Gore	Gore	Gore	Bush	Bush
Gore	Bush	Bush	Gore	Gore
Gore	Gore	Gore	Bush	Gore
Gore	Gore	Gore	Gore	Bush
Gore	Gore	Gore	Gore	Gore
Gore	Nader	Gore	Bush	Bush
Gore	Bush	Bush	Gore	Bush

Determine the mode. Gore

24. Hospital Admissions The following data represent the diagnosis of a random sample of 20 patients admitted to a hospital:

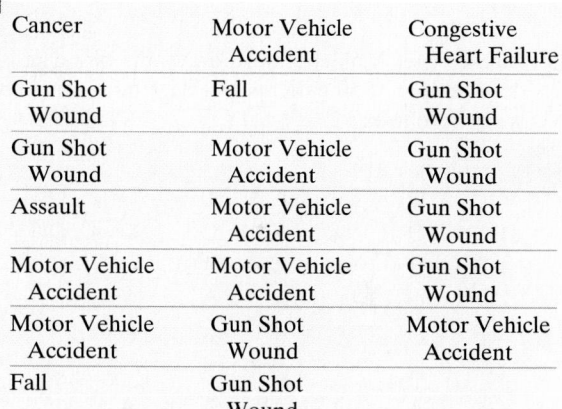

Cancer	Motor Vehicle Accident	Congestive Heart Failure
Gun Shot Wound	Fall	Gun Shot Wound
Gun Shot Wound	Motor Vehicle Accident	Gun Shot Wound
Assault	Motor Vehicle Accident	Gun Shot Wound
Motor Vehicle Accident	Motor Vehicle Accident	Gun Shot Wound
Motor Vehicle Accident	Gun Shot Wound	Motor Vehicle Accident
Fall	Gun Shot Wound	

Source: Tamela Ohm, Student at Joliet Junior College

Determine the mode diagnosis. Gun shot wound

25. Which Position in Baseball Is the Highest Paying? You are a prospective baseball agent and are in search of some clients. You would like to recruit the highest-paid players as clients so you perform a study in which you identify the 36 most highly paid players and their positions.

Player	Position	Player	Position	Player	Position
Kevin Brown	Pitcher	Derek Jeter	Shortstop	John Smoltz	Pitcher
Randy Johnson	Pitcher	Raul Mondesi	Right Field	Jim Thome	1st Base
Albert Belle	Right Field	Gary Sheffield	Right Field	Todd Stottlemyre	Pitcher
Bernie Williams	Center Field	Tom Glavine	Pitcher	Robin Ventura	3rd Base
Mike Piazza	Catcher	Shawn Green	Right Field	Chuck Finley	Pitcher
Larry Walker	1st Base	Ken Griffey, Jr.	Center Field	Al Leiter	Pitcher
David Cone	Pitcher	Mark McGwire	1st Base	Brian Jordan	Center Field
Pedro Martinez	Pitcher	Wilson Alvarez	Pitcher	Ray Lankford	Center Field
Mo Vaughn	1st Base	Rafael Palmeiro	1st Base	Juan Gonzalez	1st Base
Greg Maddux	Pitcher	Ivan Rodriguez	Catcher	Kenny Rogers	Pitcher
Sammy Sosa	Right Field	Matt Williams	3rd Base	Kenny Lofton	Center Field
Barry Bonds	Right Field	Andres Gallarraga	1st Base	Alex Rodriguez	Shortstop

Source: SLAM! Baseball

Determine the mode position. Pitcher

---

26. Blood Type A phlebotomist draws the blood of a random sample of 50 patients and determines their blood types as follows:

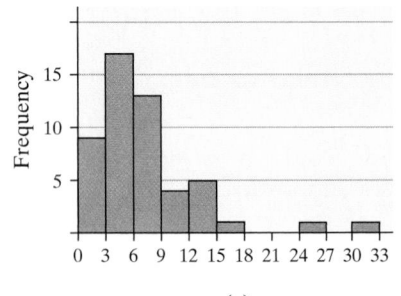

O	O	A	A	O	O	O
B	O	B	A	O	O	O
AB	B	A	B	AB	O	
O	O	A	A	O	A	
AB	O	A	B	A	O	
O	A	A	O	A	O	
O	A	O	AB	A	A	
O	B	A	A	O	A	

Determine the mode blood type. O

27. Refer to the tensile strength data from Problem 15. Suppose that the data value 185.97 was accidentally entered as 815.97. Recompute the mean and median with the incorrect data. How did this change affect the mean and median? 229.134; 207.88

28. Refer to the mileage data from Problem 16. Suppose the data value 17,685 was accidentally recorded as 117,685. Recompute the mean and median for the incorrect data set. How did this change affect the mean and median? 36,020.4; 34,505.5

(a) $\bar{x} > M$ (b) $\bar{x} = M$
(c) $\bar{x} < M$

29. For each of the three histograms shown, determine whether the mean is greater than, less than, or approximately equal to the median, and justify your answer.

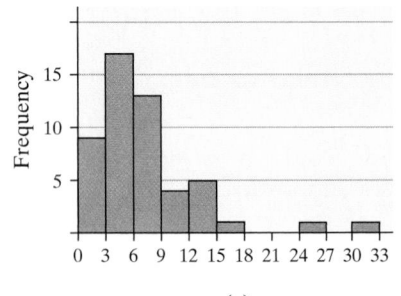

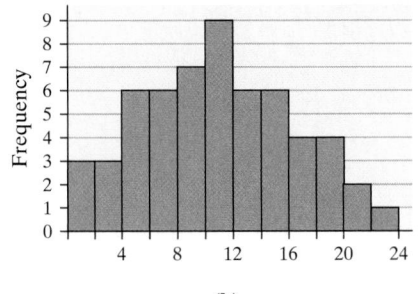

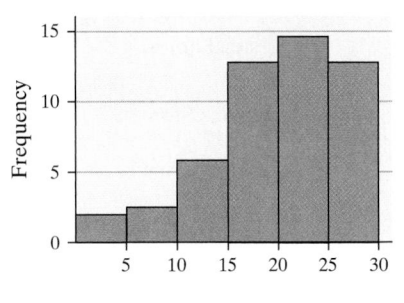

(a)   (b)   (c)

30. Match the histograms shown to the summary statistics:

(a) IV
(b) III
(c) II
(d) I

	Mean	Median
(I)	42	42
(II)	31	36
(III)	31	26
(IV)	31	32

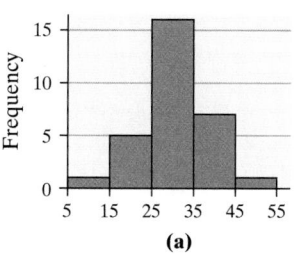

(a)

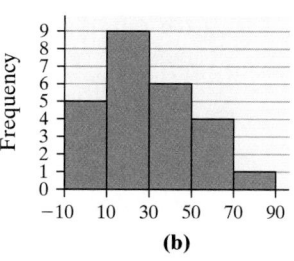

(b)

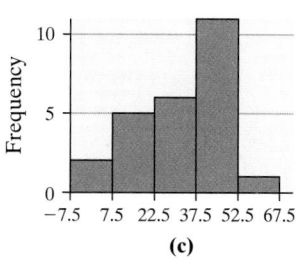

(c)

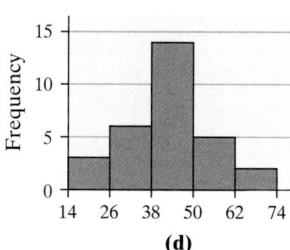

(d)

31. You are negotiating a contract for the Players' Association of the NBA. Which measure of central tendency will you use to support your claim that the average player's salary needs to be increased? Why? As the chief negotiator for the owners, which measure would you use to refute the claim made by the Player's Association?

32. In October of 2000, the mean amount of money lost per visitor to the Harrah's River Boat was $110. Do you think the median was more than, less than, or equal to this amount? Why?

33. Suppose that the mean of a set of six data values is 34. What is the sum of the six data values?

34. Use the five test scores of 65, 70, 71, 75, and 95 to answer the following questions:

(a) Find the sample mean. 75.2
(b) Find the median. 71
(c) Which measure of central tendency best describes the typical test score? Median
(d) Suppose the professor decides to curve the exam by adding 4 points to each person's score. Compute the sample mean based on the adjusted scores. 79.2
(e) Compare the unadjusted test score mean with the curved test score mean. What effect did adding 4 to each score have on the mean?

35. For each of the following situations, determine which measure of central tendency is most appropriate:

(a) Average price of a home sold in Pittsburgh, Pennsylvania, in 2002 Median
(b) Most popular major for students enrolled in a statistics course Mode
(c) Average test score when the scores are distributed symmetrically Mean
(d) Average test score when the scores are skewed right Median
(e) Average income of a player in the National Football League Median

36. Trimmed Mean Another measure of central tendency is the trimmed mean. It is computed by determining the arithmetic mean of a data set after deleting the smallest and largest observed value. Compute the trimmed mean for the data in Problem 19. Is the trimmed mean resistant? Explain. 0.875

37. Midrange The midrange is also a measure of central tendency. It is computed by adding the smallest and largest observed value of a data set and dividing the result by 2; that is,

$$\text{Midrange} = \frac{\text{Largest Data Value} + \text{Smallest Data Value}}{2}$$

Compute the midrange for the data in Problem 19. Is the midrange resistant? Explain. 0.85; No

38. Geometric Mean The **geometric mean** is often used as a measure of central tendency when the data are measured in percents or indexes. The geometric mean of r_1, r_2, and r_3 is

$$\sqrt[3]{(1 + r_1)(1 + r_2)(1 + r_3)} - 1$$

The geometric mean is more resistant to extreme values than the arithmetic mean. For example, suppose a stock's price increases 10, 20, 3, and 9 percent over the past four years. The geometric mean is

$$\sqrt[4]{(1.10)(1.20)(1.03)(1.09)} - 1 = 0.103 = 10.3\%$$
percent.

(a) The monthly rate of return of Cisco Systems stock from June, 2000–August, 2000 has been 11.6 percent, 2.9 percent, and 4.9 percent. Compute the geometric mean rate of return. 6.4%
(b) The consumer price index for medical services has had percentage changes of 4.5 percent, 3.5 percent, 2.8 percent, and 3.2 percent for the years 1995–1998. Compute the geometric mean percentage change in prices for medical services over this time period. 3.5%

39. Harmonic Mean The **harmonic mean** is often used as a measure of central tendency when the data are measured as a rate of change such as 50 miles per hour. For example, suppose we wanted to know the mean time to download 500 kilobytes (Kb) of information using a 56K modem. In three separate downloads, the download speeds are 4.4 Kb per second, 3.8 Kb per second, and 4 Kb per second. Determining the average download rate is not as simple as computing $(4.4 + 3.8 + 4)/3$.

To compute the average download speed, we must observe that $3(500) = 1,500$ kilobytes were downloaded. In addition, the download time of each of the three 500 Kb files is $\dfrac{500\,\text{Kb}}{4.4\,\text{Kb/sec}} = 113.6$ seconds, $\dfrac{500\,\text{Kb}}{3.8\,\text{Kb/sec}} = 131.6$ seconds, and $\dfrac{500\,\text{Kb}}{4\,\text{Kb/sec}} = 125$ seconds. So, the average download speed (the harmonic mean) of the three files is

$$\frac{3(500\,\text{Kb})}{113.6\,\text{sec} + 131.6\,\text{sec} + 125\,\text{sec}} = 4.05\,\text{Kb per second}.$$

The harmonic mean is found using the formula:

$$\text{HM} = \frac{n}{\dfrac{1}{x_1} + \dfrac{1}{x_2} + \cdots + \dfrac{1}{x_n}} = \frac{n}{\Sigma\dfrac{1}{x_i}}$$

where x_i are the n rates of change. Notice that the size of the file being downloaded does not play a role in the computation.

For each of the following, compute the harmonic mean.

(a) This past summer, we drove from Chicago, Illinois, to Naples, Florida. The distance each way is about 1200 miles. The trip from Chicago to Naples resulted in an average speed of 48 miles per hour, while the return trip resulted in an average speed of 51 miles per hour. Compute the average speed for the entire trip. *49.5 mph*

(b) A 300-Kb file is downloaded four separate times resulting in download speeds of 4.3 Kb/sec, 4.1 Kb/sec, 3.8 Kb/sec and 4.3 Kb/sec. Compute the average download time. *4.1 Kb/sec*

(c) A chef purchases $100 worth of ground sirloin at $2.50 per pound and $100 worth of ground beef at $1.00 per pound. Determine the average cost per pound of the meat. *$1.43 per lb*

Technology Step-By-Step
Determining the Mean and Median

TI-83 Plus | **Step 1:** Enter the raw data in L1 by pressing STAT and selecting 1:Edit.

Step 2: Press STAT, highlight the CALC menu, and select 1:1-Var Stats.

Step 3: With 1-Var Stats appearing on the HOME screen, press 2nd 1 to insert L1 on the HOME screen. Press ENTER.

MINITAB | **Step 1:** Enter the data in C1.

Step 2: Select the **Stat** menu, highlight **Basic Statistics** and then highlight **Display Descriptive Statistics**.

Step 3: In the **Variables** window, enter C1. Click OK.

Excel | **Step 1:** Enter the data in column A.

Step 2: Select the **Tools** menu and highlight **Data Analysis**...

Step 3: In the Data Analysis window, highlight **Descriptive Statistics** and click OK.

Step 4: With the cursor in the **Input Range** window, use the mouse to highlight the data in column A.

Step 5: Select the **Summary statistics** option and click OK.

3.2   Measures of Dispersion

Objectives   Compute the range of a variable from raw data
 Compute the variance of a variable from raw data
 Compute the standard deviation of a variable from raw data
 Use the Empirical Rule
 Use Chebyshev's theorem

In Section 3.1, we discussed measures of central tendency. The purpose of these measures is to describe the typical value of a variable or the center of the distribution. However, in addition to measuring the central tendency of a variable, we would also like to know the amount of dispersion in the variable. By dispersion, we mean the degree to which the data are "spread out". An example should help to explain why measures of central tendency are not sufficient in describing a distribution.

▶ **EXAMPLE 1**   **Comparing Two Sets of Data**

Problem: The data in Table 7 represent the IQ scores of a random sample of 100 students from two different universities. For each university, compute the arithmetic mean IQ score and draw a histogram, using a lower class limit of 50 for the first class and a class width of 10.

TABLE 7																			
University A										**University B**									
73	103	91	93	136	108	92	104	90	78	86	91	107	94	105	107	89	96	102	96
108	93	91	78	81	130	82	86	111	93	92	109	103	106	98	95	97	95	109	109
102	111	125	107	80	90	122	101	82	115	93	91	92	91	117	108	89	95	103	109
103	110	84	115	85	83	131	90	103	106	110	88	97	119	90	99	96	104	98	95
71	69	97	130	91	62	85	94	110	85	87	105	111	87	103	92	103	107	106	97
102	109	105	97	104	94	92	83	94	114	107	108	89	96	107	107	96	95	117	97
107	94	112	113	115	106	97	106	85	99	98	89	104	99	99	87	91	105	109	108
102	109	76	94	103	112	107	101	91	107	116	107	90	98	98	92	119	96	118	98
107	110	106	103	93	110	125	101	91	119	97	106	114	87	107	96	93	99	89	94
118	85	127	141	129	60	115	80	111	79	104	88	99	97	106	107	112	97	94	106

Approach: Use statistical software to compute the arithmetic mean and draw a histogram for each university.

Solution: We enter the data into Minitab and determine that the arithmetic mean IQ score of both universities is 100.0. Figure 11 on page 132 shows the histograms.   ◀◀

We notice that both universities have the same mean IQ, but the histograms indicate the IQs from University A are more spread out—that is, more dispersed. While an IQ of 100.0 is "typical" for both universities, it appears to be a more reliable description of the typical student from

Figure 11

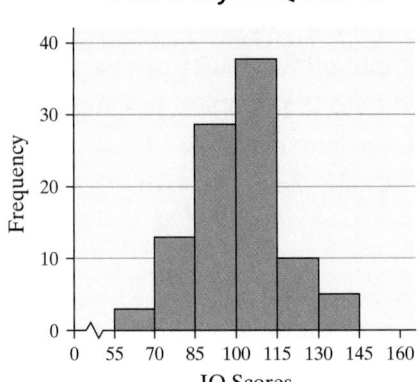

University A IQ Scores

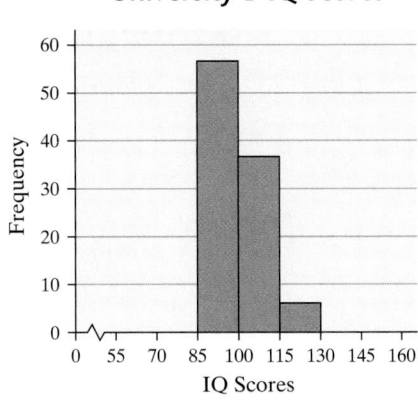

University B IQ Scores

University B than that of University A. That is, a higher proportion of students have IQ scores within, say, 15 points of the mean of 100.0 from University B than from University A.

Our goal in this section is to discuss numerical measures of dispersion so that we can quantify the spread of data. In this section, we discuss three numerical measures for describing the dispersion or spread of data: the range, variance, and standard deviation. In Section 3.4, we will discuss another measure of dispersion, the *interquartile range* (IQR).

Note to Instructor
You may want to share with students that the smallest data value is also referred to as the minimum and the largest data value is referred to as the maximum, as a preview of the "Five-Number Summary."

① The Range

The simplest measure of dispersion is the range. In order to compute the range, the data must be quantitative.

Definition

The **range**, **R**, of a variable is the difference between the largest data value and the smallest data value. That is,

$$\text{Range} = R = \text{Largest Data Value} - \text{Smallest Data Value}$$

TABLE 8

Team	Home Runs
1. Anaheim Angels	158
2. Baltimore Orioles	136
3. Boston Red Sox	198
4. Chicago White Sox	214
5. Cleveland Indians	212
6. Detroit Tigers	139
7. Kansas City Royals	152
8. Minnesota Twins	164
9. New York Yankees	203
10. Oakland Athletics	199
11. Seattle Mariners	169
12. Tampa Bay Devil Rays	121
13. Texas Rangers	246
14. Toronto Blue Jays	195

Source: Major League Baseball

▶ **EXAMPLE 2   Determining the Range of a Set of Data**

Problem: The data in Table 8 represent the number of home runs hit by all teams in the American League in 2001. Compute the range.

Approach: The range is found by computing the difference between the largest and smallest data values. In other words, we determine the difference between the highest and lowest numbers.

Solution: The Texas Rangers hit the most home runs, 246, while the Tampa Bay Devil Rays hit the fewest home runs, 121. The range, R, is

$$R = 246 - 121 = 125$$

All the teams in the American League hit between 121 and 246 home runs. The difference between the best home-run-hitting team and the worst home-run-hitting team in the American League is 125 home runs.   ◀◀

NW *Now compute the range of the data in Problem 3.*

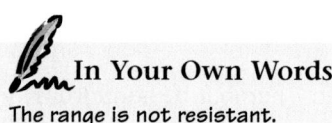
In Your Own Words

The range is not resistant.

Notice the range is affected by extreme values in the data set, so the range is not resistant. If the Texas Rangers had hit 500 home runs in 2001, the range would be $R = 500 - 121 = 379$. In addition, the range is computed using only two values in the data set (the largest and smallest). The variance and the standard deviation, on the other hand, use all the data values in the computations.

 ## Variance

Note to Instructor
Stress to the students that the variance is difficult to interpret because it is measured in units squared (such as home runs squared). However, the variance plays an important role in statistical inference.

Just as there is a population mean and sample mean, we have a population variance and a sample variance. Variance is based upon the difference between each observation and the arithmetic mean; that is, it is based upon the **deviation about the mean**. For a population, the deviation about the mean for the ith observation is $x_i - \mu$. For a sample, the deviation about the mean for the ith observation is $x_i - \overline{x}$. The further an observation is from the mean, the larger the absolute deviation.

Because the mean represents the "center of gravity," the sum of all deviations about the mean must equal zero. That is,

$$\Sigma(x_i - \mu) = 0 \qquad \text{and} \qquad \Sigma(x_i - \overline{x}) = 0$$

In other words, observations larger than the mean are offset by observations smaller than the mean.

Definition

The **population variance** of a variable is the sum of the squared deviations about the population mean divided by the number of observations in the population, N. That is, it is the arithmetic mean of the squared deviations about the population mean. The population variance is symbolically represented by σ^2 (lower case Greek sigma squared).

$$\sigma^2 = \frac{\Sigma(x_i - \mu)^2}{N} = \frac{(x_1 - \mu)^2 + (x_2 - \mu)^2 + \cdots + (x_N - \mu)^2}{N} \, * \quad \textbf{(1)}$$

where $x_1, x_2, \ldots, x_N$ are the N observations in the population and μ is the population mean.

NOTE: In using Formula (1), do not round until the last computation. Use as many decimal places as allowed by your calculator in order to avoid round-off errors.

▶ **EXAMPLE 3**   ## Computing a Population Variance

Note to Instructor
You can use the data collected from the students in Section 3.1 to illustrate Examples 3, 4, and 5.

Problem: Use the data in Table 8 to compute the population variance of the home runs hit by American League teams in 2001.

---

*An algebraically equivalent formula for computing the population variance is

$$\sigma^2 = \frac{\Sigma x_i^2 - \dfrac{(\Sigma x_i)^2}{N}}{N},$$ where Σx_i^2 means to square each observation and then sum these squared values, and $(\Sigma x_i)^2$ means to add up all the observations and then square the sum.

Approach:

Step 1: Create a table with the population data (number of home runs) in the first column. In the second column, enter the population mean: $\mu = 179$.
Step 2: Compute the deviation about the mean for each of the data values. That is, compute $x_i - \mu$ for each data value. Enter these values in column 3.
Step 3: Square the values in column 3 and enter the results in column 4.
Step 4: Sum the squared deviations in column 4 and divide this result by the size of the population, N.

Solution:

Step 1: See Table 9. Column 1 lists the observations in the data set, and column 2 contains the population mean.
Step 2: Compute the deviations about the mean, $x_i - \mu$, for each observation as shown in column 3. For example, the deviation about the mean for the Anaheim Angels is $158 - 179 = -21$.
Step 3: Column 4 shows the squared deviations about the mean.

			TABLE 9	
Number of Home Runs	Population Mean, μ	Deviation about the Mean, $x_i - \mu$	Squared Deviations about the Mean, $(x_i - \mu)^2$
158	179	$158 - 179 = -21$	$(-21)^2 = 441$
136	179	−43	1849
198	179	19	361
214	179	35	1225
212	179	33	1089
139	179	−40	1600
152	179	−27	729
164	179	−15	225
203	179	24	576
199	179	20	400
169	179	−10	100
121	179	−58	3364
246	179	67	4489
195	179	16	256
		$\Sigma(x_i - \mu) = 0$	$\Sigma(x_i - \mu)^2 = 16{,}704$

Step 4: We sum the entries in column 4 to obtain the numerator of Formula (1), $\Sigma(x_i - \mu)^2$. We compute the population variance by dividing the sum of the entries in column 4 by the number of teams, 14:

$$\sigma^2 = \frac{\Sigma(x_i - \mu)^2}{N} = \frac{16{,}704}{14} = 1{,}193.1 \qquad \blacktriangleleft\blacktriangleleft$$

Notice the unit of measure of the variance in Example 3 is home runs squared. This unit of measure results from squaring the deviations about the mean. Because home runs squared does not have any real meaning, the use of the variance for any practical purpose is limited.

The sample variance is computed using sample data.

Definition

The **sample variance**, s^2, is computed by determining the sum of the squared deviations about the sample mean and dividing this result by $n - 1$. The formula for the sample variance from a sample of size n is

$$s^2 = \frac{\sum(x_i - \overline{x})^2}{n - 1} = \frac{(x_1 - \overline{x})^2 + (x_2 - \overline{x})^2 + \cdots + (x_n - \overline{x})^2}{n - 1} \quad ^* \quad (2)$$

where $x_1, x_2, \ldots, x_n$ are the n observations in the sample and $\overline{x}$ is the sample mean.

Caution

When computing the sample variance, be sure to divide by $n - 1$, not n.

Notice that the sample variance is obtained by dividing by $n - 1$. If we divided by n, as we would expect, the sample variance would consistently underestimate the population variance. Whenever a statistic consistently overestimates or underestimates a parameter, it is called **biased**. To obtain an unbiased estimate of the population variance, divide the sum of the squared deviations about the mean by $n - 1$.

To help understand the idea of a biased estimator, consider the following situation: Suppose you work for a carnival in which you must guess a person's age. After 20 people come to your booth, you notice that you have a tendency to underestimate people's age. (You guess too low.) What would you do about this? In all likelihood, you would adjust your guesses higher so that you don't underestimate any more. In other words, before the adjustment, your guesses were biased. To remove the bias, you increase your guess. That's what dividing by $n - 1$ in the sample variance formula accomplishes. Dividing by n results in an underestimate, so we divide by a smaller number to increase our "guess."

Although a proof that establishes why we divide by $n - 1$ is beyond the scope of the text, we can provide an explanation that has intuitive appeal. We already know that the sum of the deviations about the mean, $\sum(x_i - \overline{x})$ must equal zero. Therefore, if the sample mean is known and the first $n - 1$ observations are known, then the nth observation must be the value that causes the sum of the deviations to equal zero. For example, suppose $\overline{x} = 4$ based upon a sample of size three. In addition, suppose $x_1 = 2$ and $x_2 = 3$, then we can determine x_3.

Note to Instructor
In-class concept check: Ask students to explain why $\sum(x_i - \overline{x}) = 0$? When calculating $\sum(x_i - \overline{x})$, why does it sometimes turn out to be a little more/less than 0?

$$\frac{x_1 + x_2 + x_3}{3} = \overline{x}$$

$$\frac{2 + 3 + x_3}{3} = 4 \qquad x_1 = 2, x_2 = 3, \overline{x} = 4$$

$$5 + x_3 = 12$$

$$x_3 = 7$$

*An algebraically equivalent formula for computing the sample variance is

$$s^2 = \frac{\sum x_i^2 - \frac{(\sum x_i)^2}{n}}{n - 1}, \text{ where } \sum x_i^2 \text{ means to square each observation and then sum these}$$

squared values, whereas $(\sum x_i)^2$ means to add up all the observations and then square the sum.

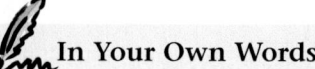
In Your Own Words

We have $n-1$ degrees of freedom in the computation of s^2 because an unknown parameter, μ, is estimated with $\bar{x}$. For each parameter estimated, we lose one degree of freedom.

Therefore, the first $n-1$ observations have freedom to be whatever value they wish, but the nth value has no freedom; it must be whatever value forces the sum of the deviations about the mean to equal zero. In this regard, we say that there are $n-1$ **degrees of freedom**.

Again, you should notice that Greek letters are used for parameters while Roman letters are used for statistics. Do not use rounded values of the sample mean in Formula (2).

▶ EXAMPLE 4 **Computing a Sample Variance**

Problem: Compute the sample variance of the sample obtained in Example 1(b) on page 113 from Section 3.1.

Approach: We follow the same approach that we used to compute the population variance, but this time using the sample mean instead of the population mean.

Solution: The Anaheim Angels (158 home runs), Baltimore Orioles (136 home runs), Detroit Tigers (139 home runs), Tampa Bay Devil Rays (121 home runs), and Seattle Mariners (169 home runs) are in our sample.

Step 1: We create a table just as we did in the computation of the population variance. Column 1 in Table 10 lists the data in the sample and column 2 contains the unrounded sample mean, $\bar{x} = 144.6$.

Step 2: Compute the deviations about the mean, $x_i - \bar{x}$, for each observation as shown in column 3.

Step 3: Column 4 in Table 10 shows the squared deviations about the mean.

TABLE 10			
Number of Home Runs	Sample Mean, $\bar{x}$	Deviation about the Mean, $x_i - \bar{x}$	Squared Deviations about the Mean, $(x_i - \bar{x})^2$
158	144.6	$158 - 144.6 = 13.4$	$13.4^2 = 179.56$
136	144.6	-8.6	73.96
139	144.6	-5.6	31.36
121	144.6	-23.6	556.96
169	144.6	24.4	595.36
		$\Sigma(x_i - \bar{x}) = 0$	$\Sigma(x_i - \bar{x})^2 = 1437.2$

Step 4: We sum the entries in column 4 and obtain $\Sigma(x_i - \bar{x})^2 = 1437.2$. We compute the sample variance by dividing the sum of the entries in column 4 by the number of individuals in the sample less one, $5 - 1 = 4$:

$$s^2 = \frac{\Sigma(x_i - \bar{x})^2}{n-1} = \frac{1437.2}{5-1} = 359.3 \qquad ◀◀$$

Notice that the sample variance obtained for this sample is an underestimate of the population variance. This discrepancy does not violate our definition of an unbiased estimator, however. A biased estimator is one that *consistently* under- or overestimates.

EXPLORATION   Using the results from the Exploration in Section 3.1 on page 115, compute two additional sample variances. Conclude that different samples lead to different sample variances.   ◀◀

③ Standard Deviation

The standard deviation and the arithmetic mean are the most popular methods for numerically describing the distribution of a variable. This is because these two measures are used for most types of statistical inference.

Definitions

The **population standard deviation**, σ, is obtained by taking the square root of the population variance. That is,

$$\sigma = \sqrt{\sigma^2}$$

The **sample standard deviation**, s, is obtained by taking the square root of the sample variance. That is,

$$s = \sqrt{s^2}$$

▶ **EXAMPLE 5**   **Obtaining the Population and Sample Standard Deviation**

Problem: Use the results obtained in Examples 3 and 4 to compute the population and sample standard deviation number of home runs hit in 2001 by teams in the American League.

Approach: The population standard deviation is the square root of the population variance. The sample standard deviation is the square root of the sample variance.

Solution: The population standard deviation is

$$\sigma = \sqrt{\sigma^2} = \sqrt{\frac{\sum (x_i - \mu)^2}{N}} = \sqrt{\frac{16{,}704}{14}} = 34.5 \text{ home runs}$$

The sample standard deviation for the sample obtained in Example 1 from Section 3.1 is

$$s = \sqrt{s^2} = \sqrt{\frac{\sum (x_i - \overline{x})^2}{n-1}} = \sqrt{\frac{1437.2}{5-1}} = 19.0 \text{ home runs} \quad ◀◀$$

Caution

Never use the rounded variance to compute the standard deviation.

To avoid round-off error, never use the rounded value of the variance to compute the standard deviation.

EXPLORATION   Compute the two sample standard deviations using the two sample variances obtained in the Exploration on the top of this page. Conclude that different samples result in different sample standard deviations.   ◀◀

NW *Now Work Problem 11.*

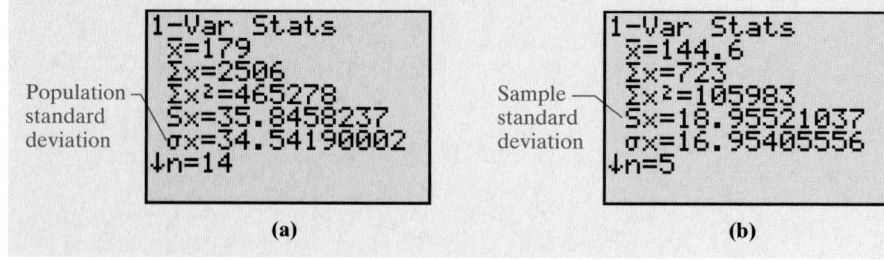

Using Technology: Statistical spreadsheets and many calculators have the ability to compute the variance and standard deviation. Figure 12(a) shows the population standard deviation obtained in Example 5, and Figure 12(b) shows the sample standard deviation obtained in Example 5 using a TI-83 Plus graphing calculator.

Figure 12

Interpretations of the Standard Deviation

The standard deviation is used in conjunction with the mean in order to numerically describe distributions. The mean measures the center of the distribution, while the standard deviation measures the spread of the distribution. So how does the value of the standard deviation relate to the dispersion of the distribution? If we are comparing two populations, then **the larger the standard deviation, the more dispersion the distribution has**. This rule of thumb is true provided that the variable of interest from the two populations has the same unit of measure. The units of measure must be the same so that we are comparing "apples" with "apples." For example, a standard deviation of $100 is not the same as 100 Japanese yen, because $1 is equivalent to about 120 yen. This means a standard deviation of $100 is substantially higher than a standard deviation of 100 yen.

▶ **EXAMPLE 6** **Comparing the Variance and Standard Deviation of Two Data Sets**

Problem: Refer to the data in Example 1 on page 131. Use the standard deviation to determine whether University A or University B has more dispersion in the IQ scores of its students.

Approach: We will use Minitab to compute the standard deviation of IQ for each university. The university with the higher standard deviation will be the university with more dispersion in IQ scores. Recall that on the basis of the histograms, it was apparent that University A had more dispersion. Therefore, we would expect University A to have a higher sample standard deviation.

Solution: We enter the data into Minitab and compute the descriptive statistics. See Figure 13.

Figure 13 **Descriptive statistics**

Variable	N	Mean	Median	TrMean	StDev	SEMean
UnivA	100	100.00	102.00	99.97	16.08	1.61
UnivB	100	100.00	98.000	99.73	8.35	0.83

Variable	Minimum	Maximum	Q1	Q3
UnivA	60.00	141.00	90.00	110.00
UnivB	86.00	119.00	94.00	107.00

The sample standard deviation is larger for University A (16.1) than University B (8.4).* Therefore, University A has IQ scores that are more dispersed.   ◄◄

 The Empirical Rule

If data have a distribution that is bell shaped, the following rule can be used to determine the percentage of data that will lie within k standard deviations of the mean.

Theorem

The Empirical Rule

If a distribution is roughly bell shaped, then
- Approximately 68% of the data will lie within one standard deviation of the mean. That is, approximately 68% of the data lie between $\mu - 1\sigma$ and $\mu + 1\sigma$.
- Approximately 95% of the data will lie within two standard deviations of the mean. That is, approximately 95% of the data lie between $\mu - 2\sigma$ and $\mu + 2\sigma$.
- Approximately 99.7% of the data will lie within three standard deviations of the mean. That is, approximately 99.7% of the data lie between $\mu - 3\sigma$ and $\mu + 3\sigma$.

Figure 14 illustrates the Empirical Rule.

Figure 14

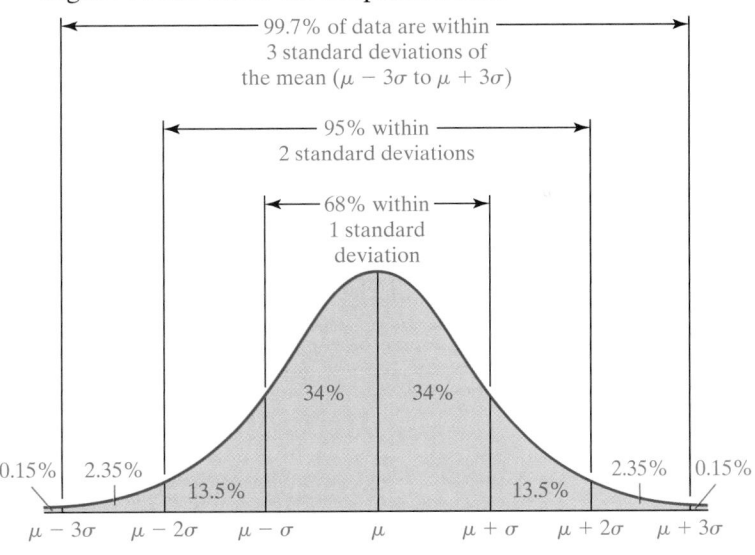

Let's revisit the data from University A in Table 7.

► **EXAMPLE 7**   **Using the Empirical Rule**

Problem: Using the data from University A in Table 7 on page 131.

(a) Determine the percentage of students that have IQ scores within three standard deviations of the mean according to the Empirical Rule.

(b) Determine the percentage of students that have IQ scores between 67.8 and 132.2 according to the Empirical Rule.

(c) Determine the actual percentage of students that have IQ scores between 67.8 and 132.2.

*Don't forget that we agreed to round the mean and standard deviation to one more decimal place than the original data.

Figure 15

University A IQ Scores

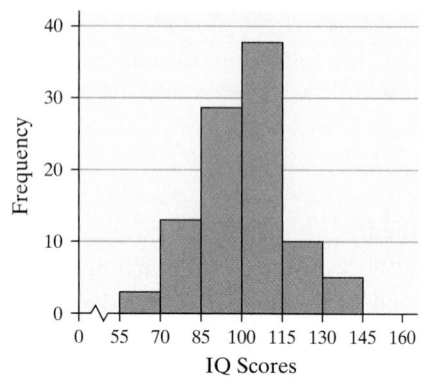

Approach: To use the Empirical Rule, a histogram of the data must be roughly bell shaped. Figure 15 shows the histogram of the data from University *A*.

Solution: The histogram of the data drawn in Figure 15 is roughly bell shaped.

(a) According to the Empirical Rule, approximately 99.7% of the IQ scores will be within three standard deviations of the mean. That is, approximately 99.7% of the data will be greater than or equal to $100 - 3(16.1) = 51.7$ and less than or equal to $100 + 3(16.1) = 148.3$.

(b) Since 67.8 is exactly two standard deviations below the mean $(100 - 2(16.1) = 67.8)$ and 132.2 is exactly two standard deviations above the mean $(100 + 2(16.1) = 132.2)$, we use the Empirical Rule to determine that approximately 95% of all IQ scores lie between 67.8 and 132.2.

(c) Of the 100 IQ scores listed, 96, or 96%, are between 67.8 and 132.2. This is very close to the approximation given by the Empirical Rule. ◀◀

 Now Work Problems 25(a) and 25(b).

Chebyshev's Theorem

Chebyshev's theorem was developed by the Russian mathematician Pafnuty Chebyshev (1821–1894). The theorem is used to determine a lower bound on the percentage of observations that lie within k standard deviations of the mean, where $k > 1$. What's amazing about this theorem is that these bounds are arrived at regardless of the basic shape of the distribution (skewed left, skewed right, or symmetric).

Theorem

Chebyshev's Inequality

For any data set, regardless of the shape of the distribution, at least $\left(1 - \dfrac{1}{k^2}\right)100\%$ of the observations will lie within k standard deviations of the mean where k is any number greater than 1. That is, at least $\left(1 - \dfrac{1}{k^2}\right)100\%$ of the data will lie between $\overline{x} - ks$ and $\overline{x} + ks$ for $k > 1$.

Note to Instructor
If pressed for time, Chebyshev's inequality can be skipped without loss of continuity.

Caution

The Empirical Rule holds only if the distribution is bell shaped. Chebyshev's Inequality holds regardless of the shape of the distribution.

For example, at least $\left(1 - \dfrac{1}{2^2}\right)100\% = 75\%$ of all observations will lie within $k = 2$ standard deviations of the mean and at least $\left(1 - \dfrac{1}{3^2}\right)100\% = 88.9\%$ of all observations will lie within $k = 3$ standard deviations of the mean.

Notice the theorem does not state that exactly 75% of all observations lie within two standard deviations of the mean, but instead states that 75% or more of the observations will lie within two standard deviations of the mean.

▶ **EXAMPLE 8** **Using Chebyshev's Inequality**

Problem: Using the data from University A in Table 7 on page 131,

(a) Determine the minimum percentage of students who have IQ scores within three standard deviations of the mean according to Chebyshev's theorem.

(b) Determine the minimum percentage of students who have IQ scores between 67.8 and 132.2, according to Chebyshev's theorem.

(c) Determine the actual percentage of students who have IQ scores between 67.8 and 132.2.

Approach:

(a) We use Chebyshev's inequality with $k = 3$.

(b) We need to determine the number of standard deviations 67.8 and 132.2 are from the mean of 100.0. We then substitute this value of k into Chebyshev's inequality.

(c) We refer to Table 7 and count the number of observations between 67.8 and 132.2. We divide this result by 100, the number of observations in the data set.

Solution:

(a) We use Chebyshev's inequality with $k = 3$ and determine that at least $\left(1 - \dfrac{1}{3^2}\right)100\% = 88.9\%$ of all students have IQ scores within three standard deviations of the mean. Since the mean of the data set is 100.0 and the standard deviation is 16.1, at least 88.9% of the students have IQ scores between $\bar{x} - ks = 100.0 - 3(16.1) = 51.7$ and $\bar{x} + ks = 100 + 3(16.1) = 148.3$.

(b) Since 67.8 is exactly two standard deviations below the mean $(100 - 2(16.1) = 67.8)$ and 132.2 is exactly two standard deviations above the mean $(100 + 2(16.1) = 132.2)$, we use Chebyshev's inequality with $k = 2$ to determine that at least $\left(1 - \dfrac{1}{2^2}\right)100\% = 75\%$ of all IQ scores lies between 67.8 and 132.2.

(c) Of the 100 IQ scores listed, 96 or 96% are between 67.8 and 132.2. Notice that Chebyshev's inequality provides a rather conservative result.

◀◀

NW *Now Work Problems 25(c) and 25(d).*

Because the Empirical Rule requires that the distribution be bell shaped, while Chebyshev's theorem applies to all distributions, the Empirical Rule provides results that are more precise.

Historical Notes

Pafnuty Chebyshev was born on May 16, 1821, in Okatovo, Russia. In 1847, he began teaching mathematics at the University of St. Petersburg. Some of his more famous work was done on prime numbers. In particular, he discovered a way to determine the number of prime numbers less than or equal to a given number. Chebyshev also studied mechanics, including rotary motion. Chebyshev was elected a Fellow of the Royal Society in 1877. He died November 26, 1894, in St. Petersburg.

3.2 Assess Your Understanding

Concepts and Vocabulary

1. Would it be appropriate to say that a distribution with a standard deviation of 10 centimeters is more dispersed than a distribution with a standard deviation of 5 inches? Support your position.

2. What is meant by the phrase "degrees of freedom" as it pertains to the computation of the sample variance?

3. Are any of the measures of dispersion mentioned in this section resistant?

4. The sum of the deviations about the mean always equals _____.

5. What does it mean when a statistic is biased?

Exercises

• Skill Building

1. **Crash Test Results** The Insurance Institute for Highway Safety crashed the 2001 Honda Civic four times at 5 miles per hour. The cost of repair for each of the four crashes is as follows:

$$\$420, \ \$462, \ \$409, \ \$236$$

Compute the range, sample variance, and sample standard deviation cost of repair. *$226, 9962.9, $99.8*

2. **Cell Phone Usage** The following data represent the monthly cell phone bill for my wife's phone for six randomly selected months:

$$\$35.34, \ \$42.09, \ \$39.43, \ \$38.93, \ \$43.39, \ \$49.26$$

Compute the range, sample variance, and sample standard deviation phone bill. *$13.92; 22.584; $4.75*

3. **Concrete Mix** A certain type of concrete mix is designed to withstand 3000 pounds per square inch (psi) of pressure. The strength of concrete is measured by pour-

ing the mix into casting cylinders 6 inches in diameter and 12 inches tall. The cylinder is allowed to "set up" for 28 days. The cylinders are then stacked upon one another until the cylinders are crushed. The following data represent the strength of nine randomly selected casts:

3960, 4080, 3200, 3100, 2940, 3830, 4090, 4040, 3780

Compute the range, sample variance, and sample standard deviation for strength of the concrete (in pounds per square inch). *1150; 210,236.1; 458.5*

4. **Flight Time** The following data represent the flight time (in minutes) of a random sample of seven flights from Las Vegas, Nevada, to Newark, New Jersey, on Continental Airlines:

$$282, 270, 260, 266, 257, 260, 267$$

Compute the range, sample variance, and sample standard deviation of flight time. *25; 71; 8.4*

• Applying the Concepts

5. **Corn Production** The following data represent the number of corn plants in randomly sampled rows (a 17-foot by 5-inch strip) for various types of plot. Compute the range and sample standard deviation for each type of plot. Which type has the most dispersion based upon the range? Which type has the most dispersion based upon the standard deviation?

Plot Type	Number of Plants
Sludge Plot	25 27 33 30 28 27
Spring Disk	32 30 33 35 34 34
No Till	30 26 29 32 25 29
Spring Chisele	30 32 26 28 31 29
Great Lakes Bt	28 32 27 30 29 27

Source: Andrew Dieter and Brad Schmidgall, Joliet Junior College

6. **Soybean Yield** The following data represent the number of pods on a random sample of soybean plants for various types of plots. Compute the range and sample standard deviation for each type of plot. Which type has the most dispersion based upon the range? Which type has the most dispersion based upon the standard deviation?

Plot Type	Pods								
Liberty	32	31	36	35	41	34	39	37	38
Fall Plowed	29	31	33	22	7	19	30	36	30
No Till	34	30	31	27	40	33	37	42	39
Chisele Plowed	34	37	24	23	32	33	27	34	30
Round-up Ready	49	27	34	46	32	35	20	29	35

Source: Andrew Dieter and Brad Schmidgall, Joliet Junior College

7. **Day of Birth** A researcher wanted to know whether more births occur on Mondays than on Saturdays. She collects the following data that represent the number of live births on Mondays and Saturdays for the first six weeks in 1997 from the National Center for Health Statistics. Compute the range and sample standard deviation for each day. Does there appear to be more variability in the number of births on Monday versus Saturday? What might account for any difference?

Births on Monday		Births on Saturday	
10,456	10,527	8,617	8,634
10,267	10,596	8,368	8,488
10,444	10,778	8,340	8,411

Source: National Center for Health Statistics

7. Monday: 511; 170.8 Saturday: 294; 126.0

8. **Month of Birth** A researcher wants to know whether more births occur in September than in March. She randomly selects seven weekdays in March 1997 and seven weekdays in September 1997 and records the number of births on those days. The data are presented in the table. Compute the range and sample standard deviation for each month. Does there appear to be a difference in the variability of births in March versus those in September? What might account for any difference? *March: 1661; 571.4 September: 1584; 575.4*

Births in March		Births in September	
11,726	11,571	11,307	11,453
11,944	11,523	12,462	12,132
11,570	10,283	12,891	12,457
10,903		12,372	

Source: National Center for Health Statistics

9. **Rats in Space** In the experiment "Regulation of Erythropoiesis during Spaceflight," led by NASA scientist Dr. Robert D. Lange, rats were sent to space on Spacelab Life Sciences I to measure the effect of space travel on weight. The following data represent the weights (in grams) of rats in an Animal Enclosure Module (AEM) on the flight return day for both a ground (control) group and a flight (experimental) group. Compute the range and sample standard deviation for both the control and the experimental groups. Does there appear to be a difference in the variability of weights? What might account for any difference? *Control: 40; 15.1 Flight: 73; 28.5*

Control Group		Flight Group	
305	330	330	320
320	316	310	326
345		383	

Source: NASA Life Sciences Data Archive

10. **Reaction Time** In an experiment conducted on-line at the University of Mississippi, study participants are asked to react to a stimulus. In one experiment, the participant must press a key upon seeing a blue screen. The time (in seconds) to press the key is measured. The same person is then asked to press a key upon seeing a red screen, again with the time to react measured. The results for six study participants are listed in the table. Compute the range and sample standard deviation reaction time for both blue and red. Does there appear to be a difference in the variability of reaction time? What might account for any difference? *Blue: 0.574; 0.1994 Red: 0.14; 0.0647*

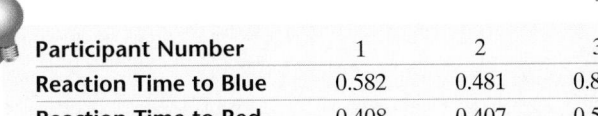

Participant Number	1	2	3	4	5	6
Reaction Time to Blue	0.582	0.481	0.841	0.267	0.685	0.45
Reaction Time to Red	0.408	0.407	0.542	0.402	0.456	0.533

Source: PsychExperiments at the University of Mississippi (http://www.olemiss.edu/psychexps/)

11. **Pulse Rates** The following data represent the pulse rates (beats per minute) of the nine students enrolled in a section of Sullivan's course in introductory statistics. Treat the nine students as a population.

(a) Compute the population variance and population standard deviation. *58.8; 7.7*

Student	Pulse
Perpectual Bempah	76
Megan Brooks	60
Jeff Honeycutt	60
Clarice Jefferson	81
Crystal Kurtenbach	72
Janette Lantka	80
Kevin McCarthy	80
Tammy Ohm	68
Kathy Wojdyla	73

(b) Determine two simple random samples of size three, and compute the sample variance and sample standard deviation of each sample.

(c) Which samples underestimate the population standard deviation? Which overestimate the population standard deviation?

12. **Travel Time** The following data represent the travel time (in minutes) to school for the nine students enrolled in Sullivan's College Algebra course. Treat the nine students as a population.

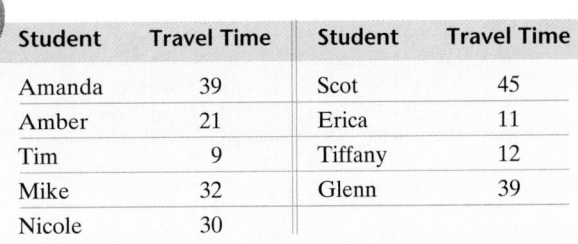

Student	Travel Time	Student	Travel Time
Amanda	39	Scot	45
Amber	21	Erica	11
Tim	9	Tiffany	12
Mike	32	Glenn	39
Nicole	30		

(a) Compute the population variance and population standard deviation. *164.9; 12.8*

(b) Determine three simple random samples of size four, and compute the sample variance and sample standard deviation of each sample.

(c) Which samples underestimate the population standard deviation? Which overestimate the population standard deviation?

In Problems 13–20, compute the range, sample variance, and sample standard deviation.

13. Waiting for a Table The following data represent the number of customers waiting for a table at 6:00 P.M. on Saturday for 40 consecutive Saturdays at Bobak's Restaurant: *11, 7.4, 2.7*

11	6	5	8	11	6	3	7
4	6	5	4	13	14	9	11
13	8	10	10	9	9	6	5
10	8	8	8	7	7	3	8
7	8	9	6	10	11	4	8

14. Highway Repair The following data represent the number of potholes on 50 randomly selected 1-mile stretches of highway in the city of Chicago: *9, 4.7, 2.2*

2	7	4	7	2	7
2	2	2	3	4	3
1	2	3	2	1	4
2	2	5	2	3	4
4	1	7	10	3	5
4	3	3	2	2	
1	6	5	7	9	
2	2	2	1	5	
3	5	1	3	5	

15. Tensile Strength Tensile strength is the maximum stress at which one can be reasonably certain failure will not occur. The following data represent tensile strength (in thousands of pounds per square inch) of a composite material to be used in an aircraft. *82.32; 335.638; 18.320*

203.41	185.97	184.41	160.44	174.63
209.58	190.67	200.73	180.95	185.34
213.35	207.88	206.51	201.95	205.59
218.56	210.80	209.84	204.60	212.00
242.76	231.46	212.15	219.51	225.25

Source: Vangel, Mark G., "New Methods for One-sided Tolerance Limits for a One-way Balanced Random-Effects ANOVA Model," *Technometrics*; May, 1992, Vol. 34, Issue 2, pp. 176–185.

16. Miles on a Cavalier A random sample of 36 three-year-old Chevy Cavaliers was obtained in the Miami, Florida area and the number of miles on the car was recorded. The data are listed in the following table.

34,122	34,511	17,595	30,500	31,883
39,416	34,500	44,224	35,936	32,923
28,281	41,620	26,455	44,448	40,614
37,021	30,283	27,368	41,043	42,398
30,747	15,499	37,904	30,739	
35,439	26,051	23,221	38,995	
17,685	32,305	38,041	41,194	
29,307	39,884	35,295	29,289	

Source: cars.com

17. Serum HDL Dr. Paul Oswiecmiski randomly selects 40 of his 20–29-year-old patients and obtains the following data regarding their serum HDL cholesterol:

70	56	48	48	53	52	66	48
36	49	28	35	58	62	45	60
38	73	45	51	56	51	46	39
56	32	44	60	51	44	63	50
46	69	53	70	33	54	55	52

18. Volume of Philip Morris Stock The following data represent the number of millions of shares of Philip Morris stock sold in a random sample of 35 trading days in 2000: *23.56; 33.4; 5.8*

3.98	8.90	10.40	7.52	13.84
14.04	9.14	7.96	11.40	13.30
5.29	9.69	8.94	12.10	13.25
4.62	10.85	24.52	14.62	16.10
4.24	8.54	11.59	6.75	27.54
16.06	17.62	7.17	6.13	25.32
7.71	10.14	4.28	7.24	10.88

Source: http://finance.yahoo.com

16. *28,949; 54, 141, 591.0; 7358.1*   17. *45; 118.0; 10.9*

19. **M&Ms** The following data represent the weights (in grams) of a simple random sample of 50 M&M plain candies: *0.18; 0.002, 0.040*

0.87	0.88	0.82	0.90	0.90	0.84	0.84
0.91	0.94	0.86	0.86	0.86	0.88	0.87
0.89	0.91	0.86	0.87	0.93	0.88	
0.83	0.94	0.87	0.93	0.91	0.85	
0.91	0.91	0.86	0.89	0.87	0.93	
0.88	0.88	0.89	0.79	0.82	0.83	
0.90	0.88	0.84	0.93	0.76	0.90	
0.88	0.92	0.85	0.79	0.84	0.86	

Source: Michael Sullivan

20. **Old Faithful** The following data represent the length of eruption (in seconds) for a random sample of eruptions of the Old Faithful geyser in California: *30; 39.1; 6.2*

108	108	99	105	103	103	94
102	99	106	90	104	110	110
103	109	109	111	101	101	
110	102	105	110	106	104	
104	100	103	102	120	90	
113	116	95	105	103	101	
100	101	107	110	92	108	

Source: Ladonna Hansen, Park Curator

21. **Rates of Return of Stocks** Stocks may be categorized by industry. The following data represent the five-year rates of return for a simple random sample of financial stocks and energy stocks for the period ending December 28, 2001:

(21a) Financial:
$\bar{x} = 11.12$, M = 9.33;
Energy:
$\bar{x} = 9.71$, M = 9.09

Financial Stocks

16.12	18.61	4.04	13.93	17.85
3.34	8.39	21.32	34.22	16.56
28.51	13.29	11.03	14.61	6.67
2.98	14.06	28.90	11.26	9.24
10.97	7.13	5.32	0.63	13.43
17.10	22.21	6.18	5.80	1.39
0.83	5.63	8.39	8.02	1.23
3.32	9.42	2.98	13.62	6.36

Source: Morningstar.com

Energy Stocks

2.49	9.70	21.67	8.31	5.07
7.70	23.72	5.59	6.09	9.69
1.82	12.68	6.07	11.09	6.35
2.00	14.22	13.17	6.29	6.25
7.39	9.09	30.39	11.25	7.17
9.48	9.23	9.70	5.41	10.29
6.11	7.38	11.60	12.10	13.38

Source: Morningstar.com

(a) Compute the arithmetic mean and the median for each industry. Which sector has the higher arithmetic mean rate of return? Which sector has the higher median rate of return?

(b) Compute the standard deviation for each industry. In finance, the standard deviation rate of return is called **risk**. Which sector is riskier? *Financial: s = 8.06; Energy: s = 5.852; Financial*

22. **American League versus National League** The following data represent the earned-run average of the top 37 pitchers in both the American League and the National League during the 2001 season:

(22a) AL: $\bar{x} = 4.124$; M = 4.090
NL: $\bar{x} = 3.928$; M = 4.050
(22b) AL: s = 0.676;
NL: s = 0.638; AL

American League

3.05	3.15	3.16	3.29	3.37
3.43	3.45	3.49	3.51	3.59
3.60	3.65	3.77	3.90	3.94
3.99	4.05	4.08	4.09	4.09
4.09	4.25	4.32	4.36	4.37
4.39	4.42	4.45	4.45	4.50
4.76	4.93	5.02	5.08	5.17
5.54	5.82			

National League

2.49	2.98	3.04	3.05	3.09
3.16	3.29	3.31	3.36	3.40
3.42	3.50	3.57	3.57	3.69
3.70	3.80	4.03	4.05	4.05
4.19	4.31	4.33	4.34	4.42
4.42	4.45	4.46	4.46	4.47
4.48	4.49	4.63	4.79	4.81
4.85	4.90			

(a) Compute the arithmetic mean and the median for each league. Which league has the higher arithmetic mean earned-run average? Which league has the higher median earned-run average?

(b) Compute the standard deviation for each league. Which league has more dispersion?

23. **Golf Scores** The following data represent the golf scores of Michael and Kevin for their most recent 15 rounds of golf:
    (a) Compute the arithmetic mean score of each golfer.
    (b) Compute the median score of each golfer.
    (c) Compute the mode score of each golfer.
    (d) Compute the range of each golfer. M: 13; K: 17
    (e) Compute the sample standard deviation of each golfer. M: 3.2; K: 5.9
    (f) Which player is more consistent? Why? Michael

    (a) M: 81.1; K: 81.2 (b) M: 81; K: 82 (c) M: 83; K: 73

Michael's Scores				
83	88	81	75	79
80	83	85	82	80
77	78	82	83	81

Kevin's Scores				
90	73	73	80	85
89	78	83	75	79
88	84	86	82	73

24. **SAT Scores** The following data represent SAT Math scores for 15 randomly selected students in two different high school districts:

District 115					District 231				
377	412	530	594	561	409	445	519	559	538
415	565	464	523	529	447	540	478	514	518
537	459	468	532	495	523	474	480	520	497

    (a) Compute the arithmetic mean SAT Math score of each district. D 115: 497.4; D 231: 497.4
    (b) Compute the median SAT Math score of each district. 115: 523; 231: 514
    (c) Compute the mode SAT Math score of each district. 115: None; 231: None
    (d) Compute the range of each district. 115: 217; 231: 150
    (e) Compute the sample standard deviation of each district. 115: 62.9; 231: 41.3
    (f) Which district has less dispersion in the scores? Why? District 231

25. **Chebyshev's Theorem and the Empirical Rule** A random sample of 50 gas stations in Cook County, Illinois, resulted in a mean price per gallon of $1.60 and a standard deviation of $0.07.
    (a) A histogram of the data indicates that the data follow a bell-shaped distribution. Use the Empirical Rule to determine the percentage of gas stations that have prices within three standard deviations of the mean. 99.7%
    (b) Determine the percentage of gas stations that have prices between $1.46 and $1.74, according to the Empirical Rule. 95%
    (c) Determine the minimum percentage of gas stations with prices within three standard deviations of the mean according to Chebyshev's theorem. 88.9%
    (d) Determine the minimum percentage of gas stations that have prices between $1.46 and $1.74 according to Chebyshev's theorem. 75%

26. **Chebyshev's Theorem and the Empirical Rule** The weight, in grams, of both kidneys based upon a random sample of 30 normal men aged 40–49 resulted in a mean of 325 grams, with a standard deviation of 30 grams.
    (a) A histogram of the data indicates that the data follow a bell-shaped distribution. Use the Empirical

    (26a) 99.7%

Rule to determine the percentage of kidneys that weigh within three standard deviations of the mean.
    (b) Determine the percentage of kidneys that weigh between 265 grams and 385 grams, according to the Empirical Rule. 95%
    (c) Determine the minimum percentage of kidneys that weigh within three standard deviations of the mean according to Chebyshev's theorem. 88.9%
    (d) Determine the minimum percentage of kidneys that weigh between 265 grams and 385 grams according to Chebyshev's theorem. 75%

27. **Chebyshev's Theorem and the Empirical Rule** Use the results of Problem 17 in this section, Problem 17 in Section 3.1, and Problem 21 in Section 2.2.
    (a) On the basis of the histogram drawn in Problem 21 in Section 2.2, comment on the appropriateness of using the Empirical Rule. Okay to use
    (b) Use the Empirical Rule to determine the percentage of patients with serum HDL within three standard deviations of the mean. 99.7%
    (c) Use the Empirical Rule to determine the percentage of patients with serum HDL between 29.3 and 72.9. *Hint*: $\bar{x} = 51.1$, $s = 10.9$. 95%

(d) Determine the minimum percentage of patients with serum HDL within three standard deviations of the mean, according to Chebyshev's theorem.

(e) Determine the minimum percentage of patients with serum HDL between 29.3 and 72.9, according to Chebyshev's theorem. *Hint*: $\bar{x} = 51.1$, $s = 10.9$.

(f) Determine the actual percentage of patients with serum HDL between 29.3 and 72.9. Compare the results to those obtained from the Empirical Rule and Chebyshev's theorem. 95%

28. Chebyshev's Theorem and the Empirical Rule Use the results of Problem 19 in this section, Problem 19 in Section 3.1 and Problem 23 in Section 2.2.

(a) On the basis of the histogram drawn in Problem 23 in Section 2.2, comment on the appropriateness of using the Empirical Rule.

(b) Use the Empirical Rule to determine the percentage of M&Ms within three standard deviations of the mean. 99.7%

(c) Use the Empirical Rule to determine the percentage of M&Ms that weigh between 0.794 and 0.954 grams. *Hint*: $\bar{x} = 0.874$, $s = 0.040$. 95%

(d) Determine the minimum percentage of M&Ms within three standard deviations of the mean, according to Chebyshev's theorem. 88.9%

(e) Determine the minimum percentage of M&Ms that weigh between 0.794 and 0.954 grams, according to Chebyshev's theorem. 75%

(27d) 88.9%   (27e) 75%   29. Range = 655.53; s = 123.57
(31b) s = 11.6   (31d) s = 23.3

(f) Determine the actual percentage of M&Ms that weigh between 0.794 miles and 0.954 grams. Compare the results to those obtained from the Empirical Rule and Chebyshev's theorem. 94%

29. Refer to the tensile strength data from Problem 15. Suppose the data value entered as 185.97 was accidentally recorded as 815.97. Recompute the range and standard deviation for the corrected data set. How did this change affect the statistics? Are the data more or less dispersed? Are these statistics resistant?

30. Refer to the data from Problem 16. Suppose the data value entered as 17,685 should have been recorded as 117,685. Recompute the range, and standard deviation for the corrected data set. How did this change affect the statistics? Are the data more or less dispersed? Are these statistics resistant? Range = 102,186; s = 15,589

31. Use a sample of five test scores of 65, 70, 71, 75, and 95 to answer the following questions:

(a) Compute the sample standard deviation. s = 11.6

(b) Suppose the professor decides to curve the exam by adding 4 points to each person's score. Compute the sample standard deviation of the adjusted scores.

(c) Compare the unadjusted test score's standard deviation to the curved test score's standard deviation. What effect did adding 4 to each score have on the sample standard deviation? None

(d) Multiply each exam score by 2 and determine the sample standard deviation of the new test scores.

(e) What effect did multiplying the scores by 2 have on the sample standard deviation? Double

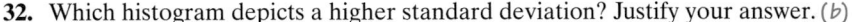

32. Which histogram depicts a higher standard deviation? Justify your answer. (b)

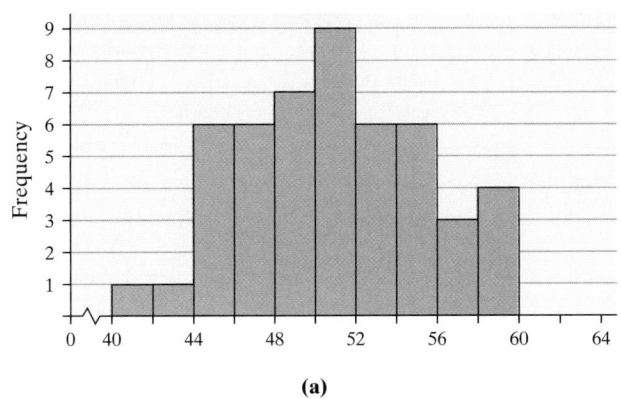

(a)

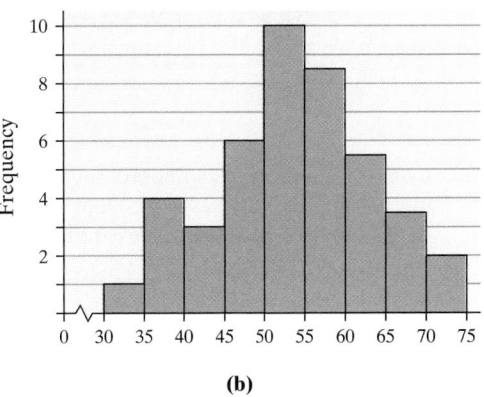

(b)

33. Match the histograms to the summary statistics given.

(a) III
(b) I
(c) IV
(d) II

	Mean	Median	Standard Deviation
(I)	53	53	1.3
(II)	60	60	11
(III)	53	53	9
(IV)	53	53	0.12

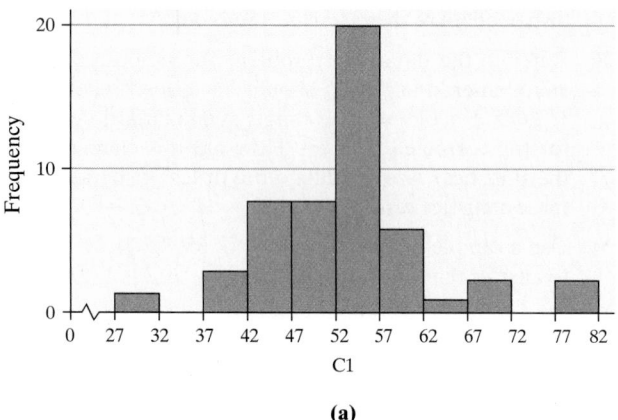

(a)

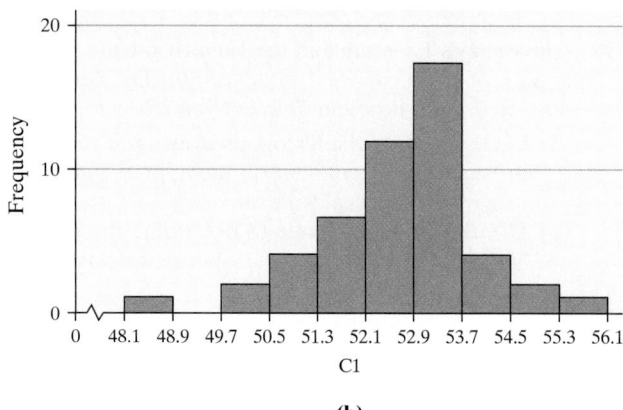

(b)

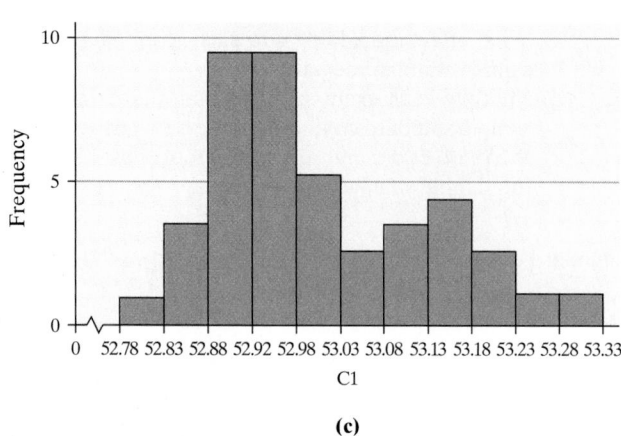

(c)

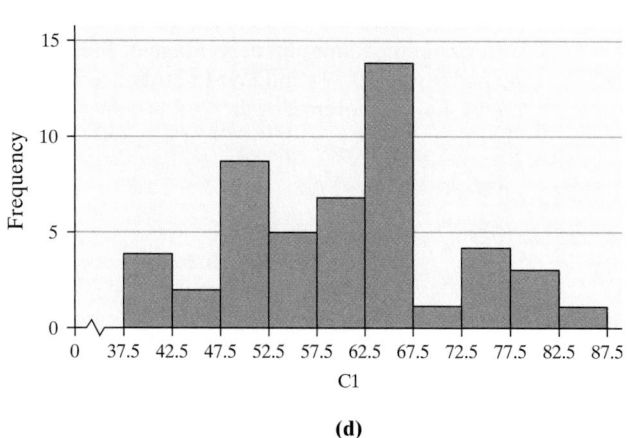

(d)

34. Compute the sample standard deviation of the following test scores: 78, 78, 78, 78. What can be said about a data set in which all the values are identical? $s = 0$

35. **Coefficient of Variation** The coefficient of variation is a measure that allows for the comparison of two or more variables measured on a different scale. It measures the relative variability in terms of the mean and does not have a unit of measure. The lower the coefficient of variation, the less is the variation in the data. The coefficient of variation is defined as

$$CV = \frac{\text{standard deviation}}{\text{arithmetic mean}} \cdot 100\%$$

For example, suppose the senior class of a school district has a mean ACT score of 23 with a standard deviation of 4 and a mean SAT score of 1100 with a standard deviation of 150. Which test has more variability? The co-efficient of variation for the ACT exam is $\frac{4}{23} \cdot 100\% = 17.4\%$, while the coefficient of variation for the SAT exam is $\frac{150}{1100} \cdot 100\% = 13.6\%$. The ACT has more variability.

(a) Suppose the systolic blood pressure of a random sample of 100 students before exercising has a sample mean of 121, with a standard deviation of 14.1. The systolic blood pressure after exercising is 135.9, with a standard deviation of 18.1. Is there more variability in systolic blood pressure before exercise or after exercise? After

(b) An investigation between intracellular calcium and blood pressure was conducted by Erne, Bolli, Buergisser, and Buehler in 1984 and published in the *New England Journal of Medicine*, 310: 1084–1088. The researchers measured the free calcium concentration in the blood platelets of 38 people with normal blood pressure and 45 people with high blood pressure. The mean and the standard deviation of the normal blood pressure group were 107.9 and 16.1, respectively. The mean and the standard deviation of the high blood pressure group were 168.2 and 31.7, respectively. Is there more variability in free calcium concentration in the normal blood pressure or the high blood pressure group?

36. **Mean Absolute Deviation** Another measure of variation is the mean absolute deviation. It is computed using the formula

$$\text{MAD} = \frac{\sum |x_i - \bar{x}|}{n}$$

Compute the mean absolute deviation of the data in Problem 1 and compare the results with the sample standard deviation. MAD = 72.875

37. **Coefficient of Skewness** Karl Pearson developed a measure that describes the skewness of a distribution, called the **coefficient of skewness**. The formula is

$$\text{Skewness} = \frac{3(\text{mean} - \text{median})}{\text{standard deviation}}$$

The value of this measure generally lies between −3 and +3. The closer the value lies to −3, the more the distribution is skewed left; the closer the value lies to +3, the more the distribution is skewed right. A value close to 0 is indicative of a symmetric distribution. Find the coefficient of skewness of the following distributions and comment on the skewness:

(a) Mean = 50, median = 40, standard deviation = 10
(b) Mean = 100, median = 100, standard deviation = 15 0
(c) Mean = 400, median = 500, standard deviation = 120 −2.5
(d) Compute the coefficient of skewness for the data in Problem 15. −0.4
(e) Compute the coefficient of skewness for the data in Problem 16. −0.4
(f) Compute the coefficient of skewness for the data in Problem 17. 0.03
(g) Compute the coefficient of skewness for the data in Problem 18. 0.5

38. **Diversification** A popular theory in investment states that one should invest a certain amount of money in foreign investments in order to reduce risk. The risk of a portfolio is defined as the standard deviation of the rate of return. Refer to the following graph, which depicts the relation between risk and reward (mean rate of return).

How Foreign Stocks Benefit a Domestic Portfolio

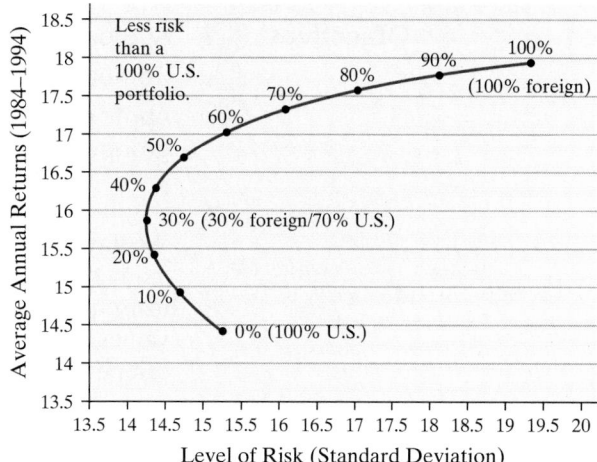

Source: T. Rowe Price

(a) Determine the average annual return and level of risk in a portfolio that is 10% foreign.
(b) Determine the percentage that should be invested in foreign stocks in order to minimize risk. 30%
(c) Why do you think risk initially decreases as the percent of foreign investments increases?
(d) A portfolio that is 30% foreign and 70% American has a mean rate of return of about 15.8%, with a standard deviation of 14.3%. According to Chebyshev's theorem, at least 75% of returns will be between what values? According to Chebyshev's theorem, at least 88.9% of returns will be between what two values? Should an investor be surprised if she has a negative rate of return? Why? Between −12.8% and 44.4%; Between −27.1% and 58.7%

Technology Step-by-Step
Determining the Range, Variance, and Standard Deviation

The same steps followed to obtain the measures of central tendency from raw data can be used to obtain the measures of dispersion.

(35b) High   (37a) 3   (38a) Return: 14.9%; Risk: 14.7%

3.3 Measures of Central Tendency and Dispersion from Grouped Data

Preparing for This Section   Before getting started, review the following:

✓ Summarizing discrete data in tables (Section 2.2, pp. 67–68)

✓ Summarizing continuous data in tables (Section 2.2, pp. 69–71)

✓ Class midpoint (Section 2.3, p. 85)

Objectives Approximate the mean of a variable from grouped data

 Compute the weighted mean

 Approximate the variance and standard deviation of a variable from grouped data

Note to Instructor
The formulas used in this section can be overwhelming. Therefore, it is recommended that "by hand" computations be de-emphasized.

We have discussed how to compute descriptive statistics from raw data, but many times the data that we have access to have already been summarized in frequency distributions (grouped data). While we cannot obtain exact values of the mean or standard deviation without raw data, these measures can be approximated using the techniques discussed in this section.

 Arithmetic Mean

Since raw data cannot be retrieved from a frequency table, we assume that, within each class, all the data values are equal to the class midpoint. We then multiply the class midpoint by the frequency. This product is expected to be close to the sum of the data that lie within the class. We repeat the process for each class and sum the results. This sum approximates the sum of all the data.

Definition   **The Approximate Mean of a Variable from a Frequency Distribution**

Population Mean

$$\mu = \frac{\sum x_i f_i}{\sum f_i} = \frac{x_1 f_1 + x_2 f_2 + \cdots + x_n f_n}{f_1 + f_2 + \cdots + f_n}$$

Sample Mean

$$\bar{x} = \frac{\sum x_i f_i}{\sum f_i} = \frac{x_1 f_1 + x_2 f_2 + \cdots + x_n f_n}{f_1 + f_2 + \cdots + f_n} \tag{1}$$

where x_i is the midpoint or value of the *i*th class

f_i is the frequency of the *i*th class

n is the number of classes

In Formula (1), $x_1 f_1$ approximates the sum of all the data values in the first class, $x_2 f_2$ approximates the sum of all the data values in the second class, and so on. Notice that the formulas for the population mean and sample mean are identical, just as they were for computing the mean from raw data.

▶ **EXAMPLE 1**   **Approximating the Mean for Continuous Quantitative Data from the Frequency Distribution**

TABLE 11

Class (three-year rate of return)	Frequency
10.0–14.9	7
15.0–19.9	11
20.0–24.9	8
25.0–29.9	6
30.0–34.9	3
35.0–39.9	3
40.0–44.9	0
45.0–49.9	2

Problem: The frequency distribution in Table 11 represents the three-year rate of return of a random sample of 40 small-capitalization growth mutual funds. Approximate the mean three-year rate of return.

Approach: We perform the following steps to approximate the mean:

Step 1: Determine the class midpoint of each class. Recall that the class midpoint is found by adding the lower class limit and the upper class limit and dividing the result by 2.

Step 2: Compute the sum of the frequencies, $\sum f_i$.

Step 3: Multiply the class midpoint by the frequency to obtain $x_i f_i$ for each class.

Step 4: Compute $\sum x_i f_i$.

Step 5: Substitute into Formula (1) to obtain the mean from grouped data.

Solution:

Step 1: The class midpoint of the first class is $\dfrac{10.0 + 14.9}{2} = 12.45$, so $x_1 = 12.45$. The remaining class midpoints are listed in column 2 of Table 12.

Step 2: We add the frequencies in column 3 to obtain $\sum f_i = 7 + 11 + \dots + 2 = 40$.

Step 3: Compute the values of $x_i f_i$ by multiplying each class midpoint by the corresponding frequency and obtain the results shown in column 4 of Table 12.

Step 4: We add the values in column 4 of Table 12 to obtain $\sum x_i f_i = 928$.

TABLE 12			
Class (three-year rate of return)	Class Midpoint, x_i	Frequency, f_i	$x_i f_i$
10.0–14.9	12.45	7	$(12.45)(7) = 87.15$
15.0–19.9	17.45	11	191.95
20.0–24.9	22.45	8	179.6
25.0–29.9	27.45	6	164.7
30.0–34.9	32.45	3	97.35
35.0–39.9	37.45	3	112.35
40.0–44.9	42.45	0	0
45.0–49.9	47.45	2	94.9
		$\sum f_i = 40$	$\sum x_i f_i = 928$

Step 5: Substituting into Formula (1), we obtain

$$\bar{x} = \frac{\sum x_i f_i}{\sum f_i} = \frac{928}{40} \approx 23.2$$

The approximate mean three-year rate of return is 23.2 percent.   ◀◀

EXPLORATION Compute the mean three-year rate of return from the raw data listed in Example 3 on page 70 from Section 2.2. Conclude that the mean from the frequency distribution does not necessarily equal the mean from the raw data. ◄◄

Note To compute the mean from a frequency distribution where the data are discrete, treat each category of data as the class midpoint. For discrete data the mean from grouped data will equal the mean from raw data. ◄

 *Now compute the mean of the frequency distribution in Problem 3.*

Note to Instructor
Idea for a classroom discussion: Suppose a company owns three cars that get 20 miles per gallon, two cars that get 22 miles per gallon and one car that gets 24 miles per gallon. Would the mean miles per gallon be 22? Discuss.

② **Weighted Mean**

Sometimes, certain data values have a higher importance or weight associated with them. In this case, we compute the *weighted mean*. For example, your grade point average is a weighted mean, with the weights equal to the number of credit hours in the course. The value of the variable is equal to the grade converted to a point value.

Definition

The **weighted mean**, $\bar{x}_w$, of a variable is found by multiplying the values of the variable by their corresponding weight and dividing the result by the sum of the weights. It can be expressed using the formula

$$\bar{x}_w = \frac{\sum w_i x_i}{\sum w_i} = \frac{w_1 x_1 + w_2 x_2 + \cdots + w_n x_n}{w_1 + w_2 + \cdots + w_n} \qquad (2)$$

where w_i is the weight of the *i*th observation
x_i is the value of the *i*th observation

► **EXAMPLE 2** **Computing the Weighted Mean**

Problem: Marissa just completed her first semester in college. She earned an "A" in her four-hour statistics course, a "B" in her three-hour sociology course, an "A" in her three-hour psychology course, a "C" in her five-hour computer programming course and an "A" in her one-hour drama course. Determine Marissa's grade point average.

Approach: We must assign point values to each grade. Let an "A" equal four points, a "B" equal three points and a "C" equal two points. The number of credit hours for each course determines its weight. So a five-hour course gets a weight of five, a four-hour course gets a weight of four, and so on. We multiply the weight of each course by the points earned in the course, sum these products, and divide the sum by the number of credit hours.

Solution:

$$\text{GPA} = \bar{x}_w = \frac{\sum w_i x_i}{\sum w_i} = \frac{4(4) + 3(3) + 3(4) + 5(2) + 1(4)}{4 + 3 + 3 + 5 + 1} = \frac{51}{16} = 3.19$$

NW *Now Work Problem 9.*

Marissa's grade point average for her first semester is 3.19. ◄◄

Approximating the Variance and Standard Deviation from Grouped Data

The procedure for approximating the variance and standard deviation from grouped data is similar to that of finding the mean from grouped data. Again, because we do not have access to the original data, the variance is approximate.

Definition

The Approximate Variance of a Variable from a Frequency Distribution:

Population Variance

Sample Variance

$$\sigma^2 = \frac{\Sigma (x_i - \mu)^2 f_i}{\Sigma f_i} \, {}^* \qquad\qquad s^2 = \frac{\Sigma (x_i - \overline{x})^2 f_i}{(\Sigma f_i) - 1} \qquad (3)$$

where x_i is the midpoint or value of the *i*th class
        f_i is the frequency of the *i*th class

We approximate the standard deviation by taking the square root of the variance.

▶ **EXAMPLE 3**   **Approximating the Variance and Standard Deviation from a Frequency Distribution**

Problem: The data in Table 11 on page 151 represent the three-year rate of return of a random sample of 40 small-capitalization growth mutual funds. Approximate the variance and standard deviation three-year rate of return.

Approach: We will use the sample variance Formula (3).

Step 1: Create a table with the class in the first column, the class midpoint in the second column, the frequency in the third column, and the unrounded mean in the fourth column.

Step 2: Compute the deviation about the mean, $x_i - \overline{x}$, for each class where x_i is the class midpoint of the *i*th class and $\overline{x}$ is the sample mean. Enter the results in column 5.

Step 3: Square the deviation about the mean and multiply this result by the frequency to obtain $(x_i - \overline{x})^2 f_i$. Enter the results in column 6.

Step 4: Add the entries in columns 3 and 6 to obtain Σf_i and $\Sigma (x_i - \overline{x})^2 f_i$.

Step 5: Substitute the values obtained in Step 4 into Formula (3) to obtain an approximate value for the sample variance.

Solution:

Step 1: We create Table 13. Column 1 contains the classes. Column 2 contains the class midpoint of each class. Column 3 contains the frequency of each class. Column 4 contains the unrounded sample mean obtained in Example 1.

---

*An algebraically equivalent formula for the population variance is $\dfrac{\Sigma x_i^2 f_i - \dfrac{(\Sigma x_i f_i)^2}{\Sigma f_i}}{\Sigma f_i}$.

Step 2: Column 5 of Table 13 contains the deviation about the mean, $x_i - \bar{x}$, for each class.

Step 3: Column 6 contains the values of the squared deviation about the mean multiplied by the frequency $(x_i - \bar{x})^2 f_i$.

Class (three-year rate of return)	Class Midpoint, x_i	Frequency, f_i	$\bar{x}$	$x_i - \bar{x}$	$(x_i - \bar{x})^2 f_i$
10.0–14.9	12.45	7	23.2	−10.75	808.9375
15.0–19.9	17.45	11	23.2	−5.75	363.6875
20.0–24.9	22.45	8	23.2	−0.75	4.5
25.0–29.9	27.45	6	23.2	4.25	108.375
30.0–34.9	32.45	3	23.2	9.25	256.6875
35.0–39.9	37.45	3	23.2	14.25	609.1875
40.0–44.9	42.45	0	23.2	19.25	0
45.0–49.9	47.45	2	23.2	24.25	1176.125
		$\Sigma f_i = 40$			$\Sigma(x_i - \bar{x})^2 f_i = 3327.5$

TABLE 13

Step 4: We add up the entries in columns 3 and 6 and obtain $\Sigma f_i = 40$ and $\Sigma(x_i - \bar{x})^2 f_i = 3327.5$.

Step 5: Substitute these values into Formula (3) to obtain an approximate value for the sample variance.

$$s^2 = \frac{\Sigma(x_i - \bar{x})^2 f_i}{(\Sigma f_i) - 1} = \frac{3327.5}{39} \approx 85.32$$

Take the square root of the unrounded estimate of the sample variance to obtain an approximation of the sample standard deviation

$$s = \sqrt{s^2} = \sqrt{\frac{3327.5}{39}} \approx 9.24 \text{ percent}$$

We approximate the sample standard deviation three-year rate of return to be 9.24 percent. ◄◄

Using Technology: Statistical software can be used to compute means and standard deviations from grouped data, but it is easier to use a graphing calculator with advanced statistical features. Figure 16 shows the results from Examples 1 and 3 using a TI-83 Plus graphing calculator.

Figure 16

Approximate mean

Approximate sample standard deviation

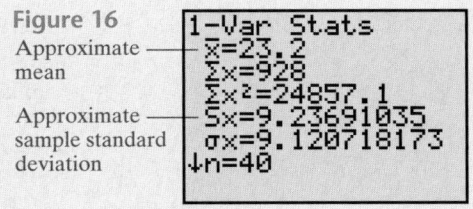

EXPLORATION Compute the sample standard deviation three-year rate of return from the raw data listed in Example 3 on page 70 from Section 2.2. Conclude that the standard deviation from the frequency distribution does not necessarily equal the standard deviation from the raw data. ◄◄

NW *Now compute the standard deviation from the frequency distribution in Problem 3.*

3.3 Assess Your Understanding

Concepts and Vocabulary

1. Explain the role of the class midpoint in the formulas to approximate the arithmetic mean and the standard deviation.

Exercises

1. Health Insurance The following data represent the number of people aged 25–64 covered by health insurance in 1998. Approximate the arithmetic mean and standard deviation age. $\mu = 42.5; \sigma = 10.4$

Age	Number (in millions)
25–34	38.5
35–44	44.7
45–54	35.2
55–64	22.9

Source: United States Census Bureau, Current Population Reports

2. Earthquakes The following data represent the magnitude of earthquakes in the United States in 2001. Approximate the arithmetic mean and standard deviation magnitude. $\mu = 2.8; \sigma = 1.3$

Magnitude	Number
0–0.9	374
1.0–1.9	2
2.0–2.9	604
3.0–3.9	760
4.0–4.9	268
5.0–5.9	37
6.0–6.9	6
7.0–7.9	1

Source: National Earthquake Information Center

3. Meteorology The following data represent the high-temperature distribution for the month of August in Chicago since 1872.

(a) Approximate the arithmetic mean and standard deviation temperature. $\mu = 80.4; \sigma = 8.2$

(b) Draw a frequency histogram of the data to verify that the data are bell shaped.

(c) According to the Empirical Rule, 95% of days in the month of August will be between what two temperatures? *64 and 96.8*

Temperature	Days
50–59	1
60–69	308
70–79	1,519
80–89	1,626
90–99	503
100–109	11

Source: NOAA

4. Multiple Births The following data represent the number of live multiple delivery births (three or more babies) in 1999 for women 15–49 years old.

(c) 21.7 and 42.5

Age	Number of Multiple Births
15–19	66
20–24	411
25–29	1,653
30–34	2,926
35–39	1,813
40–44	356
45–49	96

Source: National Vital Statistics Report, Vol. 49, No. 1; April 17, 2001

(a) Approximate the arithmetic mean and standard deviation age. $\mu = 32.1; \sigma = 5.2$

(b) Draw a frequency histogram of the data to verify that the data are bell shaped.

(c) According to the Empirical Rule, 95% of mothers of multiple births will be between what two ages?

5. Tensile Strength Use the first frequency distribution obtained in Problem 19 in Section 2.2 to approximate the arithmetic mean and standard deviation tensile strength. Compare these results to the values obtained in Problem 15 in Sections 3.1 and 3.2. $\bar{x} = 204.6; s = 17.9$

6. Miles on a Cavalier Use the first frequency distribution obtained in Problem 20 in Section 2.2 to approximate the arithmetic mean and standard deviation miles. Compare these results to the values obtained in Problem 16 in Sections 3.1 and 3.2. $\bar{x} = 33,110.6$; $s = 7436.5$

7. **Serum HDL** Use the first frequency distribution obtained in Problem 21 in Section 2.2 to approximate the arithmetic mean and standard deviation serum HDL. Compare these results to the values obtained in Problem 17 in Sections 3.1 and 3.2. $\bar{x} = 51.3$; $s = 12.1$

8. **Volume of Philip Morris Stock** Use the first frequency distribution obtained in Problem 22 in Section 2.2 to approximate the arithmetic mean and standard deviation number of shares traded. Compare these results to the values obtained in Problem 18 in Sections 3.1 and 3.2.

9. **Grade Point Average** Marissa has just completed her second semester in college. She earned a "B" in her five-hour calculus course, an "A" in her three-hour social work course, an "A" in her four-hour biology course and a "C" in her three-hour American literature course. Assuming that an "A" equals four points, a "B" equals three points, and a "C" equals two points, determine Marissa's grade point average. 3.27

10. **Computing Class Average** In Marissa's calculus course, attendance counts for 5% of the grade, quizzes count for 10% of the grade, exams count for 60% of the grade, and the final exam counts for 25% of the grade. Marissa had a 100% average for attendance, 93% for quizzes, 86% for exams, and 85% on the final. Determine Marissa's course average. 87.15%

11. **Mixed Chocolates** Michael and Kevin want to buy chocolates; however, they can't agree on whether they want chocolate-covered almonds, chocolate-covered peanuts, or chocolate-covered raisins. They agree to create a mix. They bought 4 pounds of chocolate-covered almonds at $3.50 per pound, 3 pounds of chocolate-covered peanuts for $2.75 per pound, and 2 pounds of chocolate-covered raisins for $2.25 per pound. Determine the cost per pound of the mix. $2.97

12. **Nut Mix** Michael and Kevin return to the candy store, but this time they want to purchase nuts. They can't decide between peanuts, cashews or almonds. They again agree to create a mix. They bought 2.5 pounds of peanuts for $1.30 per pound, 4 pounds of cashews for $4.50 per pound and 2 pounds of almonds for $3.75 per pound. Determine the price per pound of the mix. $3.38

13. **Population** The following data represent the male and female population by age of the United States for residents under 100 years old in 1999:

Age	Male Resident Population (in thousands)	Female Resident Population (in thousands)
0–9	19,881	18,994
10–19	20,174	19,143
20–29	18,264	18,038
30–39	21,001	21,305
40–49	20,550	21,091
50–59	14,187	15,148
60–69	9,312	10,669
70–79	6,926	9,191
80–89	2,664	4,788
90–99	384	1,112

Source: U.S. Census Bureau

(a) Approximate the population mean and standard deviation age for males. $\mu = 34.6$; $\sigma = 21.7$
(b) Approximate the population arithmetic mean and standard deviation age for females.
(c) Which gender has the higher mean age? Female
(d) Which gender has more dispersion in age? Female

14. **Age of Mother** The following data represent the age of the mother at childbirth for 1980 and 1997.

Age of Mother	Number of Births in 1980 (in thousands)	Number of Births in 1997 (in thousands)
10–14	1.1	1.2
15–19	53.0	52.9
20–24	115.1	110.9
25–29	112.9	114.3
30–34	61.9	85.4
35–39	19.8	36.0
40–44	3.9	6.9
45–49	0.2	0.3

Source: U.S. National Center for Health Statistics

(a) Approximate the population mean and standard deviation age of mothers in 1980.
(b) Approximate the population mean and standard deviation age of mothers in 1997.
(c) Which year has the higher mean age? 1997
(d) Which year has more dispersion in age? 1997

(8) $\bar{x} = 11.281$; $s = 5.844$ (13b) $\mu = 37.2$; $\sigma = 23.0$ (14a) $\mu = 25.5$; $\sigma = 5.7$ (14b) $\mu = 26.5$; $\sigma = 6.2$

Problems 15–18 use the following steps to approximate the median from grouped data:

Approximating the Median from Grouped Data

Step 1: Construct a cumulative frequency distribution.

Step 2: Identify the class in which the median lies. Remember, the median can be obtained by determining the observation that lies in the middle (i.e., the $n/2$ position, where n is the number of data values when the data is in ascending order).

Step 3: Interpolate the median using the formula

$$\text{Median} = M = L + \frac{\frac{n}{2} - CF}{f}(i)$$

where L is the lower class limit of the class containing the median

   n is the number of data values in the frequency distribution

CF is the cumulative frequency of the class immediately preceding the class containing the median

f is the frequency of the median class

i is the class width of the class containing the median

15. Approximate the median of the frequency distribution in Problem 1. *42.2*

16. Approximate the median of the frequency distribution in Problem 2. *3.06*

17. Approximate the median of the frequency distribution in Problem 3. *81.0*

18. Approximate the median of the frequency distribution in Problem 4. *32.6*

Problems 19–22 use the following definition of the modal class.

The **modal class** of a variable can be obtained from data in a frequency distribution by determining the class that has the largest frequency.

19. Determine the modal class of the frequency distribution in Problem 1. *35–44*

20. Determine the modal class of the frequency distribution in Problem 2. *3.0–3.9*

21. Determine the modal class of the frequency distribution in Problem 3. *80–89*

22. Determine the modal class of the frequency distribution in Problem 4. *30–34*

Technology Step-by-Step
Determining the Mean and Standard Deviation from Grouped Data

TI-83 Plus   **Step 1:** Enter the class midpoint in L1 and the frequency or relative frequency in L2 by pressing STAT and selecting 1:Edit.

Step 2: Press STAT, highlight the CALC menu and select 1:1-Var Stats

Step 3: With 1-Var Stats appearing on the HOME screen, press 2nd 1 to insert L1 on the HOME screen. Then press the comma and press 2nd 2 to insert L2 on the HOME screen. So, the HOME screen should have the following:

$$\text{1-Var Stats L1, L2}$$

Press ENTER to obtain the mean and standard deviation.

3.4   Measures of Position

Objectives   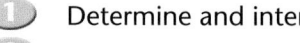   ① Determine and interpret z-scores
   ② Determine and interpret percentiles
   ③ Determine and interpret quartiles
   ④ Check a set of data for outliers

In Section 3.1, we were able to find measures of central tendency. Measures of central tendency are meant to describe the "typical" data value.

Section 3.2 discussed measures of dispersion, which describe the amount of "spread" in a set of data. In this section, we discuss measures of position—that is, we wish to describe the relative position of a certain data value within the entire set of data.

① Z-scores

During the 2000 baseball season, the city of New York sponsored a "subway" series. Both of its teams (the Yankees and Mets) were in the World Series. Which team was the better home-run-hitting team? In 2000, the New York Yankees hit 205 home runs while the New York Mets hit 198. A quick comparison might lead one to think the Yankees are a better home-run-hitting team than the Mets. However, this comparison would be unfair because the two teams play in different leagues—the Yankees play in the American League, where a designated hitter bats for the pitcher, whereas the Mets play in the National League, where the pitcher must bat (pitchers are typically poor hitters). In order to compare the two teams' home-run production, we need to determine their relative standings in their respective leagues. This can be accomplished using a *z-score*.

Definition

The **z-score** represents the number of standard deviations that a data value is from the mean. It is obtained by subtracting the mean from the data value and dividing this result by the standard deviation. There is both a population z-score and a sample z-score; their formulas follow:

$$
\text{Population Z-Score} \qquad \text{Sample Z-Score}
$$
$$
z = \frac{x - \mu}{\sigma} \qquad\qquad z = \frac{x - \bar{x}}{s} \qquad \textbf{(1)}
$$

The z-score is unitless; it has mean 0 and standard deviation 1.

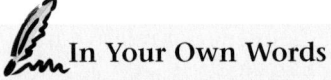
In Your Own Words

Z-scores provide a way to compare "apples" to "oranges" by converting variables with different centers and/or spreads to variables with the same center (0) and spread (1).

If a data value is larger than the mean, the z-score will be positive. If a data value is smaller than the mean, the z-score will be negative. If the data value equals the mean, the z-score will be zero. Z-scores measure the number of standard deviations above or below the mean. For example, a z-score of 1.24 would be interpreted as "the data value is 1.24 standard deviations above the mean." A z-score of -2.31 would be interpreted as "the data value is 2.31 standard deviations below the mean".

We are now prepared to determine whether the Yankees or Mets had a better year in home-run production.

► **EXAMPLE 1**   Comparing z-scores

Problem: Determine whether the New York Yankees or New York Mets had a relatively better home-run-hitting season. The Yankees hit 205 home runs and play in the American League, where the mean number of home runs was $\mu = 192$. The standard deviation was $\sigma = 36.0$. The Mets hit 198 home runs and play in the National League, where the mean number of home runs was $\mu = 186.9$. The standard deviation was $\sigma = 28.7$.

Approach: To determine which team had the relatively better home-run-hitting season, we compute each team's z-score. The team with the higher z-score had the better season. Because we know the values of the population parameters, we will compute the population z-score.

Solution: First, we compute the z-score for the Yankees:

$$z\text{-score} = \frac{x - \mu}{\sigma} = \frac{205 - 192}{36.0} = 0.36^*$$

Next, we compute the z-score for the Mets:

$$z\text{-score} = \frac{x - \mu}{\sigma} = \frac{198 - 186.9}{28.7} = 0.39$$

So, the Yankees had home-run production 0.36 standard deviation above the mean, while the Mets had home-run production 0.39 standard deviation above the mean. Therefore, the Mets had a relatively better year at hitting home runs. ◄◄

EXPLORATION   Compute the z-score for all teams in the American League in 2001, using the data from Table 1 in Section 3.1 on page 114. Compute the mean and standard deviation of the z-scores. Conclude that the mean of z-scores is 0 and the standard deviation is 1. ◄◄

NW *Now Work Problem 1.*

②   **Percentiles**

Recall that the median divides the lower 50% of a set of data from the upper 50% of the set. In general, the **kth percentile**, denoted P_k, of a set of data divides the lower k% of a data set from the upper $(100 - k)$% of the set. Percentiles divide a data set that is written in ascending order into 100 parts, so that there are 99 possible percentiles that can be computed. For example, P_1 divides the bottom 1% of the data from the top 99% of the data, while P_{99} divides the lower 99% of the data from the top 1% of the data. Figure 17 displays the 99 possible percentiles.

Figure 17

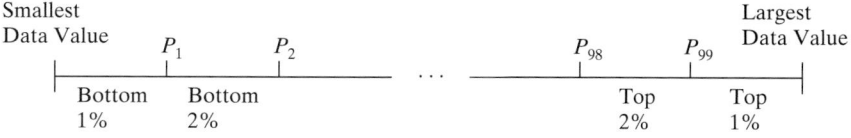

If a data value lies at the 40th percentile, then approximately 40% of the data is less than this value and approximately 60% of the data is higher than this value.

Percentiles are often used in order to give the relative standing of a data value. Many standardized exams, such as the SAT college entrance exam, use percentiles to provide students with an understanding of how they scored on the exam in relation to all other students who took the exam. For example, in 2000, an SAT verbal score of 580 was at the 75th percentile. This means approximately 75% of the scores are below 580 and 25% are above 580. Pediatricians use percentiles to describe the progress of a newborn baby's weight gain relative to other newborn babies. A three-to-five-month-old male child who weighs 14.3 pounds would be at the 15th percentile.

---

*Z-scores are typically rounded to two decimal places.

The following steps can be used to compute the kth percentile:

Determining the kth Percentile, P_k

Step 1: Arrange the data in ascending order.

Step 2: Compute an index i, using the formula

$$i = \left(\frac{k}{100}\right)n \tag{2}$$

where k is the percentile of the data value and n is the number of individuals in the data set.

Step 3: **(a)** If i is not an integer, round up* to the next highest integer. Locate the ith value of the data set written in ascending order. This number represents the kth percentile.

   (b) If i is an integer, the kth percentile is the arithmetic mean of the ith and $(i + 1)$st data value.

An example should clarify the procedure.

Note to Instructor
Try to cover two examples for finding percentiles: one that uses Step 3(a) and one that uses Step 3(b).

Caution

Don't forget to write the data in ascending order before finding the percentile.

▶ **EXAMPLE 2** **Determining the Percentile of a Data Value**

Problem: In order to qualify for "exempt" status on the PGA tour, a golfer must be in the top 130 money winners for the previous season. The data in Table 14 represent the earnings of the top 130 golfers on the PGA tour in 2000. Find the earnings that correspond to the 85th percentile.

TABLE 14						
1. 339,242	20. 425,624	39. 519,740	58. 638,422	77. 877,390	96. 1,263,585	115. 1,968,685
2. 346,569	21. 459,812	40. 527,741	59. 649,674	78. 889,153	97. 1,320,278	116. 2,002,068
3. 379,349	22. 460,024	41. 528,959	60. 660,707	79. 889,381	98. 1,368,888	117. 2,023,465
4. 387,716	23. 461,981	42. 537,105	61. 669,709	80. 896,098	99. 1,384,508	118. 2,025,781
5. 388,341	24. 464,480	43. 538,706	62. 673,387	81. 947,118	100. 1,543,818	119. 2,068,499
6. 391,075	25. 466,345	44. 548,070	63. 700,738	82. 963,974	101. 1,550,592	120. 2,099,943
7. 393,059	26. 466,712	45. 552,795	64. 724,580	83. 964,346	102. 1,557,720	121. 2,169,727
8. 393,316	27. 467,431	46. 564,918	65. 728,635	84. 990,215	103. 1,563,115	122. 2,337,765
9. 397,610	28. 469,590	47. 580,510	66. 731,925	85. 999,460	104. 1,597,139	123. 2,413,345
10. 398,393	29. 482,028	48. 583,605	67. 741,995	86. 1,004,827	105. 1,604,952	124. 2,462,846
11. 402,017	30. 482,744	49. 590,109	68. 747,312	87. 1,040,244	106. 1,631,695	125. 2,547,829
12. 403,982	31. 485,589	50. 597,021	69. 753,709	88. 1,048,166	107. 1,642,221	126. 2,573,835
13. 406,591	32. 493,906	51. 604,199	70. 762,979	89. 1,054,338	108. 1,702,317	127. 3,061,444
14. 414,123	33. 494,307	52. 608,535	71. 774,249	90. 1,063,456	109. 1,747,643	128. 3,469,405
15. 414,509	34. 495,975	53. 610,432	72. 784,754	91. 1,096,131	110. 1,804,433	129. 4,746,457
16. 415,430	35. 498,749	54. 611,209	73. 827,691	92. 1,138,749	111. 1,819,323	130. 9,188,321
17. 417,646	36. 507,308	55. 612,882	74. 838,054	93. 1,142,789	112. 1,842,221	
18. 418,780	37. 511,414	56. 617,242	75. 854,822	94. 1,207,104	113. 1,932,280	
19. 424,309	38. 514,193	57. 631,752	76. 867,372	95. 1,262,535	114. 1,940,519	

Source: Yahoo! Sports

*Rounding up is different from rounding off. Rounding up 15.2 results in 16; rounding off 15.2 results in 15.

Approach: We will follow the steps given on page 160.

Solution:

Step 1: The data provided in Table 14 are already listed in ascending order.
Step 2: To find the 85th percentile, P_{85}, we compute the index i with $k = 85$ and $n = 130$:

$$i = \left(\frac{85}{100}\right)130 = 110.5$$

Step 3: Round 110.5 up to 111. The 111th observation in the data set is $1,819,323, so $P_{85} = $1,819,323. Approximately 85% of the players in the top 130 earned less than $1,819,323, and approximately 15% of the players in the top 130 earned more than $1,819,323. ◀◀

NW *Now Work Problem 7(a).*

Often, we are interested in knowing the percentile to which a specific data value corresponds. The kth percentile of a data value, x, from a data set that contains n values is computed by using the following steps:

Finding the Percentile that Corresponds to a Data Value

Step 1: Arrange the data in ascending order.
Step 2: Use the following formula to determine the percentile of the score, x:

$$\text{Percentile of } x = \frac{\text{Number of data values less than } x}{n} \times 100 \quad \textbf{(3)}$$

Round this number to the nearest integer.

▶ **EXAMPLE 3**   **Finding the Percentile of a Specific Data Value**

Problem: In order to qualify for the last tournament of the year, the Tour Championship, a player must be among the top 30 money winners. Find the percentile that corresponds to the 30th player on the top 130 money list, Carlos Franco, with earnings $1,550,592.

Approach: We will follow the steps given above.

Solution:

Step 1: The data provided in Table 14 are in ascending order.
Step 2: There are 100 players in the top 130 who earned less than $1,550,592. Therefore,

$$\text{Percentile rank of Carlos Franco} = \frac{100}{130} \cdot 100 = 77$$

Carlos Franco's earnings are at the 77th percentile. This means approximately 77% of the players in the top 130 earned less than Carlos and approximately 23% of players in the top 130 earned more than Carlos. ◀◀

NW *Now Work Problem 7(d).*

③ Quartiles

The most common percentiles are quartiles. **Quartiles** divide data sets into fourths, or four equal parts. The first quartile, denoted Q_1, divides the bottom 25% of the data from the top 75%. Therefore, the first quartile is equivalent to the 25th percentile. The second quartile divides the bottom 50% of the data from the top 50% of the data, so the second quartile is equivalent to the 50th percentile, which is equivalent to the median. Finally, the third quartile divides the bottom 75% of the data from the top 25% of the data, so that the third quartile is equivalent to the 75th percentile. Figure 18 illustrates the concept of quartiles.

In Your Own Words

The first quartile, Q_1, is equivalent to the 25th percentile, P_{25}. The 2nd quartile, Q_2, is equivalent to the 50th percentile, P_{50}, which is equivalent to the median, M. Finally, the third quartile, Q_3, is equivalent to the 75th percentile, P_{75}.

Figure 18

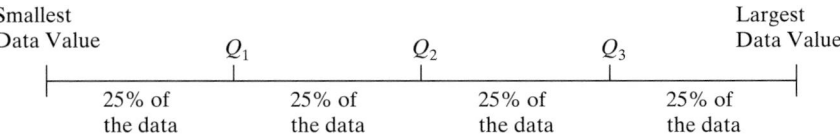

▶ **EXAMPLE 4** **Finding the Quartiles of a Data Set**

Problem: Find the first, second, and third quartiles for the earnings of top 130 PGA golfers listed in Table 14.

Approach:

Step 1: The first quartile, Q_1, is the 25th percentile, P_{25}. We let $k = 25$ in Formula (2) to obtain the index, i.
Step 2: The second quartile, Q_2, is the 50th percentile, P_{50}. We let $k = 50$ in Formula (2) to obtain the index, i.
Step 3: The third quartile, Q_3, is the 75th percentile, P_{75}. We let $k = 75$ in Formula (2) to obtain the index, i.

Note to Instructor
Ask your students whether quartiles are resistant. What about the interquartile range?

Solution:

Step 1: The index for the first quartile, Q_1, is

$$i = \left(\frac{25}{100}\right)130 = 32.5$$

Round this value up to 33. The 33rd observation will be the first quartile. So we have $Q_1 = P_{25} = \$494,307$.
Step 2: The index for the second quartile, Q_2, is

$$i = \left(\frac{50}{100}\right)130 = 65$$

Because the index is an integer, the second quartile will be the arithmetic mean of the 65th and 66th data values.

$$Q_2 = P_{50} = M = \frac{\$728,635 + \$731,925}{2} = \$730,280$$

Step 3: The index for the third quartile, Q_3, is

$$i = \left(\frac{75}{100}\right)130 = 97.5$$

Now Work Problem 9(b).

Round this value up to 98. The 98th observation will be the third quartile. So, we have $Q_3 = P_{75} = \$1,368,888$. ◀◀

④ Outliers

Whenever performing any type of data analysis, we should always check for extreme observations in the data set. Extreme observations are referred to as **outliers**. Whenever outliers are encountered, their origin must be investigated. They can occur because of error in the measurement of a variable, during data entry, or from errors in sampling. For example, in the 2000 presidential election, a precinct in New Mexico accidentally recorded 610 absentee ballots for Al Gore as 110. Workers in the Gore camp discovered the data-entry error through an analysis of vote totals.

Sometimes, extreme observations are in the nature of the population. For example, suppose we wanted to estimate the mean price of a European car. We might take a random sample of size 5 from the population of all European automobiles. If our sample included a Ferrari 360 Spider (approximately $170,000), it probably would be an outlier, because this car costs much more than the typical European automobile. This type of outlier would be considered *unusual* because it is not a "typical" value from the data set.

We can check for outliers with quartiles. The following steps can be followed in order to check for outliers by using quartiles.

> ### Checking for Outliers by Using Quartiles
>
> **Step 1:** Determine the first and third quartiles of the data.
>
> **Step 2:** Compute the interquartile range. The **interquartile range** or **IQR** is the difference between the third and first quartile. That is,
>
> $$\text{IQR} = Q_3 - Q_1$$
>
> **Step 3:** Determine the fences. **Fences** serve as cutoff points for determining outliers.
>
> $$\text{Lower Fence} = Q_1 - 1.5(\text{IQR})$$
>
> $$\text{Upper Fence} = Q_3 + 1.5(\text{IQR})$$
>
> **Step 4:** If a data value is less than the lower fence or greater than the upper fence, then it is considered an outlier.

► **EXAMPLE 5** **Checking for Outliers**

Problem: Check the data that represent the earnings of the top 130 PGA golfers in 2000 for outliers.

Approach: We follow the preceding steps. Any data value that is less than the lower fence or greater than the upper fence will be considered an outlier.

Solution: We consider the top 130 PGA golfers to be a population. Figure 19* shows the output provided by Minitab. Notice that the mean is much larger than the median, so the data is skewed right.

---

*A comparison of the quartiles reported by Minitab and those obtained by hand in Example 4 reveals a discrepancy. Minitab uses a sophisticated approach to computing the quartiles and can be considered more accurate. Be aware that different software use different techniques for finding quartiles and, therefore, the results can differ.

Caution

Outliers distort both the arithmetic mean and the standard deviation, since neither is resistant. Because these measures often form the basis for most statistical inference, any conclusions drawn from a set of data that contains outliers can be flawed.

Note to Instructor

A second method for identifying outliers utilizes z-scores. If the z-score is less than −2 or greater than 2, the data value can be considered to be an outlier. However, this method should be used only if the distribution is symmetric, because it is based on the Empirical Rule.

Figure 19

Descriptive Statistics

Variable	N	Mean	Median	Tr Mean	StDev	SE Mean
Earnings	130	1070682	730280	935458	1020972	89545

Variable	Min	Max	Q1	Q3
Earnings	339242	9188321	494207	1372793

Minitab's quartiles are more accurate than the ones obtained by hand in Example 4, so we will use $Q_1 =$ \$494,207, and $Q_3 =$ \$1,372,793; so IQR = \$1,372,793 − \$494,207 = \$878,586. Substitute these values into the formulas for the lower and upper fence:

$$\text{Lower Fence} = Q_1 - 1.5(\text{IQR}) = \$494{,}207 - 1.5(\$878{,}586) = -\$823{,}672$$

$$\text{Upper Fence} = Q_3 + 1.5(\text{IQR}) = \$1{,}372{,}793 + 1.5(\$878{,}586) = \$2{,}690{,}672$$

Note to Instructor
In class discussion: Why is it inappropriate to only use histograms to identify outliers?

Clearly, there are no outliers resulting from the value of the lower fence; however, we do have outliers resulting from the upper fence: \$9,188,321; \$4,746,457; \$3,469,405; and \$3,061,444. These earnings correspond to Tiger Woods, Phil Mickelson, Ernie Els, and Hal Sutton, respectively. ◄◄

NW *Now Work*
Problem 9(c) and (d).

Figure 20 shows a histogram of the data. We can easily identify the outliers corresponding to Tiger Woods and Phil Mickelson in Figure 20; however, the outliers for the other two players are less obvious.

Figure 20

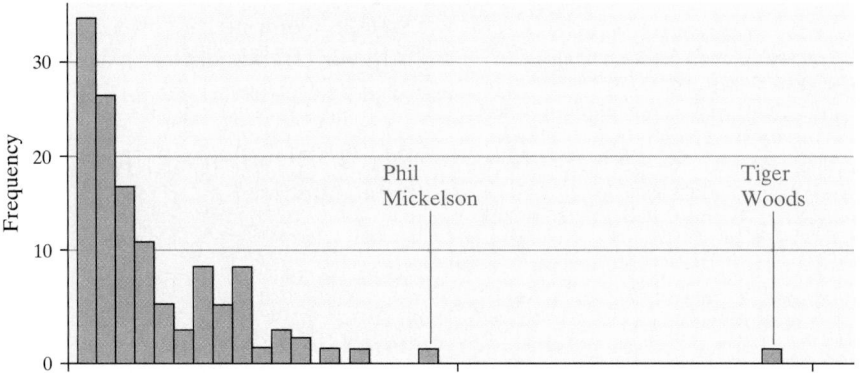

PGA Earnings, 2000

3.4 Assess Your Understanding

Concepts and Vocabulary

1. Write a paragraph that explains the meaning of percentiles.
2. Suppose you received the highest score on an exam. Your friend scored the second-highest score, yet you both were in the 99th percentile. How can this be?
3. Morningstar is a mutual fund rating agency. They rank a fund's performance by using from one to five stars. A one-star mutual fund is in the bottom 20% of its investment class; a five-star mutual fund is in the top 20% of its investment class. Interpret the meaning of a four-star mutual fund.
4. When outliers are discovered, should they always be removed from the data set before further analysis?
5. Mensa is an organization designed for people of high intelligence. One qualifies for Mensa if one's intelligence is measured at or above the 98th percentile. Explain what this means.

Exercises

1. **ACT versus SAT** You are registering for classes during your first semester at college. The advisor asks to see either your ACT math score or your SAT math score so she can enroll you in the appropriate math class. You scored 25 on the ACT math portion and 650 on the SAT math score. In the math portion of the ACT exam, the mean score is 20.7, with a standard deviation of 5, while the SAT math portion has a mean score of 514, with a standard deviation of 113. Which test score should you provide to the advisor, assuming that you wish to enroll in the highest-level course possible? Why? SAT

2. **ACT versus SAT** You are filling out an application for college. The application requests either your ACT or SAT I score. You scored 26 on the ACT composite and 650 on the SAT I. On the ACT exam, the composite mean score is 21 with a standard deviation of 5, while the SAT I has a mean score of 514 with a standard deviation of 113. Which test score should you provide on the application? Why? SAT

3. **Birth Weights** In 1998, babies born after a gestation period of 32–35 weeks had a mean weight of 2600 grams and a standard deviation of 680 grams. In the same year, babies born after a gestation period of 40 weeks had a mean weight of 3500 grams and a standard deviation of 480 grams. Suppose a 34-week-gestation-period baby weighs 2400 grams and a 40-week-gestation-period baby weighs 3300 grams. Which baby weighs less relative to the gestation period? 40-week baby

4. **Birth Weights** In 1998, babies born after a gestation period of 32–35 weeks had a mean weight of 2600 grams and a standard deviation of 680 grams. In the same year, babies born after a gestation period of 40 weeks had a mean weight of 3500 grams and a standard deviation of 480 grams. Suppose a 34-week-gestation-period baby weighs 3000 grams and a 40-week-gestation-period baby weighs 4000 grams. Which baby weighs more relative to the gestation period? 40-week baby

5. **Men versus Women** The average 20–29 year old man is 69.9 inches tall, with a standard deviation of 3.0 inches, while the average 20–29 year old woman is 64.6 inches tall, with a standard deviation of 2.8 inches. Who is relatively taller, a 75-inch man or a 70-inch woman? Woman

6. **Men versus Women** The average 20–29 year old man is 69.9 inches tall, with a standard deviation of 3.0 inches, while the average 20–29 year old women is 64.6 inches tall, with a standard deviation of 2.8 inches. Who is relatively taller, a 67-inch man or a 62-inch woman? Woman

7. **PGA Earnings** Use the data in Table 14 regarding the earnings of PGA tour players in 2000 to answer the following questions.

(a) Find and interpret the 40th percentile. $609,483.50
(b) Find and interpret the 95th percentile $2,462,846
(c) Find and interpret the 10th percentile. $410,357
(d) What is the percentile rank of $459,812?
(e) What is the percentile rank of $1,563,115?

8. **PGA Earnings** Use the data in Table 14 regarding the earnings of PGA tour players in 2000 to answer the following questions.

(a) Find and interpret the 30th percentile. $523,740.50
(b) Find and interpret the 90th percentile. $2,024,623
(c) Find and interpret the 5th percentile. $393,059
(d) What is the percentile rank of $507,308?
(e) What is the percentile rank of $1,804,433?

9. **April Showers** The following data represent the number of inches of rain in Chicago, Illinois, during the month of April for 20 randomly selected years.

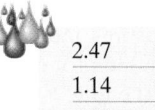

2.47	3.97	3.94	4.11
1.14	4.02	3.41	1.85
5.22	0.97	6.14	2.34
3.48	4.77	2.78	4.00
6.28	5.50	7.69	5.79

Source: NOAA, Climate Diagnostics Center

(a) Compute the z-score corresponding to the rainfall in 1971, 0.97 inches. Interpret this result. −1.70
(b) Determine the quartiles.
(c) Compute the interquartile range, IQR. 2.735
(d) Determine the lower and upper fences. Are there any outliers, according to this criterion?

10. **Hemoglobin in Cats** The following data represent the hemoglobin (in g/dL) for 20 randomly selected cats.

7.8	9.6	13.4	9.5	5.7
8.7	8.9	12.9	10.3	9.6
7.7	11.2	9.9	10.0	11.7
13.0	11.0	9.4	10.6	10.7

Source: Joliet Junior College Veterinarian Technology Program

(a) Compute the z-score corresponding to the hemoglobin of Blackie, 7.8 g/dL. Interpret this result. −1.21
(b) Determine the quartiles.
(c) Compute the interquartile range, IQR. 1.95
(d) Determine the lower and upper fences. Are there any outliers, according to this criterion?

(7d) 15th percentile   (7e) 78th percentile   (8d) 27th percentile   (8e) 84th percentile
(9b) $Q_1 = 2.625$, $Q_2 = 3.985$, $Q_3 = 5.36$ (9d) −1.478; 9.463; No   (10b) $Q_1 = 9.15$, $Q_2 = 9.95$, $Q_3 = 11.1$
(10d) 6.225; 14.025; Yes

11. **Red Blood Cell Count** The following data represent the red blood cell count (in M/μL) for 20 randomly selected dogs.

6.2	6.0	8.1	6.8	6.8
6.8	5.2	5.6	8.2	7.0
6.1	6.1	7.1	6.6	6.1
6.9	0.2	5.3	6.3	7.5

Source: Laura Blackburn, Student, Joliet Junior College

(a) Compute the z-score corresponding to the red blood cell count of Sampson, 0.2 M/μL. Interpret this result. −3.70
(b) Determine the quartiles.
(c) Compute the interquartile range, IQR. 0.9
(d) Determine the lower and upper fences. Are there any outliers, according to this criterion?

12. **Acid Rain** A biologist measures the pH level of the rain in Pierce County, Washington for a random sample of 19 rain dates and obtains the following data.

5.08	4.66	4.70	4.87
4.78	5.00	4.50	4.73
4.79	4.65	4.91	5.07
5.03	4.78	4.77	4.60
4.73	5.05	4.70	

Source: National Atmospheric Deposition Program

(a) Compute the z-score corresponding to 5.08. Interpret this result. 1.57
(b) Determine the quartiles.
(c) Compute the interquartile range, IQR. 0.3
(d) Determine the lower and upper fences. Are there any outliers, according to this criterion?

13. **Concentration of Dissolved Organic Carbon** The following data represent the concentration of organic carbon (mg/l) collected from organic soil.

22.74	29.8	27.1	16.51	6.51
8.81	5.29	20.46	14.9	33.67
30.91	14.86	15.91	15.35	9.72
19.8	14.86	8.09	17.9	18.3
5.2	11.9	14	7.4	17.5
10.3	11.4	5.3	15.72	20.46
16.87	15.42	22.49		

Source: Lisa Emili, Ph.D. Candidate, University of Waterloo

(a) Compute the z-score corresponding to 20.46. Interpret this result. 0.61
(b) Determine the quartiles.
(c) Compute the interquartile range, IQR. 10.12
(d) Determine the lower and upper fences. Are there any outliers, according to this criterion? −5.17, 35.31; No

14. **Concentration of Dissolved Organic Carbon** The following data represent the concentration of organic carbon (mg/l) collected from mineral soil.

8.5	3.91	9.29	21	10.89
10.3	11.56	7	3.99	3.79
5.5	4.71	7.66	11.72	11.8
8.05	10.72	21.82	22.62	10.74
3.02	7.45	11.33	7.11	9.6
12.57	12.89	9.81	17.99	21.4
8.37	7.92	17.9	7.31	16.92
4.6	8.5	4.8	4.9	9.1
7.9	11.72	4.85	11.97	7.85
9.11	8.79			

Source: Lisa Emili, Ph.D. Candidate, University of Waterloo

(a) Compute the z-score corresponding to 17.99. Interpret this result. 1.60
(b) Determine the quartiles.
(c) Compute the interquartile range, IQR. 4.61
(d) Determine the lower and upper fences. Are there any outliers, according to this criterion? 0.195, 18.635; Yes

15. **Rates of Return of Stocks** Stocks can be categorized by industry. The following data represent the five-year rates of return for a simple random sample of financial stocks and energy stocks ending December 28, 2001.
(a) Determine whether there are any outliers in either industry.
(b) Draw histograms for these data, and label the outliers if any.

Financial Stocks				
16.12	18.61	4.04	13.93	17.85
3.34	8.39	21.32	34.22	16.56
28.51	13.29	11.03	14.61	6.67
2.98	14.06	28.90	11.26	9.24
10.97	7.13	5.32	0.63	13.43
17.10	22.21	6.18	5.80	1.39
0.83	5.63	8.39	8.02	1.23
3.32	9.42	2.98	13.62	6.36

Source: Morningstar.com

(11b) $Q_1 = 6.05$, $Q_2 = 6.45$, $Q_3 = 6.95$ (11d) 4.7, 8.3; Yes   (12b) $Q_1 = 4.70$, $Q_2 = 4.78$, $Q_3 = 5$ (12d) 4.25, 5.45; No
(13b) $Q_1 = 10.01$, $Q_2 = 15.42$, $Q_3 = 20.13$ (14b) $Q_1 = 7.11$, $Q_2 = 9.1$, $Q_3 = 11.72$

Energy Stocks

2.49	9.70	21.67	8.31	5.07
7.70	23.72	5.59	6.09	9.69
1.82	12.68	6.07	11.09	6.35
2.00	14.22	13.17	6.29	6.25
7.39	9.09	30.39	11.25	7.17
9.48	9.23	9.70	5.41	10.29
6.11	7.38	11.60	12.10	13.38

Source: Morningstar.com

16. **American League versus National League** The following data represent the earned-run averages of the top 37 pitchers in the American League and the top 37 in the National League during the 2001 season.

American League

3.05	3.15	3.16	3.29	3.37
3.43	3.45	3.49	3.51	3.59
3.60	3.65	3.77	3.90	3.94
3.99	4.05	4.08	4.09	4.09
4.09	4.25	4.32	4.36	4.37
4.39	4.42	4.45	4.45	4.50
4.76	4.93	5.02	5.08	5.17
5.54	5.82			

National League

2.49	2.98	3.04	3.05	3.09
3.16	3.29	3.31	3.36	3.40
3.42	3.50	3.57	3.57	3.69
3.70	3.80	4.03	4.05	4.05
4.19	4.31	4.33	4.34	4.42
4.42	4.45	4.46	4.46	4.47
4.48	4.49	4.63	4.79	4.81
4.85	4.90			

(a) Determine whether there are any outliers in either league.
(b) Draw histograms for these data, and label the outliers if any.

17. **Student Survey of Income** A survey of 50 randomly selected full-time Joliet Junior College students was conducted during the Fall 2000 semester; in the survey, the students were asked to disclose their weekly income from employment. If the student did not work, $0 was entered. The results of the survey are as follows:

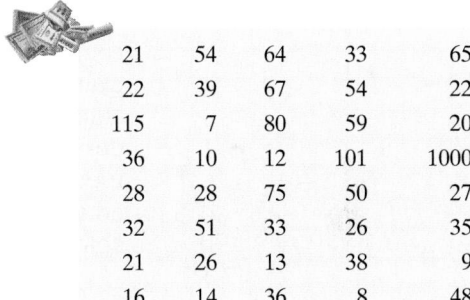

0	262	0	635	0
244	521	476	100	650
12777	567	310	527	0
83	159	0	547	188
719	0	367	316	0
479	0	82	579	289
375	347	331	281	628
0	203	149	0	403
0	454	67	389	0
671	95	736	300	181

(a) Check the data set for outliers.
(b) Provide an explanation for the outliers.

18. **Student Survey of Entertainment Spending** A survey of 40 randomly selected full-time Joliet Junior College students was conducted in the Fall 2000 semester; in the survey, the students were asked to disclose their weekly spending on entertainment. The results of the survey are as follows:

21	54	64	33	65
22	39	67	54	22
115	7	80	59	20
36	10	12	101	1000
28	28	75	50	27
32	51	33	26	35
21	26	13	38	9
16	14	36	8	48

(a) Check the data set for outliers.
(b) Provide an explanation for the outliers.

19. **Pulse Rate** Use the results of Problem 11 in Sections 3.1 and 3.2 to compute the z-scores for all the students. Compute the mean and standard deviation of these z-scores.

20. **Travel Time** Use the results of Problem 12 in Sections 3.1 and 3.2 to compute the z-scores for all the students. Compute the mean and standard deviation of these z-scores.

Technology Step-by-Step
Determining Percentiles

TI-83 Plus   The TI-83 Plus can only compute the quartiles. Follow the same Steps as were given to compute the mean and median from raw data.

MINITAB   Minitab can only compute the quartiles. Follow the same Steps as were given to compute the mean and median from raw data.

Excel   ***Step 1:*** Enter the raw data into column A.

Step 2: With the data analysis tool pak enabled, select the **Tools** menu and highlight **Data Analysis** . . . .

Step 3: Select **Rank and Percentile** from the Data Analysis window.

Step 4: With the cursor in the **Input Range** cell, highlight the data. Press OK.

3.5   The Five-Number Summary; Boxplots

Objectives   Compute the five-number summary

 Draw and interpret boxplots

Some aspects of statistical analysis attempt to verify a conjecture by means of observational studies or designed experiments. In other words, a theory is conjectured, and then data is collected in order to support the theory. For example, a dietitian might conjecture that exercise will lower an individual's cholesterol. The dietitian would carefully design an experiment that randomly divides study participants into two groups—the control group, and the experimental (treatment) group. She would impose the treatment (exercise) on the two groups and then measure the effect on the response variable, cholesterol levels.

However, there is another aspect of statistics that looks at data in order to spot any interesting results that might be concluded from the data. In other words, rather than develop a theory and use data to support or disprove the theory, a researcher would start with data and look for a theory. This area of statistics is referred to as **exploratory data analysis (EDA)**. The idea behind exploratory data analysis is to draw graphs of data and obtain measures of central tendency and spread, in order to form some conjectures regarding the data.

The methods of exploratory data analysis were developed by John Tukey (1915–2000). A complete presentation of the materials found in this chapter can be found in his text *Exploratory Data Analysis* (Addison-Wesley, 1977).

 The Five-Number Summary

Rather than numerically describing a distribution via the mean and standard deviation, exploratory data analysis summarizes a distribution by using measures that are resistant to extreme observations. Recall that the median is a measure of central tendency that divides the lower 50% from

the upper 50% of the data. This particular measure of central tendency is resistant to extreme values and hence is the preferred measure of central tendency when data is skewed to either the right or the left. The three measures of dispersion presented in Section 3.2 are not resistant to extreme values. However, the interquartile range, $Q_3 - Q_1$ is resistant; it measures the spread of the data by determining the difference between the 25th and 75th percentiles. It is interpreted as the range of the middle 50% of the data. However, the median, Q_1 and Q_3 do not provide information about the tails of the distribution of the data. To get this information, we need to know the smallest and largest values in the data set. The **five-number summary** of a set of data consists of the smallest data value, Q_1, the median, Q_3, and the largest data value. Symbolically, the five-number summary is presented as follows.

The Five-Number Summary

MINIMUM Q_1 M Q_3 MAXIMUM

▶ **EXAMPLE 1**   **Obtaining the Five-Number Summary**

Problem: Use the data in Table 12 on page 70 from Section 2.2 to obtain the five-number summary of the three-year rates of return of 40 small-capitalization growth mutual funds.

Approach: The five-number summary requires that we determine the minimum data value, Q_1 (the 25th percentile), M (the median), Q_3 (the 75th percentile), and the maximum data value. We will need to arrange the data in ascending order, then use the procedures introduced in Section 3.4 to obtain Q_1, M, and Q_3.

Solution: The data in ascending order are as follows:

10.8, 10.9, 11.6, 12.7, 12.8, 14.7, 14.7, 15.8, 16.6, 16.7, 17.4, 18.2, 18.4, 18.4, 18.4, 18.5, 19.2, 19.6, 21.3, 21.9, 22.2, 22.6, 23.3, 23.7, 23.7, 24.1, 25.5, 27.0, 27.4, 28.5, 29.1, 29.6, 31.1, 32.0, 32.1, 35.9, 37.0, 38.1, 45.9, 47.7

The smallest number in the data set (i.e., the lowest return) is 10.8. The largest number in the data set is 47.7. The first quartile, Q_1, is 17.05. The median, M, is 22.05. The third quartile, Q_3, is 28.8. The five-number summary is

10.8   17.05   22.05   28.8   47.7   ◀◀

Using Technology: Many calculators and statistical software packages have the ability to present the five-number summary. For example, Figure 21 presents the five-number summary for the data in Example 1, obtained from a TI-83 Plus graphing calculator.

Figure 21

```
1-Var Stats
↑n=40
  minX=10.8
  Q₁=17.05
  Med=22.05
  Q₃=28.8
  maxX=47.7
```

 Boxplots

The five-number summary can be used to create another graph, called the *boxplot*.

Drawing a Boxplot

Step 1: Determine the lower and upper fences:

$$\text{Lower fence} = Q_1 - 1.5(\text{IQR})$$

$$\text{Upper fence} = Q_3 + 1.5(\text{IQR})$$

Step 2: Draw vertical lines at Q_1, M, and Q_3. Enclose these vertical lines in a box.

Step 3: Label the lower and upper fences.

Step 4: Draw a line from Q_1 to the smallest data value that is larger than the lower fence. Draw a line from Q_3 to the largest data value that is smaller than the upper fence.

Step 5: Any data values less than the lower fence or greater than the upper fence are outliers and are marked with an asterisk (*).

▶ **EXAMPLE 2**   **Constructing a Boxplot**

Problem: Use the results from Example 1 to a construct a boxplot of the three-year rates of return of small-capitalization growth mutual funds.

Approach: Follow the steps presented above.

Solution: From the results of Example 1, we know that $Q_1 = 17.05$, $M = 22.05$, $Q_3 = 28.8$. Therefore, the interquartile range $= IQR = Q_3 - Q_1 = 28.8 - 17.05 = 11.75$. The difference between the 75th percentile and 25th percentile is a rate of return of 11.75 percent.

Step 1: We compute the lower and upper fences:

$$\text{Lower fence} = Q_1 - 1.5(\text{IQR}) = 17.05 - 1.5(11.75) = -0.575$$

$$\text{Upper fence} = Q_3 + 1.5(\text{IQR}) = 28.8 + 1.5(11.75) = 46.425$$

Step 2: Draw a horizontal number line with a scale that will accommodate our graph. Draw vertical lines at $Q_1 = 17.05$, $M = 22.05$, and $Q_3 = 28.8$. Enclose these lines in a box. See Figure 22(a).

Step 3: We label the lower and upper fence with brackets ([and]). See Figure 22(b).

Step 4: The smallest data value that is larger than −0.575 (the lower fence) is 10.8. The largest data value that is smaller than 46.425 (the upper fence) is 45.9. We draw horizontal lines from Q_1 to 10.8 and from Q_3 to 45.9. See Figure 22(c).

Step 5: Label any values less than −0.575 (the lower fence) or greater than 46.425 (the upper fence) as outliers. We label 47.7 as an outlier. See Figure 22(d). ◀◀

Note to Instructor
Emphasize how to "read" a boxplot. They will be utilized throughout the text.

Boxplots can be interpreted the same way that histograms can be interpreted. In fact, we can describe the shape of the distribution using the boxplot.

Figure 22

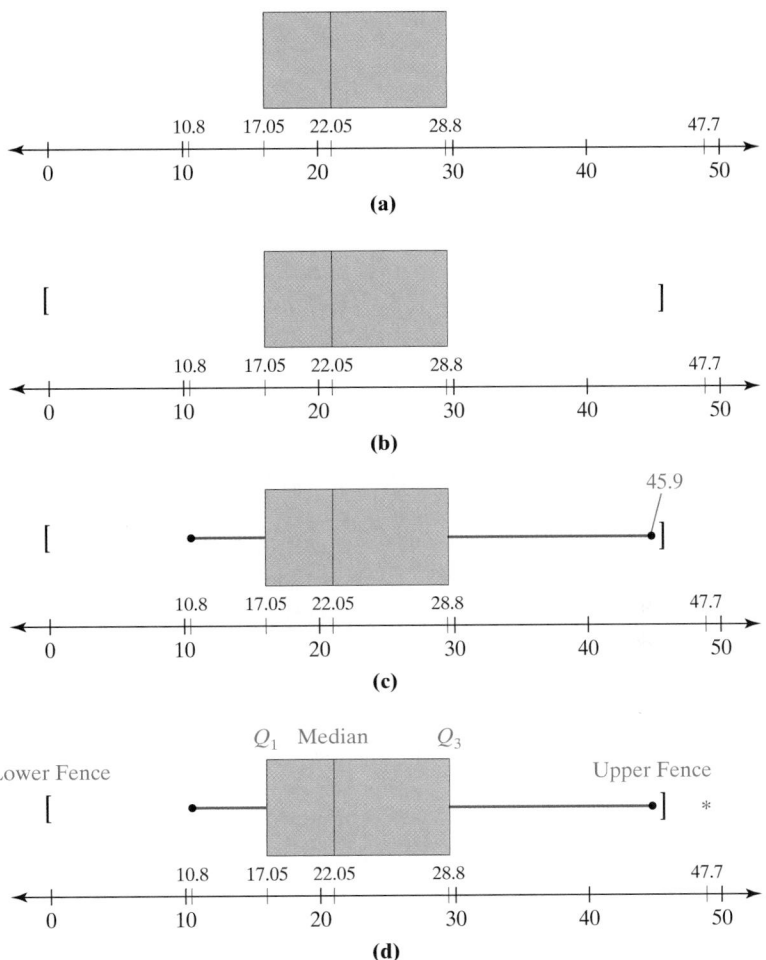

Theorem

Distribution Shape Based upon Boxplot

1. If the median is near the center of the box and each of the horizontal lines is of approximately equal length, then the distribution is roughly symmetric.
2. If the median is to the left of the center of the box or the right line is substantially longer than the left line, the distribution is skewed right.
3. If the median is to the right of the center of the box or the left line is substantially longer than the right line, the distribution is skewed left.

Figure 23 on page 172 provides examples of boxplots that are (a) symmetric, (b) skewed right, and (c) skewed left, along with the corresponding histograms.

The boxplot in Figure 22(d) suggests that the distribution is skewed right, since the right line is longer than the left and the median is in the left of the center of the box. (Refer to Figure 9 on page 72 in Section 2.2 to see the histogram of these data.)

NW   *Now Work Problem 9.*

Figure 23

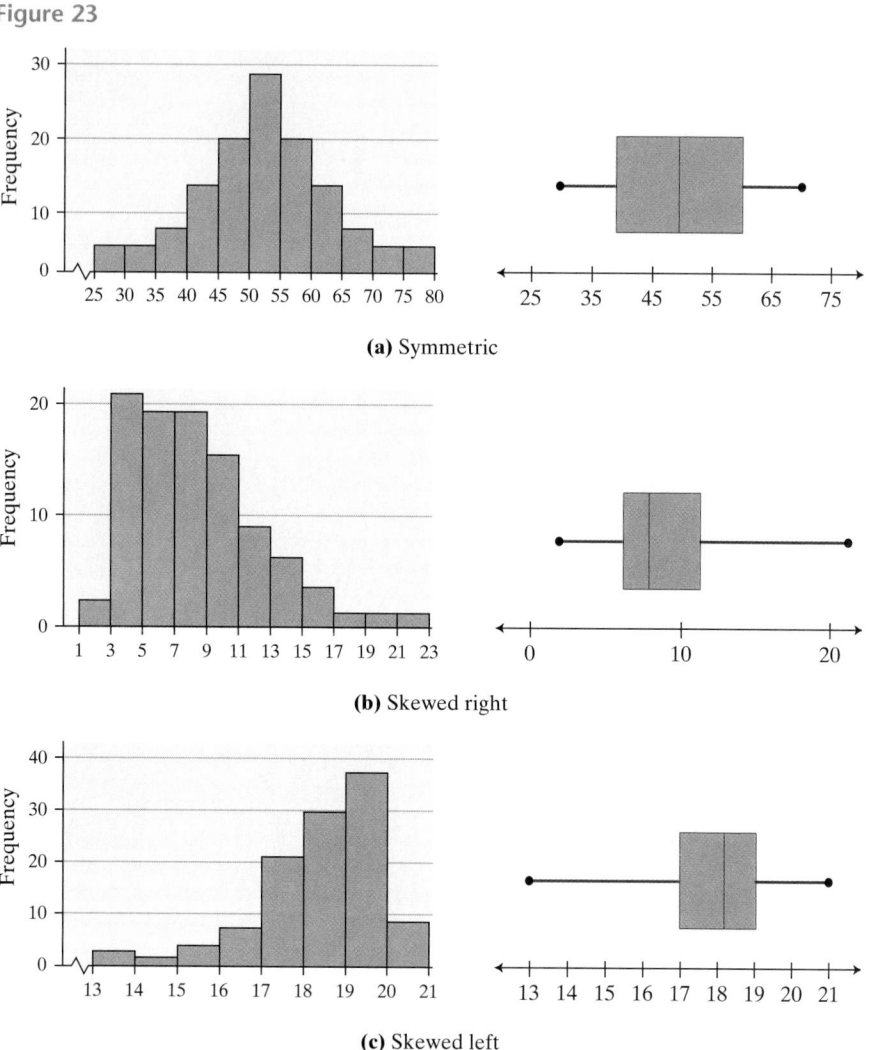

(a) Symmetric

(b) Skewed right

(c) Skewed left

Historical Note

John Tukey was born on July 16, 1915 in New Bedford, Massachusetts. His parents graduated numbers 1 and 2 from Bates College and were elected "the couple most likely to give birth to a genius." In 1936, Tukey graduated from Brown University with an undergraduate degree in chemistry. He went on to earn a master's degree in chemistry at Brown. In 1939, Tukey earned his doctorate in mathematics from Princeton. He remained at Princeton and in 1965 became the founding chair of the Department of Statistics. Among his many accomplishments, Tukey is credited with coining the terms software and bit. In the early 1970s, he discussed the negative effects of aerosol cans on the ozone layer. Tukey recommended that the 1990 Census be adjusted by means of statistical formulas. John Tukey died in New Brunswick, New Jersey, July 26, 2000.

▶ **EXAMPLE 3** **Comparing Two Distributions by Using Boxplots**

The Problem: In the Spacelab Life Sciences 2, 14 male rats were sent to space. Upon their return, the red blood cell mass (in milliliters) of the rats was determined. A control group of 14 male rats was held under the same conditions (except for spaceflight) as the space rats, and their red blood cell mass was also determined when the space rats returned. The project was led by Dr. Paul X. Callahan. The data in Table 15 were obtained. Construct boxplots for red blood cell mass for the flight group and control group. Does it appear that the flight to space affected the red blood cell mass of the rats?

Approach: When comparing two data sets, we draw the boxplots on the same horizontal number line to make comparison easy. Therefore, we draw boxplots for flight and control, using the same number line.

Solution: See Figure 24. From the boxplots, it appears that the spaceflight has reduced the red blood cell mass of the rats.

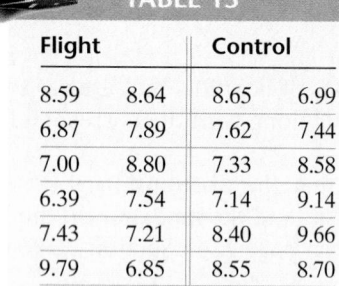

TABLE 15

Flight		Control	
8.59	8.64	8.65	6.99
6.87	7.89	7.62	7.44
7.00	8.80	7.33	8.58
6.39	7.54	7.14	9.14
7.43	7.21	8.40	9.66
9.79	6.85	8.55	8.70
9.30	8.03	9.88	9.94

Source: NASA Life Sciences Data Archive

Figure 24

Flight versus Control

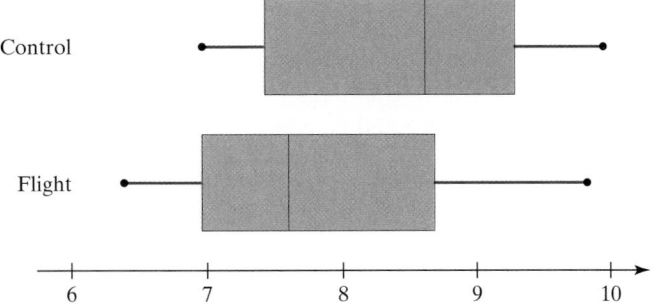

3.5 Assess Your Understanding

Concepts and Vocabulary

1. Explain the circumstances under which the median and interquartile range would be better measures of central tendency and dispersion than the mean and standard deviation.

Exercises

• Skill Building

In Problems 1 and 2, (a) identify the shape of the distribution, and (b) determine the five-number summary. Assume that each of the numbers in the five-number summary is an integer.

1.

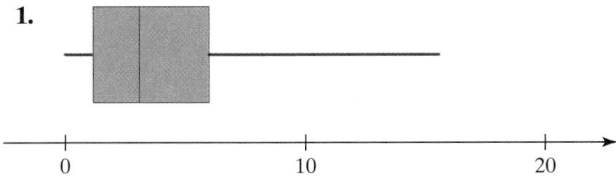

2.

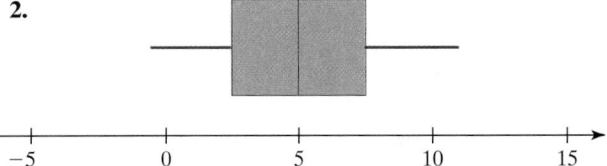

• Applying the Concepts

In Problems 3–6, find the five-number summary, and construct a boxplot for the data in the indicated problem. Comment on the shape of the distribution.

3. Age at Inauguration The following data represent the age of United States presidents on their respective inauguration days.

57	61	57	57	58	57	61
54	68	51	49	64	50	48
65	52	56	46	54	49	50
47	55	55	54	42	51	56
55	51	54	51	60	62	43
55	56	61	52	69	64	46
54						

4. Divorce Rate The following data represent percentage of divorces (as a percentage of marriages in 1996) for selected countries. (*Note*: The United States is at 49%. The highest is Belarus, at 68%, and the lowest is Macedonia, at 5%.)

68	65	64	63	63	61	56
56	55	53	52	49	46	45
43	43	41	41	40	39	39
38	35	34	28	26	26	25
24	21	19	18	18	18	17
15	15	13	13	12	12	12
7	6	5				

Source: Time Almanac 2000

5. Grams of Fat in McDonald's Breakfast The following data represent the number of grams of fat in breakfast meals offered at McDonald's.

12	23	28	2	31	37	34
15	23	38	31	16	11	8
8	17	20				

Source: McDonald's Corporation

6. Miles Per Gallon The following data represent the number of miles per gallon on the highway of domestic cars for the 2001 model year.

30	30	30	29	24	27	26
26	30	34	28	32	32	32
37	28	26	26	27	26	28
35	20	25	38	38	30	28
28	25	25	34	24	28	32
28	28	35	23	29	30	30
29	33	40	33	40		

Source: Road and Track magazine

7. Tensile Strength Tensile strength is the maximum stress at which one can be reasonably certain that failure will not occur. The following data represent tensile strength (in thousands of pounds per square inch) of a composite material to be used in an aircraft.
(a) *160.44, 188.32, 206.51, 212.75, 242.76*

203.41	185.97	184.41	160.44	174.63
209.58	190.67	200.73	180.95	185.34
213.35	207.88	206.51	201.95	205.59
218.56	210.80	209.84	204.60	212.00
242.76	231.46	212.15	219.51	225.25

Source: Vangel, Mark G., "New Methods for One-sided Tolerance Limits for a One-way Balanced Random-Effects ANOVA Model," *Technometrics*; May, 1992, Vol. 34, Issue 2, pp. 176–185.

(a) Compute the five-number summary.
(b) Draw a boxplot of the data.
(c) Determine the shape of the distribution from the boxplot. Refer to the histogram drawn in Problem 19 in Section 2.2 to test your answer.

8. Miles on a Cavalier A random sample of 36 three-year-old Chevy Cavaliers was obtained in the Miami, Florida area, and the number of miles on each car was recorded.

(a) Compute the five-number summary.
(b) Draw a boxplot of the data.
(c) Determine the shape of the distribution from the boxplot. Refer to the histogram drawn in Problem 20 in Section 2.2 to test your answer.
(a) *15,499; 29,298; 34,311; 39,205.5; 44,448*

34,122	34,511	17,595	30,500	31,883
39,416	34,500	44,224	35,936	32,923
28,281	41,620	26,455	44,448	40,614
37,021	30,283	27,368	41,043	42,398
30,747	15,499	37,904	30,739	
35,439	26,051	23,221	38,995	
17,685	32,305	38,041	41,194	
29,307	39,884	35,295	29,289	

Source: cars.com

9. Serum HDL Dr. Paul Oswiecmiski randomly selects forty of his 20–29-year-old patients and obtains the following data regarding their serum HDL cholesterol:

(a) *28, 45, 51, 57.5, 73*

70	56	48	48	53	52	66	48
36	49	28	35	58	62	45	60
38	73	45	51	56	51	46	39
56	32	44	60	51	44	63	50
46	69	53	70	33	54	55	52

(a) Compute the five-number summary.
(b) Draw a boxplot of the data.
(c) Determine the shape of the distribution from the boxplot. Refer to the histogram drawn in Problem 21 in Section 2.2 to test your answer.

10. Volume of Philip Morris Stock The following data represent a random sample of the number of millions of shares of Philip Morris stock traded for 35 days in 2000.
(a) *3.98, 7.24, 10.14, 13.84, 27.54*

3.98	8.90	10.40	7.52	13.84
14.04	9.14	7.96	11.40	13.30
5.29	9.69	8.94	12.10	13.25
4.62	10.85	24.52	14.62	16.10
4.24	8.54	11.59	6.75	27.54
16.06	17.62	7.17	6.13	25.32
7.71	10.14	4.28	7.24	10.88

Source: http://finance.yahoo.com

(a) Compute the five-number summary.
(b) Draw a boxplot of the data.
(c) Determine the shape of the distribution from the boxplot. Refer to the histogram drawn in Problem 22 in Section 2.2 to test your answer.

11. M&Ms The following data represent the weights (in grams) of a simple random sample of 50 M&M plain candies.   (a) *0.76, 0.85, 0.88, 0.90, 0.94*

0.87	0.88	0.82	0.90	0.90	0.84	0.84
0.91	0.94	0.86	0.86	0.86	0.88	0.87
0.89	0.91	0.86	0.87	0.93	0.88	
0.83	0.94	0.87	0.93	0.91	0.85	
0.91	0.91	0.86	0.89	0.87	0.93	
0.88	0.88	0.89	0.79	0.82	0.83	
0.90	0.88	0.84	0.93	0.76	0.90	
0.88	0.92	0.85	0.79	0.84	0.86	

Source: Michael Sullivan

(a) Compute the five-number summary.
(b) Draw a boxplot of the data.
(c) Determine the shape of the distribution from the boxplot. Refer to the histogram drawn in Problem 23 in Section 2.2 to test your answer.

12. Old Faithful The following data represent the length of eruption (in seconds) for a random sample of eruptions of the Old Faithful geyser in California.

(a) 90, 101, 104, 108.5, 120

108	108	99	105	103	103	94
102	99	106	90	104	110	110
103	109	109	111	101	101	
110	102	105	110	106	104	
104	100	103	102	120	90	
113	116	95	105	103	101	
100	101	107	110	92	108	

Source: Ladonna Hansen, Park Curator

(a) Compute the five-number summary.
(b) Draw a boxplot of the data.
(c) Determine the shape of the distribution from the boxplot. Refer to the histogram drawn in Problem 24 in Section 2.2 to test your answer.

In Problems 13–16, compare the two data sets by determining the five-number summary and constructing boxplots on the same scale.

13. Vehicle Death Rates The following data represent the death rates for a sample of passenger minivans and sport utility vehicles (SUVs). The death rates are expressed as deaths per 1 million registered vehicles. For example, the Nissan Quest had 18 deaths for each 1 million vehicles registered. Which vehicles appear to be safer, according to the boxplots?

Van: 18, 23.5, 41, 47, 81
UV: 39, 45, 90.5, 151, 231

Van	Death Rate	SUV	Death Rate
Nissan Quest	18	Chevy Suburban	44
Dodge Grand Caravan	22	Ford Explorer (4 door)	103
Chevy Astro	25	Isuzu Rodeo	151
Ford Windstar	33	Chevy S10 Blazer	195
Honda Odyssey	41	Jeep Grand Cherokee	78
Chrysler Town and Country	45	Ford Explorer (2 door)	231
Mercury Villager	46	Jeep Cherokee	74
Dodge Caravan	48	Ford Expedition	39
GMC Safari	81	Chevy Tahoe	45
		Toyota 4Runner	125

Source: Insurance Institute for Highway Safety

14. Automobile Batteries The following data represent the number of cold cranking amps of group size 24 and group size 35 batteries. The cold cranking amps number measures the amps produced by the battery at $0°$ Fahrenheit. Which type of battery would you prefer?

Group Size 24 Batteries			Group Size 35 Batteries		
800	600	675	525	620	550
600	525	700	560	675	550
500	660	550	530	570	640
585	675		525	640	640

Source: Consumer Reports, October 2000

15. **Thermocouples** A thermocouple is a temperature sensor. One use of a thermocouple is to measure the temperature inside a furnace. A company has three thermocouples, but one is suspected of being broken. They wrap the three thermocouples together, place them in an oven and record the temperature. They repeat this process 20 times and obtain the following data. Which thermocouple appears to be broken? Which thermocouple provides the most consistent measurement?

Thermo 1: 325.97, 326.04, 326.08, 326.13, 326.20

Thermo 2: 323.55, 323.60, 323.64, 323.70, 323.76

Thermo 3: 325.95, 326.01, 326.04, 326.11, 326.20

Thermocouple 1		Thermocouple 2		Thermocouple 3	
326.06	326.20	323.59	323.55	326.03	325.97
326.09	326.00	323.63	323.76	326.06	326.20
326.07	325.97	323.62	323.55	326.03	325.95
326.08	326.20	323.64	323.74	326.06	326.18
326.05	326.07	323.64	323.66	326.02	326.04
326.05	326.11	323.60	323.66	326.02	326.08
326.03	326.00	323.62	323.57	326.01	325.98
326.08	326.20	323.64	323.75	326.01	326.16
326.00	326.13	323.58	323.70	325.99	326.12
326.16	326.12	323.70	323.68	326.13	326.08

Source: Christenson, Ronald and Blackwood, Larry, "Tests for Precision and Accuracy of Multiple Measuring Devices" *Technometrics*, Nov. 93, Vol 35, Issue 4, pp. 411–421.

16. **Homicide Rates** The following data represent the homicide rates (homicides per 100,000 residents) for 14–24 year olds in all states (except Florida and Kansas) in 1999. A researcher wanted to know whether the homicide rates for states west of the Mississippi differed from those for states east of the Mississippi. Which part of the country appears to have the higher homicide rate?

West: 2.07, 3.49, 5.65, 11.98, 19.77

East: 0.00, 5.53, 10.75, 14.01, 23.96

West			East		
16.84	3.49	8.60	6.49	10.56	1.22
13.98	2.49	11.98	13.51	18.25	10.94
9.08	2.07	3.22	7.92	5.04	6.02
5.01	19.77	10.49	6.99	23.96	11.29
2.44	15.51	2.58	2.75	4.09	11.92
3.96	11.91	5.65	14.20	13.81	0.00
4.84	4.52	4.39	21.99	15.88	8.93
13.45	11.91		13.20	15.87	4.94

Source: United States Department of Justice

Technology Step-by-Step
Drawing Boxplots Using Technology

TI-83 Plus   **Step 1:** Enter the raw data into L1.

Step 2: Press 2nd Y = and select 1:Plot 1.

Step 3: Turn the plots ON. Use the cursor to highlight the boxplot icon. Your screen should look as follows:

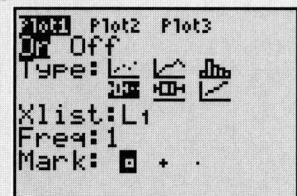

Step 4: Press ZOOM and select 9: ZoomStat.

MINITAB   **Step 1:** Enter the raw data into column C1.

Step 2: Select the **Graph** menu and highlight **Boxplot**...

Step 3: Select the data to be graphed. If you want the boxplot to be horizontal rather than vertical, select the OPTIONS button and transpose X and Y. Click OK.

Excel   **Step 1:** Start the PHStat Add-in.

Step 2: Enter the raw data into column A.

Step 3: Select the **PHStat** menu and highlight **Box-and-Whisker Plot**... With the cursor in the "Data Variable Cell Range" cell, highlight the data in column A.

Step 4: Click OK.

CHAPTER 3 REVIEW

Summary

This chapter concentrated on describing distributions numerically. Measures of central tendency are used to indicate the "typical" value in a distribution. Three measures of central tendency were discussed. The arithmetic mean measures the center of gravity of the distribution; the median separates the bottom 50% of the data from the top 50%. Both of these measures require that the data be quantitative. The mode measures the most frequent observation. The data can be either quantitative or qualitative in order to compute the mode. The median is resistant to extreme values, while the mean is not. A comparison between the median and mean can help determine the shape of the distribution.

Measures of dispersion describe how "spread out" the data are. The range is the difference between the highest and lowest data value. The variance measures the average squared deviation about the mean. The standard deviation is the square root of the variance. The mean and standard deviation are used in many types of statistical inference.

The mean, median, and mode can be approximated from grouped data. The variance and standard deviation can also be approximated from grouped data.

We can determine the relative position of an observation in a data set by using z-scores and percentiles. Z-scores determine the number of standard deviations from the mean that an observation is, whereas percentiles determine the percent of observations that lie above and below an observation. The interquartile range can be used to identify potential outliers. Any potential outlier must be investigated to determine whether it was the result of a data entry error, of some other error in the data collection process, or of an unusual value in the data set.

Exploratory data analysis is used to investigate data without any preconceived notions as to the distribution of the data. The five-numbers summary provides an idea about the center and spread of a data set, through the median and the interquartile range. The length of the tails in the distribution can be determined from the smallest and the largest data values. The five-number summary is used to construct boxplots. Boxplots can be used to describe the shape of the distribution.

Formulas

Population Mean

$$\mu = \frac{\sum x_i}{N}$$

Sample Mean

$$\overline{x} = \frac{\sum x_i}{n}$$

Population Variance

$$\sigma^2 = \frac{\sum (x_i - \mu)^2}{N}$$

Sample Variance

$$s^2 = \frac{\sum (x_i - \overline{x})^2}{n - 1}$$

Population Standard Deviation

$$\sigma = \sqrt{\sigma^2}$$

Sample Standard Deviation

$$s = \sqrt{s^2}$$

Range = Largest Data Value − Smallest Data Value

Weighted Mean

$$\overline{x}_w = \frac{\sum w_i x_i}{\sum w_i}$$

Population Mean from Grouped Data

$$\mu = \frac{\sum x_i f_i}{\sum f_i}$$

Sample Mean from Grouped Data

$$\overline{x} = \frac{\sum x_i f_i}{\sum f_i}$$

Population Variance from Grouped Data

$$\sigma^2 = \frac{\sum (x_i - \mu)^2 f_i}{\sum f_i}$$

Approximating the Sample Variance from Grouped Data

$$s^2 = \frac{\sum (x_i - \overline{x})^2 f_i}{(\sum f_i) - 1}$$

Population z-score

$$z = \frac{x - \mu}{\sigma}$$

Sample z-score

$$z = \frac{x - \overline{x}}{s}$$

Percentile of x $= \dfrac{\text{Number of data values less than } x}{n} \cdot 100$

Interquartile Range

$$IQR = Q_3 - Q_1$$

Lower and Upper Fences

Lower Fence $= Q_1 - 1.5(IQR)$
Upper Fence $= Q_3 + 1.5(IQR)$

Vocabulary

Parameter (p. 112)
Statistic (p. 112)
Arithmetic mean (p. 113)
Median (p. 116)
Mode (p. 118)
Resistant (p. 119)
Range (p. 132)
Deviation about the mean (p. 133)

Population variance (p. 133)
Sample variance (p. 135)
Biased (p. 135)
Degrees of freedom (p. 136)
Population standard deviation (p. 137)
Sample standard deviation (p. 137)
Weighted mean (p. 152)
Z-score (p. 158)

kth percentile (p. 159)
Quartiles (p. 162)
Interquartile range (p. 163)
Outlier (p. 163)
Fences (p. 163)
Exploratory data analysis (p. 168)
Five-number summary (p. 169)
Boxplot (p. 170)

Objectives

Review Exercises

1. Muzzle Velocity The following data represent the muzzle velocity (in meters per second) of rounds fired from a 155-mm gun.

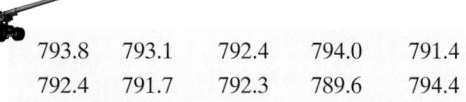

793.8	793.1	792.4	794.0	791.4
792.4	791.7	792.3	789.6	794.4

Source: Christenson, Ronald and Blackwood, Larry; "Tests for Precision and Accuracy of Multiple Measuring Devices," *Technometrics*, Nov. 93, Vol. 35, Issue 4, pp. 411–421.

(a) Compute the sample mean and median muzzle velocity. $\bar{x} = 792.51$, M $= 792.40$
(b) Compute the range, sample variance, and sample standard deviation. Range $= 4.8$, $s^2 = 2.03$, $s = 1.42$

2. Pulse Rates The following data represent the pulse rate of 8 randomly selected females after stepping up and down on a 6 inch platform for 3 minutes. Pulse is measured in beats per minute.   (a) $\bar{x} = 126.8$, M $= 128.5$

136	169	120	128	129
143	115	146	96	86

Source: Michael McCraith, Joliet Junior College

(a) Compute the sample mean and median pulse.
(b) Compute the range, sample variance, and sample standard deviation. Range $= 83$, $s^2 = 589.07$, $s = 24.3$

3. Price of Chevy Cavaliers The following data represent the sales price for nine two-year-old Chevrolet Cavaliers. (a) $\bar{x} = \$13,068.1$; M $= \$12,995$

16,495	15,300	13,995	13,995	12,995
11,990	10,995	10,948	10,900	

Source: cars.com

(a) Compute the sample mean and median price.
(b) Compute the range, and sample standard deviation. Range $= \$5595$, $s = \$2034.2$
(c) Redo (a) and (b) as if the data value 16,495 and incorrectly been entered as 61,495. How does this change affect the mean? The median? The range? The standard deviation? Which of these values is resistant?

4. Home Sales The following data represent the closing prices (in U.S. dollars) of 15 randomly selected homes sold in Joliet, Illinois, in December 1999. (a) $\bar{x} = \$138,068.3$; $\$136,924$

138,820	140,794	136,833	157,216
169,541	153,146	115,000	149,380
135,512	99,000	124,757	136,529
149,143	136,924	128,429	

Source: Transamerica Intellitech

(a) Compute the sample mean and median sale price.
(b) Compute the range, and sample standard deviation. Range $= \$70,541$, $s = \$17,286.3$

5. **Chief Justices** The following data represent the ages of chief justices of the United States Supreme Court when they were appointed.

Justice	Age
John Jay	44
John Rutledge	56
Oliver Ellsworth	51
John Marshall	46
Roger B. Taney	59
Salmon P. Chase	56
Morrison R. Waite	58
Melville W. Fuller	55
Edward D. White	65
William H. Taft	64
Charles E. Hughes	68
Harlan F. Stone	69
Frederick M. Vinson	56
Earl Warren	62
Warren E. Burger	62
William H. Rehnquist	62

Source: Information Please Almanac

(a) Compute the population mean, median, and mode ages. $\mu = 58.3$, M $= 58.5$, Bimodal: 56 and 62
(b) Compute the range and population standard deviation ages. Range $= 25$, $\sigma = 6.9$
(c) Obtain two simple random samples of size four, and compute the sample mean and sample deviation ages.

6. **National Champion Trees** The following data represent the height (in feet) of the 10 National Champion trees, as selected by *American Forests*.

(a) $\mu = 171.8$, M $= 131.5$, No mode

Tree	Height (in feet)
American Beech	115
Black Willow	76
Coast Douglas-Fir	329
Coast Redwood	313
Giant Sequoia	275
Loblolly Pine	148
Pinyon Pine	69
Sugar Maple	65
Sugar Pine	232
White Oak	96

Source: World Almanac, 2000

(a) Compute the population mean, median, and mode.
(b) Compute the range and population standard deviation. Range $= 264$, $\sigma = 99.8$
(c) Obtain two simple random samples of size four, and compute the sample mean and sample standard deviation.

7. **Family Size** By random sample, 36 married couples who had been married seven years were asked the number of children they had. The results of the survey follow:

0	0	3	1	2	3
3	4	3	3	0	3
1	2	1	3	0	3
4	2	3	2	2	4
2	1	3	4	1	3
0	3	3	3	2	1

(a) Compute the sample mean and the median number of children. $\bar{x} = 2.2$, M $= 2.5$
(b) Compute the range and the sample standard deviation. Range $= 4$, $s = 1.3$

8. **Waiting in Line** The following data represent the number of cars that arrived at a McDonald's drive through between 11:50 A.M. and 12:00 noon each Wednesday for the past 30 weeks:

1	3	2	8	6
6	6	3	3	1
5	6	3	3	1
4	9	5	3	5
2	6	7	5	8
7	8	3	2	3

(a) Compute the sample mean and the median number of cars. $\bar{x} = 4.5$, M $= 4.5$
(b) Compute the range and the sample standard deviation waiting time. Range $= 8$, $s = 2.3$

9. **Chebyshev's Theorem and the Empirical Rule** Lightbulbs from a sample of 200 lightbulbs have a mean life of 600 hours and a standard deviation of 53 hours.
(a) Use Chebyshev's theorem to determine the minimum percentage of lightbulbs with a life within 2.5 standard deviations of the mean. 84%
(b) Use Chebyshev's theorem to determine the minimum percentage of lightbulbs that have a life between 494 and 706 hours. 75%
(c) Suppose a histogram of the data indicates the sample data follow a bell-shaped distribution. According to the Empirical Rule, 99.7% of lightbulbs will have life times between _____ and _____ hours. 441; 759
(d) Assuming the distribution of the data is bell shaped, determine the percentage of lightbulbs that will have a life between 494 and 706 hours. 95%

(e) If the company that manufactures the lightbulb guarantees to replace any bulb that doesn't last at least 441 hours, what percent of lightbulbs can the firm expect to have to replace, according to the Empirical Rule? 0.15%

10. **Chebyshev's Theorem and the Empirical Rule** In a random sample of 250 toner cartridges, the mean number of pages a toner cartridge can print is 4302 and the standard deviation is 340.   (c) 3282; 5322
(a) Use Chebyshev's theorem to determine the minimum percentage of toner cartridges with a page count within 1.5 standard deviations of the mean. 55.6%
(b) Use Chebyshev's theorem to determine the minimum percentage of toner cartridges that print between 3282 and 5322 pages. 88.9%
(c) Suppose a histogram of the data indicates that the sample data follow a bell-shaped distribution. According to the Empirical Rule, 99.7% of toner cartridges will print between _____ and _____ pages.
(d) Assuming that the distribution of the data is bell shaped, determine the percentage of toner cartridges whose print total is between 3,622 and 4,982 pages. 95%
(e) If the company that manufactures the toner cartridges guarantees to replace any cartridge that doesn't print at least 3,622 pages, what percent of cartridges can the firm expect to be responsible for replacing, according to the Empirical Rule? 2.5%

11. **Vehicle Fatalities** The frequency distribution listed in the table represents the number of drivers in fatal crashes in 1996, by age, for males aged 20 to 84 years old.

Age	Number of Drivers
20–24	6,148
25–29	5,073
30–34	4,834
35–39	4,414
40–44	3,563
45–49	2,935
50–54	2,164
55–59	1,655
60–64	1,398
65–69	1,154
70–74	1,055
75–79	894
80–84	684

Source: National Highway Traffic Safety Administration

(a) Approximate the mean age of a male involved in a traffic fatality. $\mu = 40.3$
(b) Approximate the standard deviation age of a male involved in a traffic fatality. $\sigma = 16.0$

12. **Vehicle Fatalities** The frequency distribution shown in the table represents the number of drivers in fatal crashes in 1996, by age, for females aged 20 to 84 years old.

Age	Number of Drivers
20–24	1,747
25–29	1,558
30–34	1,561
35–39	1,503
40–44	1,180
45–49	957
50–54	752
55–59	522
60–64	498
65–69	491
70–74	550
75–79	485
80–84	314

(a) Approximate the mean age of a female involved in a traffic fatality. $\mu = 42.6$
(b) Approximate the standard deviation age of a female involved in a traffic fatality. $\sigma = 17.1$
(c) Compare the results to those obtained in Problem 11. How do you think an insurance company might use this information?

13. **Weighted Mean** Michael has just completed his first semester in college. He earned an "A" in his 5-hour calculus course, a "B" in his 4-hour chemistry course, an "A" in his 3-hour speech course, and a "C" in his 3-hour psychology course. Assuming an "A" equals 4 points, a "B" equals 3 points, and a "C" equals 2 points, determine Michael's grade-point average if grades are weighted by class hours. 3.33

14. **Weighted Mean** Yolanda wishes to develop a new type of meat loaf to sell at her restaurant. She decides to combine 2 pounds of ground sirloin (cost $2.70 per pound), 1 pound of ground turkey ($1.30 per pound) and $\frac{1}{2}$ pound of ground pork (cost $1.80 per pound). What is the cost per pound of the meat loaf? $2.17

15. **Mets versus Yankees** The following data represent the salaries of the 25 players on the playoff rosters of the 2000 New York Mets and the 2000 New York Yankees.

New York Mets		New York Yankees	
Player	**Salary**	**Player**	**Salary**
Mike Piazza	12,121,428	Bernie Williams	12,357,143
Robin Ventura	8,000,000	David Cone	12,000,000
Al Leiter	7,750,000	Derek Jeter	10,000,000
Mike Hampton	5,750,000	Mariano Rivera	7,250,000
Bobby J. Jones	5,366,667	Andy Pettitte	7,000,000
Edgardo Alfonzo	4,375,000	David Justice	7,000,000
Rick Reed	4,375,000	Paul O'Neill	6,500,000
Todd Zeile	4,333,333	Roger Clemens	6,350,000
Darryl Hamilton	3,633,333	Chuck Knoblauch	6,000,000
Armando Benitez	3,437,500	Scott Brosius	5,250,000
John Franco	3,350,000	Tino Martinez	4,800,000
Mike Bordick	3,025,000	Denny Neagle	4,750,000
Dennis Cook	2,200,000	Jose Vizcaino	3,500,000
Turk Wendell	2,050,014	Jose Canseco	3,000,000
Lenny Harris	1,100,000	Mike Stanton	2,400,000
Rick White	610,000	Orlando Hernandez	1,950,000
Kurt Abbott	500,000	Jeff Nelson	1,916,666
Todd Pratt	500,000	Glenallen Hill	1,500,000
Matt Franco	462,500	Jorge Posada	1,250,000
Glendon Rusch	270,000	Jason Grimsley	750,000
Bubba Trammell	253,000	Luis Sojo	450,000
Joe McEwing	250,000	Chris Turner	375,000
Benny Agbayani	220,000	Clay Bellinger	206,650
Jay Payton	215,000	Dwight Gooden	200,000
Timo Perez	200,000	Luis Polonia	200,000

Source: USA Today research by Hal Bodley

(a) Compute the population mean salary for each team. $\mu_M = \$2,973,911$; $\mu_y = \$4,278,218.4$
(b) Compute the median salary for each team. $M_m = \$2,200,000$; $M_y = \$3,500,000$
(c) Given the results of (a) and (b), decide whether the distribution is symmetric, skewed right, or skewed left. *Skewed right*
(d) Compute the population standard deviation salary for each team. Which team has it's salaries more dispersed? $\sigma_m = \$3,005,819.2$; $\sigma_y = \$3,581,882.8$; *Yankees*
(e) Compute the five-number summary for each team.
(f) On the same graph, draw boxplots for the two teams. Annotate the graph with some general remarks comparing the team salaries.
(g) Describe the shape of the distribution of each team, as illustrated by the boxplots. Does this confirm the result obtained in part (c)?
(h) Determine whether the data for each team contain outliers.

16. **Air-Traffic Control Errors** An air-traffic control error is said to occur when planes come too close to one another. The following data represent the number of air-traffic control errors for a random sample of regions around the United States for fiscal years 1996 and 2000.

Center	Errors, 2000	Errors, 1996	Center	Errors, 2000	Errors, 1996
Washington	102	24	Cleveland	74	32
New York ARTCC	71	44	Chicago ARTCC	70	26
Indianapolis	54	39	Atlanta	40	36
Memphis	38	21	Dallas–Fort Worth	34	23
Los Angeles	33	19	Denver	33	11
Jacksonville, FL	30	27	Kansas City, MO	28	20
New York TRACON	27	33	Albuquerque	25	21
Miami	21	15	Boston	21	13
Northern California	18	30	Houston	18	7
Oakland	17	20	Minneapolis	15	13
Chicago TRACON	14	13	Salt Lake City	12	8
Oakland Bay	8	6	Miami	8	2
Washington Dulles	7	2			

Source: Associated Press

(a) Compute the sample mean number of errors in 1996 and 2000. $\bar{x}_{1996} = 20.2$; $\bar{x}_{2000} = 32.7$

(b) Compute the median number of errors in 1996 and 2000. $M_{1996} = 20$; $M_{2000} = 27$

(c) 1996: Symmetric; 2000: Skewed right

(c) Given the results of (a) and (b), decide whether the distribution of "number of errors in 1996" is symmetric, skewed right, or skewed left. What about "number of errors in 2000"?

(d) Compute the sample standard deviation number of errors in 1996 and 2000. Which year is more dispersed? $S_{1996} = 11.42$; $S_{2000} = 24.11$

(e) Compute the five-number summary for each year.

(f) On the same graph, draw boxplots for the two years. Add some general remarks comparing each year's errors.

(g) Describe the shape of the distribution of each year, as shown in the boxplots. Does this confirm the result obtained in part (c)?

(h) Determine whether the data for each year contain outliers.

(i) Explain why comparing 1996 data to 2000 data may be misleading.

17. **Cholesterol** According to the National Center for Health Statistics, the mean serum total cholesterol for females 20 years and older is 206, with a standard deviation of 44.7. The mean serum total cholesterol for males 20 years and older is 202, with a standard deviation of 41.0. Who has a relatively higher serum total cholesterol: a female whose serum total cholesterol is 230 or a male whose serum total cholesterol is 230? Why? Male

18. **Weights of Males versus Females** According to the National Center for Health Statistics, the mean weight of a 20–29-year-old female is 141.7 pounds, with a standard deviation of 27.2 pounds. The mean weight of a 20–29-year-old male is 172.1 pounds, with a standard deviation of 36.5 pounds. Who is relatively heavier: a 20–29-year-old female who weighs 150 pounds or a 20–29-year-old male who weighs 185 pounds? Why? Male

19. **Infant Mortality Rate** The following data represent the infant mortality rate (deaths per 1000 infants) for 226 countries throughout the world. The data have already been sorted in ascending order.

(a) Find the 20th percentile. 7.9

(b) Find the 95th percentile. 120.06

(c) Find the 99th percentile. 148.66

(d) What is the percentile rank of the United States? 17th percentile

(e) What is the percentile rank of Nepal? 82nd percentile

(f) Find the quartiles. $Q_1 = 9.61$; $M = 24.7$, $Q_3 = 64.9$

(g) Draw a boxplot. Are there any outliers?

Country	Infant Mortality Rate	Country	Infant Mortality Rate	Country	Infant Mortality Rate
1. Sweden	3.49	56. Chile	9.6	109. Saint Helena	23.23
2. Iceland	3.58	57. Poland	9.61	110. Oman	23.28
3. Singapore	3.65	58. Virgin Islands	9.64	111. Tuvalu	23.3
4. Finland	3.82	59. Puerto Rico	9.71	112. North Korea	24.29
5. Japan	3.91	60. Guadeloupe	9.77	113. Colombia	24.7
6. Norway	3.98	61. Bermuda	9.82	114. Cook Islands	24.7
7. Andorra	4.08	62. Cayman Islands	10.44	115. Suriname	25.06
8. Netherlands	4.42	63. American Samoa	10.63	116. Bosnia/Herzegovina	25.17
9. Macau	4.49	64. Nauru	10.9	117. Solomon Islands	25.26
10. Austria	4.5	65. Montenegro	10.97	118. Anguilla	25.44
11. France	4.51	66. Costa Rica	11.49	119. Trinidad and Tobago	25.76
12. Switzerland	4.53	67. Kuwait	11.55	120. Belize	25.97
13. Slovenia	4.56	68. Netherlands	11.74	121. Gaza Strip	25.97
14. Belgium	4.76	69. Antilles Barbados	12.37	122. Venezuela	26.17
15. Germany	4.77	70. Estonia	12.92	123. Mexico	26.19
16. Luxembourg	4.83	71. Macedonia	13.35	124. China	28.92
17. Spain	4.99	72. French Guiana	13.99	125. El Salvador	29.22
18. Australia	5.04	73. Fiji	14.45	126. Lebanon	29.3
19. Guernsey	5.07	74. Tonga	14.45	127. Philippines	29.52
20. Liechtenstein	5.07	75. Jamaica	14.61	128. Iran	30.02
21. Canada	5.08	76. Belarus	14.63	129. Libya	30.08
22. Denmark	5.11	77. Grenada	14.63	130. Tunisia	30.09
23. Gibraltar	5.6	78. Lithuania	14.67	131. Paraguay	30.81
24. Ireland	5.62	79. Brunei	14.84	132. Vietnam	31.13
25. Czech Republic	5.63	80. Bulgaria	15.13	133. Honduras	31.29
26. United Kingdom	5.63	81. Uruguay	15.14	134. Thailand	31.48
27. Jersey	5.71	82. Saint Lucia	15.64	135. Samoa	32.75
28. Northern Mariana Islands	5.79	83. Latvia	15.71	136. Micronesia	33.48
29. Italy	5.92	84. Sri Lanka	16.51	137. Nicaragua	34.79
30. Monaco	5.92	85. Saint Kitts and Nevis	16.72	138. Syria	34.86
31. Hong Kong	5.93	86. Bahamas	16.99	139. Ecuador	35.13
32. Malta	5.94	87. Saint Vincent and the Grenadines	17.06	140. Dominican Republic	35.93
33. Portugal	6.05	88. Palau	17.12	141. Brazil	38.04
34. San Marino	6.33	89. Dominica	17.13	142. Guyana	39.07
35. New Zealand	6.39	90. United Arab Emirates	17.17	143. Peru	40.6
36. Aruba	6.51	91. Mauritius	17.73	144. Marshall Islands	40.95
37. Greece	6.51	92. Seychelles	17.74	145. Mongolia	41.22
38. Man, Isle of	6.54	93. Greenland	18.26	146. Albania	41.33
39. United States	6.82	94. Argentina	18.31	147. Armenia	41.48
40. Guam	6.83	95. Turks and Caicos Islands	18.66	148. Algeria	41.97
41. Faroe Islands	6.94	96. Romania	19.84	149. Indonesia	42.21
42. Taiwan	7.06	97. Serbia	20.13	150. Moldova	43.32
43. Croatia	7.35	98. Russia	20.33	151. Guatemala	47.03
44. Cuba	7.51	99. Bahrain	20.48	152. Turkey	48.9
45. South Korea	7.85	100. Panama	20.8	153. Morocco	49.72
46. Israel	7.9	101. Malaysia	20.96	154. São Tomé and Principe	50.41
47. Martinique	7.97	102. Maldives	20.96	155. Saudi Arabia	52.9
48. Cyprus	8.07	103. British Virgin Islands	21.05	156. Georgia	52.94
49. New Calendonia	8.57	104. Jordan	21.11	157. Cape Verde	54.58
50. Saint Pierre and Miquelon	8.61	105. Ukraine	21.67	158. Kiribati	55.36
51. Reunion	8.67	106. Qatar	22.14	159. Ghana	57.43
52. Montserrat	9.1	107. West Bank	22.33	160. Senegal	58.08
53. Hungary	9.15	108. Antigua and Barbuda	23.05	161. South Africa	58.88
54. Slovakia	9.18			162. Kazakhstan	59.39
55. French Polynesia	9.3			163. Papua New Guinea	59.89
				164. Bolivia	60.44
				165. Botswana	61.68

Country	Infant Mortality Rate	Country	Infant Mortality Rate	Country	Infant Mortality Rate
166. Zimbabwe	62.25	188. Mauritania	78.15	208. Djibouti	103.32
167. Egypt	62.32	189. Gambia, The	79.29	209. Central African	
168. Iraq	62.49	190. Tanzania	80.97	Republic	106.69
169. Vanuatu	62.52	191. Pakistan	82.49	210. Burkina Faso	108.53
170. India	64.9	192. Lesotho	82.97	211. Swaziland	108.95
171. Cambodia	66.82	193. Azerbaijan	83.41	212. Bhutan	110.99
172. Kenya	68.74	194. Madagascar	85.26	213. Guinea-Bissau	112.25
173. Sudan	70.21	195. Comoros	86.33	214. Tajikistan	117.42
174. Yemen	70.28	196. Benin	90.84	215. Rwanda	120.06
175. Cameroon	70.87	197. Zambia	92.38	216. Malawi	122.28
176. Namibia	70.88	198. Uganda	93.25	217. Mali	123.25
177. Mayotte	71.31	199. Laos	94.8	218. Niger	124.9
178. Burundi	71.5	200. Equatorial Guinea	94.83	219. Somalia	125.77
179. Togo	71.55	201. Cote d'Ivoire	95.06	220. Guinea	130.98
180. Bangladesh	71.66	202. Gabon	96.3	221. Western Sahara	133.59
181. Uzbekistan	72.13	203. Chad	96.66	222. Liberia	134.63
182. Turkmenistan	73.3	204. Haiti	97.1	223. Mozambique	139.86
183. Nigeria	74.18	205. Ethiopia	101.29	224. Sierra Leone	148.66
184. Burma	75.3	206. Congo, Republic		225. Afghanistan	149.28
185. Nepal	75.93	of the	101.55	226. Angola	195.78
186. Eritrea	76.66	207. Congo, Democratic			
187. Kyrgyzstan	77.08	Republic of the	101.71		

20. Crime Rate Answer the accompanying questions regarding the boxplot, which illustrates crime-rate data for the 50 United States:

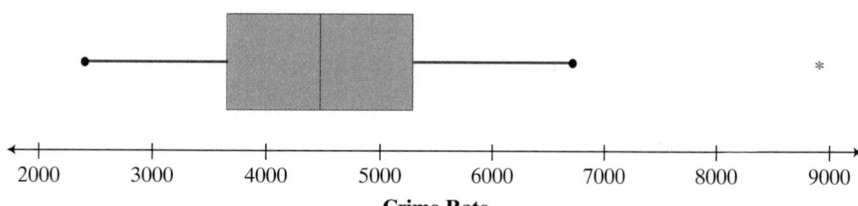

Crime Rate

(a) Approximately, what is the median crime rate in the United States? 4500
(b) Approximately, what is the 25th percentile crime rate in the United States? 3600
(c) Are there any outliers? If so, identify them. Yes, 8900
(d) What is the lowest crime rate? 2200

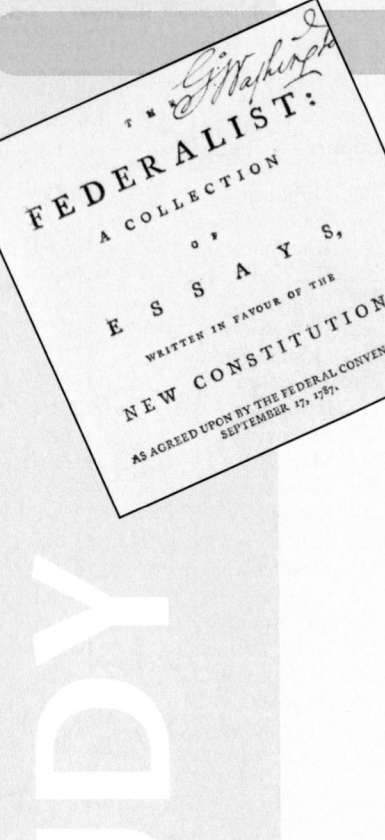

Who wrote the plays attributed to William Shakespeare? Which colonial patriot penned the VINDEX essay in the January 8, 1770, issue of *The Boston Gazette and Country Journal*? Who wrote the 12 contested *Federalist* papers? Such questions about authorship of unattributed documents are one of the many problems confronting historians. Statistical analyses, when combined with other historical facts, often help resolve these mysteries.

One such historical conundrum is the identity of the writer known simply as "A MOURNER." A letter appeared in the February 26, 1770, issue of *The Boston Gazette and Country Journal*. The text of the letter is as follows:

The general Sympathy and Concern for the Murder of the Lad by the base and infamous Richardson on the 22d Instant, will be sufficient Reason for your Notifying the Publick that he will be buried from his Father's House in Frogg Lane, opposite Liberty-Tree, on Monday next, when all the Friends of Liberty may have an Opportunity of paying their last Respects to the Remains of this little Hero and first Martyr to the noble Cause—Whose manly Spirit (after this Accident happened) appear'd in his discreet Answers to his Doctor, his Thanks to the Clergymen who prayed with him, and Parents, and while he underwent the greatest Distress of bodily Pain; and with which he met the King of Terrors. These Things, together with the several heroic Pieces found in his Pocket, particularly *Wolfe's Summit of human Glory*, gives Reason to think he had a *martial Genius*, and would have made a clever Man.

A MOURNER.

The "Lad" the writer refers to is Christopher Sider, an 11-year-old son of a poor German immigrant. Young Sider was shot and killed on February 22, 1770, in a civil disturbance involving schoolboys, patriot supporters of the nonimportation agreement, and champions of the English crown. This event preceded the bloody Boston Massacre by just a couple of weeks. Of Sider's funeral, John Adams wrote, "My eyes never beheld such a funeral. The Procession extended further than can be well imagined." (Diary of John Adams entry for 1770. MONDAY FEB. 26 OR THEREABOUTS.)

From a historical perspective, the identity of "A MOURNER" remains a mystery. However, it seems clear from the letter's text that the author supported the patriot position. This assumption somewhat narrows the field of possible writers.

Ordinarily, a statistical analysis of the frequencies of various words contained in the contested document, when compared with frequency analyses for known authors, would permit an identity inference to be drawn. Unfortunately, in this case, the letter is too short for this strategy to be useful. Another possibility is based upon the frequencies of word lengths. In this instance, a simple count of letters is generated for each word in the document. Proper names, numbers, abbreviations, and titles are removed from consideration, because these do not represent normal vocabulary use. Care must be taken in choosing comparison texts, since colonial publishers habit-

CASE STUDY

ually incorporated their own spellings into the essays they printed. Therefore, it is desirable to get comparison texts from the same printer the contested material came from.

The table below contains the summary analysis for six passages printed in *The Boston Gazette, and Country Journal* in early 1770. The Tom Sturdy (probably a pseudonym) text was included because of the use of the phrase "Friends of Liberty," which appears in "A MOURNER"'s letter, as opposed to the more familiar "Sons of Liberty." Alexander Hamilton, James Otis, and Samuel Adams are included because they are well-known patriots who frequently wrote articles that were carried by the Boston papers. In the case of Samuel Adams, the essay used in this analysis was signed VINDEX, one of his many pseudonyms. The table presents three summaries of work penned by Adams. The first two originate from two separate sections of the VINDEX essay. The last summary is a compilation of the first two.

Summary Statistics of Word Length from Sample Passages by Various Potential Authors of the Letter Signed "A MOURNER"

	Tom Sturdy	Alexander Hancock	James Otis	Samuel Adams-1	Samuel Adams-2	Samuel Adams-1&2
Mean	4.08	4.69	4.58	4.60	4.52	4.56
Median	4	4	4	3	4	4
Mode	2	3	2	2	2	2
Standard Deviation	2.17	2.60	2.75	2.89	2.70	2.80
Sample Variance	4.70	6.76	7.54	8.34	7.30	7.84
Range	13	9	14	12	16	16
Minimum	1	1	1	1	1	1
Maximum	14	10	15	13	17	17
Sum	795	568	842	810	682	1492
Count	195	121	184	176	151	327

1. Acting as a historical detective, generate a data set consisting of the length of each word used in the letter signed by "A MOURNER." Be sure to disregard any text that uses proper names, numbers, abbreviations, or titles.

2. Calculate the summary statistics for the letter's word lengths. Compare your findings with those of the known authors, and speculate about the identity of "A MOURNER."

3. Compare the two Adams summaries. Discuss the viability of word-length analysis as a tool for resolving disputed documents.

4. What other information would be useful to identify "A MOURNER"?

Suppose you were in the market to purchase a used car. In order to make an informed decision regarding your purchase, you would need to collect as much information as possible. Among the information you might consider are the typical price of the car, the typical number of miles the car should have, its crash test results, its insurance costs, and its expected repair costs.

1. Make a list of at least three cars that you would consider purchasing. To be fair, the cars should be in the same class (such as compact, midsize, and so on). They should also be of the same age.

2. Collect information regarding the three cars in your list by finding at least eight cars of each type that are for sale. Obtain such information as the asking price and the number of miles the car has. Sources of data include your local newspaper, classified ads, and car Web sites (such as http://www.cars.com/ and http://www.autobytel.com/). Compute summary statistics for asking price, number of miles, and other variables of interest.

3. Go to the Insurance Institute for Highway Safety Web site, http://www.hwysafety.org. Select the Vehicle Ratings link. Choose the make and model for each car you are considering. Obtain information regarding crash testing for each of the cars under consideration. Compare cars in the same class. How does each of your cars compare? Is one of the cars you are considering substantially safer than the others? What about repair costs? Compute summary statistics for crash tests and repair costs.

4. Obtain information about insurance costs. Contact various insurance companies to determine the cost of insuring the cars you are considering. Compute summary statistics for insurance costs.

5. Write a report supporting your conclusion regarding which car you would purchase.

DECISIONS

A waterproofing coating can be an inexpensive and easy way to deal with leaking basements. But how effective are they? In a recent study, Consumer Reports (June 2002) tested nine waterproofers to rate their effectiveness in controlling water seepage though concrete foundations.

In order to compare the products' ability to control water seepage, we applied two coats of each product to slabs cut from concrete block. For statistical validity, this process was repeated at least six times. In each test run, four blocks (each coated with a different product) were simultaneously placed in a rectangular aluminum chamber. See the picture below.

The chamber was sealed and filled with water and the blocks were subjected to progressively increasing hydrostatic pressures. Water that leaked out during each period was channeled to the bottom of the chamber opening, collected and weighed.

The table on the right contains a subset of the data collected for two of the products tested:

Using this data,

(a) Calculate the mean, median and mode weight of water collected for product A.

(b) Calculate the standard deviation of the weight of water collected for product A.

(c) Calculate the mean, median, and mode weight of water collected for product B.

Product	Replicate	Weight of Collected Water (in grams)
A	1	91.2
A	2	91.2
A	3	90.9
A	4	91.3
A	5	90.8
A	6	90.8
B	1	87.1
B	2	87.2
B	3	86.8
B	4	87.0
B	5	87.2
B	6	87.0

(d) Calculate the standard deviation of the weight of water collected for product B.

(e) Construct a stem and leaf diagram for these data.

Does there appear to be a difference in these two products' ability to mitigate water seepage? Why?

Note to Readers: In many cases, our test protocol and analytical methods are more complicated than described in these examples. The data and discussions have been modified to make the material more appropriate for the audience.

Basement Waterproofer Test Chamber

In Chapters 2 and 3 we examined data in which a single variable was measured for each individual in the study (**univariate data**), such as the three-year rate of return (the variable) for various mutual funds (the individual). We obtained descriptive measures for the variable that were both graphical and numerical.

However, much research is designed in order to describe the relation that may exist between two variables. For example, a researcher may be interested in the relationship between per capita gross domestic product (GDP) and the life expectancy of residents of a country (per capita GDP can be thought of as the average income of residents of the country). Here, the individual is the country and the two variables are per capita GDP and life expectancy. This type of data is referred to as *bivariate data*. **Bivariate data** is data in which two variables are measured on an individual. In order to describe the relation between the two variables, we first graphically represent the data and then obtain some numerical descriptions of the data, just as we did when analyzing univariate data.

CHAPTER 4

Describing the Relation between Two Variables

Outline

 For additional study help, go to www.prenhall.com/sullivanstats

Materials include

- Self-Graded Quizzes
- "Preparing for This Section" Quizzes
- STATLETs
- PowerPoint Downloads
- Step-by-Step Technology Guide
- Graphing Calculator Help

4.1 Scatter Diagrams; Correlation

Preparing for This Section Before getting started, review the following:

✓ Mean (Section 3.1, pp. 113–115)

✓ Standard deviation (Section 3.2, pp. 137–138)

✓ Z-scores (Section 3.4, pp. 158–159)

Objectives Draw scatter diagrams

 Interpret scatter diagrams

 Understand the properties of the linear correlation coefficient

Compute and interpret the linear correlation coefficient

Note to Instructor
Remind students that we looked at relations between two qualitative variables when we drew side-by-side bar graphs (Section 2.1). Problems 29 and 30 in Section 2.2 discussed how we can graphically represent relations between a quantitative and qualitative variable. We now look at a graph of two quantitative variables.

Before we can graphically represent bivariate data, a fundamental question must be asked. Am I interested in using the value of one variable to predict the value of the other variable? For example, it seems reasonable to think that as the level of per capita gross domestic product (GDP) within a country increases, the life expectancy of the country's residents also increases. Therefore, we might use per capita GDP to predict life expectancy. We call life expectancy the *response* (or *dependent*) *variable* and per capita GDP the *predictor* (or *independent*) *variable*.

Definition

The **response variable** is the variable whose value can be explained by, or is determined by, the value of the **predictor variable**.

Caution

If bivariate data are observational, then the predictor and response are not causally related.

It is important to recognize that if the data used in the study are observational, then the relation determined between the two variables is not a causal relation. We cannot say that changes in the level of the predictor variable *cause* changes in the level of the response variable. In fact, it may be that the two are related through some *lurking variable*. Recall that a **lurking variable** is a variable that is related to either the response or predictor variable or both, but is excluded from the analysis. For example, air-conditioning bills can be used to predict lemonade sales: As air-conditioning bills rise, the sales of lemonade rise. This relation does not mean that high air-conditioning bills cause high lemonade sales, because both high air-conditioning bills and high lemonade sales are associated with high summer temperatures. Therefore, summer temperature is a lurking variable.

 Scatter Diagrams

The first step in identifying the type of relation, if any, that might exist between two variables is to draw a picture. Bivariate data can be represented graphically through a *scatter diagram*.

Definition

Note to Instructor
A fun activity is to randomly select six students from class. Have them determine their "at rest" pulse. Now have the same six students run in place for two minutes and then recompute their pulse. You now have bivariate data to analyze!

A **scatter diagram** is a graph that shows the relationship between two quantitative variables measured on the same individual. Each individual in the data set is represented by a point in the scatter diagram. The predictor variable is plotted on the horizontal axis and the response variable is plotted on the vertical axis. Do not connect the points when drawing a scatter diagram.

▶ **EXAMPLE 1**   **Drawing a Scatter Diagram**

Problem: The per capita gross domestic product (GDP) of a country is the average income of a resident of the country. A researcher would like to know if per capita GDP could be used to predict life expectancy. The data in Table 1 represent the per capita GDP (in thousands of U.S. dollars) for randomly selected countries in Western Europe and the life expectancy of residents of the country. Draw a scatter diagram of the data.

TABLE 1					
Country	Per Capita GDP (000s)	Life Expectancy	Country	Per Capita GDP (000s)	Life Expectancy
Austria	21.4	77.48	Ireland	18.6	76.39
Belgium	23.2	77.53	Italy	21.5	78.51
Finland	20.0	77.32	Netherlands	22.0	78.15
France	22.7	78.63	Switzerland	23.8	78.99
Germany	20.8	77.17	United Kingdom	21.2	77.37

Source: Time Almanac 2000

Approach: Because the researcher wants to use per capita GDP to predict life expectancy, per capita GDP will be the predictor variable (horizontal axis) and life expectancy will be the response variable (vertical axis). We plot the ordered pairs (21.4, 77.48), (23.2, 77.53), and so on, in a rectangular coordinate system.

Solution: The scatter diagram is shown in Figure 1.

Figure 1

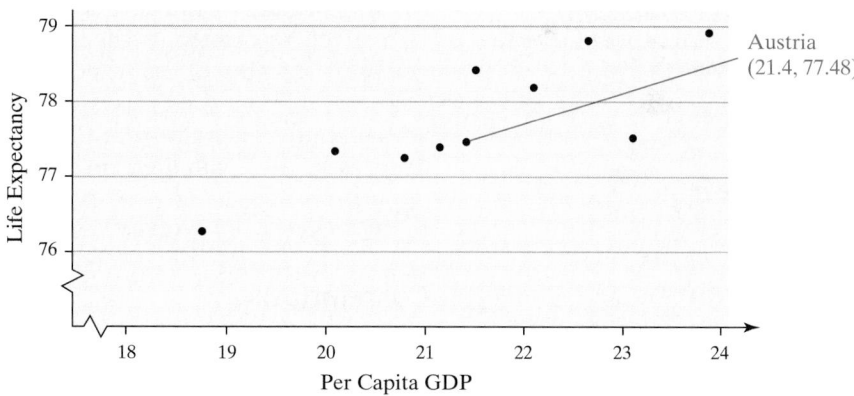

It would appear from the graph that as per capita GDP rises, the life expectancy of the country's residents rise as well.   ◀◀

It is not always clear which variable should be considered the response variable and which should be considered the predictor variable. For example, does high school GPA predict a student's SAT score or can the SAT score be used to predict GPA? The researcher must determine which variable plays the role of predictor variable based upon the questions he or she wants answered. For example, if the researcher is interested in predicting SAT scores on the basis of high school GPA, then high school GPA will play the role of predictor variable.

NW *Now Work Problems 11(a) and 11(b).*

Interpreting Scatter Diagrams

Scatter diagrams show the type of relation that exists between two variables. Our goal in interpreting scatter diagrams will be to distinguish scatter diagrams that imply a linear relation from those which imply a nonlinear relation and those which imply no relation. Figure 2 displays various scatter diagrams and the type of relation implied.

Figure 2

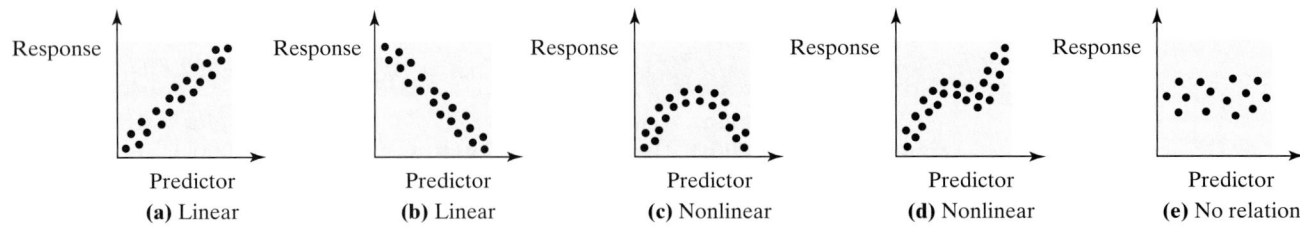

| (a) Linear | (b) Linear | (c) Nonlinear | (d) Nonlinear | (e) No relation |

As we compare Figure 2(a) with Figure 2(b), we notice a distinct difference. In Figure 2(a), the data follow a linear pattern that slants upward to the right, while the data in Figure 2(b) follow a linear pattern that slants downward to the right.

Definitions

Two variables that are linearly related are said to be **positively associated** when above-average values of one variable are associated with above-average values of the corresponding variable. That is, two variables are positively associated if, whenever the values of the predictor variable increase, the values of the response variable also increase.

Two variables that are linearly related are said to be **negatively associated** when above-average values of one variable are associated with below-average values of the corresponding variable. That is, two variables are negatively associated if, whenever the values of the predictor variable increase, the values of the response variable decrease.

> **In Your Own Words**
>
> If two variables that are linearly related are positively associated, then as one goes up the other also goes up. If two variables that are linearly related are negatively associated, then as one goes up the other goes down.

So the scatter diagram from Figure 1 implies that per capita GDP is positively associated with life expectancy.

 Now Work Problem 1.

 Correlation

It is dangerous to use only a scatter diagram to conclude whether two variables might follow a linear relation. Suppose we redraw the scatter diagram in Figure 1 using a different scale. See Figure 3.

> **Caution**
>
> The horizontal or vertical scale of a scatter diagram can be set so that the scatter diagram misleads a reader.

Figure 3

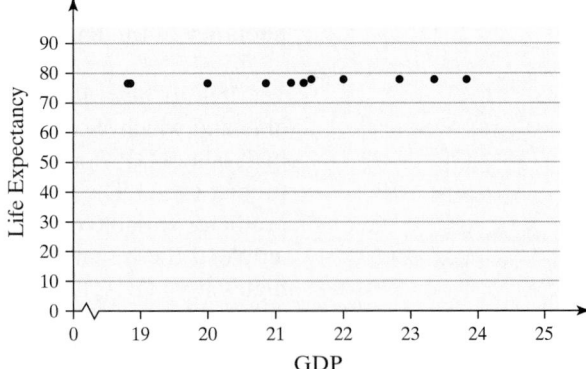

From Figure 3, we might conclude that per capita GDP and life expectancy are not related. The moral of the story is this: Just as we can manipulate the scale of graphs of univariate data, we can also manipulate the scale of the graphs of bivariate data, thereby encouraging incorrect conclusions. Therefore, numerical summaries of bivariate data should be used in conjunction with graphs in order to determine the type of relation, if any, that exists between two variables.

Definition

The **linear correlation coefficient** or **Pearson product moment correlation coefficient** is a measure of the strength of linear relation between two quantitative variables. We use the Greek letter ρ (rho) to represent the population correlation coefficient and r to represent the sample correlation coefficient. We shall present only the formula for the sample correlation coefficient.

Sample Correlation Coefficient

$$r = \frac{\sum \left(\dfrac{x_i - \overline{x}}{s_x}\right)\left(\dfrac{y_i - \overline{y}}{s_y}\right)}{n - 1} \; * \tag{1}$$

where $\overline{x}$ is the sample mean of the predictor variable

s_x is the sample standard deviation of the predictor variable

$\overline{y}$ is the sample mean of the response variable

s_y is the sample standard deviation of the response variable

n is the number of individuals in the sample

The Pearson linear correlation coefficient is named in honor of Karl Pearson (1857–1936).

Properties of the Linear Correlation Coefficient

1. The linear correlation coefficient is always between -1 and 1, inclusive. That is, $-1 \le r \le 1$.
2. If $r = +1$, there is a perfect positive linear relation between the two variables. See Figure 4(a).
3. If $r = -1$, there is a perfect negative linear relation between the two variables. See Figure 4(d).
4. The closer r is to $+1$, the stronger is the evidence of positive association between the two variables. See Figures 4(b) and 4(c).
5. The closer r is to -1, the stronger is the evidence of negative association between the two variables. See Figures 4(e) and 4(f).
6. If r is close to 0, there is evidence of no *linear* relation between the two variables. Because the linear correlation coefficient is a measure of strength of linear relation, r close to 0 does not imply no relation, just no linear relation. See Figures 4(g) and 4(h).
7. The linear correlation coefficient is a unitless measure of association. So the unit of measure for x and y plays no role in the interpretation of r.

*An equivalent formula for the linear correlation coefficient is

$$r = \frac{\sum x_i y_i - \dfrac{\sum x_i \sum y_i}{n}}{\sqrt{\left(\sum x_i^2 - \dfrac{\left(\sum x_i\right)^2}{n}\right)}\sqrt{\left(\sum y_i^2 - \dfrac{\left(\sum y_i\right)^2}{n}\right)}} = \frac{S_{xy}}{\sqrt{S_{xx}}\sqrt{S_{yy}}}$$

Historical Note

Karl Pearson was born March 27, 1857. Pearson's proficiency as a statistician was recognized early in his life. It is said that his mother told him not to suck his thumb, because otherwise his thumb would wither away. Pearson analyzed the size of each thumb and said to himself, "They look alike to me. I can't see that the thumb I suck is any smaller than the other. I wonder if she could be lying to me."

Karl Pearson graduated from Cambridge University in 1879. From 1893 to 1911, he wrote 18 papers on genetics and heredity. Through this work, he developed ideas regarding correlation and the chi-square test. (See Chapter 11.) In addition, Pearson came up with the term "standard deviation."

Pearson and Ronald Fisher didn't get along. The dispute between the two was bad enough to have Fisher turn down the post of chief statistician at the Galton Laboratory in 1919 on the grounds that it would have meant working under Pearson. Pearson died on April 27, 1936.

Figure 4 demonstrates these properties through various scatter diagrams, along with their linear correlation coefficients.

Figure 4

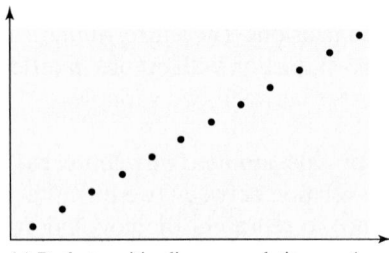

(a) Perfect positive linear correlation, $r = 1$

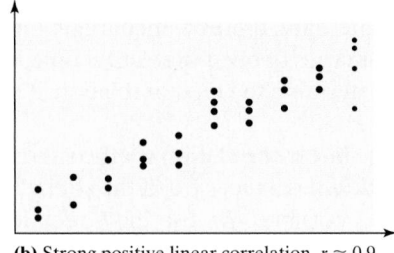

(b) Strong positive linear correlation, $r \approx 0.9$

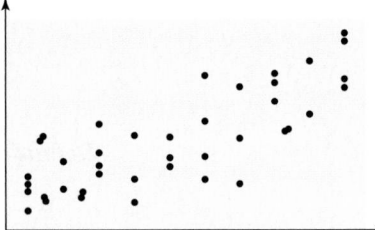

(c) Weak positive linear correlation, $r \approx 0.4$

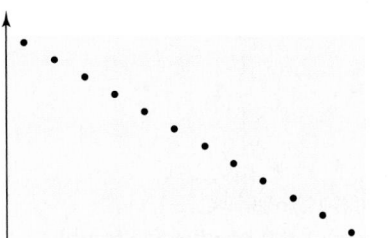

(d) Perfect negative linear correlation, $r = -1$

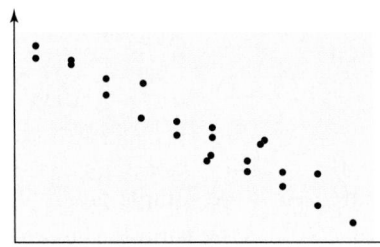

(e) Strong negative linear correlation, $r \approx -0.9$

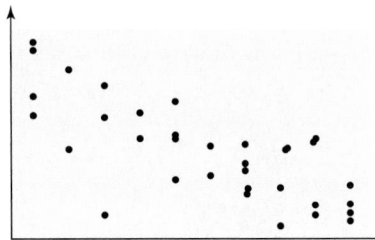

(f) Weak negative linear correlation, $r \approx -0.4$

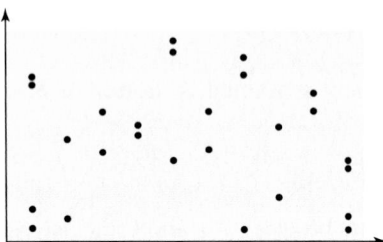

(g) No linear correlation, r close to 0.

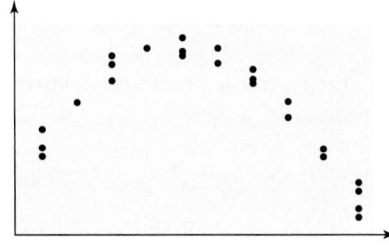

(h) No linear correlation, r close to 0.

Caution

A linear correlation coefficient close to 0 does not imply no relation, just no linear relation. For example, although the scatter diagram drawn in Figure 4(h) indicates that the predictor and response variables are related, the linear correlation coefficient of this data is close to 0.

In looking carefully at Formula (1), we should notice that the numerator of the formula is the product of z-scores for the predictor (x) and response (y) variables. A positive linear correlation coefficient means that the sum of the product of the z-scores for x and y must be positive. Under what circumstances does this occur? Figure 5 shows a scatter diagram that implies a positive association between x and y. The vertical dashed line represents the value of $\overline{x}$ and the horizontal dashed line represents the value of $\overline{y}$. These two dashed lines divide our scatter diagram into 4 quadrants, labeled I, II, III, and IV.

Notice that a majority of the data lie in quadrants I and III. If a certain x-value is above its mean, $\overline{x}$, then the corresponding y-value will be above its mean, $\overline{y}$. If a certain x-value is below its mean, $\overline{x}$, then the corresponding y-value will be below its mean, $\overline{y}$. Therefore, for data in quadrant I, we would have $\left(\dfrac{x_i - \overline{x}}{s_x}\right)$ positive and $\left(\dfrac{y_i - \overline{y}}{s_y}\right)$ positive, so that their product is positive. For data in quadrant III, we would have $\left(\dfrac{x_i - \overline{x}}{s_x}\right)$ negative and $\left(\dfrac{y_i - \overline{y}}{s_y}\right)$ negative, so that their product is positive. The sum of these products will be positive, and therefore we have a positive linear correlation coefficient. A similar argument can be made for negative correlation.

Figure 5

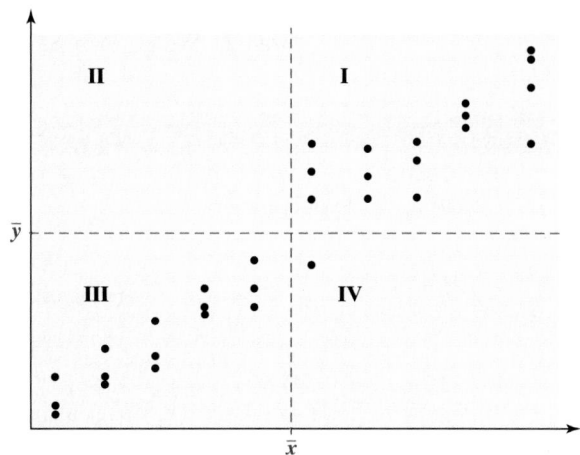

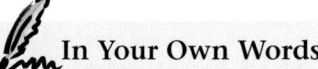In Your Own Words

The correlation coefficient describes the strength and the direction of the linear relationship between a predictor and a response variable.

Now suppose the data are equally dispersed in the four quadrants. Then the negative products (resulting from data in quadrants II and IV) will offset the positive products (resulting from data in quadrants I and III). The result is a linear correlation coefficient close to 0.

 *Now Work Problem 5.*

④ ▶ EXAMPLE 2   **Computing and Interpreting the Correlation Coefficient**

Problem: In Table 2, columns 2 and 3 represent the per capita gross domestic product (in thousands of U.S. dollars) and the average life expectancy of the population, for randomly selected countries in Western Europe. Compute and interpret the linear correlation coefficient.

Approach: We treat per capita GDP as the predictor variable, x, and life expectancy as the response variable, y.

Step 1: Compute $\bar{x}$, s_x, $\bar{y}$, and s_y.

Step 2: Determine $\dfrac{x_i - \bar{x}}{s_x}$ and $\dfrac{y_i - \bar{y}}{s_y}$.

Step 3: Compute $\left(\dfrac{x_i - \bar{x}}{s_x}\right)\left(\dfrac{y_i - \bar{y}}{s_y}\right)$.

Step 4: Determine $\displaystyle\sum\left(\dfrac{x_i - \bar{x}}{s_x}\right)\left(\dfrac{y_i - \bar{y}}{s_y}\right)$ and substitute this value into Formula (1).

Solution:

Step 1: We compute $\bar{x}$, s_x, $\bar{y}$, and s_y:

$$\bar{x} = 21.52, \; s_x = 1.531738301, \; \bar{y} = 77.754, \text{ and } s_y = 0.794847295$$

Notice we do not round these values. This is to avoid round-off error when using Formula (1).

Step 2: We determine $\dfrac{x_i - \bar{x}}{s_x}$ and $\dfrac{y_i - \bar{y}}{s_y}$ in Columns 4 and 5 in Table 2.

			TABLE 2		
Country	Per Capita GDP, x_i	Life Expectancy, y_i	$\dfrac{x_i - \bar{x}}{s_x}$	$\dfrac{y_i - \bar{y}}{s_y}$	$\left(\dfrac{x_i - \bar{x}}{s_x}\right)\left(\dfrac{y_i - \bar{y}}{s_y}\right)$
Austria	21.4	77.48	$\dfrac{21.4 - 21.52}{1.531738301}$ $= -0.0783424$	$\dfrac{77.48 - 77.754}{0.794847295}$ $= -0.34472$	$(-0.0783424)(-0.34472)$ $= 0.027006$
Belgium	23.2	77.53	1.0967931	−0.28182	−0.30909
Finland	20.0	77.32	−0.9923366	−0.54602	0.541832
France	22.7	78.63	0.7703666	1.102098	0.84902
Germany	20.8	77.17	−0.4700542	−0.73473	0.345364
Ireland	18.6	76.39	−1.9063309	−1.71605	3.271365
Italy	21.5	78.51	−0.0130571	0.951126	−0.01242
Netherlands	22.0	78.15	0.3133695	0.498209	0.156123
Switzerland	23.8	78.99	1.4885049	1.555016	2.314648
United Kingdom	21.2	77.37	−0.2089130	−0.48311	0.100928

$$\sum\left(\frac{x_i - \bar{x}}{s_x}\right)\left(\frac{y_i - \bar{y}}{s_y}\right) = 7.284776$$

Step 3: We multiply the entries in columns 4 and 5 to obtain the entries in column 6.

Step 4: We add up the entries in column 6 to obtain $\sum\left(\dfrac{x_i - \bar{x}}{s_x}\right)\left(\dfrac{y_i - \bar{y}}{s_y}\right) = 7.284776$. Substitute this value into Formula (1) to obtain the correlation coefficient.

$$r = \frac{\sum\left(\dfrac{x_i - \bar{x}}{s_x}\right)\left(\dfrac{y_i - \bar{y}}{s_y}\right)}{n - 1} = \frac{7.284776}{10 - 1} = 0.809$$

The linear correlation between per capita GDP and life expectancy is 0.809, indicating a strong positive association between the two variables. The higher the per capita GDP of a country, the longer its residents can expect to live. ◄◄

Notice in Example 2 that we carry many decimal places in the computation of the correlation coefficient, in order to avoid rounding error. Also, compare the signs of the entries in columns 4 and 5. Notice that negative values in column 4 correspond with negative values in column 5 and that positive values in column 4 correspond with positive values in column 5 (except for Belgium and Italy). This means that above-average values of x are associated with above-average values of y and below-average values of x are associated with below-average values of y. This is why the linear correlation coefficient is positive.

Using Technology: Many calculators and statistical software have the ability to compute the correlation between two quantitative variables. Figure 6 shows the correlation coefficient computed in Example 2 using Excel. Notice Excel provides a **correlation matrix**, which means it will compute the correlation between every pair of columns and display the correlation in the bottom triangle of the matrix.

Figure 6

	Per Capita GDP	*Life Expectancy*
Per Capita GDP	1	
Life Expectancy	**0.809419506**	1

NW *Now Work Problems 11(c) and 11(d).*

Recall from Chapter 1 we stated that there are two types of studies—observational and experimental. When data analysis is performed upon observational data, a researcher cannot make claims regarding causation. It is vital that this point be understood, as it pertains to the linear correlation coefficient.

The data used in Example 2 are observational data. Therefore, we cannot claim that a high per capita GDP causes a higher life expectancy. It may be that a lurking variable is related to both per capita GDP and a higher life expectancy. Recall that a lurking variable is a variable that is correlated to both the response and predictor variables. For example, high per capita GDP and life expectancy may be related through a lurking variable such as the quality of health care. If data are obtained through a controlled experiment, then a linear correlation coefficient that implies a strong positive or negative association also implies causation.

Caution!

A linear correlation coefficient that implies a strong positive or negative association that is computed using observational data does not imply causation.

4.1 Assess Your Understanding

Concepts and Vocabulary

1. Describe the difference between univariate and bivariate data.
2. Explain what is meant by a lurking variable. Provide an example.
3. What does it mean to say that two variables are positively associated?
4. What does it mean to say that the linear correlation coefficient between two variables equals one? What would the scatter diagram look like?

5. What does it mean if $r = 0$?
6. Is the linear correlation coefficient a resistant measure? Support your answer.
7. Explain what is wrong with the following statement: "We have concluded that there is a high correlation between male drivers and rates of automobile accidents."
8. Write a statement that explains the concept of correlation. Include a discussion of the role that $x_i - \bar{x}$ and $y_i - \bar{y}$ play in the computation.

Exercises

• **Skill Building**

In Problems 1–4, determine whether the scatter diagram indicates that a linear relation may exist between the two variables. If the relation is linear, determine whether it is indicative of positive or negative association between the variables.

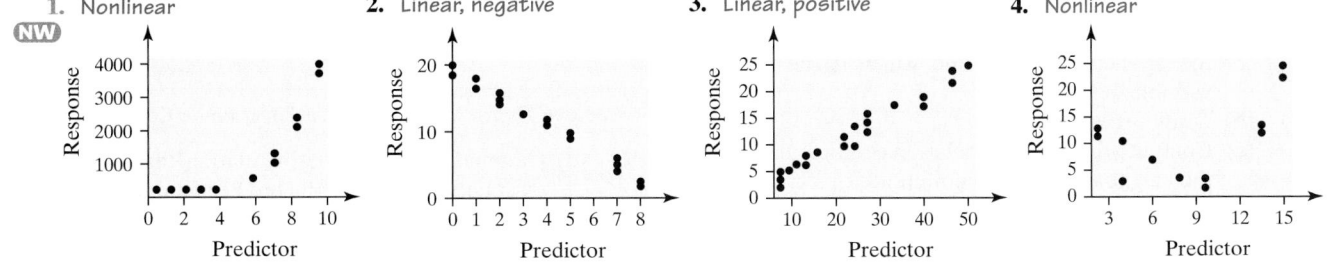

1. Nonlinear
NW

2. Linear, negative

3. Linear, positive

4. Nonlinear

5. Match the linear correlation coefficient to the scatter diagram. The scales on the *x*- and *y*-axis are the same for each scatter diagram.

(a) *r* = 0.787 III   (b) *r* = 0.523 IV   (c) *r* = 0.810 II   (d) *r* = 0.946 I

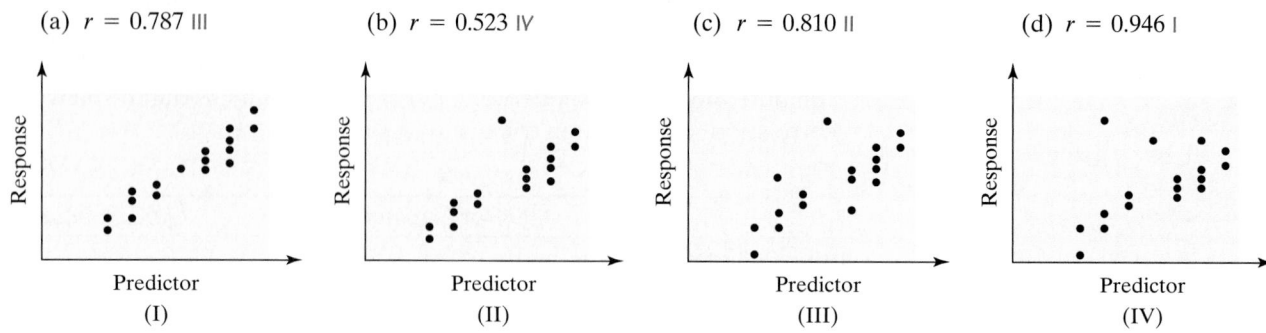

6. Match the linear correlation coefficient to the scatter diagram. The scales on the *x*- and *y*-axis are the same for each scatter diagram.

(a) *r* = −0.969 IV   (b) *r* = −0.049 III   (c) *r* = −1 I   (d) *r* = −0.992 II

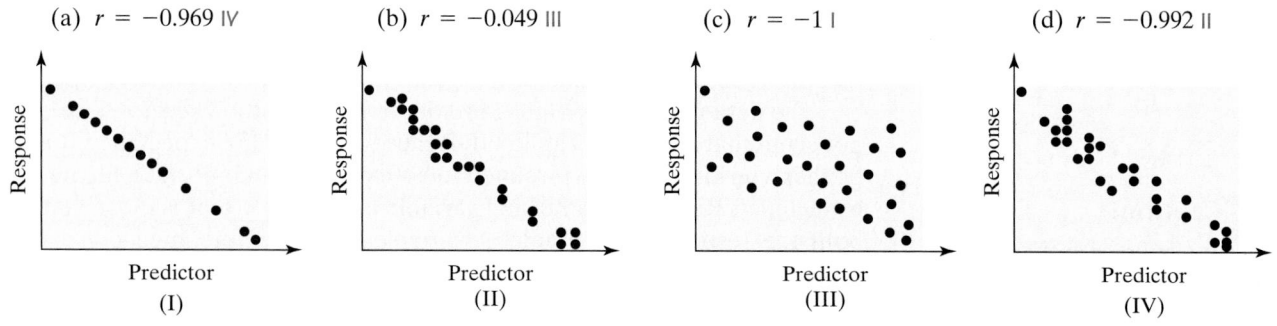

In Problems 7–10, (a) draw a scatter diagram of the data, (b) by hand, compute the correlation coefficient, (c) comment on the type of relation that appears to exist between x and y.

7. *r* = 0.9572

x	2	4	8	8	9
y	1.4	1.8	2.1	2.3	2.6

8. *r* = −0.9922

x	2	3	5	6	6
y	5.7	5.2	2.8	1.9	2.2

9. −0.9703

x	1.2	1.8	2.3	3.5	4.1
y	8.4	7	7.3	4.5	2.4

10. *r* = 0.9806

x	0	0.5	1.4	2.1	3.9	4.6
y	0.8	1.3	1.9	2.5	5.0	6.8

• **Applying the Concepts**

11. **Height versus Head Circumference** A pediatrician wants to determine the relation that may exist between a child's height and head circumference. She randomly selects 11 three-year-old children from her practice, measures their height and head circumference, and obtains the data shown in the table.

(a) If the pediatrician wants to use height to predict head circumference, determine which variable is the predictor variable and which is the response variable. Predictor: Height

(b) Draw a scatter diagram.

(c) Compute the linear correlation coefficient between the height and head circumference of a child. 0.911

Height (inches)	Head Circumference (inches)	Height (inches)	Head Circumference (inches)
27.75	17.5	26.5	17.3
24.5	17.1	27	17.5
25.5	17.1	26.75	17.3
26	17.3	26.75	17.5
25	16.9	27.5	17.5
27.75	17.6		

Source: Denise Slucki, Student at Joliet Junior College

(d) Comment on the type of relation that appears to exist between the height and head circumference of a child on the basis of the scatter diagram and linear correlation coefficient.

12. **Round-cut Diamonds** A gemologist is interested in determining the relation that exists between the size of a diamond (carats) and the price. The following data represent the weight and price of D color, VS1 clarity, round-cut diamonds.

Carats	Price	Carats	Price
0.66	$3282	0.80	$4378
0.75	$3950	0.90	$5682
0.70	$3543	0.91	$6426
0.71	$3788	1.18	$9362
0.77	$4108		

Source: diamonds.com

(a) The researcher wants to use the number of carats to predict price. Determine which variable is the predictor variable and which is the response variable.
(b) Draw a scatter diagram.
(c) Compute the linear correlation coefficient between the number of carats and the price of a diamond.
(d) Comment on the type of relation that appears to exist between the number of carats and the price, based upon the scatter diagram and linear correlation coefficient.
(e) Remove the diamond that weighs 1.18 carats from the data set and recompute the linear correlation coefficient between the number of carats and price of a diamond. What effect did the removal of the data value have on the linear correlation coefficient? Provide a justification for this result. *0.9707*

13. **Gestation Period versus Life Expectancy** A researcher would like to know if the gestation period of an animal can be used to predict the life expectancy. She collects the following data.

Animal	Gestation (or Incubation) Period (days)	Life Expectancy (years)
Cat	63	11
Chicken	22	7.5
Dog	63	11
Duck	28	10
Goat	151	12
Lion	108	10
Parakeet	18	8
Pig	115	10
Rabbit	31	7
Squirrel	44	9

Source: Time Almanac 2000

(a) Suppose a researcher wants to use the gestation period of an animal to predict its life expectancy. Determine which variable is the predictor variable and which is the response variable.
(b) Draw a scatter diagram.
(c) Compute the linear correlation coefficient between gestation period and life expectancy. *0.7257*
(d) Comment on the type of relation that appears to exist between gestation period and life expectancy based upon the scatter diagram and linear correlation coefficient.
(e) Remove the goat from the data set and recompute the linear correlation coefficient between the gestation period and life expectancy. What effect did the removal of the data value have on the linear correlation coefficient? Provide a justification for this result.

14. **Tar and Nicotine** Every year the Federal Trade Commission must report tar and nicotine levels in cigarettes to the Congress. It obtains the tar and nicotine levels of over 1200 brands of cigarettes. A sample from those reported to Congress is given in the following table.

Brand	Tar (mg)	Nicotine (mg)
Barclay 100	5	0.4
Benson and Hedges King	16	1.1
Camel Regular	24	1.7
Chesterfield King	24	1.4
Doral	8	0.5
Kent Golden Lights	9	0.8
Kool Menthol	9	0.8
Lucky Strike	24	1.5
Marlboro Gold	15	1.2
Newport Menthol	18	1.3
Salem Menthol	17	1.3
Virginia Slims Ultra Light	5	0.5
Winston Light	10	0.8

Source: Federal Trade Commission

(a) Suppose a researcher wants to use the level of tar to predict the nicotine level in a cigarette. Determine which variable is the predictor variable and which is the response variable. *Predictor: tar*
(b) Draw a scatter diagram.
(c) Compute the linear correlation coefficient between the amount of tar and nicotine. *0.9666*
(d) Comment on the type of relation that appears to exist between the amount of tar and nicotine, based upon the scatter diagram and linear correlation coefficient.

(12a) Predictor: Carats   (12c) *0.9917*
(13a) Predictor: gestation period   (13e) *0.592*

15. **Bone Length** Research performed at NASA and led by Dr. Emily R. Morey-Holton measured the lengths of the right humerus and right tibia in 11 rats that were sent to

Right Humerus (mm)	Right Tibia (mm)	Right Humerus (mm)	Right Tibia (mm)
24.8	36.05	25.9	37.38
24.59	35.57	26.11	37.96
24.59	35.57	26.63	37.46
24.29	34.58	26.31	37.75
23.81	34.2	26.84	38.5
24.87	34.73		

Source: NASA Life Sciences Data Archive

space on Spacelab Life Sciences 2. The following data were collected.

(a) Draw a scatter diagram treating the length of the right humerus as the predictor variable and the length of the right tibia as the response variable.
(b) Compute the linear correlation coefficient between the length of the right humerus and the length of the right tibia. *0.9513*
(c) Comment on the type of relation that appears to exist between the length of the right humerus and the length of the right tibia based upon the scatter diagram and the linear correlation coefficient.
(d) Convert the data to inches (1 mm = 0.03937 inch) and recompute the linear correlation coefficient. What effect did the conversion from millimeters to inches have on the linear correlation coefficient? *None*

16. **Weight of a Car versus Miles per Gallon** An engineer wanted to determine how the weight of a car affected the gas mileage. The following data represent the weight of various domestic cars and their miles per gallon in the city for the 2001 model year.

Car	Weight (pounds)	Miles Per Gallon
Buick LeSabre	3565	19
Buick Regal	3440	20
Cadillac Seville	3970	17
Chevrolet Camaro	3305	19
Chevrolet Monte Carlo	3340	20
Chrysler PT Cruiser	3200	20
Chrysler Sebring Sedan	3230	19
Dodge Neon	2560	28
Ford Focus	2520	28
Ford Mustang	3065	20
Lincoln LS	3600	18
Mercury Sable	3300	19
Oldsmobile Aurora	3625	19
Pontiac Bonneville	3590	19
Pontiac Sunfire	2605	23
Saturn Coupe	2370	28

Source: Road and Track magazine

(a) Determine which variable is the likely predictor variable and which is the likely response variable.
(b) Draw a scatter diagram.
(c) Compute the linear correlation coefficient between the weight of a car and its miles per gallon in the city.
(d) Comment on the type of relation that appears to exist between the weight of a car and its miles per gallon in the city based upon the scatter diagram and the linear correlation coefficient.

17. **General Electric versus the S&P 500** An investor wants to determine whether the rate of return of the S&P 500 can be used to predict the rate of return of the stock of General Electric (GE). The following data represent the rate of return of GE stock for 13 months versus the rate of return of the Standard & Poor's Index of 500 stocks.

Month	Rate of Return of S&P 500	Rate of Return of GE
Sep-99	−2.9	5.6
Oct-99	6.3	14.3
Nov-99	1.9	−4.0
Dec-99	5.8	18.9
Jan-00	−5.0	−13.4
Feb-00	−2.0	−1.2
Mar-00	10.0	17.6
Apr-00	−3.1	1.0
May-00	−2.2	0.4
Jun-00	2.4	0.7
Jul-00	−1.6	−2.5
Aug-00	6.1	13.4
Sep-00	−5.3	−1.2

Source: Yahoo! Finance

(a) Draw a scatter diagram treating the rate of return of the S&P 500 as the predictor variable.
(b) Compute the linear correlation coefficient between the rate of return of GE stock and the rate of return of the S&P 500. *0.8290*
(c) Comment on the type of relation that appears to exist between the rate of return of GE stock and the rate of return of the S&P 500, on the basis of the scatter diagram and the linear correlation coefficient.

(16a) Predictor: weight (16c) −0.9163

18. Fat-free Mass versus Energy Expenditure In an effort to measure the dependence of energy expenditure on body build, researchers used underwater weighing techniques to determine the fat-free body mass for seven men. In addition, they measured the total 24-hour energy expenditure during inactivity. The results are shown in the table.

Fat-free Mass (kg)	Energy Expenditure (Kcal)
49.3	1894
59.3	2050
68.3	2353
48.1	1838
57.6	1948
78.1	2528
76.1	2568

Source: Webb, P. Energy expenditure and fat-free mass in men and women. *American Journal of Clinical Nutrition,* **34,** (1981):1816–1826.

(a) Determine which variable is the likely predictor variable and which is the likely response variable.
(b) Draw a scatter diagram.
(c) Compute the linear correlation coefficient between fat-free mass and energy expenditure. *0.9814*
(d) Comment on the type of relation that appears to exist between fat-free mass and energy expenditure on the basis of the scatter diagram and the linear correlation coefficient.

19. Age versus HDL Cholesterol A doctor wanted to determine whether there was a relation between a male's age and his HDL (so-called "good") cholesterol. He randomly selected 17 of his patients and determined their HDL cholesterol. He obtained the following data.

Age	HDL Cholesterol	Age	HDL Cholesterol
38	57	38	44
42	54	66	62
46	34	30	53
32	56	51	36
55	35	27	45
52	40	52	38
61	42	49	55
61	38	39	28
26	47		

Source: Data based upon information obtained from the National Center for Health Statistics

(a) Draw a scatter diagram of the data treating age as the predictor variable. What type of relation, if any, appears to exist between age and HDL cholesterol?

(18a) Predictor: Fat-free mass

(b) Compute the linear correlation coefficient between age and HDL cholesterol. *−0.164*
(c) Comment on the type of relation that appears to exist between age and HDL cholesterol on the basis of the scatter diagram and the linear correlation coefficient.

20. Intensity of a Lightbulb Cathy is conducting an experiment to measure the relation between a lightbulb's intensity and the distance from the light source. She measures a 100-watt lightbulb's intensity 1 meter from the bulb and at 0.1-meter intervals up to 2 meters from the bulb and obtains the following data.

Distance (meters), x	Intensity, y	Distance (meters), x	Intensity, y
1.0	0.29645	1.6	0.11450
1.1	0.25215	1.7	0.10243
1.2	0.20547	1.8	0.09231
1.3	0.17462	1.9	0.08321
1.4	0.15342	2.0	0.07342
1.5	0.13521		

(a) Draw a scatter diagram of the data, treating distance as the predictor variable.
(b) Do you think that it is appropriate to compute the linear correlation between distance and intensity? Why?

21. Does Size Matter? Researchers Willerman, Schultz, Rutledge, and Bigler wondered whether the size of a person's brain was related to the individual's mental capacity. They selected a sample of right-handed introductory psychology students who had Scholastic Aptitude Test Scores higher than 1350. The subjects were administered the Wechsler (1981) Adult Intelligence Scale-Revised in order to obtain their IQ scores. The MRI Scans were performed at the same facility for the subjects. The scans consisted of 18 horizontal MR images. The computer counted all pixels with nonzero gray scale in each of the 18 images and the total count served as an index for brain size.

Gender	MRI Count	IQ	Gender	MRI Count	IQ
Female	816,932	133	Male	949,395	140
Female	951,545	137	Male	1,001,121	140
Female	991,305	138	Male	1,038,437	139
Female	833,868	132	Male	965,353	133
Female	856,472	140	Male	955,466	133
Female	852,244	132	Male	1,079,549	141
Female	790,619	135	Male	924,059	135
Female	866,662	130	Male	955,003	139
Female	857,782	133	Male	935,494	141
Female	948,066	133	Male	949,589	144

Source: Willerman, L., Schultz, R., Rutledge, J. N., and Bigler, E. (1991), "In Vivo Brain Size and Intelligence," *Intelligence,* 15, 223–228.

(a) Draw a scatter diagram, treating MRI Count as the predictor variable and IQ as the response variable. Comment on what you see.
(b) Compute the linear correlation coefficient between MRI Count and IQ. Do you think that MRI Count and IQ are linearly related?
(c) A lurking variable in the analysis is gender. Draw a scatter diagram, treating MRI Count as the predictor variable and IQ as the response variable, but use a different plotting symbol for each gender. For example, use a circle for males and a triangle for females. What do you notice?
(d) Compute the linear correlation coefficient between MRI Count and IQ for females. Compute the linear correlation coefficient between MRI Count and IQ for males. Do you still believe that MRI Count and IQ are linearly related? What is the moral?

22. **Male versus Female Drivers** The following data represent the number of licensed drivers in various age groups and the number of accidents within the age group by gender.

Age Group	Number of Male Licensed Drivers (000s)	Number of Crashes Involving a Male (000s)	Number of Female Licensed Drivers (000s)	Number of Crashes Involving a Female (000s)
16	816	244	764	178
17	1198	233	1115	175
18	1342	243	1212	164
19	1454	229	1333	145
20–24	7866	951	7394	618
25–29	9356	899	8946	595
30–34	10,121	875	9871	571
35–39	10,521	901	10,439	566
40–44	9776	692	9752	455
45–49	8754	667	8710	390
50–54	6840	390	6763	247
55–59	5341	290	5258	165
60–64	4565	218	4486	133
65–69	4234	191	4231	121
70–74	3604	167	3749	104
75–79	2563	118	2716	77
80–84	1400	61	1516	45
≥ 85	767	34	767	20

Source: National Highway and Traffic Safety Institute

(a) On the same graph, draw a scatter diagram for both males and females. Be sure to use a different plotting symbol for each group. For example, use a square (□) for males and a plus sign (+) for females. Treat number of licensed drivers as the predictor variable.
(b) Based on the scatter diagrams, do you think that insurance companies are justified in charging different insurance rates for males and females? Why?
(c) Compute the linear correlation coefficient between number of licensed drivers and number of crashes for males. 0.899
(d) Compute the linear correlation coefficient between number of licensed drivers and number of crashes for females. 0.863
(e) Which gender has the stronger linear relation between number of licensed drivers and number of crashes. Why? Males

23. **Gestation Period versus Life Expectancy** Suppose we add humans to the data in Problem 13. Humans have a gestation period of 268 days and a life expectancy of 76.5 years.
(a) Redraw the scatter diagram with humans included.
(b) Recompute the linear correlation coefficient with humans included. 0.847
(c) Compare the results of (a) and (b) with the results of Problem 13. Provide a statement that explains the results.

24. Weight of a Car versus Miles per Gallon Suppose we add the Dodge Viper to the data in Problem 16. A Dodge Viper weighs 3425 pounds and gets 11 miles per gallon.

(a) Redraw the scatter diagram with the Viper included.

(b) Recompute the linear correlation coefficient with the Viper included. -0.819

(c) Compare the results of (a) and (b) with the results of Problem 16. Why are the results reasonable?

25. Consider the following set of data:

x	2.2	3.7	3.9	4.1	2.6	4.1	2.9	4.7
y	3.9	4.0	1.4	2.8	1.5	3.3	3.6	4.9

(a) Draw a scatter diagram of the data and compute the linear correlation coefficient. 0.2280

(b) Draw a scatter diagram of the data and compute the linear correlation coefficient with the additional data point (10.4, 9.3). Comment on the effect of the additional data point. Conclude that correlations should always be reported with scatter diagrams. 0.8598

26. On the basis of the accompanying scatter diagram, explain what is wrong with the following statement: "Because the linear correlation coefficient between them is 0.012, there is no relation between age and median income."

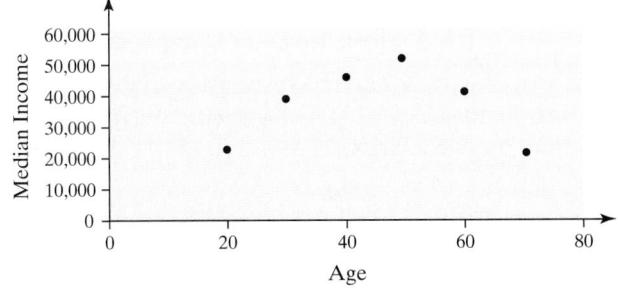

27. For each of the following statements, explain whether you think the variables will have positive correlation, negative correlation, or no correlation. Support your opinion.

(a) Number of children in the household under the age of 3 and expenditures on diapers Positive

(b) Interest rates on car loans and number of cars sold

(c) Number of hours per week on the treadmill and cholesterol level Negative

(d) Price of a Big Mac and number of McDonald's french fries sold in a week Negative

(e) Shoe size and IQ No correlation

28. Consider the following data set:

x	5	6	7	7	8	8	8	8
y	4.2	5	5.2	5.9	6	6.2	6.1	6.9
x	9	9	10	10	11	11	12	12
y	7.2	8	8.3	7.4	8.4	7.8	8.5	9.5

(a) Draw a scatter diagram with the x-axis starting at 0 and ending at 30, the y-axis starting at 0 and ending at 20.

(b) Compute the linear correlation coefficient. 0.9518

(c) Now multiply both x and y by 2.

(d) Draw a scatter diagram of the new data with the x-axis starting at 0 and ending at 30, the y-axis starting at 0 and ending at 20. Compare the scatter diagrams.

(e) Compute the linear correlation coefficient. 0.9518

(f) Conclude that multiplying each value in the data set does not affect the correlation between the variables. Explain why this is the case.

(27b) Negative

---

 29. Consider the following four data sets:

Data Set 1		Data Set 2		Data Set 3		Data Set 4	
x	**y**	**x**	**y**	**x**	**y**	**x**	**y**
10	8.04	10	9.14	10	7.46	8	6.58
8	6.95	8	8.14	8	6.77	8	5.76
13	7.58	13	8.74	13	12.74	8	7.71
9	8.81	9	8.77	9	7.11	8	8.84
11	8.33	11	9.26	11	7.81	8	8.47
14	9.96	14	8.10	14	8.84	8	7.04
6	7.24	6	6.13	6	6.08	8	5.25
4	4.26	4	3.10	4	5.39	8	5.56
12	10.84	12	9.13	12	8.15	8	7.91
7	4.82	7	7.26	7	6.42	8	6.89
5	5.68	5	4.47	5	5.73	19	12.50

Source: Anscombe, Frank, "Graphs in statistical analysis," *American Statistician* 27 (1973):17–21.

(a) Compute the linear correlation coefficient for each data set. $r = 0.82$ for all four

(b) Draw a scatter diagram for each data set. Conclude that linear correlation coefficients and scatter diagrams must be used together in any statistical analysis of bivariate data.

30. In a study published in the Journal of the American Medical Association (May 16, 2001), researchers found that breast-feeding may help to prevent obesity in kids. In an interview, the head investigator stated, "It's not clear whether breast milk has obesity-preventing properties or the women who are breast-feeding are less likely to have fat kids because they are less likely to be fat themselves and may be more health-conscious". Using this researcher's statement, explain what might be wrong with the conclusion that breast-feeding prevents obesity. Identify some lurking variables in the study.

31. Compute the linear correlation coefficient between the points $(3, 8)$ and $(5, 12)$. Explain why the result is reasonable. 1

32. Compute the linear correlation coefficient between the points $(2, 4)$ and $(6, 1)$. Explain why the result is reasonable. -1

33. Explain how you might use the linear correlation coefficient to identify lurking variables in an observational study.

Technology Step-by-Step
Drawing Scatter Diagrams and Determining the Correlation Coefficient

TI-83 Plus **Scatter Diagrams**

Step 1: Enter the predictor variable in L1 and the response variable in L2.

Step 2: Press 2nd Y = to bring up the StatPlot menu. Select 1: Plot1.

Step 3: Turn Plot 1 ON by putting the cursor on the ON button and pressing ENTER.

Step 4: Highlight scatter diagram icon (see the figure) and press ENTER. Be sure that Xlist is L1 and Ylist is L2.

Step 5: Press ZOOM and select 9: ZoomStat.

Correlation Coefficient

Step 1: Turn the diagnostics on by selecting the catalog $(2^{nd} \emptyset)$. Scroll down and select DiagnosticOn. Hit ENTER to activate diagnostics.

Step 2: With the predictor variable in L1 and the response variable in L2, press STAT, highlight CALC and select 4: LinReg (ax + b). With LinReg on the HOME screen press ENTER.

MINITAB **Scatter Diagrams**

Step 1: Enter the predictor variable in C1 and the response variable in C2. You may want to name the variables.

Step 2: Select the **Graph** menu and highlight **Plot**...

Step 3: With the cursor in the Y column, select the response variable. With the cursor in the X column, select the predictor variable. Click OK.

Correlation Coefficient

Step 1: With the predictor variable in C1 and the response variable in C2, select the **Stat** menu, highlight **Basic Statistics**. Highlight **Correlation**.

Step 2: Select the variables whose correlation you wish to determine and click OK.

Excel **Scatter Diagrams**

Step 1: Enter the predictor variable in column A and the response variable in column B. Select the Chart Wizard icon.

Step 2: Follow the instructions in the Chart Wizard.

Correlation Coefficient

Step 1: Be sure the Data Analysis Tool Pak is activated, by selecting the **Tools** menu and highlighting **Add-Ins**... Check the box for the Analysis ToolPak and select OK.

Step 2: Select **Tools** and highlight **Data Analysis**... Highlight **Correlation** and select OK.

Step 3: With the cursor in the Input Range, highlight the data. Select OK.

4.2   Least-Squares Regression

Preparing for This Section   Before getting started, review the following:

✓ Lines (Appendix B, pp. A-21–A-25)

Objectives   1   Find the least-squares regression line
2   Interpret the slope and the *y*-intercept of the least-squares regression line
3   Predict the value of the response variable based upon the least-squares regression line
4   Determine residuals based upon the least-squares regression line
5   Compute the sum of squared residuals

Note to Instructor
Encourage students to review lines in
Appendix B.

Once the scatter diagram and linear correlation coefficient indicate that a linear relation exists between two variables, we proceed to find a linear equation that describes the relation between the two variables. One way to obtain a line that describes the relation would be to select two points from the data that appear to provide a good "fit" and find the equation of the line through these points.

▶ EXAMPLE 1   **Finding an Equation that Describes Linearly Related Data**

Problem: The data in Table 3 represent the per capita gross domestic product of randomly selected countries in Western Europe and the life expectancy of the residents. We determined that these data are linearly related in the last section.

(a) Find a linear equation that relates per capita GDP, *x* (the predictor variable), and life expectancy, *y* (the response variable), by selecting two points and finding the equation of the line containing the points.
(b) Graph the equation on the scatter diagram.
(c) Use the equation to predict the life expectancy of a resident of Spain where per capita GDP is $16.4 thousand.

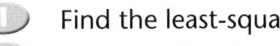

Country	Per Capita GDP, *x*	Life Expectancy, *y*	*(x, y)*
TABLE 3			
Austria	21.4	77.48	(21.4, 77.48)
Belgium	23.2	77.53	(23.2, 77.53)
Finland	20.0	77.32	(20.0, 77.32)
France	22.7	78.63	(22.7, 78.63)
Germany	20.8	77.17	(20.8, 77.17)
Ireland	18.6	76.39	(18.6, 76.39)
Italy	21.5	78.51	(21.5, 78.51)
Netherlands	22.0	78.15	(22.0, 78.15)
Switzerland	23.8	78.99	(23.8, 78.99)
United Kingdom	21.2	77.37	(21.2, 77.37)

Source: Time Almanac, 2000

Approach: To answer Part (a), we perform the following steps:

Step 1: Select two points from Table 3 such that a line drawn through the points appears to give a "good fit." Call the points (x_1, y_1) and (x_2, y_2). Refer to Figure 1 on page 193 for the scatter diagram.

Step 2: Find the slope of the line containing these two points using $m = \dfrac{y_2 - y_1}{x_2 - x_1}$.

Step 3: Use the point-slope formula, $y - y_1 = m(x - x_1)$, to find the line through the points selected in Step 1. Express the line in the form $y = mx + b$, where m is the slope and b is the y-intercept.

For part (b), draw a line through the points selected in Step 1 of part (a). Finally, for part (c), we let $x = 16.4$ in the equation found in part (a).

Solution:

(a) *Step 1:* We will select Ireland, $(x_1, y_1) = (18.6, 76.39)$, and Switzerland, $(x_2, y_2) = (23.8, 78.99)$, because a line drawn through these two points seems to give a good fit.

Step 2: $m = \dfrac{y_2 - y_1}{x_2 - x_1} = \dfrac{78.99 - 76.39}{23.8 - 18.6} = \dfrac{2.6}{5.2} = 0.5*$

Step 3: We use the point-slope form of a line to find the equation of the line.

$$y - y_1 = m(x - x_1)$$

$$y - 76.39 = 0.5(x - 18.6) \qquad \text{\small $m = 0.5$, $x_1 = 18.6$, $y_1 = 76.39$}$$

$$y - 76.39 = 0.5x - 9.3$$

$$y = 0.5x + 67.09 \qquad\qquad\qquad \textbf{(1)}$$

The slope of the line is 0.5 and the y-intercept is 67.09.

(b) Figure 7 shows the scatter diagram along with the line drawn through the points $(18.6, 76.39)$ and $(23.8, 78.99)$.

Figure 7

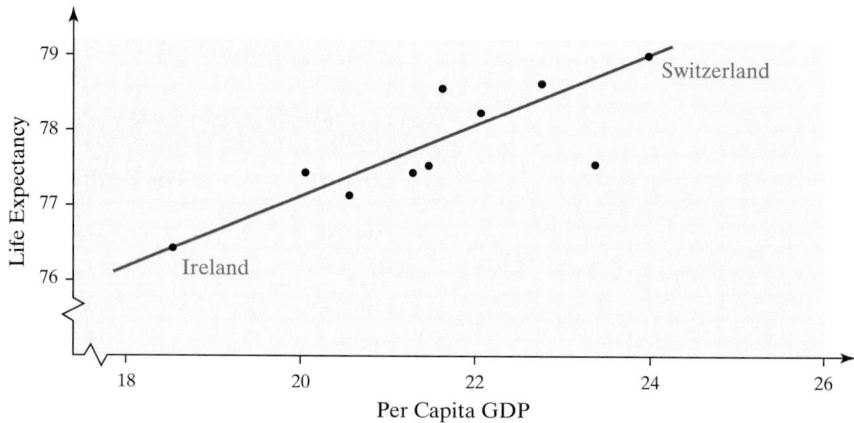

(c) We let $x = 16.4$ in equation (1) to predict the life expectancy of a resident of Spain.

$$y = 0.5(16.4) + 67.09$$

$$= 75.29$$

*Unless otherwise noted, we will round to four decimal places. As always, do not round until the last computation.

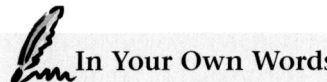

In Your Own Words

The residual represents how close our prediction comes to actual observation. The smaller the residual, the better is the prediction.

Historical Note

Adrien Marie Legendre was born on September 18, 1752. He was born into a wealthy family and educated in mathematics and physics at the College Mazarin in Paris. From 1775 to 1780, he taught at Ecole Militaire. On March 30, 1783, Legendre was appointed an adjoint in the Académie des Sciences. On May 13, 1791, he became a member of the committee of the Académie des Sciences and was charged with the task of standardizing weights and measures. The committee worked to compute the length of the meter. During the revolution, Legendre lost his small fortune. In 1794, Legendre published Eléments de géométrie, which was the leading elementary text in geometry for around 100 years. In 1806, Legendre published a book on orbits, in which he developed the theory of least squares. He died on January 10, 1833.

We predict that a resident of Spain can expect to live 75.29 years. In fact, in Spain, the life expectancy is 77.71 years, so we underestimated the life expectancy of a resident of Spain. ◀◀

 Now Work Problems 3(a), 3(b), and 3(c).

Least-Squares Regression

Although the line that we found in Example 1 appears to describe the relation between per capita GDP and life expectancy well, is there a line that fits the data better? Is there a line that fits the data "best"?

Consider Figure 8. Each y-coordinate on the line corresponds to a predicted life expectancy for a given level of per capita GDP. For example, the per capita GDP of Italy is \$21.5 thousand, so the predicted life expectancy is $0.5(21.5) + 67.09 = 77.84$ years. The observed life expectancy in Italy is 78.51 years. The difference between the observed value of y and the predicted value of y is the error or **residual**. For Italy, the residual is

$$\text{Residual} = \text{observed } y - \text{predicted } y$$
$$= 78.51 - 77.84$$
$$= 0.67 \text{ years}$$

The residual for Italy is labeled in Figure 8.

Figure 8

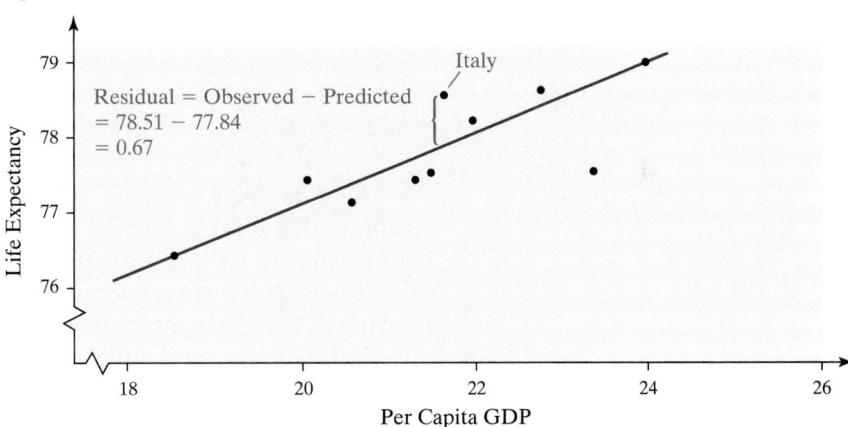

The line that "best" describes the relation between two variables is the one that makes the residuals "as small as possible." The most popular technique for making the residuals "as small as possible" is the *method of least squares*, discovered by Adrien Marie Legendre.

Definition

Least-Squares Regression Criterion

The **least-squares regression line** is the one that minimizes the sum of the squared errors. It is the line that minimizes the square of the vertical distance between observed values of y and those predicted by the line, $\hat{y}$ (read "y-hat"). We represent this as

$$\text{Minimize } \sum \text{residuals}^2$$

The advantage of the least-squares criterion is that it allows for statistical inference on the predicted value and slope (Chapter 12). Another advantage of the least-squares criterion is explained by Legendre in his text *Nouvelles méthodes pour la determination des orbites des comètes*, published in 1805.

> Of all the principles that can be proposed for this purpose, I think there is none more general, more exact, or easier to apply, than that which we have used in this work; it consists of making the sum of squares of the errors a *minimum*. By this method, a kind of equilibrium is established among the errors which, since it prevents the extremes from dominating, is appropriate for revealing the state of the system which most nearly approaches the truth.

Theorem

Equation of the Least-Squares Regression Line

The equation of the least-squares regression line is given by

$$\hat{y} = b_1 x + b_0$$

where

$b_1 = r \cdot \dfrac{s_y}{s_x}$ is the **slope** of the least-squares regression line*   (2)

and

$b_0 = \bar{y} - b_1 \bar{x}$ is the **y-intercept** of the least-squares regression line   (3)

Note: $\bar{x}$ is the sample mean and s_x is the sample standard deviation of the predictor variable x; $\bar{y}$ is the sample mean and s_y is the sample standard deviation of the response variable y.

The notation $\hat{y}$ is used in the least-squares regression line to serve as a reminder that it is a predicted value of y for a given value of x. An interesting property of the least-squares regression line, $\hat{y} = b_1 x + b_0$, is that the line always contains the point $(\bar{x}, \bar{y})$. This property can be useful in the drawing of the least-squares regression line by hand.

Since s_y and s_x must both be positive, the sign of the linear correlation coefficient determines the sign of the slope of the least-squares regression line.

▶ **EXAMPLE 2**   **Finding the Least-Squares Regression Line**

Problem: For the data in Table 3 on page 207,

(a) Find the least-squares regression line.
(b) Interpret the slope and intercept.
(c) Predict the life expectancy of a resident of Italy where per capita GDP is $21.5 thousand.

*An equivalent formula is $b_1 = \dfrac{S_{xy}}{S_{xx}} = \dfrac{\sum x_i y_i - \dfrac{(\sum x_i)(\sum y_i)}{n}}{\sum x_i^2 - \dfrac{(\sum x_i)^2}{n}}$

(d) Compute the residual for Italy.

(e) Draw the least-squares regression line on the scatter diagram of the data.

Approach:

(a) From Example 2 in Section 4.1, we have the following: $r = 0.8094$, $\bar{x} = 21.52$, $s_x = 1.531738$, $\bar{y} = 77.754$ and $s_y = 0.794847$. We substitute these values into Formula (2) to find the slope of the least-squares regression line. We use Formula (3) to find the intercept of the least-squares regression.

(b) The slope represents the change in life expectancy divided by the change in per capita GDP, so we interpret the slope as the additional life expectancy if per capita GDP rises by $1 thousand. The intercept represents the value of the response variable when the predictor variable is 0.

(c) Substitute $x = 21.5$ into the least-squares regression line found in part (a) to find $\hat{y}$.

(d) The residual is the difference between the observed y and the predicted y. That is, residual $= y - \hat{y}$.

(e) To draw the least-squares regression line, select two values of x and use the equation to find the predicted values of y. Plot these points on the scatter diagram and draw a line through the points.

Solution:

(a) Substituting $r = 0.8094$, $s_x = 1.531738$, and $s_y = 0.794847$ into Formula (2), we obtain

$$b_1 = r \cdot \frac{s_y}{s_x} = 0.8094 \cdot \frac{0.794847}{1.531738} = 0.4200*$$

We have that $\bar{x} = 21.52$ and $\bar{y} = 77.754$. Substituting these values into Formula (3), we obtain

$$b_0 = \bar{y} - b_1\bar{x} = 77.754 - 0.4200(21.52) = 68.7156$$

The least-squares regression line is

$$\hat{y} = 0.4200x + 68.7156$$

(b) The slope of the least-squares regression line is 0.4200. If per capita GDP increases by $1 thousand, life expectancy increases by 0.42 years. The intercept is 68.7156 years. The intercept is found by letting $x = 0$, so the intercept is the life expectancy in a country where per capita GDP is $0. It is probably unreasonable to interpret the intercept since countries with per capita GDP of $0 do not occur in our data set.

(c) We let $x = 21.5$ in the equation $y = 0.4200x + 68.7156$ to predict the life expectancy in Italy.

$$\hat{y} = 0.4200(21.5) + 68.7156$$

$$= 77.75 \text{ years}$$

We predict that the life expectancy in Italy is 77.75 years.

*Throughout the text, we will round the slope and y-intercept values to four decimal places.

Historical Note

Sir Francis Galton was born on February 16, 1822. Galton came from a wealthy and well-known family. His first cousin was Charles Darwin. Galton studied medicine at Cambridge. After receiving a large inheritance, he left the medical field and traveled the world. He explored Africa from 1850–1852. In the 1860s, his study of meteorology led him to discover "anticyclones." Influenced by Darwin, Galton always had an interest in genetics and heredity. He studied heredity through experiments with sweet peas. He noticed that the weight of the "children" of the "parent" peas reverted or "regressed" to the mean weight of all peas. Hence, the term "regression analysis." Galton died January 17, 1911.

④ (d) The actual life expectancy in Italy is 78.51 years. The residual is

$$\text{residual} = \text{observed } y - \text{predicted } y$$
$$= y - \hat{y}$$
$$= 78.51 - 77.75$$
$$= 0.76 \text{ years}$$

We underestimated life expectancy in Italy by 0.76 years.

(e) Figure 9 shows the graph of the least-squares regression line drawn on the scatter diagram with the residual labeled.

Figure 9

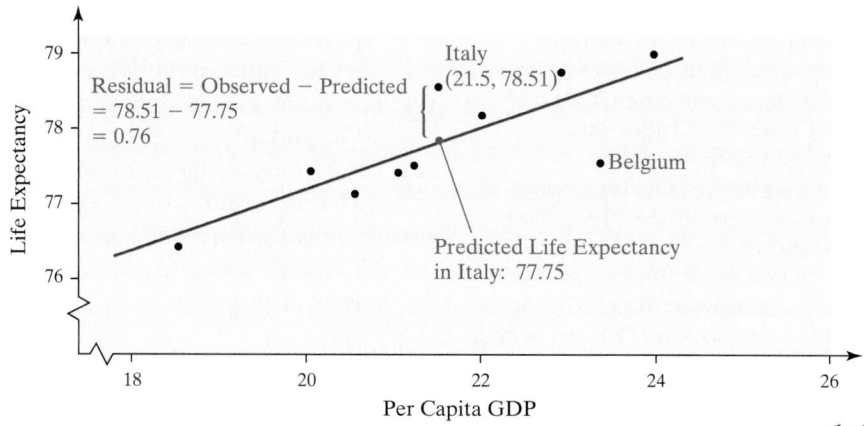

Notice that an underestimate results in a positive residual, while an overestimate will result in a negative residual.

We can think of any point on the least-squares regression line as the mean value of the response variable for a given value of the predictor variable. For example, the mean life expectancy for a country that has per capita GDP of $21.5 thousand is 77.75 years. Because the life expectancy in Italy is 78.51 years, the Italians have a life expectancy that is higher than the mean life expectancy of countries that have per capita GDP of $21.5 thousand. Perhaps it's the red wine!

Look back at Figure 9. Which country would result in the worst prediction? The worst prediction would be the country whose residual differs the most from zero (i.e., has the furthest vertical distance from the line of best fit). From Figure 9, it would seem that Belgium (per capita GDP: $23.2 thousand, life expectancy: 77.53) would result in the worst prediction. The predicted life expectancy for Belgium is

$$\hat{y} = 0.4200(23.2) + 68.7156$$
$$= 78.46 \text{ years}$$

The residual for Belgium is then

$$\text{Residual} = \text{observed } y - \text{predicted } y$$
$$= y - \hat{y}$$
$$= 77.53 - 78.46$$
$$= -0.93 \text{ years}$$

We overestimated the life expectancy in Belgium by 0.93 years. Which country results in the best prediction?

In Your Own Words

An underestimate means the residual is positive; an overestimate means the residual is negative. A residual of zero means the prediction is right on!

The Scope of the Model

It is important to note that the *y*-intercept will have meaning only if the following two conditions are met:

1. A value of 0 for the predictor variable makes sense.

2. There are observed values of the predictor variable near 0.

Caution

Never use the least-squares regression line to make predictions for values of the predictor variable that are much larger or much smaller than those observed.

The second condition is especially important because statisticians do not use the regression model to make predictions **outside the scope of the model**. In other words, statisticians do not recommend using the regression model to make predictions for values of the predictor variable that are much larger or much smaller than those observed because we cannot be certain of the behavior of the data for which we have no observations.

For example, it would be inappropriate to use the line we determined in Example 2 to predict life expectancy in a country where per capita GDP is $40 thousand. The highest observed per capita GDP in our data set is $23.8 thousand and we cannot be certain that the linear relation between per capita GDP and life expectancy will continue. It is likely that at high levels of per capita GDP, life expectancy will level off. See Figure 10.

Figure 10

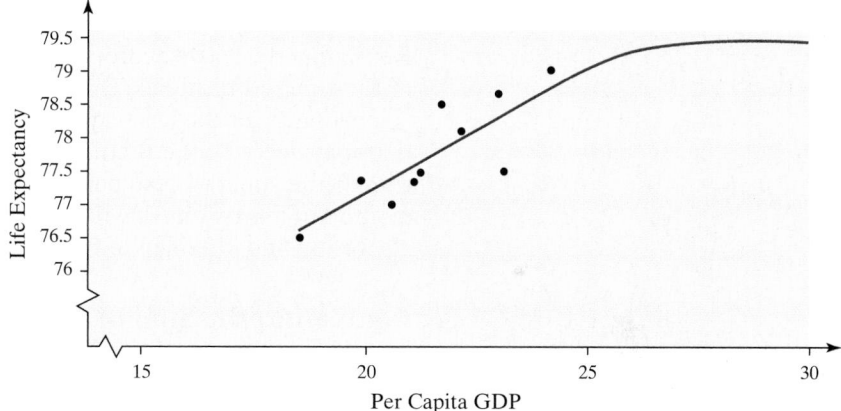

Using Technology: While we have presented the procedure for computing the least-squares regression line by hand, in practice a calculator or statistical spreadsheet program is used to determine the least-squares regression line. Figure 11(a) shows the output obtained from a TI-83 Plus graphing calculator, and Figure 11(b) shows the output obtained from Minitab with the slope and *y*-intercept highlighted. Figure 11(c) shows partial output from Excel with the slope and intercept highlighted.

Figure 11

Slope ———

y-intercept ———

```
LinReg
y=ax+b
a=.4200227316
b=68.71511082
r²=.6551599375
r=.8094195065
```

(a)

Figure 11 (cont.)

Regression

```
The regression equation is
y = 68.7 + 0.420 x

Predictor          Coef    StDev        T        P
Constant         68.715    2.324    29.57    0.000
X                0.4200   0.1077     3.90    0.005

S = 0.4951     R-Sq = 65.5%      R-Sq(adj) = 61.2%
```

(b)

	Coefficients	Standard Error	t Stat	P-value
Intercept	68.71511082	2.323769861	29.57053	1.85E-09
X Variable 1	0.420022732	0.107736532	3.89861	0.004554

(c)

NW *Now Work Problems 3(d) and 3(e).*

5 ## Least-Squares Criterion Revisited

Recall that the least-squares regression line is the line that minimizes the sum of the squared residuals. This means that the sum of the squared residuals, $\sum \text{residuals}^2$ for the least-squares line will be smaller than for any other line that may describe the relation between the two variables. In particular, the sum of the squared residuals for the line obtained in Example 2 using the method of least-squares will be smaller than the sum of the squared residuals for the line obtained in Example 1. It is worthwhile to verify this result.

▶ EXAMPLE 3 ### Comparing the Sum of Squared Residuals

Problem: Compare the sum of squared residuals for the lines obtained in Examples 1 and 2.

Approach: We compute $\sum \text{residuals}^2$ using the predicted values of y, $\hat{y}$, for the lines obtained in Examples 1 and 2. This is best done by creating a table of values.

Solution: We create Table 4, which contains the value of the predictor variable in Column 1. Column 2 contains the corresponding response variable. Column 3 contains the predicted value of the response variable using the equation obtained in Example 1, $\hat{y} = 0.5x + 67.09$. In Column 4, we compute the residuals for each observation, residual = observed y–predicted y. For example, the first residual using the equation found in Example 1 is observed y– predicted y = 77.48–77.79 = −0.31. Column 5 contains the squares of the residuals obtained in Column 4. Column 6 contains the predicted value of the response variable using the least-squares regression equation obtained in Example 2: $\hat{y} = 0.4200x + 68.7156$. Column 7 represents the residuals for each observation and Column 8 represents the squared residuals.

Per Capita GDP	Life Expectancy	$y = 0.5x +$ 67.09 EXAMPLE 1	residual	residual^2	$\hat{y} = 0.4200x +$ 68.7156 EXAMPLE 2	residual	residual^2
21.4	77.48	0.5(21.4) + 67.09 = 77.79	77.48 − 77.79 = −0.31	$(−.31)^2$ = 0.0961	0.4200(21.4) + 68.7156 = 77.70	77.48 − 77.70 = −0.22	$(−0.22)^2$ = 0.0484
23.2	77.53	78.69	−1.16	1.3456	78.46	−0.93	0.8649
20	77.32	77.09	0.23	0.0529	77.12	0.20	0.04
22.7	78.63	78.44	0.19	0.0361	78.25	0.38	0.1444
20.8	77.17	77.49	−0.32	0.1024	77.45	−0.28	0.0784
18.6	76.39	76.39	0	0	76.53	−0.14	0.0196
21.5	78.51	77.84	0.67	0.4489	77.75	0.76	0.5776
22	78.15	78.09	0.06	0.0036	77.96	0.19	0.0361
23.8	78.99	78.99	0	0	78.71	0.28	0.0784
21.2	77.37	77.69	−0.32	0.1024	77.62	−0.25	0.0625
			$\sum$ residual = −0.96	$\sum$ residual^2 = 2.188		$\sum$ residual = −0.01*	$\sum$ residual^2 = 1.9503

TABLE 4

The sum of the squared residuals for the line found in Example 1 is 2.188, while the sum of the squared residuals for the least-squares regression line is 1.9503. Again, any line that describes the relation between per capita GDP and life expectancy will have a sum of squared residuals that is greater than 1.9503.

◄◄

NW *Now Work Problems 3(f) and 3(g)*

We draw the graphs of the two lines obtained in Examples 1 and 2 on the same scatter diagram in Figure 12 to help the reader visualize the difference.

Figure 12

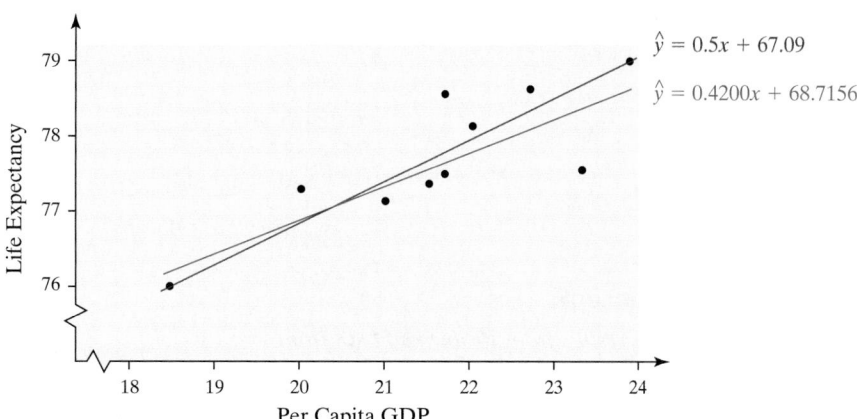

$\hat{y} = 0.5x + 67.09$

$\hat{y} = 0.4200x + 68.7156$

Look back at Table 4. Notice that the sum of the residuals based on the line found in Example 1 (Column 4) does not add up to zero. Because the sum of the residuals adds up to −0.96, the model is consistently overestimating life expectancy. In least-squares regression models, the fact that the sum of the residuals is always zero means that the overestimates are offset by underestimates. That is, the predicted value is an **unbiased estimator** of the actual observation.

* The sum of the residuals for the least-squares regression line does not sum to zero due to rounding error.

4.2 Assess Your Understanding

Concepts and Vocabulary

1. Explain the least-squares regression criterion.
2. What is a residual? What does it mean when a residual is positive?
3. Explain the phrase "outside the scope of the model." Why is it dangerous to make predictions "outside the scope of the model"?
4. If the linear correlation between two variables is negative, what can be said about the slope of the regression line?
5. What is meant by an unbiased estimator as it pertains to least-squares regression?
6. In your own words, explain the meaning of Legendre's quote given on page 210.

Exercises

• Skill Building

1. For the data set

x	0	2	3	5	6	6
y	5.8	5.7	5.2	2.8	1.9	2.2

   (a) Draw a scatter diagram. Comment on the type of relation that appears to exist between x and y.
   (b) Given that $\bar{x} = 3.667$, $s_x = 2.42212$, $\bar{y} = 3.933$, $s_y = 1.8239152$, and $r = -0.9476938$, determine the least-squares regression line. $\hat{y} = -0.7136x + 6.55$
   (c) Graph the least-squares regression line on the scatter diagram drawn in part (a).

2. For the data set

x	2	4	8	8	9
y	1.4	1.8	2.1	2.3	2.6

   (a) Draw a scatter diagram. Comment on the type of relation that appears to exist between x and y.
   (b) Given that $\bar{x} = 6.2$, $s_x = 3.03315$, $\bar{y} = 2.04$, $s_y = 0.461519$, and $r = 0.957241$, determine the least-squares regression line. $\hat{y} = 0.1457x + 1.1370$
   (c) Graph the least-squares regression line on the scatter diagram drawn in part (a).

In Problems 3–8:

   (a) Draw a scatter diagram treating x as the predictor variable and y as the response variable.
   (b) Select two points from the scatter diagram and find the equation of the line containing the points selected.
   (c) Graph the line found in part (b) on the scatter diagram.
   (d) Determine the least-squares regression line.
   (e) Graph the least-squares regression line on the scatter diagram.
   (f) Compute the sum of the squared residuals for the line found in part (b).
   (g) Compute the sum of the squared residuals for the least-squares regression line found in part (d).
   (h) Comment on the "fit" of the line found in part (b) versus the least-squares regression line found in part (d).

3. (NW)

x	3	4	5	7	8
y	4	6	7	12	14

4.

x	3	5	7	9	11
y	0	2	3	6	9

5.

x	−2	−1	0	1	2
y	−4	0	1	4	5

6.

x	−2	−1	0	1	2
y	7	6	3	2	0

7.

x	20	30	40	50	60
y	100	95	91	83	70

8.

x	5	10	15	20	25
y	2	4	7	11	18

• Applying the Concepts

Problems 9–16 use the results from Problems 11–18 from Section 4.1.

9. **Height versus Head Circumference** A pediatrician wants to determine the relation that exists between a child's height and head circumference. She randomly selects 11 children from her practice, measures their height and head circumference, and obtains the following data.

   (a) Find the least-squares regression line treating height as the predictor variable and head circumference as the response variable. Head = 0.1827 Height + 12.4932
   (b) Interpret the slope and intercept, if appropriate.
   (c) Use the regression equation to predict the head circumference of a child who is 25 inches tall. 17.1 inches

Height (inches)	Head Circumference (inches)	Height (inches)	Head Circumference (inches)
27.75	17.5	26.5	17.3
24.5	17.1	27	17.5
25.5	17.1	26.75	17.3
26	17.3	26.75	17.5
25	16.9	27.5	17.5
27.75	17.6		

Source: Denise Slucki, Student at Joliet Junior College

(d) Compute the residual based upon the observed head circumference of the 25-inch-tall child in the table. Is the head circumference of this 25-inch-tall child above average or below average? −0.2 inches; below

(e) Draw the least-squares regression line on the scatter diagram of the data and label the residual.

(f) Notice that there are two children that are 26.75 inches tall. One of the children has a head circumference that is 17.3 inches, while the other has a head circumference that is 17.5 inches. How can this be?

(g) Would it be reasonable to use the least-squares regression line to predict the head circumference of a child who was 32 inches tall? Why? No

10. **Round-cut Diamonds** A gemologist is interested in determining the relation that exists between the size of a diamond (carats) and the price. The following data represent the weight and price of D color, VS1 clarity, round-cut diamonds.

Carats	Price	Carats	Price
0.66	$3282	0.80	$4378
0.75	$3950	0.90	$5682
0.70	$3543	0.91	$6426
0.71	$3788	1.18	$9362
0.77	$4108		

Source: diamonds.com

(a) Find the least-squares regression line treating carats as the predictor variable and price as the response variable. Price = 12092.16 · Carats − 4969.01

(b) Interpret the slope and intercept, if appropriate.

(c) Use the regression equation to predict the price of a color D, VS1 clarity round-cut diamond that weighs 0.91 carats. $6034.86

(d) Compute the residual of a color D, VS1 clarity round-cut diamond that weighs 0.91 carats and costs $6426. Is this diamond priced above average or below average? $391.14; above

(e) Draw the least-squares regression line on the scatter diagram of the data and label the residual.

(f) Predict the price of a color D, VS1 clarity round-cut diamond that weights 0.85 carats. $5309.33

(g) Suppose the gemologist had two 0.85 carat, color D, VS1 clarity round-cut diamonds, but one was priced at $4503 and the other at $5420. What might account for the difference in price of these two diamonds?

(h) Would it be reasonable to use the least-squares regression line to predict the price of a color D, VS1 clarity, round-cut diamond that weighs 0.25 carats? Why? No

11. **Gestation Period versus Life Expectancy** The following data represent the gestation period of various animals along with their life expectancy.

Animal	Gestation (or Incubation) Period (days)	Life Expectancy (years)
Cat	63	11
Chicken	22	7.5
Dog	63	11
Duck	28	10
Goat	151	12
Lion	108	10
Parakeet	18	8
Pig	115	10
Rabbit	31	7
Squirrel	44	9

Source: Time Almanac 2000

(a) Find the least-squares regression line treating gestation period as the predictor variable and life expectancy as the response variable.

(b) Interpret the slope and intercept, if appropriate.

(c) Suppose a new animal species has been discovered. After breeding the species in captivity, it is determined that the gestation period is 95 days. Use the least-squares regression line to predict the life expectancy of the animal. 10.4 years

(d) Use the regression equation to predict the life expectancy of a parakeet. 8.3 years

(e) Use the regression equation to predict the life expectancy of a guinea pig (gestation period = 68 days. 9.6 years

(f) Compute the residual of the prediction made in part (e) if the life expectancy of a guinea pig is three years. Conclude that the least-squares regression line sometimes provides accurate predictions (as in the case of the parakeet) and sometimes provides inaccurate predictions (as in the case of the guinea pig). Unfortunately, when the value of the response variable is unknown (as in the case of the new animal species from part [c]), we don't know the accuracy of the prediction. −6.6 years

(11a) Life = 0.0261 · gestation + 7.8738

12. Tar and Nicotine Every year the Federal Trade Commission must report tar and nicotine levels in cigarettes to the Congress. It obtains the tar and nicotine levels in over 1200 brands of cigarettes. A sample from those reported to Congress is given in the following table.

Brand	Tar (mg)	Nicotine (mg)
Barclay 100	5	0.4
Benson and Hedges King	16	1.1
Camel Regular	24	1.7
Chesterfield King	24	1.4
Doral	8	0.5
Kent Golden Lights	9	0.8
Kool Menthol	9	0.8
Lucky Strike	24	1.5
Marlboro Gold	15	1.2
Newport Menthol	18	1.3
Salem Menthol	17	1.3
Virginia Slims Ultra Light	5	0.5
Winston Light	10	0.8

Source: Federal Trade Commission

(a) Find the least-squares regression line treating tar as the predictor variable and nicotine as the response variable. Nicotine = 0.0575 tar + 0.2088
(b) Interpret the slope and intercept, if appropriate.
(c) Determine the residual of a cigarette that has 18 mg of tar and 1.3 mg of nicotine. Is the amount of nicotine in this cigarette above average or below average?
(d) Draw the least-squares regression line on the scatter diagram of the data and label the residual from part (c).
(e) Suppose a cigarette has 21 mg of tar. Use the least-squares regression line to predict the level of nicotine.

13. Bone Length Research performed at NASA and led by Dr. Emily R. Morey-Holton measured the lengths of the right humerus and right tibia in 11 rats that were sent to space on Spacelab Life Sciences 2. The following data were collected.

Right Humerus (mm)	Right Tibia (mm)	Right Humerus (mm)	Right Tibia (mm)
24.8	36.05	25.9	37.38
24.59	35.57	26.11	37.96
24.59	35.57	26.63	37.46
24.29	34.58	26.31	37.75
23.81	34.2	26.84	38.5
24.87	34.73		

Source: NASA Life Sciences Data Archive

(a) Find the least-squares regression line treating the length of the right humerus as the predictor variable and the length of the right tibia as the response variable. Tibia = 1.3902 Humerus + 1.1140
(b) Interpret the slope and intercept, if appropriate.
(c) Determine the residual if the length of the right humerus is 26.11 mm and the actual length of the right tibia is 37.96 mm. Is the length of this tibia above average or below average? 0.55 mm; above
(d) Draw the least-squares regression line on the scatter diagram and label the residual.
(e) Suppose one of the rats sent to space received a broken right tibia due to a severe landing. The length of the right humerus is determined to be 25.31 mm. Use the least-squares regression line to estimate the length of the right tibia. 36.30 mm

14. Weight of a Car versus Miles per Gallon An engineer wanted to determine how the weight of a car affected the gas mileage. The following data represent the weight of various domestic cars and their miles per gallon in the city for the 2001 model year.

Car	Weight (pounds)	Miles Per Gallon
Buick LeSabre	3565	19
Buick Regal	3440	20
Cadillac Seville	3970	17
Chevrolet Camaro	3305	19
Chevrolet Monte Carlo	3340	20
Chrysler PT Cruiser	3200	20
Chrysler Sebring Sedan	3230	19
Dodge Neon	2560	28
Ford Focus	2520	28
Ford Mustang	3065	20
Lincoln LS	3600	18
Mercury Sable	3300	19
Oldsmobile Aurora	3625	19
Pontiac Bonneville	3590	19
Pontiac Sunfire	2605	23
Saturn Coupe	2370	28

Source: *Road and Track* magazine

(a) Find the least-squares regression line treating weight as the predictor variable and miles per gallon as the response variable.
(b) Interpret the slope and intercept, if appropriate.
(c) Predict the miles per gallon of an Oldsmobile Aurora and compute the residual. Is the miles per gallon of an Aurora above average or below average for cars of this weight? 18; above

(12c) 0.1 mg; above (12e) 1.4 mg
(14a) MPG = −0.0073 weight + 44.2657

(d) Draw the least-squares regression line on the scatter diagram of the data and label the residual.

(e) Would it be reasonable to use the least-squares regression line to predict the miles per gallon of a Honda Insight—a hybrid gas and electric car? Why? No

15. **General Electric versus the S&P 500** The following data represent the rate of return of GE stock for 13 months versus the rate of return of the Standard & Poor's Index of 500 stocks.

Month	Rate of Return of S&P 500	Rate of Return of GE
Sep-99	−2.9	5.6
Oct-99	6.3	14.3
Nov-99	1.9	−4.0
Dec-99	5.8	18.9
Jan-00	−5.0	−13.4
Feb-00	−2.0	−1.2
Mar-00	10.0	17.6
Apr-00	−3.1	1.0
May-00	−2.2	0.4
Jun-00	2.4	0.7
Jul-00	−1.6	−2.5
Aug-00	6.1	13.4
Sep-00	−5.3	−1.2

Source: Yahoo! Finance

(a) Find the least-squares regression line treating the rate of return of the S&P 500 as the predictor variable and the rate of return of General Electric as the response variable. GE = 1.6028 S&P 500 + 2.5331

(b) Interpret the slope and y-intercept, if appropriate. The slope of the line is referred to as the **beta** of the stock. Stock analysts use beta to determine how a stock will perform relative to the market. For example, a beta of 1.1 means that in a month in which the S&P 500 increases 1%, the stock will increase 1.1%. So stocks with betas greater than 1 have more price movement than the overall market; they are, therefore, considered riskier than those stocks with betas less than 1.

(c) Predict the rate of return of General Electric if the rate of return of the S&P 500 is 8.9 percent. 16.8%

16. **Fat-free Mass versus Energy Expenditure** In an effort to measure the dependence of energy expenditure on body build, researchers used underwater weighing techniques to determine the fat-free body mass for seven men. In addition, they measured the total 24-hour energy expenditure during inactivity. The results are shown in the table.

(16a) Energy = 25.0116 Mass + 607.7034

Fat-free Mass (kg)	Energy Expenditure (Kcal)
49.3	1894
59.3	2050
68.3	2353
48.1	1838
57.6	1948
78.1	2528
76.1	2568

Source: Webb, P. (1981) Energy expenditure and fat-free mass in men and women. *American Journal of Clinical Nutrition, 34,* 1816–1826

(a) Find the least-squares regression line treating fat-free mass as the predictor variable and energy expenditure as the response variable.

(b) Interpret the slope and intercept, if appropriate.

(c) Predict the energy expenditure where fat-free mass is 52.4 kg. 1918 Kcal

17. **Does Size Matter?** Researchers Willerman, Schultz, Rutledge, and Bigler wondered whether the size of a person's brain was related to the individual's mental capacity. They selected a sample of right-handed Anglo introductory psychology students who had Scholastic Aptitude Test Scores higher than 1350. The subjects were administered the Wechsler (1981) Adult Intelligence Scale-Revised in order to obtain their IQ scores. The MRI Scans, performed at the same facility, consisted of 18 horizontal MR images. The computer counted all pixels with nonzero gray scale in each of the 18 images and the total count served as an index for brain size. The resulting data are presented in the table below.

Gender	MRI Count	IQ	Gender	MRI Count	IQ
Female	816,932	133	Male	949,395	140
Female	951,545	137	Male	1,001,121	140
Female	991,305	138	Male	1,038,437	139
Female	833,868	132	Male	965,353	133
Female	856,472	140	Male	955,466	133
Female	852,244	132	Male	1,079,549	141
Female	790,619	135	Male	924,059	135
Female	866,662	130	Male	955,003	139
Female	857,782	133	Male	935,494	141
Female	948,066	133	Male	949,589	144

Source: Willerman, L., Schultz, R., Rutledge, J. N., and Bigler, E. (1991), "In Vivo Brain Size and Intelligence," *Intelligence,* 15, 223–228.

(a) Find the least-squares regression line treating MRI Count as the predictor variable and IQ as the response variable. IQ = 0.00003 MRI + 109.8940

(b) What do you notice about the value of the slope? Why does this result seem reasonable based upon the scatter diagram and linear correlation coefficient obtained in Problem 21 of Section 4.1?

(c) When there is no relation between the predictor and response variable, we use the mean value of the response variable, $\bar{y}$, to predict. Predict the IQ of an individual whose MRI Count is 1,000,000. Predict the IQ of an individual whose MRI Count is 830,000. 136; 136

18. **Male versus Female Drivers** The following data represent the number of licensed drivers in various age groups and the number of accidents within the age group by gender.

Age Group	Number of Male Licensed Drivers (000s)	Number of Crashes Involving a Male (000s)	Number of Female Licensed Drivers (000s)	Number of Crashes Involving a Female (000s)
16	816	244	764	178
17	1198	233	1115	175
18	1342	243	1212	164
19	1454	229	1333	145
20–24	7866	951	7394	618
25–29	9356	899	8946	595
30–34	10,121	875	9871	571
35–39	10,521	901	10,439	566
40–44	9776	692	9752	455
45–49	8754	667	8710	390
50–54	6840	390	6763	247
55–59	5341	290	5258	165
60–64	4565	218	4486	133
65–69	4234	191	4231	121
70–74	3604	167	3749	104
75–79	2563	118	2716	77
80–84	1400	61	1516	45
≥ 85	767	34	767	20

Source: National Highway and Traffic Safety Institute

(a) Find the least-squares regression line for males, treating number of licensed drivers as the predictor variable and number of crashes as the response variable. Repeat this procedure for females.

(b) Interpret the slope of the least-squares regression line for each gender, if appropriate. How might an insurance company use this information?

(c) Predict the number of accidents for males if there were 8700 thousand licensed drivers. Predict the number of accidents for females if there were 8700 thousand licensed drivers.

(18a) Males: Crash = 0.0802 Drivers + 8.14; Females: Crash = 0.0505 Drivers + 15.1611
(18c) Males: 706 thousand; Females: 455 thousand

Technology Step-by-Step
Determining the Least-Squares Regression Line

TI-83 Plus	Use the same steps that were followed to obtain the correlation coefficient.
MINITAB	**Step 1:** With the predictor variable in C1 and the response variable in C2, select the **Stat** menu and highlight **Regression**. Highlight **Regression**. . . .
	Step 2: Select the predictor and response variables and click OK.
Excel	**Step 1:** Be sure the Data Analysis Tool Pak is activated by selecting the **Tools** menu and highlighting **Add-Ins** . . . Check the box for the Analysis ToolPak and select OK.
	Step 2: Enter the predictor variable in column A and the response variable in column B.
	Step 3: Select the **Tools** menu and highlight **Data Analysis** . . .
	Step 4: Select the **Regression** option.
	Step 5: With the cursor in the Y-range cell, highlight the column that contains the response variable. With the cursor in the X-range cell, highlight the column that contains the predictor variable. Press OK.

4.3   Diagnostics on the Least-Squares Regression Line

Preparing for This Section   Before getting started, review the following:

- ✓ Z-scores (Section 3.4, pp. 158–159)
- ✓ Outliers (Section 3.4, pp. 163–164)

Objectives   ① Compute and interpret the coefficient of determination
② Perform residual analysis on a regression model
③ Identify influential observations

In Section 4.2, we discussed the procedure for obtaining the least-squares regression line. In this section, we discuss additional characteristics of the least-squares regression line, along with graphical diagnostic tests that should be performed on every least-squares regression line.

① The Coefficient of Determination

In Your Own Words

Just as a doctor performs tests in order to diagnose her or his patients, a researcher must use tests to diagnose what, if anything, is wrong with the least-squares regression line.

Consider the per capita GDP versus life expectancy data introduced in Section 4.1. If we were asked to predict the life expectancy of a randomly selected Western European, what would a good guess be? Our best guess might be the average life expectancy of all Western Europeans. Since we don't know this value, we would use the average life expectancy from the sample data given in Table 1 on page 193, $\bar{y} = 77.75$.

Now suppose we were told this particular European lives in France where the per capita GDP is $22.7 thousand. We could use the least-squares regression line to adjust our "guess" to $\hat{y} = 0.4200(22.7) + 68.7156 = 78.25$ years. Knowing the linear relation that exists between per capita GDP and life expectancy allows us to increase our estimate of the life expectancy of the individual. In statistical terms, we say that some of the variation in life expectancy is explained by the linear relation between per capita GDP and life expectancy.

A descriptive measure of the percentage of variation in life expectancy that is explained by the least-squares regression line is the *coefficient of determination*.

Definition

> The **coefficient of determination,** R^2, measures the percentage of total variation in the response variable that is explained by the least-squares regression line.

![feather pen icon] **In Your Own Words**

The coefficient of determination is a measure of how well the least-squares regression line describes the relation between the predictor and response variable. The closer R^2 is to 1, the better the line describes how changes in the predictor affect the value of the response.

The coefficient of determination is a number between 0 and 1, inclusive. That is, $0 \le R^2 \le 1$. If $R^2 = 0$, the least-squares regression line has no explanatory value; if $R^2 = 1$, the least-squares regression line explains 100% of the variation in the response variable.

Consider Figure 13, where a horizontal line is drawn at $\bar{y} = 77.75$. This value represents the predicted life expectancy of a Western European without any knowledge of her or his country's per capita GDP. Armed with the additional information that the individual is from France, we increased our "guess" to 78.25 years. The difference between the predicted life expectancy of 78.25 years and the predicted life expectancy of 77.75 years is due to the fact that the individual is from France. In other words, the difference between the prediction of $\hat{y} = 78.25$ and $\bar{y} = 77.75$ is explained by the linear relation between per capita GDP and life expectancy. The actual life expectancy in France is 78.63 years. The difference between our predicted value, $\hat{y} = 78.25$, and the actual value, $y = 78.63$, is due to factors other than the per capita GDP in France (perhaps the French have a healthy life style) and random error. In general, these differences are called **deviations**.

Figure 13

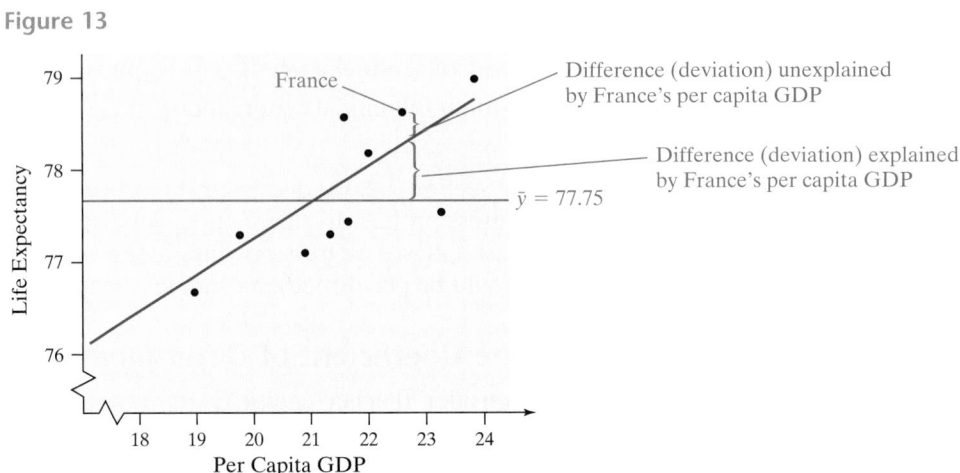

The deviation between the observed value of the response variable, y, and the mean value of the response variable, $\bar{y}$, is called the **total deviation**, so total deviation $= y - \bar{y}$. The deviation between the predicted value of the response variable, $\hat{y}$, and the mean value of the response variable, $\bar{y}$, is called the **explained deviation**, so explained deviation $= \hat{y} - \bar{y}$. Finally, the deviation between the observed value of the response variable, y, and the predicted value of the response variable, $\hat{y}$, is called the **unexplained deviation**, so unexplained deviation $= y - \hat{y}$. See Figure 14.

![feather pen icon] **In Your Own Words**

The word "deviations" comes from "deviate." "To deviate" means "to stray."

Figure 14

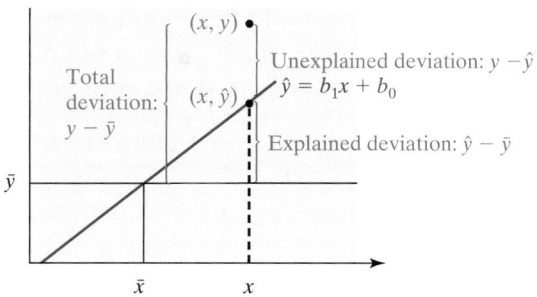

From the figure, it should be clear that

$$y - \bar{y} = (y - \hat{y}) + (\hat{y} - \bar{y})$$

or

Total deviation = unexplained deviation + explained deviation.

Although beyond the scope of this text, it can be shown that

$$(y - \bar{y})^2 = (y - \hat{y})^2 + (\hat{y} - \bar{y})^2$$

or

Total variation = unexplained variation + explained variation

Dividing both sides by total variation we obtain

$$1 = \frac{\text{unexplained variation}}{\text{total variation}} + \frac{\text{explained variation}}{\text{total variation}}$$

Subtracting $\dfrac{\text{unexplained variation}}{\text{total variation}}$ from both sides, we obtain

$$R^2 = \frac{\text{explained variation}}{\text{total variation}} = 1 - \frac{\text{unexplained variation}}{\text{total variation}}$$

Unexplained variation is found by summing the squares of the residuals, $\sum \text{residuals}^2$. So, the smaller the sum of squared residuals, the smaller the unexplained variation, and therefore, the larger R^2 will be. Therefore, the closer the observed y's are to the regression line (the predicted y's), the larger R^2 will be.

Theorem

The coefficient of determination, R^2, is the square of the linear correlation coefficient for the least-squares regression model.

▶ EXAMPLE 1   **Computing the Coefficient of Determination, R^2**

Problem: Compute and interpret the coefficient of determination, R^2, for the per capita GDP versus life-expectancy data shown in Table 1 on page 193 in Section 4.1.

Approach: To compute R^2, we square the linear correlation coefficient, r, found in Example 2 from Section 4.1 on page 197.

Solution: $R^2 = r^2 = 0.8094^2 = 0.6551 = 65.51\%$.

Interpretation: 65.51% of the variation in life expectancy is explained by the least-squares regression line, while 34.49% of the variation in life expectancy is explained by other factors.   ◀◀

Caution

Squaring the linear correlation coefficient to obtain the coefficient of determination works only for the least-squares linear regression model

$$\hat{y} = b_0 + b_1 x.$$

The method does not work in general.

To help reinforce the concept of the coefficient of determination, consider the three data sets in Table 5.

TABLE 5					
DATA SET A		**DATA SET B**		**DATA SET C**	
x	y	x	y	x	y
3.6	8.9	3.1	8.9	2.8	8.9
8.3	15.0	9.4	15.0	8.1	15.0
0.5	4.8	1.2	4.8	3.0	4.8
1.4	6.0	1.0	6.0	8.3	6.0
8.2	14.9	9.0	14.9	8.2	14.9
5.9	11.9	5.0	11.9	1.4	11.9
4.3	9.8	3.4	9.8	1.0	9.8
8.3	15.0	7.4	15.0	7.9	15.0
0.3	4.7	0.1	4.7	5.9	4.7
6.8	13.0	7.5	13.0	5.0	13.0

Figure 15(a) represents the scatter diagram of data set A, Figure 15(b) represents the scatter diagram of data set B, and Figure 15(c) represents the scatter diagram of data set C.

Figure 15

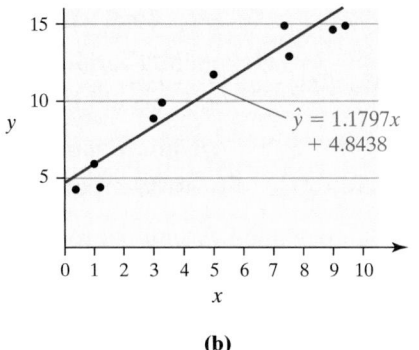

$\hat{y} = 1.2922x + 4.2159$

(a)

$\hat{y} = 1.1797x + 4.8438$

(b)

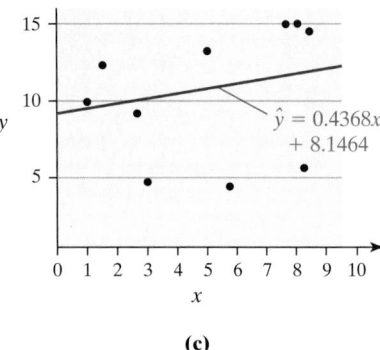

$\hat{y} = 0.4368x + 8.1464$

(c)

Notice that the y-values in each of the three data sets are the same. The variance of y is 17.49. If we look at the scatter diagram in Figure 15(a), we notice that 100% of the variability in y can be explained by the least-squares regression line, because all of the data lie on a straight line. In Figure 15(b), a high percentage of the variability in y can be explained by the least-squares regression line because the data have a strong linear relation. (Higher x values are associated with higher y values.) Finally, in Figure 15(c), a low percentage of the variability in y is explained by the least-squares regression line. (If x increases, we cannot easily predict the change in y.) If we compute the coefficient of determination, R^2, for the three data sets in Table 5, we obtain the following results:

Coefficient of Determination for Data Set A: 100%

Coefficient of Determination for Data Set B: 94.7%

Coefficient of Determination for Data Set C: 9.4%

Notice that as the explanatory ability of the line decreases, so does the coefficient of determination, R^2.

Figure 16

SUMMARY OUTPUT

Regression Statistics	
Multiple R	0.80942
R Square	0.65516
Adjusted R Square	0.612055
Standard Error	0.495073
Observations	10

Using Technology: Statistical spreadsheets and graphing calculators with advanced statistical features have the ability to compute the coefficient of determination. Figure 16 displays partial output from Excel using the per capita GDP data with the value of R^2 highlighted. Notice the results differ slightly from the value of R^2 we obtained in Example 1. The difference is due to rounding error.

 NW *Now Work Problems 5 and 15(a).*

② Residual Analysis

Recall that a residual is the difference between the observed value of y and the predicted value, $\hat{y}$. Residuals play an important role in determining the adequacy of the linear model. In fact, residuals can be used for the following purposes:

- to determine whether a linear model is appropriate to describe the relation between the predictor and response variables,
- to determine whether the variance of the residuals is constant,
- to check for outliers.

Let's see how the residuals can be used to verify the adequacy of the linear model.

Is a Linear Model Appropriate?   To answer this question, we plot the residuals against the corresponding values of the predictor variable.

> If a plot of the residuals against the predictor variable shows a discernible pattern, such as a curve, then the response and predictor variable may not be linearly related.

Figure 17 shows two residual plots. The residual plot in Figure 17(a) does not show any pattern, so a linear model is appropriate. However, the residual plot in Figure 17(b) shows an obvious pattern which indicates that a linear model is inappropriate.

Figure 17

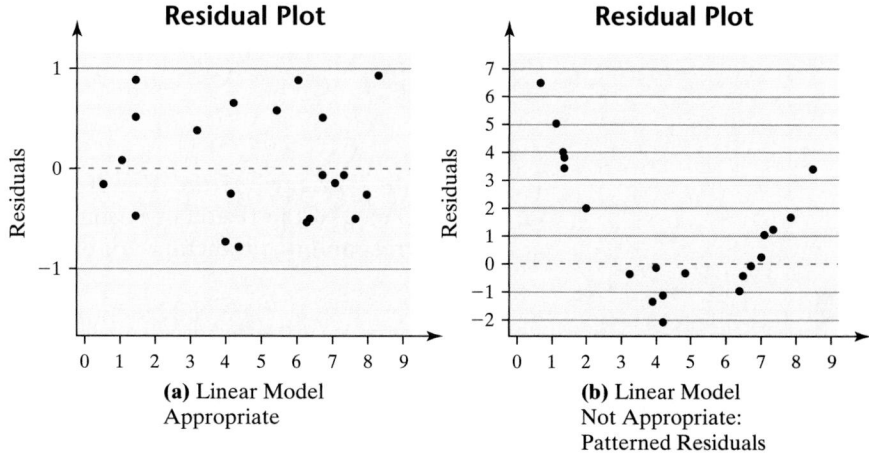

(a) Linear Model
Appropriate

(b) Linear Model
Not Appropriate:
Patterned Residuals

▶ **EXAMPLE 2** **Is a Linear Model Appropriate?**

TABLE 6

Year, x	Closing Price, y
1994	6.8032
1995	7.0328
1996	11.5585
1997	13.4799
1998	23.5424
1999	31.9342
2000	39.7277
2001	54.31

Source: Yahoo! Finance

Problem: The data in Table 6 represent the closing price of Harley David-son stock at the end of each year from 1994 through 2001. Determine whether the relation between the closing price and the year is linear.

Approach: We will find the least-squares regression line and compute the residuals. We then plot the residuals against the predictor variable, time. If an obvious pattern results, then we conclude that the linear model is not appropriate.

Solution: Enter the data into statistical software or a graphing calculator with advanced statistical features. Figure 18(a) shows a scatter diagram of the data. It would appear that perhaps closing price and year are linearly re-lated with a positive slope. In fact, the linear correlation coefficient between these two variables is 0.960. We use statistical software to compute the least-squares regression line and store the residuals. Figure 18(b) shows a plot of residuals versus the predictor variable, year. The U-shaped pattern in the plot indicates the linear model is not appropriate. The predicted values underestimate the stock price for early and late years, while they overestimate the stock price in the middle years.

Figure 18

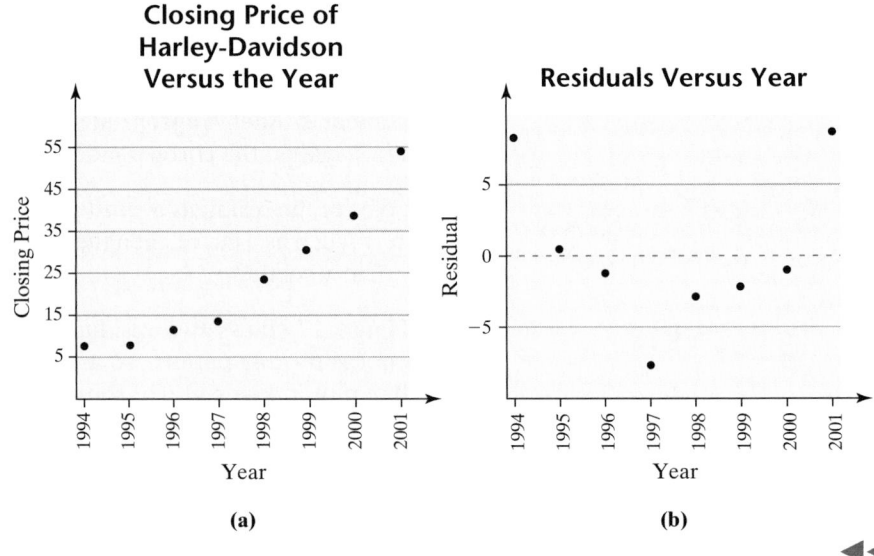

(a)   (b)

◀◀

NW *Now Work Problem 11.*

Is the Variance of the Residuals Constant? To determine whether the variance of the residuals is constant, we also plot the residuals against the corresponding predictor variable.

Caution

If the model does not have constant error variance, statistical inference using the regression model is not reliable.

If a plot of the residuals against the predictor variable shows the spread of the residuals increasing or decreasing as the predictor increases, then a strict requirement of the linear model is violated. This requirement is called constant error variance.*

*The statistical term for constant error variance is **homoscedasticity**.

▶ **EXAMPLE 3**   **Constant Error Variance**

Figure 19 illustrates the idea behind constant error variance. Notice that in Figure 19(a) the data appear more "spread out" about the regression line for large x. In Figure 19(b), we see the absolute value of the residuals is larger for large x and smaller for the smaller x. This means that the predictions made using the regression equation will be less reliable for large x because there is more variability in y.

Figure 19

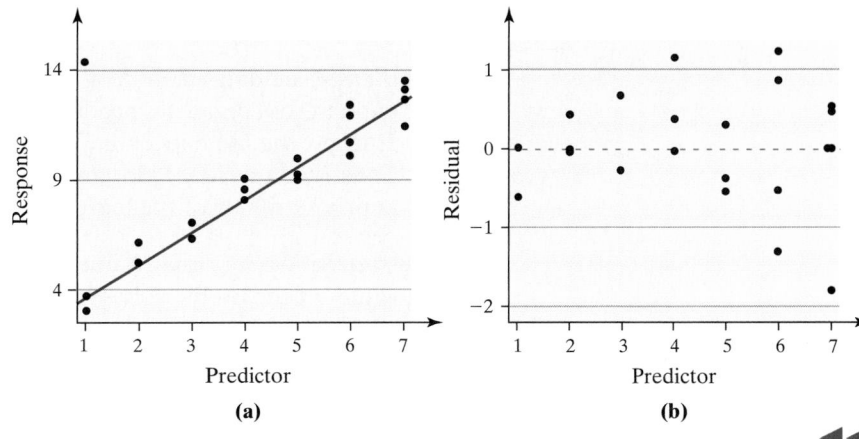

(a)   (b)

◀◀

Are There Any Outliers?   In Section 3.4 we said that outliers are extreme observations. An outlier can also be thought of as an observation that does not fit the overall pattern of the data. To determine outliers, we can either construct a plot of residuals against the predictor variable or draw a boxplot of the residuals.

We can find outliers from the residual plot because the residual will lie far from the rest of the plot. Outliers can be found from a boxplot because they will appear as asterisks (∗) in the plot.

▶ **EXAMPLE 4**   **Identifying Outliers**

Problem: Figure 20(a) shows a scatter diagram of a set of data. After the least-squares regression line was obtained, the residual plot in Figure 20(b) and the boxplot of the residuals in Figure 20(c) was obtained. Do the data have any outliers?

Figure 20

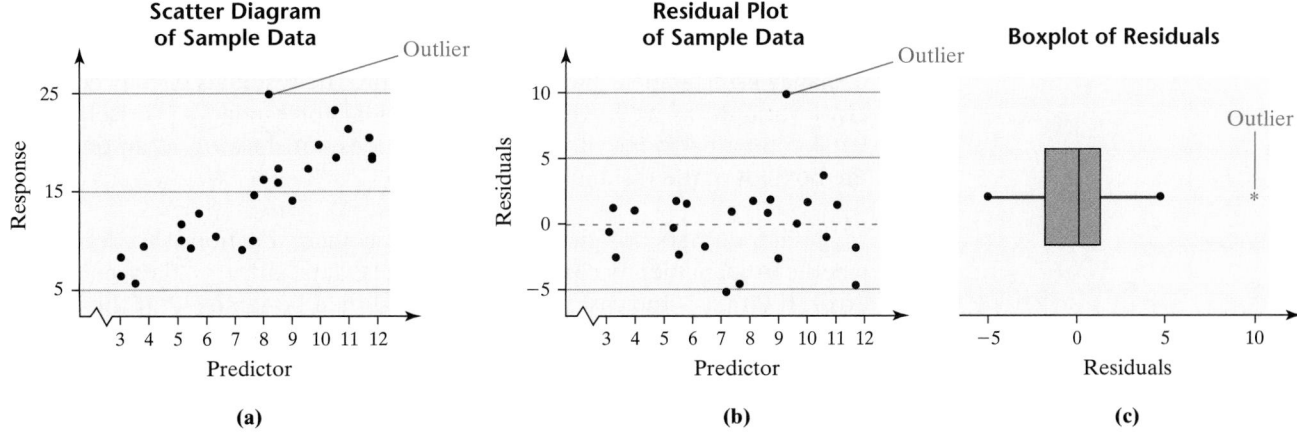

(a)   (b)   (c)

Approach: We look at the residual plot and boxplot for outliers.

Solution: We can see that the data do contain an outlier. We label the outlier in the scatter diagram given in Figure 20(a). ◄◄

We will follow the practice of removing outliers only if they are the result of an error in recording, a miscalculation, or some other obvious blunder in the data collection process.

► EXAMPLE 5   Graphical Residual Analysis

Problem: The data in Table 4 on page 215 from Section 4.2 represent the per capita gross domestic product of randomly selected countries in Western Europe, the life expectancy of residents of the country, and the residuals. Construct a residual plot and boxplot of the residuals and comment on the appropriateness of the least-squares regression model.

Approach: We plot the residuals on the vertical axis and the corresponding values of the predictor variable on the horizontal axis. We then look for any violations of the requirements of the regression model. We use the boxplot to identify any outliers.

Solution: Figure 21 shows the residual plot. Figure 22 shows the boxplot.

Figure 21

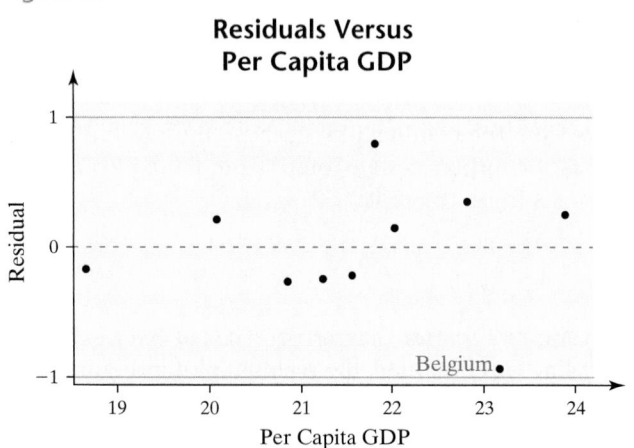

Figure 22

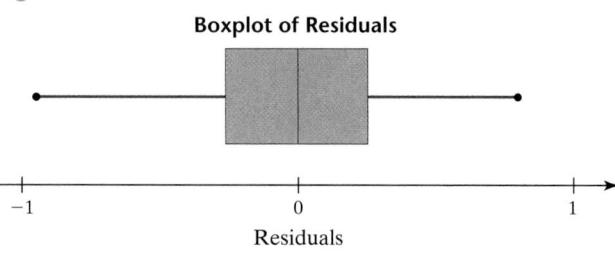

Because there is no discernible pattern in the residual plot, it would seem that describing the relation between per capita GDP and life expectancy using a linear model is appropriate. The residuals display constant error variance as well. Although the residual corresponding to Belgium is large compared to the other residuals, it does not show up as an outlier in the boxplot of the residuals. ◄◄

When outliers are identified, the first course of action is to determine whether the outlier occurred because of a data entry or data collection error. If either is the case, the data value should be removed. If there is no data entry or data collection error, the outlier should be removed only if there is reason to do so.

Influential Observations

An **influential observation** is an observation that significantly affects the value of the slope and/or y-intercept of the least-squares regression line. How do we identify influential observations? We first remove the point that is believed to be influential from the data set and then we recompute the regression line. If the slope or y-intercept changes significantly, then we say that the removed point is influential. Consider the scatter diagram in Figure 23.

Figure 23

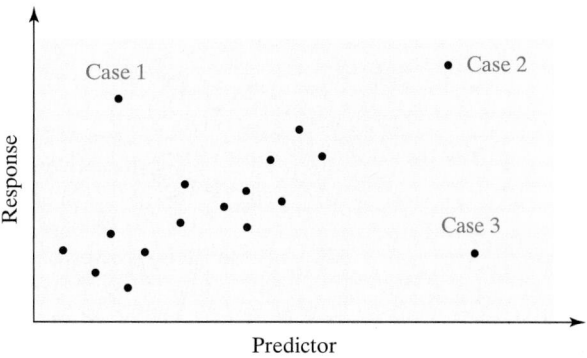

Case 1 would be an outlier because its Y value is large relative to its X value. Notice, however, that there are enough points to offset the effect Case 1 would have on the least-squares regression, so it is not influential. Case 2 is large relative to both its X value and Y value. It may or may not be influential because the point appears to lie along the linear pattern of the data. Case 3 is large relative to its X value and its Y value is not consistent with the pattern of the data. This point would influence the values of the slope and y-intercept in the regression equation. We conclude the following:

Influential observations typically exist when the point is an outlier relative to its X value.

Note to Instructor
Ask students to describe in their own words the difference between an influential observation and an outlier.

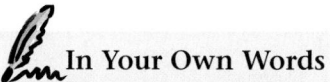 **In Your Own Words**

Draw a boxplot of the predictor variable. If an outlier appears, then the observation corresponding to the outlier may be influential.

▶ **EXAMPLE 6** **Identifying Influential Observations**

Problem: Suppose the country of Greece is added to the data in Table 4. The per capita GDP of Greece is $13.9 thousand and the life expectancy is 78.44 years. Determine whether Greece is an influential observation.

Approach: To determine whether Greece is influential, we recompute the least-squares regression line with Greece included. If the slope or y-intercept of the least-squares regression line changes substantially, we will conclude that Greece is influential.

Solution: Figure 24 shows partial output obtained from Minitab with Greece included in the data set.

Figure 24

Regression Analysis

```
The regression equation is
Life Expectancy = 76.7 + 0.0557 Per Capita GDP

Predictor        Coef       StDev        T          P
Constant        76.656      1.974      38.83      0.000
Per Capi        0.05571     0.09406     0.59      0.568

S = 0.8086     R-Sq = 3.8%     R-Sq(adj) = 0.0%
```

The least-squares regression line with Greece included in the data set is

$$\hat{y} = 0.0557x + 76.656$$

We graph the regression lines with Greece included (blue) and with Greece excluded (red) on the same scatter diagram. See Figure 25.

Figure 25

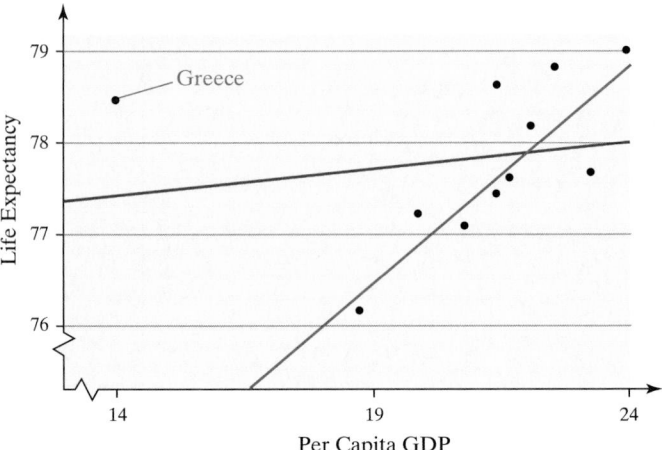

The inclusion of Greece in the data set causes the slope of the regression line to decrease. In other words, Greece "pulls" the least-squares regression line toward itself. Greece is influential. ◀◀

As with outliers, influential observations should be removed only if there is justification to do so. When an influential observation occurs in a data set and its removal is not warranted, two popular courses of action are to (1) collect more data so that additional points near the influential observation are obtained or (2) use techniques that reduce the influence of the influential observation. (These techniques are beyond the scope of this text.) In the case of Example 5, we are justified in removing Greece from the data set because it is the only Eastern European country in the set.

NW *Now Work Problem 7.*

4.3 Assess Your Understanding

Concepts and Vocabulary

1. Suppose it is determined that $R^2 = 0.75$ when a linear regression is performed. Interpret this result.
2. Explain what is meant by total deviation, explained deviation, and unexplained deviation.
3. What does it mean if a plot of the residuals against the predictor variable shows a discernible pattern (such as U-shaped)?
4. What is constant error variance? Why is it important?

5. What is an influential observation? If an influential observation is identified, what should be done?
6. Explain the difference between an outlier and an influential observation.
7. Explain how an influential observation affects the least-squares regression line.
8. Explain how a violation of the constant error variance assumption might affect the confidence placed upon a predicted value.

Exercises

• Skill Building

In Problems 1–4, analyze the residual plots and identify which, if any, of the conditions for an adequate linear model is not met.

1. Constant error variance

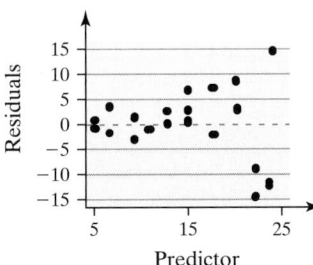

Predictor

2. None

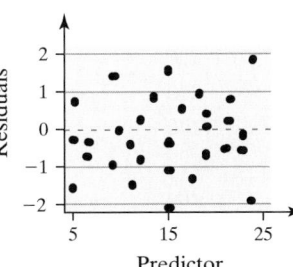

Predictor

3. Outlier

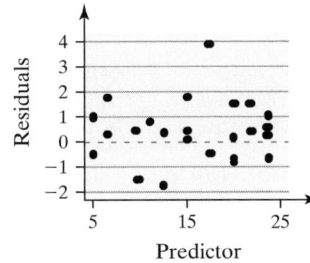

Predictor

4. Patterned residuals

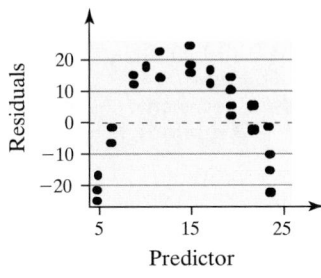

Predictor

5. Match the coefficient of determination to the scatter diagram. The scales on the horizontal and vertical axis are the same
(NW) for each scatter diagram.

(a) $R^2 = 0.58$ III

(b) $R^2 = 0.90$ II

(c) $R^2 = 1$ IV

(d) $R^2 = 0.12$ I

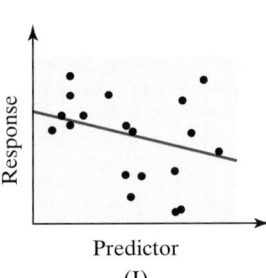

Predictor
(I)

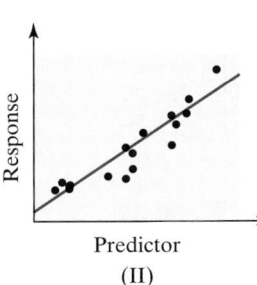

Predictor
(II)

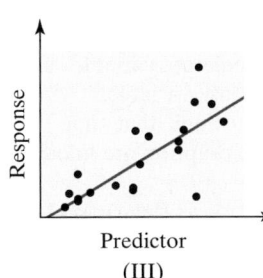

Predictor
(III)

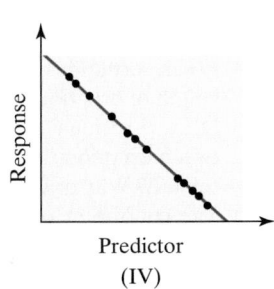

Predictor
(IV)

6. Use the linear correlation coefficient given to determine the coefficient of determination, R^2. Interpret each R^2.

(a) $r = -0.32$
     $R^2 = 10.24\%$

(b) $r = 0.13$
     $R^2 = 1.69\%$

(c) $r = 0.40$
     $R^2 = 16\%$

(d) $r = 0.93$
     $R^2 = 86.49\%$

In Problems 7–10, a scatter diagram is given with one of the points drawn in blue. In addition, there are two least-squares regression lines drawn: The line drawn in red is the least-squares regression line with the point in blue excluded; The line drawn in blue is the least-squares regression line with the point in blue included. On the basis of these graphs, do you think the point in blue is influential? Why?

7. Yes

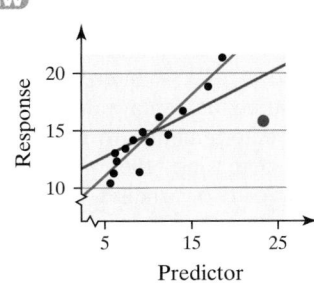

Predictor

8. No

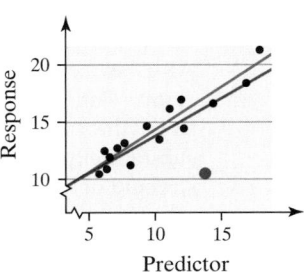

Predictor

9. Yes

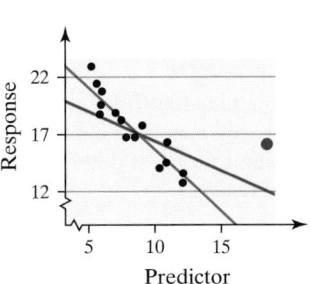

Predictor

10. No

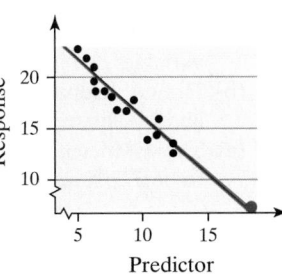

Predictor

• Applying the Concepts

11. The Other Old Faithful Perhaps you are familiar with the famous Old Faithful geyser in Yellowstone National Park. There is another Old Faithful geyser located in Calistoga in California's Napa Valley. The following data represent the time between eruptions and the length of eruption for 11 randomly selected eruptions.

Time Between Eruptions, x	Length of Erup-tion, y	Time Between Eruptions, x	Length of Erup-tion, y
12.17	1.88	11.70	1.82
11.63	1.77	12.27	1.93
12.03	1.83	11.60	1.77
12.15	1.83	11.72	1.83
11.30	1.70		

Source: Ladonna Hansen, Park Curator

(a) Draw a scatter diagram of the data, treating time between eruptions as the predictor variable. Find the least-squares regression treating the time between eruptions as the predictor variable and length of eruption as the response variable.
(b) Draw a residual plot. Do you think that time between eruptions and length of eruption are linearly related? Why or why not? Yes
(c) The coefficient of determination is determined to be 83.0%. Interpret this result.

12. Concrete As concrete cures, it gains strength. The following data represent the 7-day and 28-day strength (in pounds per square inch) of a certain type of concrete.

7-day Strength, x	28-day Strength, y	7-day Strength, x	28-day Strength, y
2300	4070	2480	4120
3390	5220	3380	5020
2430	4640	2660	4890
2890	4620	2620	4190
3330	4850	3340	4630

(a) Draw a scatter diagram of the data treating the 7-day strength as the predictor variable. Find the least-squares regression treating 7-day strength as the predictor variable and 28-day strength as the response variable. $\hat{y} = 0.6764x + 2675.6$
(b) Draw a residual plot. Do you think that 7-day strength and 28-day strength are linearly related? Why? Yes
(c) The coefficient of determination, R^2, is determined to be 57.5%. Interpret this result.

(11a) $\hat{y} = 0.1854x - 0.3779$

13. Calories versus Sugar The following data represent the number of calories per serving and the number of grams of sugar per serving for a random sample of high-fiber cereals.

Calories, x	Sugar, y	Calories, x	Sugar, y
200	18	210	23
210	23	210	16
170	17	210	17
190	20	190	12
200	18	190	11
180	19	200	11

Source: Consumer Reports, October, 1999

(a) A scatter diagram with the least-squares regression line is shown. The least-squares regression equation is $\hat{y} = 0.0821x + 0.93$. Do you think that calories and sugar content are linearly related? Why? No

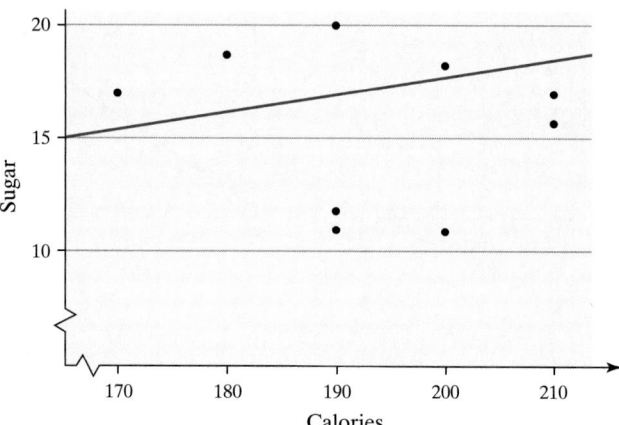

(b) The coefficient of determination, R^2, for these data is 6.8%. Interpret this result. Does this support your conclusion from part (a)? Why or why not?
(c) Suppose that we add Kellogg's All-Bran cereal, which has 80 calories and 6 grams of sugar per serving, to the data set. Draw a scatter diagram of the data, with this cereal included. Do you think that Kellogg's All-Bran cereal is influential? *Hint:* The least-squares regression line with All-Bran included is $\hat{y} = 0.0933x - 1.288$. Why? Yes
(d) The coefficient of determination, R^2, with Kellogg's All-Bran cereal included, is 42.1%. Interpret this result. Conclude that influential data values can cause the coefficient of determination to increase substantially, thereby increasing the apparent strength of relation between two variables.

14. Consumption versus Income The following data represent the per capita disposable income (income after taxes) and per capita consumption in constant 1996 dollars in the United States for 1993–2001.

Year	Per Capita Disposable Income, x	Per Capita Consumption, y
1993	20,233	18,796
1994	20,504	19,253
1995	20,795	19,630
1996	21,069	20,058
1997	21,464	20,563
1998	22,354	21,303
1999	22,641	22,098
2000	23,148	22,917
2001	23,691	23,312

Source: Bureau of Economic Analysis

(a) A scatter diagram with the least-squares regression line is shown. Do you think that per capita disposable income and per capita consumption are linearly related? Why or why not? Yes

(14c) Possible outlier

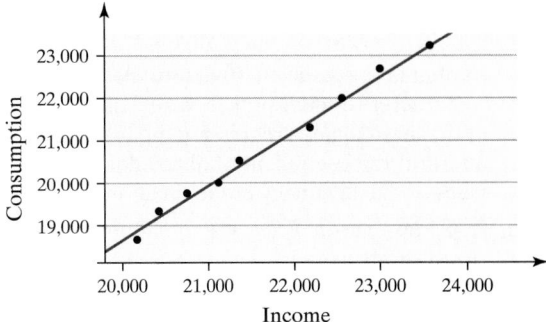

(b) The coefficient of determination, R^2, for the data is 99.0%. Interpret this result. Does this support your conclusion from part (a)? Why?

(c) A residual plot is shown below. Which, if any, of the requirements of the linear model are violated?

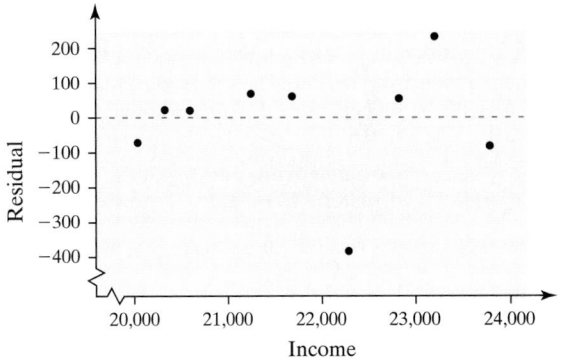

Problems 15–22 use the results from Problems 11–18 in Section 4.1 and Problems 9–16 in Section 4.2.

15. Height versus Head Circumference Use the results from Problem 11 in Section 4.1 and Problem 9 in Section 4.2 to   (a) $R^2 = 83.0\%$

(a) compute the coefficient of determination, R^2.

(b) construct a residual plot to verify the assumptions of the least-squares regression model.

(c) interpret the coefficient of determination and comment on the adequacy of the linear model.

16. Round-Cut Diamonds Use the results from Problem 12 in Section 4.1 and Problem 10 in Section 4.2 to

(a) compute the coefficient of determination, R^2. 98.3%

(b) construct a residual plot to verify the assumptions of the least-squares regression model.

(c) interpret the coefficient of determination and comment on the adequacy of the linear model.

17. Gestation Period versus Life Expectancy Use the results from Problem 13 in Section 4.1 and Problem 11 in Section 4.2 to

(a) compute the coefficient of determination, R^2. 52.7%

(b) construct a residual plot to verify the assumptions of the least-squares regression model.

(c) interpret the coefficient of determination and comment on the adequacy of the linear model.

18. Tar and Nicotine Use the results from Problem 14 in Section 4.1 and Problem 12 in Section 4.2 to

(a) compute the coefficient of determination, R^2. 93.4%

(b) construct a residual plot to verify the assumptions of the least-squares regression model.

(c) interpret the coefficient of determination and comment on the adequacy of the linear model.

19. Bone Length Use the results from Problem 15 in Section 4.1 and Problem 13 in Section 4.2 to

(a) compute the coefficient of determination, R^2. 90.5%

(b) construct a residual plot to verify the assumptions of the least-squares regression model.

(c) interpret the coefficient of determination and comment on the adequacy of the linear model.

20. Weight of a Car versus Miles per Gallon Use the results from Problem 16 in Section 4.1 and Problem 14 in Section 4.2 to

(a) compute the coefficient of determination, R^2. 84.0%

(b) construct a residual plot to verify the assumptions of the least-squares regression model.

(c) interpret the coefficient of determination and comment on the adequacy of the linear model.

21. General Electric versus the S&P 500 Use the results from Problem 17 in Section 4.1 and Problem 15 in Section 4.2 to

(a) compute the coefficient of determination, R^2. 68.7%

(b) construct a residual plot to verify the assumptions of the least-squares regression model.

(c) interpret the coefficient of determination and comment on the adequacy of the linear model.

22. Fat-Free Mass versus Energy Expenditure Use the results from Problem 18 in Section 4.1 and Problem 16 in Section 4.2 to

(a) compute the coefficient of determination, R^2. 96.3%

(b) construct a residual plot to verify the assumptions of the least-squares regression model.

(c) interpret the coefficient of determination and comment on the adequacy of the linear model.

23. Kepler's Law of Planetary Motion The time it takes for a planet to complete its orbit around the sun is called the planet's sidereal year. In 1618, Johann Kepler discovered that the sidereal year of a planet is related to the distance the planet is from the sun. The following data show the distances of the planets from the sun and their sidereal years.

Planet	Distance from Sun, x (millions of miles)	Sidereal Year, y
Mercury	36	0.24
Venus	67	0.62
Earth	93	1.00
Mars	142	1.88
Jupiter	483	11.9
Saturn	887	29.5
Uranus	1,785	84.0
Neptune	2,797	165.0
Pluto	3,675	248.0

(a) Draw a scatter diagram of the data, treating distance from the sun as the predictor variable.

(b) Compute the least-squares regression line.

(c) Plot the residuals against the distance from the Sun.

(d) Do you think the least-squares regression line is a good model? Why? No

24. Wind Chill Factor The wind chill factor depends upon wind speed and the air temperature. The following data represent the wind speed (in mph) and wind chill factor at an air temperature of 15° Fahrenheit.

Wind Speed (mph)	Wind Chill Factor	Wind Speed (mph)	Wind Chill Factor
5	12	25	−22
10	−3	30	−25
15	−11	35	−27
20	−17		

Source: Information Please Almanac

(a) Draw a scatter diagram of the data treating wind speed as the predictor variable.

(b) Compute the least-squares regression line.

(c) Plot the residuals against the wind speed.

(d) Do you think the least-squares regression line is a good model? Why? No

25. Gestation Period versus Life Expectancy Suppose we add humans to the data in Problem 11 in Section 4.2. Humans have a gestation period of 268 days and a life expectancy of 76.5 years.

(a) Compute the coefficient of determination of the expanded data set. What effect does the addition of humans to the data set have on R^2? 71.7%

(b) Is the point corresponding to humans influential? Is it an outlier? Yes; Yes

(c) Remove humans from the data set. Suppose elephants are added to the data set (gestation period: 624 days, life expectancy: 35 years). Is the point corresponding to elephants influential? Is it an outlier? Yes; No

26. Weight of a Car versus Miles per Gallon Suppose we add the Dodge Viper to the data in Problem 14 in Section 4.2. A Dodge Viper weighs 3425 pounds and gets 11 miles per gallon.

(a) Compute the coefficient of determination of the expanded data set. What effect does the addition of the Viper to the data set have on R^2? $R^2 = 67.0\%$

(b) Is the point corresponding to the Dodge Viper influential? Is it an outlier? No; Yes

27. Height versus Weight The following data represent the heights and weights of various professional baseball players.

Player	Height (inches)	Weight (pounds)
Albert Belle	74	225
Alex Rodriguez	75	210
Derek Jeter	75	195
Greg Maddux	72	185
Randy Johnson	82	230
David Justice	75	200
Al Leiter	75	220
Barry Bonds	74	210
Mike Bordick	71	175
Ron Grant	72	196
Pete Harnisch	72	228
Randy Velarde	72	200
Ray Lankford	71	200
Jason Isringhausen	75	210

Source: Yahoo! Sports

(23b) $\hat{y} = 0.0657x - 12.4967$

(24b) Chill $= -1.2286$ speed $+ 11.2857$

(a) Draw a scatter diagram of the data, treating height as the predictor variable and weight as the response variable.

(b) Compute the least-squares regression line and the correlation coefficient.

(c) Remove the value corresponding to Randy Johnson and recompute the least-squares regression line and the correlation coefficient. What effect does Randy Johnson have on the regression line and correlation coefficient?

(d) Do you think that Randy Johnson is an influential observation? Why? Yes

28. Height versus Weight in the WNBA The following data represent the heights and weights of centers of the Eastern Conference in the Women's National Basketball Association.

Player	Height (inches)	Weight (pounds)
Summer Erb	78	240
Rhonda Map	74	190
Ann Wauters	76	193
Chasity Melvin	75	185
Pollyanna Johns	75	185
Oksana Zakaluzhnaya	78	174
Katryna Galther	75	170
Kara Wolters	79	225
Shantia Owens	74	175
Jamie Cassidy	75	187
Tamika Whitmore	74	190
Olga Firsova	78	215
Taj McWilliams	74	184
Heather Owen	77	220

Source: Yahoo! Sports

(a) Draw a scatter diagram of the data treating height as the predictor variable and weight as the response variable.

(b) Compute the least-squares regression line and the correlation coefficient.

(c) Remove the value corresponding to Oksana Zakaluzhnaya and recompute the least-squares regression line and the correlation coefficient.

(d) Do you think that Oksana Zakaluzhnaya is an influential observation? Why? Yes

29. Age versus Study Time Professor McCraith feels that there is a relation between the number of hours a statistics student studies each week and the student's age. He conducts a survey in which 26 statistics students are asked their age and the number of hours they study statistics each week. He obtains the results shown below.

Age	Number of Hours Studying	Age	Number of Hours Studying	Age	Number of Hours Studying
18	4.2	19	5.1	22	2.1
18	1.1	19	2.3	22	3.6
18	4.6	20	1.7	24	5.4
18	3.1	20	6.1	25	4.8
18	5.3	20	3.2	25	3.9
18	3.2	20	5.3	26	5.2
19	2.8	21	2.5	26	4.2
19	2.3	21	6.4	35	8.1
19	3.2	21	4.2		

(a) Draw a scatter diagram of the data. Comment on any potential influential observations.

(b) Find the least-squares regression line using all the data points. Hours = 0.232age − 0.920

(c) Find the least-squares regression line with the data point (35, 8.1) removed. Hours = 0.1549age + 0.635

(d) Draw each least-squares regression line on the scatter diagram obtained in part (a).

(e) Comment on the influence the point (35, 8.1) has on the regression line.

30. Tar and Nicotine Refer to the data given in Problem 12 in Section 4.2. Suppose the nicotine level of a Marlboro Gold cigarette was incorrectly entered as 2.1 mg. Will the data value appear as an outlier? Yes

31. Height versus Head Circumference Refer to the data given in Problem 9 in Section 4.2. Suppose the child whose height is 25 inches has his head circumference recorded as 19.6 inches. Will the data value appear as an outlier? Yes

(27b) Weight = 3.28height − 36.77; r = 0.572
(27c) Weight = 3.948height − 85.3; r = 0.429
(28b) Weight = 8.113height − 420.2; r = 0.685
(28c) Weight = 10.5360height − 600.6; r = 0.872

Technology Step-by-Step
Determining R^2 and Residual Plots

TI-83 Plus   **The Coefficient of Determination, R^2**
Use the same steps that were followed to obtain the correlation coefficient to obtain R^2. Diagnostics must be on.

Residual Plots
Step 1: Enter the raw data in `L1` and `L2`. Obtain the least-squares regression line.

Step 2: Access `STAT PLOTS`. Select `Plot1`. Choose the scatter diagram icon and let XList be `L1`. Let YList be `RESID` by putting the cursor on List2, pressing 2nd `STAT` and choosing the list entitled `RESID`.

Step 3: Press `ZOOM` and select `9: ZoomStat`.

MINITAB   **The Coefficient of Determination, R^2**
Step 1: This is provided in the standard regression output.

Residual Plots
Step 1: Follow the same steps as those used to obtain the regression output. Before selecting OK, click GRAPHS. In the cell that says "Residuals versus the variables" enter the name of the predictor variable. Click OK.

Excel   **The Coefficient of Determination, R^2**
Step 1: This is provided in the standard regression output.

Residual Plots
Step 1: Follow the same steps as those used to obtain the regression output. Before selecting OK, click **Residual Plots**. Click OK.

4.4   Nonlinear Regression: Transformations

Objectives

 Change exponential expressions to logarithmic expressions and logarithmic expressions to exponential expressions

 Simplify expressions containing logarithms

 Use logarithmic transformations to linearize exponential relations

 Use logarithmic transformations to linearize power relations

Note to Instructor
The material in this section is optional and may be omitted without loss of continuity.

Up to now, we concentrated on finding an equation that describes the relationship between two variables that were linearly related. However, there are many situations where two variables have a relation that is not linear. In this section, we present methods for describing the relation between two variables, x and y, that are related through an exponential equation, $y = ab^x$, or are related through a power equation, $y = ax^b$. The method that we use requires that we *transform* the equations into linear form. This way, we can use the method of least-squares to estimate the values of a and b.

As before, we will draw a scatter diagram of the data to help determine the appropriate model to use. Figure 26 shows scatter diagrams that typically will be observed for the **exponential model**, $y = ab^x$, or the **power model**, $y = ax^b$.

Figure 26

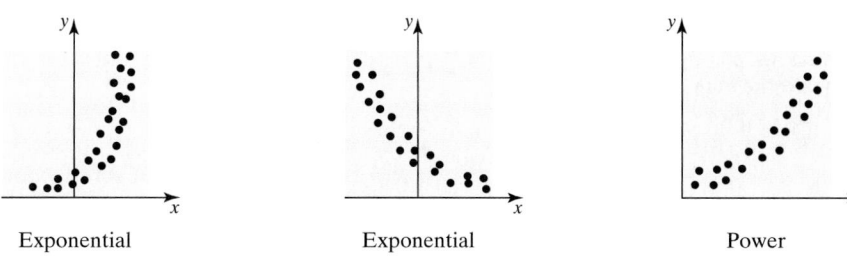

Exponential   Exponential   Power

The material in this section requires that certain properties of logarithms be reviewed. We start with the definition of a logarithm.

Definition

> The **logarithm to the base a**, where $a > 0$ and $a \neq 1$, is denoted by $y = \log_a x$ (read as "y is the logarithm to the base a of x") and is defined by
>
> $$y = \log_a x \quad \text{if and only if} \quad x = a^y$$
>
> In order for the logarithm to be defined, x must be positive ($x > 0$).

▶ **EXAMPLE 1**   **Using the Definition of the Logarithm**

Problem: Rewrite the logarithmic expressions to an equivalent expression involving an exponent. Rewrite the exponential expressions to an equivalent logarithmic expression.

(a) $\log_a 12 = 5$

(b) $\log_{10} x = 2$

(c) $4^y = 13$

(d) $10^{1.5} = x$

Approach: We use the fact that $y = \log_a x$ if and only if $x = a^y$.

Solution:

(a) If $\log_a 12 = 5$, then $12 = a^5$

(b) If $\log_{10} x = 2$, then $10^2 = x$

(c) If $4^y = 13$, then $\log_4 13 = y$

(d) If $10^{1.5} = x$, then $\log_{10} x = 1.5$ ◀◀

NW *Now Work Problems 1 and 9.*

In order to transform an exponential equation or power equation into linear form, we need to utilize certain properties of logarithms. We will make use of the following properties of logarithms in this section.

**In Your Own Words**

Property (1) is easily expressed in words as "the log of a product equals the sum of the logs."

> In the following properties, M, N, and a are positive real numbers, with $a \neq 1$, and r is any real number.
>
> $$\log_a (MN) = \log_a M + \log_a N \qquad \textbf{(1)}$$
>
> $$\log_a M^r = r \log_a M \qquad \textbf{(2)}$$

It will be helpful to present some examples that utilize Properties (1) and (2).

▶ **EXAMPLE 2** **Simplifying Logarithms Using Properties (1) and (2)**

Problem: Write the following expressions as a sum of logarithms. Express powers as factors.

(a) $\log_a x^2$ **(b)** $\log_a (x^4 y^3)$ **(c)** $\log_a (4x^3)$

Approach: We use Properties (1) and (2).

Solution:

(a) $\log_a x^2 \qquad = 2 \log_a x$ Property (2)

(b) $\log_a (x^4 y^3) = \log_a x^4 + \log_a y^3$ Property (1)
$\qquad\qquad = 4 \log_a x + 3 \log_a y$ Property (2)

(c) $\log_a (4x^3) \quad = \log_a 4 + \log_a x^3$ Property (1)
$\qquad\qquad = \log_a 4 + 3 \log_a x$ Property (2) ◀◀

NW *Now Work Problem 17.*

**Historical Note**

Logarithms were invented by John Napier in 1590. Napier was a Scottish lord, a secretive man whose neighbors thought that he was in league with the devil. In 1614, Napier published a table of natural logarithms that was difficult to use. A London professor named Henry Briggs became interested in Napier's tables, and together they developed the idea of a common logarithm. These tables became an important tool for calculation until 1972, when the inexpensive handheld calculator decreased their value.

In this section, we shall always let the base a equal 10. The resulting logarithm is referred to as the *common logarithm*.

Definition

> **The Common Logarithm**
>
> If $a = 10$ in the expression $y = \log_a x$, the resulting logarithm, $y = \log_{10} x$ is called the **common logarithm**. It is common practice to omit the base, a, when it is equal to 10 and write the common logarithm as $y = \log x$.

▶ **EXAMPLE 3** **Evaluating Exponential and Logarithmic Expressions**

Problem: Evaluate the following expressions. Round your answers to three decimal places.

(a) $\log 4.5$ **(b)** $10^{3.4}$

Approach: To evaluate these expressions, we shall use a calculator.

Solution:

(a) $\log 4.5 = 0.653$ rounded to three decimal places.

(b) $10^{3.4} = 2{,}511.886$ rounded to three decimal places.

NW *Now Work Problems 25 and 29.*

We are now prepared to discuss nonlinear curve fitting.

3 ## Exponential Curve Fitting

Many variables are related exponentially. For example, the future value of a lump sum of money, the growth of bacteria, and the decay of a radioactive substance all behave exponentially. When data are related exponentially, we can describe this relationship through the equation $y = ab^x$ where $y > 0$. In order to find the exponential equation of best fit, we first need to linearize the equation so that we can use the method of least-squares to estimate the values of a and b.

Caution

In order to use logarithms to linearize an exponential equation, the y values must be greater than 0.

$$y = ab^x$$

$$\log y = \log(ab^x) \qquad \text{Take the common logarithm of both sides}$$

$$\log y = \log a + \log b^x \qquad \text{Property (1)}$$

$$\log y = \log a + x \log b \qquad \text{Property (2)}$$

The resulting equation is linear. If we let $Y = \log y$, $B = \log b$ and $A = \log a$, the expression $\log y = \log a + x \log b$ can be written as follows:

$$Y = A + Bx \qquad Y = \log y;\ A = \log a;\ B = \log b$$

The exponential equation $y = ab^x$ has been transformed into a linear equation with slope B and y-intercept A. This means the method of least squares can be performed on the ordered pairs $(x, \log y)$ in order to identify the values of A and B. To estimate the values of a and b, we simply undo the transformation as follows:

$$\text{Slope:} \qquad B = \log b$$

$$b = 10^B \qquad y = \log_a x \text{ if and only if } x = a^y$$

$$\text{Intercept:} \quad A = \log a$$

$$a = 10^A$$

So, to find the value of b in $y = ab^x$, we raise 10 to the slope, B, of the least-squares regression of the transformed data. To find a in $y = ab^x$, we raise 10 to the y-intercept, A, of the least-squares regression of the transformed data. An example should help to clarify the procedure.

▶ EXAMPLE 4 **Finding the Curve of Best Fit to an Exponential Model**

Problem: The data in Table 7 represent the closing price of Harley Davidson, Incorporated, stock for the years ended 1987–2001. We let $x = 1$ represent 1987, $x = 2$ represent 1988, and so on.

(a) Draw a scatter diagram of the data treating the year, x, as the predictor variable. Comment on the shape of the scatter diagram.

(b) Determine $Y = \log y$. Draw a scatter diagram treating the year, x, as the predictor variable and $Y = \log y$ as the response variable. Comment on the shape of the scatter diagram.

(c) Find the least-squares regression line of the transformed data.

TABLE 7	
Year, x	Closing Price, y
1987 (x = 1)	0.392
1988 (x = 2)	0.7652
1989 (x = 3)	1.1835
1990 (x = 4)	1.1609
1991 (x = 5)	2.6988
1992 (x = 6)	4.5381
1993 (x = 7)	5.3379
1994 (x = 8)	6.8032
1995 (x = 9)	7.0328
1996 (x = 10)	11.5585
1997 (x = 11)	13.4799
1998 (x = 12)	23.5424
1999 (x = 13)	31.9342
2000 (x = 14)	39.7277
2001 (x = 15)	54.31

Source: Yahoo! Finance

(d) Determine the exponential equation of best fit and graph it on the scatter diagram obtained in Part (a).

(e) Use the exponential equation of best fit to predict the closing price of Harley Davidson stock at the end of 2002.

Approach:

(a) We plot the ordered pairs (x, y).

(b) First we must determine the logarithm of the y-values so that $Y = \log y$. Then we plot the ordered pairs $(x, Y) = (x, \log y)$.

(c) We use Minitab to find the least-squares regression line using the transformed data.

(d) The least-squares regression line will be of the form, $\log y = \log a + x \log b = A + Bx$ where A is the y-intercept and B is the slope of the least-squares regression line. To find a and b, we let $a = 10^A$ and $b = 10^B$. The exponential equation of best fit will be $y = ab^x$. To graph the equation, we evaluate the exponential equation of best fit at various values of x to determine the corresponding value of y. We then plot these points and connect them into a smooth curve.

(e) Let $x = 16$ in the exponential equation of best fit to predict the closing price of Harley Davidson stock at the end of 2002.

Solution:

(a) Figure 27 shows a scatter diagram of the data presented in Table 7. The data appear to exhibit exponential behavior.

(b) We perform a log transformation on the y-values. The third column in Table 8 represents the transformed values.

Figure 27

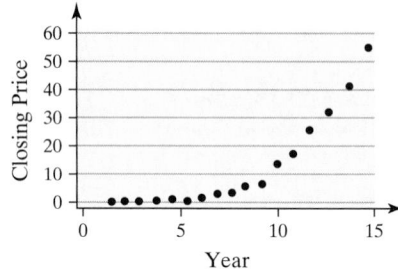

TABLE 8		
Year, x	Closing Price, y	$Y = \log y$
1987 (x = 1)	0.392	$\log 0.392 = -0.4067$
1988 (x = 2)	0.7652	$\log 0.7652 = -0.1162$
1989 (x = 3)	1.1835	$\log 1.1835 = 0.0732$
1990 (x = 4)	1.1609	0.0648
1991 (x = 5)	2.6988	0.4312
1992 (x = 6)	4.5381	0.6569
1993 (x = 7)	5.3379	0.7274
1994 (x = 8)	6.8032	0.8327
1995 (x = 9)	7.0328	0.8471
1996 (x = 10)	11.5585	1.0629
1997 (x = 11)	13.4799	1.1297
1998 (x = 12)	23.5424	1.3719
1999 (x = 13)	31.9342	1.5043
2000 (x = 14)	39.7277	1.5991
2001 (x = 15)	54.31	1.7349

Figure 28 shows a scatter diagram of the transformed data.

Figure 28

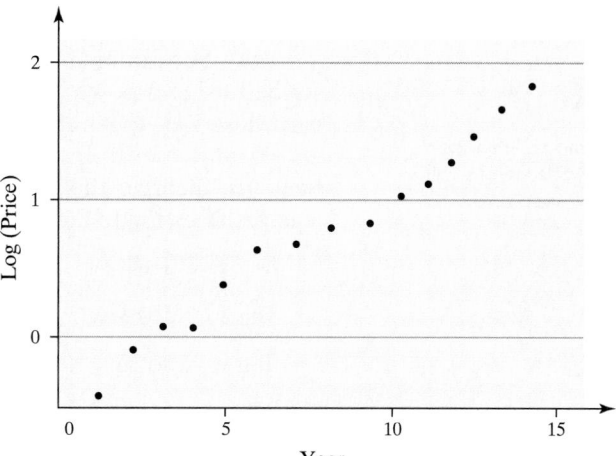

The scatter diagram of the transformed data appears to exhibit a linear pattern.

(c) We use Minitab to find the least-squares regression line of the transformed data and obtain the results shown in Figure 29.

Figure 29

Regression Analysis

```
The regression equation is
Log(Price) = -0.395 + 0.145 Year

Predictor        Coef      StDev         T        P
Constant     -0.39516    0.05060     -7.81    0.000
Year         0.145336   0.005565     26.11    0.000

S = 0.09313     R-Sq = 98.1%      R-Sq(adj) = 98.0%
```

From the output, we see that the slope of the least-squares regression line, B, is 0.145336 and the intercept, A, is -0.39516.

(d) To find the values of a and b in the exponential equation of best fit, $y = ab^x$, we let $a = 10^A = 10^{-0.39516} = 0.4026$ and $b = 10^B = 10^{0.145336} = 1.3974$. The exponential equation of best fit is

$$y = ab^x = 0.4026(1.3974)^x$$

Figure 30 shows the scatter diagram of the original data, along with the exponential equation of best fit.

Figure 30

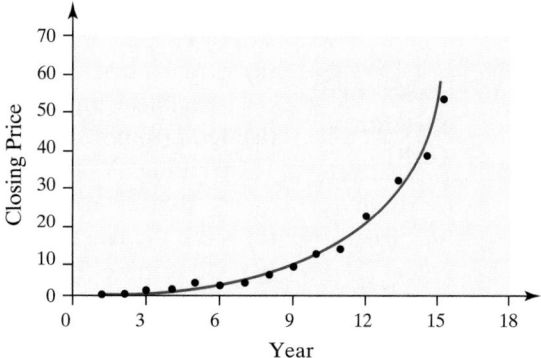

(e) Letting $x = 16$ in the exponential equation of best fit, we predict the closing price of Harley Davidson at the end of 2002 will be

NW *Now Work Problem 33.*

$$y = 0.4026(1.3974)^{16} = \$85.11$$

◄◄

Caution

To use logarithms to linearize a power equation, the x and y values must be greater than zero.

④ Power Curve Fitting

Variables may also be related through a power equation of the form $y = ax^b$. For example, the distance that an object falls over time can be described using a power equation. When data are related in this fashion, we can describe the relationship through the equation $y = ax^b$ where $x > 0$ and $y > 0$. In order to find the power equation of best fit, we first need to linearize the equation so that we can use the method of least-squares to estimate the values of a and b.

$$y = ax^b$$
$$\log y = \log (ax^b) \qquad \text{Take the common logarithm of both sides}$$
$$\log y = \log a + \log x^b \qquad \text{Property (1)}$$
$$\log y = \log a + b \log x \qquad \text{Property (2)}$$

Notice that the resulting equation is linear. If we let $Y = \log y$, $A = \log a$, and $X = \log x$, the expression $\log y = \log a + b \log x$ can be written

$$Y = A + bX \qquad \text{\small $Y = \log y$; $A = \log a$; $X = \log x$}$$

The power equation $y = ax^b$ has been transformed into a linear equation. This means the method of least squares can be performed on the ordered pairs $(\log x, \log y)$. The slope of the least-squares regression line will be b, and the y-intercept will be $A = \log a$. To find the value of a, we simply undo the transformation, as follows:

$$y\text{-intercept:} \quad A = \log a$$
$$a = 10^A$$

So, to find the value of a in $y = ax^b$, we raise 10 to the y-intercept, A, of the least-squares regression of the transformed data. An example should help to clarify the procedures.

▶ **EXAMPLE 5**   **Finding the Curve of Best Fit to a Power Model**

Problem: Scott drops a ball from various heights and records the time, x, that it takes for the ball to hit the ground, using a motion detector. He obtains the data displayed in Table 9.

(a) Draw a scatter diagram of the data, treating the time, x, as the predictor variable. Comment on the shape of the scatter diagram.
(b) Determine $Y = \log y$ and $X = \log x$, and draw a scatter diagram treating $X = \log x$ as the predictor variable and $Y = \log y$ as the response variable. Comment on the shape of the scatter diagram.
(c) Find the least-squares regression line of the transformed data.
(d) Determine the power equation of best fit, and graph it on the scatter diagram obtained in part (a).
(e) Use the power equation of best fit to predict the distance a ball would have to fall in order to take 4.2 seconds to hit the ground.

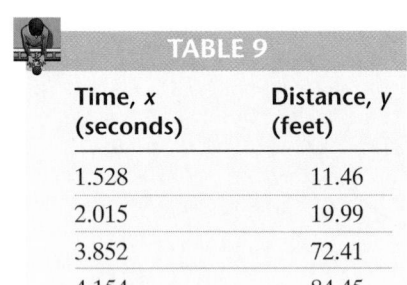

TABLE 9	
Time, x (seconds)	Distance, y (feet)
1.528	11.46
2.015	19.99
3.852	72.41
4.154	84.45
4.625	104.23

Approach:

(a) We plot the ordered pairs (x, y).

(b) First, we must determine the logarithms of the x-values and y-values, so that $X = \log x$ and $Y = \log y$. We then plot the ordered pairs $(X, Y) = (\log x, \log y)$.

(c) We use Minitab to find the least-squares regression line, using the transformed data.

(d) The least-squares regression line will be of the form $\log y = \log a + b \log x = A + bX$, where A is the y-intercept and b is the slope of the least-squares regression line. To find a, we let $a = 10^A$. The power equation of best fit will be $y = ax^b$. To graph the equation, we evaluate the power equation of best fit at various values of x to determine the corresponding value of y. We then plot these points and connect them into a smooth curve.

(e) Let $x = 4.2$ in the power equation of best fit.

Solution:

(a) Figure 31 shows a scatter diagram of the data presented in Table 9.

Figure 31

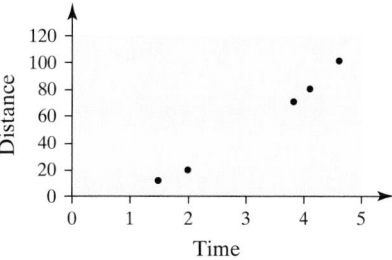

(b) We perform a log transformation on the x-values and y-values. The third column in Table 10 represents the transformed values $X = \log x$; the fourth column represents the transformed values $Y = \log y$. Figure 32 shows a scatter diagram of the transformed data. The scatter diagram of the transformed data appears to exhibit a linear pattern.

Figure 32

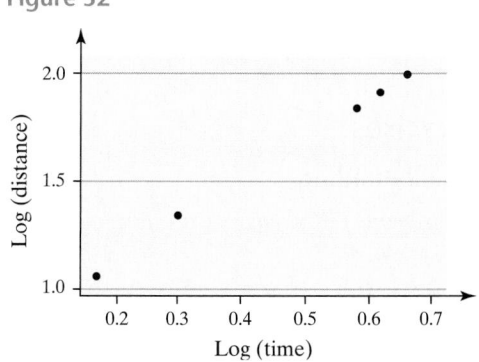

TABLE 10			
Time, x	Distance, y	X = log x	Y = log y
1.528	11.46	log 1.528 = 0.184	log 11.46 = 1.06
2.015	19.99	log 2.015 = 0.304	log 19.99 = 1.30
3.852	72.41	0.586	1.86
4.154	84.45	0.618	1.93
4.625	104.23	0.665	2.02

(c) We use Minitab to find the least-squares regression line, using the transformed data; we obtain the results shown in Figure 33.

Figure 33

Regression Analysis

```
The regression equation is
log(distance) = 0.693 + 1.99 log(time)

Predictor        Coef       StDev        T        P
Constant      0.693190    0.001377    503.30    0.000
log(time)     1.99284     0.00271     736.19    0.000

S = 0.001157     R-Sq = 100.0%     R-Sq(adj) = 100.0%
```

From the output, we see that the slope of the least-squares regression line, b, is 1.99284 and that the y-intercept, A, is 0.693190.

(d) To find the value of a in the power equation of best fit, $y = ax^b$, we let $a = 10^A = 10^{0.693190} = 4.934$. The power equation of best fit is, then,

$$y = ax^b = 4.934x^{1.99284}$$

Figure 34

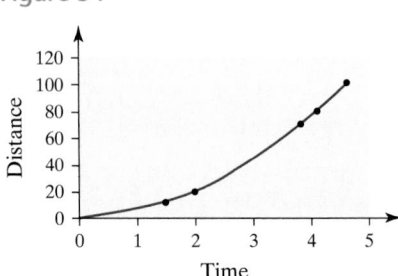

Distance vs. Time

Figure 34 shows the scatter diagram of the original data along with the power equation of best fit.

(e) Letting $x = 4.2$ in the power equation of best fit, we predict the distance a ball will fall in taking 4.2 seconds to hit the ground:

$$y = 4.934x^{1.99284} = 4.934(4.2)^{1.99284} = 86.15 \text{ feet} \quad \blacktriangleleft\blacktriangleleft$$

NW *Now Work Problem 37.*

4.4 Assess Your Understanding

Concepts and Vocabulary

1. State the definition of a logarithm.
2. What is a common logarithm?
3. What is the linear form of $y = ab^x$?

4. Suppose data are known to be related through the equation $y = ax^b$. What variables need to be transformed in order to use linear least squares to estimate a and b?

Exercises

• Skill Building

In Problems 1–8, change each exponential expression to an equivalent expression involving a logarithm.

1. $4^2 = 16$ $\quad 2 = \log_4 16$
   NW

2. $2^5 = 32$ $\quad 5 = \log_2 32$

3. $x^5 = 18$ $\quad 5 = \log_x 18$

4. $c^3 = 21$ $\quad 3 = \log_c 21$

5. $7^x = 15$ $\quad x = \log_7 15$

6. $12^x = 43$ $\quad x = \log_{12} 43$

7. $5^3 = y$ $\quad 3 = \log_5 y$

8. $6^{1.5} = y$ $\quad 1.5 = \log_6 y$

In Problems 9–16, change each logarithmic expression to an equivalent expression involving an exponent.

9. $\log_3 81 = 4$ $3^4 = 81$

10. $\log_4 64 = 3$ $4^3 = 64$

11. $\log_a 14 = 3$ $a^3 = 14$

12. $\log_b 19 = 4$ $b^4 = 19$

13. $\log_4 c = 3$ $4^3 = c$

14. $\log_5 b = 4$ $5^4 = b$

15. $\log_2 5 = k$ $2^k = 5$

16. $\log_6 24 = w$ $6^w = 24$

In Problems 17–24, write each expression as a sum of logs. Express powers as factors.

17. $\log_3 (uv)$ $\log_3 u + \log_3 v$

18. $\log_2 (ab)$ $\log_2 a + \log_2 b$

19. $\log_5 x^4$ $4 \log_5 x$

20. $\log_7 y^3$ $3 \log_7 y$

21. $\log_a (uv^2)$
$\log_a u + 2 \log_a v$

22. $\log_a (x^3 y)$
$3 \log_a x + \log_a y$

23. $\log (x^4 y^3)$
$4 \log x + 3 \log y$

24. $\log (x^6 y^2)$
$6 \log x + 2 \log y$

In Problems 25–32, use a calculator to evaluate each expression. Round your answers to three decimal places.

25. $\log 34$ 1.531

26. $\log 18$ 1.255

27. $\log 13.2$ 1.121

28. $\log 34.1$ 1.533

29. $10^{1.6}$ 39.811

30. $10^{2.3}$ 199.526

31. $10^{0.36}$ 2.291

32. $10^{0.74}$ 5.495

- **Applying the Concepts**

33. **Biology** A strain of E-coli Beu 397-recA441 is placed into a petri dish at 30° Celsius and allowed to grow. The following data are collected. Theory states that the number of bacterium in the petri dish will grow initially according to the law of uninhibited growth. This law states that the population grows exponentially over time. The population is estimated by means of an optical device in which the amount of light that passes through the petri dish is measured.

Time (hours), x	Population, y
0	0.09
2.5	0.18
3.5	0.26
4.5	0.35
6	0.50

Source: Dr. Polly Lavery, Joliet Junior College

(a) Draw a scatter diagram treating time as the predictor variable.
(b) Determine the logarithm of the y-values so that $Y = \log y$. Draw a scatter diagram of the transformed data.
(c) Find the least-squares regression line for the transformed data. $Y = 0.1266x - 1.0443$
(d) Find the exponential equation of best fit.
(e) Use the exponential equation of best fit to predict the population at $x = 7$ hours. 0.69

34. **Chemistry** A chemist has a 100-gram sample of a radioactive material. He records the amount of radioactive material in the sample every week for 6 weeks and obtains the following data. Theory states that the amount of radioactive material will decline according to the law of uninhibited decay. This law states the amount of radioactive material in the sample will decline exponentially over time.

Week, x	Weight (in grams), y	Week, x	Weight (in grams), y
0	100.0	4	59.1
1	88.3	5	51.8
2	75.9	6	45.5
3	69.4		

(a) Draw a scatter diagram treating time as the predictor variable.
(b) Determine the logarithm of the y-values so that $Y = \log y$. Draw a scatter diagram of the transformed data.
(c) Find the least-squares regression line for the transformed data. $Y = -0.0571x + 2.0014$
(d) Find the exponential equation of best fit.
(e) Use the exponential equation of best fit to predict the amount of radioactive material after 10 weeks. 27.0 grams

(33d) $y = 0.0903(1.3384)^x$ (34d) $y = 100.32(0.877)^x$

35. The United States Population The following data, obtained from the U.S. Census Bureau, represent the population of the United States. An ecologist is interested in finding an equation that describes the population of the United States over time. She is convinced that the population is growing exponentially.

Year, x	Population, y
1900	76,212,168
1910	92,228,496
1920	106,021,537
1930	123,202,624
1940	132,164,569
1950	151,325,798
1960	179,323,175
1970	203,302,031
1980	226,542,203
1990	248,709,873
2000	281,421,906

Source: United States Census Bureau

(a) Draw a scatter diagram treating time as the predictor variable.
(b) Determine the logarithm of the y-values so that $Y = \log y$. Draw a scatter diagram of the transformed data.
(c) Find the least-squares regression line for the transformed data. $Y = 0.0056x - 2.6593$
(d) Find the exponential equation of best fit.
(e) Use the exponential equation of best fit to predict the population of the United States in 2010, the year of the next census. $339,805,699$
(f) Do you think your prediction will overestimate or underestimate the actual population in 2005? Why?
(g) Compare your prediction with that provided by the U.S. Census Bureau. Is your prediction higher or lower than the Census Bureau's prediction?

36. Finance The following data, represent the amount of money an investor has in an investment account each year for the last six years. The theory of finance states that account values grow exponentially over time.

Year, x	Value of Account, y	Year, x	Value of Account, y
0	$20,000	4	$27,484
1	$21,516	5	$30,053
2	$23,355	6	$32,622
3	$24,885		

(a) Draw a scatter diagram treating time as the predictor variable.
(b) Determine the logarithm of the y-values so that $Y = \log y$. Draw a scatter diagram of the transformed data.
(c) Find the least-squares regression line for the transformed data. $Y = 0.0357x + 4.2971$
(d) Find the exponential equation of best fit.
(e) Use the exponential equation of best fit to predict the value of the account after 30 years. $235,504$
(f) If we subtract 1 from the base, b, in the exponential equation of best fit, we obtain the average annual rate of return on the investment. What was the average rate of return on this investment over the past seven years? 8.56%

37. Kepler's Law of Planetary Motion The time it takes for a planet to complete its orbit around the sun is called the planet's sidereal year. In 1618, Johann Kepler discovered that the sidereal year of a planet is related to the distance of the planet from the sun through a power equation. The following data, show the distances that the planets are from the sun and their sidereal years.

Planet	Distance from Sun, x (millions of miles)	Sidereal Year, y
Mercury	36	0.24
Venus	67	0.62
Earth	93	1.00
Mars	142	1.88
Jupiter	483	11.9
Saturn	887	29.5
Uranus	1,785	84.0
Neptune	2,797	165.0
Pluto	3,675	248.0

(a) Draw a scatter diagram treating distance from the sun as the predictor variable.
(b) Determine the logarithm of both the x- and y-values so that $X = \log x$ and $Y = \log y$. Draw a scatter diagram of the transformed data.
(c) Find the least-squares regression line for the transformed data. $Y = 1.4994X - 2.9506$
(d) Find the power equation of best fit.

38. Gravity David is conducting an experiment to estimate the acceleration of an object due to gravity. He takes a ball, drops it from different heights, and records the time that it takes for the ball to hit the ground. Using an optic laser connected to a stop watch in order to determine the time, he collects the following data.

(35d) $y = 0.0022(1.0129)^x$ (36d) $Y = 19820(1.0856)^x$ (37d) $y = 0.0011x^{1.4994}$

Time, x (seconds)	Distance, y (feet)
1.003	16
1.365	30
1.769	50
2.093	70
2.238	80

Physics theory states that the distance that an object falls depends upon time through a power equation.

(a) Draw a scatter diagram treating time as the predictor variable.

(b) Determine the logarithm of both the x- and y-values so that $X = \log x$ and $Y = \log y$. Draw a scatter diagram of the transformed data.

(c) Find the least-squares regression line for the transformed data. $Y = 2.0018X + 1.2034$

(d) Find the power equation of best fit.

(e) Use the power equation of best fit to predict the distance the object will fall in 1.85 seconds.

(f) Physics theory states that the distance that an object falls is given by the equation $s = \dfrac{1}{2}gt^2$, where s is distance, g is acceleration due to gravity, and t is time. What is David's estimate of g? (It is known that the acceleration due to gravity is approximately 32 feet/second^2.) 31.95 ft/sec^2

39. Intensity of a Lightbulb Cathy is conducting an experiment to measure the relation between a lightbulb's intensity and the distance from the light source. She measures a 100-watt lightbulb's intensity 1 meter from the bulb and at 0.1-meter intervals up to 2 meters from the bulb and obtains the following data.

Distance (meters), x	Intensity, y	Distance (meters), x	Intensity, y
1.0	0.29645	1.6	0.11450
1.1	0.25215	1.7	0.10243
1.2	0.20547	1.8	0.09231
1.3	0.17462	1.9	0.08321
1.4	0.15342	2.0	0.07342
1.5	0.13521		

Physics theory states that the intensity of a lightbulb is related to the distance from the light bulb through a power equation.

(a) Draw a scatter diagram treating distance as the predictor variable.

(b) Determine the logarithm of both the x- and y-values so that $X = \log x$ and $Y = \log y$. Draw a scatter diagram of the transformed data.

(c) Find the least-squares regression line for the transformed data. $Y = -2.012X - 0.5236$

(d) Find the power equation of best fit.

(e) Use the power equation of best fit to predict the intensity of a 100-watt lightbulb that is 2.3 meters away. 0.05605

40. Pendulums The period of a pendulum is the time required for one oscillation; the pendulum is usually referred to as simple when the angle made with the vertical is less than 5°. An experiment is conducted in which simple pendulums are constructed with different lengths and the corresponding periods are recorded. The following data are collected.

Length (in feet), x	Period (in seconds), y
1	1.10
2	1.55
3	1.89
4	2.24
5	2.51
6	2.76
7	2.91

Physics theory states that the period of a simple pendulum is related to the length of the pendulum through a power equation.

(a) Draw a scatter diagram treating length as the predictor variable.

(b) Determine the logarithm of both the x- and y-values so that $X = \log x$ and $Y = \log y$. Draw a scatter diagram of the transformed data.

(c) Find the least-squares regression line for the transformed data. $Y = 0.5098X + 0.0394$

(d) Find the power equation of best fit. $y = 1.095x^{0.5098}$

(e) Use the power equation of best fit to predict the period of a simple pendulum whose length is 2.3 feet. 1.67 seconds

(38d) $Y = 15.973x^{2.0018}$ (38e) 54.7 feet
(39d) $y = 0.2995x^{-2.012}$

Technology Step-by-Step
Nonlinear Curve Fitting

TI-83 Plus   Use the same steps that were followed to obtain the linear regression, except select `Ø: ExpReg` for exponential regression or `A: PwrReg` for power regression.

MINITAB   Minitab does not directly determine exponential and power regressions. The user must transform the data and then use the linear regression option.

Excel   **Step 1:** Draw a scatter diagram of the data.

Step 2: Place the mouse cursor on one of the data points and double-click.

Step 3: Select the TYPE tab, and click on the type of regression you wish to perform.

Step 4: Select the OPTIONS tab, and select "Display equation on chart" and "Display R-squared value on chart." Click OK.

CHAPTER 4 REVIEW

Summary

In this chapter, we introduced techniques that allow us to describe the relation between two quantitative variables. The first step in identifying the type of relation that might exist is to draw a scatter diagram. The predictor variable is plotted on the horizontal axis, the corresponding response variable on the vertical axis. The scatter diagram can be used to discover whether the relation between the predictor and the response variable is linear. In addition, for linear relations, we can judge whether the linear relation shows positive or negative association.

A numerical measure for the strength of linear relation between two variables is the linear correlation coefficient. It is a number between -1 and 1, inclusive. Values of the correlation coefficient near -1 are indicative of a negative linear relation between the two variables; values of the correlation coefficient near $+1$ indicate a positive linear relation between the two variables. If the correlation coefficient is near 0, then there is little *linear* relation between the two variables.

Once a linear relation between the two variables has been discovered, we describe the relation by finding the least-squares regression line. This line best describes the linear relation between the predictor and the response variables. We can use the least-squares regression line to predict a value of the response variable for a given value of the predictor variable.

The coefficient of determination, R^2, measures the percent of variation in the response variable that is explained by the least-squares regression line. It is a measure between 0 and 1 inclusive. The closer R^2 is to 1, the more explanatory value the line has. Whenever a least-squares regression line is obtained, certain diagnostics must be performed. These include verifying that the residuals have constant variance, verifying that the linear model is appropriate, and checking for outliers and influential observations.

In Section 4.4, we introduced methods that can be used to discover exponential equations and power equations of best fit. This method requires that we transform the data via logarithmic transformations.

One item worth mentioning again is that a researcher should never claim causation between two variables in a study unless the data are experimental. Observational data allow us to say that two variables might be associated, but we cannot claim causation.

Formulas

Correlation Coefficient

$$r = \frac{\sum\left(\dfrac{x_i - \overline{x}}{s_x}\right)\left(\dfrac{y_i - \overline{y}}{s_y}\right)}{n - 1}$$

Equation of the Least-Squares Regression Line
The equation of the least-squares regression line is given by

$$\hat{y} = b_1 x + b_0$$

where

$\hat{y}$ is the predicted value of the response variable,

$b_1 = r \cdot \dfrac{s_y}{s_x}$ is the slope of the least-squares regression

line, and

$b_0 = \overline{y} - b_1\overline{x}$ is the intercept of the least-squares regression line.

Coefficient of Determination, R^2

$$R^2 = \frac{\text{variation explained by predictor variable}}{\text{total variation}}$$

$$= 1 - \frac{\text{unexplained variation}}{\text{total variation}}$$

$= r^2$ for the least-squares regression model $\hat{y} = b_0 + b_1 x$

Exponential Equation of Best Fit

$$y = ab^x$$

$$\log y = \log a + x \log b$$

Power Equation of Best Fit

$$y = ax^b$$

$$\log y = \log a + b \log x$$

Vocabulary

Bivariate data (p. 190)
Response variable (p. 192)
Predictor variable (p. 192)
Lurking variable (p. 192)
Scatter diagram (p. 192)
Positively associated (p. 194)

Negatively associated (p. 194)
Linear correlation coefficient (p. 195)
Residuals (p. 209)
Least-squares regression line (p. 209)
Outside the scope of the model (p. 213)
Coefficient of determination (p. 222)

Total deviation (p. 222)
Explained deviation (p. 222)
Unexplained deviation (p. 222)
Influential observation (p. 229)
Logarithm (p. 237)
Common logarithm (p. 238)

Objectives

Section	You should be able to . . .	Review Exercises
4.1	1 Draw scatter diagrams (p. 192)	1–4, 9(a), 10(a), 20, 33–35(a)
	2 Interpret scatter diagrams (p. 194)	1–4(c)
	3 Understand the properties of the linear correlation coefficient (p. 194)	36
	4 Compute and interpret the linear correlation coefficient (p. 197)	1–4(c), 9(d), 10(d)
4.2	1 Find the least-squares regression line (p. 209)	5–8(a), 19(a), 20(b)
	2 Interpret the slope and y-intercept of the least-squares regression line (p. 211)	5–8(c)
	3 Predict the value of the response variable, based upon the least-squares regression line (p. 211)	5–8(d)
	4 Determine residuals, based upon the least-squares regression line (p. 212)	5–8(e)
	5 Compute the sum of squared residuals (p. 214)	9, 10 (f) and (g)
4.3	1 Compute and interpret the coefficient of determination (p. 221)	15–18(a)
	2 Perform residual analysis on a regression model (p. 225)	11–14; 15–18(b),(c); 20(c), (d)
	3 Identify influential observations (p. 229)	15(d), (e); 16–18(d); 19(b)
4.4	1 Change exponential expressions to logarithmic expressions and logarithmic expressions to exponential expressions (p. 237)	21–28
	2 Simplify expressions containing logarithms (p. 238)	29–32
	3 Use logarithmic transformations to linearize exponential relations (p. 239)	33
	4 Use logarithmic transformations to linearize power relations (p. 242)	34

Review Exercises

1. **Engine Displacement versus Fuel Economy** The following data represent the size of a car's engine (in liters) versus its miles per gallon in the city for various 2001 domestic automobiles.
   (a) Draw a scatter diagram treating engine displacement as the predictor variable and miles per gallon as the response variable.
   (b) Compute the linear correlation coefficient between engine displacement and miles per gallon. −0.871
   (c) Based upon the scatter diagram and the linear correlation coefficient, comment on the type of relation that appears to exist between the two variables.

Car	Engine Displacement (in liters)	City Miles per Gallon
Buick Century	3.1	20
Buick LeSabre	3.8	19
Cadillac DeVille	4.6	16
Chevrolet Camaro	3.8	19
Chevrolet Cavalier	2.2	24
Chevrolet Malibu	3.1	23
Chrysler LHS	3.5	18
Dodge Intrepid	2.7	19
Ford Crown Victoria	4.6	17
Ford Focus	2.0	28
Ford Mustang	3.8	20
Oldsmobile Aurora	3.5	19
Pontiac Grand Am	2.4	22
Pontiac Sunfire	2.2	23
Saturn Coupe	1.9	28

Source: Road and Track magazine

2. **Temperature versus Cricket Chirps** Crickets make a chirping noise by sliding their wings rapidly over each other. Perhaps you have noticed that the number of chirps seems to increase with the temperature. The following data list the temperature (in Fahrenheit) and the number of chirps per second for the striped ground cricket.

(a) Draw a scatter diagram treating temperature as the predictor variable and chirps per second as the response variable.

(b) Compute the linear correlation coefficient between temperature and chirps per second. 0.835

(c) Based upon the scatter diagram and the linear correlation coefficient, comment on the type of relation that appears to exist between the two variables.

Temperature	Chirps per Second	Temperature	Chirps per Second
88.6	20.0	71.6	16.0
93.3	19.8	84.3	18.4
80.6	17.1	75.2	15.5
69.7	14.7	82.0	17.1
69.4	15.4	83.3	16.2
79.6	15.0	82.6	17.2
80.6	16.0	83.5	17.0
76.3	14.4		

Source: The Songs of Insects, Pierce, George W., Cambridge, Mass.: Harvard University Press, 1949, pp. 12–21

3. **Apartments** The following data represent the square footage and rents for apartments in North Chicago and in the western suburbs of Chicago.

Location	Square Footage	Rent Per Month
North Chicago	800	1320
North Chicago	820	1507
North Chicago	1050	1895
North Chicago	1415	2195
North Chicago	936	1555
North Chicago	800	1615
North Chicago	891	1125
North Chicago	970	1660
North Chicago	950	1600
North Chicago	1250	1900
North Chicago	1050	1830
West Suburbs	1161	1265
West Suburbs	1000	1050
West Suburbs	1034	915
West Suburbs	910	1003
West Suburbs	934	920
West Suburbs	860	890
West Suburbs	1056	1035
West Suburbs	1000	1190
West Suburbs	784	730
West Suburbs	962	1005
West Suburbs	897	940

Source: apartments.com

(a) On the same graph, draw a scatter diagram for both North Chicago and West Suburban apartments treating square footage as the predictor variable. Be sure to use a different plotting symbol for each group.

(b) Compute the linear correlation coefficient between square footage and rent for each location.

(c) Given the scatter diagram and the linear correlation coefficient, comment on the type of relation that appears to exist between the two variables for each group.

(d) Does location appear to be a factor in rent?

4. **Boys versus Girls** The following data represent the height (in inches) of boys and girls between the ages of 2 and 10 years. Data are based upon results obtained from the National Center for Health Statistics.

Age	Boy Height	Girl Height	Age	Boy Height	Girl Height
2	36.1	39.0	6	49.8	43.7
2	34.2	38.6	7	43.2	50.5
2	31.1	33.6	7	47.9	47.7
3	36.3	41.3	8	51.4	44
3	39.5	40.9	8	48.3	62.1
4	41.5	43.2	8	50.9	44.8
4	38.6	39.8	9	52.2	50.9
5	45.6	50.5	9	51.3	55.6
5	44.8	38.3	10	55.6	61.4
5	44.6	43.9	10	59.5	50.8

(a) On the same graph, draw a scatter diagram for both boys and girls treating age as the predictor variable. Be sure to use a different plotting symbol for each gender.

(b) Compute the linear correlation coefficient between age and height for each gender. Boys: 0.949; Girls: 0.802

(3b) Chicago: 0.835; Suburbs: 0.829

(c) Based upon the scatter diagram and the linear correlation coefficient, comment on the type of relation that appears to exist between the two variables for each gender.

(d) Does gender appear to be a factor in determining height?

5. Using the data and results from Problem 1, do the following:
   (a) Find the least-squares regression line, treating engine displacement as the predictor variable and miles per gallon as the response variable.
   (b) Draw the least-squares regression line on the scatter diagram.
   (c) Interpret the slope and intercept, if appropriate.
   (d) Predict the miles per gallon of a Ford Mustang whose engine displacement is 3.8 liters. 18.7
   (e) Compute the residual of the prediction found in part (d). 1.3
   (f) Is the miles per gallon above or below average for a Ford Mustang? Above

6. Using the data and results from Problem 2, do the following:
   (a) Find the least-squares regression line, treating temperature as the predictor variable and chirps per second as the response variable.
   (b) Draw the least-squares regression line on the scatter diagram.
   (c) Interpret the slope and intercept, if appropriate.
   (d) Predict the chirps per second if it is 83.3°F. 17.3

(e) Compute the residual of the prediction found in part (d). −1.1
(f) Were chirps per second above or below average at 83.3°F? Below

7. Using the "West Suburbs" data and results from Problem 3, do the following:
   (a) Find the least-squares regression line, treating square footage as the predictor variable and rent as the response variable.
   (b) Draw the least-squares regression line on the scatter diagram.
   (c) Interpret the slope and intercept, if appropriate.
   (d) Predict the rent of a 934-square-foot apartment. $960
   (e) Compute the residual of the prediction found in part (d). −$40
   (f) Is this apartment's rent above or below average?

8. Using the "boy height" data and results from Problem 4, do the following:
   (a) Find the least-squares regression line, treating age as the predictor variable and height as the response variable. Height = 2.6351 · age + 29.705
   (b) Draw the least-squares regression line on the scatter diagram.
   (c) Interpret the slope and intercept, if appropriate.
   (d) Predict the height of a six-year-old boy. 45.5 inches
   (e) Compute the residual of the prediction found in part (d). 4.3 inches
   (f) Is this boy's height above or below average? Above

(5a) mpg = −3.5339 engine + 32.1201 (6a) Chirps = 0.2119 Temp − 0.309 (7a) Rent = 1.1702 Area − 132.6
(7f) Below

In Problems 9 and 10, do the following:

(a) Draw a scatter diagram treating x as the predictor variable and y as the response variable.
(b) Select two points from the scatter diagram and find the equation of the line containing the points selected.
(c) Graph the line found in part (b) on the scatter diagram.
(d) Determine the least-squares regression line.
(e) Graph the least-squares regression line on the scatter diagram.
(f) Compute the sum of the squared residuals for the line found in part (b).
(g) Compute the sum of the squared residuals for the least-squares regression line found in part (d).
(h) Comment on the "fit" of the line found in part (b) versus the least-squares regression line found in part (d).

9.

x	3	4	6	7	9
y	2.1	4.2	7.2	8.1	10.6

10.

x	10	14	17	18	21
y	105	94	82	76	63

In Problems 11–14, a residual plot is given. From the residual plot, determine whether a linear model is appropriate. If not, state your reason.

11. Yes   **12.** No   **13.** No   **14.** No

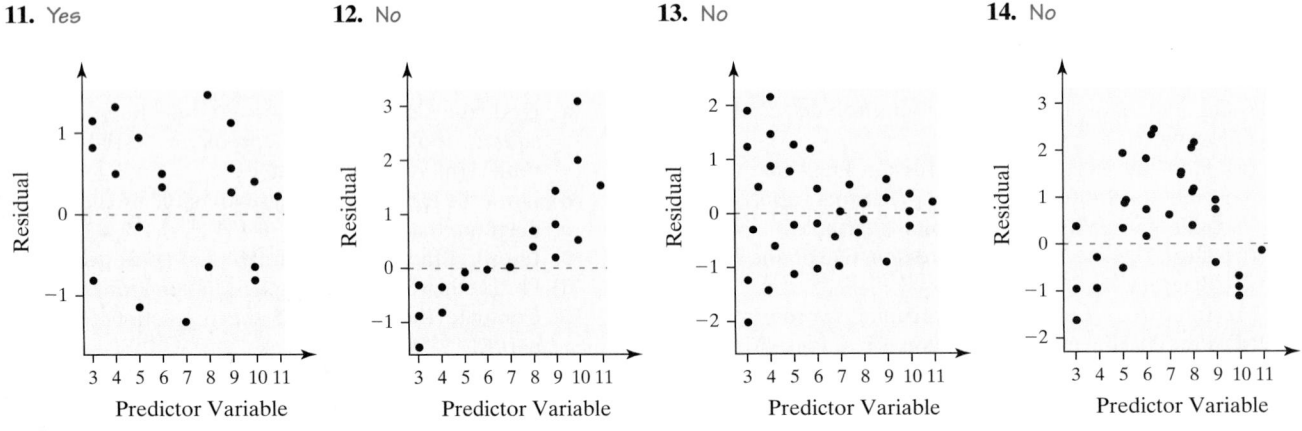

Predictor Variable

15. Use the results from Problems 1 and 5 for the following:
    (a) Compute and interpret R^2. 75.9%
    (b) Plot the residuals against engine displacement.
    (c) For the graph obtained in part (b), is a linear model appropriate?
    (d) Are there any outliers or influential observations? No
    (e) Add a Dodge Viper to the data set in Problem 1 (8.0 liter engine, 11 miles per gallon), then redo Problems 1, 7, and 15. Comment on the effect the Viper has on the regression model.

16. Use the results from Problems 2 and 6 for the following:
    (a) Compute and interpret R^2. 69.7%
    (b) Plot the residuals against temperature.
    (c) For the graph obtained in part (b), is a linear model appropriate? Yes
    (d) Are there any outliers or influential observations? No

17. Use the results from Problems 3 and 7 for the following:
    (a) Compute and interpret R^2. 68.7%
    (b) Plot the residuals against square footage.
    (c) For the graph obtained in part (b), is a linear model appropriate? Yes
    (d) Are there any outliers or influential observations? No

18. Use the results from Problems 4 and 8 for the following:
    (a) Compute and interpret R^2. 90.1%
    (b) Plot the residuals against age.
    (c) For the graph obtained in part (b), is a linear model appropriate? Yes
    (d) Are there any outliers or influential observations? No

19. **Apartment Rents** Using the "North Chicago" apartments rent data and the results of Problem 3, do the following:
    (a) Find the least-squares regression line, treating square footage as the predictor variable and rent as the response variable. Rent = 1.2787 Footage + 384.0
    (b) Are there any outliers or influential observations? Yes

20. **Depreciation** The following data represent the price of a random sample of used Chevy Camaros, by age.

Age (in years)	Price (in dollars)	Age (in years)	Price (in dollars)
2	$15,900	1	$20,365
5	$10,988	2	$16,463
2	$16,980	6	$10,824
5	$9,995	1	$19,995
4	$11,995	1	$18,650
5	$10,995	4	$10,488

Source: www.onlineauto.com

(a) Draw a scatter diagram treating the age of the car as the predictor variable and price as the response variable.
(b) Find the least-squares regression line.
(c) Plot the residuals against the age of the car.
(d) Do you think that a linear model is appropriate for describing the relation between the age of the car and price? Why? No

(20b) Price = −2054.6 age + 20,976.2

In Problems 21–24, change each exponential expression to an equivalent expression involving a logarithm.

21. $5^3 = 125$ $3 = \log_5 125$ **22.** $4^5 = 1024$ $5 = \log_4 1024$ **23.** $a^6 = 22$ $6 = \log_a 22$ **24.** $b^2 = 7$ $2 = \log_b 7$

In Problems 25–28, change each logarithmic expression to an equivalent expression involving an exponent.

25. $\log_4 x = 8$ $4^8 = x$ **26.** $\log_6 b = 2$ $6^2 = b$ **27.** $\log_a 11 = 5$ $a^5 = 11$ **28.** $\log_b 9 = 4$ $b^4 = 9$

In Problems 29–32, write each expression as a sum of logs. Express powers as factors.

29. $\log (u^2 v)$ $2 \log u + \log v$ **30.** $\log (a^4 b)$ $4 \log a + \log b$ **31.** $\log x^6$ $6 \log x$ **32.** $\log y^8$ $8 \log y$

---

33. Newton's Law of Cooling The following data were collected by placing a temperature probe in a portable heater, removing the probe, and then recording the temperature over time.

Time (seconds)	Temperature (°F)
0	165.07
1	164.77
2	163.99
3	163.22
4	162.82
5	161.96
6	161.20
7	160.45
8	159.35
9	158.91
10	157.89
11	156.83
12	156.11
13	155.08
14	154.40
15	153.72

Newton's law of cooling states that the temperature of a heated object decreases exponentially over time toward the temperature of the surrounding medium (such as the room in which the object is located).
(a) Draw a scatter diagram treating time as the predictor variable and temperature as the response variable.
(b) Determine the logarithm of the y-values so that $Y = \log y$. Draw a scatter diagram of the transformed data.
(c) Find the least-squares regression line for the transformed data. $Y = -0.0022x + 2.2194$
(d) Find the exponential equation of best fit.
(e) Use the exponential equation of best fit to predict the temperature of the probe at 16 seconds. $152.96°F$

(33d) $y = 165.73(0.995)^x$

34. Gravity on the Moon Neil Armstrong wishes to estimate the acceleration due to gravity on the Moon. He drops a ball (with a special chip that measures the distance to the ground in two-second intervals) into a crater that is known to be 1000 feet deep. The following data represent the distance the object has fallen over two-second intervals.

Time (seconds), x	Distance (in feet), y
2	10.7
4	42.5
6	96.0
8	170.9
10	265.9
12	384.1
14	523.5

Physics theory states that the distance s that an object travels after t seconds is given by the power equation $s = \frac{1}{2}gt^2$ where g is the acceleration due to gravity.
(a) Draw a scatter diagram treating time as the predictor variable and distance as the response variable.
(b) Determine the logarithm of the x-values so that $X = \log x$. Determine the logarithm of the y-values so that $Y = \log y$. Draw a scatter diagram of the transformed data.
(c) Find the least-squares regression line for the transformed data. $Y = 2x + 0.4263$
(d) Find the power equation of best fit. $y = 2.669x^2$
(e) What is Neil Armstrong's estimate of the acceleration due to gravity on the Moon? 5.34 ft/sec^2

Picture a sweltering planet covered in the blistering heat of the sun. In the dog days of summer, it is probably not too difficult to imagine such a sweltering Earth. Is it so easy to visualize a sweltering planet in the dead of winter?

Magazine covers and nightly-news anchors detail the latest predictions of global warming. We are told that, as greenhouse gases rise, so will the oceans, from the melting of glaciers. These forecasters maintain that, as the glaciers melt from the heat, we are rushing into a catastrophic climate change of our own making. In some places, they say, where once rich farmland existed, there will be only the sand of a desert. Film-makers and story writers capitalize on these predictions, creating catastrophic visions of a future in which the world's land is overcome by the water of the melted glaciers. Where does science end and science fiction begin?

Recently reported predictions suggest an increase in the annual-average global temperature. Estimates of the temperature increase range from a low of about 2°C to as much as 5°C, with most forecasts coming in at around 4°C. Increasing emissions, due to human activity, of so-called greenhouse gases, such as carbon dioxide, methane, nitrous oxide, and CFCs (chlorofluorocarbons), are seen as the leading culprits in the forecasted planetary warming. Additionally, reports indicating an unusually high concentration of warm seasons or years in recent decades appear to support these predictions.

However, not all climatologists agree with the forecasters' predictions. Some scientists suggest that the recent rise in reported mean temperatures is a phenomenon that is isolated, affecting primarily urban areas. The climatic effect of urban areas, known as urban heat islands, is well documented. The term simply refers to the fact that urban areas, with their high density of materials such as asphalt and concrete, generally exhibit higher temperatures than their rural counterparts. The impact of the Philadelphia heat island can be seen in the following table:

Average Temperature (in °C) for Philadelphia Airport and Downtown Philadelphia (10-Year Averages)		
	Downtown	**Airport**
Annual Mean	13.6	12.8
Mean June Maximum	28.2	27.8
Mean December maximum	6.7	6.4
Mean June minimum	17.7	16.5
Mean December minimum	−0.4	−2.1

Source: Frederick Lutgens and Edward Tarbuck. *The Atmosphere*, 5th edition; Englewood Cliffs, NJ: Prentice Hall, 1992, p. 321. Original source: Hans Neuberger and John Cahir. *Principles of Climatology*; New York: Holt, Rheinhart, & Winston, 1969, p. 128.

Examining the temperature trends of both rural and urban areas can provide some insight into the global-warming issue. For a very large number of locations throughout the United States, a simple linear regression equation was determined with each site's annual mean temperature as the response variable and time as the predictor variable. Temperature declines over time result in negative slopes; temperature increases cause positive slopes. The following tables contain the regression results for five rural and five urban areas:

CASE STUDY

Regression Results for the Mean Annual Temperature for Five Rural U.S. Sites
(Mean Annual Temperature $= b_0 + b_1(\text{Year}))$ (1910–1994)

Location	b_1	b_0	R^2
Lake City, FL	−0.014	95.16	9.61
Lampasas, TX	−0.037	136.70	34.23
Tejon Rancho, CA	0.016	31.34	1.93
Cedar Lake, WA	−0.019	84.83	10.47
Pembina, ND	0.005	27.96	0.33

Regression Results for the Mean Annual Temperature for Five Urban U.S. Sites
(Mean Annual Temperature $= b_0 + b_1(\text{Year}))$ (1910–1994)

Location	b_1	b_0	R^2
Baltimore, MD	0.035	−11.01	40.42
San Antonio, TX	−0.008	85.06	3.20
Newport Beach, CA	0.020	22.35	4.46
Seattle, WA	0.025	4.24	24.67
Minneapolis, MN	−0.001	47.78	0.04

Source: Original data are from the United States Historical Climatology Network Data set. The regression trend statistics are available at http://www.co2science.org/ushcn/ushcn.htm. This Web site provides trend calculations for locations in all fifty states.

1. Examine these results. Does it appear that rising temperatures over time are associated with urban areas?

2. List some other predictor variables that might be used in a least-squares regression model. With these variables in mind, what are the limitations, if any, of these regression equations? Is there any additional information you would like to have before coming to a final conclusion concerning the usefulness of these equations? Write a report detailing your findings.

3. What would be the danger of predicting a location's annual mean temperature 100 years into the future? Explain.

4. To explore the temperature trends for these locations further, go to the Web site mentioned above. For any of these locations, select another time period for your analysis. For example, for Lake City, Florida, calculate a regression equation for the years 1890 through 1994. How does your choice of data alter your results?

5. To further explore the impact of rural and urban sites on temperature trends, go to the aforementioned Web site and select other urban locations, such as New York City, Pasadena, California, and Tucson, Arizona, and rural locations such as Indian Lake, New York, and Grand Canyon, Arizona. Calculate regression equations for these locations. How do these results affect your previous conclusion regarding the claim that rising temperatures over time are associated with urban areas?

What Car Should I Buy?

You are still in the market to buy a car. As we all know, cars lose value over time. Therefore, another item to consider when purchasing a car is its depreciation rate. The higher the depreciation rate, the more value the car loses each year. Using the same three cars that you used in the Chapter 3 "decision," answer the following in order to determine depreciation rate.

1. Collect information regarding the 3 cars in your list by finding at least 12 cars of each car type that are for sale. Obtain the asking price and age of the car. Sources of data include your local newspaper classified ads and car Web-sites, such as http://www.cars.com/ and http://www.autobytel.com/.

2. For each car type, draw a scatter diagram, treating age of the car as the predictor variable and asking price as the response variable.

3. The asking price of a car and the age of a car are related through the exponential equation $y = ab^x$, where y is the price of the car and x is the age of the car. The depreciation rate will be $1 - b$. To estimate the values of a and b via least-squares regression, we need to linearize the equation. This is accomplished by computing the logarithm of the asking price. For example, if the asking price of a car is $8,000, compute $\log(8{,}000) = 3.9031$. Compute the logarithm of each asking price for each car.

4. For each car type, draw a scatter diagram, treating age of the car as the predictor variable and the logarithm of asking price as the response variable.

5. For each car type, find the least-squares regression line, treating age of the car as the predictor variable and the logarithm of asking price as the response variable. The line will be $Y = \log a + (\log b)x = A + Bx$.

6. To determine a and b for the exponential equation $y = ab^x$, let $a = 10^A$ and $b = 10^B$. Graph the exponential equation on each scatter diagram from question (2).

7. For each exponential equation determined in question (6), the depreciation rate is $1 - b$. What are the depreciation rates for the 3 cars considered? Will this result affect your decision about which car to buy?

DECISIONS

256

The taste, color, and clarity of the water coming out of home faucets have long concerned consumers. Recent reports of lead and parasite contamination have made unappetizing water a health, as well as an aesthetic, concern. Water companies are struggling to contain cryptosporidium, a parasite that has caused outbreaks of illness that may be fatal to people with a weakened immune system. Even chlorination, which has rid drinking water of infectious organisms that once killed people by the thousands, is under suspicion as an indirect cause of miscarriages and cancer.

Concerns about water quality and taste have made home filtering increasingly popular. To find out how well they work, technicians at Consumer Reports tested 14 models to determine how well they filtered contaminants and whether they could improve the taste of our cabbage-soup testing mixture (October, 1999).

To test chloroform and lead removal, we added concentrated amounts of both to our water, along with calcium nitrate to increase water hardness. Every few days we analyzed the water to measure chloroform and lead content. The following table contains the lead measurements for one of the models tested.

# Gallons Processed	% Lead Removed
25	85%
26	87%
73	86%
75	88%
123	90%
126	87%
175	92%
177	94%

(a) Construct a scatter diagram of the data using "% Lead Removed" as the response variable.

(b) Does the relationship between "# Gallons Processed" and "% Lead Removed" appear to be linear? If not, describe the relationship.

(c) Calculate the linear correlation coefficient between "# Gallons Processed" and "% Lead Removed." Based on the scatter diagram constructed in part (a) and your answer to part (b), is this measure useful? What is R^2? Interpret R^2.

(d) Fit a linear regression model to this data. Using this model, construct a residual plot. What does the residual plot suggest?

(e) Using statistical software or a graphing calculator with advanced statistical features, fit a quadratic model to this data. Construct a residual plot. What is R^2? Which model appears to fit the data better?

(f) Given the nature of the variables being measured, describe the type of curve you would expect to describe the true relationship between these variables (linear, quadratic, exponential, s-shaped). Support your position.

Note to Readers: In many cases, our test protocol and analytical methods are more complicated than described in these examples. The data and discussions have been modified to make the material more appropriate for the audience.

Putting It All Together

In Chapter 1, we learned the methods of collecting data. In Chapters 2 through 4, we learned how to summarize raw data through tables, graphs, and numbers. As far as the statistical process goes, we have discussed the collecting, organizing and summarizing part of the process.

Before we can proceed with the analysis of data, we introduce probability, which forms the basis of inferential statistics. Why? Well, we can think of the probability of an occurrence as the likelihood of observing that occurrence. If something has a high likelihood of occurring, we assign it a high probability (close to 1).

If something has a small chance of occurring, we assign it a low probability (close to 0). For example, in rolling a single die, it is unlikely that we would roll five straight sixes, so we assign this result a low probability. In fact, the probability of rolling five straight sixes is 0.0001286. So if we were playing a game that entailed throwing a single die, and one of the players threw five sixes in a row, we would consider the player to be lucky (or a cheater) because it is such an unusual occurrence. Statisticians use probability in the same way. If something occurs that has a low probability, we investigate to find out "what's up."

Probability

Outline

 For additional study help, go to
www.prenhall.com/sullivanstats

Materials include

- Self-Graded Quizzes
- "Preparing for This Section" Quizzes
- STATLETs
- PowerPoint Downloads
- Step-by-Step Technology Guide
- Graphing Calculator Help

5.1 Probability of Simple Events

Preparing for This Section   Before getting started, review the following:

✓ Relative frequency (Section 2.1, pp. 53–54)

Objectives

1. Understand the properties of probabilities
2. Compute and interpret probabilities using the classical method
3. Compute and interpret probabilities using the empirical method
4. Use simulation to obtain probabilities
5. Understand subjective probabilities

Note to Instructor
Probabilities can be expressed as fractions, decimals, or percents. You may want to give a mini-review of how to convert from one form to the other.

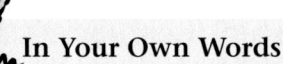**In Your Own Words**

Probability describes how likely it is that some event will occur. If we can look at the proportion of times an event has occurred over a long period of time (or over a large number of trials), we can be more certain of the likelihood of its occurrence.

Probability is a measure of the likelihood of a random phenomenon or chance behavior. Probability describes the long-term proportion with which a certain **outcome** will occur in situations with short-term uncertainty. The long-term predictability of chance behavior is best understood through a simple experiment. Flip a coin 100 times and compute the proportion of heads observed after each toss of the coin. Suppose the first flip is tails, so the proportion of heads is 0/1; the second flip is heads, so the proportion of heads is 1/2; the third flip is heads, so the proportion of heads is 2/3, and so on. Plot the proportion of heads versus the number of flips and obtain the graph in Figure 1(a). We repeat this experiment with the results shown in Figure 1(b).

Look at the graphs in Figures 1(a) and (b). Notice that in the short term (fewer flips of the coin), the proportion of heads is different and unpredictable for each experiment. As the number of flips of the coin increases, however, both graphs tend toward a proportion of 0.5. This is the basic premise of probability. Probability deals with experiments that yield random short-term results or outcomes, yet reveal long-term predictability. **The long-term proportion with which a certain outcome is observed is**

Figure 1

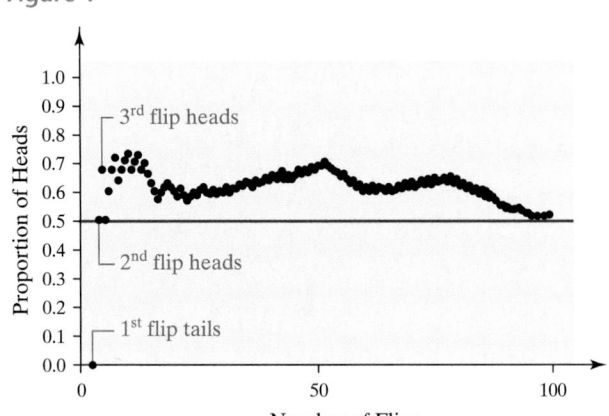

(a)

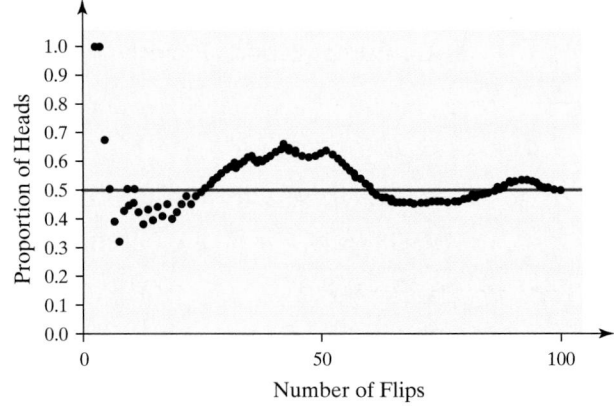

(b)

the probability of that outcome. Therefore, we say that the probability of observing a head is $\frac{1}{2}$ or 50% because as the number of repetitions of the experiment increases (as we flip the coin more and more), the proportion of heads tends toward $\frac{1}{2}$. This phenomenon is referred to as the *Law of Large Numbers*.

Theorem

> **The Law of Large Numbers**
>
> As the number of repetitions of a probability experiment increases, the proportion with which a certain outcome is observed gets closer to the probability of the outcome.

Note to Instructor
In class activity: Have each student flip a coin three times. Use the results to find the probability of a head. Repeat this experiment a few times. Use the cumulative results to illustrate the Law of Large Numbers.

The Law of Large Numbers is illustrated in Figure 1. For a few flips of the coin, the probability fluctuates wildly around 0.5, but as the number of flips increases, the proportion of heads settles down near 0.5. Jakob Bernoulli (a major contributor to the field of probability) felt that The Law of Large Numbers was common sense. This is evident by the following quote from his text *Ars Conjectandi*: "For even the most stupid of men, by some instinct of nature, by himself and without any instruction, is convinced that the more observations have been made, the less danger there is of wandering from one's goal."

In probability, an **experiment** is any process that can be repeated in which the results are uncertain. Probability experiments do not always produce the same results or outcome, so the result of any single trial of the experiment is not known ahead of time. However, the results of the experiment over many trials do produce regular patterns that enable us to predict with remarkable accuracy. For example, an insurance company cannot know ahead of time whether a specific 16-year-old driver will be involved in an accident over the course of a year. However, based upon historical records, the company can be fairly certain that about three out of every ten 16-year-old male drivers will be involved in a traffic accident during the course of a year. Therefore, of the 816,000 16-year-old drivers (816,000 repetitions of the experiment), the insurance company is fairly confident that about 30%, or 244,800, of the 816,000 drivers will be involved in an accident. This prediction forms the basis for establishing insurance rates for any particular 16-year-old male driver.

We now introduce some terminology that is required in the study of computing probabilities.

Definitions

In Your Own Words

A simple event is the result of one trial of a probability experiment. The sample space is a list of all possible results of a probability experiment.

A **simple event** is any single outcome from a probability experiment. Each simple event is denoted e_i.

The **sample space, S**, of a probability experiment is the collection of all possible simple events.

An **event** is any collection of outcomes from a probability experiment. An event may consist of one or more simple events. Events are denoted using capital letters such as E.

We present an example to illustrate the definitions.

▶ **EXAMPLE 1** **Identifying Events and the Sample Space of a Probability Experiment**

Problem: A probability experiment consists of rolling a single "fair" die.*

(a) Identify the simple events of the probability experiment.
(b) Determine the sample space.
(c) Define the event E = "roll an even number."

Approach: The simple events are the possible outcomes that can occur based upon one trial of the experiment. The sample space is a list of all possible simple events. So we need to make a list of all possible ways the die can land.

Solution:

(a) The simple events from rolling a single fair die are e_1 = "rolling a one" = $\{1\}$, e_2 = "rolling a two" = $\{2\}$, e_3 = "rolling a three" = $\{3\}$, e_4 = "rolling a four" = $\{4\}$, e_5 = "rolling a five" = $\{5\}$, and e_6 = "rolling a six" = $\{6\}$.

(b) Combining these simple events, we form the sample space, $S = \{1, 2, 3, 4, 5, 6\}$. There are 6 simple events in the sample space.

(c) The event E = "roll an even number" = $\{2, 4, 6\}$. ◀◀

① **Properties of Probabilities**

We define the **probability of an event**, denoted $P(E)$, as the likelihood of that event occurring. Probabilities have some properties that must be satisfied.

Properties of Probabilities

1. The probability of any event E, $P(E)$, must be between 0 and 1 inclusive. That is, $0 \le P(E) \le 1$.

2. If an event is **impossible**, the probability of the event is 0.

3. If an event is a **certainty**, the probability of the event is 1.

4. If $S = \{e_1, e_2, \ldots, e_n\}$, then $P(e_1) + P(e_2) + \ldots + P(e_n) = 1$.

- Property 1 states that a probability less than 0 or greater than 1 is not possible. Therefore, probabilities of 1.13 or −0.32 are not possible.

- Property 2 states that impossible events have a probability of 0. For example, in the United States of America it is impossible for Thanksgiving to be on Monday; therefore, the probability of Thanksgiving occurring on Monday is 0.

---

*A fair die is one in which each possible outcome is equally likely. For example, rolling a 2 is just as likely as rolling a 5. We contrast this with a "loaded" die in which a certain outcome is more likely. For example, if rolling a 1 is more likely than rolling a 2, 3, 4, 5, or 6, then the die is loaded.

- Property 3 states that events that are certain have a probability of 1. Because every Thanksgiving occurs on Thursday, the probability that Thanksgiving occurs on Thursday next year is 1.
- Property 4 states that the sum of the probabilities of all the simple events must be 1.

The closer a probability is to 1, the more likely the event is to occur. The closer a probability is to 0, the less likely the event is to occur. For example, an event with probability 0.8 is more likely to occur than an event with probability 0.75. An event with probability 0.8 will occur about 80 times out of 100 repetitions of the experiment, while an event with probability 0.75 will occur about 75 times out of 100. Be careful of this interpretation. Just because an event has probability of 0.75 does not mean that the event *must* occur 75 times out of 100. It simply means that we *expect* the number of occurrences to be close to 75 in 100 trials of the experiment. The more repetitions of the probability experiment, the closer the proportion with which the event occurs will be to 0.75 (The Law of Large Numbers).

One of the main goals of this section is to learn how probabilities can be used to identify *unusual events*. An **unusual event** is an event that has a low probability of occurring. Typically, an event whose probability is less than 5% is considered unusual, but this "cut-off point" is not set in stone. Ultimately, the researcher must decide the probability that separates unusual events from "not so unusual events." The context of the problem dictates this "cut-off point." For example, suppose the probability of being wrongly convicted of a capital crime punishable by death is 3%. The probability is too high in light of the consequences (death for the wrongly convicted). In other words, the probability indicates the event is not unusual (unlikely) enough. We would want this probability to be as close to zero as possible. Now suppose that you are planning a picnic on a day in which there is a 3% chance of rain. In this context, you would consider "rain" an unusual (unlikely) event and proceed with the picnic plans. The point is this: Selecting a probability that separates unusual events from "not so unusual" events is a subjective practice. The probability selected will depend upon the situation. With that said, statisticians typically use "cut-off" points of 1%, 5%, and 10%. For most circumstances, any event that occurs with probability of 5% or less will be considered unusual.

 **In Your Own Words**

An unusual event is an event that is not likely to occur.

Note to Instructor
Ask students to cite some real-life examples of unusual events.

Caution

A probability of 0.05 should not always be used to separate unusual events from "not so unusual events."

NW   *Now Work Problem 1.*

Next, we introduce three methods for determining the probability of an event: (1) the classical method, (2) the empirical method, and (3) the subjective method.

② The Classical Method

The classical method of computing probabilities requires *equally likely outcomes*. An experiment is said to have **equally likely outcomes** when each simple event has the same probability of occurring. For example, in throwing a fair die once, each of the six simple events in the sample space, $\{1, 2, 3, 4, 5, 6\}$, has an equal chance of occurring. Contrast this situation with a loaded die in which a five or six is twice as likely to occur as a one, two, three, or four.

Theorem

Computing Probability Using the Classical Method

If an experiment has n equally likely simple events and if the number of ways that an event E can occur is m, then the probability of E, $P(E)$, is

$$P(E) = \frac{\text{Number of ways that } E \text{ can occur}}{\text{Number of possible outcomes}} = \frac{m}{n} \quad \text{(1)}$$

So, if S is the sample space of this experiment, then

$$P(E) = \frac{N(E)}{N(S)} \quad \text{(2)}$$

where $N(E)$ is the number of simple events in E and $N(S)$ is the number of simple events in the sample space.

▶ **EXAMPLE 2** **Computing Probabilities Using the Classical Method**

Problem: A pair of fair dice are rolled.

(a) Compute the probability of rolling a seven.
(b) Compute the probability of rolling "snake eyes"; that is, compute the probability of rolling a two.
(c) Comment on the likelihood of rolling a seven versus rolling a two.

Approach: To compute probabilities using the classical method, we count the number of simple events in the sample space and count the number of ways the event can occur.

Solution:

(a) In rolling a pair of fair dice, there are 36 equally likely outcomes, as shown in Figure 2.

Figure 2

There are 36 simple events in the sample space, so $N(S) = 36$. The event $E = $ "roll a seven" $= \{(1, 6), (2, 5), (3, 4), (4, 3), (5, 2), (6, 1)\}$ is composed of six simple events, so $N(E) = 6$. Using Formula (2), the probability of rolling a seven is

$$P(E) = P(\text{roll a seven}) = \frac{N(E)}{N(S)} = \frac{6}{36} = \frac{1}{6}$$

(b) The event F = "rolling a two" = $\{(1, 1)\}$ has one simple event, so $N(E) = 1$. Using Formula (2), the probability of rolling a two is

$$P(F) = P(\text{roll a two}) = \frac{N(E)}{N(S)} = \frac{1}{36}$$

(c) Since $P(\text{rolling a seven}) = 6/36$ and $P(\text{rolling a two}) = 1/36$, we are six times as likely to roll a seven as a two. In other words, in 36 rolls of the dice, we would *expect* to observe about 6 sevens and only 1 two.

◀◀

In simple random sampling, each individual has the same chance of being selected. Therefore, we can use the classical method to compute the probability of obtaining a specific sample.

▶ **EXAMPLE 3**   **Computing Probabilities Using Equally Likely Outcomes**

Problem: Sophia has three tickets to a concert. Yolanda, Michael, Kevin, and Marissa have all stated they would like to go to the concert with Sophia. To be fair, Sophia decides to randomly select the two people who can go to the concert with her.

(a) Determine the sample space of the experiment. In other words, list all possible simple random samples of size $n = 2$.
(b) Compute the probability of the event "Michael and Kevin attend the concert."
(c) Compute the probability of the event "Marissa attends the concert."

Approach: First, we determine the simple events in the sample space by making a table. The probability of each event is the number of simple events in the event divided by the number of simple events in the sample space.

Solution:
(a) The sample space is listed in Table 1.

TABLE 1		
Yolanda, Michael	Yolanda, Kevin	Yolanda, Marissa
Michael, Marissa	Kevin, Marissa	Michael, Kevin

(b) We have $N(S) = 6$ and there is one way the event "Michael and Kevin attend the concert" can occur. Therefore, the probability that Michael and Kevin attend the concert is 1/6.
(c) We have $N(S) = 6$ and there are three ways the event "Marissa attends the concert" can occur. The probability that Marissa will attend is 3/6 = 50%.

◀◀

NW *Now Work Problems 11 and 27.*

③ **Empirical Probabilities**

When using the classical method, we obtain the probability of an event without actually conducting the probability experiment. Consider Example 2, where we computed the probability of rolling a seven to be 1/6 without actually rolling a pair of dice. Often, however, attempts to count the number of ways an event can occur are difficult or impossible. For example, the probability of winning in the card game Black Jack can be computed using classical methods, but the tedious amount of work that needs to be done to figure out the equally likely events is overwhelming! It may also be the case that the simple events are not equally likely, in which case the classical method is inappropriate. For these reasons, we introduce a second method for determining probabilities that relies on empirical evidence, that is, evidence based upon the outcomes of a probability experiment.

Theorem

> **Approximating Probabilities through the Empirical Approach**
>
> The probability of an event E is approximately the number of times event E is observed divided by the number of repetitions of the experiment.
>
> $$P(E) \approx \text{relative frequency of } E = \frac{\text{frequency of } E}{\text{number of trials of experiment}} \quad (3)$$

In Your Own Words

When probabilities are computed by using the classical approach, they are exact. When probabilities are computed by using the empirical approach, they are approximate. Probabilities computed from population data are exact; probabilities computed from survey (or sample) data are approximate.

Why is the probability obtained using the empirical approach approximate? Because different "runs" of the probability experiment will lead to different outcomes, and therefore different estimates of $P(E)$. Consider flipping a coin 20 times and recording the number of heads. Use the results of the experiment to estimate the probability of obtaining a head. Now repeat the experiment. Because the results of the second "run" of the experiment do not necessarily yield the same results, we cannot say the probability *equals* some proportion, but rather say the probability is *approximately* some value. Of course, as we increase the number of trials of a probability experiment, we have more confidence in our estimate (again, the Law of Large Numbers).

When we survey a random sample of individuals, the probabilities computed from the surveys are approximate. In fact, we can think of a survey as a probability experiment because the results of a survey will be different each time the survey is conducted (because there will be different people in it).

▶ **EXAMPLE 4**   **Using Relative Frequencies to Approximate Probabilities**

Problem: The data in Table 2 represent the results of a survey in which 200 people were asked their means of travel to work. The data are based on information obtained from the United States Census Bureau.

TABLE 2	
Travel Mean	**Frequency**
Drive Alone	153
Carpool	22
Public Transportation	10
Walk	5
Other Means	3
Work at Home	7

(a) Approximate the probability that a randomly selected individual carpools to work.

(b) Would it be unusual to randomly select an individual who walks to work?

Approach: To estimate the probability of each event, we determine the relative frequency of the event.

Solution:

(a) There are $153 + 22 + \ldots + 7 = 200$ individuals in the survey. The relative frequency of the event "carpool" is $22/200 = 0.11 = 11\%$. We estimate that there is an 11% probability that a randomly selected individual carpools to work.

(b) The probability that an individual walks to work is $5/200 = 0.025 = 2.5\%$. It is somewhat unusual for individuals to walk to work. ◀◀

▶ **EXAMPLE 5** **Comparing the Classical Method and Empirical Method**

Problem: Suppose a survey is conducted in which 50 families with three children are asked to disclose the gender of their children. Based upon the results, it was found that 18 of the families had two boys and one girl.

(a) Estimate the probability of having two boys and one girl in a three-child family using the empirical method.

(b) Compute the probability of having two boys and one girl in a three-child family using the classical method, assuming boys and girls are equally likely.

Approach: To answer part (a), we determine the relative frequency of the event "two boys and one girl." To answer part (b), we must count the number of ways the event "two boys and one girl" can occur and divide this by the number of possible outcomes for this experiment.

Solution:

(a) The empirical probability of the event $E =$ "two boys and one girl" is

$$P(E) \approx \text{ relative frequency of } E = \frac{18}{50} = 0.36 = 36\%$$

There is about a 36% probability that a family of three children will have two boys and one girl.

(b) To determine the sample space, we construct a **tree diagram** to list the equally likely outcomes of the experiment. We draw two branches corresponding to the two possible outcomes (boy or girl) for the first repetition of the experiment (i.e., the first child). For the second child, we draw four branches: two branches originate from the first boy and two branches originate from the first girl. This is repeated for the third child. (See Figure 3 on page 268, where B stands for boy and G stands for girl.)

The sample space S of this experiment is found by following each branch to identify all the possible outcomes of the experiment:

$$S = \{\text{BBB, BBG, BGB, BGG, GBB, GBG, GGB, GGG}\}$$

So $N(S) = 8$.

For the event $E =$ "two boys and a girl" $= \{\text{BBG, BGB, GBB}\}$, we have $N(E) = 3$. Since the outcomes are equally likely (for example, BBG is just as likely as BGB), the probability of E is

$$P(E) = \frac{N(E)}{N(S)} = \frac{3}{8} = 0.375 = 37.5\%$$

Historical Note

Girolamo Cardano (in English Jerome Cardan) was born in Pavia, Italy, on September 24, 1501. He was an illegitimate child whose father was Fazio Cardano, a lawyer in Milan. Fazio was a part-time mathematician and taught Girolamo. In 1526, Cardano earned his medical degree; shortly thereafter, his father died. Unable to maintain a medical practice, Cardano spent his inheritance and turned to gambling to help support himself. Cardano developed an understanding of probability which helped him to win. He wrote a booklet on probability, *Liber de Ludo*, which wasn't printed until 1663, 87 years after his death. The booklet is a practical guide to gambling, including cards, dice, and cheating. Eventually Cardano became a lecturer of mathematics at the Piatti Foundation. This position allowed him to practice medicine and develop a favorable reputation as a doctor. In 1545, he published his greatest work, *Ars Magna*.

Historical Note

Pierre de Fermat was born into a wealthy family. His father was a leather merchant and second consul of Beaumont-de-Lomagne. Pierre attended the University of Toulouse. He moved to Bordeaux in the second half of the 1620s. From Bordeaux, Fermat went to Orleans to study law. By 1631, Fermat was a lawyer and government official. He rose quickly through the ranks because of all the deaths from the plague. In fact, in 1653, Fermat's death was incorrectly reported. Fermat considered mathematics his passionate hobby and true love. He is most famous for his "Last Theorem." This theorem states that the equation $x^n + y^n = z^n$ has no nonzero integer solutions for $n > 2$. The theorem was scribbled in the margin of a book by Diophantus, a Greek mathematician. Fermat stated, "I have discovered a truly marvelous proof of this theorem, which, however, the margin is not large enough to contain." The status of "Fermat's Last Theorem" baffled mathematicians until Andrew Wiles proved it to be true in 1994. In 1654, Fermat received a correspondence from Blaise Pascal in which Pascal asked Fermat to confirm his ideas on probability. Pascal knew of Fermat through his father, who had died three years before. They discussed the problem of how to divide the stakes in a game that is interrupted before completion, knowing how many points each player needs to win. Their short correspondence laid the foundation for the theory of probability and, on the basis of it, they are now regarded as joint founders of the subject.

Figure 3

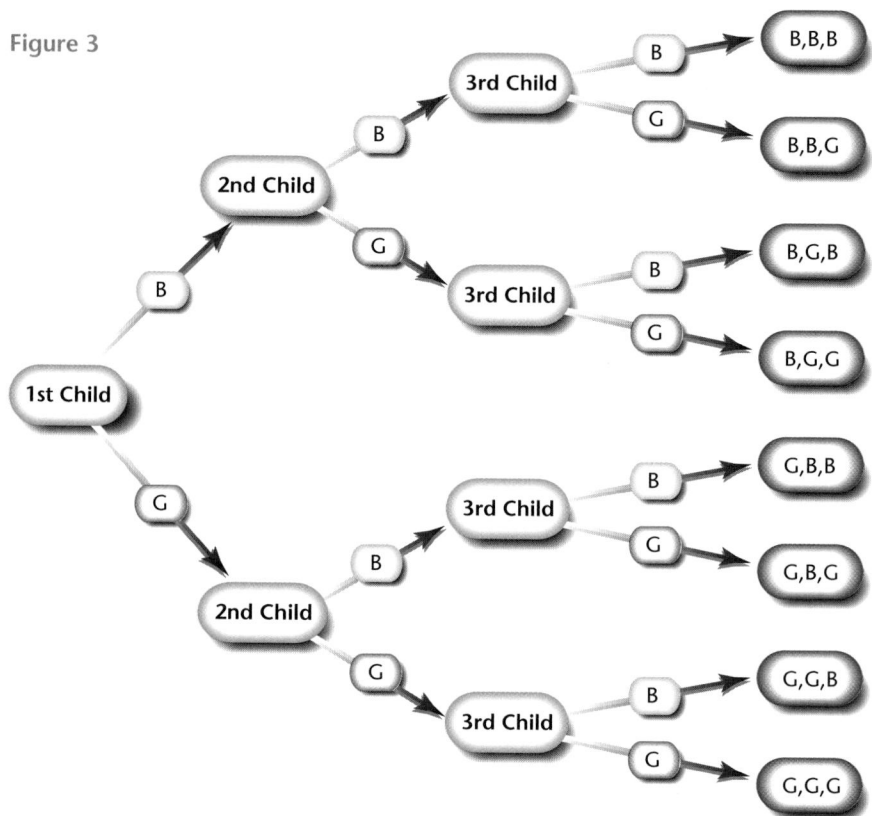

There is a 37.5% probability that a family of three children will have two boys and one girl. ◀◀

In comparing the results of Examples 5(a) and 5(b), we notice that the two probabilities are slightly different. Empirical probabilities and classical probabilities often differ in value. However, as the number of repetitions in a probability experiment increase, the empirical probability gets closer to the classical probability. That is, the classical probability is the theoretical relative frequency of an event after a large number of trials of the probability experiment. It is also possible that the two probabilities differ because having a boy or girl are not equally likely events. (Maybe the probability of having a boy is 50.5% and the probability of having a girl is 49.5%.) If this is the case, the empirical probability will not get closer to the classical probability.

 Now Work Problem 17.

4 Simulation

Suppose we wanted to determine the probability of having a boy. Using classical methods, we assume that having a boy is just as likely as having a girl, so the probability of having a boy is 50%. We could also approximate this probability by looking in the *Statistical Abstract of the United States* under "Vital Statistics" and determining the number of boys and girls born for the most recent year for which data are available. For example, in 1996, there were 1,990,000 boys born and 1,901,000 girls born. Based upon empirical evidence, the probability of a boy is approximately $1,990,000/(1,990,000 + 1,901,000) = 0.511 = 51.1\%$.

Historical Note

Blaise Pascal was born on June 19, 1623, in Clermont, France. He was the third of four children. His mother died when he was three years old. Pascal was home schooled by his father, Etienne. Pascal's father felt that Blaise should not be taught mathematics before age 15. Pascal couldn't resist studying mathematics on his own and at the age of 12 started to teach himself geometry. In December 1639, the Pascal family moved to Rouen, where Pascal's father had been appointed as a tax collector. Between 1642 and 1645, Pascal worked on developing a calculator to help his father collect taxes. Around 1646, he began to experiment with atmospheric pressure. By 1647, he felt that he had proved that a vacuum existed. In correspondence with Fermat, he helped develop the theory of probability. This correspondence consisted of five letters and occurred in the summer of 1654. They considered the dice problem and the problem of points. The dice problem deals with determining the expected number of times a pair of dice must be thrown before a pair of sixes is observed. The problem of points asks how to divide the stakes if a game of dice is incomplete. They solved the problem of points for a two-player game but did not solve it for three or more players. Pascal's last work was on the cycloid, the curve traced by a point on the outside of a rolling circle. Pascal died on August 19, 1662, from a malignancy in his stomach that spread to the brain.

However, instead of obtaining data from existing sources, we could simulate having babies by using a graphing calculator or statistical software to replicate the experiment as many times as we like.

▶ **EXAMPLE 6   Simulating Probabilities**

Problem:

(a) Simulate the experiment of sampling 100 babies.
(b) Simulate the experiment of sampling 1000 babies.

Approach: To simulate probabilities, we use a random number generator available in statistical software and most calculators. We assume the simple events "have a boy" and "have a girl" are equally likely.

Solution:

(a) We use Minitab to perform the simulation. Set the seed in Minitab to any value you wish, say 1204. Use the Integer Distribution* to generate random data that simulate having babies. If we agree to let 0 represent a boy and 1 represent a girl, we can approximate the probability of having a girl by summing the number of 1's (adding up the number of girls) and dividing by the number of repetitions of the experiment, 100. See Figure 4.

Figure 4

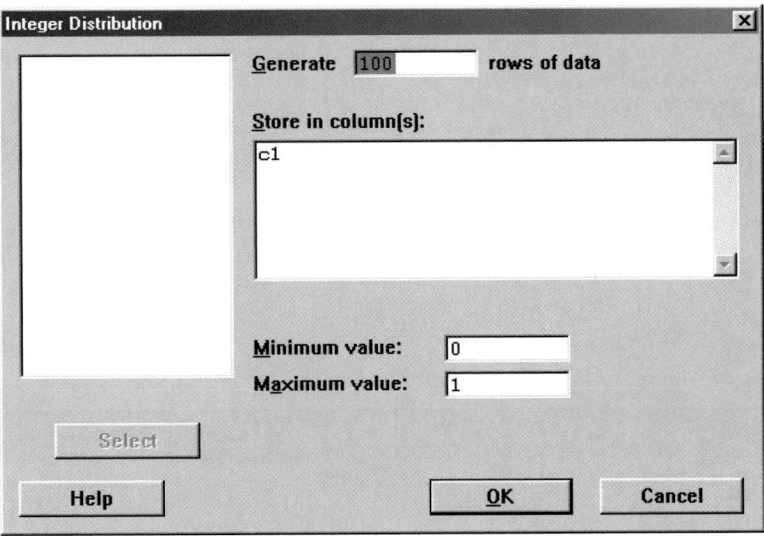

Using Minitab's Tally command we can determine the number of 0s and 1s that Minitab randomly generated. See Figure 5.

Figure 5

Summary Statistics for Discrete Variables

C1	Count	Percent
0	48	48.00
1	52	52.00
N=	100	

Based upon Figure 5, we approximate that there is a 48% probability of having a boy and a 52% probability of having a girl.

*The Integer Distribution involves a mathematical formula that uses a seed number to generate a sequence of equally likely random integers. Consult the technology manuals for setting the seed and generating sequences of integers.

(b) Again, set the seed to 1204. Figure 6 shows the results of simulating the birth of 1000 babies.

Figure 6   **Summary Statistics for Discrete Variables**

```
C1    Count    Percent
0      501      50.10
1      499      49.90
N=    1000
```

We approximate that there is a 50.1% probability of having a boy and a 49.9% probability of having a girl.   ◀◀

Notice that more repetitions of the experiment (100 babies versus 1000 babies) result in a probability closer to the expected values of $\frac{1}{2}$ for each gender. Again, this result demonstrates the Law of Large Numbers.

 *Now Work Problem 31.*

⑤   ## Subjective Probabilities

Subjective probabilities are probabilities obtained based upon an educated guess. For example, three different economists were asked "What is the probability the economy will fall into recession next year?" Each economist provided a different answer. The first economist said the probability is about 25%. The second economist was more gloomy and said the probability is about 50%. Finally, the third economist stated the probability was about 10%. How can three well-trained economists have such different opinions regarding the probability of a recession? Because the probabilities they stated are educated guesses based upon information they currently have available. The differences in the probabilities come from the fact that people interpret information differently!

 Caution!

Because subjective probabilities are based upon personal judgments, they should be interpreted with extreme skepticism.

5.1 Assess Your Understanding

Concepts and Vocabulary

1. Describe the difference between classical and empirical probability.

2. What is the probability of an impossible event? Suppose a probability is approximated to be zero based upon empirical results. Does this mean the event is impossible?

3. Why should subjective probabilities be interpreted with caution?

4. Suppose a coin is flipped and a die is cast. List all simple events for this probability experiment.

5. In computing classical probabilities, all simple events must be equally likely. Explain what this means.

6. Describe the idea behind using probabilities to identify unusual events.

Exercises

• **Basic Skills**

1. Which of the following numbers could be the probability of an event? *0, 0.01, 0.35, 1*

$$0, 0.01, 0.35, -0.4, 1, 1.4$$

2. Which of the following numbers could be the probability of an event? *1/2, 3/4, 2/3, 0*

$$1.5, \tfrac{1}{2}, \tfrac{3}{4}, \tfrac{2}{3}, 0, -\tfrac{1}{4}$$

For Problems 3–6, let the sample space be S $= \{1, 2, 3, 4, 5, 6, 7, 8, 9, 10\}$. *Suppose the simple events are equally likely.*

3. Compute the probability of the event $E = \{1, 2, 3\}$. $\frac{3}{10}$

4. Compute the probability of the event $F = \{3, 5, 9, 10\}$. 2/5

5. Compute the probability of the event $E =$ "an even number". 1/2

6. Compute the probability of the event $F =$ "an odd number". 1/2

• Applying the Concepts

7. Family of Three Using the results of Example 5(b) and Figure 3, compute the probability of having three boys in a three-child family. 1/8

8. Family of Three Using the results of Example 5(b) and Figure 3, compute the probability of having three girls in a three-child family. 1/8

9. Family of Four Compute the probability of having one boy and three girls in a four-child family assuming boys and girls are equally likely. 1/4

10. Family of Four Compute the probability of having two girls and two boys in a four-child family assuming boys and girls are equally likely. 3/8

11. Planting Tulips A bag of 100 tulip bulbs was purchased from a nursery. The bag contains 40 red tulip bulbs, 35 yellow tulip bulbs, and 25 purple tulip bulbs.
   (a) What is the probability that a randomly selected tulip bulb will be red? 0.4
   (b) What is the probability that a randomly selected tulip bulb will be purple? 0.25

12. Golf Balls The local golf store sells an "onion bag" that contains 80 "experienced" golf balls. Suppose the bag contains 35 Titleists, 25 Maxflis, and 20 Top-Flites.
   (a) What is the probability that a randomly selected golf ball will be a Titleist? 0.4375
   (b) What is the probability that a randomly selected golf ball will be a Top-Flite? 0.25

13. Roulette In the game of roulette a wheel consists of 38 slots numbered 0, 00, 1, 2, ..., 36. (See the photo.) To play the game, a metal ball is spun around the wheel and is allowed to fall into one of the numbered slots. (b) 1/38

   (a) Determine the sample space. $\{0, 00, 1, 2, \ldots, 36\}$
   (b) Determine the probability that the metal ball falls into the slot marked "8." Interpret this probability.
   (c) Determine the probability that the metal ball lands in an odd slot. Interpret this probability. 9/19

14. A Deck of Cards A standard deck of cards contains 52 cards. There are 4 suits in the deck: 13 hearts, 13 diamonds, 13 clubs and 13 spades. Each suit has one "ace," one "two," one "three," one "four," one "five," one "six," one "seven," one "eight," one "nine," one "ten," one "jack," one "queen," and one "king." Consider the probability experiment of drawing one card from a deck of cards. (d) 1/13
   (a) Determine the sample space of the probability experiment. 52 cards
   (b) Determine the probability of randomly selecting the king of hearts from the deck of cards. Interpret this probability. 1/52
   (c) Determine the probability of randomly selecting any heart from a deck of cards. Interpret this probability. 1/4
   (d) Determine the probability of randomly selecting a king from a deck of cards. Interpret this probability.

15. Birthdays Exclude leap years from the following calculations:
   (a) Determine the probability that a randomly selected person has a birthday on the 1st day of a month. Interpret this probability. 12/365
   (b) Determine the probability that a randomly selected person has a birthday on the 31st day of a month. Interpret this probability. 7/365
   (c) Determine the probability that a randomly selected person was born in December. Interpret this probability. 31/365
   (d) Determine the probability that a randomly selected person has a birthday on November 8. Interpret this probability. 1/365
   (e) If you just met somebody and she asked you to guess her birthday, are you likely to be correct? No
   (f) Do you think it is appropriate to use the methods of classical probability to compute the probability that a person is born in December?

   (a) $\{SS, Ss, sS, ss\}$

16. Genetics A gene is composed of two alleles. An allele can be either a dominant allele or a recessive allele. Suppose a husband and wife decide to have a child. Each of these parents has one dominant normal cell allele, S, and one recessive normal cell allele, s. Therefore,

the genotype of each parent is *Ss*. This means that each parent is a carrier of the disease, but does not have the disease. Each parent contributes one allele to his or her offspring with each allele being equally likely.

(a) List the possible genotypes of their offspring.
(b) What is the probability that the offspring will have sickle cell anemia? In other words, what is the probability that the offspring will have genotype *ss*? Interpret this probability. 1/4
(c) What is the probability that the offspring will not have sickle cell anemia, but will be a carrier? In other words, what is the probability that the offspring will have one dominant normal cell allele and one recessive sickle cell allele? Interpret this probability. 1/2

17. **College Survey** In a national survey conducted by the Centers for Disease Control in order to determine college students' health-risk behaviors, college students were asked: "How often do you wear a seat belt when riding in a car driven by someone else?" The frequencies appear in the following table:

Response	Frequency
Never	125
Rarely	324
Sometimes	552
Most of the time	1,257
Always	2,518

(a) Approximate the probability that a randomly selected college student never wears a seat belt when riding in a car driven by someone else. 0.026
(b) Would you consider it unusual to find somebody who never wears a seat belt when riding in a car driven by someone else? Why?
(c) Approximate the probability that a randomly selected college student sometimes wears a seat belt when riding in a car driven by someone else. Interpret this probability. 0.116

18. **College Survey** In a national survey conducted by the Centers for Disease Control in order to determine college students' health-risk behaviors, college students were asked, "How often do you wear a seat belt when driving a car?" The frequencies appear in the following table:

Response	Frequency
Never	118
Rarely	249
Sometimes	345
Most of the time	716
Always	3,093

(a) Approximate the probability that a randomly selected college student never wears a seat belt when driving a car. 0.026
(b) Is it unusual for a college student never to wear a seat belt when driving a car? Why?
(c) Approximate the probability that a randomly selected college student sometimes wears a seat belt when driving a car. Interpret this probability. 0.076

19. **Foreign-Born Population** A survey of 300 randomly selected foreign-born residents of the United States was conducted in which the respondents were asked to disclose the region of their birth. The data, based on information obtained from the United States Census Bureau, are as follows: (c) Yes

Region	Frequency	Region	Frequency
Europe	46	Oceania	2
Asia	83	Latin America	152
Africa	9	North America	8

(a) Approximate the probability that a randomly selected foreign-born resident of the United States is from Asia. Interpret this probability. 0.277
(b) Approximate the probability that a randomly selected foreign-born resident is from Oceania. 0.007
(c) Are foreign-born residents from Oceania unusual?

20. **Larceny Theft** A police officer randomly selected 595 police records of larceny thefts. The following data, based on information obtained from the U.S. Federal Bureau of Investigation, represent the number of offenses for various types of larceny thefts:

Type of Larceny Theft	Number of Offenses
Pocket picking	5
Purse snatching	5
Shoplifting	118
From motor vehicles	197
Motor vehicle accessories	77
Bicycles	43
From buildings	105
From coin-operated machines	45

(a) Approximate the probability that a randomly selected larceny theft is shoplifting. Interpret this probability. 0.198
(b) Approximate the probability that a randomly selected larceny theft is pocket picking. 0.008
(c) As far as larceny theft goes, is pocket picking unusual? Yes

21. Birth Weight The following data represent the birth weight of all babies born in the United States in 1998:

Weight (in grams)	Number
Less than 500	5,950
500–999	22,471
1,000–1,499	28,555
1,500–1,999	58,921
2,000–2,499	182,311
2,500–2,999	649,658
3,000–3,499	1,457,401
3,500–3,999	1,135,572
4,000–4,499	335,087
4,500–4,999	54,809
5,000 or more	6,200
Total	**3,936,935**

Source: National Vital Statistics Report, Vol. 48, No. 3, March 28, 2000

(a) What is the probability that a randomly selected baby born in 1998 weighs 1000–1499 grams at birth. Interpret this probability. 0.007
(b) What is the probability that a randomly selected baby born in 1998 weighs 4000–4499 grams at birth. Interpret this probability. 0.085
(c) What is the probability that a randomly selected baby born in 1998 weighs 5000 grams or more. Is this unusual? 0.002; Yes

22. Multiple Births The following data represent the number of live multiple delivery births (three or more babies) in 1999 for women 15–44 years old:

Age	Number of Multiple Births
15–19	66
20–24	411
25–29	1653
30–34	2926
35–39	1813
40–44	956

Source: National Vital Statistics Report, Vol. 49, No. 1, April 17, 2001

(a) What is the probability that a randomly selected multiple birth in 1999 had a mother 30–34 years old. Interpret this probability. 0.374
(b) What is the probability that a randomly selected multiple birth in 1999 had a mother 40–44 years old. Interpret this probability. 0.122
(c) What is the probability that a randomly selected multiple birth in 1999 had a mother 15–19 years old. Is a multiple birth where the mother is 15–19 years old unusual? 0.008; Yes

23. Tornadoes Of the 28,538 tornadoes that occurred between 1916 and 1985 in the United States, 3262 of them occurred between the hours of 5:00 P.M. and 6:00 P.M. If a tornado occurs, approximate the probability it occurs between 5:00 P.M. and 6:00 P.M. Is it unusual for tornadoes to occur between 5:00 P.M. and 6:00 P.M.? Source: Dr. T. Fujita, *U.S. Tornadoes*, Part I. 0.114; No

24. Tornadoes Of the 28,538 tornadoes that occurred between 1916 and 1985 in the United States, 324 of them occurred between the hours of 5:00 A.M. and 6:00 A.M. If a tornado occurs, approximate the probability that it occurs between 5:00 A.M. and 6:00 A.M. Is it unusual for tornadoes to occur between 5:00 A.M. and 6:00 A.M.? Source: Dr. T. Fujita, *U.S. Tornadoes*, Part I. 0.011; Yes

25. Chicago Weather In Chicago, during the month of June, 11.5 days are partly cloudy, 7.3 days are clear, and 11.2 days are cloudy. Approximate the probability that a randomly selected day is clear. Interpret this probability.

26. Chicago Weather In Chicago, during the month of July, 12.3 days are partly cloudy, 8.2 days are clear, and 10.5 days are cloudy. Approximate the probability that a randomly selected day is clear. Interpret this probability.

27. Randomly Selecting Cabinet Members During the (NW) presidency of Andrew Jackson there were six cabinet positions: secretary of state, secretary of the treasury, secretary of war, attorney general, postmaster general, and secretary of the navy. Suppose two members of the cabinet are to be randomly selected to represent the United States at the funeral of a foreign diplomat.

(a) List the sample space.
(b) What is the probability the two representatives will be the secretary of state and the secretary of the treasury? 1/15
(c) What is the probability one of the two representatives will be the secretary of state? 1/3

28. Presidential Elections Prior to 1804 Prior to the presidential election of 1804, the individual running for president who received the most votes was declared president, while the individual receiving the second most votes was declared vice president. In 1792, the individuals running in the presidential election were (1) George Washington, (2) John Adams, (3) George Clinton, (4) Thomas Jefferson, and (5) Aaron Burr.

(a) List sample space for president and vice president. Remember order matters here, so (Washington, Adams) is different from (Adams, Washington).
(b) Suppose the election were purely random. What is the probability that Washington would be president and Adams vice president? 1/20
(c) Suppose the election were purely random. What is the probability that Washington would be selected as president? 1/5

29. Mark McGwire On September 8, 1998, Mark McGwire hit his 62nd home run of the season. Of the 62 home runs he hit, 26 went to left field, 21 went to left center, 12
25. 0.243   26. 0.265

went to center field, 3 went to right center field and 0 went to right field.

(a) What is the probability that a randomly selected home run was hit to left field? Interpret this probability. *26/62 = 0.419*

(b) What is the probability that a randomly selected home run was hit to right field? *0*

(c) Is it impossible for Mark McGwire to hit a homer to right field? *No*

30. **Rolling a Die**

(a) Roll a single die 50 times, recording the result of each throw of the die. Use the results to approximate the probability of throwing a three.

(b) Roll a single die 100 times, recording the result of each throw of the die. Use the results to approximate the probability of throwing a three.

(c) Compare the results of (a) and (b) to the classical probability of rolling a three.

31. **Simulation** Use a graphing calculator or statistical soft-

NW ware to simulate rolling a six-sided die 100 times, using the Integer Distribution with numbers one through six.

(a) Use the results of the simulation to compute the probability of obtaining a one.

(b) Repeat the simulation. Compute the probability of rolling a one.

(c) Simulate rolling a six-sided die 500 times. Compute the probability of rolling a one.

(d) Which simulation resulted in the closest estimate to the probability that would be obtained using the classical method?

32. **Blood Types** A person can have one of four blood types: A, B, AB, or O. If people are randomly selected, is the probability they have blood type A equal to $\frac{1}{4}$? Why? *No*

33. **Rolling Dice** When rolling a pair of dice, there are 11 possible outcomes: "rolling a 2", "rolling a 3", … "rolling a 12." Is the probability of "rolling a 2" equal to 1/11? Why? *No*

34. **Classifying Probability** Determine whether the following probabilities are computed using classical methods, empirical methods, or subjective methods.

(a) The probability of having eight girls in an eight-child family is 0.390625%. *Classical*

(b) On the basis of a study of families with eight children, the probability of a family having eight girls is 0.54%. *Empirical*

(c) According to a sports analyst, the probability that the Chicago Bears will win their next game is about 30%. *Subjective*

(d) On the basis of clinical trials, the probability of efficacy of a new drug is 75%. *Empirical*

35. **Checking for Loaded Dice** You suspect a pair of dice to be loaded and conduct a probability experiment by rolling each die 200 times. The outcome of the experiment is listed in the following table:

Value of Die	Frequency	Value of Die	Frequency
1	105	4	49
2	47	5	51
3	44	6	104

Do you think the die is loaded? Why?

36. Conduct a survey in your school by randomly asking 50 students whether they drive to school. Based upon the results of the survey, approximate the probability that a randomly selected student drives to school.

37. **Median Income** In 1998, the median income of families in the United States was $46,737. What is the probability that a randomly selected family will have a median income greater than $46,737? *0.5*

38. **Education** In 1998, 17% of Americans aged 25 years old or older did not have a high-school diploma. What is the probability that a randomly selected American aged 25 years old or older does not have a high school diploma? *0.17*

Technology Step-by-Step
Simulation

TI-83 Plus   **Step 1:** Set the seed by entering any number on the HOME screen. Press the STO ⇒ button, press the MATH button, highlight the PRB menu and highlight 1:rand and hit ENTER. With the cursor on the HOME screen, hit ENTER.

Step 2: Press the MATH button and highlight the PRB menu. Highlight 5:randInt(and hit ENTER.

Step 3: After the randInt(on the HOME screen type 1,n, number of repetitions of experiment) where *n* is the number of equally likely simple events. For example, to simulate rolling a single die 50 times, we type

randInt(1, 6, 50)

Step 4: Press the STO $\Rightarrow$ button and then 2nd 1, and hit ENTER to store the data in L1.

Step 5: Draw a histogram of the data using the simple events as classes. TRACE to obtain outcomes.

MINITAB **Step 1:** Set the seed by selecting the **Calc** menu and highlighting **Set Base** . . . Insert any seed you wish into the cell and click OK.

Step 2: Select the **Calc** menu, highlight **Random Data** and then highlight **Integer**. To simulate rolling a single die one hundred times, fill in the window as shown in Figure 4.

Step 3: Select the **Stat** menu, highlight **Tables**, and then highlight **Tally** . . . Enter C1 into the variables cell. Make sure that the Counts box is checked and click OK.

Excel **Step 1:** With cell A1 selected, press the *fx* button.

Step 2: Highlight Math & Trig in the Function category window. Then highlight RANDBETWEEN in the Function Name: window. Click OK.

Step 3: To simulate rolling a die 50 times, enter 1 for the lower limit and 6 for the upper limit. Click OK.

Step 4: Copy the contents of cell A1 into cells A2 through A50.

5.2   The Addition Rule; Complements

Objectives ① Use the Addition Rule

② Compute the probability of an event using complements

① In rolling a single die, the probability of the event E = "rolling an even number" is $3/6 = 1/2$. The probability of the event F = "rolling a 1 or 2" is $1/3$, but what is the probability of "rolling an even number" or "rolling a 1 or 2"? To answer this question, we need methods for finding **compound probabilities**.

Note to Instructor
The "or" that we use here is not the "exclusive or." An "exclusive or" is the event consisting of simple events that belong to either E or F, but not both.

Definition

Let E and F be two events. **E and F** is the event consisting of simple events that belong to both E and F. **E or F** is the event consisting of simple events that belong to either E or F or both.

We will discuss probabilities involving the word "and" in the next section. The *Addition Rule* is used to find compound probabilities involving the word "or." The notation used for these types of probabilities is $P(E \text{ or } F)$, which means the probability of event E or F or both.

▶ **EXAMPLE 1** **Illustrating the Addition Rule**

Problem: Suppose a single die is cast. Let E = "roll an even number" and let F = "roll a 1 or 2." Find $P(E \text{ or } F)$.

Approach: We list the sample space of the experiment and count the simple events in each event. The probability will be the number of ways E or F could occur divided by the number of simple events in the sample space.

Figure 7

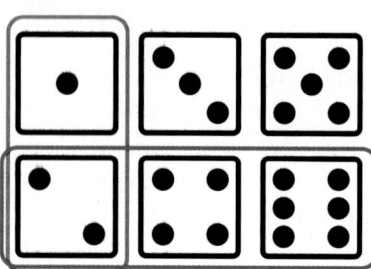

Solution: Figure 7 lists all the simple events in the sample space.

In blue, we circle all the simple events corresponding to the event E = "roll an even number." In red, we circle all the simple events corresponding to the event F = "roll a one or two". We now count the number of simple events in "E or F". To avoid double counting, we count the "two" only once. There are, therefore, four ways the event "E or F" can occur and we have the following result:

$$P(E \text{ or } F) = \frac{4}{6} = \frac{2}{3}$$ ◄◄

Example 1 illustrates a general rule, called the **Addition Rule** of probability.

Theorem

Addition Rule

For any two events E and F,

$$P(E \text{ or } F) = P(E) + P(F) - P(E \text{ and } F) \qquad (1)$$

For example, we can use the Addition Rule to find $P(E \text{ or } F)$ in Example 1:

$$P(E \text{ or } F) = P(E) + P(F) - P(E \text{ and } F) = \frac{3}{6} + \frac{2}{6} - \frac{1}{6} = \frac{4}{6} = \frac{2}{3}$$

It is often helpful to draw pictures of events. Such pictures, called **Venn diagrams**, represent events as circles enclosed in a rectangle. The rectangle represents the sample space and each circle represents an event. Such diagrams help us to visualize relationships among events. We can explain the Addition Rule using Venn diagrams. Figure 8 shows two intersecting circles. The area of the circle on the left represents $P(E)$ while the area of the circle on the right represents event $P(F)$. The region where the two circles overlap represents the event $P(E \text{ and } F)$. If we compute $P(E \text{ or } F)$ by adding the area of the left circle to the area of the right circle, we double count the overlapping region, $P(E \text{ and } F)$. To avoid the double counting, we subtract $P(E \text{ and } F)$ from the sum of $P(E)$ and $P(F)$.

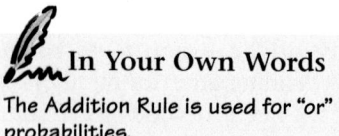

In Your Own Words

The Addition Rule is used for "or" probabilities.

Figure 8

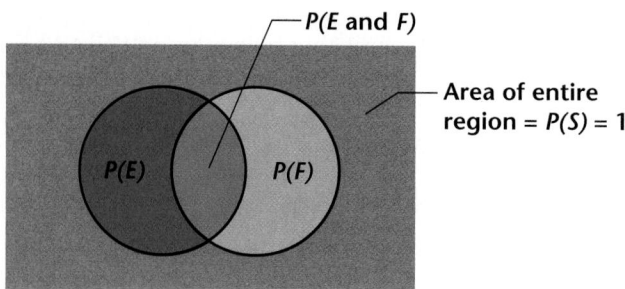

If events E and F have no simple events in common or cannot occur simultaneously, they are said to be **disjoint** or **mutually exclusive**. For example, in rolling a single die, we cannot simultaneously observe "rolling a three" and "rolling a four". Therefore, these events are mutually exclusive. If two events are mutually exclusive, then $P(E \text{ and } F) = 0$ and the Addition Rule takes on the following form:

Theorem

Addition Rule for Mutually Exclusive Events

If E and F are mutually exclusive events, then

$$P(E \text{ or } F) = P(E) + P(F) \qquad (2)$$

In general, if $E, F, G, \ldots$ are mutually exclusive events, then

$$P(E \text{ or } F \text{ or } G \text{ or } \ldots) = P(E) + P(F) + P(G) + \ldots \qquad (3)$$

In Your Own Words

"Mutually exclusive" basically means that the events cannot occur at the same time.

Figure 9(a) demonstrates mutually exclusive events for two events using Venn diagrams. Figure 9(b) demonstrates mutually exclusive events for three events using Venn diagrams.

Figure 9

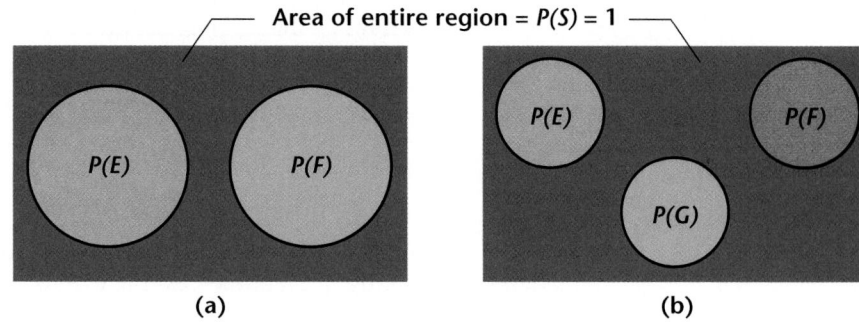

Area of entire region = $P(S)$ = 1

(a)　　　　　(b)

▶ **EXAMPLE 2** **Computing Probabilities Using the Addition Rule**

Problem: Suppose a single card is selected from a standard 52-card deck.

(a) Compute the probability of the event E = "drawing a king."

(b) Compute the probability of the event E = "drawing a king" or F = "drawing a queen."

(c) Compute the probability of the event E = "drawing a king" or F = "drawing a queen" or G = "drawing a jack."

(d) Compute the probability of the event E = "drawing a king" or H = "drawing a diamond."

Approach: We will use the classical method for computing probabilities because the outcomes are equally likely and easy to count. The probabilities in parts (a)–(d) are "or" probabilities, so we use the Addition Rule. Notice parts (a)–(c) involve mutually exclusive events, while events E and H in part (d) are not mutually exclusive.

Solution: The sample space consists of the 52 cards in the deck, so $N(S) = 52$. Figure 10 on page 278 shows a standard deck of cards.

(a) A standard deck of cards has four kings, so $N(E) = 4$. Therefore $P(\text{king}) = P(E) = N(E)/N(S) = 4/52 = 1/13$.

(b) A standard deck of cards also has four queens. Because events E and F are mutually exclusive (you can't draw a king and queen simultaneously), we use the Addition Rule for Mutually Exclusive Events Formula (2). So, $P(\text{king or queen}) =$

$$P(E \text{ or } F) = P(E) + P(F) = \frac{4}{52} + \frac{4}{52} = \frac{8}{52} = \frac{2}{13}$$

Historical Note

John Venn was born on August 4, 1834, in Humberside, England. In 1853 he enrolled in Gonville and Caius College in Cambridge, and in 1857 he earned his B.A. degree. Venn's father's involvement in the church, led John Venn to become a priest in 1859. At around the same time, he became interested in logic and published three texts on the subject. His text, *Symbolic Logic*, written in 1881, introduced the concept of Venn diagrams. While studying logic, Venn became disenchanted with the church and gave up his priesthood in 1883. In the same year, he was elected to the Royal Society. John Venn died on April 4, 1923, in Cambridge, England.

Figure 10

(c) Because events E, F and G are mutually exclusive, we use the Addition Rule for Mutually Exclusive Events Formula (3). So,

$$P(\text{king or queen or jack}) = P(E \text{ or } F \text{ or } G) = P(E) + P(F) + P(G) = \frac{4}{52} + \frac{4}{52} + \frac{4}{52} = \frac{12}{52} = \frac{3}{13}$$

(d) There are four kings and 13 diamonds. However, one of the kings is the king of diamonds. So the events are not mutually exclusive. Therefore,

$$P(\text{king or diamond}) = P(\text{king}) + P(\text{diamond}) - P(\text{king of diamonds})$$
$$= \frac{4}{52} + \frac{13}{52} - \frac{1}{52}$$
$$= \frac{16}{52} = \frac{4}{13}$$
◀◀

NW *Now Work Problem 23.*

▶ **EXAMPLE 3** **Using the Addition Rule**

Problem: The data in Table 3 represent the marital status of males and females 18 years old or older in the United States in 1998.

TABLE 3			
	Males (in millions)	Females (in millions)	Totals (in millions)
Never Married	25.5	21.0	46.5
Married	58.6	59.3	117.9
Widowed	2.6	11.0	13.6
Divorced	8.3	11.1	19.4
Totals (in millions)	95.0	102.4	197.4

Source: U.S. Census Bureau, Current Population Reports

(a) Determine the probability that a randomly selected United States resident 18 years old or older is male.

(b) Determine the probability that a randomly selected United States resident 18 years old or older is widowed.

(c) Determine the probability that a randomly selected United States resident 18 years old or older is widowed or divorced.

(d) Determine the probability that a randomly selected United States resident 18 years old or older is male or widowed.

Approach: We first add up the entries in each row and column so that we get the total number of people in each category. We can then determine the probabilities using the Addition Rule.

Solution: Add up the entries in each column. For example, in the "male" column, we find that there are $25.5 + 58.6 + 2.6 + 8.3 = 95$ million males 18 years old or older in the United States. Add up the entries in each row. For example, in the "never married" row, we find there are $25.5 + 21.0 = 46.5$ million United States residents 18 years old or older that have never married. Adding up the row totals or column totals, we find there are $95 + 102.4 = 46.5 + 117.9 + 13.6 + 19.4 = 197.4$ million United States residents 18 years old or older.

(a) There are 95 million males 18 years old or older and 197.4 million United States residents 18 years old or older. The probability that a randomly selected United States resident 18 years old or older is male is $95/197.4 = 0.481 = 48.1\%$.

(b) There are 13.6 million United States residents 18 years old or older who are widowed. The probability that a randomly selected United States resident 18 years old or older is widowed is $13.6/197.4 = 0.069 = 6.9\%$.

(c) The events "widowed" and "divorced" are mutually exclusive. Do you see why? We use the Addition Rule for Mutually Exclusive Events:

$$P(\text{widowed or divorced}) = P(\text{widowed}) + P(\text{divorced}) = \frac{13.6}{197.4} + \frac{19.4}{197.4} = \frac{33}{197.4} = 0.167 = 16.7\%$$

(d) The events "male" and "widowed" are not mutually exclusive. In fact, there are 2.6 million males that are widowed in the United States. Therefore, we use the Addition Rule Formula (1) to compute $P(\text{male or widowed})$:

$$P(\text{male or widowed}) = P(\text{male}) + P(\text{widowed}) - P(\text{male and widowed})$$

$$= \frac{95}{197.4} + \frac{13.6}{197.4} - \frac{2.6}{197.4} = \frac{106}{197.4} = 0.537 = 53.7\% \quad \blacktriangleleft\blacktriangleleft$$

NW *Now Work Problem 35.*

② Complements

Suppose the probability of an event E is known and we would like to determine the probability that E does not occur. This can easily be accomplished using the idea of *complements*.

Definition

Complement of an Event

Let S denote the sample space of a probability experiment and let E denote an event. The **complement of E**, denoted $\overline{E}$, is all simple events in the sample space S that are not simple events in the event E.

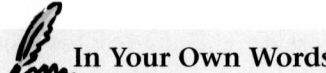

In Your Own Words

The Complement Rule is used when you know the probability that some event will occur and you want to know the opposite: the chance it will not occur.

Because E and $\overline{E}$ are mutually exclusive,

$$P(E \text{ or } \overline{E}) = P(E) + P(\overline{E}) = P(S) = 1$$

Subtracting $P(E)$ from both sides, we obtain

$$P(\overline{E}) = 1 - P(E)$$

We have the following result.

Theorem

Complement Rule

If E represents any event and $\overline{E}$ represents the complement of E, then

$$P(\overline{E}) = 1 - P(E)$$

Figure 11 illustrates the Complement Rule using a Venn diagram.

Figure 11

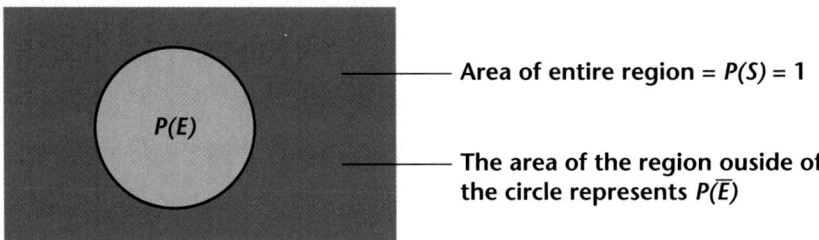

Area of entire region = P(S) = 1

The area of the region ouside of the circle represents P($\overline{E}$)

▶ **EXAMPLE 4**   **Computing Probabilities Using Complements**

Problem: According to the National Gambling Impact Study Commision, 52% of Americans have played state lotteries. What is the probability that a randomly selected American has not played a state lottery?

Approach: Not playing a state lottery is the complement of playing a state lottery. We compute the probability using the Complement Rule.

Solution:

$$P(\text{not played state lottery}) = 1 - P(\text{played state lottery}) = 1 - 0.52 = 0.48$$

There is a 48% probability of randomly selecting an American that has not played a state lottery. ◀◀

▶ **EXAMPLE 5**   **Computing Probabilities Using Complements**

Problem: The data in Table 4 represent the income distribution of households in the United States in 2000.

TABLE 4			
Annual Income	Number (in thousands)	Annual Income	Number (in thousands)
Less than $10,000	10,023	$50,000 to $74,999	20,018
$10,000 to $14,999	6,995	$75,000 to $99,999	10,480
$15,000 to $24,999	13,994	$100,000 to $149,999	8,125
$25,000 to $34,999	13,491	$150,000 to $199,999	2,337
$35,000 to $49,999	17,032	$200,000 or more	2,239

Source: U.S. Bureau of the Census

(a) Compute the probability that a randomly selected household earned $200,000 or more in 2000.

(b) Compute the probability that a randomly selected household earned less than $200,000 in 2000.

(c) Compute the probability that a randomly selected household earned at least $10,000 in 2000.

Approach: The probabilities will be determined by finding the relative frequency of each event. We need to find the total number of households in the United States in 2000.

Solution:

(a) There were a total of $10{,}023 + 6995 + \ldots + 2239 = 104{,}734$ thousand households in the United States in 2000 and 2239 thousand of them earned $200,000 or more. The probability that a randomly selected household in the United States earned $200,000 or more in 2000 is $2239/104{,}734 = 0.021 = 2.1\%$.

(b) We could compute the probability of randomly selecting a household that earned less than $200,000 in 2000 by adding the relative frequencies of each category less than $200,000, but it is easier to use complements. The complement of earning less than $200,000 is earning $200,000 or more. Therefore,

$$P(\text{less than }\$200{,}000) = 1 - P(\$200{,}000 \text{ or more}) = 1 - 0.021 = 0.979 = 97.9\%$$

There is a 97.9% probability of randomly selecting a household that earned less than $200,000 in 2000.

(c) The phrase "at least" means greater than or equal to. The complement of "at least $10,000" is "less than $10,000." 10,023 thousand households earned less than $10,000. The probability of randomly selecting a household that earned at least $10,000 is

$$P(\text{at least }\$10{,}000) = 1 - P(\text{less than }\$10{,}000) = 1 - \frac{10{,}023}{104{,}734} = 0.904 = 90.4\%$$

 *Now Work Problem 31.*

There is a 90.4% probability of randomly selecting a household that earned $10,000 or more. ◀◀

5.2 Assess Your Understanding

Concepts and Vocabulary

1. What does it mean when two events are mutually exclusive?

2. Why is $P(E \text{ and } F)$ subtracted from $P(E) + P(F)$ in the Addition Rule when E and F are not mutually exclusive?

3. What does it mean when two events are complements?

Exercises

• Basic Skills

In Problems 1–8, a probability experiment is conducted in which the sample space of the experiment is $S = \{1, 2, 3, 4, 5, 6, 7, 8, 9, 10, 11, 12\}$. *Let event* $E = \{2, 3, 4, 5, 6, 7\}$, *event* $F = \{5, 6, 7, 8, 9\}$, *event* $G = \{9, 10, 11, 12\}$, *and event* $H = \{2, 3, 4\}$.

1. List the simple events in "E and F." Are E and F mutually exclusive? $\{5, 6, 7\}$; No

2. List the simple events in "F and G." Are F and G mutually exclusive? $\{9\}$; No

7. $\{1, 8, 9, 10, 11, 12\}$; 1/2   8. $\{1, 2, 3, 4, 10, 11, 12\}$; 7/12

3. List the simple events in F or G. Now find $P(F$ or $G)$ by counting the number of simple events in F or G. Determine $P(F$ or $G)$ using the Addition Rule. 2/3

4. List the simple events in E or H. Now find $P(E$ or $H)$ by counting the number of simple events in E or H. Determine $P(E$ or $H)$ using the Addition Rule. 1/2

5. List the simple events in E and G. Are E and G mutually exclusive? $\{\ \}$; Yes

6. List the simple events in F and H. Are F and H mutually exclusive? $\{\ \}$; Yes

7. List the simple events in $\overline{E}$. Find $P(\overline{E})$.

8. List the simple events in $\overline{F}$. Find $P(\overline{F})$.

In Problems 9–14, find the probability of the indicated event if $P(A) = 0.25$ and $P(B) = 0.45$.

9. $P(A$ or $B)$ if $P(A$ and $B) = 0.15$ 0.55

10. $P(A$ and $B)$ if $P(A$ or $B) = 0.6$ 0.1

11. $P(A$ or $B)$ if A and B are mutually exclusive 0.7

12. $P(A$ and $B)$ if A and B are mutually exclusive 0

13. $P(\overline{A})$ 0.75

14. $P(\overline{B})$ 0.55

15. If $P(A) = 0.60$, $P(A$ or $B) = 0.85$, and $P(A$ and $B) = 0.05$, find $P(B)$. 0.3

16. If $P(B) = 0.30$, $P(A$ or $B) = 0.65$, and $P(A$ and $B) = 0.15$, find $P(A)$. 0.5

• Applying the Concepts

In Problems 17–20, a golf ball is selected at random from a golf bag. If the golf bag contains 9 Titleists, 8 Maxflis, and 3 Top-Flites, find the probability of each event.

17. The golf ball is a Titleist or Maxfli. 17/20

18. The golf ball is a Maxfli or Top-Flite. 11/20

19. The golf ball is not a Titleist. 11/20

20. The golf ball is not a Top-Flite. 17/20

21. **Family of Three** Compute the probability of having one or two boys in a three-child family. 0.75

22. **Family of Three** Compute the probability of having two or three girls in a three-child family. 0.5

23. **A Deck of Cards** A standard deck of cards contains 52 cards as shown in Figure 10. One card is randomly selected from the deck.
    (a) Compute the probability of randomly selecting a heart or club from a deck of cards. 1/2
    (b) Compute the probability of randomly selecting a heart or club or diamond from a deck of cards. 3/4
    (c) Compute the probability of randomly selecting an ace or heart from a deck of cards. 4/13

24. **A Deck of Cards** A standard deck of cards contains 52 cards as shown in Figure 10. One card is randomly selected from the deck.
    (a) Compute the probability of randomly selecting a two or three from a deck of cards. 2/13
    (b) Compute the probability of randomly selecting a two or three or four from a deck of cards. 3/13
    (c) Compute the probability of randomly selecting a two or club from a deck of cards. 4/13

25. **Birthdays** Exclude leap years from the following calculations.   (a) 364/365
    (a) Compute the probability that a randomly selected person does not have a birthday on November 8.
    (b) Compute the probability that a randomly selected person does not have a birthday on the 1st day of a month. 353/365

    (c) Compute the probability that a randomly selected person does not have a birthday on the 31st day of a month. 358/365
    (d) Compute the probability that a randomly selected person was not born in December. 334/365

26. **Roulette** In the game of roulette a wheel consists of 38 slots numbered $0, 00, 1, 2, \ldots 36$. The odd-numbered slots are red, while the even-numbered slots are black. The numbers 0 and 00 are green. To play the game, a metal ball is spun around the wheel and is allowed to fall into one of the numbered slots.
    (a) What is the probability that the metal ball lands on green or red? 10/19
    (b) What is the probability that the metal ball does not land on green? 18/19

27. **College Survey** In a national survey conducted by the Centers for Disease Control in order to determine college students' health-risk behaviors, college students were asked: "How often do you wear a seat belt when riding in a car driven by someone else?" The frequencies appear in the following table:

Response	Frequency
Never	125
Rarely	324
Sometimes	552
Most of the time	1,257
Always	2,518

    (a) Approximate the probability that a randomly selected college student never or rarely wears a seat belt when riding in a car driven by someone else. 0.094
    (b) Approximate the probability that a randomly selected college student does not always wear a seat belt when riding in a car driven by someone else. 0.473

28. College Survey In a national survey conducted by the Centers for Disease Control in order to determine college students' health-risk behaviors, college students were asked: "How often do you wear a seat belt when driving a car?" The frequencies are displayed in the following table:

Response	Frequency
Never	118
Rarely	249
Sometimes	345
Most of the time	716
Always	3,093

(a) Approximate the probability that a randomly selected college student never or rarely wears a seat belt when driving a car. *0.081*
(b) Approximate the probability that a randomly selected college student does not always wear a seat belt when driving a car. *0.316*

29. Foreign-Born Population A survey of 300 randomly selected foreign-born residents of the United States was conducted in which the respondents were asked to disclose the region of their birth. The data, based on information obtained from the United States Census Bureau, are as follows:

Region	Frequency	Region	Frequency
Europe	46	Oceania	2
Asia	83	Latin America	152
Africa	9	North America	8

(a) Approximate the probability that a randomly selected foreign-born resident of the United States is from Europe or Asia. *0.43*
(b) Approximate the probability that a randomly selected foreign-born resident of the United States is from Europe, Asia, or Latin America. *0.937*
(c) Approximate the probability that a randomly selected foreign-born resident of the United States is not from Europe. *0.847*

30. Larceny Theft A police officer randomly selected 595 police records of larceny thefts. The following data, based on information obtained from the U.S. Federal Bureau of Investigation, represent the number of offenses for various types of larceny thefts. (a) *0.207*

(a) Approximate the probability that a randomly selected larceny theft is shoplifting or purse snatching.
(b) Approximate the probability that a randomly selected larceny theft is shoplifting or purse snatching or pocket picking. *0.215*
(c) Approximate the probability that a randomly selected larceny theft is not pocket picking. *0.992*

Type of Larceny Theft	Number of Offenses
Pocket picking	5
Purse snatching	5
Shoplifting	118
From motor vehicles	197
Motor vehicle accessories	77
Bicycles	43
From buildings	105
From coin-operated machines	45

31. Birth Weight The following data represent the birth weight of all babies born in the United States in 1998:

Weight (in grams)	Number	Weight (in grams)	Number
Less than 500	5,950	3,000–3,499	1,457,401
500–999	22,471	3,500–3,999	1,135,572
1,000–1,499	28,555	4,000–4,499	335,087
1,500–1,999	58,921	4,500–4,999	54,809
2,000–2,499	182,311	5,000 or more	6,200
2,500–2,999	649,658	**Total**	**3,936,935**

Source: National Vital Statistics Report, Vol. 48, No. 3, March 28, 2000

(a) Determine the probability that a randomly selected baby born in 1998 weighs less than 1000 grams at birth. *0.007*
(b) Determine the probability that a randomly selected baby born in 1998 weighs 1000 grams or more at birth. *0.993*
(c) Determine the probability that a randomly selected baby born in 1998 weighs less than 5000 grams at birth. *0.998*
(d) Determine the probability that a randomly selected baby born in 1998 weighs at least 500 grams at birth. *0.998*

32. Multiple Births The following data represent the number of live multiple delivery births (three or more babies) in 1999 for women 15–44 years old:

Age	Number of Multiple Births
15–19	66
20–24	411
25–29	1653
30–34	2926
35–39	1813
40–44	956

Source: National Vital Statistics Report, Vol. 49, No. 1, April 17, 2001

(a) Determine the probability that a randomly selected multiple birth in 1999 for women 15–44 years old had a mother 30–39 years old. *0.606*

(b) Determine the probability that a randomly selected multiple birth in 1999 for women 15–44 years old had a mother that was not 30–39 years old. *0.394*

(c) Determine the probability that a randomly selected multiple birth in 1999 for women 15–44 years old had a mother who was less than 40 years old. *0.878*

(d) Determine the probability that a randomly selected multiple birth in 1999 for women 15–44 years old had a mother who was at least 20 years old. *0.992*

33. Tornadoes Of the 28,538 tornadoes that occurred between 1916 and 1985 in the United States, 3262 of them occurred between the hours of 5:00 P.M. and 6:00 P.M.. If a tornado occurs, approximate the probability it does not occur between 5:00 P.M. and 6:00 P.M.. *Source:* Dr. T. Fujita, U.S. Tornadoes Part I. *0.886*

34. Tornadoes Of the 28,538 tornadoes that occurred between 1916 and 1985 in the United States, 324 of them occurred between the hours of 5:00 A.M. and 6:00 A.M.. If a tornado occurs, approximate the probability it does not occur between 5:00 A.M. and 6:00 A.M.. *Source:* Dr. T. Fujita, U.S. Tornadoes Part I. *0.989*

35. Medicaid The following data, in thousands, represent the age of persons receiving Medicaid and their poverty level:

	AGE			
	<18	18–44	45–64	>65
Below Poverty Level	8,550	4,356	1,520	958
Above Poverty Level	5,884	3,741	1,756	1,943

Source: U.S. Census Bureau

(a) Determine the probability that a randomly selected individual receiving Medicaid has income below the poverty line. *0.536*

(b) Determine the probability that a randomly selected individual receiving Medicaid is less than 18 years old. *0.503*

(c) Determine the probability that a randomly selected individual receiving Medicaid has income below the poverty line and is less than 18 years old. *0.298*

(d) Determine the probability that a randomly selected individual receiving Medicaid has income below the poverty line or is less than 18 years old. *0.741*

36. SAT Verbal Scores The following data represent the scores received on the 2000 SAT I: Reasoning Test—Verbal, by gender:

	Male	Female
200–249	6,755	7,512
250–299	9,594	10,816
300–349	25,630	30,058
350–399	50,042	60,139
400–449	78,276	95,780
450–499	98,989	117,976
500–549	102,423	120,183
550–599	84,524	96,381
600–649	62,205	68,515
650–699	36,202	39,843
700–749	18,044	18,716
750–800	10,647	11,028
TOTAL	**583,331**	**676,947**

Source: College Board

(a) If a test taker is randomly selected, what is the probability that the test taker is female? *0.537*

(b) If a test taker is randomly selected, what is the probability that the test taker scored 600–649? *0.104*

(c) If a test taker is randomly selected, what is the probability that the test taker is female and scored 600–649? *0.054*

(d) If a test taker is randomly selected, what is the probability that the test taker is female or scored 600–649? *0.586*

37. Driver Fatalities The following data represent the number of driver fatalities in 1996 by age group for male and female drivers:

	Male	Female
16–19	1922	762
20–24	2814	699
25–29	2126	617
30–34	1986	627
35–39	1743	604
40–44	1437	485
45–49	1169	391
50–54	859	347
55–59	684	260
60–64	637	270
65–69	614	268
70–74	598	358
75–79	554	323
80–84	474	230
85 or older	329	146
TOTAL	**17,946**	**6,387**

Source: National Highway Traffic Institute

(a) Determine the probability that a randomly selected driver fatality involves a male driver. *0.738*

(b) Determine the probability that a randomly selected driver fatality involves a 20–24 year old. *0.144*

(c) 0.116

(c) Determine the probability that a randomly selected driver fatality involves a 20–24 year old male driver.

(d) Determine the probability that a randomly selected driver fatality involves a 20–24 year old or a male driver. *0.766*

---

38. Marital Status The following data represent the marital status of Americans 25 years old or older and their level of education in 1999:

	Did Not Graduate High School	High School Graduate	Some College	College Graduate
Never Married	4,012	7,790	6,565	7,685
Married, Spouse Present	15,122	36,076	27,003	29,811
Married, Spouse Absent	1,877	2,006	1,435	1,489
Separated	1,094	1,515	1,214	598
Widowed	5,000	4,757	2,264	1,456
Divorced	2,951	7,047	5,649	3,766

Source: U.S. Census Bureau

(a) 0.146
(b) 0.332

(a) Determine the probability that a randomly selected person has never married.

(b) Determine the probability that a randomly selected person is a high school graduate.

(c) Determine the probability that a randomly selected person has never married and is a high school graduate. *0.044*

(d) Determine the probability that a randomly selected person has never married or is a high school graduate. *0.435*

5.3   The Multiplication Rule

Objectives Compute probabilities using the Multiplication Rule

 Compute probabilities using the Multiplication Rule for Independent Events

 Compute "at least" probabilities

 In Section 5.2 we studied the probability of event E or F occurring in a single trial of an experiment. In this section, we concentrate on methods for computing the probability of events E and F.

▶ **EXAMPLE 1**   **Illustrating the Multiplication Rule**

Problem: Two members from a five-member committee are to be randomly selected to serve as chairperson and secretary. The first person selected is the chairperson and the second person selected is the secretary. The members of the committee are Bob, Faye, Elena, Melody, and Dave. Determine the probability that Elena is chairperson and Dave is secretary.

Approach: The first person randomly selected is chairperson. Because an individual cannot serve as both chairperson and secretary, we are sampling without replacement.* We list the possibilities for chairperson and

*Recall from Chapter 1 that sampling without replacement means that once an individual is selected, the individual is removed from the sample space and cannot be selected again.

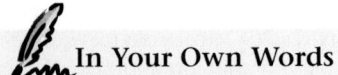

secretary in a tree diagram. We count the number of ways Elena can be chairperson and Dave can be secretary and divide this result by the number of possible outcomes of the experiment.

In Your Own Words

A tree diagram is a great way to list outcomes in a probability experiment.

Solution: We list the possibilities for chairperson and secretary in the tree diagram in Figure 12. The first trial of the experiment involves selecting the chairperson. There are five branches on the tree diagram corresponding to

Figure 12

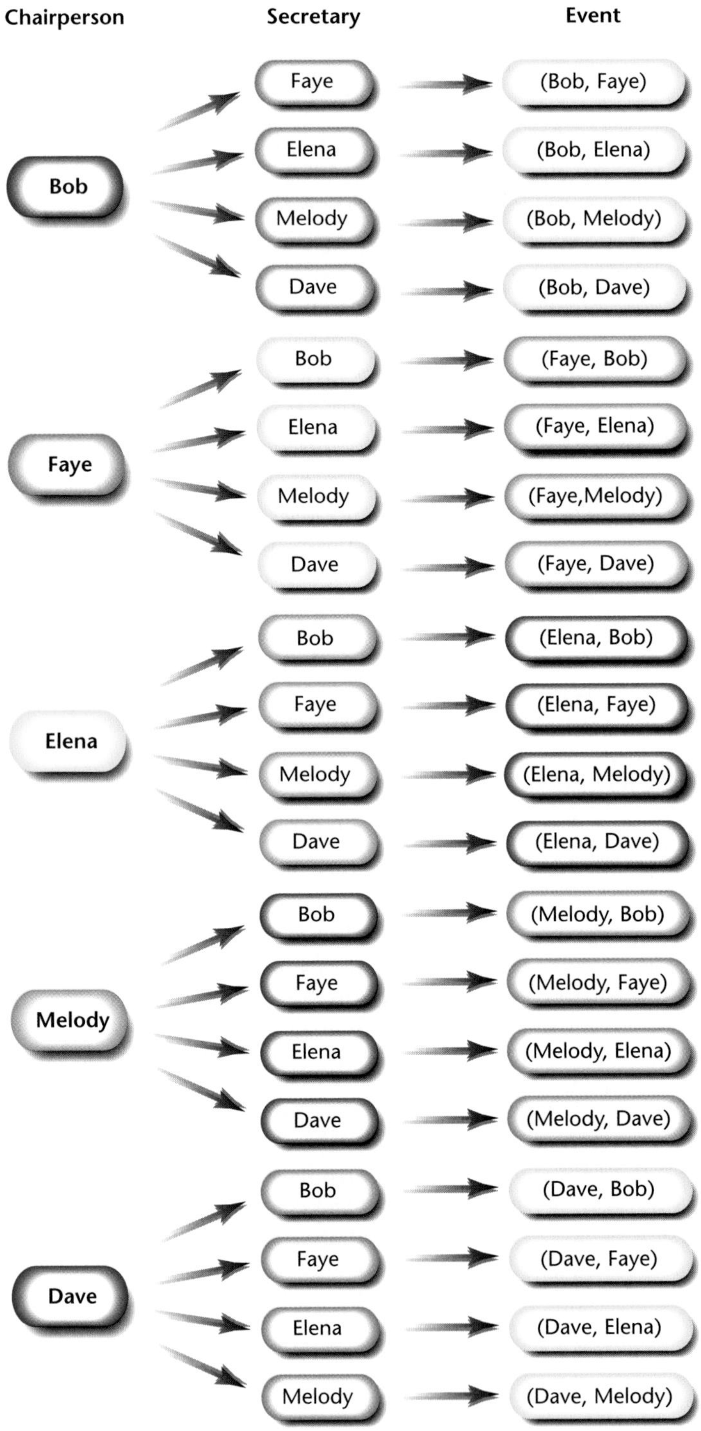

Chairperson
Secretary
Event
Bob
Faye
Elena
Melody
Dave
(Bob, Faye)
(Bob, Elena)
(Bob, Melody)
(Bob, Dave)
Faye
Bob
Elena
Melody
Dave
(Faye, Bob)
(Faye, Elena)
(Faye,Melody)
(Faye, Dave)
Elena
Bob
Faye
Melody
Dave
(Elena, Bob)
(Elena, Faye)
(Elena, Melody)
(Elena, Dave)
Melody
Bob
Faye
Elena
Dave
(Melody, Bob)
(Melody, Faye)
(Melody, Elena)
(Melody, Dave)
Dave
Bob
Faye
Elena
Melody
(Dave, Bob)
(Dave, Faye)
(Dave, Elena)
(Dave, Melody)

the five possible choices for chairperson. For each choice of chairperson, there are four remaining choices for secretary. Therefore, four branches are drawn from each choice of chairperson. From the diagram, we see there are twenty ways the chairperson and secretary can be selected. There is one way the chairperson can be Elena and the secretary can be Dave. Therefore, the probability that Elena is chairperson and Dave is secretary is 1/20.   ◄◄

The method used to obtain the probability in Example 1 was rather tedious. Imagine the amount of work involved had there been 20 members on the original committee! Fortunately, the *Multiplication Rule* can be used to obtain probabilities of the form *E* and *F*. Before we present the Multiplication Rule, we discuss the concept of *conditional probability*.

Definition

Conditional Probability

The notation $P(F \mid E)$ is read "the probability of event *F* given event *E*." It is the probability of an event *F* occurring given the occurrence of the event *E*.

For example, we might compute the probability of selecting Dave to serve on the committee as secretary given that Elena has already been selected as chairperson. Under this scenario, we concentrate on the branch of the tree diagram in which Elena is chairperson. Look back at Figure 12. If we let E = "Elena is chairperson" and F = "Dave is secretary," then $P(F \mid E) = P(\text{Dave is secretary given that Elena is chairperson}) = \frac{1}{4}$ since there is one way for Dave to be secretary and four possible outcomes after Elena was chosen as the chairperson.

We now present the Multiplication Rule.

Theorem

The Multiplication Rule

The probability that two events *E* and *F* both occur is

$$P(E \text{ and } F) = P(E) \cdot P(F \mid E)$$

In words, the probability of *E* and *F* is the probability of event *E* occurring times the probability of event *F* occurring given the occurrence of event *E*.

✍ **In Your Own Words**

The Addition Rule is used for "or" probabilities. The Multiplication Rule is for "and" probabilities.

Let's redo Example 1 using the Multiplication Rule.

► **EXAMPLE 2**   **Computing Probabilities Using the Multiplication Rule**

Problem: Redo Example 1 using the Multiplication Rule.

Approach: We first compute the probability that Elena is selected as chairperson. We multiply this result by the probability Dave is secretary given Elena is chairperson.

Solution: We define event E = "Elena is chairperson" and event F = "Dave is secretary." The first trial of the experiment is randomly selecting a chairperson. Since there are five members on the committee, then $P(\text{Elena is chairperson}) = P(E) = 1/5$. The second trial of the experiment is randomly selecting a secretary given that Elena has already been selected as chairperson. Therefore, $P(\text{"Dave is secretary" given that "Elena is chairperson"}) = P(F \mid E) = \frac{1}{4}$ since there is one way Dave can be selected and there are four different outcomes of the experiment (since Elena is not available to serve as secretary). Using the Multiplication Rule we find

$$P(\text{Elena is chairperson and Dave is secretary}) = P(E \text{ and } F) = P(E) \cdot P(F \mid E)$$

$$= \frac{1}{5} \cdot \frac{1}{4} = \frac{1}{20}$$

This is the same result as Example 1, and we obtained it without drawing a tree diagram.　◀◀

NW *Now Work Problem 7.*

The Multiplication Rule applies to more than just a sequence of events (such as selecting a chair and then selecting a secretary). Consider the next example.

▶ **EXAMPLE 3**　**Using the Multiplication Rule**

Problem: The probability that a police officer is hiding behind the billboard next to the highway is 0.08. The probability that a randomly selected driver is speeding, given that a police officer is behind the billboard, is 0.2. What is the probability that a randomly selected driver is speeding and there is a police officer hiding behind the billboard next to the highway?

Approach: Let E represent the event "police officer hiding behind the billboard" and let F represent the event "driver is speeding." We use the Multiplication Rule to compute $P(E \text{ and } F)$.

Solution: P(driver is speeding and a police officer is hiding behind the billboard) $= P(E \text{ and } F) = P(E) \cdot P(F \mid E) = 0.08(0.2) = 0.016 = 1.6\%$. There is a 1.6% probability that a driver is speeding and there is a police officer hiding behind the billboard.　◀◀

NW *Now Work Problem 17.*

In certain experiments, the probability of one event is not affected by some other event. In this case, we say the two events are *independent*.

Definition

> Two events E and F are **independent** if the occurrence of event E in a probability experiment does not affect the probability of event F. Two events are **dependent** if the occurrence of event E in a probability experiment affects the probability of event F.

To contrast independent and dependent events, consider an experiment in which an urn contains three red chips and five blue chips. Suppose two chips are drawn without replacement and the first chip drawn is red. The probability that the second chip is blue is 5/7 because there are now seven chips left in the urn and five of them are blue. However, if the two chips are drawn with replacement (we put the red chip back after selecting it), the probability that the second chip drawn is blue is 5/8, the same as the probability of selecting a blue chip on the first trial. In sampling without replacement, the events "the first chip is red" and "the second chip is blue"

✎ In Your Own Words

In determining whether two events are independent, ask yourself whether the probability of one event is affected by the other event. For example, what is the probability that a 20-to-29-year-old male has high cholesterol? What is the probability that a 20-to-29-year-old male has high cholesterol, given that he eats fast food four times a week? Does the fact that the individual eats fast food four times a week change the probability that he has high cholesterol? If yes, the events are not independent.

are dependent because selecting a red chip on the first draw affects the probability that the second draw will result in a blue chip. In sampling with replacement, the events "the first chip is red" and "the second chip is blue" are independent because the occurrence of the first chip being red does not affect the probability of the second chip being blue.

In Example 1, the events "Elena is chairperson" and "Dave is secretary" are dependent because the probability of Dave being selected as secretary *before* Elena is chosen as chairperson is 1/5. However, once Elena is selected as chairperson, the probability Dave is secretary is $\frac{1}{4}$.

We now formalize the definition of independence.

Definition

Independent Events

Two events E and F are independent if and only if $P(F \mid E) = P(F)$ or $P(E \mid F) = P(E)$.

This means that if events E and F are independent, then knowledge of the event E has no effect on the probability of the event F occurring.

▶ **EXAMPLE 4**   Distinguishing Independent and Dependent Events

Caution

Independence is different from mutually exclusive. For example, the event "not a cloud in the sky" and the event "raining" are mutually exclusive. However, the two events are not independent. $P(\text{rain}) \neq P(\text{rain} \mid \text{not a cloud in the sky})$.

According to the National Center for Health Statistics, the probability that a randomly selected mother will have a low birth-weight baby is 0.078. The probability that a randomly selected mother will have a low birth-weight baby given that the mother smokes is 0.121. Since $P(\text{low birth weight}) \neq P(\text{low birth weight} \mid \text{mother smokes})$, the events "low birth weight" and "mother smokes" are not independent. In fact, if a mother smokes there is an increased probability of a low birth-weight baby.   ◀◀

 Now Work Problem 3.

② If events E and F are independent, then we can modify the Multiplication Rule.

Theorem

Multiplication Rule for Independent Events

If E and F are independent events, the probability that E and F both occur is

$$P(E \text{ and } F) = P(E) \cdot P(F)$$

In words, the probability of E and F is the probability of event E times the probability of event F.

▶ **EXAMPLE 5**   Computing Probabilities of Independent Events

Problem: In the game of roulette, there is a wheel with slots numbered 0, 00, and 1 through 36. A metal ball is allowed to roll around a wheel until it falls into one of the numbered slots. You decide to play the game and place a bet on the number 17. What is the probability the ball will land in the slot numbered 17 two times in a row?

Approach: There are 38 simple events in the sample space corresponding to the 38 possible outcomes of the experiment. We use the classical method of computing probabilities because the simple events are equally likely. In addition, we use the Multiplication Rule for Independent Events. The events "17 on first trial" and "17 on second trial" are independent because the ball does not remember it landed on 17 on the first trial, so this cannot affect the probability of landing on 17 on the second trial.

Solution: Because there are 38 possible outcomes to the experiment, the probability of the ball landing on 17 is 1/38. Because the events "17 on first trial" and "17 on second trial" are independent, we have

$$P(\text{ball lands in slot 17 in the first game and ball lands in slot 17 in the second game})$$
$$= P(\text{ball lands in slot 17 in the first game}) \cdot P(\text{ball lands in slot 17 in the second game})$$
$$= \frac{1}{38} \cdot \frac{1}{38} = \frac{1}{1{,}444} \approx 0.0006925$$

It is very unlikely that the ball will land on 17 twice in a row. We'd expect the ball to land on 17 twice in a row about 7 times in 10,000 trials. ◀◀

We can extend the Multiplication Rule for three or more independent events.

Theorem

> **Multiplication Rule for *n* Independent Events**
>
> If events $E, F, G, \ldots$ are independent, then
>
> $$P(E \text{ and } F \text{ and } G \text{ and } \cdots) = P(E) \cdot P(F) \cdot P(G) \cdots$$

▶ **EXAMPLE 6 Life Expectancy**

Problem: The probability that a randomly selected male 24 years old will survive the year is 99.85% according to the National Vital Statistics Report, Vol. 47, No. 28. What is the probability that three randomly selected 24-year-old males will survive the year?

Approach: We can safely assume that the outcomes of the probability experiment are independent because there is no indication that the survival of one of the males affects the survival of the other two. For example, if two of the males lived in the same house, then a house fire could kill both males and we lose independence. (Knowledge that one of the males died in a house fire certainly would affect the probability that the other died.) By randomly selecting the males, we minimize the chances that they are related in any way.

Solution:

$$P(\text{All three males survive}) = P(\text{first survives and second survives and third survives})$$
$$= P(\text{first survives}) \cdot P(\text{second survives}) \cdot P(\text{third survives})$$
$$= (0.9985)(0.9985)(0.9985)$$
$$= 0.9955$$

There is a 99.55% probability that all three males survive the year. ◀◀

NW *Now Work Problem 19(a) and 19(b).*

Whenever a small random sample is taken from a large population, it is reasonable to compute probabilities of events assuming independence. Consider the following example.

▶ **EXAMPLE 7**   **Sickle Cell Anemia**

Problem: In a survey of 10,000 African-Americans, it was determined that 27 had sickle cell anemia.

(a) Suppose we randomly select one of the 10,000 African-Americans surveyed. What is the probability that he or she will have sickle cell anemia?

(b) If two individuals from this group are randomly selected, what is the probability that both have sickle cell anemia?

(c) Compute the probability of randomly selecting two individuals from this group who have sickle cell anemia, assuming independence.

Approach: We will let the event E = "sickle cell anemia," so that $P(E)$ = number of African-Americans who have sickle cell anemia divided by the number in the survey. To answer part (b), we let E_1 = "first person has sickle cell anemia" and E_2 = "second person has sickle cell anemia," and then we compute $P(E_1 \text{ and } E_2) = P(E_1) \cdot P(E_2 \mid E_1)$. To answer part (c), we use the Multiplication Rule for Independent Events.

Solution:

(a) If one individual is selected, $P(E)$ = 27/10,000 = 0.0027 = 0.27%.

(b) Using the Multiplication Rule, we have

$$P(E_1 \text{ and } E_2) = P(E_1) \cdot P(E_2 \mid E_1) = \frac{27}{10000} \cdot \frac{26}{9999} \approx 0.00000702$$

Notice $P(E_2 \mid E_1) = \dfrac{26}{9999}$ because we are sampling without replacement, so after event E_1 occurs there is one less person with sickle cell anemia and one less person in the sample space.

(c) The assumption of independence means that the outcome of the first trial of the experiment does not impact the probability of the second trial. (It's like sampling with replacement.) Therefore, we assume $P(E_1) = P(E_2)$ = 27/10,000. Then

$$P(E_1 \text{ and } E_2) = P(E_1) \cdot P(E_2) = \frac{27}{10,000} \cdot \frac{27}{10,000} \approx 0.00000729 \quad ◀◀$$

The probabilities in Examples 7(b) and 7(c) are extremely close in value. Based upon these results, we infer the following principle:

> If small random samples are taken from large populations without replacement, it is reasonable to assume independence of the events. As a general rule of thumb, if the sample size is less than 5% of the population size, then we treat the events as independent.

Historical Note

For example, in Example 7, we can compute the probability of randomly selecting two African-Americans that have sickle cell anemia using independence because the sample size is less than 5% of the population size $\left(\dfrac{2}{10,000} = 0.0002 = 0.02\% \right)$.

NW *Now Work Problem 29.*

③   We now present an example in which we compute "at least" probabilities. These probabilities utilize the Complement Rule. The phrase "at least" means greater than or equal to. For example, a person must be at least 17 years old to see an "R" rated movie.

▶ **EXAMPLE 8**   **Computing "At Least" Probabilities**

Note to Instructor
Remind students that "at least"
means greater than or equal to. "At
least" probabilities are usually
determined using the Complement Rule.
For Example 8, ask students to
distinguish between $1 - 0.9985^{1000}$
and $(1 - 0.9985)^{1000}$.

Problem: Compute the probability that at least 1 male out of 1000 aged 24 years will die during the course of the year if the probability that a randomly selected 24-year-old male survives the year is 0.9985.

Approach: The phrase "at least" means greater than or equal, so we wish to know the probability that 1 or 2 or 3 or ... or 1000 males will die during the year. These events are mutually exclusive, so

$$P(1 \text{ or } 2 \text{ or } 3 \text{ or} \ldots \text{or } 1000 \text{ die}) = P(1 \text{ dies}) + P(2 \text{ die}) + P(3 \text{ die}) + \ldots + P(1000 \text{ die}).$$

Clearly, computing these probabilities would be very time consuming. However, we should notice that the complement of "at least one dying" is "none die." We shall use the Complement Rule to compute the probability.

Solution:

$$\begin{aligned}
P(\text{at least one dies}) &= 1 - P(\text{none die}) \\
&= 1 - P(\text{first survives and second survives and} \ldots \text{and thousandth survives}) \\
&= 1 - P(\text{first survives}) \cdot P(\text{second survives}) \cdot \ldots \cdot P(\text{thousandth survives}) \quad \text{independent events} \\
&= 1 - (0.9985)^{1000} \\
&= 1 - 0.2229 \\
&= 0.7771 \\
&= 77.71\%
\end{aligned}$$

There is a 77.71% probability that at least one 24-year-old male out of 1000 will die during the course of the year. ◀◀

NW *Now Work Problem 19(c).*

You may have noticed that "or" probabilities utilize the Addition Rule, while "and" probabilities utilize the Multiplication Rule. Accordingly, "or" probabilities imply addition, while "and" probabilities imply multiplication.

5.3 Assess Your Understanding

Concepts and Vocabulary

1. The word "and" in probability implies that we use the _____ Rule. The word "or" in probability implies that we use the _____ Rule. Multiplication; Addition
2. Describe the concept of independence.
3. State two methods for determining whether two events are independent.
4. Describe the difference between mutually exclusive events and independent events.
5. Comment on the difference between sampling with replacement and sampling without replacement.
6. Describe the circumstances under which sampling without replacement can be assumed to be independent.

Exercises

• **Basic Skills**

1. Determine whether the events E and F are independent or dependent. Justify your answer.
   (a) E: It rains on June 30
      F: It is cloudy on June 30 Dependent
   (b) E: Your car has a flat tire
      F: The price of gasoline increases overnight Independent
   (c) E: You live at least 80 years
      F: You smoke a pack of cigarettes every day of your life Dependent

2. Determine whether the events A and B are independent or dependent. Justify your answer.
   (a) A: You earn an "A" on an exam
      B: You study for an exam Dependent
   (b) A: You are late for work
      B: Your car has a flat tire Dependent
   (c) A: You earn more than \$50,000 per year
      B: You are born in the month of July Independent

3. According to the United States Census Bureau, the probability a randomly selected individual in the United States earns more than \$75,000 per year is 18.4%. The probability a randomly selected individual in the United States earns more than \$75,000 per year given that the individual has earned a bachelor's degree is 35.0%. Are the events "earn more than \$75,000 per year" and "earned a bachelor's degree" independent? No

4. Are events E and F independent if $P(F) = 0.95$; $P(F\,|\,E) = 0.95$? Yes

5. Consider an experiment in which a single card is drawn from a deck. Let E be the event "draw a face card." Let F be the event "draw a club."
   (a) What is $P(F)$? 1/4
   (b) What is $P(F\,|\,E)$? 1/4
   (c) Are events E and F independent? Why? Yes

6. Consider an experiment in which a single card is drawn from a deck.   (b) 1/13
   (a) What is the probability of the event E = "draw an ace"? 1/13
   (b) Let F be the event "draw a club." What is $P(E\,|\,F)$?
   (c) Are events E and F independent? Why? Yes

• **Applying the Concepts**

7. **Acceptance Sample** Suppose you just received a shipment of six televisions. Two of the televisions are defective. If two televisions are randomly selected, use a tree diagram to compute the probability both televisions work. Then compute the probability using the Multiplication Rule. 0.4

8. **Committee** A committee consists of four women and three men. The committee will randomly select two people to attend a conference in Hawaii. Use a tree diagram to find the probability that both are women. Then compute the probability using the Multiplication Rule. 2/7

9. **Drawing Cards** Suppose two cards are randomly selected from a standard 52-card deck.
   (a) What is the probability that the first card is a king and the second card is a king if the sampling is done without replacement? 1/221
   (b) What is the probability that the first card is a king and the second card is a king if the sampling is done with replacement? 1/169

10. **Drawing Cards** Suppose two cards are randomly selected from a standard 52-card deck.
    - (a) What is the probability that the first card is a club and the second card is a club if the sampling is done without replacement? 1/17
    - (b) What is the probability that the first card is a club and the second card is a club if the sampling is done with replacement? 1/16

11. **Board Work** This past semester, I had a small business calculus section. The students in the class were Mike, Neta, Jinita, Kristin and Dave. Suppose I randomly select two people to go to the board to do homework. What is the probability that Dave is the first person chosen to go to the board and Neta is the second? 1/20

12. **Party** My wife has organized a monthly neighborhood party. There are five people involved in the group: Yolanda (my wife), Lorrie, Laura, Kim, and Anne Marie. They decide to randomly select the first and second home that will host the party. What is the probability that my wife hosts the first party and Lorrie hosts the second? NOTE: Once a home has hosted, it cannot host again until all other homes have hosted. 1/20

13. **Playing a CD on the "Random" Setting** Suppose a compact disk (CD) you just purchased has 13 tracks. After listening to the CD, you decide that you like 5 of the songs. With the random feature on your CD player, each of the 13 songs is played once in random order. Find the probability that among the first two songs played,
    - (a) You like both of them. Would this be unusual? 5/39
    - (b) You like neither of them. 14/39
    - (c) You like exactly one of them. 20/39
    - (d) Redo (a)–(c) if a song can be replayed before all 13 songs are played (if, for example, track 2 can play twice in a row).

14. **Packaging Error** Due to a manufacturing error, three cans of regular soda were accidentally filled with diet soda and placed into a 12-pack. Suppose that two cans are randomly selected from the case.
    - (a) Determine the probability that both contain diet soda. 1/22
    - (b) Determine the probability that both contain regular soda. Would this be unusual? 6/11; No
    - (c) Determine the probability that exactly one is diet and one is regular. 9/22

15. **Planting Tulips** A bag of 30 tulip bulbs was purchased from a nursery. The bag contains 12 red tulip bulbs, 10 yellow tulip bulbs, and 8 purple tulip bulbs.
    - (a) What is the probability that two randomly selected tulip bulbs will both be red? 0.152
    - (b) What is the probability that the first bulb selected is red and the second yellow? 0.138
    - (c) What is the probability that the first bulb selected is yellow and the second is red? 0.138
    - (d) What is the probability that one bulb is red and the other yellow? 0.276

16. **Golf Balls** The local golf store sells an "onion bag" that contains 35 "experienced" golf balls. Suppose the bag contains 20 Titleists, 8 Maxflis, and 7 Top-Flites.
    - (a) What is the probability that two randomly selected golf balls will both be Titleists? 0.319
    - (b) What is the probability that the first ball selected will be a Titleist and the second will be a Maxfli? 0.134
    - (c) What is the probability that the first ball selected will be a Maxfli and the second will be a Titleist? 0.134
    - (d) What is the probability that one golf ball is a Titleist and the other is a Maxfli? 0.269

17. **Smokers** According to the National Center for Health (NW) Statistics, there is a 23.4% probability that a randomly selected resident of the United States aged 25 years or older is a smoker. In addition, there is a 21.7% probability that a randomly selected resident of the United States aged 25 years or older is female, given that he or she smokes. What is the probability that a randomly selected resident of the United States aged 25 years or older is female and smokes? Would it be unusual to randomly select a resident of the United States aged 25 years or older who is female and smokes? 0.051

18. **Multiple Jobs** According to the United States Bureau of Labor Statistics, there is a 5.84% probability that a randomly selected employed individual has more than one job (a multiple job holder). In addition, there is a 52.6% probability that a randomly selected employed individual is male given that he has more than one job. What is the probability that a randomly selected employed individual is a multiple job holder and male? Would it be unusual to randomly select an employed individual who is a multiple job holder and male? 0.031

19. **Life Expectancy** The probability that a randomly se-(NW) lected 40-year-old male will live to be 41 years old is 0.99718 according to the National Vital Statistics Report, Vol. 48, No. 18.
    - (a) What is the probability that two randomly selected 40-year-old males will live to be 41 years old? 0.994
    - (b) What is the probability that five randomly selected 40-year-old males will live to be 41 years old? 0.986
    - (c) What is the probability that at least one of five randomly selected 40-year-old males will not live to be 41 years old? Would it be unusual that at least one of five randomly selected 40-year-old males will not live to be 41 years old? 0.014

20. **Life Expectancy** The probability that a randomly selected 40-year-old female will live to be 41 years old is 0.99856 according to the National Vital Statistics Report, Vol. 48, No. 18.
    - (a) What is the probability that two randomly selected 40-year-old females will live to be 41 years old? 0.997

$$(13d) \left(\frac{5}{13}\right)^2 ; \left(\frac{8}{13}\right)^2 ; 0.473$$

(b) What is the probability that five randomly selected 40-year-old females will live to be 41 years old? *0.993*

(c) What is the probability that at least one of five randomly selected 40-year-old females will not live to be 41 years old? Would it be unusual that at least one of five randomly selected 40-year-old females will not live to be 41 years old? *0.007; Yes*

21. Blood Types Blood types can be classified as either Rh^+ or Rh^-. According to the Information Please Almanac, 99% of the Chinese population has Rh^+ blood.

(a) What is the probability that two randomly selected Chinese have Rh^+ blood? *0.9801*

(b) What is the probability that six randomly selected Chinese have Rh^+ blood? *0.9415*

(c) What is the probability that at least one of six randomly selected Chinese has Rh^- blood? Would it be unusual that at least one of six randomly selected Chinese has Rh^- blood? *0.0585*

22. Quality Control Suppose a company selects two people who work independently inspecting two-by-four timbers. Their job is to identify low-quality timbers. Suppose the probability that an inspector does not identify a low-quality timber is 20%.

(a) What is the probability that two inspectors do not identify a low-quality timber? *0.04*

(b) How many inspectors should be hired in order to keep the probability of not identifying a low-quality timber below 1%? *3*

23. The Birthday Problem Determine the probability that at least two people in a room of ten people share the same birthday, ignoring leap years, by answering the following questions: (a) *0.883*

(a) Compute the probability that 10 people have different birthdays. (*Hint*: The first person's birthday can occur 365 ways, the second person's birthday can occur 364 ways because he or she can't have the same birthday as the first person, the third person's birthday can occur 363 ways because he or she can't have the same birthday as the first or second person, and so on.)

(b) The complement of "10 people have different birthdays" is "At least 2 share a birthday." Use this information to compute the probability that at least 2 people out of 10 share the same birthday. *0.117*

24. The Birthday Problem Using the procedure given in Problem 23, compute the probability that at least 2 people in a room of 23 people share the same birthday. *0.507*

25. A Flush A flush in the card game of poker occurs if a player gets five cards that are all the same suit (clubs, diamonds, hearts, or spades). Answer the following questions to obtain the probability of being dealt a flush in five cards.

(a) We initially concentrate on one suit, say clubs. There are 13 clubs in a deck. Compute P(five clubs) = P(first card is clubs and second card is

26. 0.00000154

clubs and third card is clubs and fourth card is clubs and fifth card is clubs). *0.000495*

(b) A flush can occur if we get five clubs or five diamonds or five hearts or five spades. Compute P(five clubs or five diamonds or five hearts or five spades). Note the events are mutually exclusive. *0.002*

26. A Royal Flush A royal flush in the game of poker occurs if the player gets the cards Ten, Jack, Queen, King, and Ace all in the same suit. Use the results of Problem 25 to compute the probability of being dealt a royal flush.

27. Cold Streaks Players in sports are said to have "hot streaks" and "cold streaks." For example, a batter in baseball might be considered to be in a "slump" or "cold streak" if he has made 10 outs in 10 consecutive at-bats. Suppose a hitter successfully reaches base 30% of the time he comes to the plate.

(a) Find the probability that the hitter makes 10 outs in 10 consecutive at-bats, assuming that at-bats are independent events. (*Hint*: The hitter makes an out 70% of the time.) *0.028*

(b) Are "cold streaks" unusual?

28. Hot Streaks Wilt Chamberlain holds the National Basketball Association record for most consecutive field goals in a game with 18. Over his career, Wilt made 54% of his field goal attempts.

(a) Find the probability of Wilt Chamberlain making 18 consecutive field goals, assuming that field goal attempts are independent events. *0.000015*

(b) Is this record likely to be broken?

29. (NW) **Independence in Small Samples from Large Populations** Suppose a computer chip company has just shipped 10,000 computer chips to a computer company. Unfortunately, 50 of the chips are defective. (a) *0.0000245*

(a) Compute the probability that two randomly selected chips are defective using conditional probability.

(b) There are 50 defective chips out of 10,000 shipped. The probability that the first chip randomly selected is defective is 50/10,000 = 0.005 = 0.5%. Compute the probability that two randomly selected chips are defective under the assumption of independent events. Compare your results to part (a). Conclude that when small samples are taken from large populations without replacement, the assumption of independence does not significantly affect the probability. *0.000025*

30. Independence in Small Samples from Large Populations Suppose a poll is being conducted in the Village of Lemont. The pollster identifies her target population as all residents of Lemont 18 years old or older. The list of this population has 6494 people on it.

(a) Compute the probability that the first resident selected to participate in the poll is Roger Cummings and the second is Rick Whittingham. [These people are my neighbors in Lemont.] *0.0000000237*

(b) The probability that any particular resident of Lemont is the first person picked is 1/6494. Compute the probability that the two people selected are Roger and Rick assuming independence. Compare your results to part (a). Conclude that when small samples are taken from large populations without replacement, the assumption of independence does not significantly affect the probability.

31. **Playing Five-Card Stud** In the game of five-card stud, one card is dealt face down to each player and the remaining four cards are dealt face up. After two cards are dealt (one down and one up), the players bet. Players continue to bet after each additional card is dealt. Suppose three cards have been dealt to each of the five players at the table. You currently have three clubs in your hand, so you will attempt to get a flush (all cards in

(30b) 0.0000000237

the same suit). Of the cards dealt, there are two clubs showing in other player's hands.   (b) 41; 8
(a) How many clubs are in a standard 52-card deck? 13
(b) How many cards remain in the deck or are not known by you? Of this amount, how many are clubs?
(c) What is the probability you get dealt a club on the next card? 8/41
(d) What is the probability you get dealt two clubs in a row? 0.034
(e) Should you stay in the game?

32. Refer back to the tree diagram in Figure 12.
(a) What is the probability of Dave's being chairperson? 1/5
(b) What is the probability of Dave's being secretary, given that he has been selected as chairperson? 0

5.4 Conditional Probability

Objectives Compute conditional probabilities

 Use the Multiplication Rule to check for independent events

Note to Instructor
For those instructors who wish to have lighter coverage of probability, the material in this section can be omitted without loss of continuity.

Oftentimes, we have knowledge that affects the probability of an event. For example, in Example 4 from Section 5.3, we saw that the probability that a randomly selected mother gives birth to a low-birth-weight baby is 0.078. However, if we know that the mother is a smoker, the probability increases to 0.121.

 We use conditional probabilities in the Multiplication Rule as follows:

$$P(E \text{ and } F) = P(E) \cdot P(F|E)$$

Solving this expression for $P(F|E)$, we obtain the *conditional probability rule.*

Theorem   **Conditional Probability Rule**

If E and F are any two events, then

$$P(F|E) = \frac{P(E \text{ and } F)}{P(E)} = \frac{N(E \text{ and } F)}{N(E)} \qquad \textbf{(1)}$$

The probability of event F occurring given the occurrence of event E is found by dividing the probability of E and F by the probability of E. Or, the probability of event F occurring given the occurrence of event E is found by dividing the number of simple events in E and F by the number of simple events in E.

▶ **EXAMPLE 1**   **Computing a Conditional Probability**

Problem: The data in Table 5 represent the marital status and gender of the residents of the United States aged 18 years old or older in 1998.

TABLE 5			
	Males (in millions)	Females (in millions)	Totals (in millions)
Never Married	25.5	21.0	46.5
Married	58.6	59.3	117.9
Widowed	2.6	11.0	13.6
Divorced	8.3	11.1	19.4
Totals (in millions)	95.0	102.4	197.4

Source: U.S. Census Bureau, Current Population Reports

(a) Compute the probability that a randomly selected male has never married.

(b) Compute the probability that a randomly selected individual who has never married is male.

Approach:

(a) We are given that the randomly selected person is male, so we concentrate on the "male" column. There are 95 million males and 25.5 million people who are male and never married, so $N(\text{male}) = 95$ million and $N(\text{male and never married}) = 25.5$ million. Compute the probability via the Conditional Probability Rule.

(b) We are given that the randomly selected person has never married, so we concentrate on the "never married" row. There are 46.5 million people who have never married and 25.5 million people who are male and have never married, so $N(\text{never married}) = 46.5$ million and $N(\text{male and never married}) = 25.5$ million. Compute the probability via the Conditional Probability Rule.

Solution:

(a) Substituting into Formula (1), we obtain

$$P(\text{never married} \mid \text{male}) = \frac{N(\text{never married and male})}{N(\text{male})} = \frac{25.5}{95} \approx 0.268$$

There is a 26.8% probability the randomly selected individual has never married, given that he is male.

(b) Substituting into Formula (1), we obtain

$$P(\text{male} \mid \text{never married}) = \frac{N(\text{male and never married})}{N(\text{never married})} = \frac{25.5}{46.5} \approx 0.548$$

There is a 54.8% probability the randomly selected individual is male, given that he or she has never married. ◄◄

What is the difference between the results of Example 1(a) and (b)? In Example 1(a), we found that 26.8% of males have never married, while in Example 1(b), we found that 54.8% of individuals who have never married are male. Do you see the difference?

NW *Now Work Problem 7.*

▶ **EXAMPLE 2** **Birth Weights of Preterm Babies**

Problem: In 1998, 11.47% of all births were preterm. (The gestation period of the pregnancy was less than 37 weeks.) Also in 1998, for 0.23% of all births, the baby was preterm and weighed 8 pounds, 13 ounces or more. What is the probability that a randomly selected baby weighs 8 pounds, 13 ounces or more, given that the baby was preterm?

Approach: We want to know the probability that the baby weighs 8 pounds, 13 ounces or more given the baby was preterm. We know that 0.23% of all babies weighed 8 pounds, 13 ounces or more and were preterm, so P(Weighs 8 pounds, 13 ounces or more and preterm) = 0.23%. We also know that 11.47% of all births were preterm, so P(preterm) = 11.47%. We compute the probability by dividing the probability that a baby will weigh 8 pounds, 13 ounces or more *and* be preterm by the probability that a baby will be preterm.

Solution: P(Weighs 8 pounds, 13 ounces or more | preterm)

$$= \frac{P(\text{Weighs 8 pounds, 13 ounces or more and preterm})}{P(\text{preterm})}$$

$$= \frac{0.23\%}{11.47\%} = \frac{0.0023}{0.1147} \approx 0.0201 = 2.01\%$$

$$\approx 2.01\%$$

There is a 2.01% probability that a randomly selected baby will weigh 8 pounds, 13 ounces or more, given the baby is preterm. It is unusual for preterm babies to weigh 8 pounds, 13 ounces or more. ◀◀

 Now Work Problem 11.

② Checking for Independence

In Section 5.3, we said two events E and F are independent if $P(E|F) = P(E)$ or $P(F|E) = P(F)$. An alternative method for checking for independence is through the Multiplication Rule.

Theorem | **Checking for Independence**
If $P(E \text{ and } F) = P(E) \cdot P(F)$, then events E and F are independent.

▶ **EXAMPLE 3** **Checking for Independence**

Problem: Table 5 on page 297 represents the gender and marital status of the residents of the United States aged 18 years old and older. Determine whether the events "male" and "never married" are independent.

Approach: In order for the events to be independent, P(male|never married) = P(male) or P(never married|male) = P(never married). Alternatively, we could check for independence by determining whether P(male and never married) = P(male) · P(never married).

 **Caution**

The method of checking for independence presented here works only for population data. To determine whether sample data are independent requires procedures introduced in Section 11.3.

Solution: From Example 1(b), we found that P(male|never married) = 0.548. In Example 3(a) of Section 5.2, we computed P(male) = 95/197.4 ≈ 0.481. Because P(male|never married) ≠ P(male), the events are dependent. In fact, knowing that individuals have never married increases the probability that they are male. Another method for checking for independence would be to determine whether $P(\text{male and never married}) = P(\text{male}) \cdot P(\text{never married})$. From Table 5, we find that $P(\text{male and never married}) = 25.5/197.4 \approx 0.129$. We also find that

$$P(\text{male}) \cdot P(\text{never married}) = \frac{95}{197.4} \cdot \frac{46.5}{197.4} \approx 0.113.$$ Because $P(\text{male}$ and never married$) \neq P(\text{male}) \cdot P(\text{never married})$, the events "male" and "never married" are dependent. ◀◀

 *Now Work Problem 15.*

Mutually Exclusive Events versus Independent Events It is important that we understand that mutually exclusive events and independent events are different concepts. Recall that two events are mutually exclusive if they have no simple events in common. That is, two events are mutually exclusive if the occurrence of one of the events precludes the other event from occurring. However, two events are independent if knowledge of one event does not affect the probability of the other. Consider a simple experiment in rolling a single die. Let E = "roll an even number" and let F = "roll an odd number." Clearly, E and F are mutually exclusive, but they are not independent, because $P(E) = 1/2$ and $P(E|F) = 0$.

Caution
Two events that are mutually exclusive are not independent.

5.4 Assess Your Understanding

Concepts and Vocabulary

1. State two methods for discovering whether two events are independent.

2. Describe the difference between mutually exclusive events and independent events.

Exercises

• **Basic Skills**   1. *0.75*   2. *0.525*   3. *0.568*   4. *0.411*

1. Suppose that E and F are two events and that $P(E \text{ and } F) = 0.6$ and $P(E) = 0.8$. What is $P(F|E)$?

2. Suppose that A and B are two events and that $P(A \text{ and } B) = 0.21$ and $P(A) = 0.4$. What is $P(B|A)$?

3. Suppose that E and F are two events and that $N(E \text{ and } F) = 420$ and $N(E) = 740$. What is $P(F|E)$?

4. Suppose that A and B are two events and that $N(A \text{ and } B) = 380$ and $N(A) = 925$. What is $P(B|A)$?

5. Suppose that E and F are two events and that $P(E \text{ and } F) = 0.24$, $P(E) = 0.4$, and $P(F) = 0.6$. Are E and F independent? Why? *Yes*

6. Suppose that A and B are two events and that $P(A \text{ and } B) = 0.3$, $P(A) = 0.5$, and $P(B) = 0.8$. Are E and F independent? Why? *No*

• Applying the Concepts

7. **Medicaid** The data to the right, in thousands, represent the age of persons receiving Medicaid and their poverty level.

   (a) What is the probability that a randomly selected individual who is less than 18 years old is below the poverty level? *0.592*

   (b) What is the probability that a randomly selected individual who is below the poverty level is less than 18 years old? *0.556*

	AGE			
	<18	**18–44**	**45–64**	**>65**
Below Poverty Level	8,550	4,356	1,520	958
Above Poverty Level	5,884	3,741	1,756	1,943

Source: U.S. Census Bureau

8. SAT Verbal Scores The following data represent the scores received on the 2000 SAT I: Reasoning Test—Verbal, by gender:

	Male	Female		Male	Female
200–249	6,755	7,512	550–599	84,524	96,381
250–299	9,594	10,816	600–649	62,205	68,515
300–349	25,630	30,058	650–699	36,202	39,843
350–399	50,042	60,139	700–749	18,044	18,716
400–449	78,276	95,780	750–800	10,647	11,028
450–499	98,989	117,976	TOTAL	583,331	676,947
500–549	102,423	120,183			

Source: College Board

(a) What is the probability that a randomly selected female scored 750–800 on the 2000 SAT I: Reasoning Test—Verbal? 0.016
(b) What is the probability that a randomly selected individual who scored 750–800 on the 2000 SAT I: Reasoning Test—Verbal is female? 0.509

9. Driver Fatalities The following data represent the number of driver fatalities in 1996, by age group, for male and female drivers:

	Male	Female		Male	Female
16–19	1922	762	60–64	637	270
20–24	2814	699	65–69	614	268
25–29	2126	617	70–74	598	358
30–34	1986	627	75–79	554	323
35–39	1743	604	80–84	474	230
40–44	1437	485	85 or older	329	146
45–49	1169	391	TOTAL	17,946	6,387
50–54	859	347			
55–59	684	260			

Source: National Highway Traffic Institute

(a) What is the probability that a randomly selected driver fatality who was male was 20–24 years old? 0.157
(b) What is the probability that a randomly selected driver fatality who was 20–24 years old was male? 0.801
(c) Suppose you are a police officer called to the scene of a traffic accident with a fatality. The dispatcher states the victim is 20–24 years old, but the gender is not known. Is the victim more likely to be male or female? Why?

10. Marital Status The following data represent the marital status of Americans 25 years old or older and their level of education in 1999:

	Did Not Graduate High School	High School Graduate	Some College	College Graduate
Never Married	4,012	7,790	6,565	7,685
Married, Spouse Present	15,122	36,076	27,003	29,811
Married, Spouse Absent	1,877	2,006	1,435	1,489
Separated	1,094	1,515	1,214	598
Widowed	5,000	4,757	2,264	1,456
Divorced	2,951	7,047	5,649	3,766

Source: U.S. Census Bureau

(a) What is the probability that a randomly selected individual who has never married is a high school graduate? 0.299
(b) What is the probability that a randomly selected individual who is a high school graduate has never married? 0.132

11. Rainy Days For the month of June in the city of Chicago, 37% of the days are cloudy. Also in the month of June in the city of Chicago, 21% of the days are cloudy and rainy. What is the probability that a randomly selected day in June will be rainy if it is cloudy? 0.568

12. Cause of Death According to the U.S. National Center for Health Statistics, in 1997, 0.2% of deaths in the United States were of 25–34 year olds whose cause of death was cancer. In addition, 1.97% of all decedants were 25–34 years old. What is the probability that a randomly selected death is the result of cancer if the individual is known to have been 25–34 years old? 0.102

13. High School Dropout According to the U.S. Census Bureau, 9.1% of 16–17-year-olds drop out of high school. In addition, 5.8% of White 16–17-year-olds drop out of high school. What is the probability a randomly selected dropout is White, given that he or she is 16–17 years old? *0.637*

14. Income by Region According to the U.S Census Bureau, 19.1% of the U.S. households are in the Northeast. In addition, 4.4% of American households earn $75,000 per year or more and are located in the Northeast. Determine the probability that a randomly selected American household earns more than $75,000 per year, given that the house is located in the Northeast. *0.230*

15. **Medicaid** Refer to the table in Problem 7. Are the (NW) events " < 18 years old" and "below poverty level" independent? *No*

16. SAT Verbal Scores Refer to the table in Problem 8. Are the events "female" and "scored 750–800" independent? *No*

17. Driver Fatalities Refer to the table in Problem 9. Are the events "male" and "20–24 years old" independent? *No*

18. Marital Status Refer to the table in Problem 10. Are the events "never married" and "high school graduate" independent? *No*

19. Household Income In 1997, 18.4% of all households earned more than $75,000 per year. Also in 1997, 4.2% of all households earned more than $75,000 per year and lived in the Northeast. What is the probability that a randomly selected household lives in the Northeast, given that the household earns more than $75,000 per year? *0.228*

5.5   Counting Techniques

Objectives Solve counting problems using the Multiplication Principle
 Solve counting problems using permutations
 Solve counting problems using combinations
 Solve counting problems using permutations with repetition
 Compute probabilities involving permutations and combinations

Note to Instructor
Most of the material in this section is optional. However, the material on combinations should be covered if you intend to present binomial probabilities (Section 6.2).

   Counting plays a major role in many diverse areas, including probability. In this section, we look at special types of counting problems and develop general formulas for solving them.

We begin with an example that will demonstrate a general counting principle.

▶ **EXAMPLE 1**   **Counting the Number of Possible Meals**

Problem: The fixed-price dinner at Mabenka Restaurant provides the following choices:

Appetizer:	soup or salad
Entrée:	baked chicken, broiled beef patty, baby beef liver, or roast beef au jus
Dessert:	ice cream or cheese cake

How many different meals can be ordered?

Approach: Ordering such a meal requires three separate decisions:

Choose an Appetizer	**Choose an Entrée**	**Choose a Dessert**
2 choices	4 choices	2 choices

We will draw a tree diagram that lists the possible meals that can be ordered.

Figure 13

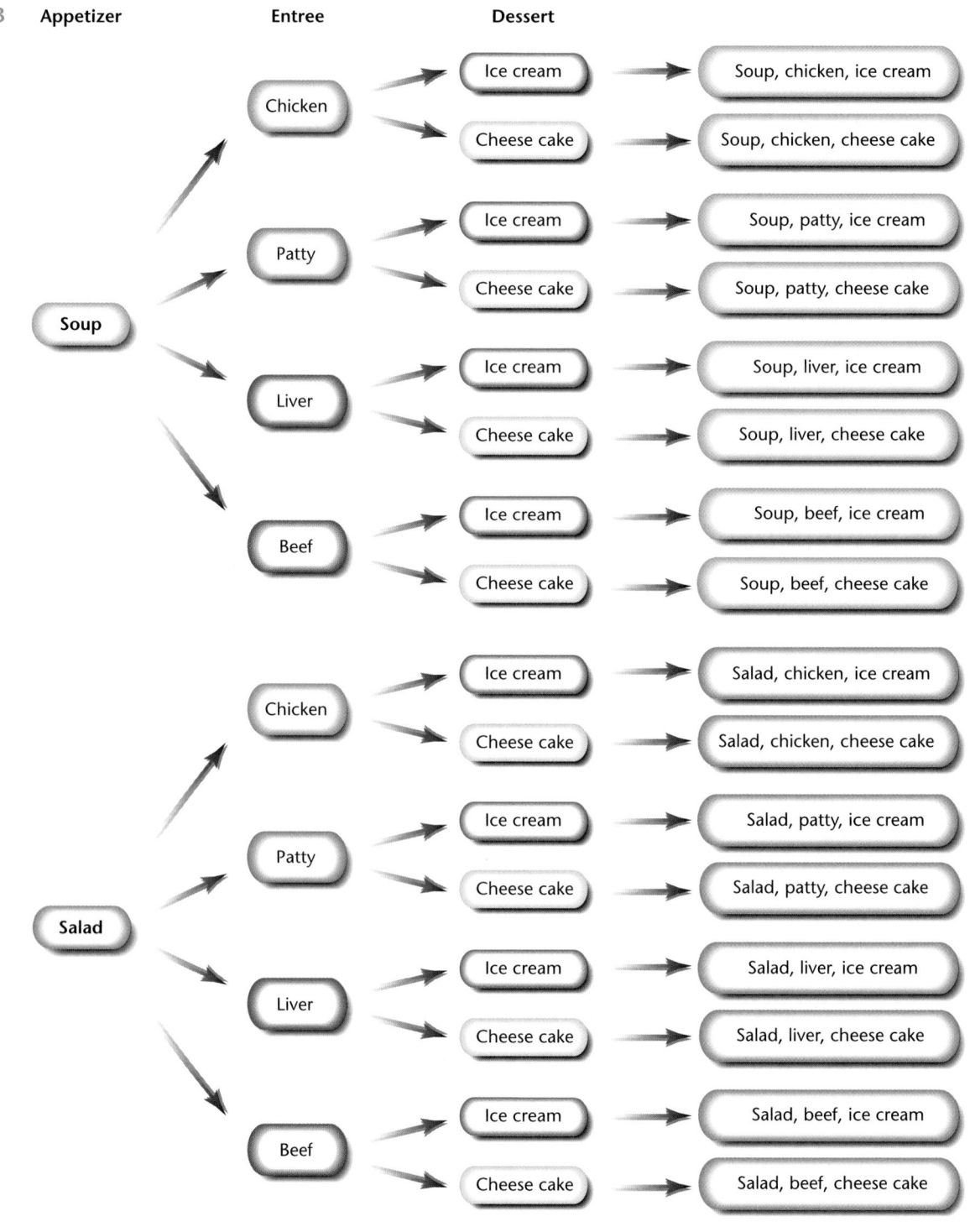

Solution: Look at the tree diagram in Figure 13. We see that, for each choice of appetizer, there are 4 choices of entrée—and that, for each of these $2 \cdot 4 = 8$ choices, there are 2 choices for dessert. A total of

$$2 \cdot 4 \cdot 2 = 16$$

different meals can be ordered.

◀◀

Example 1 illustrates a general counting principle.

Theorem

Multiplication Principle of Counting

If a task consists of a sequence of choices in which there are p selections for the first choice, q selections for the second choice, r selections for the third choice, and so on, then the task of making these selections can be done in

$$p \cdot q \cdot r \cdot \ldots$$

different ways.

▶ **EXAMPLE 2   Counting Airport Codes**

Problem: The International Airline Transportation Association (IATA) assigns three-letter codes to represent airport locations. For example, the airport code for Fort Lauderdale is FLL. How many different airport codes are possible?

Approach: We are choosing 3 letters from 26 letters and arranging them in order. We notice that repetition of letters is allowed. We use the Multiplication Principle of Counting, recognizing there are 26 ways to choose the first letter, 26 ways to choose the second letter, and 26 ways to choose the third letter.

Solution: By the Multiplication Principle, there are

$$26 \cdot 26 \cdot 26 = 17,576$$

different airport codes possible.   ◀◀

In Example 2, we were allowed to repeat a letter. For example, a valid airport code is FLL (Ft. Lauderdale International Airport), in which the letter L appears twice. In the next example, repetition is not allowed.

▶ **EXAMPLE 3   Counting without Repetition**

Problem: Three members from a 14-member committee are to be randomly selected to serve as chair, vice chair, and secretary. The first person selected is the chair, the second person selected vice chair, and the third secretary. How many different committee structures are possible?

Approach: The task consists of making three selections. The first selection requires choosing from 14 members. Because a member cannot serve in more than one capacity, the second selection requires choosing from 13 members. The third selection requires choosing from 12 members. (Do you see why?) We use the Multiplication Principle to determine the number of possible committees.

Solution: By the Multiplication Principle, there are

$$14 \cdot 13 \cdot 12 = 2184$$

different committee structures possible.   ◀◀

 *Now Work Problem 27.*

The Factorial Symbol

We now introduce a special symbol that can assist us in representing certain types of counting problems.

Definition   If $n \geq 0$ is an integer, the **factorial symbol $n!$** is defined as follows:

$$0! = 1 \qquad 1! = 1$$

$$n! = n(n - 1) \cdot \ldots \cdot 3 \cdot 2 \cdot 1$$

For example, $2! = 2 \cdot 1 = 2, 3! = 3 \cdot 2 \cdot 1 = 6, 4! = 4 \cdot 3 \cdot 2 \cdot 1 = 24$, and so on. Table 8 lists the values of $n!$ for $0 \leq n \leq 6$.

TABLE 8						
n	0	1	2	3	4	5	6
$n!$	1	1	2	6	24	120	720

Using Technology: Your calculator has a factorial key. Use it to see how fast factorials increase in value. Find the value of 69!. What happens when you try to find 70!? In fact, 70! is larger than 10^{100} (a *googol*), the largest number most calculators can display.

▶ **EXAMPLE 4**   **The Traveling Salesman**

Problem: You have just been hired as a book representative for Prentice Hall. On your first day, you must travel to seven schools to introduce yourself. How many different routes are possible?

Approach: The seven schools are different. Let's call the schools *A, B, C, D, E, F,* and *G.* School *A* can be visited first, second, third, fourth, fifth, sixth or seventh. So, we have seven choices for school *A.* We would then have six choices for school *B,* five choices for school *C* and so on. We can use the factorial to find our solution.

NW *Now Work Problems 1 and 29.*

Solution: There are $7 \cdot 6 \cdot 5 \cdot 4 \cdot 3 \cdot 2 \cdot 1 = 7! = 5040$ different routes possible.   ◀◀

② **Permutations**

Examples 3 and 4 illustrate a type of counting problem referred to as a *permutation.*

Definition   A **permutation** is an ordered arrangement in which r objects are chosen from n distinct (different) objects and repetition is not allowed. The symbol $_nP_r$ represents the number of permutations of r objects selected from n objects.

So we could represent the solution to the question posed in Example 3 as

$$_nP_r = {}_{14}P_3 = 14 \cdot 13 \cdot 12 = 2184$$

and the solution to Example 4 could be represented as

$$_7P_7 = 7 \cdot 6 \cdot 5 \cdot 4 \cdot 3 \cdot 2 \cdot 1 = 5040$$

To arrive at a formula for $_nP_r$, we note that there are n choices for the first selection, $n - 1$ choices for the second selection, $n - 2$ choices for the third selection, ..., and $n - (r - 1)$ choices for the rth selection. By the Multiplication Principle, we have

$$
\begin{array}{ccccccccc}
 & & 1^{st} & & 2^{nd} & & 3^{rd} & & r^{th} \\
_nP_r & = & n & \cdot & (n - 1) & \cdot & (n - 2) & \cdot \ldots \cdot & [n - (r - 1)] \\
 & = & n & \cdot & (n - 1) & \cdot & (n - 2) & \cdot \ldots \cdot & (n - r + 1)
\end{array}
$$

This formula for $_nP_r$ can be written in **factorial notation**:

$$_nP_r = n \cdot (n - 1) \cdot (n - 2) \cdot \ldots \cdot (n - r + 1)$$

$$= n \cdot (n - 1) \cdot (n - 2) \cdot \ldots \cdot (n - r + 1) \cdot \frac{(n - r) \cdot \ldots \cdot 3 \cdot 2 \cdot 1}{(n - r) \cdot \ldots \cdot 3 \cdot 2 \cdot 1} = \frac{n!}{(n - r)!}$$

We have the following result.

Theorem

> **Number of Permutations of n Distinct Objects Taken r at a Time**
>
> The number of arrangements of r objects chosen from n objects, in which
> **1.** the n objects are distinct
> **2.** once an object is used it cannot be repeated, and
> **3.** order is important,
>
> is given by the formula
>
> $$_nP_r = \frac{n!}{(n - r)!} \tag{1}$$

▶ **EXAMPLE 5**   **Computing Permutations**

Problem: Evaluate: **(a)** $_7P_5$ **(b)** $_8P_2$ **(c)** $_5P_5$

Approach: To answer (a), we use Formula (1) with $n = 7$ and $r = 5$. To answer (b), we use Formula (1) with $n = 8$ and $r = 2$. To answer (c), we use Formula (1) with $n = 5$ and $r = 5$.

Solution:

(a) $_7P_5 = \dfrac{7!}{(7 - 5)!} = \dfrac{7!}{2!} = \dfrac{7 \cdot 6 \cdot 5 \cdot 4 \cdot 3 \cdot 2!}{2!} = \underbrace{7 \cdot 6 \cdot 5 \cdot 4 \cdot 3}_{5 \text{ factors}} = 2{,}520$

(b) $_8P_2 = \dfrac{8!}{(8 - 2)!} = \dfrac{8!}{6!} = \dfrac{8 \cdot 7 \cdot 6!}{6!} = \underbrace{8 \cdot 7}_{2 \text{ factors}} = 56$

(c) $_5P_5 = \dfrac{5!}{(5 - 5)!} = \dfrac{5!}{0!} = 5! = 5 \cdot 4 \cdot 3 \cdot 2 \cdot 1 = 120$ ◀◀

Using Technology: We can use a graphing calculator to compute permutations. Figure 14 shows the result of doing Example 5(a) on a TI-83 Plus calculator.

Figure 14

```
7 nPr 5
            2520
```

NW   *Now Work Problem 7.*

Example 5(c) illustrates a general result.

Theorem

$$_rP_r = r!$$

We need to recognize that, in a permutation, order matters. That is, if we wanted to permute the letters ABC by selecting them 3 at a time, the following arrangements are all different:

$$ABC, ACB, BAC, BCA, CAB, CBA$$

▶ **EXAMPLE 6** **Betting on the Trifecta**

Problem: In how many ways can horses in a 10-horse race finish first, second, and third?

Approach: The 10 horses are distinct. Once a horse crosses the finish line, that horse will not cross the finish line again, and, in a race, order is important. We have a permutation of 10 objects taken 3 at a time.

Solution: The top three horses can finish a 10-horse race in

$$_{10}P_3 = \frac{10!}{(10-3)!} = \frac{10!}{7!} = \frac{10 \cdot 9 \cdot 8 \cdot 7!}{7!} = \underbrace{10 \cdot 9 \cdot 8}_{3 \text{ factors}} = 720 \text{ ways} \blacktriangleleft\blacktriangleleft$$

NW *Now Work Problem 41.*

③ Combinations

In a permutation, order is important; for example, the arrangements *ABC, ACB, BAC, BCA, CAB,* and *CBA* are considered different arrangements of the letters *A, B,* and *C*. In many situations, though, order is unimportant. If order is unimportant, the six arrangements of the letters *A, B,* and *C* given above are not different. That is, we do not distinguish *ABC* from *BAC*, for example. In the card game of poker, the order in which the cards are received does not matter; the *combination* of the cards is what matters.

Definition

A **combination** is a collection, without regard to order, of n distinct objects without repetitions. The symbol $_nC_r$ represents the number of combinations of n distinct objects taken r at a time.

▶ **EXAMPLE 7** **Listing Combinations**

Problem: Roger, Rick, Randy and Jay are going to play golf. They will randomly select teams of two players each. List all possible team combinations. That is, list all the combinations of the four people Roger, Rick, Randy, and Jay taken two at a time. What is $_4C_2$?

Approach: We list the possible teams. We note that order is unimportant, so {Roger, Rick} is the same as {Rick, Roger}.

Solution: The list of all such teams (combinations) is

Roger, Rick; Roger, Randy; Roger, Jay; Rick, Randy; Rick, Jay; Randy, Jay

Thus,

$$_4C_2 = 6$$

There are six ways of forming teams of two from a group of four players.

We can find a formula for $_nC_r$ by noting that the only difference between a permutation and a combination is that we disregard order in combinations. To determine $_nC_r$, we eliminate from the formula for $_nP_r$ the number of permutations that were rearrangements of a given set of r objects. In Example 7, for example, selecting {Roger, Rick} was the same as selecting {Rick, Roger}, so there were $2! = 2$ rearrangements of the two objects. This can be determined from the formula for $_nP_r$ by calculating $_rP_r = r!$. So, if we divide $_nP_r$ by $r!$, we will have the desired formula for $_nC_r$:

$$_nC_r = \frac{_nP_r}{r!} = \frac{n!}{r!(n-r)!}$$

We have proven the following result.

Theorem

Number of Combinations of n Distinct Objects Taken r at a Time

The number of different arrangements of n objects using $r \le n$ of them, in which

1. the n objects are distinct

2. once an object is used, it cannot be repeated, and

3. order is not important

is given by the formula

$$_nC_r = \frac{n!}{r!(n-r)!} \tag{2}$$

Using Formula (2) to solve the problem presented in Example 7, we obtain

$$_4C_2 = \frac{4!}{2!(4-2)!} = \frac{4!}{2!2!} = \frac{4 \cdot 3 \cdot 2!}{2 \cdot 1 \cdot 2!} = \frac{12}{2} = 6$$

▶ **EXAMPLE 8**   **Using Formula (2)**

Problem: Use Formula (2) to find the value of each expression.

(a) $_4C_1$

(b) $_6C_4$

(c) $_6C_2$

Approach: We will use Formula (2).

Solution:

(a) $_4C_1 = \dfrac{4!}{1!(4-1)!} = \dfrac{4!}{1! \cdot 3!} = \dfrac{4 \cdot 3!}{1 \cdot 3!} = 4$

(b) $_6C_4 = \dfrac{6!}{4!(6-4)!} = \dfrac{6!}{4! \cdot 2!} = \dfrac{6 \cdot 5 \cdot 4!}{4! \cdot 2 \cdot 1} = \dfrac{30}{2} = 15$

(c) $_6C_2 = \dfrac{6!}{2!(6-2)!} = \dfrac{6!}{2!4!} = \dfrac{6 \cdot 5 \cdot 4!}{2 \cdot 1 \cdot 4!} = \dfrac{30}{2} = 15$ ◀◀

Using Technology: We can use a graphing calculator to compute combinations. Figure 15 shows the result of doing Example 8(b) an a TI-83+ graphing calculator.

Figure 15

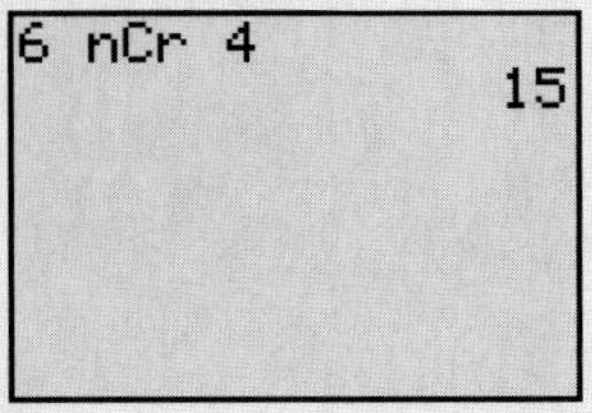

```
6 nCr 4
                    15
```

Notice in Example 8 that $_6C_4 = {}_6C_2$. This result can be generalized.

Theorem

$$_nC_r = {}_nC_{n-r}$$

NW *Now Work Problem 15.*

▶ **EXAMPLE 9**   **Simple Random Samples**

Problem: How many different simple random samples of size 4 can be obtained from a population whose size is 20?

Approach: The 20 individuals in the population are distinct. In addition, the order in which an individual is selected to be in the sample is unimportant. Thus, the number of simple random samples of size 4 from a population of size 20 is a combination of 20 objects taken 4 at a time.

Solution: Use Formula (2) with $n = 20$ and $r = 4$:

$$_{20}C_4 = \frac{20!}{4!(20-4)!} = \frac{20!}{4!16!} = \frac{20 \cdot 19 \cdot 18 \cdot 17 \cdot 16!}{4 \cdot 3 \cdot 2 \cdot 1 \cdot 16!} = \frac{116{,}280}{24} = 4845$$

There are 4845 different simple random samples of size 4 from a population whose size is 20. ◀◀

NW *Now Work Problem 47.*

④ **Permutations with Repetition**

Let's begin with an example.

▶ **EXAMPLE 10**   **Forming Different Words**

Problem: How many distinguishable strings of letters can be formed by using all the letters in the word REARRANGE?

Approach: Each string formed will have nine letters: three R's, two A's, two E's, one N, and one G. To construct each word, we need to fill in nine positions with the nine letters:

$$\overline{1} \quad \overline{2} \quad \overline{3} \quad \overline{4} \quad \overline{5} \quad \overline{6} \quad \overline{7} \quad \overline{8} \quad \overline{9}$$

The process of forming a word consists of five tasks:

Task 1: Choose the positions for the three R's.
Task 2: Choose the positions for the two A's.
Task 3: Choose the positions for the two E's.
Task 4: Choose the position for the one N.
Task 5: Choose the position for the one G.

Task 1 can be done in $_9C_3$ ways. There then remain six positions to be filled, so Task 2 can be done in $_6C_2$ ways. There remain four positions to be filled, so Task 3 can be done in $_4C_2$ ways. There remain two positions to be filled, so Task 4 can be done in $_2C_1$ ways. The last position can be filled in $_1C_1$ way.

Solution: By the Multiplication Principle, the number of possible words that can be formed is

$$_9C_3 \cdot {}_6C_2 \cdot {}_4C_2 \cdot {}_2C_1 \cdot {}_1C_1 = \frac{9!}{6! \cdot 3!} \cdot \frac{6!}{4!2!} \cdot \frac{4!}{2! \cdot 2!} \cdot \frac{2!}{1! \cdot 1!} \cdot \frac{1!}{1!0!} = \frac{9!}{3! \cdot 2! \cdot 2! \cdot 1! \cdot 1!} = 15{,}120 \quad \blacktriangleleft\blacktriangleleft$$

The form of the answer to Example 10 is suggestive of a general result. Had the letters in REARRANGE each been different, there would have been $_9P_9 = 9!$ possible words formed. This is the numerator of the answer. The presence of three R's, two A's, and two E's reduces the number of different words, as the entries in the denominator illustrate. We are led to the following result:

Theorem

> **Permutations with Repetition**
>
> The number of permutations of n objects of which n_1 are of one kind, n_2 are of a second kind, ..., and n_k are of a kth kind is given by
>
> $$\frac{n!}{n_1! \cdot n_2! \cdot \ldots \cdot n_k!} \qquad \textbf{(3)}$$
>
> where $n = n_1 + n_2 + \ldots + n_k$.

▶ **EXAMPLE 11**   **Arranging Flags**

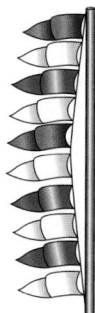

Problem: How many different vertical arrangements are there of 10 flags if 5 are white, 3 are blue and 2 are red?

Approach: We seek the number of permutations of 10 objects, of which 5 are of one kind (white), 3 are of a second kind (blue), and 2 are of a third kind (red).

Solution: Using Formula (3), we find that there are

$$\frac{10!}{5! \cdot 3! \cdot 2!} = \frac{10 \cdot 9 \cdot 8 \cdot 7 \cdot 6 \cdot 5!}{5! \cdot 3! \cdot 2!} = 2520 \text{ different arrangements} \quad \blacktriangleleft\blacktriangleleft$$

NW   *Now Work Problem 51.*

Summary

To summarize the differences between combinations and the various types of permutations, we present Table 6 on page 310.

⑤   ## Probabilities Involving Permutations and Combinations

The counting techniques presented in this section can be used to determine probabilities of certain events by utilizing the classical method of computing probabilities. Recall that this method stated the probability of an event E is the number of ways event E can occur divided by the number of different possible outcomes of the experiment.

TABLE 6		
	Description	**Formula**
Combination	The selection of r objects from a set of n different objects where the order in which the objects is selected does not matter (so AB is the same as BA) and an object cannot be selected more than once (repetition is not allowed)	${}_nC_r = \dfrac{n!}{r!(n-r)!}$
Permutation of Distinct Items with Replacement	The selection of r objects from a set of n different objects where the order in which the objects are selected matters (so AB is different from BA) and an object may be selected more than once (repetition is allowed)	n^r
Permutation of Distinct Items without Replacement	The selection of r objects from a set of n different objects where the order in which the objects are selected matters (so AB is different from BA) and an object cannot be selected more than once (repetition is not allowed)	${}_nP_r = \dfrac{n!}{(n-r)!}$
Permutation of Non-distinct Items without Replacement	The number of ways n objects can be arranged (order matters) in which there are n_1 of one kind, n_2 of a second kind, $\dots$, and n_k of a kth kind, where $n = n_1 + n_2 + \dots + n_k$	$\dfrac{n!}{n_1!n_2!\cdots n_k!}$

▶ **EXAMPLE 12** **Winning the Lottery**

Problem: In the Illinois Lottery, an urn contains balls numbered 1–54. From this urn, 6 balls are randomly chosen without replacement. For a \$1 bet, a player chooses two sets of 6 numbers. In order to win, all six numbers must match those chosen from the urn. The order in which the balls are selected does not matter. What is the probability of winning Lotto?

Approach: The probability of winning is given by the number of ways a ticket could win, divided by the size of the sample space. Each ticket has two sets of six numbers, so there are two chances (for the two sets of numbers) of winning for each ticket. The size of the sample space S is the number of ways that 6 objects can be selected from 54 objects without replacement and without regard to order, so that $N(S) = {}_{54}C_6$.

Solution: The size of the sample space is

$$N(S) = {}_{54}C_6 = \frac{54!}{6! \cdot (54-6)!} = \frac{54 \cdot 53 \cdot 52 \cdot 51 \cdot 50 \cdot 49 \cdot 48!}{6! \cdot 48!} = 25{,}827{,}165$$

Each ticket has two sets of 6 numbers, so a player has two chances of winning for each \$1. If E is the event "winning ticket," then $N(E) = 2$. The probability of E is

$$P(E) = \frac{2}{25{,}827{,}165} \approx 0.000000077$$

There is about a 1 in 13,000,000 chance of winning the Illinois Lottery! ◀◀

▶ **EXAMPLE 13** **Probabilities Involving Combinations**

Problem: A shipment of 120 fasteners that contains 4 defective fasteners was sent to a manufacturing plant. The quality-control manager at the manufacturing plant randomly selects five fasteners and inspects them. What is the probability that exactly one of the fasteners is defective?

Approach: The probability that exactly one fastener is defective is found by calculating the number of ways of selecting exactly 1 defective fastener in 5 fasteners and then dividing this result by the number of ways of selecting 5 fasteners from 120 fasteners. To choose exactly 1 defective in the 5 requires choosing one defective from the four defectives and 4 nondefectives from the 116 nondefectives. The order in which the fasteners are selected does not matter, so we use combinations.

Solution: The number of ways of choosing 1 defective fastener from 4 defective fasteners is $_4C_1$. The number of ways of choosing four nondefective fasteners from 116 nondefectives is $_{116}C_4$. Using the Multiplication Principle, we find that the number of ways of choosing 1 defective and 4 nondefective fasteners is

$$(_4C_1) \cdot (_{116}C_4) = 4 \cdot 7{,}160{,}245 = 28{,}640{,}980$$

The number of ways of selecting 5 fasteners from 120 fasteners is $_{120}C_5 = 190{,}578{,}024$. The probability of selecting exactly 1 defective fastener is

$$P(\text{one defective fastener}) = \frac{(_4C_1)(_{116}C_4)}{_{120}C_5} = \frac{4 \cdot 7{,}160{,}245}{190{,}578{,}024} \approx 0.1503 = 15.03\%$$

There is a 15.03% probability of randomly selecting exactly one defective fastener.   ◄◄

NW   *Now Work Problem 57.*

5.5 Assess Your Understanding

Concepts and Vocabulary

1. Explain the difference between a combination and a permutation.

Exercises

• Skill Building

In Problems 1–6, find the value of each factorial.

1. 5! 120

2. 7! 5040

3. 10! 3,628,800

4. 12! 479,001,600

5. 0! 1

6. 1! 1

In Problems 7–14, find the value of each permutation.

7. $_6P_2$ 30

8. $_7P_2$ 42

9. $_4P_4$ 24

10. $_7P_7$ 5040

11. $_5P_0$ 1

12. $_4P_0$ 1

13. $_8P_3$ 336

14. $_9P_4$ 3024

In Problems 15–22, find the value of each combination.

15. $_8C_3$ 56

16. $_9C_2$ 36

17. $_{10}C_2$ 45

18. $_{12}C_3$ 220

19. $_{52}C_1$ 52

20. $_{40}C_{40}$ 1

21. $_{48}C_3$ 17,296

22. $_{30}C_4$ 27,405

23. List all the permutations of five objects *a, b, c, d,* and *e* taken two at a time without repetition. What is $_5P_2$? 20

24. List all the permutations of four objects *a, b, c,* and *d* taken two at a time without repetition. What is $_4P_2$? 12

25. List all the combinations of five objects *a, b, c, d,* and *e* taken two at a time. What is $_5C_2$? 10

26. List all the combinations of four objects *a, b, c,* and *d* taken two at a time. What is $_4C_2$? 6

• Applying the Concepts

27. Clothing Options A man has six shirts and four ties. As-
NW suming that they all match, how many different shirt-and-tie combinations can he wear? 24

28. Clothing Options A woman has five blouses and three skirts. Assuming that they all match, how many different outfits can she wear? 15

29. Arranging Songs on a CD Suppose Dan is going to
NW burn a compact disk (CD) that will contain 12 songs. In how many ways can Dan arrange the 12 songs on the CD? 12!

30. Arranging Students In how many ways can 15 students be lined up? 15!

31. Traveling Salesman A salesman must travel to 8 cities in order to promote a new marketing campaign. How many different trips are possible, if any route between cities is possible? 8!

32. Randomly Playing Songs A certain compact disk play-er randomly plays each of 10 songs on a CD. Once a song is played, it is not repeated until all the songs on the CD have been played. In how many different ways can the CD player play the 10 songs? 10!

33. Stocks on the NYSE Companies whose stocks are list-ed on the New York Stock Exchange (NYSE) have their company name represented by either one, two, or three letters (repetition of letters is allowed). What is the maximum number of companies that can be listed on the New York Stock Exchange? 18,278

34. Stocks on the NASDAQ Companies whose stocks are listed on the NASDAQ stock exchange have their company name represented by either four or five let-ters (repetition of letters is allowed). What is the max-imum number of companies that can be listed on the NASDAQ? 12,338,352

35. Garage Door Code Outside of my home, there is a key-pad that can be used to open the garage if the correct four-digit code is entered.
   (a) How many codes are possible? 10,000
   (b) What is the probability of entering the correct code on the first try, assuming that I don't remember the code? 0.0001

36. Social Security Numbers A Social Security number is used to identify each resident of the United States

uniquely. The number is of the form xxx–xx–xxxx, where each *x* is a digit from 0 to 9.
   (a) How many Social Security numbers can be formed? 10^9
   (b) What is the probability of correctly guessing the So-cial Security number of the President of the United States? $1/10^9$

37. Usernames Suppose a local area network requires eight letters for user names. Lower- and uppercase let-ters are considered the same. How many user names are possible for the local area network? 26^8

38. Passwords Suppose a local area network requires eight characters for a password. The first character must be a letter, but the remaining seven characters can be either a letter or a digit (0 through 9). Lower- and uppercase letters are considered the same. How many passwords are possible for the local area network? $26 \cdot 36^7$

39. Combination Locks A combination lock has 50 num-bers on it. To open it, you turn counterclockwise to a number, then rotate clockwise to a second number, and then counterclockwise to the third number.
   (a) How many different lock combinations are there? 50^3
   (b) What is the probability of guessing a lock combina-tion on the first try? $1/50^3$

40. Forming License Plate Numbers How many different license plate numbers can be made by using one letter followed by five digits selected from the digits 0 through 9? 2,600,000

41. INDY 500 Suppose 40 cars start at the Indianapolis
NW 500. In how many ways can the top three cars finish the race? 59,280

42. Betting on the Perfecta In how many ways can the top two horses finish in a 10-horse race? 90

43. Forming a Committee Four members from a 20-person committee are to be selected randomly, to serve as chairperson, vice chairperson, secretary, and treasurer. The first person selected is the chairperson, the second person selected is the vice chairperson, the third is the secretary, and the fourth is the treasurer. How many dif-ferent leadership structures are possible? 116,280

44. Forming a Committee Four members from a 50-person committee are to be selected randomly, to serve as chairperson, vice chairperson, secretary, and treasurer. The first person selected is the chairperson, the second person selected is the vice chairperson, the third is the secretary, and the fourth is the treasurer. How many dif-ferent leadership structures are possible? $_{50}P_4$

45. Lottery Suppose a lottery exists where balls numbered 1–25 are placed in an urn. To win, you must match the four balls chosen in the correct order. How many possi-ble outcomes are there for this game? 303,600

46. **Forming a Committee** In the United States Senate, there are 21 members on the Committee on Banking, Housing, and Urban Affairs. Nine of these 21 members are selected to be on the Subcommittee on Economic Policy. How many different committee structures are possible for this subcommittee? 293,930

47. **Simple Random Sample** How many different simple (NW) random samples of size 5 can be obtained from a population whose size is 50? 2,118,760

48. **Simple Random Sample** How many different simple random samples of size 7 can be obtained from a population whose size is 100? $_{100}C_7$

49. **Children** A family has six children. If this family has exactly two boys, how many different birth and gender orders are possible? 15

50. **Children** A family has eight children. If this family has exactly three boys, how many different birth and gender orders are possible? 56

51. **Forming Words** How many different 10-letter words (NW) (real or imaginary) can be formed from the letters in the word STATISTICS? 50,400

52. **Forming Words** How many different nine-letter words (real or imaginary) can be formed from the letters in the word ECONOMICS? 90,720

53. **Landscape Design** A golf-course architect has four linden trees, five white birch trees, and two bald cypress trees to plant in a row along a fairway. In how many ways can the landscaper plant the trees in a row, assuming that the trees are evenly spaced? 6930

54. **Starting Lineup** A baseball team consists of three outfielders, four infielders, a pitcher, and a catcher. Assuming that the outfielders and infielders are indistinguishable, how many batting orders are possible? 2520

55. **Little Lotto** In the Illinois Lottery game "Little Lotto," an urn contains balls numbered 1–30. From this urn, 5 balls are chosen randomly, without replacement. For a $1 bet, a player chooses one set of 5 numbers. In order to win, all five numbers must match those chosen from the urn. The order in which the balls are selected does not matter. What is the probability of winning Little Lotto with one ticket? 1/142,506

56. **The Big Game** In the Big Game, an urn contains balls numbered 1–50, and a second urn contains balls numbered 1–36. From the first urn, 5 balls are chosen randomly, without replacement. From the second urn, 1 ball is chosen randomly. For a $1 bet, a player chooses one set of 5 numbers to match the balls selected from the first urn and one number to match the ball selected from the second urn. In order to win, all 6 numbers must match, that is, the player must match the first 5 balls selected from the first urn *and* the single ball selected from the second urn. What is the probability of winning the Big Game with a single ticket? $1/(_{50}C_5 \cdot 36)$

57. **Selecting a Jury** The grade appeal process at a university (NW) requires that a jury be structured by selecting five individuals randomly from a pool of eight students and ten faculty.
   (a) What is the probability of selecting a jury of all students? 56/8568
   (b) What is the probability of selecting a jury of all faculty? 252/8568
   (c) What is the probability of selecting a jury of two students and three faculty? 3360/8568

58. **Selecting a Committee** Suppose there are 55 Democrats and 45 Republicans in the United States Senate. A committee of seven senators is to be formed by selecting members of the Senate randomly.
   (a) What is the probability that the committee is composed of all Democrats? 0.0127
   (b) What is the probability that the committee is composed of all Republicans? 0.0028
   (c) What is the probability that the committee is composed of three Democrats and four Republicans? 0.2442

59. **Acceptance Sampling** Suppose a shipment of 120 electronic components contains 4 defective components. In order to determine whether the shipment should be accepted, a quality-control engineer randomly selects 4 of the components and tests them. If 1 or more of the components is defective, the shipment is rejected. What is the probability the shipment is rejected? 0.1283

60. **In the Dark** A box containing twelve 40-watt lightbulbs and eighteen 60-watt lightbulbs is stored in your basement. Unfortunately, the box is stored in the dark and you need two 60-watt bulbs. What is the probability, of randomly selecting two 60-watt bulbs from the box? 0.3517

61. **Randomly Playing Songs** Suppose a compact disk (CD) you just purchased has 13 tracks. After listening to the CD, you decide that you like 5 of the songs. The random feature on your CD player will play each of the 13 songs once in a random order. Find the probability that, among the first 4 songs played,
   (a) you like 2 of them; 0.3916
   (b) you like 3 of them; 0.1119
   (c) you like all 4 of them. 0.007

62. **Packaging Error** Through a manufacturing error, three cans marked "regular soda" were accidentally filled with diet soda and placed into a 12-pack. Suppose that three cans are randomly selected from the 12-pack.
   (a) Determine the probability that exactly two contain diet soda. 0.1227
   (b) Determine the probability that exactly one contains diet soda. 0.4909
   (c) Determine the probability that all three contain diet soda. 0.0045

63. **Three of a Kind** Suppose you are dealt 5 cards from a standard 52-card deck. Determine the probability of

being dealt three of a kind (i.e., three aces, three kings, etc.) by answering the following questions:

(a) How many ways can 5 cards be selected from a 52-card deck? *2,598,960*

(b) Each deck contains 4 two's, 4 three's, and so on. How many ways can three of the same card be selected from the deck? *52*

(c) The remaining 2 cards must be different from the 3 chosen and from each other. For example, if we drew three kings, the 4th card cannot be a king. After selecting the three of a kind, there are 12 of the same rank of card remaining in the deck that can be chosen. For example, if we have three aces, then we can choose two's, three's, and so on. Of the 12 ranks remaining, we choose 2 of them and there are 4 cards in each rank. How many ways can we select the remaining 2 cards? $66 \cdot 4 \cdot 4 = 1056$

(d) Use the Multiplication Rule to compute the probability of obtaining three of a kind. That is, what is the probability of selecting three of a kind and two cards that are not like? *0.0211*

64. **Two of a Kind** Follow the outline presented in Problem 63 to determine the probability of being dealt exactly a pair. *0.4226*

65. **Acceptance Sampling** Suppose you have just received a shipment of 20 modems. Although you don't know this, 3 of the modems are defective. To determine whether you will accept the shipment, you randomly select 4 modems and test them. If all 4 modems work, you accept the shipment; otherwise, the shipment is rejected. What is the probability of accepting the shipment? *0.4912*

66. **Acceptance Sampling** Suppose you have just received a shipment of 100 televisions. Although you don't know this, 6 are defective. To determine whether you will accept the shipment, you randomly select 5 televisions and test them. If all 5 televisions work, you accept the shipment; otherwise, the shipment is rejected. What is the probability of accepting the shipment? *0.7291*

Technology Step-by-Step
Factorials, Permutations, and Combinations

TI-83 Plus   **Factorials**

Step 1: To compute 7!, type 7 on the HOME screen.

Step 2: Press MATH, then highlight PRB, and then highlight 4 : ! Press ENTER. With 4! on the HOME screen, press ENTER again.

Permutations and Combinations

Step 1: To compute $_7P_3$, type 7 on the HOME screen.

Step 2: Press MATH, then highlight PRB, and then highlight $2 :_n P_r$ and press ENTER.

Step 3: Type 3 on the HOME screen, and press ENTER. NOTE: To compute $_7C_3$, select $3 :_n C_r$ instead of $2 :_n P_r$.

Excel   To do combinations or factorials, select the *fx* button. Highlight Math & Trig in the Function category. Select FACT in the function name to obtain a factorial, and fill in the appropriate cells. Select COMBIN in the function name to obtain a combination, and fill in the appropriate cells. To do permutations, select the *fx* button. Highlight Statistical in the Function category. Select PERMUT in the function name, and fill in the appropriate cells.

CHAPTER 5 REVIEW

Summary

In this chapter, we introduced the concept of probability. Probability is a measure of the likelihood of a random phenomenon or chance behavior. Because we are measuring a random phenomenon, there is short-term uncertainty. However, this short-term uncertainty gives rise to long-term predictability.

Probabilities are numbers between zero and one, inclusive. The closer a probability is to one, the more likely the event is to occur. If an event has a probability zero, it is said to be impossible; events with a probability one are said to be certain.

We introduced three methods for computing probabilities: (1) the classical method, (2) the empirical (or relative frequency) method, and (3) subjective probabilities. Classical probabilities require the events in the experiment to be equally likely. We count the number of ways an event can occur and divide this by the number of possible outcomes of the experiment. Empirical probabilities rely on the relative frequency with which an event occurs. Therefore, empirical probabilities actually require that an experiment be performed, whereas classical probability does not. Subjective probabilities are probabilities based upon the opinion of the individual providing the probability. They are simply educated guesses about the likelihood of an event's occurring.

Compound probabilities are probabilities in which we are interested in the occurrence of multiple events. For example, we might be interested in the probability that either event E or event F happens. The Addition Rule is used to compute the probability of E or F; the Multiplication Rule is used to compute the probability of both E and F. Two events are mutually exclusive if they do not have any simple events in common. Two events E and F are independent if the probability of event E occurring does not change if event F is known to have occurred. The complement of an event E, denoted $\overline{E}$, is all the simple events in the sample space that are not in E.

Finally, we introduced counting methods. The Multiplication Rule is used to count the number of ways a sequence of events can occur. Permutations are used to count the number of ways r distinct items can be arranged from a set of n items without replacement. Combinations are used to count the number of ways r distinct items can be selected from a set of n items without replacement and without regard to order. These counting techniques can be used to calculate probabilities via the classical method.

Formulas

Classical Probability

$$P(E) = \frac{\text{number of ways that } E \text{ can occur}}{\text{number of possible outcomes}} = \frac{N(E)}{N(S)}$$

Empirical Probability

$$P(E) \approx \frac{\text{frequency of } E}{\text{number of trials of experiment}}$$

Addition Rule
$$P(E \text{ or } F) = P(E) + P(F) - P(E \text{ and } F)$$

Addition Rule for Mutually Exclusive Events
$$P(E \text{ or } F) = P(E) + P(F)$$

Probabilities of Complements
$$P(\overline{E}) = 1 - P(E)$$

Multiplication Rule
$$P(E \text{ and } F) = P(E) \cdot P(F|E)$$

Multiplication Rule for Independent Events
$$P(E \text{ and } F) = P(E) \cdot P(F)$$

Multiplication Rule for n Independent Events
$$P(E \text{ and } F \text{ and } G \cdots) = P(E) \cdot P(F) \cdot P(G) \cdot \ldots$$

Conditional Probability Rule

$$P(F|E) = \frac{P(E \text{ and } F)}{P(E)} = \frac{N(E \text{ and } F)}{N(E)}$$

Factorial
$$n! = n \cdot (n - 1) \cdot (n - 2) \cdot \ldots \cdot 3 \cdot 2 \cdot 1$$

Permutation
$$_nP_r = \frac{n!}{(n - r)!}$$

Combination
$$_nC_r = \frac{n!}{r!(n - r)!}$$

Permutations with Repetition
$$\frac{n!}{n_1! \cdot n_2! \cdot \ldots \cdot n_k!}$$

Vocabulary

Probability (p. 260)
Outcome (p. 260)
Experiment (p. 261)
Simple event (p. 261)
Sample space (p. 261)
Event (p. 261)
Probability of an event (p. 262)
Impossible (p. 262)
Certainty (p. 262)

Unusual event (p. 263)
Equally likely outcomes (p. 263)
Classical probability (p. 264)
Empirical probability (p. 266)
Tree diagram (p. 267)
Subjective probability (p. 270)
Compound probability (p. 275)
Venn diagram (p. 276)
Disjoint (p. 276)

Mutually exclusive (p. 276)
Complement (p. 279)
Conditional probability (p. 287)
Independent (p. 288)
Dependent (p. 288)
Factorial (p. 304)
Permutation (p. 304)
Combination (p. 306)

Objectives

Section	You should be able to ...	Review Exercises
5.1	1 Understand the properties of probabilities (p. 262)	1, 13(d), 19(e)
	2 Compute and interpret probabilities using the classical method (p. 263)	2–4, 13(a), 14
	3 Compute and interpret probabilities using the empirical method (p. 265)	15(a), 16, 17(a) and (b), 18(a) and (b), 19(a) and (b), 20(a) and (b)
	4 Use simulation to obtain probabilities (p. 268)	34
	5 Understand subjective probabilities (p. 270)	35
5.2	1 Use the Addition Rule (p. 275)	6, 7, 13(a)–(c), 17(c), 18(d), 19(d), 20(d)
	2 Compute the probability of an event using complements (p. 279)	5, 15(b), 16
5.3	1 Compute probabilities using the Multiplication Rule (p. 285)	11, 15(c), 23, 24
	2 Compute probabilities using the Multiplication Rule for Independent Events (p. 289)	8, 9, 21(a) and (b), 22(a) and (b)
	3 Compute "at least" probabilities (p. 292)	15(d), 17(d), 21(c), 22(c)
5.4	1 Compute conditional probabilities (p. 296)	11, 18(e), 18(f), 19(f)
	2 Use the Multiplication Rule to check for independent events (p. 298)	18(h), 19(g), 21(a) and (b), 22(a) and (b)
5.5	1 Solve counting problems using the Multiplication Principle (p. 301)	25, 27
	2 Solve counting problems using permutations (p. 304)	26
	3 Solve counting problems using combinations (p. 306)	29, 30
	4 Solve counting problems using permutations with repetition (p. 308)	28
	5 Compute probabilities involving permutations and combinations (p. 309)	31–33

Review Exercises

1. (a) Which among the following numbers could be the probability of an event? *0, 0.75, 0.41*

$$0, -0.01, 0.75, 0.41, 1.34$$

(b) Which among the following numbers could be the probability of an event? *2/5, 1/3, 6/7*

$$2/5, 1/3, -4/7, 4/3, 6/7$$

For Problems 2–5, let the sample space be $S = \{$red, green, blue, orange, yellow$\}$. Suppose the simple events are equally likely.

2. Compute the probability of the event $E = \{$yellow$\}$. *1/5*

3. Compute the probability of the event $F = \{$green or orange$\}$. *2/5*

4. Compute the probability of the event $E = \{$red or blue or yellow$\}$. *3/5*

5. Suppose that $E = \{$yellow$\}$. Compute the probability of $\overline{E}$. *4/5*

6. Suppose that $P(E) = 0.76$, $P(F) = 0.45$, and $P(E$ and $F) = 0.32$. What is $P(E$ or $F)$? *0.89*

7. Suppose that $P(E) = 0.36$, $P(F) = 0.12$, and E and F are mutually exclusive. What is $P(E$ or $F)$? *0.48*

8. Suppose that events E and F are independent. In addition, $P(E) = 0.45$ and $P(F) = 0.2$. What is $P(E$ and $F)$? *0.09*

9. Suppose that $P(E) = 0.8$, $P(F) = 0.5$, and $P(E$ and $F) = 0.24$. Are events E and F independent? Why? *No*

10. Suppose that $P(E) = 0.59$ and $P(F|E) = 0.45$. What is $P(E$ and $F)$? *0.2655*

11. Suppose that $P(E \text{ and } F) = 0.35$ and $P(F) = 0.7$. What is $P(E|F)$? *0.5*

12. Determine the value of each of the following:
(a) 7! *5040*   (d) $_{10}C_3$ *120*
(b) 0! *1*   (e) $_9P_2$ *72*
(c) $_9C_4$ *126*   (f) $_{12}P_4$ *11,880*

13. Roulette In the game of roulette, a wheel consists of 38 slots, numbered $0, 00, 1, 2, \ldots, 36$. (See the photo in Problem 13 from Section 5.1.) To play the game, a metal ball is spun around the wheel and is allowed to fall into one of the numbered slots. The slots numbered 0 and 00 are green, the odd numbers are red, and the even numbers are black.   *(d) 0; impossible*
(a) Determine the probability that the metal ball falls into a "green" slot. Interpret this probability. *1/19*
(b) Determine the probability that the metal ball falls into a "green" or a "red" slot. Interpret this probability. *10/19*
(c) Determine the probability that the metal ball falls into 00 or a "red" slot. Interpret this probability. *19/38*
(d) Determine the probability that the metal ball falls into the number 31 and a "black" slot simultaneously. What term is used to describe this event?

14. Craps Craps is a dice game in which two fair dice are cast. If the roller shoots a "7" or "11" on the first roll, he or she wins. If the roller shoots a "2," "3," or "12" on the first roll, he or she loses.
(a) Compute the probability that the shooter wins on the first roll. Interpret this probability. *2/9*
(b) Compute the probability that the shooter loses on the first roll. Interpret this probability. *1/9*

15. New Year's Eve and Day There were 192 total traffic fatalities between 6:00 P.M. on Dec. 31, 1996 and 5:59 A.M. on Jan. 1, 1997. Of these 192 fatalities, 129 were alcohol related.
(a) What is the probability that a randomly selected traffic fatality that occurred between 6:00 P.M. on Dec. 31, 1996 and 5:59 A.M. on Jan. 1, 1997 was alcohol related? *129/192*
(b) What is the probability that a randomly selected traffic fatality that occurred between 6:00 P.M. on Dec. 31, 1996 and 5:59 A.M. on Jan. 1, 1997 was not alcohol related? *21/64*
(c) What is the probability that two randomly selected traffic fatalities that occurred between 6:00 P.M. on Dec. 31, 1996 and 5:59 A.M. on Jan. 1, 1997 were both alcohol related? *0.45*
(d) What is the probability that, of a two randomly selected traffic fatalities that occurred between 6:00 P.M. on Dec. 31, 1996 and 5:59 A.M. on Jan. 1, 1997, at least one was alcohol related? *0.893*

16. Cyclones According to the National Hurricane Center, about 11% of tropical cyclones occur in the North Atlantic Ocean. What is the probability that a randomly se-

lected cyclone occurs in the North Atlantic Ocean? What is the probability that a randomly selected cyclone does not occur in the North Atlantic Ocean? *0.11; 0.89*

17. October in Chicago The following data represent the distribution of daily high temperatures in Chicago in October from 1872 to 1999:

Temperature	Frequency
20–29	4
30–39	40
40–49	436
50–59	1190
60–69	1270
70–79	794
80–89	238
90–99	8

Source: Chicago Tribune

(a) What is the probability that a randomly selected October day from 1872 to 1999 in Chicago has a high in the 80s? *0.0598*
(b) What is the probability that a randomly selected October day from 1872 to 1999 in Chicago has a high in the 20s? Is it unusual to have a high temperature in the 20s in October in Chicago? *0.001; yes*
(c) What is the probability that a randomly selected October day from 1872 to 1999 in Chicago has a high in the 80s or the 90s? *0.0618*
(d) What is the probability that a randomly selected October day from 1872 to 1999 in Chicago has a high of at least 30° F? *0.999*

18. Square Footage of Housing The following data represent the square footage of housing in the United States in 1997, by geographic region:

	Region			
	North-east	Mid-west	South	West
<500 sq. ft.	82	132	356	207
500–749 sq. ft.	227	535	1127	398
750–999 sq. ft.	531	1329	2647	1079
1,000–1,499 sq. ft.	1443	3386	7045	3558
1,500–1,999 sq. ft.	1828	3387	5367	3488
2,000–2,499 sq. ft.	1992	2949	3281	1973
2,500–2,999 sq. ft.	1303	1758	1633	967
3,000–3,999 sq. ft.	1244	1651	1501	815
4,000 or more sq. ft.	801	890	903	429

Source: U.S. Census Bureau, Current Housing Reports, Series H150/97, American Housing Survey

(a) What is the probability that a randomly selected home in 1997 is located in the Northeast? *0.1518*

(b) What is the probability that a randomly selected home in 1997 has 2000–2499 square feet? *0.1638*

(c) What is the probability that a randomly selected home in 1997 is located in the Northeast and has 2000–2499 square feet? *0.0320*

(d) What is the probability that a randomly selected home in 1997 has 2000–2499 square feet or is located in the Northeast? *0.2836*

(e) What is the probability that a randomly selected home in 1997 has 2000–2499 square feet, given that it is located in the Northeast? *0.2108*

(f) What is the probability that a randomly selected home in 1997 located in the Midwest has 4000 square feet or more? *0.0556*

(g) What is the probability that a randomly selected home in 1997 located in the Midwest has less than 4000 square feet? *0.9444*

(h) Are the events "Midwest" and "2000–2499 square feet" independent? Why? *No*

19. **Gestation Period versus Weight** The following data represent the birth weights (in grams) of babies born in 1998, along with the period of gestation:

Birth Weight (in grams)	Period of Gestation		
	Preterm	Term	Postterm
Less than 500	2,365	6	0
500–999	7,753	45	4
1,000–1,499	7,868	387	74
1,500–1,999	12,550	2,419	239
2,000–2,499	22,395	21,103	1,440
2,500–2,999	25,941	105,757	8,303
3,000–3,499	18,503	192,488	18,259
3,500–3,999	6,722	105,325	12,045
4,000–4,499	1,137	23,615	2,992
4,500–4,999	187	3,441	507
Greater than 5,000	38	486	51

Source: National Vital Statistics Report, Vol. 48, No. 3, March 28, 2000

(a) What is the probability that a randomly selected baby born in 1998 was postterm? *0.0727*

(b) What is the probability that a randomly selected baby born in 1998 weighed 3000–3499 grams? *0.3793*

(c) What is the probability that a randomly selected baby born in 1998 weighed 3000–3499 grams and was postterm? *0.0302*

(d) What is the probability that a randomly selected baby born in 1998 weighed 3000–3499 grams or was postterm? *0.4217*

(e) What is the probability that a randomly selected baby born in 1998 weighed less than 500 grams and was postterm? Is this event impossible? *0; yes*

(f) What is the probability that a randomly selected baby born in 1998 weighed 3000–3499 grams, given the baby was postterm? *0.4158*

(g) Are the events "postterm baby" and "weighs 3000–3499 grams" independent? Why? *No*

20. **SAT Math Scores** The following data represent the scores received on the 2000 SAT I: Reasoning Test—Math, by gender:

SAT Score	Gender	
	Male	Female
200–249	3,497	5,752
250–299	7,773	13,263
300–349	20,124	35,052
350–399	37,524	62,879
400–449	65,945	102,487
450–499	87,624	121,762
500–549	93,742	112,520
550–599	91,264	94,200
600–649	73,272	64,686
650–699	53,880	38,989
700–749	31,534	17,935
750–800	17,152	7,422

Source: College Board

(a) If a test taker is randomly selected, what is the probability that the test taker is female? *0.5371*

(b) If a test taker is randomly selected, what is the probability that the test taker scored 600–649? *0.1095*

(c) If a test taker is randomly selected, what is the probability that the test taker is female and scored 600–649? *0.0513*

(d) If a test taker is randomly selected, what is the probability that the test taker either is female or scored 600–649? *0.5953*

21. **Home-Court Advantage** During the 2000 season, the Los Angeles Sparks of the WNBA won 97.5% of their home games. Assume the outcomes of basketball games are independent, and answer the following questions:

(a) What is the probability that the Sparks will win two home games in a row? *0.950625*

(b) What is the probability that the Sparks will win five home games in a row? *0.8811*

(c) What is the probability that the Sparks will lose at least one of their next five home games? *0.1189*

22. **Home Ice** During the 2000–2001 season, the Pittsburgh Penguins of the National Hockey League won about 43% of their home games. Assume that the outcomes of

the hockey games are independent, and answer the following questions:

(a) What is the probability that the Penguins will win two home games in a row? *0.1849*

(b) What is the probability that the Penguins will win seven home games in a row? *0.0027*

(c) What is the probability that the Penguins will lose at least one of their next seven home games? *0.9973*

23. **Acceptance Sampling** Suppose you just received a shipment of 10 DVD players. One of the DVD players is defective. You will accept the shipment if two randomly selected DVD players work. What is the probability that you will accept the shipment? *0.8*

24. **Drawing Cards** Suppose you draw three cards from a standard 52-card deck. What is the probability that all three cards are aces? *0.00018*

25. **Forming License Plates** A license plate is designed so that the first two characters are letters and the last four characters are digits (0 through 9). How many different license plates can be formed? *6,760,000*

26. **Choosing a Seat** If four students enter a classroom that has 10 vacant seats, in how many ways can they be seated? *5040*

27. **Jumble** In the game of Jumble, the letters of a word are scrambled. The player must form the correct word. In a recent game in a local newspaper, the Jumble "word" was LINCEY. How many different arrangements are there of the letters in this "word"? *6!*

28. **Arranging Flags** How many different vertical arrangements are there of 10 flags if 4 are white, 3 are blue, 2 are green, and 1 is red? *12,600*

29. **Simple Random Sampling** How many different simple random samples of size 8 can be obtained from a population whose size is 55? $_{55}C_8$

30. **Forming Committees** The United States Senate Appropriations Committee has 29 members. Suppose that a subcommittee is to be formed by randomly selecting 5 of the members of the Appropriations Committee. How many different committees could be formed? $_{29}C_5$

31. **Arizona's Fantasy 5** In one of Arizona's lotteries, balls are numbered 1–35. Five balls are selected randomly, without replacement. The order in which the balls are selected does not matter. To win, your numbers must match the five selected. Determine your probability of winning Arizona's Fantasy 5 with one ticket. *1/324,632*

32. **Pennsylvania's Cash 5** In one of Pennsylvania's lotteries, balls are numbered 1–39. Five balls are selected randomly, without replacement. The order in which the balls are selected does not matter. To win, your numbers must match the five selected. Determine your probability of winning Pennsylvania's Cash 5 with one ticket.

33. **Packaging Error** Because of a mistake in packaging, a case of 12 bottles of red wine contained 5 Merlot and 7 Cabernet, each without labels. All the bottles look alike and have an equal probability of being chosen. Three bottles are randomly selected.

(a) What is the probability that all 3 are Merlot? *0.0455*

(b) What is the probability that exactly 2 are Merlot?

(c) What is the probability that none is a Merlot? *0.1591*

34. **Simulation** Use a graphing calculator or statistical software to simulate the playing of the game of roulette, using the Integer Distribution with numbers 1 through 38. Repeat the simulation 100 times. Let the number 37 represent 0 and the number 38 represent 00. Use the results of the simulation to answer the following questions.

(a) What is the probability that the ball lands in the slot marked 7?

(b) What is the probability that the ball lands either in the slot marked 0 or in the one marked 00?

35. Explain what is meant by a subjective probability. List some examples of subjective probabilities.

32. 1/575,757 (33b) 0.3182

The Case of the Body in the Bag

The late spring morning broke sharply along the banks of a river. Robert Donkin, an elderly retiree with fishing pole in hand, slipped through the underbrush that lined the river's banks. As he neared the shore, he saw a rather large canvas bag floating in the water, held by the foliage that leaned over the river. The bag appeared to be stuffed, well-worn, and heavily stained. Upon closer inspection, Mr. Donkin observed what he believed to be hair floating through the bag's opening. Marking the spot of his discovery, the fisherman fetched the authorities.

Preliminary investigation at the scene revealed a body in the bag. Unfortunately, it was impossible to identify the corpse's sex or race immediately. Estimating age was also out of the question. Forensics was assigned the task of identifying the victim and estimating the cause and time of death. While waiting for the forensics analysis, you, as the detective in charge, have gathered the information shown on page 321 concerning victim/offender relationships from recent reports from the FBI.

Using the information contained in the tables, you are to develop a preliminary profile of the victim and offender by answering the following questions.

1. How likely is it that the offender is at least 18?
2. How likely is it that the offender is white?
3. How likely is it that the offender is male?
4. How likely is it that the offender is a white male?
5. How likely is it that the offender is either white or male?
6. How likely is it that the victim and the offender are from the same age category?
7. How likely is it that the victim and the offender are from different age categories?
8. How likely is it that the victim and the offender are of the same race?
9. How likely is it that the victim and the offender are of different races?
10. How likely is it that the victim and the offender are of the same sex?
11. How likely is it that the victim and the offender are of different sexes?
12. Without knowing the contents of the forensic team's report, what is your best prediction of the age, race, and sex of the victim? Explain your reasoning.
13. What is your best prediction as to the age, race, and sex of the offender? Explain your reasoning.

Soon after you finished this analysis, the preliminary forensics report was delivered to your desk. Although no identification had been made, the autopsy suggested that the cause of death was blunt-force trauma and that the body had been in the water at least two weeks. By using a variety of techniques, it was also determined that the victim was a white female with blonde hair. She was estimated as being in her mid-thirties, showed no signs of having had children, and was wearing no jewelry.

Based on this new information, you develop a new offender profile by answering the following questions.

14. How likely is it that the offender is at least 18?
15. How likely is it that the offender is white?

16. How likely is it that the offender is male?

Victim/Offender Relationship by Age

Age of Victim	Age of Offender		
	Less than 18	At Least 18	Unknown
Less than 18	148	596	32
At Least 18	310	4870	399
Unknown	2	66	11

Victim/Offender Relationship by Race

Race of Victim	Race of Offender			
	White	Black	Other	Unknown
White	2779	452	51	54
Black	154	2674	10	31
Other	34	17	127	3
Unknown	17	12	1	18

Victim/Offender Relationship by Sex

Sex of Victim	Sex of Offender		
	Male	Female	Unknown
Male	3946	497	65
Female	1659	196	23
Unknown	26	4	18

Race of Victim by Sex of Offender

Race of Victim	Sex of Offender		
	Male	Female	Unknown
White	2939	343	54
Black	2510	328	31
Other	156	22	3
Unknown	26	4	18

Sex of Victim by Race of Offender

Sex of Victim	Race of Offender			
	White	Black	Other	Unknown
Male	1929	2391	123	65
Female	1038	752	65	23
Unknown	17	12	1	18

Source: Uniform Crime Reports: Crime in the United States—1999.
This report can be found at http://www.fbi.gov/ucr/99cius.htm

17. How likely is it that the offender is a white male?
18. How likely is it that the offender is either white or male?
19. How likely is it that the victim and the offender are from the same age category?
20. How likely is it that the victim and the offender are from different age categories?
21. How likely is it that the victim and the offender are of the same race?
22. How likely is it that the victim and the offender are of different races?
23. How likely is it that the victim and the offender are of the same sex?
24. How likely is it that the victim and the offender are of different sexes?
25. What is your best prediction of the age, race, and sex of the offender? Explain your reasoning.

Did your answers to the offender questions change once you knew the age, race, and sex of the victim? Explain.

Suppose that 45% of murder victims were known to be related to or acquainted with the offender, that 15% were murdered by an unrelated stranger, and that for 40% of victims, relationship to their killer is unknown. Based on all of the information available, complete your offender profile for this case.

Have you ever watched a sporting event on television in which the announcer cites an obscure statistic? Where do these numbers come from? Well, pretend that you are the statistician for your favorite sports team. Your job is to compile strange probabilities regarding your favorite team and a competing team. For example, during the 2001 baseball season, the Boston Red Sox won 36% of the games they played on Wednesdays. As statisticians, we would represent this as a conditional probability as follows: $P(\text{win}|\text{Wednesday}) = 0.36$. Suppose that Boston was playing the Seattle Mariners on a Wednesday and that Seattle won 68% of the games that it played on Wednesdays. From these statistics, we'd predict that Seattle will win the game. Other ideas for conditional probabilities include home versus road games, day versus night games, weather, and so on. For basketball, consider conditional probabilities such as the probability of winning if the team's leading scorer scores less than 12 points.

Use the statistics and probabilities that you compile to make a prediction about which team will win. Write an article that presents your predictions along with the supporting numerical facts. Maybe the article could include such "keys to the game" as "Our crack statistician has found that our football team wins 80% of its games when it holds opposing teams to less than 10 points." Repeat this exercise for at least five games. Following each game, determine whether the team you chose has won or lost. Compute your winning percentage for the games you predicted. Did you predict the winner in more than 50% of the games?

A great source for these obscure facts can be found at http://www.sportssectiononline.com/. For baseball, a great site is http://www.mlb.com/NASApp/mlb/mlb/stats/mlb_stats_entry.jsp. For basketball, go to http://www.nba.com/. For football, go to http://www.nfl.com/. For hockey, go to http://www.nhl.com/.

DECISIONS

With so many men's and women's versions of different products, you might wonder how different they really are. To help answer this question, technicians at Consumers Union compared a new triple edge razor for women with a leading double edge razor for women and a leading triple edge razor for men (June 2000). We asked thirty women panelists to shave with the razors over a four week period, following a random statistical design.

After each shave, the panelists were asked to answer a series of questions related to the performance of the razor. One of the questions involved rating the razor on a 5-point scale, with 1 being "Poor" and 5 being "Excellent." The following table contains a summary of the results for this question.

Survey Results for Razor Study

Razor	"Poor"	"Fair" to "Good"	"Very Good" to "Excellent"
A	1	8	21
B	0	11	19
C	6	11	13

Using the information in the table, answer the following questions:

(a) Calculate the probability that a randomly selected razor scored "Very Good" to "Excellent."

(b) Calculate the probability that a randomly selected razor scored "Poor."

(c) Calculate the probability of randomly selecting "Razor B" given the score was "Fair" to "Good."

(d) Calculate the probability of receiving an "Excellent" rating given that "Razor C" was selected.

(e) Do you think that razor type and rating are independent?

(f) Which razor would you choose based on the information given? Support your decision.

Note to Readers: In many cases, our test protocol and analytical methods are more complicated than described in these examples. The data and discussions have been modified to make the material more appropriate for the audience.

Putting It All Together

Chapter 5 presented methods for determining probabilities of an event. We introduced two ways of assigning a probability to an event: (1) the classical method and (2) the empirical method. The classical method uses counting techniques and equally likely outcomes to determine probabilities, while the empirical method requires that the probability experiment actually be conducted. We then approximate the probability by dividing the number of times we observed the event by the number of times the experiment was conducted.

In this chapter, we introduce the concept of a *random variable* and *discrete probability distributions*. In Section 6.1, we discuss the properties of discrete probability distributions. Sections 6.2 and 6.3 present two specific discrete probability distributions: the binomial probability distribution and the Poisson probability distribution.

Discrete Probability Distributions

Outline

 For additional study help, go to
www.prenhall.com/sullivanstats

Materials include

- Self-Graded Quizzes
- "Preparing for This Section" Quizzes
- STATLETs
- PowerPoint Downloads
- Step-by-Step Technology Guide
- Graphing Calculator Help

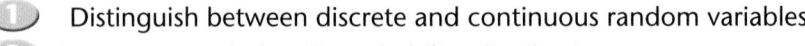

6.1   Probability Distributions

Preparing for This Section   Before getting started, review the following:

✓ Discrete versus continuous variables (Section 1.2, pp. 7–8)

✓ Relative frequency histograms for discrete data (Section 2.2, pp. 68–69)

✓ Mean (Section 3.1, pp. 113–115)

✓ Standard deviation (Section 3.2, pp. 137–138)

✓ Mean from grouped data (Section 3.3, pp. 150–152)

✓ Standard deviation from grouped data (Section 3.3, pp. 153–154)

Objectives   ① Distinguish between discrete and continuous random variables

② Construct and identify probability distributions

③ Construct probability histograms

④ Compute and interpret the mean of a discrete random variable

⑤ Compute the variance and standard deviation of a discrete random variable

⑥ Compute and interpret the expected value of a discrete random variable

① **Random Variables**

In Chapter 5, we presented the concept of an experiment and the outcomes of an experiment. When experiments are conducted in a way such that the outcome is a numerical result, we say the outcome is a *random variable*.

Definition   A **random variable** is a numerical measure of the outcome of a probability experiment, so its value is determined by chance. Random variables are denoted using letters such as X.

We will follow the practice of using a capital letter to identify the random variable and a small letter to list the possible values of the random variable, that is, the sample space of the experiment. For example, if an experiment is conducted in which a single die is cast, then X represents the number of pips showing on the die and the possible values of X are $x = 1, 2, 3, 4, 5$, or 6. As another example, suppose an experiment is conducted in which the time between arrivals of cars at a drive through is measured. The random variable T might describe the time between arrivals, so the sample space of the experiment is $t > 0$.

There are two types of random variables, *discrete* and *continuous*.

Definitions   A **discrete random variable** is a random variable that has either a finite number of possible values or a countable number of possible values.

A **continuous random variable** is a random variable that has an infinite number of possible values that is not countable.

▶ EXAMPLE 1   **Distinguishing between Discrete and Continuous Random Variables**

(a) The number of *A*s earned in a section of statistics with 15 students enrolled is a discrete random variable because the value of the random

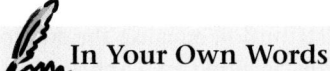

In Your Own Words

Discrete random variables typically result from counting, such as 0, 1, 2, 3, and so on. Continuous random variables are variables that result from measurement.

variable results from counting. If we let the random variable X represent the number of As, then the possible values of X are $x = 0, 1, 2, \ldots, 15$.

(b) The number of cars that travel through McDonald's drive-through in the next hour is a discrete random variable because the value of the random variable results from counting. If we let the random variable X represent the number of cars through the drive-through in the next hour, then the possible values of X are $x = 0, 1, 2, \ldots$.

(c) The speed of the next car that passes a state trooper is a continuous random variable because speed is measured. If we let the random variable S represent the speed of the next car, then the possible values of S are all positive real numbers; that is, $s > 0$. ◀◀

 Now Work Problem 1.

② ## Probability Distributions

Because the value of a random variable is determined by chance, there are probabilities that correspond to the possible values of the random variable.

Definition

> The **probability distribution** of a random variable X provides the possible values of the random variable and their corresponding probabilities. A probability distribution can be in the form of a table, graph, or mathematical formula.

▶ **EXAMPLE 2** ### A Discrete Probability Distribution

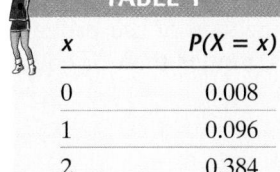

TABLE 1

x	$P(X = x)$
0	0.008
1	0.096
2	0.384
3	0.512

Suppose a basketball player historically makes 80% of her free throw attempts and free throw attempts are independent. Table 1 is a probability distribution for the random variable X, where X represents the number of successful attempts in three shots. We will present methods for constructing probability distributions such as the one shown in Table 1 in Section 6.2. ◀◀

From the probability distribution in Table 1, we can see that the probability the player makes all three free throw attempts is $0.512 = 51.2\%$. We shall follow the practice of denoting probabilities using the notation $P(X = x)$, where x is a specific value of the random variable. We read $P(X = x)$ as "the probability that the random variable X equals x." So $P(X = 3) = 0.512$ is read "the probability that the random variable X equals three is 0.512." It is important to recognize that the probabilities listed in Table 1 are theoretical probabilities. For example, *if* the player historically makes 80% of her free throws and outcomes from free throw shooting are independent, *then* we would expect her to make all three free throws about $(0.8)(0.8)(0.8) = 0.512 = 51.2\%$ of the time. If we performed this experiment 100 times and the player made all three free throws 70 times, we might conclude that the player has done something to improve her free throw shooting.

A probability distribution must satisfy some key requirements.

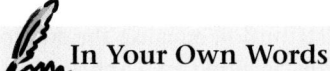

In Your Own Words

In the requirements for a discrete probability distribution, the first requirement states that the sum of the probabilities must equal 1. The second requirement states that each probability must be greater than or equal to 0 and less than or equal to 1.

Requirements for a Discrete Probability Distribution

Let $P(X = x)$ denote the probability the random variable X equals x, then

1. $\sum P(X = x) = 1$

2. $0 \leq P(X = x) \leq 1$

Table 1 from Example 2 is a probability distribution because the sum of the probabilities equals one and each probability is between 0 and 1, inclusive. The reader is encouraged to verify this.

▶ **EXAMPLE 3** **Identifying Probability Distributions**

Problem: Which of the following is a probability distribution?

(a)

x	P(X = x)
1	0.20
2	0.35
3	0.12
4	0.40
5	−0.07

(b)

x	P(X = x)
1	0.20
2	0.25
3	0.10
4	0.14
5	0.49

(c)

x	P(X = x)
1	0.20
2	0.25
3	0.10
4	0.14
5	0.31

Approach: In a probability distribution, the sum of the probabilities must equal one and all probabilities must be greater than or equal to 0 and less than or equal to 1. We will verify these requirements for (a)–(c).

Solution:

(a) This is not a probability distribution because $P(X = 5) = -0.07$, which is less than 0.

(b) This is not a probability distribution because

$$\sum P(X = x) = 0.2 + 0.25 + 0.10 + 0.14 + 0.49 = 1.18 \neq 1$$

(c) This is a probability distribution because the sum of the probabilities equals one and each of the probabilities is greater than or equal to 0 and less than or equal to 1. ◀◀

NW *Now Work Problem 3.*

Table 1 is a probability distribution in table form. Probability distributions can also be represented through graphs or mathematical formulas. We will present probability distributions using graphs now and postpone discussing probability distributions as mathematical formulas until the next section.

③ A graphical depiction of a probability distribution is typically done through a *probability histogram*.

Definition   A **probability histogram** is a histogram in which the horizontal axis corresponds to the value of the random variable and the vertical axis represents the probability of that value of the random variable.

▶ **EXAMPLE 4** **Constructing a Probability Histogram**

Problem: Construct a probability histogram of the probability distribution given in Table 1 from Example 2.

Approach: Probability histograms are constructed like relative frequency histograms, except that the vertical axis represents the probability of a value of the random variable rather than its relative frequency. Each rectangle is centered at the value of the discrete random variable.

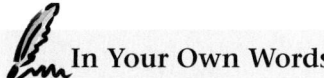

In Your Own Words

A probability histogram is constructed the same way as a relative frequency histogram for discrete data. The only difference is that the vertical axis is a probability rather than a relative frequency.

Note to Instructor
Emphasize the relation between area and probability in probability histograms as a prelude to continuous probabilities.

Solution: Figure 1 presents the probability histogram.

Figure 1

Notice that the area of each rectangle in the probability histogram equals the probability that the random variable assumes the particular value. For example, the area of the rectangle corresponding to the random variable $X = 1$ is $1 \cdot 0.096 = 0.096$ where 1 represents the width of the rectangle and 0.096 represents its height.

Probability histograms help us to determine the shape of the distribution. Recall, we describe distributions as skewed left, skewed right or symmetric. For example, the probability histogram presented in Figure 1 is skewed left.

 Now Work Problem 13(a) and (b).

Mean of a Discrete Random Variable

Remember, when we describe the distribution of a variable, we describe its center, spread, and shape. We now introduce methods for identifying the center and spread of a discrete random variable. We will use the mean to describe the center of a random variable. The variance and standard deviation are used to describe the spread of a random variable.

To help see where the formula for computing the mean of a discrete random variable comes from, consider the following. One semester I had a small statistics class of 10 students. I asked them the age of their car and obtained the following:

$$2, 4, 6, 6, 4, 4, 2, 3, 5, 5$$

What is the mean age of the 10 cars? To answer this question, we let the random variable X represent the age of a car and obtain the probability distribution in Table 2.

TABLE 2	
x	$P(X = x)$
2	2/10 = 0.2
3	1/10 = 0.1
4	3/10 = 0.3
5	2/10 = 0.2
6	2/10 = 0.2

Now, we compute the mean as follows:

$$\mu = \frac{\sum x_i}{N} = \frac{2 + 4 + 6 + 6 + 4 + 4 + 2 + 3 + 5 + 5}{10}$$

$$= \frac{\overbrace{2+2}^{2} + \overbrace{3}^{1} + \overbrace{4+4+4}^{3} + \overbrace{5+5}^{2} + \overbrace{6+6}^{2}}{10}$$

$$= \frac{2 \cdot 2 + 3 \cdot 1 + 4 \cdot 3 + 5 \cdot 2 + 6 \cdot 2}{10}$$

$$= 2 \cdot \frac{2}{10} + 3 \cdot \frac{1}{10} + 4 \cdot \frac{3}{10} + 5 \cdot \frac{2}{10} + 6 \cdot \frac{2}{10}$$

$$= 2 \cdot P(X = 2) + 3 \cdot P(X = 3) + 4 \cdot P(X = 4) + 5 \cdot P(X = 5) + 6 \cdot P(X = 6)$$

$$= 2(0.2) + 3(0.1) + 4(0.3) + 5(0.2) + 6(0.2)$$

$$= 4.1$$

Note to Instructor
Point out to students that 4.1 is not a possible value of the random variable; it just represents the mean age of all the cars in the population.

Based upon the preceding computations, we conclude that the mean of a discrete probability distribution is found by multiplying each possible value of the random variable by its corresponding probability and adding these products.

Theorem

The Mean of a Discrete Random Variable

The mean of a discrete random variable is given by the formula

$$\mu_X = \sum [x \cdot P(X = x)] \qquad (1)$$

where x is the value of the random variable and $P(X = x)$ is the probability of observing the random variable x.

In Your Own Words

To find the mean of a discrete random variable, multiply the value of each random variable by its probability. Then add up these products.

▶ **EXAMPLE 5** **Computing the Mean of a Discrete Random Variable**

Problem: Compute the mean of the discrete random variable given in Table 1 from Example 2.

Approach: The mean of a discrete random variable is found by multiplying each value of the random variable by its probability and adding up these products.

TABLE 3		
x	$P(X = x)$	$x \cdot P(X = x)$
0	0.008	$0 \cdot 0.008 = 0$
1	0.096	$1 \cdot 0.096 = 0.096$
2	0.384	0.768
3	0.512	1.536

Solution: Refer to Table 3. The first two columns represent the discrete probability distribution. The third column represents $x \cdot P(X = x)$.

We substitute into Formula (1) to find the mean number of free throws made.

$$\mu_X = \sum [x \cdot P(X = x)] = 0(0.008) + 1(0.096) + 2(0.384) + 3(0.512) = 2.4^*$$

---

*We will follow the practice of rounding the mean, variance, and standard deviation to one more decimal place than the random variable.

Interpretation of the Mean of a Discrete Random Variable

The mean of a discrete random variable can be thought of as the arithmetic mean outcome of the probability experiment if we repeated the experiment many times. Consider the result of Example 5. If we repeated the experiment of shooting three free throws many times and recorded the number of made free throws, we would expect the average number of made free throws to be around 2.4.

Interpretation of the Mean of a Discrete Random Variable

Suppose an experiment is repeated n independent times and the value of the random variable X is recorded. As the number of repetitions of the experiment, n, increases, the arithmetic mean value of the n trials will approach μ_X, the mean of the random variable X. In other words, let x_1 be the value of the random variable X after the first experiment, x_2 be the value of the random variable X after the second experiment, and so on. Then

$$\overline{X} = \frac{x_1 + x_2 + \cdots + x_n}{n}$$

The difference between $\overline{X}$ and μ_X will get closer to 0 as n increases.

► **EXAMPLE 6** **Illustrating the Interpretation of the Mean of a Discrete Random Variable**

Problem: A basketball player historically makes 80% of her free throws. She is asked to shoot three free throws 100 times. Compute the mean number of free throws made.

Approach: The player shoots three free throws and the number made is recorded. We repeat this experiment 99 more times, then compute the mean number of free throws made.

Solution: The results are presented in Table 4.

TABLE 4									
3	3	2	3	3	3	1	2	3	2
2	3	3	1	2	2	2	2	2	3
3	3	2	2	3	2	3	2	2	2
3	3	2	3	2	3	3	2	3	1
3	2	2	2	2	0	2	3	1	2
3	3	2	3	2	3	2	1	3	2
2	3	3	3	1	3	3	1	3	3
3	2	2	1	3	2	2	2	3	2
3	2	2	2	3	3	2	2	3	3
2	3	2	1	2	3	3	2	3	3

The first time the experiment was conducted, the player made all three free throws. The second time the experiment was conducted, the player made two out of three free throws. The mean number of free throws made was

$$\overline{X} = \frac{3 + 2 + 3 + \cdots + 3}{100} = 2.35$$

This is close to the mean of 2.4. As the number of repetitions of the experiment increases, we would expect $\overline{X}$ to get even closer to 2.4. ◀◀

Figure 2(a) and Figure 2(b) further demonstrate the interpretation of the mean of a discrete random variable. Figure 2(a) shows the mean number of free throws made versus the number of repetitions of the experiment for the data in Table 4. Figure 2(b) shows the mean number of free throws made versus the number of repetitions of the experiment when the same experiment of shooting three free throws 100 times is conducted a second time. In both plots the player starts off "hot" since the mean number of made free throws is above the theoretical level of 2.4. However, both graphs approach the theoretical mean of 2.4 as the number of repetitions of the experiment increases.

Figure 2

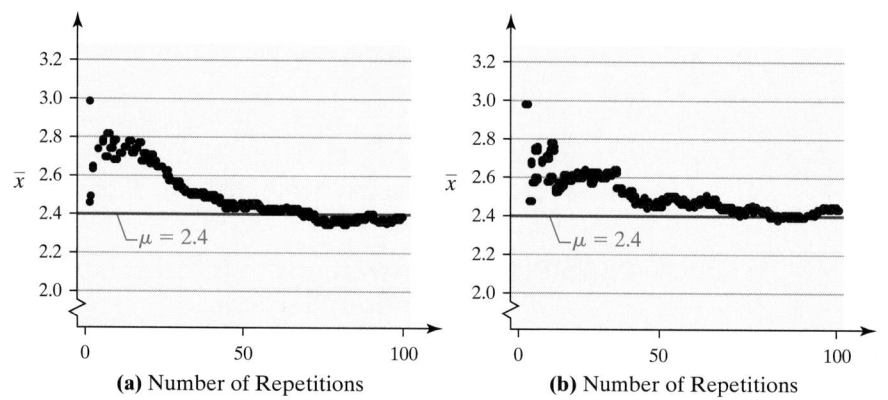

(a) Number of Repetitions (b) Number of Repetitions

NW *Now Work Problem 13(c).*

⑤ **The Variance and Standard Deviation of a Discrete Random Variable**

We now introduce a method for computing the variance and standard deviation of a discrete random variable.

Theorem

Variance and Standard Deviation of a Discrete Random Variable

The variance of a discrete random variable is given by

$$\sigma_X^2 = \sum [(x - \mu_X)^2 \cdot P(X = x)] \tag{2}$$

where x is the value of the random variable, μ_X is the mean of the random variable, and $P(X = x)$ is the probability of observing the random variable x.

To find the standard deviation of the discrete random variable, take the square root of the variance. That is, $\sigma_X = \sqrt{\sigma_X^2}$.

▶ **EXAMPLE 7** **Computing the Variance and Standard Deviation of a Discrete Random Variable**

Problem: Find the variance and standard deviation of the discrete random variable given in Table 1 from Example 2.

Approach: We know from Example 5 that $\mu_X = 2.4$. We use Formula (2).

Solution: Refer to Table 5. The first two columns represent the discrete probability distribution. The third column represents $(x - \mu_X)^2 \cdot P(X = x)$. We sum the entries in the third column.

	TABLE 5	
x	$P(X = x)$	$(x - \mu_X)^2 \cdot P(X = x)$
0	0.008	$(0 - 2.4)^2 \cdot 0.008 = 0.04608$
1	0.096	$(1 - 2.4)^2 \cdot 0.096 = 0.18816$
2	0.384	$(2 - 2.4)^2 \cdot 0.384 = 0.06144$
3	0.512	$(3 - 2.4)^2 \cdot 0.512 = 0.18432$

$$\sum(x - \mu)^2 \cdot P(X = x) = 0.48$$

The variance of the discrete random variable X is

$$\sigma_X^2 = \sum(x - \mu_X)^2 \cdot P(X = x) = 0.48^*$$

The standard deviation of the discrete random variable is found by taking the square root of the variance.

$$\sigma_X = \sqrt{\sigma_X^2} = \sqrt{0.48} = 0.692820323 \approx 0.7 \quad \blacktriangleleft\blacktriangleleft$$

The larger the standard deviation of the random variable, the more dispersed the observed values of the random variable are from the mean.

Figure 3

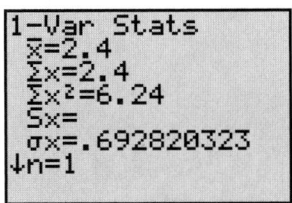

Using Technology: Graphing calculators with advanced statistical features have the ability to compute the mean and standard deviation of a discrete random variable. Figure 3 shows the results of Examples 5 and 7 using a TI-83 Plus graphing calculator.

NW *Now Work Problems 13(d) and 13(e).*

Note to Instructor
You might want to mention that expected value plays a role in game theory. For example, a negative sum game has an expected value that is negative.

6 Expected Value

The mean of a random variable is the long-run average outcome of the experiment. In this sense, as the number of trials of the experiment increases, the average result of the experiment gets closer to the mean of the random variable. For this reason, the mean of a random variable is often called the *expected value.*

Theorem

Expected Value

The **expected value** of a discrete random variable X, denoted $E(X)$, is obtained using the formula

$$E(X) = \sum[x \cdot P(X = x)]. \quad \text{(3)}$$

In Your Own Words

The expected value of a discrete random variable is the mean of the discrete random variable.

---

*If necessary, use the unrounded value of the mean in the computation of the variance in order to avoid rounding errors.

The interpretation of expected value is the same as the interpretation of the mean of a discrete random variable.

▶ **EXAMPLE 8**   **Finding the Expected Value**

Historical Note

Christiaan Huygens was born on April 14, 1629, into an influential Dutch family. He studied law and mathematics at the University of Leiden from 1645 to 1647. From 1647 to 1649, he continued to study law and mathematics at the College of Orange at Breda. Among his many great discoveries, Huygens discovered the first moon of Saturn in 1655. The following year, he discovered the shape of the rings of Saturn. While in Paris sharing his discoveries, he learned about probability through the correspondence of Fermat and Pascal. In 1657, Huygens published *De ratiociniis in ludi aleae (On Reasoning in Games of Chance)*, the first published book on probability theory. In that text, Huygens introduced the idea of mathematical expectation.

Problem: A term life insurance policy will pay a beneficiary a certain sum of money upon the death of the policyholder. These policies have premiums that must be paid annually. Suppose a life insurance company sells a $250,000 one-year term life insurance policy to a 20-year-old male for $350. According to the National Vital Statistics Report, Vol. 47, No. 28, the probability the male will survive the year is 0.99865. Compute the expected value of this policy to the insurance company.

Approach: There are two possible outcomes to the experiment: survival or death. Let the random variable X represent the "payout" (money lost or gained), depending upon survival or death of the insured. We assign probabilities to each of these random variables and substitute these values into Formula (3).

Solution:

Step 1: We have $P(\text{survives}) = 0.99865$, so that $P(\text{dies}) = 0.00135$. From the point of view of the insurance company, if the client survives the year, the insurance company makes $350. Therefore, we let $x = \$350$ if the client survives the year. If the client dies during the year, the insurance company must pay $250,000 to the client's beneficiary; however, the company still keeps the $350, so we let $x = \$350 - \$250,000 = -\$249,650$. The value is negative because it is money paid out by the insurance company. We have the probability distribution listed in Table 6.

TABLE 6	
x	*P(X = x)*
$350 (survives)	0.99865
−$249,650 (dies)	0.00135

Step 2: Substituting into Formula (3), we obtain the expected value (from the point of view of the insurance company) of the policy.

$$E(X) = \sum xP(X = x) = \$350(0.99865) + (-\$249,650)(0.00135) = \$12.50$$

Interpretation: The company expects to make $12.50 for each 20-year-old male client they insure.   ◀◀

The $12.50 profit of the insurance company is a long-term result. Of course, it does not make $12.50 on each person it insures, but rather the average profit per person insured is $12.50.

NW *Now Work Problem 21.*

6.1 Assess Your Understanding

Concepts and Vocabulary

1. What is a random variable?
2. What is the difference between a discrete random variable and a continuous random variable? Provide your own examples of each.
3. What are the two requirements for a discrete probability distribution?
4. In your own words, provide an interpretation of the mean of a discrete random variable.
5. Suppose a baseball player historically hits 0.300. (This means that the player averages three hits in every 10

at-bats.) Suppose the player has zero hits in four at-bats in a game, and enters the batter's box for the fifth time, whereupon the announcer declares that the player is "due for a hit." What is the flaw in the announcer's reasoning? If the player had four hits in the last four at-bats, is the player "due to make an out"?
6. In game theory, a game is called a zero-sum game if the expected value of the game is zero. Explain what this means.

Exercises

• Basic Skills

In Problems 1–2, determine whether the random variable is discrete or continuous. In each case, state the possible values of the random variable.

1. (a) The number of lightbulbs that burn out in the next week in a room of 20 bulbs. Discrete; $x = 0, 1, \ldots, 20$
   (b) The time it takes to fly from New York City to Los Angeles. Continuous; $t > 0$
   (c) The number of hits to a web site in a day.
   (d) The amount of snow in Toronto during the winter.
   (c) Discrete, $x = 0, 1, 2, \ldots$ (d) Continuous, $s \geq 0$

2. (a) The time it takes for a lightbulb to burn out.
   (b) The weight of a T-bone steak. Continuous, $w > 0$
   (c) The number of free throw attempts before a shot is made. Discrete, $x = 0, 1, 2, \ldots$
   (d) In a random sample of 20 people, the number who are blood type A. Discrete, $x = 0, 1, \ldots, 20$
   (a) Continuous, $t > 0$

In Problems 3–8, determine whether the distribution is a probability distribution. If not, state why.

3. Yes

x	P(X = x)
0	0.2
1	0.2
2	0.2
3	0.2
4	0.2

4. Yes

x	P(X = x)
0	0.1
1	0.5
2	0.05
3	0.25
4	0.1

5. No, $P(x = 50) < 0$

x	P(X = x)
10	0.1
20	0.23
30	0.22
40	0.6
50	−0.15

6. No, $P(x = 40) < 0$

x	P(X = x)
10	0.5
20	0.1
30	0.3
40	−0.2
50	0.3

7. No, $\sum P(X = x) \neq 1$

x	P(X = x)
100	0.1
200	0.25
300	0.2
400	0.3
500	0.1

8. No, $\sum P(X = x) \neq 1$

x	P(X = x)
100	0.25
200	0.25
300	0.25
400	0.25
500	0.25

In Problems 9 and 10, determine the required value of the missing probability in order to make the distribution a probability distribution.

9. $P(X = 4) = 0.3$

x	P(X = x)
3	0.4
4	
5	0.1
6	0.2

10. $P(X = 2) = 0.15$

x	P(X = x)
0	0.30
1	0.15
2	
3	0.20
4	0.15
5	0.05

• Applying the Concepts

11. Parental Involvement In the following probability distribution, the random variable X represents the number of activities the mother of a K–5th grade student is involved in:

x	P(X = x)
0	0.044
1	0.084
2	0.209
3	0.325
4	0.338

Source: U.S. National Center for Education Statistics

(d) $\sigma_x^2 = 1.2$

(a) Verify that this is a probability distribution.
(b) Draw a probability histogram.
(c) Compute and interpret the mean of the random variable X. $\mu_x = 2.8$
(d) Compute the variance of the random variable X.
(e) Compute the standard deviation of the random variable X. $\sigma_x = 1.1$
(f) What is the probability that a randomly selected mother is involved in three activities? 0.325
(g) What is the probability that a randomly selected mother is involved in three or four activities? 0.663

12. Parental Involvement In the following probability distribution, the random variable X represents the number of activities the mother of a 6th–8th-grade student is involved in:

x	P(X = x)
0	0.10
1	0.137
2	0.27
3	0.302
4	0.191

Source: U.S. National Center for Education Statistics

(d) $\sigma_x^2 = 1.5$

(a) Verify that this is a probability distribution.
(b) Draw a probability histogram.
(c) Compute and interpret the mean of the random variable X. $\mu_x = 2.3$
(d) Compute the variance of the random variable X.
(e) Compute the standard deviation of the random variable X. $\sigma_x = 1.2$
(f) What is the probability that a randomly selected mother is involved in three activities? 0.302
(g) What is the probability that a randomly selected mother is involved in three or four activities? 0.493

13. Hot Streak A batter historically gets on base 30% of the time. The following distribution represents the number of at-bats X before he makes an out:

x	P(X = x)
1	0.7000
2	0.2100
3	0.0630
4	0.0189
5	0.0060
6	0.0021

(d) $\sigma_x^2 = 0.6$

(a) Verify that this is a probability distribution.
(b) Draw a probability histogram.
(c) Compute and interpret the mean of the random variable X. $\mu_x = 1.4$
(d) Compute the variance of the random variable X.
(e) Compute the standard deviation of the random variable X. $\sigma_x = 0.8$
(f) What is the probability that the batter requires four at-bats before making an out? 0.0189
(g) What is the probability that the batter requires four or more at-bats before making an out? Would this be unusual? 0.027

14. Waiting in Line A Wendy's manager performed a study in order to determine the probability distribution for the number of people waiting in line X during lunch. The results were as follows:

x	P(X = x)	x	P(X = x)	x	P(X = x)
0	0.011	5	0.172	10	0.019
1	0.035	6	0.132	11	0.002
2	0.089	7	0.098	12	0.006
3	0.150	8	0.063	13	0.001
4	0.186	9	0.035	14	0.001

(d) $\sigma_x^2 = 5.0$

(a) Verify that this is a probability distribution.
(b) Draw a probability histogram.
(c) Compute and interpret the mean of the random variable X. $\mu_x = 4.9$
(d) Compute the variance of the random variable X.
(e) Compute the standard deviation of the random variable X. $\sigma_x = 2.2$
(f) What is the probability that there are 8 people waiting in line for lunch? 0.063
(g) What is the probability that there are 10 or more people waiting in line for lunch? Would this be unusual? 0.029

In Problems 15–18, (a) construct the probability distribution for the random variable X (Hint: $P(X = x_i) = f_i/N$.), (b) draw the probability histogram, (c) compute and interpret the mean of the probability distribution, and (d) compute the standard deviation of the probability distribution.

15. Age of 5–9-Year-Old Boys The following data represent the number of 5–9-year-old males in the United States in 2000:   (c) $\mu_x = 7.0$ (d) $\sigma_x = 1.4$

x (age)	Frequency (in thousands)
5	2,031
6	2,058
7	2,110
8	2,138
9	2,186

Source: United States Census Bureau

16. Age of 5–9-Year-Old Girls The following data represent the number of 5–9-year-old females in the United States in 2000:   (c) $\mu_x = 7.0$ (d) $\sigma_x = 1.4$

x (age)	Frequency (in thousands)
5	1,934
6	1,961
7	2,008
8	2,041
9	2,081

Source: United States Census Bureau

17. Grade School Enrollment The following data represent the enrollment levels in grades 1–8 in the United States in 1997:   (c) $\mu_x = 4.4$ (d) $\sigma_x = 2.3$

x (grade level)	Frequency (in thousands)
1	3,755
2	3,689
3	3,597
4	3,507
5	3,458
6	3,493
7	3,520
8	3,415

Source: U.S. National Center of Education Statistics

18. High School Enrollment The following data represent the enrollment levels in grades 9–12 in the United States in 1997:   (c) $\mu_x = 10.4$ (d) $\sigma_x = 1.1$

x (grade level)	Frequency (in thousands)
9	3,819
10	3,377
11	2,972
12	2,673

Source: U.S. National Center of Education Statistics

19. Number of Births The probability histogram to the right represents the number of live births by a mother 50–54 years old who had a live birth in 1999. The data are from the National Vital Statistics Report, Volume 49, No. 1, April 17, 2001.

(a) What is the probability that a randomly selected 50–54-year-old mother who had a live birth in 1999 has had her fourth live birth? 0.124

(b) What is the probability that a randomly selected 50–54-year-old mother who had a live birth in 1999 has had her fourth or fifth live birth? 0.148

(c) What is the probability that a randomly selected 50–54-year-old mother who had a live birth in 1999 has had her sixth or more live birth? 0.112

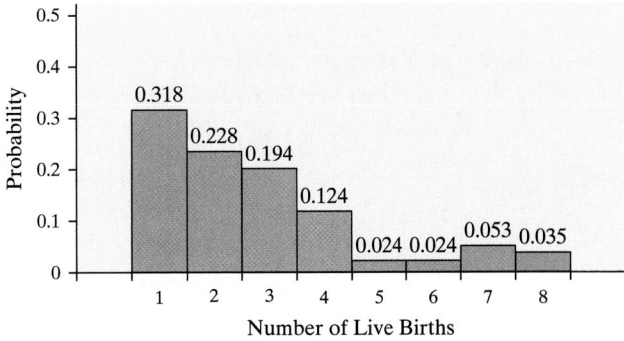

Number of Live Births, 50–54-year-old Mother

20. Rental Units The probability histogram that follows represents the number of rooms in rented housing units in 1997. The data are from the United States Census Bureau's *Current Housing Report.*

Number of Rooms in Rental Unit

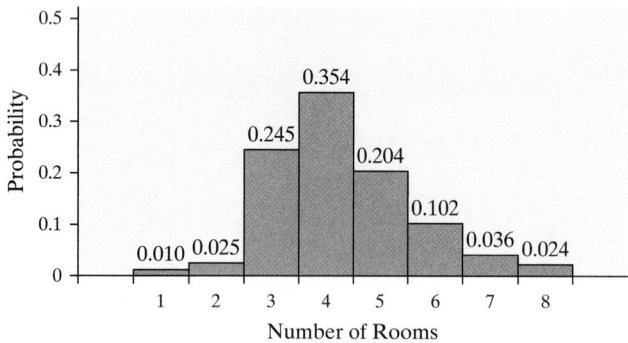

(a) What is the probability that a randomly selected rental unit has five rooms? *0.204*
(b) What is the probability that a randomly selected rental unit has five or six rooms? *0.306*
(c) What is the probability that a randomly selected rental unit has seven or more rooms? *0.06*

21. Life Insurance Suppose a life insurance company sells a $250,000 one-year term life insurance policy to a 20-year-old female for $200. According to the National Vital Statistics Report, Vol. 47, No. 28, the probability that the female survives the year is 0.99952. Compute and interpret the expected value of this policy to the insurance company. *$80*

22. Life Insurance Suppose a life insurance company sells a $500,000 one-year term life insurance policy to a 50-year-old male for $2,900. According to the National Vital Statistics Report, Vol. 47, No. 28, the probability the male survives the year is 0.99433. Compute and interpret the expected value of this policy to the insurance company. *$65*

23. Roulette In the game of roulette, a player can place a $5 bet on the number 17 and have a 1/38 probability of winning. If the metal ball lands on 17, the player wins $175, otherwise the casino takes the player's $5. What is the expected value of the game to the player? If you played the game 1,000 times, how much would you expect to lose? *− $0.26, About $260*

24. Connecticut Lottery In the Cash Five Lottery in Connecticut, a player pays $1 for a single ticket with five numbers. Five ping pong balls numbered 1 through 35 are randomly chosen from a bin without replacement. If all five numbers on a player's ticket match the five chosen, the player wins $100,000. The probability of this occurring is 1/324,632. If four numbers match, the player wins $300. This occurs with probability 1/2164. If three numbers match, the player wins $10. This occurs with probability 1/75. Compute and interpret the expected value of the game from the players point of view. *− $0.42*

25. Simulation Use the probability distribution from Problem 11 and Minitab's DISCRETE command (or some other statistical software) to simulate 100 repetitions of the experiment in which the batter bats until he makes an out. The number of at-bats is recorded. Approximate the mean and standard deviation of the random variable X, based upon the simulation. Repeat the simulation by performing 500 repetitions of the experiment. Approximate the mean and standard deviation of the random variable. Compare your results to the theoretical mean and standard deviation. What property is being illustrated?

26. Simulation Use the probability distribution from Problem 12 and Minitab's DISCRETE command (or some other statistical software) to simulate 100 repetitions of the experiment. Approximate the mean and standard deviation of the random variable X, based upon the simulation. Repeat the simulation by performing 500 repetitions of the experiment. Approximate the mean and standard deviation of the random variable. Compare your results to the theoretical mean and standard deviation. What property is being illustrated?

Technology Step-by-Step
Finding the Mean and Standard Deviation of a Discrete Random Variable Using Technology

TI-83 Plus **Step 1:** Enter the values of the random variable in L1 and their corresponding probabilities in L2.

Step 2: Press STAT, highlight CALC, and select 1: 1-Var Stats.

Step 3: With 1-Var Stats on the HOME screen, type L1 followed by a comma, followed by L2 as shown below

```
1-Var Stats L1, L2
```

Hit ENTER.

| 6.2 | The Binomial Probability Distribution |

Preparing for This Section   Before getting started, review the following:

  ✓ Independence (Section 5.3, p. 288)

  ✓ Combinations (Section 5.5, pp. 306–308)

  ✓ Multiplication Rule for Independent Events (Section 5.3, pp. 289–291)

  ✓ Addition Rule (Section 5.2, pp. 275–279)

  ✓ Complement Rule (Section 5.2, pp. 279–281)

  ✓ Empirical Rule (Section 3.2, pp. 139–140)

Objectives   Determine whether a probability experiment is a binomial experiment

   Compute probabilities of binomial experiments

   Compute the mean and standard deviation of a binomial random variable

   Construct binomial probability histograms

  Use the binomial probability distribution function to perform inference

 In Section 6.1, we stated that probability distributions could be presented using tables, graphs or mathematical formulas. Up to this point, we have only presented probability distributions using tables or graphs (probability histograms). In this section, we introduce a specific type of discrete probability distribution that can be presented using a formula, *the binomial probability distribution.*

The binomial probability distribution is a probability distribution that describes probabilities for experiments in which there are two mutually exclusive outcomes. These two outcomes are generally referred to as *success* or *failure*. For example, a basketball player can either make a free throw (success) or miss (failure). A new surgical procedure can result in either life (success) or death (failure).

Experiments in which there are only two possible outcomes are referred to as *binomial experiments*, provided that certain criteria are met.

Criteria for a Binomial Probability Experiment

An experiment is said to be a **binomial experiment** provided
1. The experiment is performed a fixed number of times. Each repetition of the experiment is called a **trial**.
2. The trials are independent. This means the outcome of one trial will not affect the outcome of the other trials.
3. For each trial, there are two mutually exclusive outcomes: success or failure.
4. The probability of success is fixed for each trial of the experiment.

If a probability experiment satisfies these four requirements, the random variable X, the number of successes in n trials, follows the binomial probability distribution. Before introducing the method for computing binomial probabilities, it is worthwhile to introduce some notation.

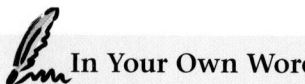

In Your Own Words

The prefix "bi" means two. This should help remind you that binomial experiments deal with situations in which there are only two outcomes: success and failure.

Notation Used in the Binomial Probability Distribution

- There are n independent trials of the experiment.
- Let p denote the probability of success so that $1 - p$ is the probability of failure.
- Let X denote the number of successes in n independent trials of the experiment. So, $0 \leq x \leq n$.

▶ **EXAMPLE 1** **Identifying Binomial Experiments**

Problem: Determine which of the following probability experiments qualify as a binomial experiment. For those that are binomial experiments, identify the number of trials, probability of success, probability of failure, and possible values of the random variable X.

(a) An experiment in which a basketball player who historically makes 80% of his free throws is asked to shoot 3 free throws and the number of made free throws is recorded.

(b) The number of people with blood type O-negative based upon a simple random sample of size 10 is recorded. According to the Information Please Almanac, 6% of the human population is blood type O-negative.

(c) A probability experiment in which three cards are drawn from a deck without replacement and the number of aces is recorded.

Approach: We need to determine whether the four conditions for a binomial experiment are satisfied.

1. The experiment is performed a fixed number of times.
2. The trials are independent.
3. There are only two possible outcomes of the experiment.
4. The probability of success for each trial is constant.

Solution:

(a) This is a binomial experiment because
   1. There are $n = 3$ trials.
   2. The trials are independent.
   3. There are two possible outcomes: make or miss.
   4. The probability of success (make) is 0.8 and the probability of failure (miss) is 0.2. They are the same for each trial.

The random variable X is the number of made free throws with $x = 0, 1, 2,$ or 3.

(b) This is a binomial experiment because
   1. There are 10 trials (the 10 randomly selected people).
   2. The trials are independent.*
   3. There are two possible outcomes: finding a person with blood type O-negative or not.
   4. The probability of success is 0.06 and the probability of failure is 0.94.

Historical Note

Jacob Bernoulli was born on December 27, 1654 in Basel, Switzerland. He studied philosophy and theology at the urging of his parents. (He resented this.) In 1671, he graduated from the University of Basel with a master's degree in philosophy. In 1676, he received a licentiate in theology. After earning his philosophy degree, Bernoulli traveled to Geneva to tutor. From there, he went to France to study with the great mathematicians of the time. One of Bernoulli's greatest works is *Ars Conjectandi*, published eight years after his death. In this publication, Bernoulli proved the binomial probability formula. To this day, each observed outcome in a binomial probability experiment is called a "Bernoulli" trial.

---

*Recall that, in sampling from large populations without replacement, the trials are assumed to be independent, provided that the sample size is small in relation to the size of the population. As a general rule of thumb, if the sample size is less than 5% of the population size, the trials can be assumed to be independent although they are technically dependent.

The random variable X is the number of people with blood type O-negative with $x = 0, 1, 2, 3, \ldots, 10$.

(c) This is not a binomial experiment because the trials are not independent. The probability of an ace on the first trial is 4/52. Because we are sampling without replacement, if an ace is selected on the first trial, the probability of an ace on the second trial is 3/51. If an ace is not selected on the first trial, the probability of an ace on the second trial is 4/51. ◀◀

 *Now Work Problem 3.*

Caution

The probability of success, *p*, is always associated with the random variable *X*, the number of successes. So if *X* represents the number of 18-year-olds involved in an accident, then *p* represents the probability of an 18-year-old being involved in an accident.

It is worth mentioning that the word *success* does not necessarily imply that something positive has occurred. Success simply means that an outcome has occurred that corresponds with p, the probability of success. For example, a probability experiment might be to randomly select ten 18-year-old male drivers. We might let X denote the number who have been involved in an accident within the last year. In this case, a success would mean obtaining an 18-year-old male who was involved in an accident. This outcome is certainly not positive, but still represents a success as far as the experiment goes.

② Computing Probabilities of Binomial Experiments

We are now prepared to compute probabilities for a binomial random variable X.

▶ EXAMPLE 2   **Constructing a Binomial Probability Distribution**

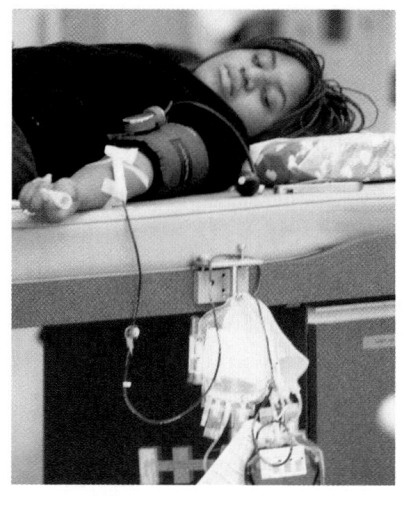

Problem: According to the Information Please Almanac, 6% of the human population is blood type O-negative. A simple random sample of size four is taken and the number of people X with blood type O-negative is recorded. Construct a probability distribution for the random variable X.

Approach: This is a binomial experiment with $n = 4$ trials. We define a success as selecting an individual with blood type O-negative. The probability of success, p, is 0.06, and X is the random variable representing the number of successes with $x = 0, 1, 2, 3$, or 4.

Step 1: Construct a tree diagram listing the various outcomes of the experiment by listing each outcome as S (success) or F (failure).

Step 2: Compute the probabilities for each value of the random variable X.

Step 3: Construct the probability distribution.

Solution:

Step 1: Figure 4 contains a tree diagram listing the 16 possible outcomes of the experiment.

Figure 4

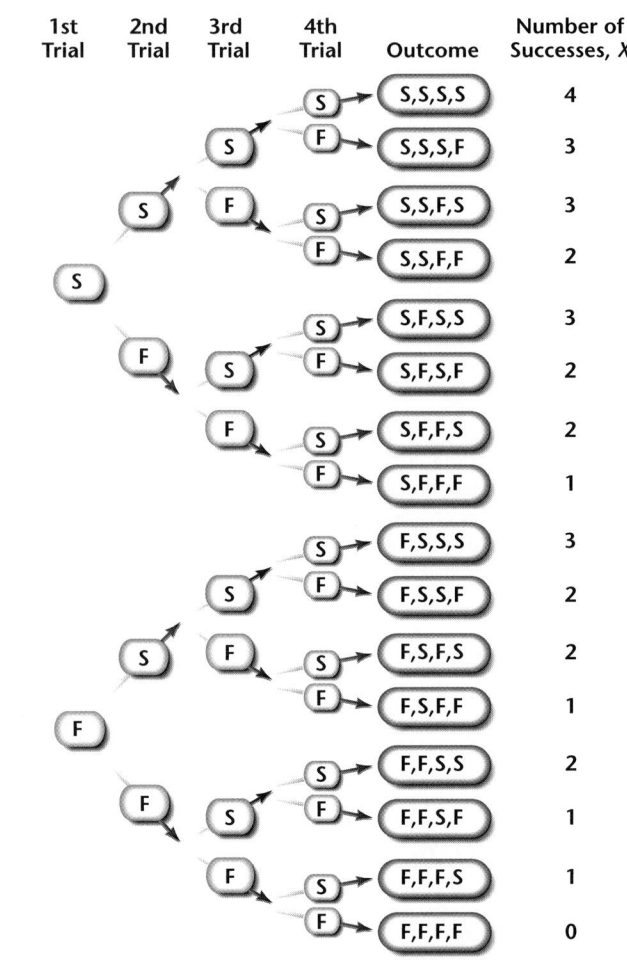

	1st Trial	2nd Trial	3rd Trial	4th Trial	Outcome	Number of Successes, X

Step 2: We now compute the probability for each possible value of the random variable X. We start with $P(X = 0)$:

$$P(X = 0) = P(FFFF) = P(F) \cdot P(F) \cdot P(F) \cdot P(F) \quad \text{Multiplication Rule for Independent Events}$$
$$= (0.94)(0.94)(0.94)(0.94)$$
$$= (0.94)^4$$
$$= 0.78075$$

$$P(X = 1) = P(SFFF \text{ or } FSFF \text{ or } FFSF \text{ or } FFFS)$$
$$= P(SFFF) + P(FSFF) + P(FFSF) + P(FFFS) \quad \text{Addition Rule for Mutually Exclusive Events}$$
$$= (0.06)^1(0.94)^3 + (0.06)^1(0.94)^3 + (0.06)^1(0.94)^3 + (0.06)^1(0.94)^3 \quad \text{Multiplication Rule for Independent Events}$$
$$= 4(0.06)^1(0.94)^3$$
$$= 0.19934$$

$$P(X = 2) = P(SSFF \text{ or } SFSF \text{ or } SFFS \text{ or } FSSF \text{ or } FSFS \text{ or } FFSS)$$
$$= P(SSFF) + P(SFSF) + P(SFFS) + P(FSSF) + P(FSFS) + P(FFSS)$$
$$= (0.06)^2(0.94)^2 + (0.06)^2(0.94)^2 + (0.06)^2(0.94)^2 + (0.06)^2(0.94)^2 + (0.06)^2(0.94)^2 + (0.06)^2(0.94)^2$$
$$= 6(0.06)^2(0.94)^2$$
$$= 0.01909$$

We compute $P(X = 3)$ and $P(X = 4)$ similarly and obtain $P(X = 3) = 0.00081$ and $P(X = 4) = 0.00001$. The reader is encouraged to verify these probabilities.

Step 3: We use these results and obtain the probability distribution in Table 7.
◄◄

TABLE 7	
x	$P(X = x)$
0	0.78075
1	0.19934
2	0.01909
3	0.00081
4	0.00001

As we look back at the solution in Example 2, we should note some interesting results. Consider the probability of obtaining $X = 1$ success:

$$P(X = 1) = 4(0.06)^1(0.94)^3$$

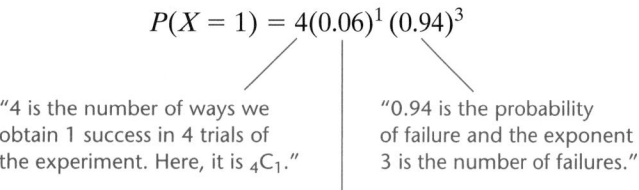

"4 is the number of ways we obtain 1 success in 4 trials of the experiment. Here, it is $_4C_1$."

"0.06 is the probability of success and the exponent 1 is the number of successes."

"0.94 is the probability of failure and the exponent 3 is the number of failures."

The coefficient 4 is the number of ways of obtaining one success in four trials. In general, the coefficient will be $_nC_x$, the number of ways of obtaining x successes in n trials. The second factor in the formula, $(0.06)^1$, is the probability of success, p, raised to the number of successes, x. The third factor in the formula, $(0.94)^3$, is the probability of failure, $1 - p$, raised to the number of failures, $n - x$. This formula holds in general and we have the *binomial probability distribution function (pdf)*.

Theorem

Binomial Probability Distribution Function

The probability of obtaining x successes in n independent trials of a binomial experiment where the probability of success is p is given by

$$P(X = x) = {_nC_x}\, p^x(1 - p)^{n-x} \quad x = 0, 1, 2, \ldots, n \qquad \textbf{(1)}$$

Caution

Before using the binomial probability distribution function, be sure the requirements for a binomial experiment are satisfied.

While reading probability problems, pay special attention to key phrases that translate into mathematical symbols. Table 8 lists various phrases and their corresponding mathematical equivalent.

TABLE 8	
Phrase	Math Symbol
"at least" or "no less than"	$\geq$
"more than" or "greater than"	$>$
"fewer than" or "less than"	$<$
"no more than" or "at most"	$\leq$
"exactly"	$=$

▶ **EXAMPLE 3** **Using the Binomial Probability Distribution Function**

Problem: According to Nielsen Media Research, 75% of all United States households have cable television.

(a) In a random sample of 15 households, what is the probability that exactly 10 have cable?
(b) In a random sample of 15 households, what is the probability that at least 13 have cable?
(c) In a random sample of 15 households, what is the probability that fewer than 13 have cable?

Approach: This is a binomial experiment with $n = 15$ independent trials with the probability of success, p, equal to 0.75. The possible values of the random variable X are $x = 0, 1, 2, \ldots, 15$. We use Formula (1) to compute the probabilities.

Solution:

(a) $P(X = 10) = {}_{15}C_{10}(0.75)^{10}(1 - 0.75)^{15-10}$ $n = 15, x = 10, p = 0.75$

$$= \frac{15!}{10!(15 - 10)!}(0.75)^{10}(0.25)^5 \quad {}_nC_x = \frac{n!}{x!(n - x)!}$$

$$= 3003(0.0563)(0.00097656)$$

$$= 0.1651$$

Interpretation: The probability of getting exactly 10 households out of 15 with cable is 0.1651. In 100 trials of this experiment, we would expect about 17 trials to result in 10 households with cable.

(b) The phrase "at least" means greater than or equal to. The values of the random variable X greater than or equal to 13 are $x = 13, 14,$ or 15.

$P(X \geq 13) = P(X = 13 \text{ or } X = 14 \text{ or } X = 15)$

$\qquad = P(X = 13) + P(X = 14) + P(X = 15)$ Addition Rule for Mutually Exclusive Events

$\qquad = {}_{15}C_{13}(0.75)^{13}(1 - 0.75)^{15-13} + {}_{15}C_{14}(0.75)^{14}(1 - 0.75)^{15-14} + {}_{15}C_{15}(0.75)^{15}(1 - 0.75)^{15-15}$

$\qquad = 0.1559 + 0.0668 + 0.0134$

$\qquad = 0.2361$

Interpretation: There is a 0.2361 probability that in a random sample of 15 households, at least 13 will have cable. In 100 trials of this experiment, we would expect about 24 trials to result in at least 13 households having cable.

(c) The values of the random variable X less than 13 are $x = 0, 1, 2, \ldots, 12$. Rather than compute $P(X \leq 12)$ directly by computing $P(X = 0) + P(X = 1) + \ldots + P(X = 12)$, we can use the Complement Rule.

$$P(x < 13) = P(x \leq 12) = 1 - P(x \geq 13) = 1 - 0.2361 = 0.7639$$

Note to Instructor
Emphasize to students that three
methods for obtaining binomial
probabilities have been introduced: tree
diagrams with the multiplication rule,
the binomial probability formula, and
technology. Encourage students to
compute a couple of binomial
probabilities using all three methods.

Interpretation: There is a 0.7639 probability that in a random sample of 15 households, less than 13 will have cable. In 100 trials of this experiment, we would expect about 76 trials to result in fewer than 13 households that have cable.   ◄◄

Using Technology: Statistical software/spreadsheets and graphing calculators with advanced statistical features have the ability to compute binomial probabilities. Figure 5(a) shows the result of Example 3(a) using Excel's formula wizard. To compute probabilities such as $P(X < 13) = P(X \le 12)$, it is best to use the **cumulative distribution function** (or **cdf**). The cumulative distribution function computes probabilities less than or equal to a specified value. For example, we can use a TI-83 Plus to compute $P(X \le 12)$ using the *binomcdf(* command. See Figure 5(b).

Figure 5

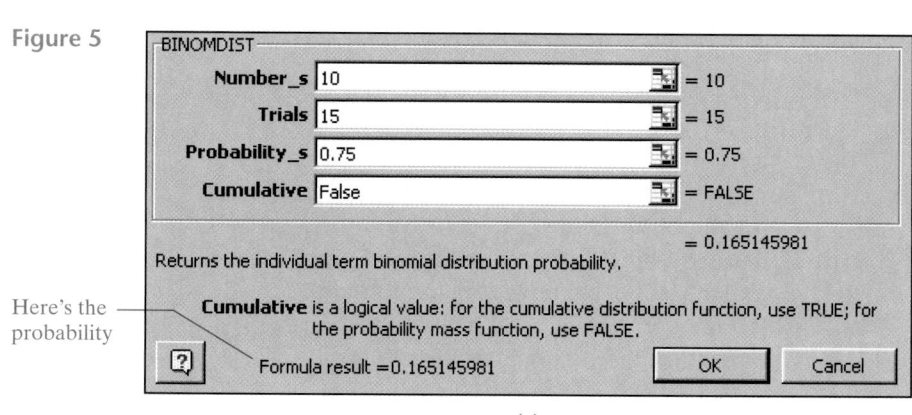

Here's the probability

(a)   (b)

NW *Now Work Problems 15(a) and 21.*

③ Mean and Standard Deviation of a Binomial Random Variable

We discussed finding the mean and standard deviation of a discrete random variable in Section 6.1. These formulas can be used to find the mean and standard deviation of a binomial random variable as well. However, there is a faster method.

Theorem

Mean and Standard Deviation of a Binomial Random Variable

A binomial experiment with n independent trials and probability of success p will have a mean and standard deviation given by the formulas

$$\mu_X = np \quad \text{and} \quad \sigma_X = \sqrt{np(1 - p)} \tag{2}$$

▶ **EXAMPLE 4**   **Finding the Mean and Standard Deviation of a Binomial Random Variable**

Note to Instructor
You many want to construct a binomial
probability distribution with $n = 3$ and
$p = 0.4$. Then use the formulas from
Section 6.1 to compute μ_X and σ_X.
Now use Formula (2) to compute μ_X
and σ_X.

Problem: According to Nielsen Media Research, 75% of all United States households have cable television. In a simple random sample of 300 households, determine the mean and standard deviation number of households that will have cable television.

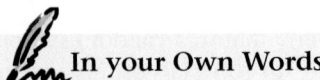

In your Own Words

The mean of a binomial random variable equals the number of trials of the experiment times the probability of success. It can be interpreted as the expected number of successes in n trials of the experiment.

Approach: This is a binomial experiment with $n = 300$ and $p = 0.75$. We can use Formula (2) to find the mean and standard deviation, respectively.

Solution: $\mu_X = np = 300(0.75) = 225$

and

$$\sigma_X = \sqrt{np(1-p)} = \sqrt{300(0.75)(1-0.75)} = \sqrt{56.25} = 7.5$$

Interpretation: We expect that in a random sample of 300 households, 225 will have cable. ◄◄

 Now Work Problems 15(b) and15(c).

4 The Binomial Probability Histogram

Constructing binomial probability histograms is no different from constructing probability histograms.

► **EXAMPLE 5** **Constructing Binomial Probability Histograms**

Problem:

(a) Construct a binomial probability histogram with $n = 10$ and $p = 0.2$. Comment on the shape of the distribution.

(b) Construct a binomial probability histogram with $n = 10$ and $p = 0.5$. Comment on the shape of the distribution.

(c) Construct a binomial probability histogram with $n = 10$ and $p = 0.8$. Comment on the shape of the distribution.

Approach: To construct a binomial probability histogram, we will first obtain the probability distribution using Minitab. We then construct the probability histogram of the probability distribution.

Solution:

(a) We obtain the probability distribution with $n = 10$ and $p = 0.2$. See Table 9. Figure 6 shows the corresponding probability histogram with the mean $\mu_X = 10(0.2) = 2$ labeled. The distribution is skewed right.

TABLE 9	
x	$P(X = x)$
0	0.107374
1	0.268435
2	0.301990
3	0.201327
4	0.088080
5	0.026424
6	0.005505
7	0.000786
8	0.000074
9	0.000004
10	0.000000

Figure 6

(b) We obtain the probability distribution with $n = 10$ and $p = 0.5$. See Table 10. Figure 7 shows the corresponding probability histogram with the mean $\mu_x = 10(0.5) = 5$ labeled. The distribution is symmetric and approximately bell shaped.

Figure 7

TABLE 10	
x	$P(X = x)$
0	0.000977
1	0.009766
2	0.043945
3	0.117188
4	0.205078
5	0.246094
6	0.205078
7	0.117188
8	0.043945
9	0.009766
10	0.000977

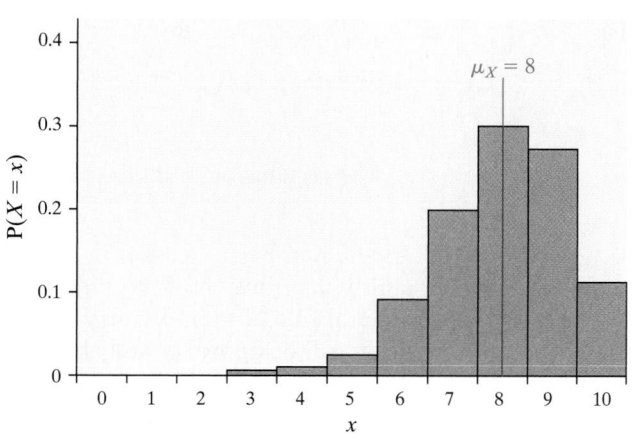

(c) We obtain the probability distribution with $n = 10$ and $p = 0.8$. See Table 11. Figure 8 shows the corresponding probability histogram with the mean $\mu_X = 10(0.8) = 8$ labeled. The distribution is skewed left.

Figure 8

TABLE 11	
x	$P(X = x)$
0	0.000000
1	0.000004
2	0.000074
3	0.000786
4	0.005505
5	0.026424
6	0.088080
7	0.201327
8	0.301990
9	0.268435
10	0.107374

NW *Now Work Problem 15(d).*

Based upon the results of Example 5, we might conclude that the binomial probability distribution is skewed right if $p < 0.5$, symmetric and approximately bell shaped if $p = 0.5$, and skewed left if $p > 0.5$. Notice that Figure 6 ($p = 0.2$) and Figure 8 ($p = 0.8$) are mirror images of each other.

Remember, the binomial probability distribution depends not only on the parameter p, but also upon n, the number of trials. What role does n play in the shape of the distribution?

EXPLORATION Construct a binomial probability histogram with $n = 10$ and $p = 0.2$. Comment on the shape of the distribution. Now construct a binomial probability histogram with $n = 30$ and $p = 0.2$. Comment on the shape of the distribution. Finally, construct a binomial probability histogram with $n = 70$ and $p = 0.2$. Comment on the shape of the distribution.

Result: We show the three probability histograms in Figures 9(a), 9(b) and 9(c).

Figure 9(a) is skewed right. Figure 9(b) is slightly skewed right and Figure 9(c) appears bell-shaped. We conclude that as the number of trials n increases, the shape of the distribution becomes more symmetric and bell shaped.

Figure 9

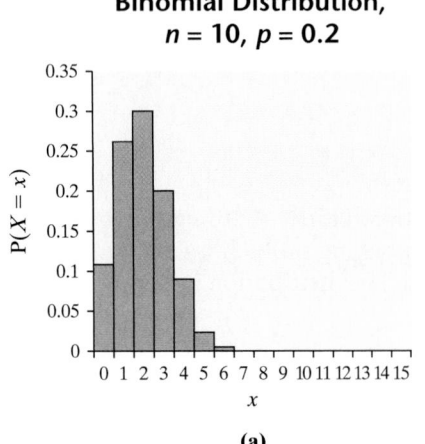

Binomial Distribution, $n = 10$, $p = 0.2$

(a)

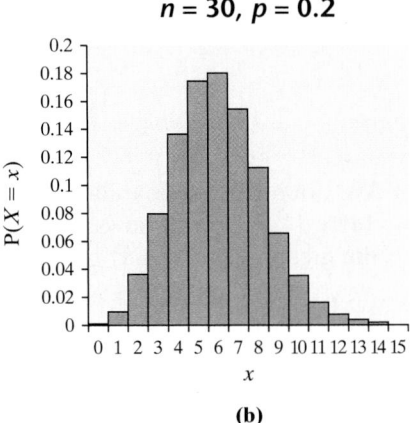

Binomial Distribution, $n = 30$, $p = 0.2$

(b)

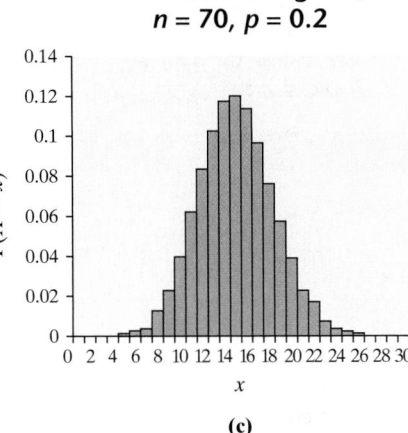

Binomial Histogram, $n = 70$, $p = 0.2$

(c)

The conclusion in the Exploration is true in general.

As the number of trials n in a binomial experiment increases, the probability distribution of the random variable X becomes bell shaped. As a general rule of thumb, if $np(1 - p) \geq 10$,* then the probability distribution will be approximately bell shaped.

This result allows us to use the Empirical Rule to identify unusual observations in a binomial experiment. Recall that the Empirical Rule states that in a bell-shaped distribution, about 95% of all observations lie within two standard deviations of the mean. That is, 95% of the observations lie

*Ramsey, P.P. and P.H. Ramsey, "Evaluating the Normal Approximation to the Binomial Test," *Journal of Educational Statistics* 13 (1998): 173–182.

between $\mu - 2\sigma$ and $\mu + 2\sigma$. Any observation that lies outside these intervals may be considered unusual because the observation occurs only 5% of the time.

▶ EXAMPLE 6

Using the Mean, Standard Deviation and Empirical Rule to Check for Unusual Results in a Binomial Experiment

Problem: According to Nielsen Media Research, in 1998, 75% of all United States households had cable television. In a simple random sample of 300 households, 244 had cable. Is this result unusual?

Approach: Because $np(1 - p) = 300(0.75)(0.25) = 56.25 \geq 10$, the binomial probability distribution is approximately bell-shaped. Therefore, we can use the Empirical Rule to check for unusual observations. If the observation is less than $\mu - 2\sigma$ or greater than $\mu + 2\sigma$, then we say it is unusual.

Solution: From Example 4, we have $\mu = 225$ and $\sigma = 7.5$.

$$\mu - 2\sigma = 225 - 2(7.5) = 225 - 15 = 210$$

and

$$\mu + 2\sigma = 225 + 2(7.5) = 225 + 15 = 240$$

Interpretation: Since any value less than 210 or greater than 240 is unusual, 244 is an unusual result. We should attempt to identify reasons for its value. It may be that the percentage of households that have cable has increased since 1998.   ◀◀

 Now Work Problem 29.

⑤ ### Inference Using the Binomial Probability Formula

Note to Instructor
The remaining material in this section is challenging and may be skipped without loss of continuity.

Suppose you are in a street game that involves rolling a single die. You decide to record the outcome in the next 100 throws of the die and obtain the results in Table 12.

Knowing that each outcome of the experiment of rolling a single die should occur about 17% (= 1/6) of the time, do you think something is "fishy" about this game? Why?

Comparing expected results of an experiment to the actual results is at the very core of statistical inference. If the two are significantly different, we might conclude the theoretical probabilities do not accurately describe the outcomes of the experiment.

In looking at Table 12, the empirical evidence indicates the die may be loaded (i.e. not "fair") since we observe "one" with a much higher frequency than the other possible outcomes. If the die is fair, we should observe each outcome in the same proportion, 1/6. If the die has a bias toward rolling a "one," we will observe "one" more often than the other outcomes. We need to ask the following question: "Are the results displayed in Table 12 likely to occur if the die is fair?" We determine the likelihood of an outcome by computing its probability, assuming that the die is fair.

TABLE 12		
Outcome	Frequency	Relative Frequency
Roll a one	32	0.32
Roll a two	14	0.14
Roll a three	13	0.13
Roll a four	9	0.09
Roll a five	19	0.19
Roll a six	13	0.13

The probability of observing 32 or more "ones" in 100 throws of a fair die is computed using the binomial probability formula with $n = 100$ and $p = 1/6$:

$$P(X \geq 32) = P(X = 32) + P(X = 33) + \ldots + P(X = 100)$$

$$= {}_{100}C_{32}(1/6)^{32}(5/6)^{100-32} + {}_{100}C_{33}(1/6)^{33}(5/6)^{100-33} + \cdots + {}_{100}C_{100}(1/6)^{100}(5/6)^{100-100}$$

$$= 0.000124$$

The probability of 0.000124 means that if we repeated this experiment 10,000 times (i.e., roll the die 100 times 10,000 times), we would expect about 1 of the 10,000 repetitions of the experiment to result in 32 or more "ones" *if* the die is fair. The likelihood of rolling 32 or more "ones" when throwing a fair die is so low that we prefer to think the die is loaded rather than say the outcome is due to chance behavior. One caveat (warning) regarding this practice is that there is a remote possibility we *would* obtain 32 or more "ones" in 100 throws of a die. Because of this, we need to be aware that we could be falsely charging the sponsor of the game.

Whenever empirical results contradict the theoretical probabilities, then one of two conclusions can be made:

1. The parameter p accurately describes the probability of success and the experiment resulted in an unusual outcome,

or

2. The parameter p does not accurately describe the probability of success of a single trial of the probability experiment.

In inference, we prefer the second explanation to the first. Let's look at another example to help clarify the procedure.

▶ **EXAMPLE 7**   **Using the Binomial Probability Distribution Function to Perform Inference**

Problem: In 1998, according to Nielsen Media Research, 75% of all United States households had cable television. Yolanda and Lorrie believe that this percentage may have increased.

(a) Yolanda conducts a simple random sample of 40 households and finds that 33 of them have cable. Assuming that 75% of the population has cable television, compute the probability that in a simple random sample of 40 households, 33 or more have cable. Do the results support Yolanda's belief that the percentage of households with cable may have increased?

(b) Lorrie conducts her own simple random sample of 40 households and finds that 38 have cable. What is the probability that in a simple random sample of 40 households, 38 or more have cable? Do the results support Lorrie's belief that the percentage of households with cable may have increased?

Approach: This is a binomial experiment with $n = 40$ and $p = 0.75$. If 75% of the population has cable television, then we would expect about $0.75(40) = 30$ households out of the 40 surveyed to have cable television. If the percentage is more than 75% of the population, we would expect more than 30 households to have cable television. The question Yolanda needs to answer is: "If 75% of households have cable, is it unusual that a random sample of 40 households results in 33 or more households with cable television?" The reason she needs to compute the probability of 33 or more households is that 33/40, 34/40, ..., 40/40 all result in proportions greater than 0.75. On the other hand, Lorrie needs to ask: "If 75% of households have cable, is it unusual that a random sample of 40 households results in 38 or more households with cable television?"

Solution:

(a) $P(X \geq 33) = P(X = 33) + P(X = 34) + \cdots + P(X = 40)$

We compute this probability using Minitab. Figure 10 shows the partial probability distribution of X using Minitab. (We don't show probabilities for X less than 30, because they are not needed for the solution.)

We have $P(X \geq 33) = P(X = 33) + P(X = 34) + \ldots + P(X = 40) = 0.0857 + 0.0530 + \ldots + 0.0000 = 0.1819 = 18.19\%$.

Interpretation: If this survey were conducted 100 times and the proportion of households with cable television were 0.75, about 18 of the surveys would result in 33 or more households having cable television. Because this is not unusual $(P(X \geq 33) = 0.1819 \geq 0.05)$, Yolanda does not have evidence to support the belief that the percentage of households with cable television has increased.

(b) Based upon Lorrie's sample, the probability that in a simple random sample of 40 households, at least 38 will have cable is $P(X \geq 38) = P(X = 38) + P(X = 39) + P(X = 40) = 0.0009 + 0.0001 + 0.0000 = 0.001 = 0.1\%$.

Interpretation: A probability of 0.001 means that about 1 sample in 1000 will result in 38 or more households having cable if the actual proportion of households with cable television is 0.75. Because this is a remote possibility, Lorrie is more inclined to believe that the percentage of households with cable has increased since the Nielsen survey of 1998. ◄◄

In Example 7(a), Yolanda cannot claim that the proportion of households with cable television has increased, even though her sample resulted in 33/40 (82.5%) of households with cable television. This is because it is not uncommon to have 33 or more successes in 40 trials of a binomial experiment with $p = 0.75$.

We present a summary for performing inference using the Binomial Probability Formula.

Inference Using the Binomial Probability Distribution Function

If a binomial experiment is conducted in which each trial of the experiment is assumed to have a probability of success, p, then

- x successes or more in n trials of the experiment will be unusual if the probability of obtaining x or more successes is low.

- x successes or fewer in n trials of the experiment will be unusual if the probability of obtaining x or fewer successes is low.

In both these cases, the low probability is an indication that the probability of success, p, for a single trial of the experiment does not accurately reflect the true probability of success.

NW *Now Work Problem 35.*

Figure 10

x	P(X = x)
30.00	0.1444
31.00	0.1397
32.00	0.1179
33.00	0.0857
34.00	0.0530
35.00	0.0272
36.00	0.0113
37.00	0.0037
38.00	0.0009
39.00	0.0001
40.00	0.0000

6.2 Assess Your Understanding

Concepts and Vocabulary

1. State the criteria for a binomial probability experiment.
2. What role does $_nC_x$ play in the binomial probability distribution function?

3. How can the Empirical Rule be used to identify unusual results from a binomial experiment? When can the Empirical Rule be used?
4. Describe how to perform inference with the Binomial Probability Distribution Function.

Exercises

• Basic Skills

In Problems 1–10, determine which of the following probability experiments represents a binomial experiment. If the probability experiment is not a binomial experiment, state why.

1. A random sample of 15 college seniors is conducted, and the individuals selected are asked to state their ages. Not binomial

2. A random sample of 30 cars in a used car lot is obtained, and their mileage recorded. Not binomial

3. An experimental drug is administered to 100 randomly (NW) selected individuals, with the number of individuals responding favorably recorded. Binomial

4. A poll of 1200 registered voters is conducted in which the respondents are asked whether they believe Congress should reform Social Security. Binomial

5. Three cards are selected from a standard 52-card deck without replacement. The number of aces selected is recorded. Not binomial

6. Three cards are selected from a standard 52-card deck with replacement. The number of aces selected is recorded. Binomial

7. A basketball player who makes 80% of her free throws is asked to shoot free throws until she misses. The number of free throw attempts is recorded. Not binomial

8. A baseball player who reaches base safely 30% of the time is allowed to bat until he reaches base safely for the third time. The number of at-bats required is recorded.

9. An investor randomly purchases 10 stocks listed on the New York Stock Exchange. Historically, the probability that a stock listed on the NYSE will increase in value over the course of a year is 48%. The number of stocks that increase in value is recorded. Binomial

10. According to Nielsen Media Research, 75% of all United States households have cable television. In a small town of 40 households, a random sample of 10 households is asked whether they have cable television. The number of households with cable television is recorded. Not binomial

8. Not binomial

In Problems 11–14, a binomial probability experiment is conducted with the given parameters. Compute the probability of x successes in the n independent trials of the experiment.

11. $n = 10$, $p = 0.4$, $x = 3$ 0.2150

12. $n = 15$, $p = 0.85$, $x = 12$ 0.2184

13. $n = 40$, $p = 0.99$, $x = 38$ 0.0532

14. $n = 50$, $p = 0.02$, $x = 3$ 0.0607

In Problems 15–20, (a) construct a binomial probability distribution with the given parameters; (b) compute the mean and standard deviation of the distribution, using the methods of Section 6.1; (c) compute the mean and standard deviation, using the methods of this section; and (d) draw the probability histogram, comment on its shape, and label the mean on the histogram.

(NW) 15. $n = 6$, $p = 0.3$ $\mu_x = 1.8$, $\sigma_x = 1.12$

16. $n = 8$, $p = 0.5$ $\mu_x = 4$, $\sigma_x = 1.41$

17. $n = 9$, $p = 0.75$ $\mu_x = 6.75$, $\sigma_x = 1.3$

18. $n = 10$, $p = 0.2$ $\mu_x = 2$, $\sigma_x = 1.26$

19. $n = 10$, $p = 0.5$ $\mu_x = 5$, $\sigma_x = 1.58$

20. $n = 9$, $p = 0.8$ $\mu_x = 7.2$, $\sigma_x = 1.2$

• **Applying the Concepts**

21. On-Time Flights United Airlines flight 1832 from Chicago to Orlando is on time 80% of the time, according to United Airlines. Suppose 15 flights are randomly selected.

(a) Find the probability that exactly 12 flights are on time. *0.2501*

(b) Find the probability that at least 12 flights are on time. *0.6482*

(c) Find the probability that fewer than 12 flights are on time. *0.3518*

(d) Find the probability that between 10 and 12 flights, inclusive, are on time. *0.5409*

22. Smokers According to the *Information Please* almanac, 80% of adult smokers started smoking before turning 18 years old. Suppose 10 smokers 18 years old or older are randomly selected.

(a) Find the probability that exactly 8 of them started smoking before 18 years of age. *0.3020*

(b) Find the probability that at least 8 of them started smoking before 18 years of age. *0.6778*

(c) Find the probability that fewer than 8 of them started smoking before 18 years of age. *0.3222*

(d) Find the probability that between 7 and 9 of them, inclusive, started smoking before 18 years of age. *0.7718*

23. Operating Systems A survey conducted by StatMarket showed that 94% of computer users use Microsoft Windows as their operating system. Suppose 12 computer users are randomly selected.

(a) Find the probability that exactly 10 of them use Microsoft Windows. *0.1280*

(b) Find the probability that 10 or more of them use Microsoft Windows. *0.9684*

(c) Find the probability that 9 or fewer of them use Microsoft Windows. *0.0316*

(d) Find the probability that between 9 and 11 of them, inclusive, use Microsoft Windows. *0.5197*

24. Murder by Firearm According to *Crime in the United States*, 1998, 65% of murders are committed with a firearm. Suppose 15 murders are randomly selected.

(a) Find the probability that exactly 13 murders are committed with a firearm. *0.0476*

(b) Find the probability that 13 or more murders are committed with a firearm. *0.0617*

(c) Find the probability that 12 or fewer murders are committed with a firearm. *0.9383*

(d) Find the probability that between 10 and 12 murders, inclusive, are committed with a firearm. *0.5025*

25. Migraine Sufferers Depakote is a medication whose purpose is to reduce the pain associated with migraine headaches. In clinical trials of Depakote, 2% of the patients in the study experienced weight gain as a side effect. Suppose a random sample of 30 Depakote users is obtained.

[*Source*: Abbott Laboratories]

(a) Find the probability that exactly 3 experienced weight gain as a side effect. *0.0188*

(b) Find the probability that 3 or fewer experienced weight gain as a side effect. *0.9971*

(c) Find the probability that 4 or more patients experienced weight gain as a side effect. *0.0029*

(d) Find the probability that between 1 and 4 patients, inclusive, experienced weight gain as a side effect.

26. Asthma Control Singulair is a medication whose purpose is to control asthma attacks. In clinical trials of the drug, 18.4% of the patients in the study experienced headaches as a side effect. Suppose a random sample of 30 Singulair users is obtained.

[*Source*: Merck and Company, Incorporated]

(a) Find the probability that exactly 5 experienced headaches as a side effect. *0.1863*

(b) Find the probability that 5 or fewer experienced headaches as a side effect. *0.5165*

(c) Find the probability that 6 or more patients experienced headaches as a side effect. *0.4835*

(d) Find the probability that between 6 and 8 patients experienced headaches as a side effect. *0.3981*

27. Softball Suppose a softball player reaches base safely 45% of the time. Assuming that trips to the plate are independent events, compute the probability that in the next 10 trips to the plate,

(a) the player reaches base safely exactly six times.

(b) the player reaches base safely six or more times.

(c) the player reaches base safely less than two times.

(d) the player reaches base safely between three and five times, inclusive. *0.6389*

28. Basketball Mark Price holds the record for percentage of free throws made in the National Basketball Association, at 90.4%. Assuming that free throws are independent events, compute the probability that in his next 10 free throws,

(a) Mark Price makes exactly 8. *0.1850*

(b) Mark Price makes 8 or more. *0.9365*

(c) Mark Price makes fewer than 7. *0.0111*

(d) Mark Price makes between 6 and 8, inclusive. *0.2471*

29. On-Time Flights United Airlines flight 1832 from Chicago to Orlando is on time 80% of the time, according to United Airlines.

(a) Compute the mean and standard deviation of a random variable X, the number of on-time flights in 100 trials of the probability experiment. $\mu_x = 80, \sigma_x = 4$

(b) Interpret the mean.

(c) Would it be unusual to observe 90 on-time flights in a random sample of 100 flights from Chicago to Orlando? Why? *Yes*

(25d) *0.4542*   (27a) *0.1596*   (27b) *0.2616*   (27c) *0.0233*

30. **Smokers** According to the *Information Please* almanac, 80% of adult smokers started smoking before turning 18 years old.   (a) $\mu_x = 160, \sigma_x = 5.66$

    (a) Compute the mean and standard deviation of a random variable X, the number of smokers who started before 18 in 200 trials of the probability experiment.

    (b) Interpret the mean.

    (c) Would it be unusual to observe 180 smokers who started smoking before turning 18 years old in a random sample of 200 adult smokers? Why? Yes

31. **Operating Systems** According to a survey conducted by StatMarket, 94% of computer users use Microsoft Windows as their operating system.

    (a) Compute the mean and standard deviation of the random variable X, the number of Windows users in 200 trials of the probability experiment.

    (b) Interpret the mean.

    (c) Would it be unusual to observe 195 users of Microsoft Windows in a random sample of 200 computer users? Why? Yes

32. **Murder by Firearm** According to *Crime in the United States, 1998*, 65% of murders are committed with a firearm.

    (a) Compute the mean and standard deviation of the random variable X, the number of firearm murders in 100 trials of the probability experiment.

    (b) Interpret the mean.

    (c) Would it be unusual to observe 70 murders by firearm in a random sample of 100 murders? Why? No

33. **Migraine Sufferers** Depakote is a medication whose purpose is to reduce the pain associated with migraine headaches. In clinical trials and extended studies of Depakote, 2% of the patients in the study experienced weight gain as a side effect.   (a) $\mu_x = 12, \sigma_x = 3.43$

    (a) Compute the mean and standard deviation of the random variable X, the number of patients experiencing weight gain in 600 trials of the probability experiment.

    (b) Interpret the mean.

    (c) Would it be unusual to observe 16 patients who experience weight gain in a random sample of 600 patients who take the medication? Why? No

34. **Asthma Control** Singulair is a medication whose purpose is to control asthma attacks. In clinical trials of Singulair, 18.4% of the patients in the study experienced headaches as a side effect.   (a) $\mu_x = 73.6, \sigma_x = 7.75$

    (a) Compute the mean and standard deviation of the random variable X, the number of patients experiencing headaches in 400 trials of the probability experiment.

    (b) Interpret the mean.

    (c) Would it be unusual to observe 86 patients who experience headaches in a random sample of 400 patients who use this medication? Why? No

35. **Males Living at Home** According to the *Information Please* almanac, 59% of males between the ages of 18 and 24 lived at home in 1998 (unmarried college students living in dorms are counted as living at home). Suppose that a survey is administered at a community college to 20 randomly selected male students between the ages of 18 and 24 years and that 17 of them respond that they live at home.

    (a) Based on the sample of 20 students, what proportion of community college males live at home? 0.85

    (b) Find the probability that 17 or more out of 20 community college male students live at home, assuming that the proportion who live at home is 59%. 0.0128

    (c) What might you conclude from this result?

36. **Females Living at Home** According to the *Information Please* almanac, 48% of females between the ages of 18 and 24 years live at home (unmarried college students living in dorms are counted as living at home). Suppose that a survey is administered at a community college to 20 randomly selected female students between the ages of 18 and 24 years and that 16 of them respond that they live at home.

    (a) Based on the sample of 20 students, what proportion of community college females live at home? 0.8

    (b) Find the probability that 16 or more out of 20 community college female students live at home, assuming that the proportion who live at home is 48%. 0.0035

    (c) What might you conclude from this result?

37. **Boys Are Preferred** In a Gallup poll conducted December 2–4, 2000, 42% of survey respondents said that, if they had only one child, they would prefer the child to be a boy. Suppose you conduct a survey of 15 randomly selected students on your campus and find that 8 of them would prefer a boy.

    (a) What proportion of students prefer a boy, according to the sample of 15 students? 0.53

    (b) Compute the probability that, in a random sample of 15 students, at least 8 would prefer a boy, assuming that the proportion that prefer a boy is 0.42. 0.2630

    (c) Do the results of your survey contradict the results of the Gallup poll? Explain. No

38. **Liars** According to a USA Today Snapshot, 3% of Americans surveyed lie frequently. Suppose you conduct a survey of 100 college students and find that 5 of them lie frequently.

    (a) Based on the sample of 100 students, what proportion of college students lie? 0.05

    (b) Compute the probability that, in a random sample of 100 college students, at least 5 lie frequently, assuming that the proportion that lie is 0.03. 0.1821

    (c) Do the results of your survey contradict the USA Today Snapshot? Explain. No

39. **Time to Graduate** According to a study done by ACT in 1997, 52.8% of students graduate from college in five years or less. Suppose you conduct a survey of 20 recent college graduates and find that 6 of them graduated in five years or less.

(31a) $\mu_x = 188, \sigma_x = 3.36$ (32a) $\mu_x = 65, \sigma_x = 4.77$

(a) What proportion of the recent college graduates surveyed graduated in five years or less? *0.3*

(b) Compute the probability that, in a random sample of 20 recent college graduates, 6 or fewer graduated in five years or less, assuming that the proportion that graduate in five years or less is 0.528. *0.0339*

(c) Do the results of your survey contradict the results of the study done by ACT? Explain. *Yes*

40. **Drunk-Driving Laws** In a Gallup poll conducted July 20–August 3, 2000, 72% of survey respondents said they would favor reducing the drunk-driving limit to 0.08% blood alcohol concentration (BAC). Survey respondents had to be 16 years old or older and a licensed driver. On October 3, 2000, President Bill Clinton signed into law a national BAC of 0.08% required to charge drunk drivers with a crime. Suppose you are a member of SADD (Students Against Drunk Driving) and conduct a survey of 20 students 16 years old or older who were licensed drivers, and 10 of them favored a drunk-driving limit of 0.08% BAC.

(a) What proportion of the 20 students surveyed favored a drunk-driving limit of 0.08% BAC? *0.5*

(b) Compute the probability that, in a random sample of 20 students, 10 or fewer would favor a drunk-driving law of 0.08% BAC, assuming that the proportion is 0.72. *0.0305*

(c) Do the results of your survey contradict the results of the Gallup poll? Explain. *Yes*

41. **Simulation** According to the United States National Center for Health Statistics, there is a 98% probability that a 20-year-old male will survive to age 30.

(a) Using statistical software, such as Minitab, simulate taking 100 random samples of size 30 from this population.

(b) Using the results of the simulation, compute the probability that exactly 29 of the 30 males survive to age 30.

(c) Compute the probability that exactly 29 of the 30 males survive to age 30, using the binomial probability distribution. Compare the results with part (b). *0.3340*

(d) Using the results of the simulation, compute the probability that at most 27 of the 30 males survive to age 30.

(e) Compute the probability that at most 27 of the 30 males survive to age 30, using the binomial probability distribution. Compare the results with part (d). *0.0217*

(f) Compute the mean number of male survivors in the 100 simulations of the probability experiment. Is it close to the expected value?

(g) Compute the standard deviation of the number of male survivors in the 100 simulations of the probability experiment. Compare the result to the theoretical standard deviation of the probability distribution.

(h) Did the simulation yield any unusual results?

42. **Simulation** According to the United States National Center for Health Statistics, there is a 99% probability that a 20-year-old female will survive to age 30.

(a) Using statistical software, such as Minitab, simulate taking 100 random samples of size 30 from this population.

(b) Using the results of the simulation, compute the probability that exactly 29 of the 30 females survive to age 30.

(c) Compute the probability that exactly 29 of the 30 females survive to age 30, using the binomial probability distribution. Compare the results with part (b). *0.2242*

(d) Using the results of the simulation, compute the probability that at most 27 of the 30 females survive to age 30.

(e) Compute the probability that at most 27 of the 30 females survive to age 30, using the binomial probability distribution. Compare the results with part (d). *0.0033*

(f) Compute the mean number of female survivors in the 100 simulations of the probability experiment. Is it close to the expected value?

(g) Compute the standard deviation of the number of female survivors in the 100 simulations of the probability experiment. Compare the result to the theoretical standard deviation of the probability distribution.

(h) Did the simulation yield any unusual results?

43. **Educational Attainment** According to the United States Census Bureau, about 25% of residents of the United States 25 years old or older have completed at least four years of college. Suppose you are performing a study and would like at least 10 people in the study to have completed at least four years of college.

(a) How many residents of the United States do you expect to have to randomly select? *40*

(b) How many residents of the United States do you need to randomly select in order to have a 99% probability that the sample contains at least 10 residents with four or more years of college? *70*

44. **Geometric Probability Distribution** A probability distribution for the random variable X, the number of trials until the first success is observed, is called the **geometric probability distribution**. It has the same requirements as the binomial distribution (see page 339), except that the number of trials is not fixed. Its probability distribution function (pdf) is

$$P(X = x) = p(1 - p)^{x-1} \quad x = 1, 2, 3, \ldots$$

where p is the probability of success.

(a) What is the probability that Shaquille O'Neal takes three free throws before he makes one? Over his career, he makes 53.6% of his free throws. That is, find $P(X = 3)$. *0.1154*

(b) Construct a probability distribution for the random variable X, the number of free throw attempts of Shaquille O'Neal before he makes a free throw. Construct the distribution for $x = 1, 2, 3, \ldots, 10$. The probabilities are small for $x > 10$.

(c) Compute the mean of the distribution, using the formula presented in Section 6.1.

(d) Compare the mean obtained in part (c) with the value $1/p$. Conclude that the mean of a geometric probability distribution is $\mu_X = 1/p$. How many free throws do we expect Shaq to take before we observe a made free throw? $\mu_X = 1.9$

45. Hypergeometric Probability Distribution Recall that, in sampling without replacement from a finite population, the trials technically are not independent. For example, suppose that a population has size 20 and that 8 of the people are female. The probability that the first person selected in the sample is female will be 8/20. If the person is not replaced, the probability that the second person is female will not be the same as with the first. So the requirements for a binomial experiment are violated. For large populations, this violation is so minor that it is overlooked. In cases where the trials are not independent, the random variable X has a **hypergeometric probability distribution**. The hypergeometric probability distribution is a distribution for the random variable X, the number of individuals in a sample of size n that have a particular attribute (such as female). The hypergeometric probability distribution function is

$$P(X = x) = \frac{(_{Np}C_x)(_{N(1-p)}C_{n-x})}{_NC_n}$$

where N is the size of the population, p is the proportion of the population with a certain attribute, x is the number of individuals from the population selected in the sample who have the attribute, and n is the number selected to be in the sample (so that $n-x$ is the number selected who do not have the attribute).

According to Nielsen Media Services, 75% of households have cable television. In a small town of $N = 500$ households, a random sample of $n = 20$ households is obtained.

(a) What is the probability exactly 15 of the households have cable? 0.2065
(b) What is the probability between 15 and 17 of the households have cable? 0.5314
(c) Verify the sample is less than 5% of the size of the population and use the binomial probability distribution to find approximate probabilities for parts (a) and (b). Compare the results. (a) 0.2023 (b) 0.5259

46. Negative Binomial Probability Distribution The **negative binomial probability distribution** can be used to compute the probability of the random variable X, the number of trials necessary to observe r successes of a binomial experiment. The probability distribution function is given by

$$P(X = x) = (_{x-1}C_{r-1})p^r(1 - p)^{x-r} \qquad x = r, r + 1, r + 2, \ldots$$

Consider a roulette wheel. Remember, a roulette wheel has 2 green slots, 18 red slots, and 18 black slots.

(a) What is the probability that it will take $x = 1$ trial before observing $r = 1$ green? 0.0526
(b) What is the probability that it will take $x = 20$ trials before observing $r = 2$ greens? 0.0199
(c) What is the probability that it will take $x = 30$ trials before observing $r = 3$ greens? 0.0137
(d) The expected number of trials before observing r successes is r/p. What is the expected number of trials before observing 3 greens? 57

Technology Step-by-Step
Computing Binomial Probabilities Via Technology

TI-83 Plus   **Computing $P(X = x)$**
Step 1: Press 2nd VARS to access the probability distribution menu.
Step 2: Highlight 0: `binompdf(` and hit ENTER.
Step 3: With `binompdf(` on the HOME screen, type the number of trials n, the probability of success, p, and the number of successes, x. For example, with $n = 10$, $p = 0.2$, and $x = 4$, type

```
binompdf(10, 0.2, 4)
```

Then hit ENTER.

Computing $P(X \le x)$
Step 1: Press 2nd VARS to access the probability-distribution menu.
Step 2: Highlight A: `binomcdf(` and hit ENTER.
Step 3: With `binomcdf(` on the HOME screen, type the number of trials n, the probability of success, p, and the number of successes, x. For example, with $n = 10$, $p = 0.2$, and $x = 4$, type

```
binomcdf(10, 0.2, 4)
```

Then hit ENTER.

MINITAB   **Computing** $P(X = x)$

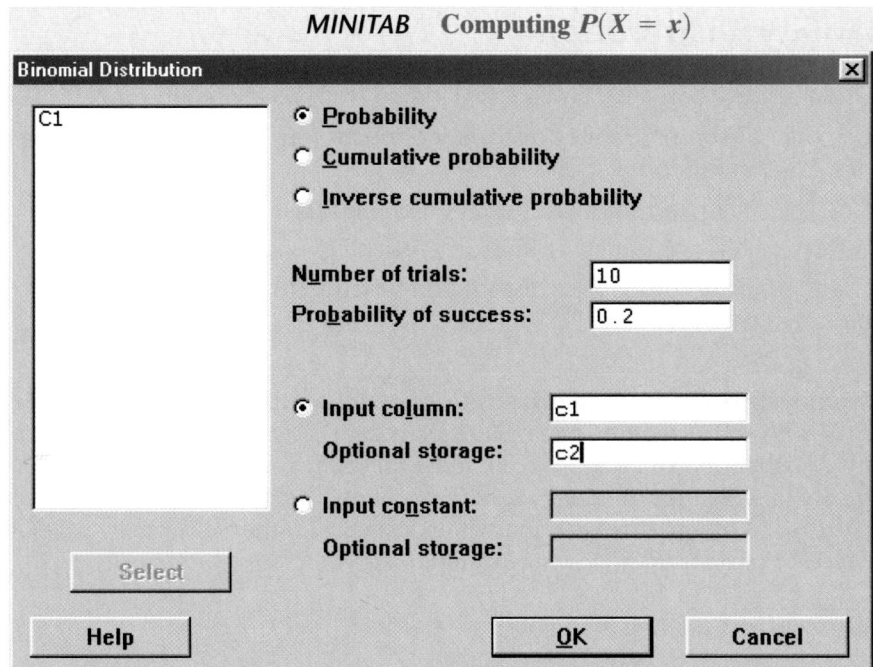

Step 1: Enter the possible values of the random variable x in C1. For example, with $n = 10$, $p = 0.2$, enter $0, 1, 2, \ldots, 10$ into C1.

Step 2: Select the **CALC** menu, highlight **Probability Distributions,** then highlight **Binomial** . . . .

Step 3: Fill in the window as shown to the left. Click OK.

Computing $P(X \leq x)$

Follow the same steps as those for computing $P(X = x)$. In the window that comes up after selecting Binomial Distribution, select Cumulative probability instead of Probability.

Excel   **Computing** $P(X = x)$

Step 1: Enter the possible values of the random variable x in column A. For example, with $n = 10$, $p = 0.2$, enter $0, 1, 2, \ldots, 10$ into A.

Step 2: With the cursor in cell B1, select the *fx* icon. Highlight Statistical in the Function category window. Highlight BINOMDIST in the Function name window.

Step 3: Fill in the window as follows:

┌─ BINOMDIST ──┐
│   **Number_s** `A1`   = 0   │
│   **Trials** `10`   = 10   │
│ **Probability_s** `0.2`   = 0.2   │
│ **Cumulative** `False`   = FALSE   │
│   │
│   = 0.107374182   │
│ Returns the individual term binomial distribution probability. │
│   │
│   **Cumulative** is a logical value: for the cumulative distribution function, use TRUE; for │
│   the probability mass function, use FALSE.   │
│   [?]   Formula result = 0.107374182   [OK] [Cancel] │
└──┘

Click OK.

Step 4: Copy the contents in cell B1 to the remaining cells.

Computing $P(X \leq x)$

Follow the same steps as those presented for computing $P(X = x)$. In the BINOMDIST window, type "TRUE" in the cumulative cell.

6.3   The Poisson Probability Distribution

Objectives   Understand when a probability experiment follows a Poisson process

Note to Instructor
This section is optional and
may be omitted without loss
of continuity.

 Use the Poisson probability distribution function to compute probabilities of a Poisson random variable

 Find the mean and standard deviation of a Poisson random variable

④ Perform inference using the Poisson probability distribution function

⑤ Use the Poisson probability distribution function to approximate binomial probabilities

①   We now introduce another discrete probability distribution, the *Poisson Probability Distribution*, named after Siméon Denis Poisson. This probability distribution can be used to compute theoretical probabilities of experiments in which the random variable X counts the number of occurrences (successes) of a particular event within a specified interval (usually time or space). Consider the following example.

▶ EXAMPLE 1   **Illustrating a Poisson Process**

Historically, a McDonald's manager knows that cars arrive at the drive-through at the constant rate of two cars per minute between the hours of 12:00 noon and 1:00 P.M. The random variable X, the number of cars that arrive between 12:20 and 12:40, follows a Poisson process.   ◀◀

We now present the criteria for a random variable to follow a *Poisson process*.

Definition   A random variable X, the number of successes in a fixed interval, follows a **Poisson process** provided the following conditions are met:

1. The probability of two or more successes in any sufficiently small subinterval* is 0.
2. The probability of success is the same for any two intervals of equal length.
3. The number of successes in any interval is independent of the number of successes in any other interval provided the intervals are not overlapping.

In the McDonald's example, if we divide the time interval into a sufficiently small length (say, 1 second), it is impossible for more than one car to arrive. This would satisfy Part 1 of the definition. Part 2 of the definition is satisfied because the cars arrive at the constant rate of 2 cars per minute over the 1-hour interval. Part 3 is satisfied because the number of cars that arrive in any 1-minute interval (say, between 12:23 P.M. and 12:24 P.M.) is independent of the number of cars that arrive in any other 1-minute interval (say, between 12:35 P.M. and 12:36 P.M.).

   If the random variable X follows a Poisson process, then we can use the following probability law to compute theoretical Poisson probabilities.

---

*For example, the fixed interval might be any time between 0 and 5 minutes. A subinterval could be any time between 1 and 2 minutes.

Theorem

Poisson Probability Distribution Function

If X is the number of successes in an interval of fixed length t, then the probability formula for X is

$$P(X = x) = \frac{(\lambda t)^x}{x!} e^{-\lambda t} \quad x = 0, 1, 2, 3, \ldots \quad (1)$$

where λ (the Greek letter lambda) represents the average number of occurrences of the event in some interval of length 1.

In Your Own Words

Poisson probabilities are used to determine the probability of the number of successes in a fixed interval of time or space.

In order to clarify the roles of λ and t, let's revisit Example 1. In the McDonald's situation, $\lambda = 2$ cars per minute, while $t = 20$ minutes (the amount of time between 12:20 P.M. and 12:40 P.M.).

NW *Now Work Problem 1.*

▶ **EXAMPLE 2**   **Computing Probabilities of a Poisson Process**

Problem: Historically, a McDonald's manager knows that cars arrive at the drive-through at the rate of 2 cars per minute between the hours of 12 noon and 1:00 P.M. She needs to determine and interpret the probability of the following events:

(a) exactly 6 cars arrive between 12 noon and 12:05 P.M.
(b) less than 6 cars arrive between 12 noon and 12:05 P.M.
(c) at least 6 cars arrive between 12 noon and 12:05 P.M.

Approach: The manager first needs a method that can be used to determine the probabilities. The cars arrive at a constant rate of 2 per minute over the time interval between 12:00 noon and 1:00 P.M. We know from Example 1 that the random variable X follows a Poisson process where $x = 0, 1, 2, \ldots$. The Poisson probability distribution function requires a value for λ and t. We are given that cars arrive at a rate of 2 per minute, so $\lambda = 2$. The interval of time we are interested in is 5 minutes, so $t = 5$.

Solution: We use the Poisson probability distribution function (1) to compute the probabilities.

(a) The probability that exactly six cars arrive between 12 noon and 12:05 P.M. is

$$P(X = 6) = \frac{[2(5)]^6}{6!} e^{-2(5)} = \frac{1,000,000}{720}(0.0000454) \approx 0.0631$$

Interpretation: About 6 out of every 100 days, exactly 6 cars will arrive between 12:00 noon and 12:05 P.M.

(b) The probability that fewer than 6 cars arrive between 12:00 noon and 12:05 P.M. is

$$P(X < 6) = P(X \le 5) = P(X = 0) + P(X = 1) + P(X = 2) + P(X = 3) + P(X = 4) + P(X = 5)$$

$$= \frac{[2(5)]^0}{0!} e^{-2(5)} + \frac{[2(5)]^1}{1!} e^{-2(5)} + \frac{[2(5)]^2}{2!} e^{-2(5)} + \frac{[2(5)]^3}{3!} e^{-2(5)} + \frac{[2(5)]^4}{4!} e^{-2(5)} + \frac{[2(5)]^5}{5!} e^{-2(5)}$$

$$= 0.00005 + 0.00045 + 0.00227 + 0.00757 + 0.01892 + 0.03783 = 0.0671$$

Interpretation: About 7 out of every 100 days, fewer than 6 cars will arrive between 12:00 noon and 12:05 P.M.

(c) The probability that at least 6 cars arrive between 12 noon and 12:05 P.M. is the complement of the probability that fewer than 6 cars arrive between 12 noon and 12:05 P.M. that is,

$$P(X \geq 6) = 1 - P(X < 6) = 1 - P(X \leq 5) = 1 - 0.0671 = 0.9329$$

Interpretation: About 93 out of every 100 days, at least six cars will arrive between 12:00 noon and 12:05 P.M. ◀◀

NW *Now Work Problem 9.*

Figure 11 shows the probability histogram for the random variable X in Example 2. We could use the histogram to approximate the probability that exactly 6 cars arrive to be 0.06 by looking at the height of the bar at $X = 6$.

Figure 11
Probability Histogram for a Random Variable X that Follows a Poisson Process with $\lambda = 2$ and $t = 5$.

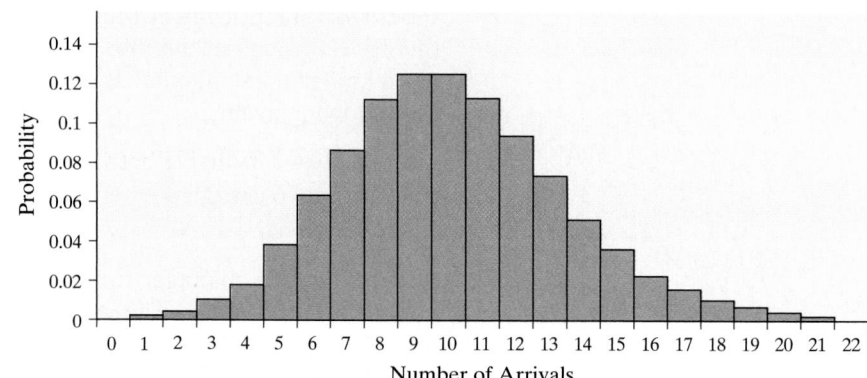

 **Caution**

"At least" probabilities must be computed using the complement rule for Poisson probabilities.

It is important to mention that "at least" probabilities for a Poisson process must be found using the complement. This is because the random variable X in a Poisson process can be any integer greater than or equal to 0.

Perhaps you found it tedious to compute the five probabilities in Example 2(b). The Poisson probability distribution function has an interesting property that simplifies the computation of probabilities. Compute the ratio of the probability of two consecutive Poisson random variables:

$$\frac{P(X = k)}{P(X = k - 1)} = \frac{\dfrac{(\lambda t)^k}{k!}e^{-\lambda t}}{\dfrac{(\lambda t)^{k-1}}{(k-1)!}e^{-\lambda t}} = \frac{(\lambda t)^k}{k!} \cdot \frac{(k-1)!}{(\lambda t)^{k-1}} = \frac{(\lambda t)^k}{(\lambda t)^{k-1}} \cdot \frac{(k-1)!}{k(k-1)!} = \frac{\lambda t}{k}$$

Therefore, $P(X = k) = \dfrac{\lambda t}{k} \cdot P(X = k - 1)$. In order to compute $P(X = 1)$ multiply $P(X = 0)$ by $\dfrac{\lambda t}{1}$, to compute $P(X = 2)$ multiply $P(X = 1)$ by $\dfrac{\lambda t}{2}$, and so on. Consider the results of Example 2(b). We had $P(X = 0) = 0.00004539992976.$* Hence,

*Keep as many decimal places as possible to avoid round-off error.

$$P(X = 1) = (0.00004539992976) \cdot \frac{2(5)}{1} = 0.0004539992976,$$

$$P(X = 2) = (0.0004539992976) \cdot \frac{2(5)}{2} = 0.0022699965,$$

and so on.

③ The Mean and Standard Deviation of a Poisson Random Variable

If cars arrive at McDonald's at the rate of 2 per minute between 12:00 noon and 1:00 P.M., how many cars would you expect to arrive between the hours of 12:00 noon and 12:05 P.M.? Considering that 2 cars arrive every minute (on average) and we are observing the arrival of cars for 5 minutes, it might seem reasonable that we expect $2(5) = 10$ cars to arrive. Since the expected value of a random variable is the mean of the random variable, it seems reasonable that $\mu_X = \lambda t$ for interval t. We demonstrate this is the case in the following example.

▶ **EXAMPLE 3**   **The Mean and Standard Deviation of a Poisson Random Variable**

Problem: We wish to determine the mean and standard deviation of a Poisson random variable with $\lambda = 2$ and $t = 5$.

Approach: Because a Poisson random variable is a discrete random variable, we can use the methods of Section 6.1 to find μ_X and σ_X. From Section 6.1, we know that

$$\mu_X = \sum x \cdot P(X = x) \quad \text{and} \quad \sigma_X = \sqrt{\sigma_X^2} = \sqrt{\sum (x - \mu_X)^2 \cdot P(X = x)}$$

So if we construct the Poisson probability distribution with $\lambda = 2$ and $t = 5$, we can find μ_X and σ_X.

Solution: We obtain the probability distribution in Table 13 with the help of Minitab. We stop evaluating probabilities after $x = 26$ because they are extremely small.

The third column represents $x \cdot P(X = x)$. If we sum the values in this column, we obtain the mean, μ_X. We have

$$\mu_X = \sum x \cdot P(X = x) = 9.999823$$

Substituting into the formula for the variance yields

$$\sigma_X^2 = \sum (x - \mu_X)^2 \cdot P(X = x) = 9.998022$$

so that

$$\sigma_X = \sqrt{9.998022} \approx 3.162$$

On the basis of these results, we might conjecture that $\mu_X = \lambda t$ and $\sigma_X = \sqrt{\lambda t}$ for a Poisson random variable X.   ◀◀

Historical Note

Siméon Denis Poisson was born on June 21, 1781, in Pithiviers, France. He was educated by his father, who wanted him to become a doctor. However, one of his first patients died within a few hours of Poisson's treatment, so Poisson decided never to practice medicine again. After this mishap, Poisson enrolled in the Polytechnic school. While there, he drew the attention of Lagrange, Legendre and Laplace. In 1837, Poisson published In *Recherches sur la probabilité des jugements*, where he first presented the Poisson probability distribution.

	TABLE 13		
x	$P(X = x)$	$x \cdot P(X = x)$	$(x - \mu_X)^2 \cdot P(X = x)$
0	0.0000453999	0	$(0 - 9.999823)^2 \cdot 0.0000453999 = 0.00454$
1	0.000453999	0.000454	$(1 - 9.999823)^2 \cdot (0.00045399) = 0.036772$
2	0.002269996	0.004540	0.145273
3	0.007566655	0.022700	0.370747
4	0.018916637	0.075667	0.680959
5	0.037833275	0.189166	0.945765
6	0.063055458	0.378333	1.008798
7	0.090079226	0.630555	0.810617
8	0.112599032	0.900792	0.450316
9	0.125110036	1.125990	0.125066
10	0.125110036	1.251100	0.000000
11	0.113736396	1.251100	0.113777
12	0.09478033	1.137364	0.379188
13	0.072907946	0.947803	0.656249
14	0.052077104	0.729079	0.833307
15	0.03471807	0.520771	0.868013
16	0.021698794	0.347181	0.781203
17	0.012763996	0.216988	0.625467
18	0.007091109	0.127640	0.453851
19	0.003732163	0.070911	0.302317
20	0.001866081	0.037322	0.186615
21	0.00088861	0.018661	0.107525
22	0.000403914	0.008886	0.058165
23	0.000175615	0.004039	0.02968
24	0.0000731728	0.001756	0.014342
25	0.0000292691	0.000732	0.006586
26	0.0000112573	0.000293	0.002882

$$\sum x \cdot P(X = x) = 9.999823 \qquad \sum (x - \mu_X)^2 \cdot P(X = x) = 9.998022$$

Theorem **Mean and Standard Deviation of a Poisson Random Variable**

A random variable X that follows a Poisson process with parameter λ has mean and standard deviation given by the formulas

$$\mu_X = \lambda t \quad \text{and} \quad \sigma_X = \sqrt{\lambda t} = \sqrt{\mu_X}$$

where t is the length of the interval.

Because $\mu_X = \lambda t$, we restate the Poisson probability distribution function in terms of its mean.

Theorem

Poisson Probability Distribution Function

If X is the number of successes in an interval of fixed length and X follows a Poisson process with mean μ, then the probability distribution function for X is

$$P(X = x) = \frac{\mu^x}{x!}e^{-\mu} \quad x = 0, 1, 2, 3 \ldots.$$

Figure 12 shows the probability histogram of a Poisson distribution for $\mu = 1, 3, 7$, and 15. Notice that as μ becomes larger, the distribution becomes more symmetric.

Figure 12

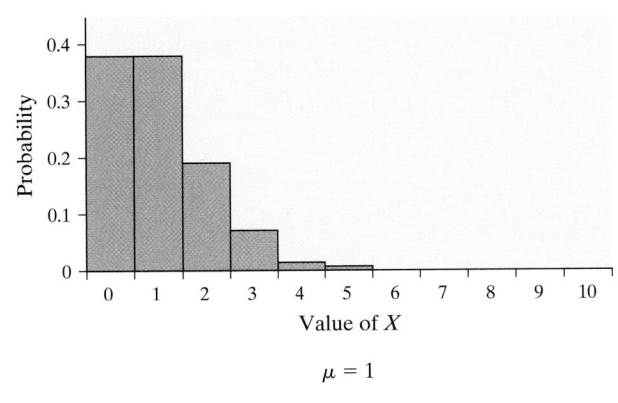

$\mu = 1$

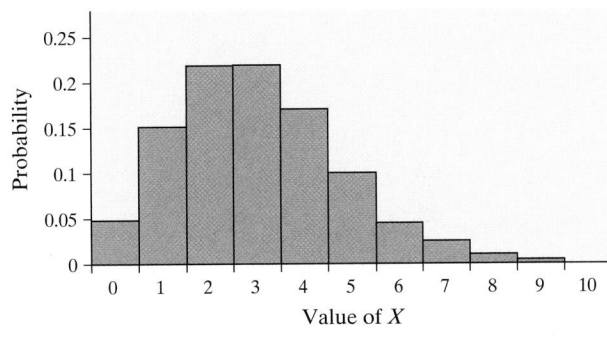

$\mu = 3$

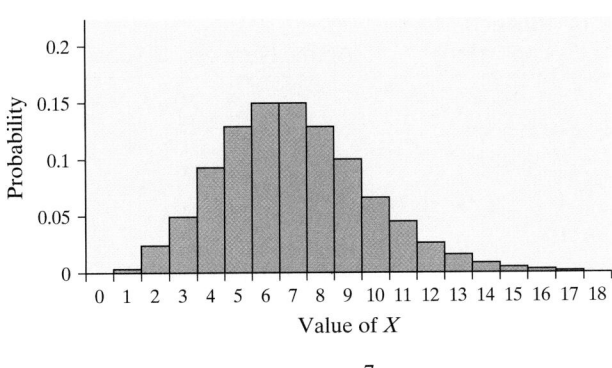

$\mu = 7$

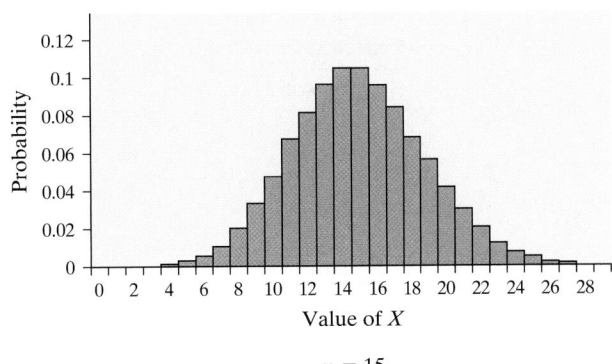

$\mu = 15$

④ Inference Using the Poisson Probability Distribution

Remember, both the binomial probability distribution function and the Poisson probability distribution function provide theoretical probabilities, which give rise to expected results of an experiment. Comparing expected results of an experiment to the empirical results is at the very core of statistical inference. If the two are significantly different, we might conclude that the theoretical probabilities do not accurately describe the outcomes of the experiment.

▶ **EXAMPLE 4**   Do the Beetles Follow a Poisson Distribution?

Problem: A biologist performs an experiment in which 2000 Asian beetles are allowed to roam in an enclosed area of 1000 square feet. The area is divided into 200 subsections of 5 square feet each. After 30 days, the biologist

TABLE 14	
k (number of beetles)	Frequency
4	3
5	7
6	14
7	18
8	19
9	30
10	30
11	21
12	20
13	15
14	8
15	6
16	4
17	2
18	2
19	1
	$\sum f = 200$

and her assistants enter the roaming area and count the number of beetles in each subsection. The frequency of the random variable X, the number of beetles in each subsection, is provided in Table 14. For example, in two of the subsections, 4 beetles were located; in six of the subsections, 5 beetles were located, and so on. The biologist wishes to know if the beetles are distributed according to the Poisson probability law (this would be an indication that the beetles evenly spread out in the enclosed area, rather than migrating together to one specific location within the enclosed area).

Approach: If the location of the beetles follows a Poisson distribution, then we would expect the beetles to be evenly distributed throughout the enclosed area. Therefore, we expect $\mu_X = 10$ beetles per subsection (2000 beetles/200 subsections). We will compare the observed proportion of beetles per subsection to the proportions predicted by the theoretical model.

Solution: We use the expected value of $\mu_X = 10$ to compute the theoretical probabilities, using Poisson probability distribution for $x = 0, 1, 2, 3, \ldots$ as shown in the first two columns of Table 15. For example, the probability a subsection contains $X = 4$ beetles is

$$P(X = 4) = \frac{10^4}{4!}e^{-10} \approx 0.018917$$

TABLE 15			
k	$P(X = k)$ Predicted Proportion	Expected Number of Subsections = $200 \cdot$ (predicted proportion)	Actual Number of Subsections
0	0.000045	200(0.000045) = 0.009	0
1	0.000454	200(0.000454) = 0.0908	0
2	0.00227	200(0.00227) = 0.454	0
3	0.007567	1.5134	0
4	0.018917	3.7834	3
5	0.037833	7.5666	7
6	0.063055	12.611	14
7	0.090079	18.0158	18
8	0.112599	22.5198	19
9	0.125110	25.022	30
10	0.125110	25.022	30
11	0.113736	22.7472	21
12	0.094780	18.956	20
13	0.072908	14.5816	15
14	0.052077	10.4154	8
15	0.034718	6.9436	6
16	0.021699	4.3398	4
17	0.012764	2.5528	2
18	0.007091	1.4182	2
19	0.003732	0.7464	1
20	0.001866	0.3732	0
21	0.000889	0.1778	0
22	0.000404	0.0808	0

In comparing the predicted frequencies (column 3) with the actual frequencies (column 4), we see the two columns are pretty close.

Interpretation: The beetles appear to be distributed according to the Poisson probability law. Because the Poisson probability law assumes that the beetles are distributed independently, the researcher might conclude from this study that beetles make decisions about where to migrate independently of other beetles.   ◄◄

NW *Now Work Problem 15.*

In Chapter 11, we will introduce a formal procedure for determining whether the expected number of beetles is "close enough" to the actual number of beetles to say that the Poisson probability law is a good model.

⑤ ## Using the Poisson Probability Distribution to Approximate a Binomial Probability Distribution

The Poisson probability distribution and binomial probability distribution are closely related to each other. In fact, the Poisson probability formula was originally used to approximate binomial probabilities.

Theorem

> The Poisson probability distribution function can be used to approximate binomial probabilities provided the number of trials $n \geq 100$ and $np \leq 10$. In other words, the number of independent trials of the binomial experiment should be large and the probability of success should be small.

► **EXAMPLE 5**   **Using the Poisson Distribution to Approximate a Binomial Probability**

Problem: According to the Information Please Almanac, 6% of the human population is blood type O-negative. O-negative is unique blood because it can be donated to people of any blood type. Suppose there is a car accident at a busy intersection and a victim is in need of an immediate blood transfusion. There are 110 bystanders at the accident. What is the probability that at least one of the bystanders is O-negative in order to give the victim an immediate transfusion?

Approach: This is a binomial experiment with $n = 110$ independent trials of an experiment. The probability of success is $p = 0.06$. Because $n = 110 \geq 100$ and $np = 110(0.06) = 6.6 \leq 10$, we can use the Poisson probability distribution function to compute this probability.

Solution: The expected number of people with blood type O-negative among the 110 is $\mu_X = np = 110(0.06) = 6.6$. To use the Poisson probability distribution function to compute $P(X \geq 1)$, we need to use the complement:

$$P(X \geq 1) = 1 - P(X < 1) = 1 - P(X = 0) = 1 - \frac{6.6^0}{0!}e^{-6.6} = 0.9986$$

It is almost a certainty that somebody at the accident scene will have blood type O-negative.   ◄◄

It is interesting to compare the results of Example 5 with the results we would obtain had we used the binomial probability formula instead. Using this formula, we get

$$P(X \geq 1) = 1 - P(X = 0) = 1 - {}_{110}C_0(0.06)^0(1 - 0.06)^{110} = 1 - 0.94^{110} = 1 - 0.0011 = 0.9989$$

NW *Now Work Problem 19.*   The results are very close indeed!

6.3 Assess Your Understanding

Concepts and Vocabulary

1. State the conditions required for the random variable X to follow a Poisson process.
2. Explain the role of λ and t in the Poisson probability formula.

3. When can the Poisson probability law be used to approximate the binomial probability law?

Exercises

• Basic Skills

In Problems 1–4, state the values of λ and t for each Poisson process.

1. The hits to a Web site occur at the rate of 10 per minute between 7:00 P.M. and 9:00 P.M. The random variable X is the number of hits to the Web site between 7:30 P.M. and 7:35 P.M. $\lambda = 10, t = 5$

2. The phone calls to a computer software help desk occur at the rate of 5 per minute between 3:00 P.M. and 4:00 P.M. The random variable X is the number of phone calls to the help desk between 3:10 P.M. and 3:20 P.M. $\lambda = 5, t = 10$

3. The flaws in a piece of timber occur at the rate of 0.07 per linear foot. The random variable X is the number of flaws in the next 20 linear feet of timber. $\lambda = 0.07, t = 20$

4. The potholes on a major highway in the city of Chicago occur at the rate of 3.4 per mile. The random variable X is the number of potholes in 10 miles of randomly selected highway. $\lambda = 3.4, t = 10$

In Problems 5 and 6, the random variable X follows a Poisson process with the given mean.

5. Assuming $\mu = 5$, compute
   (a) $P(X = 6)$ 0.1462
   (b) $P(X < 6)$ 0.6160
   (c) $P(X \geq 6)$ 0.3840
   (d) $P(2 \leq X \leq 4)$ 0.4001

6. Assuming $\mu = 7$, compute
   (a) $P(X = 10)$ 0.0710
   (b) $P(X < 10)$ 0.8305
   (c) $P(X \geq 10)$ 0.1695
   (d) $P(7 \leq X \leq 9)$ 0.3808

In Problems 7 and 8, the random variable X follows a Poisson process with the given value of λ and t.

7. Assuming $\lambda = 0.07$ and $t = 10$, compute
   (a) $P(X = 4)$ 0.0050
   (b) $P(X < 4)$ 0.9942
   (c) $P(X \geq 4)$ 0.0058
   (d) $P(4 \leq X \leq 6)$ 0.0057
   (e) μ_X and σ_X 0.7, $\sqrt{0.7}$

8. Assuming $\lambda = 0.02$ and $t = 50$, compute
   (a) $P(X = 2)$ 0.1839
   (b) $P(X < 2)$ 0.7358
   (c) $P(X \geq 2)$ 0.2642
   (d) $P(1 \leq X \leq 3)$ 0.6131
   (e) μ_X and σ_X 1,1

• Applying the Concepts

9. **Hits to a Web Site** The number of hits to a Web site follows a Poisson process; hits occur at the rate of 1.4 per minute between 7:00 P.M. and 9:00 P.M. Compute the probability that the number of hits to the Web site between 7:30 P.M. and 7:35 P.M. is
   (a) exactly seven. Interpret the result. 0.1490
   (b) less than seven. Interpret the result. 0.4497
   (c) at least seven. Interpret the result. 0.5503

10. **Calls to the Help Desk** The phone calls to a computer software help desk occur at the rate of 2.1 per minute between 3:00 P.M. and 4:00 P.M. Compute the probability that the number of calls to the help desk between 3:10 P.M. and 3:15 P.M. is

   (a) exactly eight. Interpret the result. 0.1009
   (b) less than eight. Interpret the result. 0.1785
   (c) at least eight. Interpret the result. 0.8215

11. **Insect Fragments** The Food and Drug Administration sets a Food Defect Action Level (FDAL) for the various foreign substances that inevitably end up in the food we eat and liquids we drink. For example, the FDAL level for insect filth in peanut butter is 0.3 insect fragments (larvae, eggs, body parts, and so on) per gram. Suppose that a 5-gram sample of peanut butter contains 0.3 insect fragments per gram. Compute the probability that the number of insect fragments in a 5-gram sample of peanut butter is

(a) exactly two. Interpret the result. *0.2510*
(b) less than two. Interpret the result. *0.5578*
(c) at least two. Interpret the result. *0.4422*
(d) at least one. Interpret the result. *0.7769*

12. **Potholes** The potholes on a major highway in the city of Chicago occur at the rate of 3.4 per mile. Compute the probability that the number of potholes over 3 miles of randomly selected highway is

(a) exactly seven. Interpret the result. *0.0847*
(b) less than seven. Interpret the result. *0.1180*
(c) at least seven. Interpret the result. *0.8820*

13. **Airline Fatalities** According to the *Statistical Abstract of the United States*, airline fatalities occur at the rate of 0.05 deaths per 100 million miles. Find the probability that, during the next 100 million miles of flight, there will be

(a) exactly zero deaths. Interpret the result. *0.9512*
(b) at least one death. Interpret the result. *0.0488*

14. **Traffic Fatalities** According to the *Statistical Abstract of the United States*, traffic fatalities occur at the rate of 1.6 deaths per 100 million miles. Find the probability that, during the next 100 million vehicle miles, there will be

(a) exactly zero deaths. Interpret the result. *0.2019*
(b) at least one death. Interpret the result. *0.7981*
(c) Compare these results with the results in Problem 13. Given the choice, would you rather fly or drive?

15. **Wendy's Drive-Through** Historically, cars arrive at Wendy's drive-through at a rate of 0.2 cars per minute between the hours of 11:00 P.M. and 1:00 A.M. on Saturday evening. Wendy's begins an advertising blitz that touts its late-night service. After one week of advertising, Wendy's officials count the number of cars, X, arriving at Wendy's drive-through between the hours of 12:00 midnight and 12:30 A.M. at 200 of its restaurants. The results are shown in the following table:

x (number of cars arriving)	Frequency
1	4
2	5
3	13
4	23
5	25
6	28
7	25
8	27
9	21
10	15
11	5
12	3
13	2
14	2
15	0
16	2

(a) Construct a probability distribution for the random variable X, assuming it follows a Poisson process with $\lambda = 0.2$ and $t = 30$. This is the probability distribution of X before the advertising.
(b) Compute the expected number of restaurants that will have 0 arrivals, 1 arrival, and so on.
(c) Compare these results with the number of arrivals after the advertising. Does it appear the advertising was effective? Why?

16. **Quality Control** A builder ordered two hundred 8-foot grade *A* 2-by-4s for a construction job. To qualify as a grade *A* board, each 2-by-4 will have no knots and will average no more than 0.05 imperfections per linear foot. The following table lists the number of imperfections per 2-by-4 in the two hundred ordered:

x (number of imperfections)	Frequency
0	124
1	51
2	20
3	5

(a) Construct a probability distribution for the random variable X, the number of imperfections per 8 feet of board, assuming it follows a Poisson process with $\lambda = 0.05$ and $t = 8$.
(b) Compute the expected number of 2-by-4s that will have 0 imperfections, 1 imperfection, and so on.
(c) Compare these results with the number of actual imperfections. Does it appear the 2-by-4s are of grade *A* quality? Why?

17. **Prussian Army** In 1898, Ladislaus von Bortkiewicz published *The Law of Small Numbers*, in which he demonstrated the power of the Poisson probability law. Before his publication, the law was used exclusively to approximate binomial probabilities. He demonstrated the law's power, using the number of Prussian cavalry soldiers who were kicked to death by their horses. The Prussian army monitored 10 cavalry corps for 20 years and recorded the number X of annual fatalities due to horse kicks for the 200 observations. The following table shows the data:

Number of Deaths, x	Number of Times x Deaths Were Observed
0	109
1	65
2	22
3	3
4	1

Adapted from *An Introduction to Mathematical Statistics* by Larsen, et al. Prentice Hall, 2001

(a) Compute the proportion of years in which there were 0 deaths, 1 death, 2 deaths, 3 deaths, and 4 deaths.

(b) From the data in the table, what was the mean number of deaths per year?

(c) Use the mean number of deaths per year found in part (b) and the Poisson probability law to determine the theoretical proportion of years that 0 deaths should occur. Repeat this for 1, 2, 3, and 4 deaths.

(d) Compare the observed proportions to the theoretical proportions. Do you think the data can be modeled by the Poisson probability law?

18. **Poisson Approximation to a Binomial** In clinical trials and extended studies of a medication whose purpose is to reduce the pain associated with migraine headaches, 2% of the patients in the study experienced weight gain as a side effect. A random sample of 500 users of the medication is obtained.

(a) Verify that the conditions for approximating binomial probabilities via the Poisson probability formula are satisfied.

(b) Compute the probability that exactly 4 users experience weight gain as a side effect by using the Poisson probability formula. 0.0189

(c) Compute the probability that fewer than 4 users experience weight gain as a side effect by using the Poisson probability formula. 0.0103

(d) Compare the approximate results obtained in parts (b) and (c) with the exact results that would be obtained from the binomial probability formula.

19. **Poisson Approximation to a Binomial** In clinical trials of a medication whose purpose is to treat acid reflux and stomach ulcers, 4.7% of the patients in the study experienced headaches as a side effect. A random sample of 200 users of the medication is obtained.

(a) Verify that the conditions for approximating binomial probabilities via the Poisson probability formula are satisfied.

(b) Compute the probability that exactly 5 users experience headaches as a side effect by using the Poisson probability formula. 0.0506

(c) Compute the probability that fewer than 5 users experience headaches as a side effect by using the Poisson probability formula. 0.0429

(d) Compare the approximate results obtained in parts (b) and (c) with the exact results that would be obtained from the binomial probability formula.

20. **Simulation** Data from the National Center for Health Statistics show that, in 1995, spina bifida occurred at the rate of 28 per 100,000 live births. Let the random variable X represent the number of occurrences of spina bifida in a random sample of 100,000 live births.

(a) What is the expected number of children with spina bifida per 100,000 live births in any given year? 28

(b) Using statistical software, such as Minitab, simulate taking 200 random samples of 100,000 live births assuming $\mu = 28$.

(c) Approximate the probability that fewer than 21 births per 100,000 result in spina bifida.

(d) In 1999, 20.83 births per 100,000 resulted in babies born with spina bifida. In light of the results of part (b) and (c), is this an unusual occurrence? What might you conclude?

21. **Simulation** According to the National Center for Health Statistics, the common cold occurs at the rate of 23.8 colds per 100 people during the course of a year in the 18–24-year-old age group. Let the random variable X represent the number of 18–24-year-olds out of a sample of 500 who have had a common cold in the past year.

(a) What is the expected number of colds for every 500 18–24-year-olds? 119

(b) Using statistical software, such as Minitab, simulate taking 100 random samples of size 500 from this population.

(c) Approximate the probability that at least 150 18–24-year-olds in a group of 500 will have experienced a common cold in the past year.

(d) Approximate the probability that fewer than 100 18–24-year-olds in a group of 500 will have experienced the common cold in the past year.

(e) Given the simulation, compute the mean number of 18–24-year-olds out of 500 who have experienced the common cold in the past year.

(f) Given the simulation, compute the standard deviation of the number of 18–24-year-olds out of 500 who have experienced the common cold in the past year.

(g) Compute the 5-number summary of the data. Did the simulation result in any unusual results?

22. **How Long Do I Have to Wait?** The number of hits to a Web site follows a Poisson process and occurs at the rate of 10 hits per minute between 7:00 P.M. and 9:00 P.M. How long should one expect to wait before the probability of at least one hit to the site is 95%? *Hint:* $P(X \geq 1) = 1 - P(X = 0) \approx$ 0.3 minutes

Technology Step-by-Step
Computing Poisson Probabilities Via Technology

TI-83 Plus   **Computing $P(X = x)$**

Step 1: Press 2nd VARS to access the probability distribution menu.

Step 2: Highlight B: `poissonpdf(` and hit ENTER.

Step 3: With `poissonpdf(` on the HOME screen, type the value of μ, followed by the number of successes, x. For example, with $\mu = 10$ and $x = 4$, type

```
poissonpdf(10,4)
```

Then hit ENTER.

Computing $P(X \leq x)$

Instead of selection B: `poissonpdf(`, select C: `poissoncdf(`. Everything else is the same.

MINITAB   **Computing $P(X = x)$**

Step 1: Enter the desired values of the random variable x in C1.

Step 2: Select the **CALC** menu, highlight **Probability Distributions,** then highlight **Poisson** ....

Step 3: Select Probability, enter the mean, enter the input column as C1, and select C2 as the output column. Click OK.

Computing $P(X \leq x)$

Follow the same steps as those followed for computing $P(X = x)$. In the window that comes up after selecting Poisson Distribution, select Cumulative probability instead of Probability.

Excel   **Computing $P(X = x)$**

Step 1: Enter the desired values of the random variable x in column A.

Step 2: With the cursor in cell B1, select the *fx* icon. Highlight Statistical in the Function category window. Highlight POISSON in the Function name window.

Step 3: In the cell labeled X, enter A1. In the cell labeled mean, enter the mean. In the cell labeled cumulative, type FALSE. Click OK.

Computing $P(X \leq x)$

Follow the same steps as those presented for computing $P(X = x)$. In the POISSON window, type "TRUE" in the cumulative cell.

CHAPTER 6 REVIEW

Summary

In this chapter, we discussed discrete probability distributions. A random variable represents the numerical measurement of the outcome from a probability experiment. Discrete random variables have either a finite or a countable number of outcomes. The term "countable" means that the values result from counting. Legitimate probability distributions must satisfy the following two criteria: (1) All probabilities must be between 0 and 1, inclusive, and (2) the sum of all probabilities must equal 1. Discrete probability distributions can be presented in a table, graph, or mathematical formula. The mean and standard deviation of a probability distribution describe the center and spread of the discrete random variable. The mean of a random variable is also called its expected value.

We discussed two discrete probability distributions in particular, the binomial and Poisson. A probability experiment is considered a binomial experiment if there are n independent trials of the experiment with only two outcomes.

The probability of success, p, is the same for each trial of the experiment. Special formulas exist for computing the mean and standard deviation of a binomial random variable.

The other probability distribution we discussed was the Poisson probability distribution. A Poisson process is one in which the following conditions are met: (1) The probability of two or more successes in any sufficiently small subinterval is 0. (2) The probability of success is the same for any two sufficiently short intervals of equal length. (3) Success or failure in any interval is independent of success or failure in any other interval. Special formulas exist for computing the mean and standard deviation of a random variable that follows a Poisson process. For the Poisson distribution, the mean and variance are equal.

The probability distributions presented in this chapter were constructed via classical methods. This means they are based upon what is expected to happen in a large number of trials of the experiment. If empirical evidence does not agree with the theoretical or expected values, we must investigate the reasons for the disagreement.

Formulas

Mean of a Discrete Random Variable

$$\mu_X = \sum x P(X = x)$$

Variance of a Discrete Random Variable

$$\sigma_X^2 = \sum (x - \mu_X)^2 \cdot P(X = x)$$

Expected Value of a Random Variable X

$$E(X) = \sum x P(X = x)$$

Binomial Probability Distribution Function

$$P(X = x) = {}_nC_x\, p^x (1 - p)^{n-x}$$

Mean of a Binomial Random Variable

$$\mu_X = np$$

Standard Deviation of a Binomial Random Variable

$$\sigma_X = \sqrt{np(1 - p)}$$

Poisson Probability Distribution Function

$$P(X = x) = \frac{(\lambda t)^x}{x!} e^{-\lambda t} \qquad x = 0, 1, 2, \ldots$$

Mean and Standard Deviation of a Poisson Random Variable

$$\mu_X = \lambda t \qquad \sigma_x = \sqrt{\lambda t}$$

Vocabulary

Random variable (p. 326)
Discrete random variable (p. 326)
Continuous random variable (p. 326)

Probability distribution (p. 327)
Probability histogram (p. 328)
Expected value (p. 333)

Trial (p. 339)
Binomial experiment (p. 339)
Poisson process (p. 358)

Objectives

Section	You Should Be Able to . . .	Review Exercises
6.1	1 Distinguish between discrete and continuous random variables (p. 326)	1, 2
	2 Construct and identify probability distributions (p. 327)	3, 4, 5(a), 6(a)
	3 Construct probability histograms (p. 328)	5(b), 6(b)
	4 Compute and interpret the mean of a discrete random variable (p. 329)	5(c), 6(c), 15(b), 16(b)
	5 Compute the variance and standard deviation of a discrete random variable (p. 332)	5(d), 6(d), 15(b), 16(b)
	6 Compute and interpret the expected value of a discrete random variable (p. 333)	7, 8
6.2	1 Determine whether a probability experiment is a binomial experiment (p. 339)	9, 10
	2 Compute probabilities of binomial experiments (p. 341)	11(a)–(d); 12(a)–d); 13(a)–(d); 14(a)–(d)
	3 Compute the mean and standard deviation of a binomial random variable (p. 345)	11(e), 12(e), 13(e), 14(e), 15(c), 16(c)
	4 Construct binomial probability histograms (p. 346)	15(d), 16(d)
	5 Use the binomial probability distribution function to perform inference (p. 349)	11(f), (g); 12(f), (g); 13(f), (g); 14(f), (g)
6.3	1 Understand when a probability experiment follows a Poisson process (p. 358)	23
	2 Use the Poisson probability distribution function to compute probabilities of a Poisson random variable (p. 358)	17(a)–(d); 18(a)–(d); 19(b)–(d); 20(b)–(d)
	3 Find the mean and standard deviation of the Poisson random variable (p. 361)	17(e), 18(e)
	4 Perform inference using the Poisson probability distribution function (p. 363)	21
	5 Use the Poisson probability distribution function to approximate binomial probabilities (p. 365)	11(h)

Review Exercises

In Problems 1 and 2, determine whether the random variable is discrete or continuous. In each case, state the possible values of the random variable.

1. (a) The number of inches of snow that falls in Buffalo during the winter season. Continuous; $s \geq 0$
   (b) The number of days snow accumulates in Buffalo during the winter season. Discrete, $x = 0, 1, \ldots, 91$
   (c) The number of golf balls hit into the ocean on the famous 18th hole at Pebble Beach on a randomly selected Sunday. Discrete, $x = 0, 1, 2, \ldots, n$

2. (a) The miles per gallon of gasoline in a 2002 Toyota Sienna. Continuous, $m > 0$
   (b) The number of children a randomly selected family has. Discrete, $x = 0, 1, 2, \ldots$
   (c) The number of goals scored by the Edmonton Oilers in a season. Discrete, $x = 0, 1, 2, \ldots$

In Problems 3 and 4, determine whether the distribution is a probability distribution. If not, state why.

3. No, $\sum P(X = x) \neq 1$

x	$P(X = x)$
0	0.34
1	0.21
2	0.13
3	0.04
4	0.01

4. Yes

x	$P(X = x)$
0	0.40
1	0.31
2	0.23
3	0.04
4	0.02

---

5. **Stanley Cup** The Stanley Cup is a best-of-seven series to determine the champion of the National Hockey League. The following data represent the number of games played, X, in the Stanley Cup before a champion was determined, from 1939 to 2000:

x	Frequency
4	20
5	15
6	17
7	10

Source: Information Please Almanac

   (a) Construct a probability distribution for the random variable X, the number of games in the Stanley Cup.
   (b) Draw a probability histogram.
   (c) Compute and interpret the mean of the random variable X. $\mu_x = 5.3$
   (d) Compute the standard deviation of the random variable X. $\sigma_x = 1.1$

6. **Property Crime** In 1999, 74% of crime was property crime, according to the National Crime Victimization Survey. Suppose that four crimes are randomly selected. Let the random variable X represent the number of property crimes.
   (a) Construct a probability distribution for the random variable X, by constructing a tree diagram.
   (b) Draw a probability histogram.
   (c) Compute and interpret the mean of the random variable X. $\mu_x = 2.96$
   (d) Compute the standard deviation of the random variable X. $\sigma_x = 0.88$

7. **Life Insurance** Suppose a life insurance company sells a $100,000 one-year term life insurance policy to a 35-year-old male for $200. According to the *National Vital Statistics Report*, Vol. 47, No. 28, the probability the male survives the year is 0.99802. Compute and interpret the expected value of this policy to the life insurance company. $2

8. **Roulette** In the game of roulette, a player can place a $5 bet on red and have a 9/19 probability of winning. If the metal ball lands on red, the player wins $5; otherwise, the casino takes the player's $5. What is the expected value of the game? If the player plays 100 times, how much can the player expect to lose? $-0.26; $26

In Problems 9 and 10, determine which of the following probability experiments represents a binomial experiment. If the probability experiment is not a binomial experiment, state why.

9. According to the *Chronicle of Higher Education*, there is a 54% probability that a randomly selected incoming freshman will graduate from college within six years. Suppose 10 incoming male freshmen are randomly selected. After six years, each student is asked whether he or she graduated. Binomial experiment

10. An experiment is conducted in which a single die is cast until a "3" comes up. The number of throws required is recorded. Not binomial

11. **High Cholesterol** According to the National Center for Health Statistics, 8% of 20–34-year-old females have high serum cholesterol.
    (a) In a random sample of 10 females 20–34 years old, find the probability that exactly 0 have high serum cholesterol. Interpret this result. 0.4344
    (b) In a random sample of 10 females 20–34 years old, find the probability that exactly 2 have high serum cholesterol. Interpret this result. 0.1478
    (c) In a random sample of 10 females 20–34 years old, find the probability that at least 2 have high serum cholesterol. Interpret this result. 0.1879
    (d) In a random sample of 10 females 20–34 years old, find the probability that exactly 9 will not have high serum cholesterol. Interpret this result. 0.3777
    (e) In a random sample of 250 females 20–34 years old, what is the expected number with high serum cholesterol? What is the standard deviation? 20; 4.3
    (f) If a random sample of 250 females 20–34 years old resulted in 12 of them having high serum cholesterol, would this be unusual? Why? No
    (g) Suppose a random sample of 10 females 20–34 years old resulted in 4 having high serum cholesterol. Is this result unusual? Why?
    (h) For a random sample of 100 females 20–34 years old, use the Poisson probability formula to approximate the probability that exactly 10 have high serum cholesterol. 0.0993

12. **America Reads** According to a Gallup poll conducted September 10–14, 1999, 56% of Americans 18 years old or older stated they have read at least six books (fiction and nonfiction) within the past year.
    (a) In a random sample of 15 Americans 18 years old or older, find the probability that exactly 10 have read at least six books within the past year. Interpret this result. 0.1502
    (b) In a random sample of 15 Americans 18 years old or older, find the probability that fewer than 5 have read at least six books within the past year. Interpret this result. 0.0211
    (c) In a random sample of 15 Americans 18 years old or older, find the probability that at least 5 have read at least six books within the past year. Interpret this result. 0.9789
    (d) In a random sample of 15 Americans 18 years old or older, find the probability that exactly 12 *have not* read at least six books within the past year. Interpret this result. 0.0042
    (e) In a random sample of 200 Americans 18 years old or older, what is the expected number who have read at least six books within the past year? What is the standard deviation? 112, 7.02
    (f) If a random sample of 200 Americans 18 years old or older resulted in 102 of them having read at least six books within the past year, would this be unusual? Why? No

(g) If a random sample of 15 Americans resulted in 11 having read at least six books in the past year, would this be unusual? Why? No, $P(X \geq 11) = 0.1367$

13. **Nielsen Ratings** Nielsen Media Research determines ratings for television programs by placing meters on 5000 televisions throughout the United States. A recent Monday Night Football broadcast resulted in a rating of 7.4, which means 7.4% of households were "tuned in" to the game.
    (a) In a random sample of 20 households, find the probability that exactly 6 are tuned in to Monday Night Football. 0.0022
    (b) In a random sample of 20 households, find the probability that fewer than 4 were tuned in to Monday Night Football. 0.9441
    (c) In a random sample of 20 households, find the probability that at least 2 were tuned in to Monday Night Football. 0.4417
    (d) In a random sample of 20 households, find the probability that exactly 17 were *not* tuned in to Monday Night Football. 0.1250
    (e) In a random sample of 500 households, what is the expected number who were tuned in to Monday Night Football? What is the standard deviation? 37, 5.85
    (f) If a random sample of 500 households results in 50 tuned in to Monday Night Football, would this be unusual? Why? Yes
    (g) If a random sample of 30 households resulted in 1 watching Monday Night Football, would this be unusual? Why? No, $P(X \leq 1) = 0.3384$

14. **Quit Smoking** The drug Zyban is meant to create the urge to quit smoking. In clinical trials, 35% of the study's participants experienced insomnia when taking 300 mg of Zyban per day. [*Source:* GlaxoSmithKline]
    (a) In a random sample of 25 users of Zyban, find the probability that exactly 8 will experience insomnia.
    (b) In a random sample of 25 users of Zyban, find the probability that fewer than 4 will experience insomnia.
    (c) In a random sample of 25 users of Zyban, find the probability that at least 5 will experience insomnia.
    (d) In a random sample of 25 users of Zyban, find the probability that exactly 20 will not experience insomnia. 0.0506
    (e) In a random sample of 1000 users of Zyban, what is the expected number who experience insomnia? What is the standard deviation? 350; 15.08
    (f) If a random sample of 1000 users of Zyban results in 330 who experience insomnia, would this be unusual? Why? No
    (g) If a random sample of 25 users of Zyban results in 2 who experience insomnia, would this be unusual? Why? Yes, $P(X \leq 2) = 0.0021$

(14a) 0.1607 (14b) 0.0097 (14c) 0.9680

(11g) Yes, $P(X \geq 4) = 0.0058$

In Problems 15–16, (a) construct a binomial probability distribution with the given parameters, (b) compute the mean and standard deviation of the distribution by using the methods of Section 6.1, (c) compute the mean and standard deviation by using the methods of this section, (d) draw the probability histogram, comment on its shape, and label the mean on the histogram.

15. $n = 5, p = 0.2$

16. $n = 8, p = 0.75$

In Problems 17 and 18, the random variable X follows a Poisson process with the given value of λ and t.

17. Assuming that $\lambda = 0.05$ and $t = 8$, find
   (a) $P(X = 3)$ 0.0072
   (b) $P(X < 3)$ 0.9921
   (c) $P(X \geq 3)$ 0.0079
   (d) $P(3 \leq X \leq 5)$ 0.0079
   (e) What are μ_X and σ_X? 0.4, $\sqrt{0.4}$

18. Assuming that $\lambda = 0.15$ and $t = 10$, find
   (a) $P(X = 2)$ 0.2510
   (b) $P(X < 2)$ 0.5578
   (c) $P(X \geq 2)$ 0.4422
   (d) $P(1 \leq X \leq 3)$ 0.7112
   (e) What are μ_X and σ_X? 1.5, $\sqrt{1.5}$

19. Color Blindness According to the National Center for Health Statistics, the number of Americans aged 18–44 who have color blindness follows a Poisson process and occurs at the rate of 1.0 per 100 people. Suppose a random sample of 500 18–44-year-old Americans is obtained.
   (a) Compute the probability that there are exactly three individuals with color blindness. Interpret the result.
   (b) Compute the probability that there are fewer than three individuals with color blindness. Interpret the result. 0.1247
   (c) Compute the probability that there are at least three individuals with color blindness. Interpret the result.
   (d) Find the mean and standard deviation number of color-blind individuals for a random sample of 500 18–44-year-old Americans. $\mu_x = 5, \sigma_x = \sqrt{5}$

20. Arrivals at the Bank Historically, the number of cars that arrive at a bank's drive-through window between 3:00 P.M. and 6:00 P.M. on Friday follows a Poisson process at the rate of 0.41 cars every minute. Compute the probability that the number of cars that arrive at the bank between 4:00 P.M. and 4:10 P.M. is
   (a) exactly four cars. Interpret this result. 0.1951
   (b) fewer than four cars. Interpret this result. 0.4142
   (c) at least four cars. Interpret this result. 0.5858

21. Earthquakes A great earthquake is an earthquake that measures 8.0 or higher on the Richter Scale. From 1971 to 2001 (31 years), there have been 24 great earthquakes worldwide. The following data represent the observed number of years in which there were 0, 1, 2, 3, and 4 great earthquakes:

Number of Great Earthquakes in the Year, x	Number of Years in Which x Great Earthquakes Were Observed
0	17
1	9
2	4
3	1
4	1

Source: http://neic.usgs.gov/

   (a) Compute the proportion of years in which there were 0, 1, 2, 3, and 4 great earthquakes.
   (b) What is the mean number of great earthquakes per year?
   (c) Use the mean number of great earthquakes per year found in part (b) and the Poisson probability law to determine the theoretical proportion of years that 0 great earthquakes should occur. Repeat this for 1, 2, 3, and 4 great earthquakes.
   (d) Compare the observed proportions to the theoretical proportions. Do you think the data can be modeled by the Poisson probability law?

22. State the condition required to use the Empirical Rule in order to check for unusual observations in a binomial experiment.

23. State the conditions required for a Poisson process.

24. State the conditions required in order to use the Poisson probability formula to approximate binomial probabilities.

25. In sampling without replacement, the assumption of independence required for a binomial experiment is violated. Under what circumstances can we sample without replacement and still use the binomial probability formula to approximate probabilities?

(19a) 0.1404 (19c) 0.8753

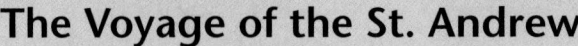

Throughout the picturesque valleys of mid-18th-century Germany echoed the song of the neuländer (newlander). Their song enticed journeymen who struggled to feed their families with the dream and promise of colonial America. Traveling throughout the German countryside, the typical neuländer sought to sign up several families from a village for immigration to a particular colony. By registering a group of neighbors, rather than isolated families, the agent increased the likelihood that his signees would not stray to the equally enticing proposals of a competitor. Additionally, by signing large groups, the neuländer fattened his purse, to the tune of one to two florins a head.

Generally, the Germans who chose to undertake the hardship of a trans-Atlantic voyage were poor, yet the cost of such a voyage was high. Records from a 1753 voyage indicate that the cost of an adult fare (one freight) from Rotterdam to Boston was 7.5 pistole. Children between the ages of four and thirteen were assessed at half the adult rate (one-half freight). Children under four were not charged. To get a sense of the expense involved, it has been estimated that the adult fare, 7.5 pistoles, is equivalent to approximately $2000 (1998 U.S.)! For a large family, the cost could easily be well beyond their means. Even though many immigrants did not have the necessary funds to purchase passage, they were determined to make the crossing. Years of indentured servitude for themselves and other family members was often the currency of last resort.

As a historian studying the influence of these German immigrants on colonial America, Hans Langenscheidt is interested in describing various demographic characteristics of these people. Unfortunately, accurate records are rare. In his research, he has discovered a partially reconstructed 1752 passenger list for a ship, the St. Andrew. This list contains the names of the head of families, a list of family members traveling with them, their parish of origin, and the number of freights each family purchased. Unfortunately, some of the data are missing for some of the families. Langenscheidt believes that the demographic parameters of this passenger list are likely to be similar to those of the other numerous voyages taken from Germany to America during the mid-eighteenth century. Assuming that he is correct, he believes that it is appropriate to create a discrete probability distribution for a number of demographic variables for this population of German immigrants. His distributions are presented below.

Probability Distribution of the Number of Families per Parish of German Immigrants on Board the 1752 *Voyage of the St. Andrew*	
Number of Families per Parish	**Probability**
1	0.706
2	0.176
3	0.000
4	0.059
5	0.000
6	0.059

Probability Distribution of the Known Number of Freights Purchased by the German Families on Board the 1752 *Voyage of the St. Andrew*	
Number of Freights	Probability
1.0	0.075
1.5	0.025
2.0	0.425
2.5	0.150
3.0	0.125
3.5	0.100
4.0	0.050
5.0	0.025
6.0	0.025

Probability Distribution of the Known Number of People in a Family for the Germans on Board the 1752 *Voyage of the St. Andrew*	
Number in Family	Probability
1	0.322
2	0.186
3	0.136
4	0.102
5	0.051
6	0.136
7	0.034
8	0.017
9	0.016

Data Source: Wilford W. Whitaker and Gary T. Horlacher, *Broad Bay Pioneers* (Rockport, Maine: Picton Press, 1998), 63–68. Distributions created from the partially reconstructed 1752 passenger list of the St. Andrew presented by Whitaker and Horlacher.

1. Using the information above, describe, through histograms and numerical summaries such as the mean and standard deviation, each of the probability distributions.

2. Does it appear that, on average, the neuländers were successful in signing more than one family from a parish? Does it seem likely that most of the families knew one another prior to undertaking the voyage? Explain your answers for both of the questions.

3. Using the mean number of freights purchased per family, estimate the average cost of the crossing for a family in pistoles and in 1998 U.S. dollars.

4. Is it appropriate to estimate the average cost of the voyage from the mean family size? Why or why not?

5. Langenscheidt came across a fragment of another ship's passenger list. This fragment listed information for six families. Of these six, five families purchased more than four freights. Using the information contained in the appropriate probability distribution for the St. Andrew, calculate the probability that at least five of six German immigrant families would have purchased more than four freights. Does it seem likely that these families came from a population similar to that of the Germans on board the St. Andrew? Explain.

6. Summarize your findings in a report. Discuss any assumptions made throughout this analysis. What are the consequences to your calculations and conclusions if your assumptions are subsequently determined to be invalid?

Should We Convict?

In 1964, a woman who was shopping in Los Angeles had her purse stolen by a young, blonde female who was wearing a ponytail. The blonde female got into a yellow car that was driven by a black male who had a mustache and a beard. The police located a blonde female named Janet Collins who wore her hair in a ponytail and had a friend who was a black male who had a mustache and beard and also drove a yellow car. The police arrested the two subjects.

Because there were no eyewitnesses and no real evidence, the prosecution used probability to make its case against the defendants. The following probabilities were presented by the prosecution for the known characteristics of the thieves:

Characteristic	Probability
Yellow car	1/10
Man with a mustache	$\frac{1}{4}$
Woman with a ponytail	1/10
Woman with blonde hair	1/3
Black man with beard	1/10
Interracial couple in car	1/1000

(a) Assuming that the characteristics listed above are independent of each other, what is the probability that a randomly selected couple would have all these characteristics? That is, what is P ("yellow car" and "man with a mustache" and ... and "interracial couple in a car")?

(b) Would you convict the defendants based on this probability? Why?

(c) Now let n represent the number of couples in the Los Angeles area that could have committed the crime. Let p represent the probability a randomly selected couple would have all six characteristics listed above. Let the random variable X represent the number of couples that have all the characteristics listed in the table. Assuming that the random variable X follows the binomial probability function, we have

$$P(X = x) = {}_nC_x \cdot p^x(1 - p)^{n-x}, \qquad x = 0, 1, 2, \ldots, n.$$

Assuming that there were $n = 1,000,000$ couples in the Los Angeles area, what is the probability that more than one of them have the characteristics listed in the table? Does this result cause you to change your mind regarding the defendants' guilt?

(d) Now, let's look at this case from a different point of view. We will compute the probability that more than one couple has the characteristics described, given that at least one couple has the characteristics:

$$P(X > 1 | X \geq 1) = \frac{P(X > 1 \text{ and } X \geq 1)}{P(X \geq 1)} \qquad \text{Conditional Probability Rule}$$

$$= \frac{P(X > 1)}{P(X \geq 1)}$$

Compute this probability, assuming $n = 1,000,000$. Compute this probability again, but this time assume that $n = 2,000,000$. Do you think that the couple should be convicted "beyond all reasonable doubt"? Why?

The Customer Relations Department at Consumers Union (CU) receives thousands of letters and e-mails from customers each month. Some people write in asking how well a product performed during CU's testing, some people write in sharing their own experiences with their household products, and the remaining people write in for an array of other reasons. In order to be able to respond to each letter and e-mail that is received, Customer Relations recently upgraded its customer contact database. Although much of the process has been automated, it still requires employees to manually draft the responses. Given the current size of the department, each Customer Relations representative is required to draft approximately 300 responses each month.

As part of a quality assurance program, the Customer Relations manager would like to develop a plan that allows him to evaluate the performance of his employees. From past experience, he knows that the probability a new employee will write an initial draft of a response that contains errors is approximately 10%. The manager would like to know how many of the 300 responses he should sample in order to have a cost effective quality assurance program.

(a) Let X be a discrete random variable that represents the number of the $n = 300$ draft responses that contain errors. Describe the probability distribution for X. Be sure to include the name of the probability distribution, possible values for the random variable X, and values of the parameters.

(b) To be effective, suppose the manager would like to have a 95% probability of finding at least one draft document that contains an error. Assuming that the probability a draft document will have errors is known to be 10%, determine the appropriate sample size to satisfy the manager's requirements. *Hint*: We are required to find the number of draft documents that must be sampled so that the probability of finding at least one document containing an error is 95%. In other words, we need to determine n by solving: $P(x \geq 1) = 0.95$.

(c) Suppose the error rate is really 20%. What sample size will the manager need to review to have a 95% probability of finding one or more documents containing an error?

(d) Now, let Y be a discrete random variable that represents the number of errors discovered in a single draft document. (It is possible for a single draft to contain more than one error.) The manager determined that errors occurred at the rate of 0.3 errors per document. Describe the probability distribution for Y. Be sure to include the name of the probability distribution, possible values for the random variable Y, and values of the parameters.

(e) What is the probability that a document contains no errors? One error? At least two errors?

Note to Readers: In many cases, our test protocol and analytical methods are more complicated than described in these examples. The data and discussions have been modified to make the material more appropriate for the audience.

Putting It All Together

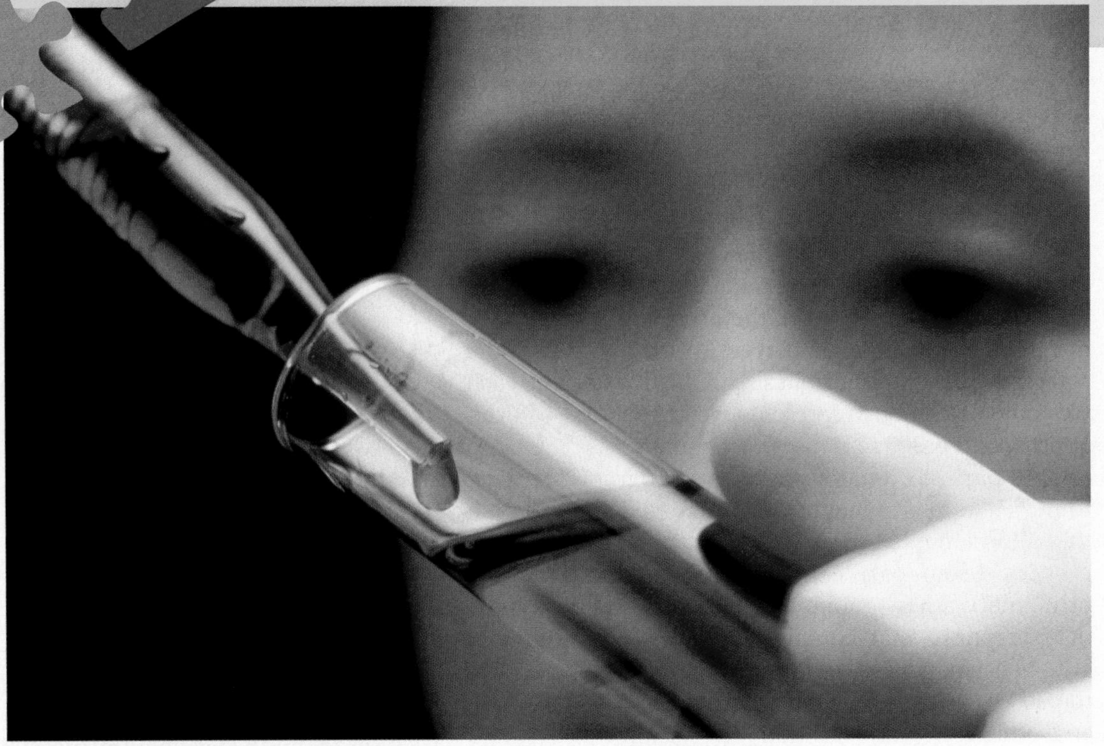

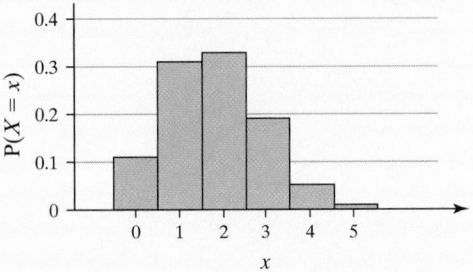

In Chapter 6, we introduced discrete probability distributions and, in particular, the binomial and Poisson probability distributions. We computed probabilities for these discrete distributions using their probability

Binomial Probability Histogram;
n = 5, p = 0.35

distribution function. However, we could also determine the probability of any discrete random variable from its probability histogram. For example, the figure shows the probability histogram for the binomial random variable X with $n = 5$ and $p = 0.35$.

From the probability histogram, we can see $P(X = 1) \approx 0.31$. Notice that the width of each rectangle in the probability histogram is one. Since the area of a rectangle equals height times width, we can think of $P(X = 1)$ as the area of the rectangle corresponding to $X = 1$. Understanding probability in this fashion makes the transition from computing discrete probabilities to continuous probabilities much easier.

In this chapter, we discuss two continuous distributions, *the uniform distribution* and *the normal distribution*. The greater part of the discussion will center on the normal distribution.

The Normal Probability Distribution

Outline

 For additional study help, go to
www.prenhall.com/sullivanstats

Materials include

- Self-Graded Quizzes
- "Preparing for This Section" Quizzes
- STATLETs
- PowerPoint Downloads
- Step-by-Step Technology Guide
- Graphing Calculator Help

7.1 Properties of the Normal Distribution

Preparing for This Section   Before getting started, review the following:

✓ Continuous variable (Section 1.1, p. 7)

✓ Requirements for a discrete probability distribution (Section 6.1, p. 327)

✓ z-score (Section 3.4, pp. 158–159)

✓ The Empirical Rule (Section 3.2, pp. 139–140)

Objectives Understand the uniform probability distribution
 Graph a normal density curve
 State the properties of the normal curve
 Understand the role of area in the normal density function
 Understand the relation between a normal random variable and a standard normal random variable with regard to area

 The Uniform Distribution

We illustrate a uniform distribution using an example.

▶ **EXAMPLE 1**   **Illustrating the Uniform Distribution**

Imagine that a friend of yours is always late. Let the random variable X represent the time from when you are supposed to meet your friend until he shows up. Further suppose that your friend could be on time ($x = 0$) or up to 30 minutes late ($x = 30$) with all 1-minute intervals of times between $x = 0$ and $x = 30$ equally likely. That is to say, your friend is just as likely to be from 3 to 4 minutes late as he is to be 25 to 26 minutes late. The random variable X can be any value in the interval from 0 to 30, that is, $0 \leq X \leq 30$. Because any two intervals of equal length between 0 and 30, inclusive, are equally likely, the random variable X is said to follow a **uniform probability distribution**.   ◀◀

Note to Instructor
To help students understand the relation between area and probability, we begin with a discussion of the Uniform Distribution. The graph of the Uniform Distribution is in the shape of a rectangle. Tell students that we will be utilizing the concept of area in this section and that the area of a rectangle is length times width.

When we compute probabilities for discrete random variables, we usually substitute the value of the random variable into a probability distribution function. Things aren't as easy for continuous random variables. Because there are an infinite number of possible outcomes for continuous random variables, the probability of observing a particular value of a continuous random variable is zero. For example, the probability that your friend is exactly 12.9438823 minutes late is zero. This result is based upon the fact that classical probability is found by dividing the number of ways an event can occur by the total number of possibilities. There is one way to observe 12.9438823 and there are an infinite number of possible values between 0 and 30, so we get a probability that is zero. To resolve this problem, we compute probabilities of continuous random variables over an interval of values. For example, we might compute the probability that your friend is between 10 and 15 minutes late. To find probabilities for continuous random variables, we do not use probability distribution functions, but instead we use *probability density functions*.

Definition

Probability Density Function

A probability density function is an equation used to compute probabilities of continuous random variables that must satisfy the following two properties.

1. The area under the graph of the equation over all possible values of the random variable must equal one.

2. The graph of the equation must be greater than or equal to zero for all possible values of the random variable. That is, the graph of the equation must lie on or above the horizontal axis for all possible values of the random variable.

In Your Own Words

To find probabilities for continuous random variables, we do not use probability distribution functions (as we did for discrete random variables). Instead, we use probability density functions.

Property 1 is similar to the property for discrete probability distributions that stated that the sum of the probabilities must add up to one. Property 2 is similar to the property that stated that all probabilities must be greater than or equal to zero.

Figure 1 illustrates the properties for your late friend example. Since all possible values of the random variable between 0 and 30 are equally likely, the graph of the probability density function for uniform random variables is a rectangle. Because the area under the graph of the equation must equal 1 and the random variable is any number between 0 and 30 inclusive, the width of the rectangle is 30. Therefore, the height of the rectangle must be 1/30.*

Figure 1
Uniform Density Function

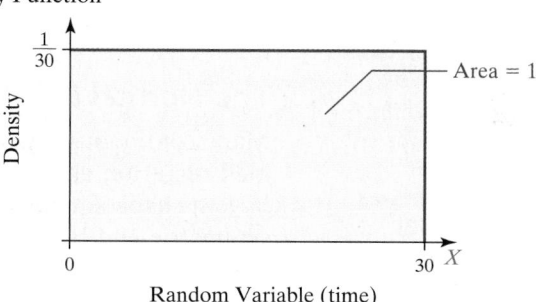

Random Variable (time)

A pressing question remains: How do we use density functions to find probabilities of continuous random variables?

The area under the graph of a density function over some interval represents the probability of observing a value of the random variable in that interval.

The following example illustrates this statement.

---

*Area of rectangle = height × width. Rather than using "Probability" as a label on the vertical axis, we use "Density" because the height of the graph does not represent a probability.

▶ **EXAMPLE 2** Area as a Probability

Problem: Refer to the situation presented in Example 1. What is the probability that your friend will be between 10 and 20 minutes late the next time you meet him?

Approach: Figure 1 presented the graph of the density function. We need to find the area under the graph between 10 and 20 minutes.

Solution: Figure 2 presents the graph of the density function with the area we wish to find shaded in green.

Figure 2

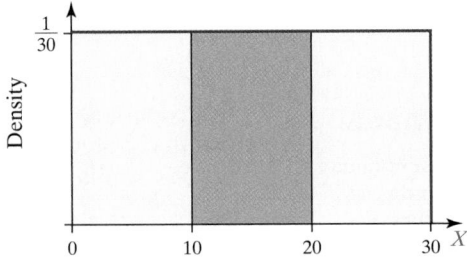

The width of the rectangle is 10 and its height is 1/30; therefore, the area between 10 and 20 is 10(1/30) = 1/3. The probability that your friend is between 10 and 20 minutes late is 1/3.   ◀◀

NW *Now Work Problem 1.*

We introduced the uniform density function so that we associate probability with area. We are now better prepared to discuss the most popular continuous distribution, the normal distribution.

② The Normal Distribution

Many continuous random variables such as IQ scores, birth weights of babies, or serum cholesterol levels have relative frequency histograms that have a shape similar to Figure 3. Relative frequency histograms that are symmetric and bell-shaped (i.e., similar to Figure 3) are said to have the shape of a **normal curve**.

Figure 3

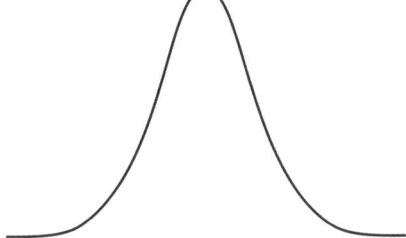

Historical Note

The normal probability distribution is often referred to as the Gaussian distribution in honor of Carl Gauss, the individual thought to have discovered the idea. However, it was actually Abraham de Moivre who first wrote down the equation of the normal distribution. Gauss was born in Brunswick, Germany, on April 30, 1777. Gauss' mathematical prowess was evident early in his life. At age eight he was able to instantly add the first 100 integers. In 1792, Gauss entered the Brunswick Collegium Carolinum and remained there for three years. In 1795, Gauss entered the University of Göttingen. In 1799, Gauss earned his doctorate. The subject of his dissertation was the Fundamental Theorem of Algebra. In 1809, Gauss published a book on the mathematics of planetary orbits. In this book, he further developed the theory of least-squares regression by analyzing the errors. The analysis of these errors led to the discovery that errors follow a normal distribution. Gauss was considered to be "glacially cold" as a person and had troubled relationships with his family. Gauss died February 23, 1855.

Definition | A continuous random variable is **normally distributed** or has a **normal probability distribution** if its relative frequency histogram of the random variable has the shape of a normal curve (bell-shaped and symmetric).

Historical Note

It was Karl Pearson who coined the phrase "normal" curve. He did not do this to imply that a distribution that is not normal is "abnormal," but rather to avoid giving the name of the distribution a proper name, such as Gaussian (as in Carl Friedrich Gauss).

Figure 4 shows a normal curve* demonstrating the role μ and σ play in drawing the curve. The mean, μ, determines the high point of the distribution. The points at $x = \mu - \sigma$ and $x = \mu + \sigma$ are the *inflection points* on the normal curve. The **inflection points** are the points on the curve where the curvature of the graph changes. To the left of $x = \mu - \sigma$ and to the right of $x = \mu + \sigma$, the curve is drawn upward $\left(\ \smile\ \text{or}\ \smile\ \right)$. In between $x = \mu - \sigma$ and $x = \mu + \sigma$, the curve is drawn downward $\left(\ \frown\ \right)$.†

Figure 4

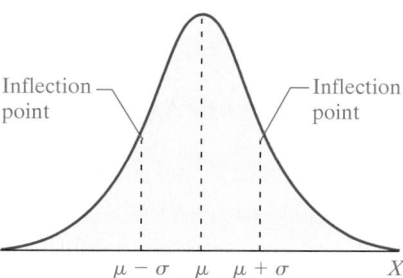

Inflection point   Inflection point

$\mu - \sigma$ μ $\mu + \sigma$ X

Figure 5 shows how changes in μ and σ change the position or shape of a normal curve. In Figure 5(a), two normal density curves are drawn with the location of the inflection points labeled. One density curve has $\mu = 0, \sigma = 1$, and the other has $\mu = 3, \sigma = 1$. We can see that increasing the mean from 0 to 3 caused the graph to shift three units to the right. In Figure 5(b), two normal density curves are drawn, again with the inflection points labeled. One density curve has $\mu = 0, \sigma = 1$ and the other has $\mu = 0, \sigma = 2$. We can see that increasing the standard deviation from 1 to 2 causes the graph to become flatter and more spread out.

Figure 5

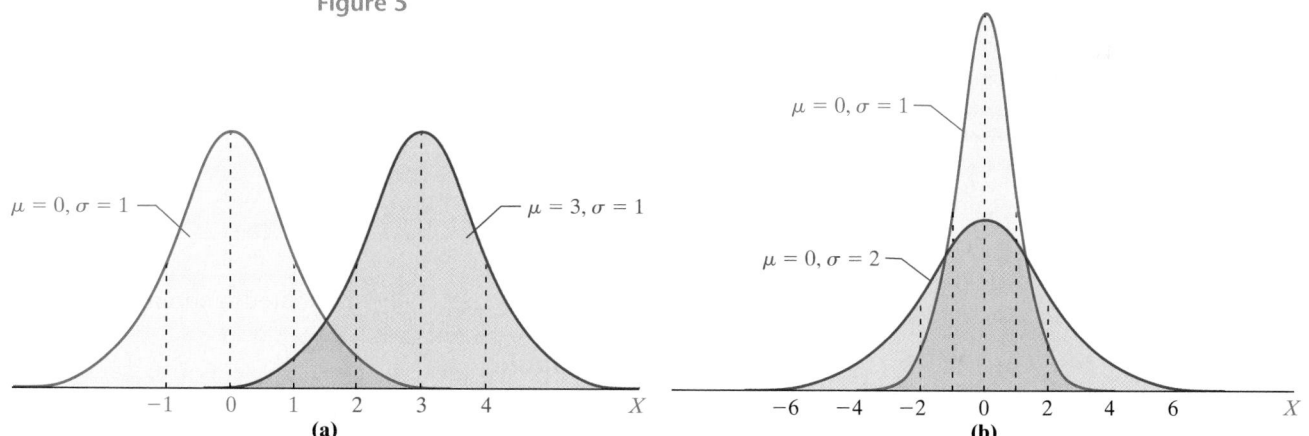

$\mu = 0, \sigma = 1$ $\mu = 3, \sigma = 1$

-1 0 1 2 3 4 X
(a)

$\mu = 0, \sigma = 1$

$\mu = 0, \sigma = 2$

-6 -4 -2 0 2 4 6 X
(b)

NW *Now Work Problem 11.*

*The equation that is used to determine the probability of continuous random variable is called a **probability density function** (or **pdf**). The **normal probability density function** is given by

$$y = \frac{1}{\sigma\sqrt{2\pi}}e^{-(x-\mu)^2/2\sigma^2}$$ where μ is the mean and σ is the standard deviation of the normal random variable. The values μ and σ are the parameters of the distribution.
†The vertical scale on the graph is purposely omitted. The vertical scale, while important, will not play a role in any of the computations utilizing this curve. We are interested simply in the basic shape of the density curve.

3

The normal probability density function satisfies all the requirements that are necessary in order to have a legitimate probability distribution. We list the properties of the normal density curve below.

Properties of the Normal Density Curve

1. It is symmetric about its mean, μ.
2. The highest point occurs at $x = \mu$.
3. It has inflection points at $\mu - \sigma$ and $\mu + \sigma$.
4. The area under the curve is one.
5. The area under the curve to the right of μ equals the area under the curve to the left of μ equals $1/2$.
6. As x increases without bound (gets larger and larger), the graph approaches, but never equals, zero. As x decreases without bound (gets larger and larger in the negative direction) the graph approaches, but never equals, zero.
7. The Empirical Rule: Approximately 68% of the area under the normal curve is between $x = \mu - \sigma$ and $x = \mu + \sigma$. Approximately 95% of the area under the normal curve is between $x = \mu - 2\sigma$ and $x = \mu + 2\sigma$. Approximately 99.7% of the area under the normal curve is between $x = \mu - 3\sigma$ and $x = \mu + 3\sigma$. See Figure 6.

Historical Note

Abraham de Moivre was born in France on May 26, 1667. He is known as a great contributor to the areas of probability and trigonometry. De Moivre studied for five years at the Protestant academy at Sedan. From 1682 to 1684, he studied logic at Saumur. In 1685, he moved to England. De Moivre was elected a fellow of the Royal Society in 1697. He was part of the commission to settle the dispute between Newton and Leibniz regarding the discoverer of calculus. He published *The Doctrine of Chance* in 1718. In 1733, he developed the equation that describes the normal curve. Unfortunately, de Moivre had a difficult time being accepted in English society (perhaps due to his accent) and was able to make only a meager living tutoring mathematics. An interesting piece of information regarding de Moivre; he correctly predicted the day of his death, Nov. 27, 1754.

Figure 6

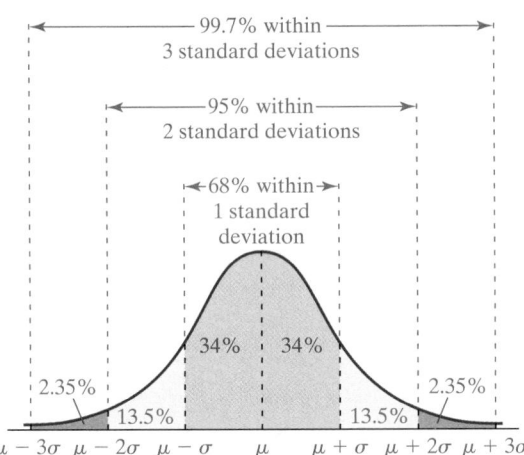

Normal Distribution

4   Let's look at an example of a normally distributed random variable.

▶ **EXAMPLE 3**   **A Normal Random Variable**

Problem: The relative frequency distribution given in Table 1 represents the heights of a pediatrician's 200 three-year-old female patients. The raw data indicate that the mean height of the patients is $\mu = 38.72$ inches with standard deviation $\sigma = 3.17$ inches.

(a) Draw a relative frequency histogram of the data. Comment on the shape of the distribution.

(b) Draw a normal curve with $\mu = 38.72$ inches and $\sigma = 3.17$ on the relative frequency histogram. Compare the area of the rectangle for heights between 40 and 40.9 inches to the area under the normal curve for heights between 40 and 40.9 inches.

TABLE 1	
Height (inches)	**Relative Frequency**
29.0–29.9	0.005
30.0–30.9	0.005
31.0–31.9	0.005
32.0–32.9	0.025
33.0–33.9	0.02
34.0–34.9	0.055
35.0–35.9	0.075
36.0–36.9	0.09
37.0–37.9	0.115
38.0–38.9	0.15
39.0–39.9	0.12
40.0–40.9	0.11
41.0–41.9	0.07
42.0–42.9	0.06
43.0–43.9	0.035
44.0–44.9	0.025
45.0–45.9	0.025
46.0–46.9	0.005
47.0–47.9	0.005

Caution

It is rare for a continuous random variable to be exactly normal. Therefore, we usually say that a random variable is approximately normal if its histogram is bell-shaped and symmetric.

Approach:

(a) Draw the relative frequency histogram. If the histogram looks like Figure 4 on page 383, we will say that height is approximately normal. We say that height is "approximately normal," rather than "normal" because it is very rare to have a perfectly normal random variable.

(b) Draw the normal curve on the histogram with the high point at μ and the inflection points at $\mu - \sigma$ and $\mu + \sigma$. Shade the rectangle corresponding to heights between 40 and 40.9 inches and compare the area of the shaded region to that under the normal curve between 40 and 40.9.

Solution:

(a) Figure 7 shows the relative frequency distribution.

Figure 7

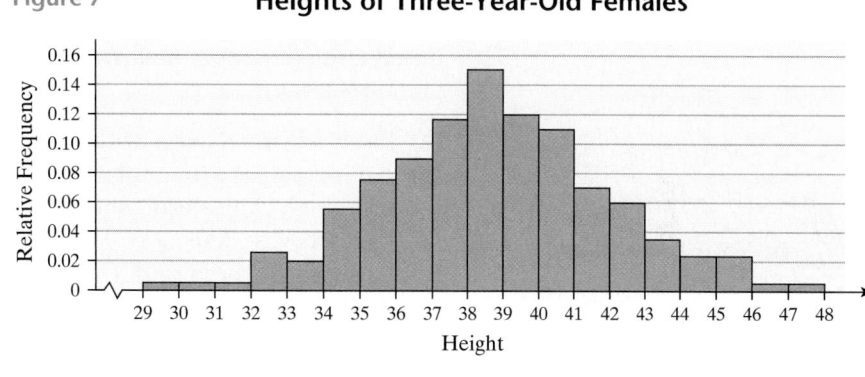

Heights of Three-Year-Old Females

The relative frequency histogram is symmetric and bell-shaped. It would appear that the random variable height of three-year-old females is approximately normally distributed.

(b) The normal curve with $\mu = 38.72$ and $\sigma = 3.17$ is superimposed on the relative frequency histogram in Figure 8. The figure demonstrates that the normal curve describes the heights of three-year-old girls fairly well. We conclude that the heights of three-year-old girls are approximately normal with $\mu = 38.72$ and $\sigma = 3.17$. Figure 8 also shows the rectangle corresponding to heights between 40 and 40.9 inches. The area of this rectangle represents the proportion of three-year-old females between 40 and 40.9 inches. Notice that the area of this shaded region is very close to the area under the normal curve for the same region. It is because of this that we can use the area under the normal curve to approximate the proportion of three-year-old females with heights between 40 and 40.9 inches!

Figure 8
Heights of Three-Year-Old Female Patients

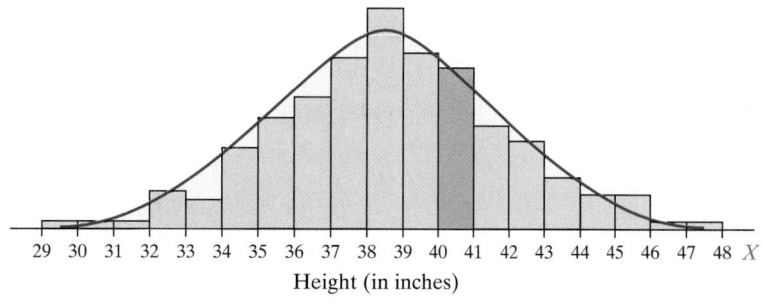

We now summarize the role area plays in the normal curve.

The Area under a Normal Curve

Suppose a random variable X is normally distributed with mean μ and standard deviation σ. The area under the normal curve for any range of values of the random variable X represents either

- the proportion of the population with the characteristics described by the range, or

- the probability that a randomly selected individual from the population will have the characteristics described by the range.

▶ **EXAMPLE 4** **Interpreting the Area under a Normal Curve**

Problem: The serum total cholesterol for males 20–29 years old is known to be approximately normally distributed with mean $\mu = 180$ and $\sigma = 36.2$ based upon data obtained from the National Health and Nutrition Examination Survey.

(a) Draw a normal curve with the parameters labeled.
(b) An individual with a total cholesterol greater than 200 is considered to have high cholesterol. Shade the region under the normal curve to the right of $X = 200$.
(c) Suppose the area under the normal curve to the right of $X = 200$ is 0.2903. (You will learn how to find this area in Section 7.3.) Provide two interpretations of this result.

In Your Own Words

The area under a normal curve is a proportion or probability.

Approach: Draw the normal curve with the mean $\mu = 180$ labeled at the high point and the inflection points at $\mu - \sigma = 180 - 36.2 = 143.8$ and $\mu + \sigma = 180 + 36.2 = 216.2$. We then shade the region under the normal curve to the right of $X = 200$. Two interpretations of this shaded region are (1) the proportion of 20–29-year-old males who have high cholesterol and (2) the probability that a randomly selected 20–29-year-old male has high cholesterol.

Solution:

(a) Figure 9(a) shows the graph of the normal curve.

Figure 9

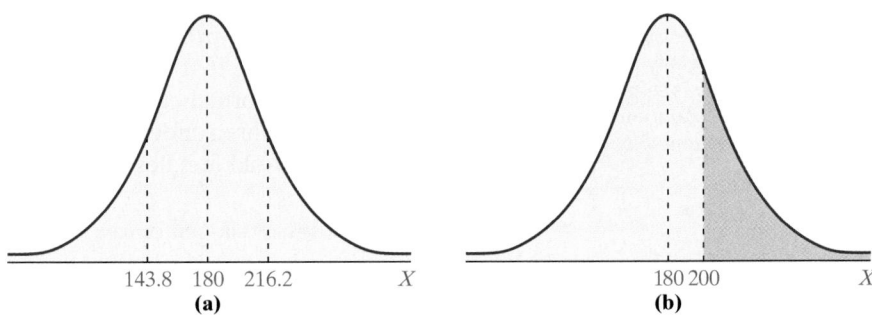

143.8 180 216.2 X
(a)

180 200 X
(b)

(b) Figure 9(b) shows the region under the normal curve to the right of $X = 200$ shaded.

(c) The two interpretations for the area of this shaded region are (1) the proportion of 20–29-year-old males that have high cholesterol is 0.2903 and (2) the probability that a randomly selected 20–29-year-old male has high cholesterol is 0.2903.   ◀◀

NW *Now Work Problems 15 and 19.*

⑤ Standardizing a Normal Random Variable

At this point, we know that a random variable X is normally distributed if its relative frequency histogram has the shape of a normal curve. The distribution of the random variable X is normal with mean μ and standard deviation σ. The area below the normal curve represents the proportion of the population with a given characteristic or the probability that a randomly selected individual from the population will have a given characteristic.

The question now becomes "How do I find the area under the normal curve?" Finding the area under a curve requires techniques introduced in calculus, which are beyond the scope of this text. An alternative would be to use a series of tables to find areas. However, this would result in an infinite number of tables being created for each possible mean and standard deviation! A solution to the problem lies in the Z-score. Recall that the Z-score allows us to transform a random variable X with mean μ and standard deviation σ into a random variable Z with mean 0 and standard deviation 1.

Standardizing a Normal Random Variable

Suppose the random variable X is normally distributed with mean μ and standard deviation σ. Then the random variable

$$Z = \frac{X - \mu}{\sigma}$$

is normally distributed with mean $\mu = 0$ and standard deviation $\sigma = 1$. The random variable Z is said to have the **standard normal distribution**.

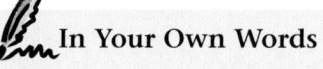
In Your Own Words

To find the area under any normal curve, we must first find the Z-score of the normal variable.

This result is powerful indeed! We need only one table of areas corresponding to the standard normal distribution. If a normal random variable has mean different from 0 or standard deviation different from 1, we simply transform the normal random variable into a standard normal random variable Z and use a table to find the area and, therefore, the probability.

We demonstrate the idea behind standardizing a normal variable in the next example.

▶ **EXAMPLE 5**   **Relation between a Normal Random Variable and a Standard Normal Random Variable**

Problem: The heights of a pediatrician's 200 three-year-old female patients are known to follow a normal distribution with mean $\mu = 38.72$ and $\sigma = 3.17$. We wish to demonstrate that the area under the normal curve between 35 and 38 inches is equal to the area under the standard normal curve between the Z-scores of 35 and 38 inches.

Approach:

Step 1: Draw a normal curve and shade the area representing the proportion of three-year-old females between 35 and 38 inches tall.
Step 2: Standardize the random variable $X = 35$ and $X = 38$ using $Z = \frac{X - \mu}{\sigma}$.

Step 3: Draw the standard normal curve with the standardized versions of $X = 35$ and $X = 38$ labeled. Shade the area that represents the proportion of three-year-old females between 35 and 38 inches tall. Comment on the relation between the two shaded regions.

Solution:

Step 1: Figure 10(a) shows the normal curve with mean $\mu = 38.72$ and $\sigma = 3.17$. The region between $X = 35$ and $X = 38$ is shaded.

Step 2: With $\mu = 38.72$ and $\sigma = 3.17$, the standardized version of $X = 35$ is

$$Z = \frac{X - \mu}{\sigma} = \frac{35 - 38.72}{3.17} = -1.17*$$

The standardized version of $X = 38$ is

$$Z = \frac{X - \mu}{\sigma} = \frac{38 - 38.72}{3.17} = -0.23$$

Step 3: Figure 10(b) shows the standard normal curve with the region between $Z = -1.17$ and $Z = -0.23$ shaded.

Figure 10
(a) Normal curve with $\mu = 38.72$ and $\sigma = 3.17$
(b) Standard normal curve

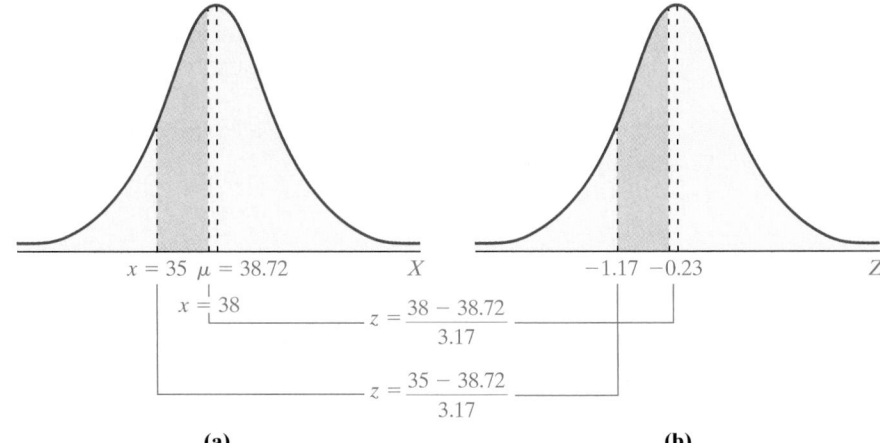

(a)   (b)

The area under the normal curve with $\mu = 38.72$ and $\sigma = 3.17$ bounded to the left by $x = 35$ and bounded to the right by $x = 38$ is equal to the area under the standard normal curve bounded to the left by $z = -1.17$ and bounded to the right by $z = -0.23$. ◀◀

NW *Now Work Problem 21.*

7.1 Assess Your Understanding

Concepts and Vocabulary

1. State the two characteristics of the graph of a probability density function.
2. List the characteristics of a normal density curve.
3. Provide two interpretations of the area under a probability density function.
4. Why do we standardize normal random variables in order to find the area under any normal curve?

5. Discuss the role of μ and σ in constructing the normal density curve.
6. As σ increases, the normal density curve becomes more spread out. Knowing the area under the density curve must be 1, what effect does increasing σ have on the height of the curve?

Exercises

• Skill Building

Problems 1–4 use the information presented in Examples 1 and 2.

1. Find the probability that your friend is between 5 and 10 minutes late. 1/6
2. Find the probability that your friend is between 15 and 25 minutes late. 1/3

3. Find the probability that your friend is at least 20 minutes late. 1/3
4. Find the probability that your friend is no more than 5 minutes late. 1/6

Recall that we round Z-scores to two decimal places.

5. **Uniform Distribution** The random number generator on calculators randomly generates a number between 0 and 1. The random variable X, the number generated, follows a Uniform Probability Distribution.
   (a) Draw the graph of the Uniform Density Function.
   (b) What is the probability of generating a number between 0 and 0.2? 0.2
   (c) What is the probability of generating a number between 0.25 and 0.6? 0.35
   (d) What is the probability of generating a number greater than 0.95? 0.05
   (e) Use your calculator or statistical software to randomly generate 200 numbers between 0 and 1.

What proportion of the numbers are between 0 and 0.2? Compare the result with part (b).

6. **Uniform Distribution** Suppose the reaction time X (in minutes) of a certain chemical process follows a Uniform Probability Distribution with $5 \leq X \leq 10$.
   (a) Draw the graph of the density curve.
   (b) What is the probability that the reaction time is between 6 and 8 minutes? 2/5
   (c) What is the probability that the reaction time is between 5 and 8 minutes? 3/5
   (d) What is the probability that the reaction time is less than 6 minutes? 1/5

In Problems 7–10, determine whether the histogram indicates that the data may be normally distributed.

7. **Birth Weights** The following relative frequency histogram represents the birth weights of babies whose term was 36 weeks:

   Normal

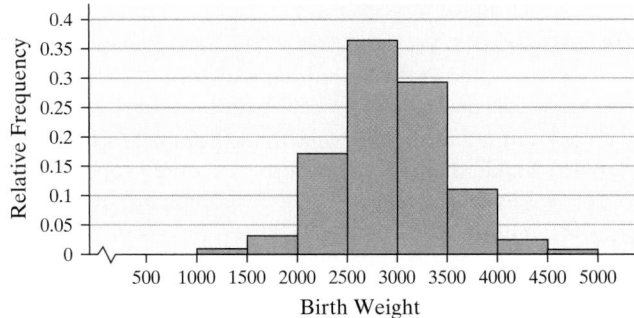

Birth Weights of Babies Whose Term Was 36 Weeks

8. **Waiting in Line** The following relative frequency histogram represents the waiting time in line (in minutes) for the Demon Roller Coaster for 2000 randomly selected people on a Saturday afternoon in the summer:

   Not normal

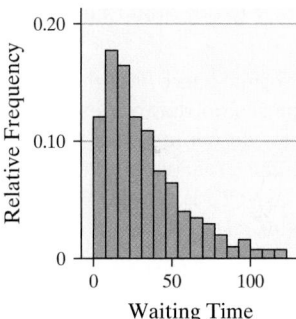

Waiting Time (in minutes) for a Roller Coaster

9. **Length of Phone Calls** The following relative frequency histogram represents the length of phone calls on my wife's cell phone during the month of September:

   Not normal

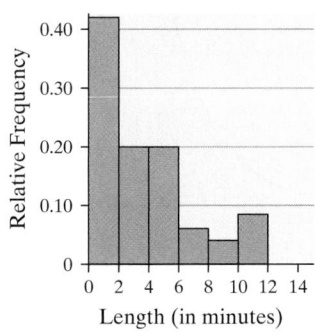

Length of Phone Calls

10. **IQ Scores** The following relative frequency histogram represents the IQ scores of a random sample of seventh grade students:

   Normal

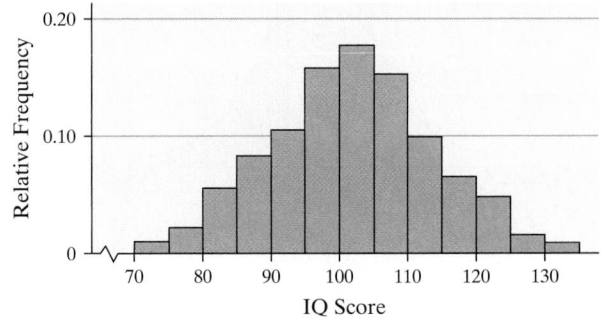

IQ Scores of 7th Grade Students

In Problems 11–14, the graph of a normal curve is given. Use the graph to identify the value of μ and σ.

11. 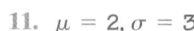 $\mu = 2, \sigma = 3$

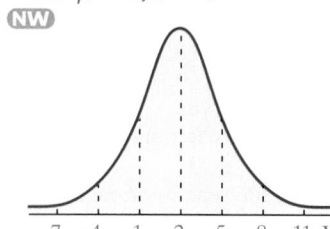

$-7 \quad -4 \quad -1 \quad 2 \quad 5 \quad 8 \quad 11 \ X$

12.  $\mu = 5, \sigma = 2$

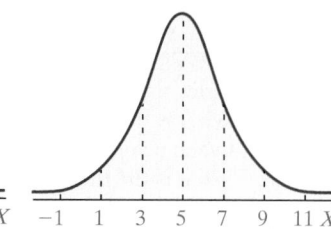

$-1 \quad 1 \quad 3 \quad 5 \quad 7 \quad 9 \quad 11 \ X$

13. $\mu = 100, \sigma = 15$

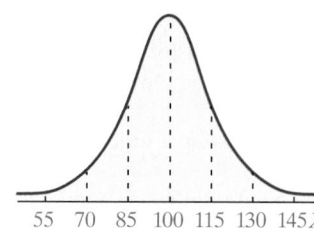

$55 \quad 70 \quad 85 \quad 100 \quad 115 \quad 130 \quad 145 X$

14. $\mu = 530, \sigma = 100$

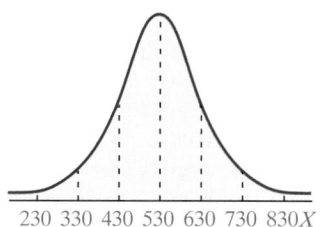

$230 \ 330 \ 430 \ 530 \ 630 \ 730 \ 830 X$

• Applying the Concepts

15. SAT Verbal Scores SAT Verbal scores are known to be normally distributed with mean $\mu = 505$ and standard deviation $\sigma = 110$ based upon data obtained from the College Board.

(a) Draw a normal curve with the parameters labeled.

(b) Shade the region that represents the proportion of test takers who scored less than 395.

(c) Suppose the area under the normal curve to the left of $X = 395$ is 0.1587. Provide two interpretations of this result.

16. ACT English ACT English scores are known to be normally distributed with mean $\mu = 20.5$ and standard deviation $\sigma = 5.5$ based upon data obtained from ACT Research.

(a) Draw a normal curve with the parameters labeled.

(b) Shade the region that represents the proportion of test takers who scored more than 27.

(c) Suppose the area under the normal curve to the right of $X = 27$ is 0.1186. Provide two interpretations of this result.

17. Birth Weights The birth weight of full-term babies is known to be normally distributed with mean $\mu = 3400$ grams and $\sigma = 505$ grams based upon data obtained from the National Vital Statistics Report, Vol. 48, No. 3.

(a) Draw a normal curve with the parameters labeled.

(b) Shade the region that represents the proportion of full-term babies who weighed more than 4410 grams.

(c) Suppose the area under the normal curve to the right of $X = 4410$ is 0.0228. Provide two interpretations of this result.

18. Height of 10-Year-Old Males The height of 10-year-old males is known to be normally distributed with mean $\mu = 55.9$ inches and $\sigma = 5.7$ inches.

(a) Draw a normal curve with the parameters labeled.

(b) Shade the region that represents the proportion of 10-year-old males who are less than 46.5 inches tall.

(c) Suppose the area under the normal curve to the left of $X = 46.5$ is 0.0496. Provide two interpretations of this result.

19. Gestation Period The length of human pregnancy is normally distributed with $\mu = 266$ days and $\sigma = 16$ days.

(a) The following figure represents the normal curve with $\mu = 266$ days and $\sigma = 16$ days:

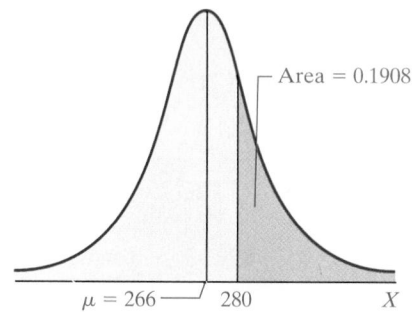

Area = 0.1908

$\mu = 266 \quad 280 \qquad X$

The area to the right of $X = 280$ is 0.1908. Provide two interpretations of this area.

(b) The following figure represents the normal curve with $\mu = 266$ days and $\sigma = 16$ days:

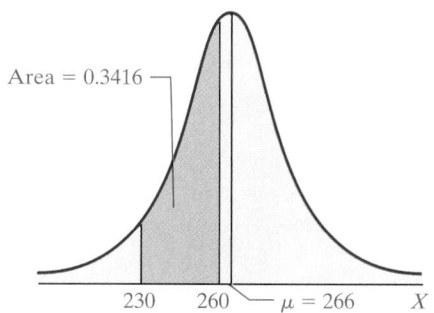

Area = 0.3416

$230 \quad 260 \quad \mu = 266 \quad X$

The area between $X = 230$ and $X = 260$ is 0.3416. Provide two interpretations of this area.

20. Miles per Gallon Elena conducts an experiment in which she fills up the gas tank on her Toyota Camry 40 times and records the miles per gallon for each fill-up. A histogram of the miles per gallon indicates the variable is normally distributed with mean of 24.6 miles per gallon and a standard deviation of 3.2 miles per gallon.

(a) The following figure represents the normal curve with $\mu = 24.6$ miles per gallon and $\sigma = 3.2$ miles per gallon:

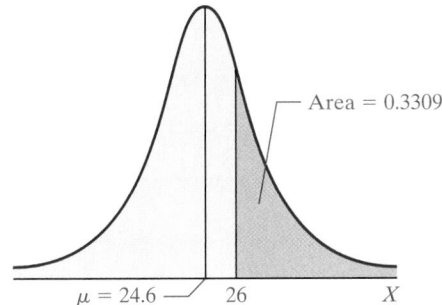

Area = 0.3309

$\mu = 24.6$ 26 X

The area under the curve to the right of $X = 26$ is 0.3309. Provide two interpretations of this area.

(b) The following figure represents the normal curve with $\mu = 24.6$ miles per gallon and $\sigma = 3.2$ miles per gallon:

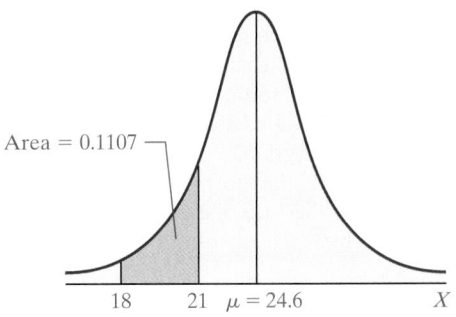

Area = 0.1107

18 21 $\mu = 24.6$ X

The area under the curve between $X = 18$ and $X = 21$ is 0.1107. Provide two interpretations of this area.

---

21. A random variable X is normally distributed with $\mu = 10$ and $\sigma = 3$.

(a) Compute $Z_1 = \dfrac{X_1 - \mu}{\sigma}$ for $X_1 = 8$. -0.67

(b) Compute $Z_2 = \dfrac{X_2 - \mu}{\sigma}$ for $X_2 = 12$. 0.67

(c) The area under the normal curve between $X_1 = 8$ and $X_2 = 12$ is 0.495. What is the area between Z_1 and Z_2? 0.495

22. A random variable X is normally distributed with $\mu = 25$ and $\sigma = 6$.

(a) Compute $Z_1 = \dfrac{X_1 - \mu}{\sigma}$ for $X_1 = 18$. -1.17

(b) Compute $Z_2 = \dfrac{X_2 - \mu}{\sigma}$ for $X_2 = 30$. 0.83

(c) The area under the normal curve between $X_1 = 18$ and $X_2 = 30$ is 0.6760. What is the area between Z_1 and Z_2? 0.6760

---

23. Hitting a Pitching Wedge In the game of golf, "distance control" is just as important as how far a player hits the ball. Suppose Michael went to the driving range with his range finder and hit 75 golf balls with his pitching wedge and measured the distance each ball traveled (in yards). He obtained the following data:

(a) Use MINITAB or some other statistical software to construct a relative frequency histogram. Comment on the shape of the distribution.

(b) Use MINITAB or some other statistical software to draw the normal density function on the relative frequency histogram.

(c) Do you think the normal density function accurately describes the distance Michael hits a pitching wedge? Why?

100	97	101	101	103	100	99	100	100
104	100	101	98	100	99	99	97	101
104	99	101	101	101	100	96	99	99
98	94	98	107	98	100	98	103	100
98	94	104	104	98	101	99	97	103
102	101	101	100	95	104	99	102	95
99	102	103	97	101	102	96	102	99
96	108	103	100	95	101	103	105	100
94	99	95						

24. Heights of Five-Year-Old Females The following frequency distribution represents the heights (in inches) of eighty randomly selected five-year-old females.

(a) Use Minitab or some other statistical software to construct a relative frequency histogram. Comment on the shape of the distribution.

(b) Use Minitab or some other statistical software to draw the normal density function on the relative frequency histogram.

(c) Do you think the normal density function accurately describes the heights of five-year-old females? Why?

44.5	42.4	42.2	46.2	45.7	44.8	43.3	39.5
45.4	43.0	43.4	44.7	38.6	41.6	50.2	46.9
39.6	44.7	36.5	42.7	40.6	47.5	48.4	37.5
45.5	43.3	41.2	40.5	44.4	42.6	42.0	40.3
42.0	42.2	38.5	43.6	40.6	45.0	40.7	36.3
44.5	37.6	42.2	40.3	48.5	41.6	41.7	38.9
39.5	43.6	41.3	38.8	41.9	40.3	42.1	41.9
42.3	44.6	40.5	37.4	44.5	40.7	38.2	42.6
44.0	35.9	43.7	48.1	38.7	46.0	43.4	44.6
37.7	34.6	42.4	42.7	47.0	42.8	39.9	42.3

7.2 The Standard Normal Distribution

Preparing for This Section Before getting started, review the following:

✓ The Complement Rule (Section 5.2, pp. 279–281)

Objectives Find the area under the standard normal curve

 Find Z-scores for the given areas

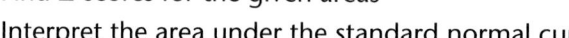 Interpret the area under the standard normal curve as a probability

In Section 7.1, we introduced the normal distribution. We learned that if X is a normally distributed random variable, we can use the area under the normal density function to obtain the proportion of a population, or the probability that a randomly selected individual from the population, has a certain characteristic. To find the area under the normal curve, we first convert the random variable X to a standard normal random variable Z with mean $\mu = 0$ and standard deviation $\sigma = 1$ and find the area under the standard normal curve. This section discusses methods for finding the area under the standard normal curve.

Properties of the Standard Normal Distribution

The standard normal distribution has a mean of 0 and a standard deviation of 1. The standard normal curve therefore, will have its high point located at 0 and inflection points located at -1 and $+1$. We use the random variable Z to represent a standard normal random variable. The graph of the standard normal curve is presented in Figure 11.

Although we stated the properties of normal curves in general in Section 7.1, it is worthwhile to restate them here as they pertain to the standard normal curve.

Figure 11

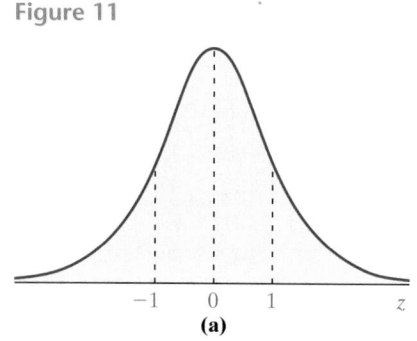

(a)

Properties of the Standard Normal Curve

1. It is symmetric about its mean, $\mu = 0$.

2. Its highest point occurs at $\mu = 0$.

3. It has inflection points at $\mu - \sigma = 0 - 1 = -1$ and $\mu + \sigma = 0 + 1 = 1$.

4. The area under the curve is 1. This characteristic is required in order to satisfy the requirement that the sum of all probabilities in a legitimate probability distribution equals 1.

5. The area under the curve to the right of $\mu = 0$ equals the area under the curve to the left of $\mu = 0$ equals $^1/_2$.

6. As z increases without bound, the graph approaches, but never equals, zero. As z decreases without bound the graph approaches, but never equals, zero.

7. The Empirical Rule: Approximately $0.68 = 68\%$ of the area under the standard normal curve is between -1 and 1. Approximately $0.95 = 95\%$ of the area under the standard normal curve is between -2 and 2. Approximately $0.997 = 99.7\%$ of the area under the standard normal curve is between -3 and 3. See Figure 12.

Figure 12

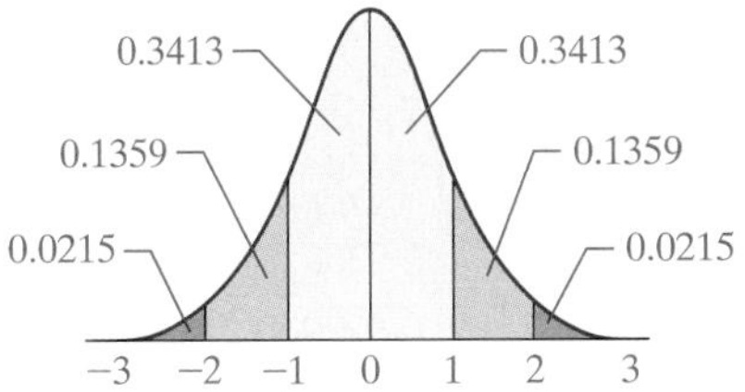

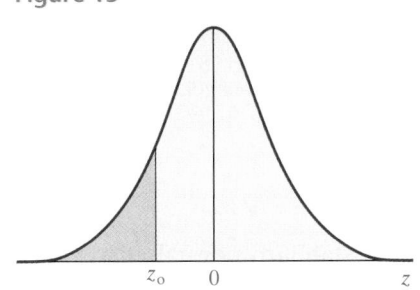

We now discuss the procedure for finding area under the standard normal curve.

① Finding Area under the Standard Normal Curve

We discuss two methods for finding area under the standard normal curve. The first method utilizes tables of areas that have been constructed for various values of Z. The second method involves the use of statistical software or a calculator with advanced statistical features.

Table II, which can be found in the front inside cover of the text or in Appendix A, gives areas under the standard normal curve. The table gives the area under the standard normal curve for values to the left of a specified Z-score, z_0, as shown in Figure 13.

Figure 13

The shaded region represents the area under the standard normal curve to the left of $Z = z_0$. Whenever finding area under a normal curve, you should sketch a normal curve and shade the area you are finding.

▶ **EXAMPLE 1**   **Finding Area under the Standard Normal Curve Left of a Z-score**

Problem: Find the area under the standard normal curve that lies to the left of $Z = 1.68$.

Approach:

Step 1: Draw a standard normal curve with $Z = 1.68$ labeled and shade the area under the curve to the left of $Z = 1.68$.

Step 2: The rows in Table II represent the ones and tenths portion of Z, while the columns represent the hundredths portion. To find the area under the curve to the left of $Z = 1.68$, we need to split 1.68 as 1.6 and 0.08. Find the row that represents "1.6" and the column that represents "0.08" in Table II. Identify where the row and column intersect. This value is the area.

Figure 14

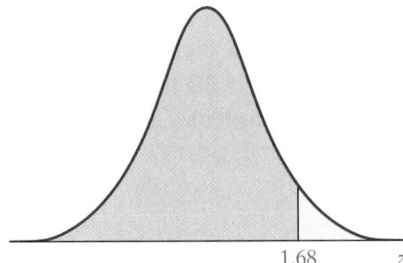

Solution:

Step 1: Figure 14 shows the graph of the standard normal curve with $Z = 1.68$ labeled. The area left of $Z = 1.68$ is shaded.

Step 2: A portion of Table II is presented in Figure 15 on page 394. We have enclosed the row that represents "1.6" and the column that represents "0.08." The point where the row and column intersect is the area we are seeking. The area to the left of $Z = 1.68$ is 0.9535.

Figure 15

z	0.00	0.01	0.02	0.03	0.04	0.05	0.06	0.07	0.08	0.09
0.0	0.5000	0.5040	0.5080	0.5120	0.5160	0.5199	0.5239	0.5279	0.5319	0.5359
0.1	0.5398	0.5438	0.5478	0.5517	0.5557	0.5596	0.5636	0.5675	0.5714	0.5753
0.2	0.5793	0.5832	0.5871	0.5910	0.5948	0.5987	0.6026	0.6064	0.6103	0.6141
0.3	0.6179	0.6217	0.6255	0.6293	0.6331	0.6368	0.6406	0.6443	0.6480	0.6517
0.4	0.6554	0.6591	0.6628	0.6664	0.6700	0.6736	0.6772	0.6808	0.6844	0.6879
0.5	0.6915	0.6950	0.6985	0.7019	0.7054	0.7088	0.7123	0.7157	0.7190	0.7224
0.6	0.7257	0.7291	0.7324	0.7357	0.7389	0.7422	0.7454	0.7486	0.7517	0.7549
0.7	0.7580	0.7611	0.7642	0.7673	0.7704	0.7734	0.7764	0.7794	0.7823	0.7852
0.8	0.7881	0.7910	0.7939	0.7967	0.7995	0.8023	0.8051	0.8078	0.8106	0.8133
0.9	0.8159	0.8186	0.8212	0.8238	0.8264	0.8289	0.8315	0.8340	0.8365	0.8389
1.0	0.8413	0.8438	0.8461	0.8485	0.8508	0.8531	0.8554	0.8577	0.8599	0.8621
1.1	0.8643	0.8665	0.8686	0.8708	0.8729	0.8749	0.8770	0.8790	0.8810	0.8830
1.2	0.8849	0.8869	0.8888	0.8907	0.8925	0.8944	0.8962	0.8980	0.8997	0.9015
1.3	0.9032	0.9049	0.9066	0.9082	0.9099	0.9115	0.9131	0.9147	0.9162	0.9177
1.4	0.9192	0.9207	0.9222	0.9236	0.9251	0.9265	0.9279	0.9292	0.9306	0.9319
1.5	0.9332	0.9345	0.9357	0.9370	0.9382	0.9394	0.9406	0.9418	0.9429	0.9441
1.6	0.9452	0.9463	0.9474	0.9484	0.9495	0.9505	0.9515	0.9525	0.9535	0.9545
1.7	0.9554	0.9564	0.9573	0.9582	0.9591	0.9599	0.9608	0.9616	0.9625	0.9633
1.8	0.9641	0.9649	0.9656	0.9664	0.9671	0.9678	0.9686	0.9693	0.9699	0.9706
1.9	0.9713	0.9719	0.9726	0.9732	0.9738	0.9744	0.9750	0.9756	0.9761	0.9767
2.0	0.9772	0.9778	0.9783	0.9788	0.9793	0.9798	0.9803	0.9808	0.9812	0.9817
2.1	0.9821	0.9826	0.9830	0.9834	0.9838	0.9842	0.9846	0.9850	0.9854	0.9857
2.2	0.9851	0.9864	0.9868	0.9871	0.9875	0.9878	0.9881	0.9884	0.9887	0.9890

◄◄

Using Technology: The area under the standard normal curve can also be computed using statistical software or graphing calculators with advanced statistical features. Figure 16 shows the results from Example 1 using Minitab. Notice the output is titled "Cumulative Distribution Function." Remember, the word cumulative means "less than or equal to," so Minitab is giving the area under the standard normal curve for Z less than or equal to 1.68.

Figure 16

Cumulative Distribution Function

```
Normal with mean = 0 and standard deviation = 1.00000

         x        P( X <= x)
     1.6800           0.9535
```

NW *Now Work Problem 1.*

Often, rather than being interested in the area under the standard normal curve to the left of $Z = z_0$, we are interested in obtaining the area under the standard normal curve to the right of $Z = z_0$. The idea behind the solution to this type of problem utilizes the fact that the area under the entire standard normal curve is 1 and the Complement Rule. Therefore,

Theorem Area under the normal curve to the right of $z_0 = 1 - $ Area to the left of z_0.

▶ **EXAMPLE 2** **Finding Area under the Standard Normal Curve Right of a Z-score**

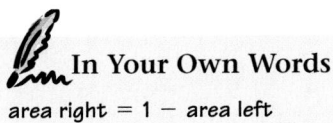

In Your Own Words

area right = 1 − area left

Problem: Find the area under the standard normal curve to the right of $Z = -0.46$.

Approach:

Step 1: Draw a standard normal curve with $Z = -0.46$ labeled and shade the area under the curve to the right of $Z = -0.46$.

Step 2: Find the row that represents "-0.4" and the column that represents "0.06" in Table II. Identify where the row and column intersect. This value is the area to the *left* of $Z = -0.46$.

Step 3: The area under the standard normal curve to the right of $Z = -0.46$ is 1 minus the area to the left of $Z = -0.46$.

Figure 17

Solution:

Step 1: Figure 17 shows the graph of the standard normal curve with $Z = -0.46$ labeled. The area to the right of $Z = -0.46$ is shaded.

Step 2: A portion of Table II is presented in Figure 18. We have highlighted the row that represents "-0.4" and the column that represents "0.06". The point where the row and column intersect is the area to the left of $Z = -0.46$. The area to the left of $Z = -0.46$ is 0.3228.

Figure 18

z	.00	.01	.02	.03	.04	.05	.06	.07	.08	.09
−3.4	0.0003	0.0003	0.0003	0.0003	0.0003	0.0003	0.0003	0.0003	0.0003	0.0002
−3.3	0.0005	0.0005	0.0005	0.0004	0.0004	0.0004	0.0004	0.0004	0.0004	0.0003
−3.2	0.0007	0.0007	0.0006	0.0006	0.0006	0.0006	0.0006	0.0005	0.0005	0.0005
−3.1	0.0010	0.0009	0.0009	0.0009	0.0008	0.0008	0.0008	0.0008	0.0007	0.0007
−3.0	0.0013	0.0013	0.0013	0.0012	0.0012	0.0011	0.0011	0.0011	0.0010	0.0010
−0.5	0.3085	0.3050	0.3015	0.2981	0.2946	0.2912	0.2877	0.2843	0.2810	0.2776
−0.4	0.3446	0.3409	0.3372	0.3336	0.3300	0.3264	0.3228	0.3192	0.3156	0.3121
−0.3	0.3821	0.3783	0.3745	0.3707	0.3669	0.3632	0.3594	0.3557	0.3520	0.3483
−0.2	0.4027	0.4168	0.4129	0.4090	0.4052	0.4013	0.3974	0.3936	0.3897	0.3859
−0.1	0.4602	0.4562	0.4522	0.4483	0.4443	0.4404	0.4364	0.4325	0.4286	0.4247
−0.0	0.5000	0.4960	0.4920	0.4880	0.4840	0.4801	0.4761	0.4721	0.4681	0.4641

Step 3: The area under the standard normal curve to the right of $Z = -0.46$ is 1 minus the area to the left of $Z = -0.46$.

$$\text{Area right of } -0.46 = 1 - (\text{Area left of } -0.46)$$

$$= 1 - 0.3228$$

$$= 0.6772$$

The area to the right of $Z = -0.46$ is 0.6772. ◀◀

NW Now Work Problem 3.

The next example presents a situation in which we are interested in the area between two Z-scores.

▶ **EXAMPLE 3** **Find the Area under the Standard Normal Curve between Two Z-scores**

Problem: Find the area under the standard normal curve between $Z = -1.35$ and $Z = 2.01$.

Approach:

Step 1: Draw a standard normal curve with $Z = -1.35$ and $Z = 2.01$ labeled. Shade the area under the curve between $Z = -1.35$ and $Z = 2.01$.

Step 2: Find the area to the left of $Z = -1.35$. Find the area to the left of $Z = 2.01$.

Figure 19

Step 3: The area under the standard normal curve between $Z = -1.35$ and $Z = 2.01$ is the area left of $Z = 2.01$ minus the area left of $Z = -1.35$.

Solution:

Step 1: Figure 19 shows the standard normal curve with the area between $Z = -1.35$ and $Z = 2.01$ shaded.

Step 2: Based upon Table II, the area left of $Z = -1.35$ is 0.0885. The area left of $Z = 2.01$ is 0.9778.

Step 3: The area between $Z = -1.35$ and $Z = 2.01$ is

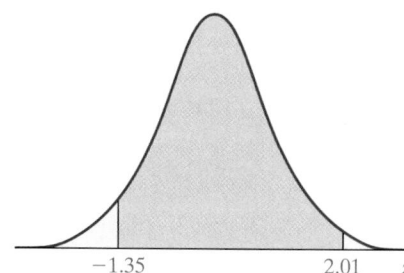

$$\text{(Area between } Z = -1.35 \text{ and } Z = 2.01) = (\text{Area left of } Z = 2.01) - (\text{Area left of } Z = -1.35)$$
$$= 0.9778 - 0.0885$$
$$= 0.8893$$

The area between $Z = -1.35$ and $Z = 2.01$ is 0.8893. ◀◀

NW Now Work Problem 5.

Caution

State the area under the standard normal curve to the left of $Z = -3.90$ as < 0.0001. State the area under the standard normal curve to the left of $Z = 3.90$ as > 0.9999.

We summarize the methods for obtaining area under the standard normal curve in Table 2 on page 397.

Because the normal curve extends indefinitely in both directions on the z-axis, there is no Z-value for which the area under the curve to the left of the Z-value is 1. For example, the area to the left of $Z = 10$ is less than 1 even though graphing calculators and statistical software state that the area is 1. This is because there is a limited number of decimal places the machines can compute. We will follow the practice of stating the area left of $Z = -3.90$ or right of $Z = 3.90$ as < 0.0001. The area under the standard normal curve left of $Z = 3.90$ or to the right of $Z = -3.90$ will be stated as > 0.9999.

TABLE 2		
Problem	**Approach**	**Solution**
Find the area left of $Z = z_o$	Shade area left of $Z = z_o$ z_o	Use Table II to find the row and column that correspond to $Z = z_o$. The area is the value where the row and column intersect. Or use technology to find the area.
Find the area right of $Z = z_o$	Shade area right of $Z = z_o$ z_o	Use Table II to find the area left of $Z = z_o$. The area right of $Z = z_o$ is 1 minus the area left of $Z = z_o$. Or use technology to find the area.
Find the area between $Z = z_o$ and $Z = z_1$	Shade the area between $Z = z_o$ and $Z = z_1$ z_o z_1	Use Table II to find the area left of $Z = z_o$ and left of $Z = z_1$. The area between $Z = z_o$ and $Z = z_1$ is (area left of $Z = z_1$) − (area left of $Z = z_o$). Or use technology to find the area.

② Finding Z-scores for Given Areas

Up to this point, we have found areas given the value of a Z-score. Often, we are interested in finding a Z-score that corresponds to a given area. The procedure to follow is essentially the reverse of the procedure to finding areas given Z-scores.

▶ **EXAMPLE 4**   **Finding a Z-score from a Specified Area to the Left**

Problem: Find the Z-score such that the area left of the Z-score is 0.32.

Approach:

Step 1: Draw a standard normal curve with the area and corresponding unknown Z-score labeled.

Step 2: We look for the area in the table closest to 0.32.

Step 3: Find the Z-score that corresponds to the area closest to 0.32.

Note to Instructor
If you are using the table to find Z-scores, be sure to emphasize that the area we are looking for may not be in the table. Therefore the closest area should be used. If the area is equidistant from two areas, the average Z-score could be used.

Figure 20

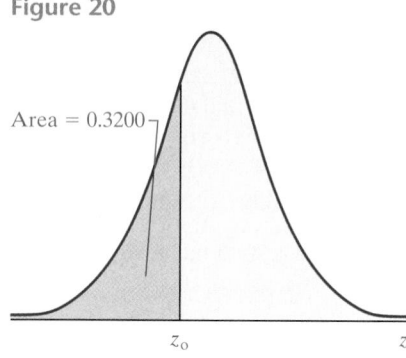

Area = 0.3200

z_o

z

Solution:

Step 1: Figure 20 shows the graph of the standard normal curve with the area of 0.32 labeled. We know z_o must be less than 0. Do you know why?

Step 2: We refer to Table II and look in the body of the table for an area closest to 0.32. The area closest to 0.32 is 0.3192. Figure 21 shows a partial representation of Table II with 0.3192 labeled.

Figure 21

z	.00	.01	.02	.03	.04	.05	.06	.07	.08	.09
−3.4	0.0003	0.0003	0.0003	0.0003	0.0003	0.0003	0.0003	0.0003	0.0003	0.0002
−3.3	0.0005	0.0005	0.0005	0.0004	0.0004	0.0004	0.0004	0.0004	0.0004	0.0003
−3.2	0.0007	0.0007	0.0006	0.0006	0.0006	0.0006	0.0006	0.0005	0.0005	0.0005
−3.1	0.0010	0.0009	0.0009	0.0009	0.0008	0.0008	0.0008	0.0008	0.0007	0.0007
−3.0	0.0013	0.0013	0.0013	0.0012	0.0012	0.0011	0.0011	0.0011	0.0010	0.0010
−0.7	0.2420	0.2389	0.2358	0.2327	0.2296	0.2266	0.2236	0.2206	0.2177	0.2148
−0.6	0.2743	0.2709	0.2676	0.2643	0.2611	0.2578	0.2546	0.2514	0.2483	0.2451
−0.5	0.3085	0.3050	0.3015	0.2981	0.2946	0.2912	0.2877	0.2843	0.2810	0.2776
−0.4	0.3446	0.3409	0.3372	0.3336	0.3300	0.3264	0.3228	0.3192	0.3156	0.3121
−0.3	0.3821	0.3783	0.3745	0.3707	0.3669	0.3632	0.3594	0.3557	0.3520	0.3483
−0.2	0.4027	0.4168	0.4129	0.4090	0.4052	0.4013	0.3974	0.3936	0.3897	0.3859

Figure 22

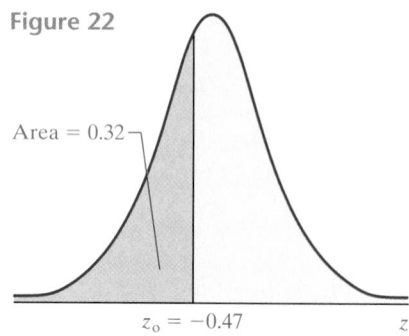

Area = 0.32

$z_o = -0.47$

z

Step 3: From reading the table in Figure 21, we can see that the approximate Z-score that corresponds to an area of 0.32 to its left is −0.47. So $z_o = -0.47$. See Figure 22. ◀◀

Using Technology: Graphing calculators with advanced statistical features and statistical software can be used to find the Z-score corresponding to an area. Figure 23 shows the result of Example 4 using a TI-83 Plus graphing calculator.

Figure 23

```
invNorm(.32,0,1)
        -.4676988012
```

It is useful to remember that if the area to the left of the Z-score is less than 0.5, the Z-score must be less than 0. If the area to the left of the Z-score is greater than 0.5, the Z-score must be greater than 0.

NW *Now Work Problem 11.*

The next example deals with situations in which the area to the right of some unknown Z-score is given. The solution utilizes the fact that the area under the normal curve is 1.

► **EXAMPLE 5** **Finding a Z-score from a Specified Area to the Right**

Problem: Find the Z-score such that the area to the right of the Z-score is 0.4332.

Approach:
Step 1: Draw a standard normal curve with the area and corresponding unknown Z-score labeled.
Step 2: Determine the area to the left of the unknown Z-score.
Step 3: Look for the area in the table closest to the area determined in Step 2 and record the Z-score that corresponds to the closest area.

Solution:
Step 1: Figure 24 shows the standard normal curve with the area and unknown Z-score labeled.
Step 2: Since the area under the entire normal curve is 1, the area left of the unknown Z-score is 1 minus the area right of the unknown Z-score. Therefore,

$$\text{area left} = 1 - \text{area right}$$
$$= 1 - 0.4332$$
$$= 0.5668$$

Step 3: We look in the body of Table II for an area closest to 0.5668. See Figure 25. The area closest to 0.5668 is 0.5675.

Figure 24

Area = 0.4332

z_0 z

Figure 25

z	0.00	0.01	0.02	0.03	0.04	0.05	0.06	0.07	0.08	0.09
0.0	0.5000	0.5040	0.5080	0.5120	0.5160	0.5199	0.5239	0.5279	0.5319	0.5359
0.1	0.5398	0.5438	0.5478	0.5517	0.5557	0.5596	0.5636	0.5675	0.5714	0.5753
0.2	0.5793	0.5832	0.5871	0.5910	0.5948	0.5987	0.6026	0.6064	0.6103	0.6141
0.3	0.6179	0.6217	0.6255	0.6293	0.6331	0.6368	0.6406	0.6443	0.6480	0.6517
0.4	0.6554	0.6591	0.6628	0.6664	0.6700	0.6736	0.6772	0.6808	0.6844	0.6879
0.5	0.6915	0.6950	0.6985	0.7019	0.7054	0.7088	0.7123	0.7157	0.7190	0.7224
0.6	0.7237	0.7291	0.7324	0.7357	0.7389	0.7422	0.7454	0.7486	0.7517	0.7549

The approximate Z-score that corresponds to an area right of 0.4332 is 0.17. Therefore, $z_0 = 0.17$. See Figure 26.

◄◄

Figure 26

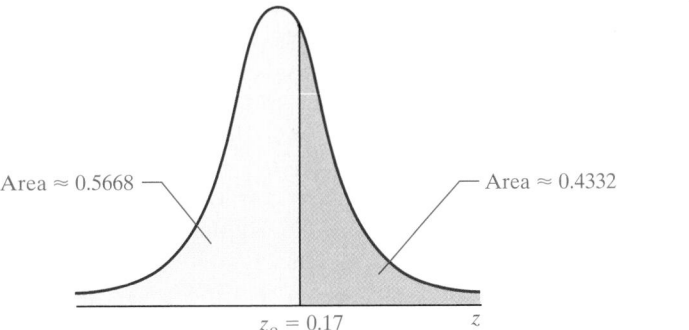

Area ≈ 0.5668   Area ≈ 0.4332

$z_0 = 0.17$ z

NW *Now Work Problem 15.*

In upcoming chapters, we will often be interested in finding Z-scores that separate the middle area of the standard normal curve from the area in its tails.

▶ **EXAMPLE 6** **Finding the Z-score from an Area in the Middle**

Problem: Find the Z-score that divides the middle 90% of the area in the standard normal distribution from the area in the tails.

Approach:

Step 1: Draw a standard normal curve with the middle 90% = 0.9 of the area separated from the area of 5% = 0.05 in each of the two tails. Label the unknown Z-scores z_0 and z_1.

Step 2: Look in the body of Table II to find the area closest to 0.05.

Step 3: Determine the Z-score in the left tail.

Step 4: The area to the right of z_1 is 0.05. Therefore, the area to the left of z_1 is 0.95. Look in Table II for an area of 0.95 and find the corresponding Z-value.

Figure 27

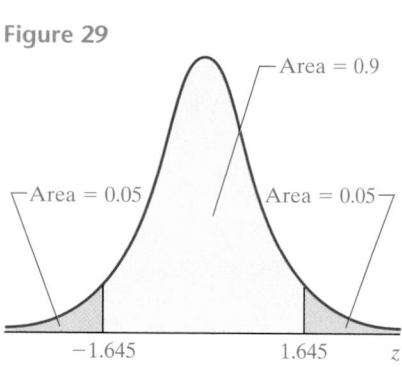

Area = 0.9

Area = 0.05   Area = 0.05

z_0 z_1 z

Solution:

Step 1: Figure 27 shows the standard normal curve with the middle 90% of the area separated from the area in the two tails.

Step 2: We look in the body of Table II for an area closest to 0.05. See Figure 28.

Figure 28

z	.00	.01	.02	.03	.04	.05	.06	.07	.08	.09
−3.4	0.0003	0.0003	0.0003	0.0003	0.0003	0.0003	0.0003	0.0003	0.0003	0.0002
−3.3	0.0005	0.0005	0.0005	0.0004	0.0004	0.0004	0.0004	0.0004	0.0004	0.0003
−3.2	0.0007	0.0007	0.0006	0.0006	0.0006	0.0006	0.0006	0.0005	0.0005	0.0005
−2.0	0.0228	0.0222	0.0217	0.0212	0.0207	0.0202	0.0197	0.0192	0.0188	0.0183
−1.9	0.0287	0.0281	0.0274	0.0268	0.0262	0.0256	0.0250	0.0244	0.0239	0.0233
−1.8	0.0359	0.0351	0.0344	0.0336	0.0329	0.0322	0.0314	0.0307	0.0301	0.0294
−1.7	0.0446	0.0436	0.0427	0.0418	0.0409	0.0401	0.0392	0.0384	0.0375	0.0367
−1.6	0.0548	0.0537	0.0526	0.0516	0.0505	0.0495	0.0485	0.0475	0.0465	0.0455
−1.5	0.0668	0.0655	0.0643	0.0630	0.0618	0.0606	0.0594	0.0582	0.0571	0.0559

We notice that 0.0495 and 0.0505 are equally close to 0.05. We agree to take the arithmetic mean of the two Z-scores corresponding to the areas.

Step 3: The Z-score corresponding to an area of 0.0495 is −1.65. The Z-score corresponding to an area of 0.0505 is −1.64. Therefore, the approximate Z-score corresponding to an area of 0.05 to the left is

$$z_0 = \frac{-1.65 + (-1.64)}{2} = -1.645$$

Step 4: The area to the right of z_1 is 0.05. Therefore, the area left of $z_1 = 1 - 0.05 = 0.95$. In Table II, we find an area of 0.9495 corresponding to $z = 1.64$ and an area of 0.9505 corresponding to $z = 1.65$ in the body. Consequently, the approximate Z-score corresponding to an area of 0.05 to the right is

$$z_1 = \frac{1.65 + 1.64}{2} = 1.645$$

Figure 29

Area = 0.9

Area = 0.05   Area = 0.05

−1.645   1.645 z

See Figure 29. ◀◀

Note to Instructor
Remind students that the standard normal curve is symmetric about its mean, 0. Therefore, once the left Z-score is known, the right is found by symmetry.

We could also obtain the solution to Example 6 using symmetry. Because the standard normal curve is symmetric about its mean, 0, the Z-score that corresponds to an area to the left of 0.05 will be the additive inverse of the Z-score that corresponds to an area to the right of 0.05. Since the area to the left of $Z = -1.645$ is 0.05, the area to the right of $Z = 1.645$ is also 0.05.

NW *Now Work Problem 19.*

We are often interested in finding the Z-score that has a specified area to the right. For this reason, we have special notation to represent this situation.

Definition

The notation z_α (pronounced "z sub alpha") is the Z-score such that the area under the standard normal curve to the right of z_α is α. Figure 30 illustrates the notation.

Figure 30

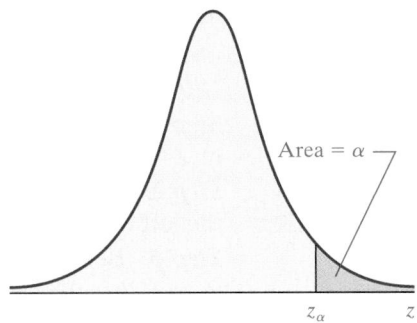

Area = α

z_α z

▶ **EXAMPLE 7**   **Finding the Value of** z_α

Figure 31

Area = 0.10

0      $z_{0.10} = 1.28$

Problem: Find the value of $z_{0.10}$

Approach: We wish to find the Z-value such that the area under the standard normal curve to the right of the Z-value is 0.10.

Solution: The area to the right of the unknown Z-value is 0.10, so the area to the left of the Z-value is $1 - 0.10 = 0.90$. We look in Table II for the area closest to 0.90. The area closest is 0.8997, which corresponds to a Z-value of 1.28. Therefore, $z_{0.10} = 1.28$. See Figure 31.   ◀◀

NW *Now Work Problem 23.*

③   Recall that the area under a normal curve can be interpreted either as a probability or as the proportion of the population with the given characteristic. When interpreting the area under the standard normal curve as a probability, we use the notation introduced in Chapter 6. For example, in Example 6, we found that the area under the standard normal curve to the left of $Z = -1.645$ is 0.05; therefore, the probability of randomly selecting a standard normal random variable that is less than -1.645 is 0.05. We write this statement with the notation $P(Z < -1.645) = 0.05$.

We will use the following notation to denote probabilities of a standard normal random variable, Z.

Notation for the Probability of a Standard Normal Random Variable

$P(a < Z < b)$	represents the probability a standard normal random variable is between a and b
$P(Z > a)$	represents the probability a standard normal random variable is greater than a.
$P(Z < a)$	represents the probability a standard normal random variable is less than a.

▶ **EXAMPLE 8**   **Finding Probabilities of Standard Normal Random Variables**

Problem: Evaluate $P(Z < 1.26)$.

Approach:

Figure 32

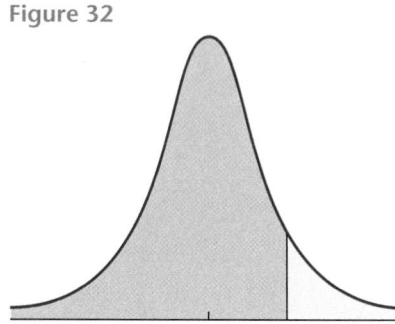

Step 1: Draw a standard normal curve with the area we desire shaded.
Step 2: Use Table II to find the area of the shaded region.
Step 3: This area represents the probability.

Solution:

Step 1: Figure 32 shows the standard normal curve with the area to the left of $Z = 1.26$ shaded.
Step 2: Using Table II, we find the area under the standard normal curve to the left of $Z = 1.26$ is 0.8962.
Step 3: Because the area under the standard normal curve to the left of $Z = 1.26$ is 0.8962, we have $P(Z < 1.26) = 0.8962$.   ◀◀

NW *Now Work Problem 29.*

For any continuous random variable, the probability of observing a specific value of the random variable is 0. For example, for a standard normal random variable, $P(Z = a) = 0$ for any value of a. This is because there is no area under the standard normal curve associated with a single value, so the probability must be 0. Hence, the following probabilities are equivalent.

Note to Instructor
Be sure to emphasize this concept with students.

$$P(a < Z < b) = P(a \le Z < b) = P(a < Z \le b) = P(a \le Z \le b)$$

For example, $P(Z < 1.26) = P(Z \le 1.26) = 0.8962$.

7.2 Assess Your Understanding

Concepts and Vocabulary

1. State the properties of the standard normal curve.
2. If the area under the standard normal curve to the left of $Z = 1.20$ is 0.8849, what is the area under the standard normal curve to the right of $Z = 1.20$?
3. True or false? The area under the standard normal curve to the left of $Z = 5.30$ is 1. Support your answer.
4. Explain why $P(Z < -1.30) = P(Z \le -1.30)$.

Exercises

• Skill Building

In Problems 1–8, find the indicated areas. For each problem, be sure to draw a standard normal curve and shade the area that is to be found.

1. Determine the area under the standard normal curve
NW that lies to the left of

  (a) $Z = -2.45$ *0.0071*
  (b) $Z = -0.43$ *0.3336*
  (c) $Z = 1.35$ *0.9115*
  (d) $Z = 3.49$ *0.9998*

2. Determine the area under the standard normal curve that lies to the left of

  (a) $Z = -3.49$ *0.0002*
  (b) $Z = -1.99$ *0.0233*
  (c) $Z = 0.92$ *0.8212*
  (d) $Z = 2.90$ *0.9981*

3. Determine the area under the standard normal curve
NW that lies to the right of

  (a) $Z = -3.01$ *0.9987*
  (b) $Z = -1.59$ *0.9441*
  (c) $Z = 1.78$ *0.0375*
  (d) $Z = 3.11$ *0.0009*

4. Determine the area under the standard normal curve that lies to the right of

  (a) $Z = -3.49$ *0.9998*
  (b) $Z = -0.55$ *0.7088*
  (c) $Z = 2.23$ *0.0129*
  (d) $Z = 3.45$ *0.0003*

5. Determine the area under the standard normal curve
NW that lies between

  (a) $Z = -2.04$ and $Z = 2.04$ *0.9586*
  (b) $Z = -0.55$ and $Z = 0$ *0.2088*
  (c) $Z = -1.04$ and $Z = 2.76$ *0.8479*

6. Determine the area under the standard normal curve that lies between

  (a) $Z = -2.55$ and $Z = 2.55$ *0.9892*
  (b) $Z = -1.67$ and $Z = 0$ *0.4525*
  (c) $Z = -3.03$ and $Z = 1.98$ *0.9749*

7. Determine the area under the standard normal curve

  (a) to the left of $Z = -2$ or to the right of $Z = 2$ *0.0455*
  (b) to the left of $Z = -1.56$ or to the right of $Z = 2.56$ *0.0646*
  (c) to the left of $Z = -0.24$ or to the right of $Z = 1.20$ *0.5202*

8. Determine the area under the standard normal curve

  (a) to the left of $Z = -2.94$ or to the right of $Z = 2.94$ *0.0033*
  (b) to the left of $Z = -1.68$ or to the right of $Z = 3.05$ *0.0476*
  (c) to the left of $Z = -0.88$ or to the right of $Z = 1.23$ *0.2988*

In Problems 9 and 10, find the area of the shaded region for each standard normal curve.

9. (a) *0.8877*

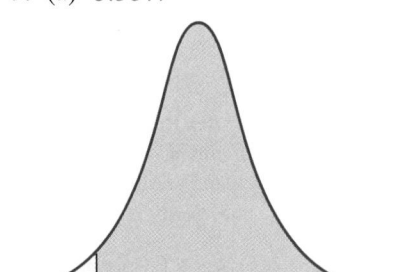

(b) *0.9802*

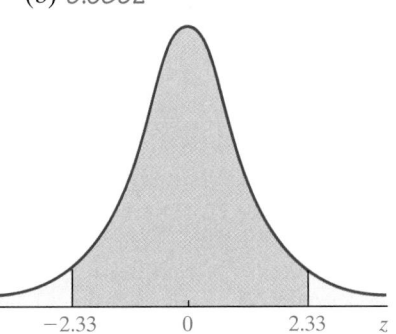

(c) *0.0198*

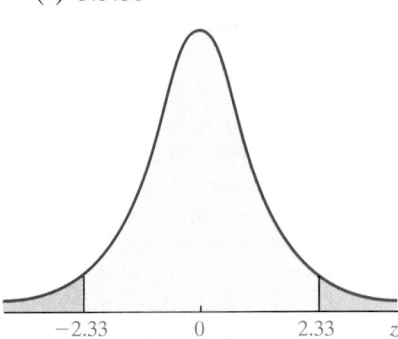

10. (a) *0.3686*

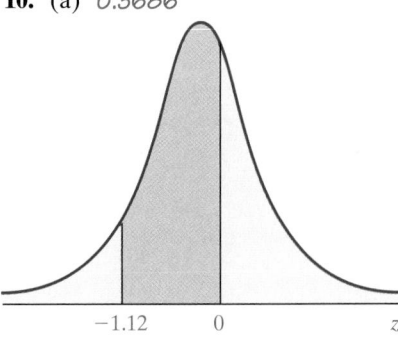

(b) *0.9500*

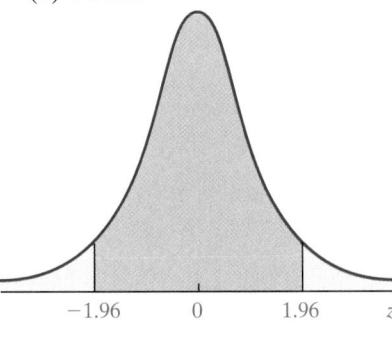

(c) *0.05*

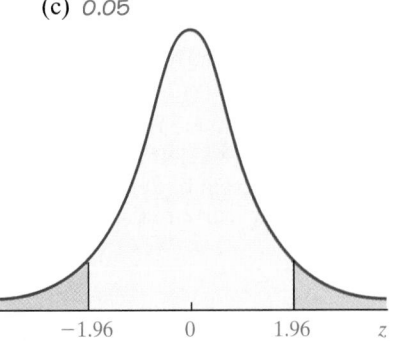

In Problems 11–22, find the indicated Z-score. Be sure to draw a standard normal curve that depicts the solution.

11. Find the Z-score such that the area under the standard
NW normal curve to the left is 0.1. −1.28

12. Find the Z-score such that the area under the standard
normal curve to the left is 0.2. −0.84

13. Find the Z-score such that the area under the standard
normal curve to the left is 0.98. 2.05

14. Find the Z-score such that the area under the standard
normal curve to the left is 0.85. 1.04

15. Find the Z-score such that the area under the standard
NW normal curve to the right is 0.25. 0.67

16. Find the Z-score such that the area under the standard
normal curve to the right is 0.35. 0.39

17. Find the Z-score such that the area under the standard
normal curve to the right is 0.89. −1.23

18. Find the Z-score such that the area under the standard
normal curve to the right is 0.75. −0.67

19. Find the Z-scores that separate the middle 80% of the
NW distribution from the area in the tails of the standard
normal distribution. −1.28; 1.28

20. Find the Z-scores that separate the middle 70% of the
distribution from the area in the tails of the standard
normal distribution. −1.04; 1.04

21. Find the Z-scores that separate the middle 99% of the
distribution from the area in the tails of the distribution.

22. Find the Z-scores that separate the middle 94% of the
distribution from the area in the tails of the distribution.

21. −2.575; 2.575

22. −1.88; 1.88

In Problems 23–28, find the value of z_α.

23. $z_{0.05}$ 1.645   **24.** $z_{0.35}$ 0.39   **25.** $z_{0.01}$ 2.33   **26.** $z_{0.02}$ 2.05   **27.** $z_{0.20}$ 0.84   **28.** $z_{0.15}$ 1.04
NW

In Problems 29–40, find the indicated probability of the standard normal random variable Z.

29. $P(Z < 1.93)$ 0.9732   **30.** $P(Z < -0.61)$ 0.2709   **31.** $P(Z > -2.98)$ 0.9986
NW

32. $P(Z > 0.92)$ 0.1788   **33.** $P(-1.20 \leq Z < 2.34)$ 0.8753   **34.** $P(1.23 < Z \leq 1.56)$ 0.0500

35. $P(Z \geq 1.84)$ 0.0329   **36.** $P(Z \geq -0.92)$ 0.8212   **37.** $P(Z \leq 0.72)$ 0.7642

38. $P(Z \leq -2.69)$ 0.0036   **39.** $P(Z < -2.56 \text{ or } Z > 1.39)$ 0.0875   **40.** $P(Z < -0.38 \text{ or } Z > 1.93)$ 0.3788

• Applying the Concepts

41. The Empirical Rule The Empirical Rule states that
about 68% of the data in a bell-shaped distribution lies
within 1 standard deviation of the mean. This means
about 68% of the data lies between $Z = -1$ and
$Z = 1$. Verify this result. Verify that about 95% of the
data lies within 2 standard deviations of the mean.
Finally, verify that about 99.7% of the data lies within 3
standard deviations of the mean.

42. According to Table II, the area under the standard normal curve to the left of $Z = -1.34$ is 0.0901. Without
consulting Table II, determine the area under the standard normal curve to the right of $Z = 1.34$. 0.0901

43. According to Table II, the area under the standard normal curve to the left of $Z = -2.55$ is 0.0054. Without
consulting Table II, determine the area under the standard normal curve to the right of $Z = 2.55$. 0.0054

44. According to Table II, the area under the standard normal curve between $Z = -1.50$ and $Z = 0$ is 0.4332.
Without consulting Table II, determine the area under
the standard normal curve between $Z = 0$ and
$Z = 1.50$. 0.4332

45. According to Table II, the area under the standard normal curve between $Z = -1.24$ and $Z = -0.53$ is
0.1906. Without consulting Table II, determine the area
under the standard normal curve between $Z = 0.53$
and $Z = 1.24$. 0.1906

46. (a) Suppose $P(Z < a) = 0.9938$; find a. 2.50
(b) Suppose $P(Z \geq a) = 0.4404$; find a. 0.15
(c) Suppose $P(-b < Z < b) = 0.8740$; find b. 1.53

Technology Step-by-Step
The Standard Normal Distribution

TI-83 Plus

Finding Areas under the Standard Normal Curve

Step 1: From the HOME screen, press 2nd VARS to access the DISTRibution menu.

Step 2: Select `2:normalcdf(`

Step 3: With `normalcdf(` on the HOME screen, type *lowerbound, upperbound, 0, 1*). For example, to find the area left of $Z = 1.26$ under the standard normal curve, type:

$$Normalcdf(-1E99, 1.26, 0, 1)$$

and hit ENTER.

NOTE: The "E" shown is scientific notation; it is 2nd, on the keyboard.

Finding Z-scores Corresponding to an Area

Step 1: From the HOME screen, press 2nd VARS to access the DISTRibution menu.

Step 2: Select `3:invNorm(`

Step 3: With `invNorm(` on the HOME screen, type *"area left", 0, 1*). For example, to find the *Z*-score such that the area under the normal curve left of the *Z*-score is 0.68, type:

$$InvNorm(0.68, 0 , 1)$$

and hit ENTER.

MINITAB

Finding Areas under the Standard Normal Curve

Step 1: Minitab will find an area to the left of a specified *Z*-score. Select the **Calc** menu, highlight **Probability Distributions**, and highlight **Normal** . . . .

Step 2: Select **Cumulative Probability**. Set the mean to 0 and the standard deviation to 1. Select **Input Constant**, and enter the specified *Z*-score. Click OK.

Finding Z-scores Corresponding to an Area

Step 1: Minitab will find the *Z*-score for an area to the left of unknown *Z*-score. Select the **Calc** menu, highlight **Probability Distributions**, and highlight **Normal** . . . .

Step 2: Select **Inverse Cumulative Probability**. Set the mean to 0 and the standard deviation to 1. Select **Input Constant**, and enter the specified area. Click OK.

Excel

Finding Areas under the Standard Normal Curve

Step 1: Excel will find the area to the left of a specified *Z*-score. Select the *fx* button from the tool bar. In **Function Category:**, select "Statistical." In **Function Name:**, select "NormsDist." Click OK.

Step 2: Enter the specified *Z*-score. Click OK.

Finding Z-scores Corresponding to an Area

Step 1: Excel will find the *Z*-score for an area to the left of unknown *Z*-score. Select the *fx* button from the tool bar. In **Function Category:**, select "Statistical." In **Function Name:**, select "NormsInv." Click OK.

Step 2: Enter the specified area. Click OK.

7.3 Applications of the Normal Distribution

Preparing for This Section Before getting started, review the following:

✓ Percentiles (Section 3.4, pp. 159–161)

Objectives Find and interpret area under a normal curve
 Find the value of a normal random variable

Suppose that a random variable X is normally distributed with mean μ and standard deviation σ. The area below the normal curve represents a proportion or probability. From the discussions in Section 7.1 we know that finding the area under a normal curve requires that we transform a normal random variable X with mean μ and standard deviation σ into a standard normal random variable Z with mean 0 and standard deviation 1. This is accomplished by letting $Z = \dfrac{X - \mu}{\sigma}$ and using Table II to find the area under the standard normal curve. This idea is illustrated in Figure 33.

Figure 33

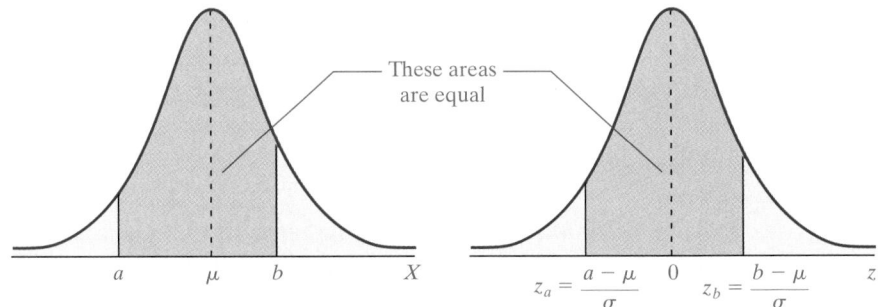

Now that we have the ability to find the area under a standard normal curve, we can find the area under any normal curve. We summarize the procedure below.

Finding the Area under any Normal Curve

Step 1: Draw a normal curve with the desired area shaded.

Step 2: Convert the values of X to Z-scores, using $Z = \dfrac{X - \mu}{\sigma}$.

Step 3: Draw a standard normal curve with the area desired shaded.

Step 4: Find the area under the standard normal curve. This is the area under the normal curve drawn in Step 1.

▶ **EXAMPLE 1** **Finding Area under a Normal Curve**

Note to Instructor
Be sure to emphasize to students that they draw the nonstandard normal curve and the corresponding standard normal curve to reinforce their conceptual understanding for finding area under any normal curve.

Problem: A pediatrician obtains the heights of her 200 three-year-old female patients. The heights are normally distributed, with mean 38.72 and standard deviation 3.17. What percent of the three-year-old females have a height less than 35 inches?

Approach: Follow the steps listed above.

Solution:

Step 1: Figure 34 shows the normal curve with the area to the left of 35 shaded.

Step 2: We convert $X = 35$ to a standard normal random variable Z with $\mu = 38.72$ and $\sigma = 3.17$.

$$Z = \frac{X - \mu}{\sigma} = \frac{35 - 38.72}{3.17} = -1.17$$

Step 3: Figure 35 shows the standard normal curve with the area left of $Z = -1.17$ shaded.

Figure 34

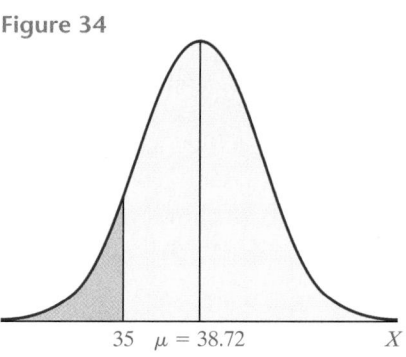

Figure 35

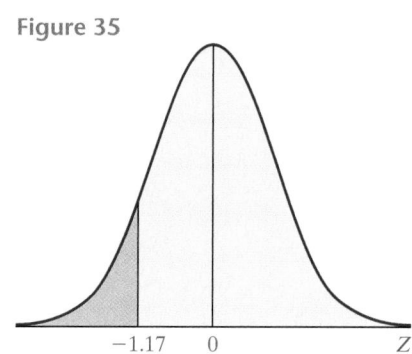

The area to the left of $Z = -1.17$ is equal to the area to the left of $X = 35$.

Step 4: Using Table II, we find the area to the left of $Z = -1.17$ is 0.121. We conclude that 12.1% of the pediatrician's three-year-old females are less than 35 inches tall.   ◄◄

TABLE 3

Height (inches)	Relative Frequency
29.0–29.9	0.005
30.0–30.9	0.005
31.0–31.9	0.005
32.0–32.9	0.025
33.0–33.9	0.02
34.0–34.9	0.055
35.0–35.9	0.075
36.0–36.9	0.09
37.0–37.9	0.115
38.0–38.9	0.15
39.0–39.9	0.12
40.0–40.9	0.11
41.0–41.9	0.07
42.0–42.9	0.06
43.0–43.9	0.035
44.0–44.9	0.025
45.0–45.9	0.025
46.0–46.9	0.005
47.0–47.9	0.005

Using Technology: Graphing calculators with advanced statistical features and statistical software can be used to compute the area below any normal curve. Figure 36 shows the results of Example 1 using a TI-83 Plus graphing calculator. The results differ from Example 1 because of rounding.

Figure 36

```
normalcdf(-1E99,
35,38.72,3.17)
        .1202974198
```

NW   *Now Work Problems 11(a) and 11(b).*

According to the results of Example 1, the probability that a randomly selected three-year-old female is shorter than 35 inches is 0.121. If the normal curve is a good model for determining probabilities (or proportions), then about 12.1% of the 200 three-year-olds in Table 1 on page 385 should be shorter than 35 inches. For convenience, the information provided in Table 1 is repeated in Table 3.

From the relative frequency distribution in Table 3, we determine that $0.005 + 0.005 + 0.005 + 0.025 + 0.02 + 0.055 = 0.115 = 11.5\%$ of the three-year olds are less than 35 inches tall. The results based upon the normal curve are in close agreement with the actual results. The normal curve accurately models the heights of three-year-old females.

► EXAMPLE 2 **Finding the Probability of a Normal Random Variable**

Problem: Use the results of Example 1 to compute the probability that a randomly selected three-year-old female is between 35 and 40 inches tall. That is, find $P(35 \le X \le 40)$.

Approach: We follow the steps listed on page 406.

Solution:

Step 1: Figure 37 shows the normal curve with the area between $X_1 = 35$ and $X_2 = 40$ shaded.

Step 2: Convert the values of $X_1 = 35$ and $X_2 = 40$ to Z-scores.

$$Z_1 = \frac{X_1 - \mu}{\sigma} = \frac{35 - 38.72}{3.17} = -1.17$$

$$Z_2 = \frac{X_2 - \mu}{\sigma} = \frac{40 - 38.72}{3.17} = 0.40$$

Step 3: Figure 38 shows the graph of the standard normal curve with the area between $Z_1 = -1.17$ and $Z_2 = 0.40$ shaded.

Figure 37

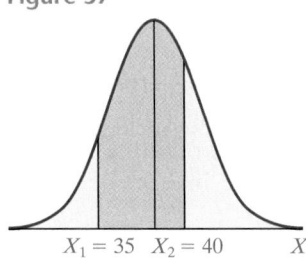

$X_1 = 35 \quad X_2 = 40 \qquad X$

Figure 38

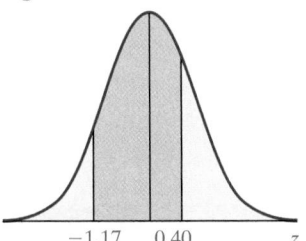

$-1.17 \quad 0.40 \qquad z$

Step 4: Using Table II, we find that the area to the left of $Z_2 = 0.40$ is 0.6554 and the area to the left of $Z_1 = -1.17$ is 0.1210. Therefore, the area between $Z_1 = -1.17$ and $Z_2 = 0.40$ is $0.6554 - 0.1210 = 0.5344$. We conclude that the probability a randomly selected three-year-old female is between 35 and 40 inches tall is 0.5344. That is, $P(35 \le X \le 40) = P(-1.17 \le Z \le 0.40) = 0.5344$. ◄◄

NW *Now Work Problem 11(c).*

In Your Own Words

The normal probability density function is used to model random variables that appear to be normal (such as girls' heights). A good model is one that yields results that are close to reality.

According to the relative frequency distribution in Table 3, the proportion of the 200 three-year-old females with heights between 35 inches and 40 inches is $0.075 + 0.09 + 0.115 + 0.15 + 0.12 = 0.55 = 55\%$. This is very close to the probability obtained in Example 2!

② **Finding Values of Normal Random Variables**

Often, rather than being interested in the proportion or probabliy of a normal random variable, we are interested in calculating the value of a normal random variable required for the variable to be at a certain proportion or probability. For example, we might want to know the height of a three-year-old girl at the 20th percentile. This means we want to know the height of a three-year-old girl who is taller than 20% of all three-year-old girls.

> **Procedure for Finding the Value of a Normal Random Variable Corresponding to a Specified Proportion or Probability**
>
> **Step 1:** Draw a normal curve with the area corresponding to the proportion or probability shaded.
>
> **Step 2:** Use Table II to find the Z-score that corresponds to the shaded area.
>
> **Step 3:** Obtain the normal value from the fact that $X = \mu + Z\sigma$.*

▶ **EXAMPLE 3**   **Finding the Value of a Normal Random Variable**

Problem: The heights of a pediatrician's 200 three-year-old females are normally distributed with mean 38.72 inches and standard deviation 3.17 inches. Find the height of a three-year-old female at the 20th percentile. That is, find the height for a three-year-old female that separates the bottom 20% from the top 80%.

Approach: We follow Steps 1–3 given above.

Solution:

Step 1: Figure 39 shows the normal curve with the unknown value of X separating the bottom 20% of the distribution from the top 80% of the distribution.

Step 2: From Table II, the area closest to 0.20 is 0.2005. The corresponding Z-score is -0.84.

Step 3: The height of a three-year-old female that separates the bottom 20% of the data from the top 80% is computed as follows:

$$X = \mu + Z\sigma$$
$$= 38.72 + (-0.84)(3.17)$$
$$= 36.1 \text{ inches} \qquad \blacktriangleleft\blacktriangleleft$$

Figure 39

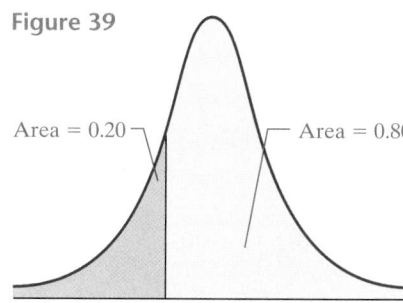

Area = 0.20
Area = 0.80
$X = ?$
X

> **Using Technology:** Graphing calculators with advanced statistical features and statistical software can be used to compute the value of a normal random variable corresponding to a given proportion. Figure 40 shows the results of Example 3 using Minitab.
>
> **Figure 40**
>
> **Inverse Cumulative Distribution Function**
>
> ```
> Normal with mean = 38.7200 and standard deviation = 3.17000
>
>
> P ( x <= x)        x
>     0.2000     36.0521
> ```

NW *Now Work Problems 21(a) and 21(b).*

$$* \, Z = \frac{X - \mu}{\sigma} \qquad \text{Formula for Standardizing a Random Variable } X$$

$$Z\sigma = X - \mu \qquad \text{Multiply both sides by } \sigma$$

$$X = \mu + Z\sigma \qquad \text{Add } \mu \text{ to both sides}$$

▶ **EXAMPLE 4** **Finding the Value of a Normal Random Variable**

Problem: The heights of a pediatrician's 200 three-year-old females are normally distributed with mean 38.72 inches and standard deviation 3.17 inches. The pediatrician wishes to determine the heights that separate the middle 98% of the distribution from the bottom and top 1%. In other words, find the 1st and 99th percentiles.

Approach: We follow Steps 1–3 given on page 409.

Solution:

Step 1: Figure 41 shows the normal curve with the unknown values of X separating the bottom and top 1% of the distribution from the middle 98% of the distribution.

Step 2: First, we will find the Z-score that corresponds to the area 0.01 to the left. From Table II, the area closest to 0.01 is 0.0099. The corresponding Z-score is -2.33. The Z-score that corresponds to the area 0.01 to the right will be the Z-score that has the area 0.99 to the left. The area closest to 0.99 is 0.9901. The corresponding Z-score is 2.33.

Step 3: The height of a three-year-old female that separates the bottom 1% of the distribution from the top 99% is

$$X_1 = \mu + Z\sigma$$
$$= 38.72 + (-2.33)(3.17)$$
$$= 31.3 \text{ inches}$$

The height of a three-year-old female that separates the top 1% of the distribution from the bottom 99% is

$$X_2 = \mu + Z\sigma$$
$$= 38.72 + (2.33)(3.17)$$
$$= 46.1 \text{ inches}$$

A three-year-old female whose height is less than 31.3 inches is in the bottom 1% of all three-year-old females and a three-year-old female whose height is more than 46.1 inches is in the top 1% of all three-year-old females. The pediatrician might use this information to identify those patients who have unusual heights. ◀◀

Figure 41

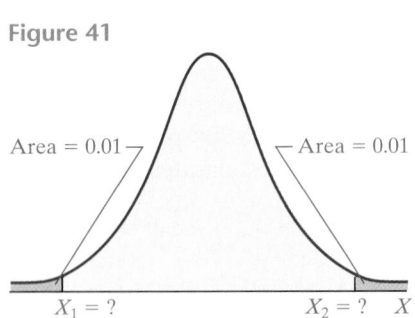

Area = 0.01   Area = 0.01

$X_1 = ?$ $X_2 = ?$ X

NW *Now Work Problem 21(c).*

7.3 Assess Your Understanding

Concepts and Vocabulary

1. Describe the procedure for finding the area under any normal curve.

2. Describe the procedure for finding the score corresponding to a probability.

Exercises

- ## Skill Building

In Problems 1–10, assume the random variable X is normally distributed with mean $\mu = 50$ and standard deviation $\sigma = 7$. Compute the following probabilities. Be sure to draw a normal curve with the area corresponding to the probability shaded.

1. $P(X > 35)$ 0.9839

2. $P(X > 65)$ 0.0161

3. $P(X \le 45)$ 0.2375

4. $P(X \le 58)$ 0.8735

5. $P(40 < X < 65)$ 0.9074

6. $P(56 < X < 68)$ 0.1906

7. $P(55 \le X \le 70)$ 0.2354

8. $P(40 \le X \le 49)$ 0.3666

9. $P(38 < X \le 55)$ 0.7192

10. $P(56 \le X < 66)$ 0.1845

- ## Applying the Concepts

11. Serum Cholesterol As reported by the U.S. National Center for Health Statistics, the mean serum high-density-lipoprotein (HDL) cholesterol of females 20–29 years old is $\mu = 53$. If serum HDL cholesterol is distributed normally with $\sigma = 13.4$, answer the following questions.

(a) What proportion of 20–29 year old females have a serum HDL cholesterol level below 39? 0.1481

(b) What proportion of 20–29 year old females have a serum HDL cholesterol above 71? 0.0896

(c) What proportion of 20–29 year old females have a serum HDL cholesterol between 60 and 75? 0.2504

(d) What is the probability a randomly selected 20–29-year-old female has a serum HDL cholesterol below 45? 0.2752

(e) What is the probability a randomly selected 20–29-year-old female has a serum HDL cholesterol between 50 and 60? 0.2879

(f) Suppose you are a doctor and a 24-year-old female patient of yours has a serum HDL cholesterol of 30. Is this unusual? A little

12. Earthquakes Since 1900, the magnitude of earthquakes that measure 0.1 or higher on the Richter Scale in California is distributed approximately normally, with $\mu = 6.2$ and $\sigma = 0.5$, according to data obtained from the United States Geological Survey.

(a) What is the probability that a randomly selected earthquake in California has a magnitude of 6.0 or higher? 0.6554

(b) What is the probability that a randomly selected earthquake in California has a magnitude less than 6.4? 0.6554

(c) What is the probability that a randomly selected earthquake in California has a magnitude between 5.8 and 7.1? 0.7522

(d) The great San Francisco Earthquake of 1906 had a magnitude of 8.25. Is an earthquake of this magnitude unusual in California? Yes

13. Stock Market Returns During the past forty years, the monthly rate of return of stocks has been approximately normally distributed, with $\mu = 0.75$ percent and $\sigma = 4.2$ percent, according to data obtained from Yahoo!Finance. (a) 0.4763

(a) What is the probability that a randomly selected month has a rate of return of at least 1 percent?

(b) What is the probability that a randomly selected month has a rate of return less than 2 percent? 0.6170

(c) What proportion of months have a positive rate of return (i.e. a rate of return greater than 0 percent)?

(d) In March, 2000, the monthly rate of return in stocks was 9.7 percent. Is this rate of return unusual? Why? Yes (c) 0.5709

14. ACT Math Scores In 2000, as reported by ACT Research Service, the mean ACT Math score was $\mu = 20.7$. If ACT Math scores are normally distributed with $\sigma = 5$, answer the following questions. (c) 0.1508

(a) What is the probability that a randomly selected student has an ACT Math score of at least 25? 0.1949

(b) What is the probability that a randomly selected student has an ACT Math score less than 18? 0.2946

(c) What is the probability that a randomly selected student has an ACT Math score between 24 and 27?

(d) If a student scores 29 on the ACT Math portion of the exam, what is her percentile rank (i.e. what percent of students scored less than 29)? 95th percentile

(e) If a student scores 17 on the ACT Math portion of the exam, what is her percentile rank? 23rd percentile

15. Heights of Females As reported by the U.S. National Center for Health Statistics, the mean height of females 20–29 years old is $\mu = 64.1$ inches. If height is normally distributed with $\sigma = 2.8$ inches, answer the following questions.

(a) What percent of 20–29-year-old females are less than 60 inches tall? 7.16%

(b) What percent of 20–29-year-old females are at least 72 inches tall? 0.24%

(c) What percent of 20–29-year-old females are between 60 and 70 inches tall? 91.09%

(d) What is the probability that a randomly selected 20–29-year-old female is between 60 and 70 inches tall? 0.9109

(e) Would it be unusual for a 20–29-year-old female to be more than 5´10˝? Yes

16. **IQ Scores** Scores on the Stanford–Binet Intelligence Test are normally distributed with mean $\mu = 100$ and standard deviation $\sigma = 16$.

    (a) People with IQ scores above 132 are considered to be "gifted." What percent of people are gifted? 2.28%
    (b) What is the probability that a randomly selected individual has an IQ score below 110? 0.7340
    (c) What is the probability that a randomly selected individual has an IQ between 90 and 120? 0.6284

17. **Blood Pressure** In a study of hypertension and optimal treatment conducted by the Center for Cardiovascular Education, 10,005 patients had a mean systolic blood pressure (the "upper reading") of 161 mm Hg with a standard deviation of 18 mm Hg. Assume systolic blood pressure is normally distributed to answer the following questions.

    (a) What percent of the people in the study have systolic blood pressure above 180, severe hypertension?
    (b) What percent of the people in the study have systolic blood pressure below 150? 27.06%
    (c) What percent of the people in the study have systolic blood pressure between 140 and 159, mild hypertension? 33.41%
    (d) What is the probability that a randomly selected individual in the study had systolic blood pressure below 143? 0.1587
    (e) What is the probability that a randomly selected individual in the study had systolic blood pressure between 155 and 170? 0.3220

18. **Gestation Period** The length of human pregnancies is normally distributed with mean $\mu = 266$ days and standard deviation $\sigma = 16$ days.   (a) 40.13%; (b) 15.87%

    (a) What percent of pregnancies last more than 270 days?
    (b) What percent of pregnancies last less than 250 days?
    (c) What percent of pregnancies last between 240 and 280 days? 75.71%
    (d) What is the probability that a randomly selected pregnancy lasts more than 280 days? 0.1908
    (e) What is the probability that a randomly selected pregnancy lasts no more than 245 days? 0.0947
    (f) A "very preterm" baby is one where the gestation period is less than 224 days. What proportion of births are "very preterm"? 0.0043

19. **Weather in Chicago** The high temperature in Chicago for the month of August is normally distributed with mean $\mu = 80°$ F and standard deviation $\sigma = 8°$ F.

    (a) What percent of the days in Chicago in August will have a high temperature above 90° F? 10.56%
    (b) What percent of the days in Chicago in August will have a high temperature below 60° F? 0.62%
    (c) What percent of the days in Chicago in August will have a high temperature between 85° F and 100° F?
    (d) What is the probability that a randomly selected day in August in Chicago will have a high temperature below 70° F? 0.1056

(e) What is the probability that a randomly selected day in August in Chicago will have a high temperature between 72° F and 80° F? 0.3413

20. **Shark Attacks** The number of shark attacks per year in the United States is distributed approximately normal, with $\mu = 31.8$ and $\sigma = 10.0$, according to data obtained from the Florida Museum of Natural History.

    (a) What percent of years will have fewer than 30 shark attacks? 42.86%
    (b) What percent of years will have more than 40 shark attacks? 20.61%
    (c) In 2000, there were 51 shark attacks in the United States. Is this an unusually high number of attacks? Why? Not that unusual

21. **Serum Cholesterol** As reported by the U.S. National Center for Health Statistics, the mean serum high-density-lipoprotein (HDL) cholesterol of females 20–29 years old is $\mu = 53$. If serum HDL cholesterol is normally distributed with $\sigma = 13.4$, answer the following questions.

    (a) Determine the 25th percentile of serum HDL cholesterol for a 20–29-year-old female. Interpret the result.
    (b) According to the U.S. National Center for Health Statistics, the 25th percentile of serum HDL cholesterol for a 20–29-year-old female is 44. How does this compare to the result obtained in part (a)?
    (c) Determine the serum HDL cholesterol levels that make up the middle 80% of serum HDL cholesterol levels. 35.8; 70.2

22. **Earthquakes** Since 1900, the magnitude of earthquakes that measure 0.1 or higher on the Richter Scale in California is distributed approximately normally, with $\mu = 6.2$ and $\sigma = 0.5$, according to data obtained from the United States Geological Survey.

    (a) Determine the 40th percentile of the magnitude of earthquakes in California. 6.1
    (b) Determine the magnitude of earthquakes that make up the middle 85% of magnitudes. 5.5; 6.9

23. **Stock Market Returns** During the past 40 years, the monthly rate of return of stocks has been distributed approximately normally, with $\mu = 0.75$ percent and $\sigma = 4.2$ percent, according to data obtained from Yahoo!Finance.

    (a) Determine the monthly rate of return that is at the 80th percentile. 4.28%
    (b) Determine the monthly rates of return that make up the middle 95% of returns. −7.48%, 8.98%

24. **ACT Math Scores** In 2000, as reported by ACT Research Service, the mean ACT Math score was $\mu = 20.7$. If ACT Math scores are normally distributed with $\sigma = 5$, answer the following questions.

    (a) If a student's ACT Math score is better than 80% of the students taking the exam (80th percentile), what was his score? 25
    (b) A certain college considers only applications in which the ACT Math score is in the top 5% of scores. What score is required to be considered? 29

(17a) 14.56% (19c) 25.98% (21a) 44

25. Heights of Females As reported by the U.S. National Center for Health Statistics, the mean height of females 20–29 years old is $\mu = 64.1$ inches. If height is normally distributed with $\sigma = 2.8$ inches, answer the following questions.

(a) Determine the 40th percentile of height for 20–29-year-old females. *63.4 inches*

(b) Determine the height required to be in the top 2% of all 20–29-year-old females. *69.9 inches*

(c) A "one-size-fits all" robe is being designed that should fit 95% of 20–29-year-old females; what heights constitute the middle 95% of all 20–29-year-old females? *58.6 inches; 69.6 inches*

26. IQ Scores Scores on the Stanford–Binet Intelligence Test are normally distributed with mean $\mu = 100$ and standard deviation $\sigma = 16$.

(a) In order to qualify for Mensa, an organization of people with high IQ scores, one must have an IQ at the 98th percentile. What IQ score is required to qualify for Mensa? *133*

(b) What range of IQ scores make up the middle 50% of the population? *89; 111*

27. Blood Pressure In the study of hypertension and optimal treatment mentioned in Problem 17, 10,005 patients had a mean systolic blood pressure of 161 mm Hg with a standard deviation of 18 mm Hg. Assume systolic blood pressure is normally distributed to answer the following questions. *(b) 146; 176*

(a) Determine the 70th percentile of systolic blood pressure for this group. *170*

(b) What range of systolic blood pressures make up the middle 60% of the participants in the study?

28. Gestation Period The length of human pregnancies is approximately normally distributed with mean $\mu = 266$ days and standard deviation $\sigma = 16$ days.

(a) Suppose an unusually long pregnancy is one that is in the top 2%. Determine the length of pregnancy that separates an unusually long pregnancy from one that is not unusually long. *299 days*

(b) Determine the length of pregnancy that would be considered typical if we define typical to be the middle 96% of pregnancies. *233–299 days*

29. Weather in Chicago The high temperature in Chicago for the month of August is distributed approximately normally, with mean $\mu = 80°$ F and standard deviation $\sigma = 8°$ F.

(a) Determine the high temperature required for a day to be in the bottom 10%. *70° F*

(b) If we define an unusually warm day in August as one that is in the top 4%, what temperatures qualify as unusually warm? *≥94° F*

(c) Determine the temperatures that constitute the middle 80% of high temperatures in August.

30. Shark Attacks The number of shark attacks per year in the United States is distributed approximately normally, with $\mu = 31.8$ and $\sigma = 10.0$, according to data obtained from Florida Museum of Natural History. *(a) 52 attacks*

(a) Determine the number of shark attacks per year that separates the top 2% from the bottom 98%.

(b) Determine the numbers of shark attacks per year that constitute the middle 80% of shark attacks per year. *19–45 attacks*

31. SAT Math Scores The following relative frequency distribution represents the scores on the SAT I: Reasoning Test—Math in 2000:

Score	Relative Frequency	Score	Relative Frequency
200–249	0.0073	500–549	0.1637
250–299	0.0167	550–599	0.1472
300–349	0.0438	600–649	0.1095
350–399	0.0797	650–699	0.0737
400–449	0.1336	700–749	0.0393
450–499	0.1661	750–800	0.0195

Source: College Board Online

SAT math scores are known to be normally distributed. The mean SAT math score is $\mu = 514$ and the standard deviation is $\sigma = 113$.

(a) Compute the theoretical proportion of test takers in each class by finding the area under the normal curve.

(b) Compare the theoretical proportions to the actual proportions. Are you convinced that the SAT math scores are normally distributed?

32. SAT Verbal Scores The following relative-frequency distribution represents the scores on the SAT I: Reasoning Test—Verbal in 2000:

Score	Relative Frequency	Score	Relative Frequency
200–249	0.0113	500–549	0.1766
250–299	0.0162	550–599	0.1435
300–349	0.0442	600–649	0.1037
350–399	0.0874	650–699	0.0603
400–449	0.1381	700–749	0.0292
450–499	0.1722	750–800	0.0172

Source: College Board Online

SAT verbal scores are known to be normally distributed. The mean SAT verbal score is $\mu = 505$ and the standard deviation is $\sigma = 111$.

(a) Compute the theoretical proportion of test takers in each class by finding the area under the normal curve.

(b) Compare the theoretical proportions to the actual proportions. Are you convinced the SAT verbal scores are normally distributed?

(29c) 70° F − 90° F

33. Weather in Chicago The following frequency distribution represents the daily high temperature in Chicago, Nov. 16–30, for the years 1872–1999:

Temperature	Frequency	Temperature	Frequency
5.0–9.9	1	40.0–44.9	375
10.0–14.9	10	45.0–49.9	281
15.0–19.9	15	50.0–54.9	233
20.0–24.9	40	55.0–59.9	160
25.0–29.9	95	60.0–64.9	101
30.0–34.9	217	65.0–69.9	21
35.0–39.9	325	70.0–74.9	1

Source: Chicago Tribune, November 27, 2000

(a) Construct a relative frequency distribution.
(b) Draw a relative frequency histogram. Does the distribution of high temperatures appear to be normal?
(c) Compute the mean and standard deviation of (the variable) high temperature. $\mu = 43.5°, \sigma = 10.5°$
(d) Use the information obtained in part (c) to compute the theoretical proportion of high temperatures in each class by finding the area under the normal curve.
(e) Are you convinced that high temperatures are normally distributed?

Technology Step-by-Step
The Normal Distribution

TI-83 Plus

Finding Areas under the Normal Curve

Step 1: From the HOME screen, press 2nd VARS to access the DISTRibution menu.

Step 2: Select `2:normalcdf(`

Step 3: With `normalcdf(` on the HOME screen, type *lowerbound, upperbound,* μ, σ). For example, to find the area to the left of $X = 35$ under the normal curve with $\mu = 40$ and $\sigma = 10$, type

```
Normalcdf(-1E99, 35, 40, 10)
```

and hit ENTER.

Note: The "E" shown is scientific notation; it is 2nd,

Finding Scores Corresponding to an Area

Step 1: From the HOME screen, press 2nd VARS to access the DISTRibution menu.

Step 2: Select `3:invNorm(`

Step 3: With `invNorm(` on the HOME screen, type "*area*", μ, σ). For example, to find the score such that the area under the normal curve to the left of the score is 0.68 with $\mu = 40$ and $\sigma = 10$, type

```
InvNorm(0.68, 40, 10)
```

and hit ENTER.

MINITAB

Finding Areas under the Normal Curve

Step 1: Minitab will find an area to the left of a specified observation. Select the **Calc** menu, highlight **Probability** **Distributions**, and highlight **Normal** ....

Step 2: Select **Cumulative Probability**. Enter the mean, μ, and the standard deviation, σ. Select **Input Constant**, and enter the observation. Click OK.

Finding Z-scores Corresponding to an Area

Step 1: Minitab will find the score corresponding to a specified area. Select the **Calc** menu, highlight **Probability** **Distributions**, and highlight **Normal** ...

Step 2: Select **Inverse Cumulative Probability**. Enter the mean, μ, and the standard deviation, σ. Select **Input Constant**, and enter the area left of the unknown score. Click OK.

Excel **Finding Areas under the Normal Curve**
Step 1: Excel will find an area to the left of a specified observation. Select the *fx* button from the tool bar. In **Function Category:**, select "Statistical." In **Function Name:**, select NormDist. Click OK.
Step 2: Enter the specified observation, μ, and σ, and set **cumulative** to True. Click OK.

Finding Scores Corresponding to an Area
Step 1: Select the *fx* button from the tool bar. In **Function Category:**, select "Statistical." In **Function Name:**, select NormInv. Click OK.
Step 2: Enter the area left of the unknown score, μ, and σ. Click OK.

7.4 Assessing Normality

Preparing for This Section Before getting started, review the following:

✓ Shape of a distribution (Section 3.1, pp. 119–122)

Objectives   Draw normal probability plots to assess normality

Suppose that we obtain a simple random sample from a population whose distribution is unknown. Many of the statistical tests that we perform on small data sets (sample size less than 30) require that the population from which the sample is drawn be normally distributed. Up to this point, we have said that a random variable X is normally distributed, or at least approximately normal, provided the histogram of the data is symmetric and bell-shaped. This method works well for large data sets, but the shape of a histogram drawn from a small sample of observations does not always accurately represent the shape of the population. For this reason, we need additional methods for assessing the normality of a random variable X when we are looking at a small set of sample data.

In Your Own Words

Normal probability plots are used to assess normality in small data sets.

Normal Probability Plots

A **normal probability plot** plots observed data versus *normal scores*. A **normal score** is the expected Z-score of the data value if the distribution of the random variable is normal. The expected Z-score of an observed value will depend upon the number of observations in the data set.

To draw a normal probability plot requires the following steps.

Drawing a Normal Probability Plot

Step 1: Arrange the data in ascending order.

Step 2: Compute $f_i = \dfrac{i - 0.375}{n + 0.25}$,* where i is the index (the ith number in the list) and n is the number of observations. This value represents the expected proportion of observations less than or equal to the ith data value.

Step 3: Find the Z-score corresponding to f_i from Table II.

Step 4: Plot the observed values on the horizontal axis and the corresponding expected Z-scores on the vertical axis.

*The derivation of this formula is beyond the scope of this text.

Figure 42

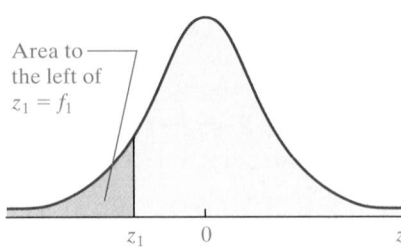

Area to the left of $z_1 = f_1$

The idea behind finding the expected Z-score is that, if the data come from a population that is normally distributed, we should be able to predict the area to the left of each of the data values. The value of f_i represents the expected area to the left of the ith data value when the data come from a population that is normally distributed. For example, f_1 is the expected area to the left of the smallest data value, f_2 is the expected area to the left of the second-smallest data value, and so on. Figure 42 illustrates the idea.

Once we determine each of the f_i, we find the Z-scores corresponding to f_1, f_2, and so on. The smallest observation in the data set will be the smallest expected Z-score, and the largest observation in the data set will be the largest expected Z-score. In addition, because of the symmetry of the normal curve, the expected Z-scores are always paired as positive and negative values.

Normal random variables X and their Z-scores are linearly related $[X = \mu + Z\sigma]$, so a plot of observations of normal variables against their expected normal scores will be linear. We conclude the following:

If sample data are taken from a population that is normally distributed, a normal probability plot of the actual values versus the expected Z-scores will be approximately linear.

Note to Instructor
The goal of this section is for students to be able to understand what a normal probability plot is. In addition, we want students to be able to read the output provided by a computer or calculator. Do not emphasize the "by hand" solution. Rather emphasize how to interpret normal probability plots.

Fortunately, graphing calculators with advanced statistical features and statistical software have the ability to create normal probability plots.

Normal probability plots are typically drawn by using graphing calculators or statistical software; however, it is worthwhile to go through an example that demonstrates the procedure so that we can better understand the results supplied by software.

▶ **EXAMPLE 1**   Constructing a Normal Probability Plot

TABLE 4			
15.8	18.5	22.6	27.4
16.7	19.2	23.7	28.5
18.2	19.5	23.7	29.1
18.4	21.3	25.5	29.6
18.4	22.2	27.0	

Source: Morningstar.com

Problem: The data in Table 4 represent the three-year rate of return of 19 randomly selected small-capitalization growth mutual funds. Is there evidence to support the belief that the variable "three-year rate of return" is normally distributed?

Approach: We follow Steps 1–4 listed earlier.

Solution:

Step 1: The first column in Table 5 represents the index i. The second column in Table 5 represents the observed values in the data set, written in ascending order.

Step 2: The third column in Table 5 represents $f_i = \dfrac{i - 0.375}{n + 0.25}$ for each observation. Remember, this is the expected area under the normal curve to the left of the ith observation, under the assumption of normality. For example, $i = 1$ corresponds to the rate of return of 15.8 percent.

$$f_1 = \frac{1 - 0.375}{19 + 0.25} = 0.0325$$

So, the area to the left of 15.8 would be 0.0325 if the sample data come from a population that is normally distributed.

Note to Instructor
As an alternative to using Minitab to assess the linearity of the normal probability plot, we can use the linear correlation coefficient using the following steps.
Step 1: Compute the linear correlation between the data and the expected Z-scores.
Step 2: Compare the linear correlation coefficient to the critical values supplied below ($\alpha = 0.05$). If the linear correlation coefficient is greater than or equal to the critical value, then there is evidence to support the belief that the data come from a population that is normally distributed.

Sample size, n	Critical Value
5	0.880
6	0.888
7	0.898
8	0.906
9	0.912
10	0.918
11	0.923
12	0.928
13	0.932
14	0.935
15	0.939
16	0.941
17	0.944
18	0.946
19	0.949
20	0.951
21	0.952
22	0.954
23	0.956
24	0.957
25	0.959
30	0.960

Source: S.W. Looney and T.R. Gulledge, Jr. "Use of the Correlation Coefficient with Normal Probability Plots," *The American Statistician;* Vol. 39 (Feb, 1985), pp. 75–79

Step 3: We use Table II to find the Z-scores that correspond to f_i. The expected Z-scores are listed in the fourth column of Table 5. For example, the area to the left of 15.8 is $f_1 = 0.0325$ if the data come from a population that is normally distributed. Look in Table II for the area closest to $f_1 = 0.0325$. The expected Z-score is -1.85. Notice that for each negative expected Z-score, there is a corresponding positive expected Z-score, as a result of the symmetry of the normal curve.

		TABLE 5	
Index, i	Observed Value	f_i	Expected Z-score
1	15.8	$\dfrac{1 - 0.375}{19 + 0.25} = 0.0325$	-1.85
2	16.7	$\dfrac{2 - 0.375}{19 + 0.25} = 0.0844$	-1.38
3	18.2	0.1364	-1.10
4	18.4	0.1883	-0.88
5	18.4	0.2403	-0.71
6	18.5	0.2922	-0.55
7	19.2	0.3442	-0.40
8	19.5	0.3961	-0.26
9	21.3	0.4481	-0.13
10	22.2	0.5	0
11	22.6	0.5519	0.13
12	23.7	0.6039	0.26
13	23.7	0.6558	0.40
14	25.5	0.7078	0.55
15	27.0	0.7597	0.71
16	27.4	0.8117	0.88
17	28.5	0.8636	1.10
18	29.1	0.9156	1.38
19	29.6	0.9675	1.85

Step 4: We plot the actual observations on the horizontal axis and the expected Z-scores on the vertical axis. See Figure 43.

Figure 43
Normal Probability Plot

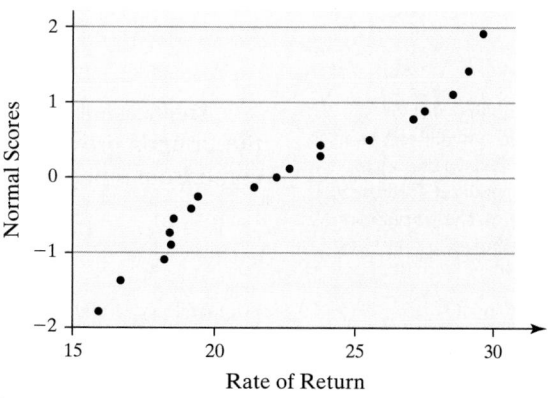

Although the normal probability plot in Figure 43 does show some curvature, it is roughly linear.* We conclude that the three-year rate of return of small-capitalization growth mutual funds is approximately normally distributed. ◄◄

Typically, normal probability plots are drawn by using either a graphing calculator with advanced statistical features or statistical software. Certain software, such as Minitab, provides bounds that the data must lie within in order to support the belief that the sample data come from a population that is normally distributed.

► EXAMPLE 2   Assessing Normality Via Statistical Software

Problem: Using Minitab, or some other statistical software, draw a normal probability plot of the data in Table 4 and determine whether there is evidence to support the belief that the sample data come from a population that is normally distributed.

Approach: We will construct a normal probability plot using Minitab. Minitab provides curved "bounds" that can be used to assess normality. If the normal probability plot is roughly linear and all the data lie within the bounds provided by the software, then we have reason to believe the data come from a population that is approximately normal.

Solution: Figure 44 shows the normal probability plot.

Figure 44

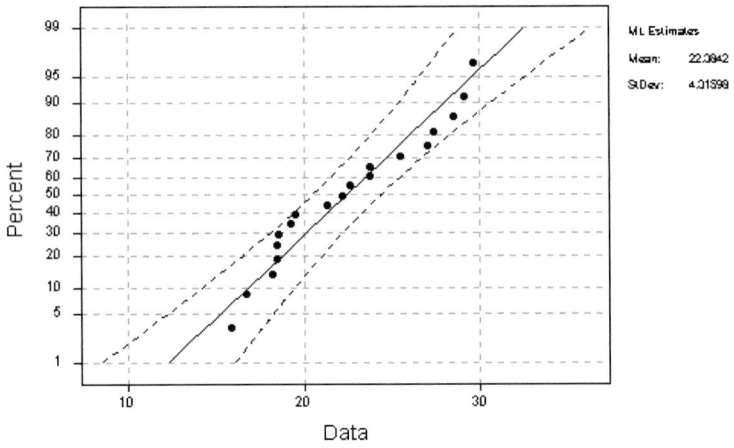

Normal Probability Plot for Rate of Return

    Caution

If a normal probability plot of sample data is roughly linear, then it is reasonable to believe that the population is normally distributed. We do not say that the population is normally distributed.

The normal probability plot is roughly linear, and all the data lie within the bounds provided by Minitab. We conclude that the sample data could come from a population that is normally distributed. ◄◄

*In fact, the correlation between the observed value and expected *Z*-score is 0.974.

Figure 45 shows a histogram drawn for the data analyzed in Example 2. Judging from the histogram whether the sample data come from a population that is normally distributed would be very difficult.

Figure 45

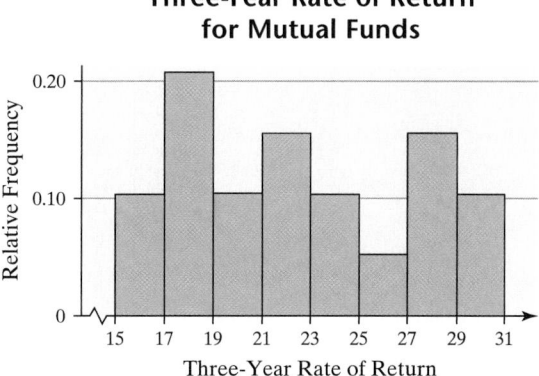

Throughout the text, we will provide normal probability plots drawn with Minitab, so that assessing normality is straightforward.

▶ EXAMPLE 3   Assessing Normality

Problem: The data in Table 6 represent the time spent waiting in line (in minutes) for the Demon Roller Coaster for 100 randomly selected riders. Is the random variable "waiting time" normally distributed?

TABLE 6																
7	3	5	107	8	37	16	41	7	25	22	19	1	40	1	29	93
33	76	14	8	9	45	15	81	94	10	115	18	0	18	11	60	34
30	6	21	0	86	6	11	1	1	3	9	79	41	2	9	6	19
4	3	2	7	18	0	93	68	6	94	16	13	24	6	12	121	30
35	39	9	15	53	9	47	5	55	64	51	80	26	24	12	0	
94	18	4	61	38	38	21	61	9	80	18	21	8	14	47	56	

Approach: We will use Minitab to draw a normal probability plot. If the normal probability plot is roughly linear and the data lie within the bounds provided by Minitab, conclude that it is reasonable to believe that the sample data come from a population that follows a normal distribution.

Solution: Figure 46 shows a normal probability plot of the data drawn using Minitab.

Figure 46

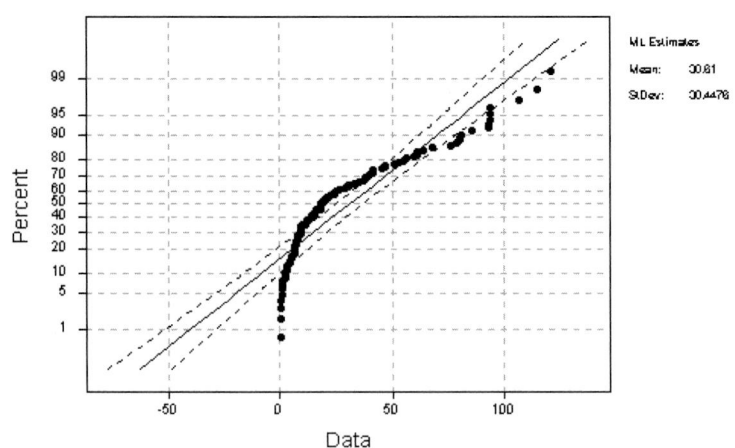

Normal Probability Plot for Wait Time

Clearly, the normal probability plot is not linear. We conclude that the random variable "wait time" is not normally distributed. ◄◄

Figure 47 shows a histogram of the data in Table 6. The histogram indicates that the data are skewed right.

Figure 47

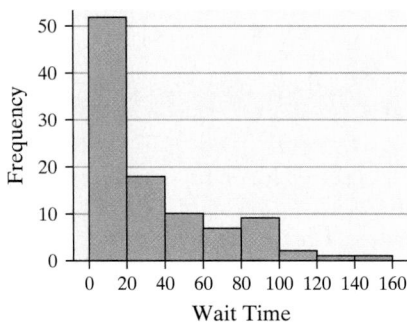

Histogram of Wait Time

NW *Now Work Problems 1 and 5.*

7.4 Assess Your Understanding

Concepts and Vocabulary

1. Explain why normal probability plots should be linear if the data is normally distributed.

2. What does f_i represent?

Exercises

⇒ Skill Building

In Problems 1–6, determine whether the normal probability plot indicates that the sample data could have come from a population that is normally distributed.

1. Not normal
2. Not normal
3. Normal
4. Not normal
5. Normal
6. Normal

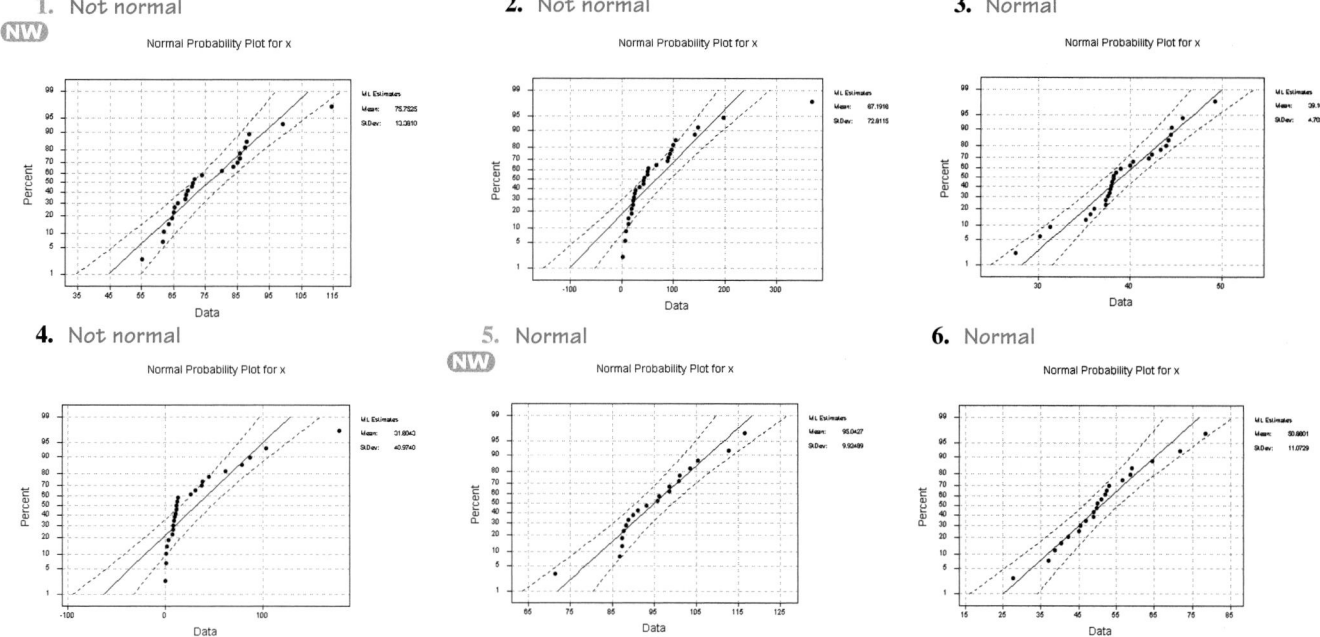

• Applying the Concepts

In Problems 7–10, use a normal probability plot to assess whether the sample data could have come from a population that is normally distributed.

7. **Achievement Scores** A school psychologist conducted an experiment in which 40 third-grade students who were identified as "at-risk" by their teachers were randomly divided into two equal groups of size 20. Group 1 participated in a new school success program; group 2 participated in an ongoing school success program. The following data represent the achievement scores of the students in Group 1 at post-trial assessment. Normal

75	110	80	134	102	82	109
114	83	110	89	89	98	104
104	99	98	111	104	92	

8. **Miles on a Cavalier** A random sample of eighteen three-year-old Chevy Cavaliers was obtained in the Miami, FL area, and the number of miles on each car was recorded. Normal

34,122	17,685	15,499	26,455	30,500
39,416	29,307	26,051	27,368	35,936
28,281	34,511	32,305	37,904	44,448
41,194	29,289	31,883		

Source: cars.com

9. **Volume of Philip Morris Stock** The following data represent a random sample of the number of shares of Philip Morris stock traded for 20 days in 2000. Not normal

3.98	8.90	10.40	7.52	13.84
5.29	9.69	8.94	12.10	13.25
4.24	8.54	11.59	6.75	27.54
7.71	10.14	4.28	7.24	10.88

Source: http://finance.yahoo.com

10. **Baseball Salaries** The following data represent the baseball salaries of 24 randomly selected players from the 2000 season (data are in thousands, so 2350 means $2,350,000). Not normal

2350	208	260	215	6000	3333
1400	225	1000	270	2750	4000
3950	4000	269	225	305	200
2400	300	962	15,714	950	213

Source: espn.com

Technology Step-by-Step
Normal Probability Plots

TI-83 Plus   **Step 1:** Enter the raw data into L1.

Step 2: Press 2nd Y = to access STAT PLOTS.

Step 3: Select 1:Plot1.

Step 4: Turn Plot1 ON by highlighting ON and pressing ENTER. Press the down-arrow key. Highlight the *normal probability plot* icon. It is the icon in the lower-right corner under Type:. Press ENTER to select this plot type. The Data List should be set at L1. The data axis should be the *x*-axis.

Step 5: Press ZOOM, and select 9:ZoomStat.

MINITAB   **Step 1:** Enter the raw data into C1.

Step 2: Select the **Graph** menu. Highlight **Probability Plot** ....

Step 3: In the Variables cell, enter the column that contains the raw data. Make sure Distribution is set to Normal. Click OK.

Excel   **Step 1:** Load the PHStat Add-in.

Step 2: Enter the raw data into column A.

Step 3: Select the **PHStat** menu. Highlight **Probability Distributions**, then highlight **Normal Probability Plot** ....

Step 4: With the cursor in the "Variable Cell Range:" cell, highlight the raw data. Enter a graph title, if desired. Click OK.

7.5   Sampling Distributions; The Central Limit Theorem

Preparing for This Section   Before getting started, review the following:

✓ Simple random sampling (Section 1.2, pp. 15–18)

✓ The arithmetic mean (Section 3.1, pp. 113–115)

✓ The standard deviation (Section 3.2, pp. 137–138)

Objectives   **①** Understand the concept of a sampling distribution

② Compute the mean and standard deviation of a sampling distribution of the mean

③ Compute probabilities of a sample mean obtained from a normal population

④ Compute probabilities of a sample mean utilizing the Central Limit Theorem

① Recall the process of statistics presented in Chapter 1.

Step 1: A research question is posed.

Step 2: Information (data) is collected so that the question posed can be answered. This information typically is collected through an experiment or survey.

Step 3: The information is organized and summarized. This is done through a pictorial representation of the data collected in Step 2 and through numerical summaries, such as the mean and standard deviation.

Step 4: Draw conclusions from the data.

The methods for conducting Steps 1 and 2 were discussed in Chapter 1. The methods for conducting Step 3 were discussed in Chapters 2, 3, and 4.

If the information that is organized in Step 3 is based upon sample data, then we use this data to make inferences about the population. For example, we might compute a sample mean from the information collected in Step 2 and use this information to draw conclusions regarding the population mean.

From our discussions of sampling methods, we know that the values of statistics such as $\bar{x}$ vary from sample to sample (because the individuals in the samples are different). So, using statistics to make inferences regarding a population is subject to variability and, hence, uncertainty. Therefore, we need a way to assess the reliability of inferences made regarding a population. This is where the information learned in Chapters 5 and 6 and in the sections in Chapter 7 preceding this one comes in handy.

Inferential statistics is based upon probability statements. If we know the probability distribution of a random variable, we can obtain probability statements regarding that random variable. For example, suppose IQ scores are normally distributed with mean 100 and standard deviation 16. Given this information, we can make a probability statement regarding the likelihood of randomly selecting an individual with an IQ of 120 or higher.

Because statistics such as $\bar{x}$ vary from sample to sample, they are random variables. As such, statistics have probability distributions associated with them. For example, there is a probability distribution for the sample mean, one for the sample variance, and so on. In order to make probability statements regarding a sample statistic, we need to know the probability distribution of the sample statistic—that is to say, we need to know the shape, center, and spread of the sample statistic's distribution.

Sampling Distributions

In general, a sampling distribution of a statistic is a probability distribution (such as the normal distribution) for all possible values of the statistic computed from a sample of size n. The **sampling distribution of the mean** is a probability distribution of all possible values of the random variable $\bar{x}$ computed from a sample of size n from a population with mean μ and standard deviation σ.

The idea behind obtaining the sampling distribution of the mean is as follows:

Step 1: Obtain a simple random sample of size n.

Step 2: Compute the sample mean.

Step 3: Assuming that we are sampling from a finite population, repeat Steps 1 and 2 until all simple random samples of size n have been obtained.

We present an example to illustrate the idea behind a sampling distribution.

▶ EXAMPLE 1

Illustrating a Sampling Distribution

Note to Instructor
In-class activity: Treat the pulse of 6 students in your class as a population. Obtain the population mean. List all samples of size $n = 2$, and compute the sample means. Form a probability distribution for the sample means.

Problem: One semester, I had a small statistics class of 7 students. I asked them the age of their cars and obtained the following data:

$$2, 4, 6, 8, 4, 3, 7$$

Construct a sampling distribution of the mean for samples of size $n = 2$. The population mean is $\mu = \dfrac{34}{7} \approx 4.9$ years. What is the probability of obtaining a sample mean between 4 and 6 years, inclusive—that is, what is $P(4 \leq \bar{x} \leq 6)$?

Approach: We follow Steps 1–3 just listed to construct the probability distribution.

Solution: There are a total of 7 individuals in the population. We are selecting them two at a time without replacement. Therefore, there are $_7C_2 = 21$ samples of size $n = 2$. We list these 21 samples along with the sample means in Table 7.

TABLE 7					
Sample	Sample Mean	Sample	Sample Mean	Sample	Sample Mean
2, 4	3	4, 8	6	6, 7	6.5
2, 6	4	4, 4	4	8, 4	6
2, 8	5	4, 3	3.5	8, 3	5.5
2, 4	3	4, 7	5.5	8, 7	7.5
2, 3	2.5	6, 8	7	4, 3	3.5
2, 7	4.5	6, 4	5	4, 7	5.5
4, 6	5	6, 3	4.5	3, 7	5

Table 8 displays the sampling distribution of the sample mean, $\bar{x}$.

TABLE 8		
Sample Mean	Frequency	Probability
2.5	1	1/21
3	2	2/21
3.5	2	2/21
4	2	2/21
4.5	2	2/21
5	4	4/21
5.5	3	3/21
6	2	2/21
6.5	1	1/21
7	1	1/21
7.5	1	1/21

From Table 8, we can see that

$$P(4 \leq \bar{x} \leq 6) = \frac{2}{21} + \frac{2}{21} + \frac{4}{21} + \frac{3}{21} + \frac{2}{21} = \frac{13}{21} = 0.619$$

If we took 10 simple random samples of size 2 from this population, about 6 of them would result in sample means between 4 and 6 years, inclusive. ◀◀

The population mean of the data in Example 1 is μ = 4.9, rounded to one decimal place. Notice that the sample mean with the highest probability is $\overline{x}$ = 5. Also notice that the further the sample mean is from 4.9, the lower the probability of obtaining the sample mean. Figure 48 is a probability histogram of the sampling distribution for the sample mean given in Table 8.

Figure 48

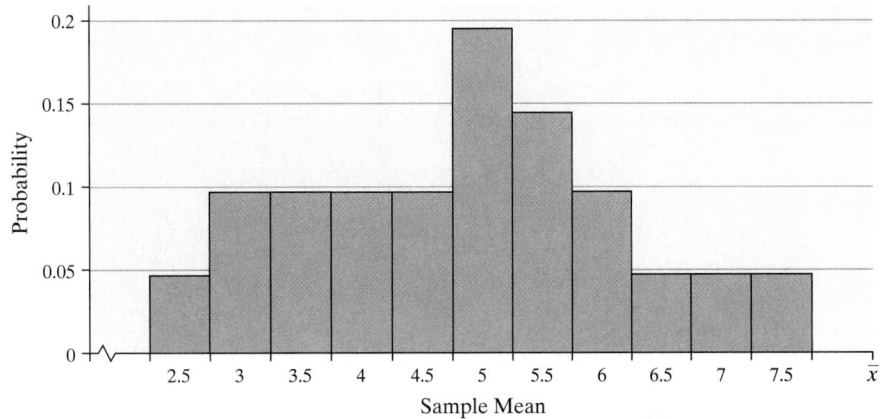

Probability Distribution of the Sample Mean

NW   *Now Work Problem 19.*

The point of Example 1 is to help you realize that statistics such as $\overline{x}$ vary and so have distributions associated with them. In practice, a single random sample of size n is obtained from a population. The probability distribution of the sample statistic (or sampling distribution) is determined from statistical theory. We will use simulation to help justify the result that statistical theory provides. We consider two possibilities. In the first case, we sample from a population that is known to be normally distributed. In the second case, we sample from a distribution that is not normally distributed.

▶ EXAMPLE 2   **Sampling Distribution of the Sample Mean— Population Normal**

Problem: The weight of three-year-old female patients is normally distributed with μ = 38.72 pounds and σ = 3.17 pounds. Approximate the sampling distribution of $\overline{x}$ by taking 100 simple random samples of size n = 5.

Approach: Use Minitab, Excel, or some other statistical software package to perform the simulation. We will perform the following steps.

Step 1: Obtain 100 simple random samples of size n = 5 from the population, using simulation.
Step 2: Compute the mean of each of the samples.
Step 3: Draw a histogram of the sample means.
Step 4: Compute the mean and standard deviation of the sample means.

Solution:

Step 1: We obtain 100 simple random samples of size n = 5. All the samples of size n = 5 are shown in Table 9.

Sample	Sample of Size $n = 5$					Sample Mean
1	36.48	39.94	42.57	39.53	33.81	38.47
2	43.13	37.97	42.41	39.61	43.30	41.28
3	41.64	39.01	37.77	38.94	41.10	39.69
4	40.37	43.49	37.60	40.14	38.88	40.10
5	38.62	33.43	45.17	42.66	39.98	39.97
6	38.98	41.35	36.80	43.56	39.92	40.12
7	42.48	37.00	35.87	39.62	38.74	38.74
8	39.38	37.02	41.60	40.34	37.62	39.19
9	42.82	45.77	35.16	42.56	39.75	41.21
10	36.19	35.20	37.74	40.46	37.47	37.41
11	36.59	41.62	42.18	39.23	39.26	39.77
12	38.57	42.13	45.39	38.22	46.18	42.10
13	38.40	39.06	43.60	31.46	37.03	37.91
14	34.29	47.73	37.27	41.82	33.33	38.89
15	42.28	43.29	37.69	37.32	40.06	40.13
16	34.31	43.58	40.02	41.13	42.99	40.41
17	38.71	39.03	39.39	42.62	38.41	39.63
18	38.63	39.66	39.47	41.13	38.01	39.38
19	39.09	33.86	37.57	41.65	35.22	37.48
20	40.94	37.50	38.72	41.64	35.48	38.86
21	38.72	35.89	37.82	35.04	37.06	36.91
22	39.64	36.30	35.54	40.40	38.74	38.12
23	38.22	38.49	33.60	40.18	39.07	37.91
24	40.93	40.53	37.55	37.30	37.16	38.70
25	33.27	38.92	37.14	39.90	33.83	36.61
26	39.44	37.28	35.70	41.97	36.80	38.24
27	38.83	41.41	38.87	39.40	37.20	39.14
28	40.10	36.96	35.73	43.00	38.11	38.78
29	41.93	36.57	37.55	35.14	38.75	37.99
30	31.25	38.85	39.25	35.07	39.77	36.84
31	38.47	34.45	30.43	41.76	41.61	37.34
32	37.98	35.56	43.97	44.96	37.81	40.06
33	43.34	40.94	35.17	41.74	37.59	39.76
34	39.80	44.44	37.53	40.52	41.95	40.85
35	41.98	42.02	40.73	40.47	36.81	40.40
36	40.98	35.08	34.61	40.78	37.26	37.74
37	35.75	40.81	40.13	35.99	36.52	37.84
38	36.39	45.97	40.59	37.64	42.42	40.60
39	36.20	35.63	37.43	38.35	34.81	36.48
40	33.58	33.87	41.60	45.10	38.68	38.57
41	31.77	38.34	41.79	37.93	40.83	38.13
42	43.03	33.12	34.98	36.58	37.78	37.10
43	35.76	35.17	42.58	39.10	41.08	38.74
44	38.44	38.45	35.93	35.32	44.60	38.55
45	44.54	41.88	35.84	42.64	42.38	41.46
46	41.89	36.81	41.83	40.24	39.28	40.01
47	38.00	40.08	35.57	34.44	39.51	37.52
48	39.92	38.05	39.96	38.04	32.11	37.61
49	36.37	38.62	32.25	41.35	40.91	37.90
50	34.38	36.65	32.97	39.93	41.34	37.05

Table 9 (cont'd)

51	40.32	39.80	41.00	38.62	38.24	39.59
52	37.95	45.26	38.67	34.96	41.13	39.60
53	36.82	42.63	41.62	39.43	37.48	39.59
54	41.63	37.65	38.58	39.03	37.53	38.88
55	37.91	37.20	38.72	36.87	45.40	39.22
56	41.05	34.01	39.11	38.23	35.74	37.63
57	42.09	45.44	35.52	39.87	37.28	40.04
58	39.31	35.79	37.82	39.15	35.57	37.53
59	41.16	39.98	41.11	39.21	39.98	40.29
60	35.68	45.60	39.34	36.65	43.30	40.12
61	36.07	39.63	42.55	41.72	36.81	39.36
62	38.97	36.83	41.01	38.12	35.27	38.04
63	33.70	39.15	34.81	34.13	39.00	36.16
64	37.19	34.69	36.21	34.34	39.07	36.30
65	33.99	44.87	42.52	40.22	39.26	40.17
66	41.40	27.62	34.57	40.08	34.65	35.66
67	40.14	34.45	38.26	38.09	39.72	38.13
68	33.64	42.62	32.08	34.30	37.34	35.99
69	35.36	39.02	43.98	41.19	32.47	38.40
70	43.26	37.85	35.82	37.11	36.22	38.05
71	36.24	38.07	33.38	38.43	39.88	37.20
72	38.55	43.06	41.07	36.58	37.02	39.25
73	41.26	36.99	36.17	38.98	36.03	37.89
74	37.31	38.41	41.18	39.76	39.64	39.26
75	36.26	41.84	42.50	37.70	41.21	39.90
76	39.27	38.61	44.53	38.08	35.01	39.10
77	39.14	40.83	39.83	37.78	36.51	38.82
78	42.53	43.41	41.01	33.71	39.47	40.03
79	45.34	32.61	33.81	39.03	40.32	38.22
80	36.31	35.55	37.12	38.74	40.80	37.70
81	31.40	41.80	40.15	42.53	37.62	38.70
82	41.01	39.02	39.68	36.61	38.44	38.95
83	34.15	36.19	35.98	36.02	36.32	35.73
84	31.50	37.61	43.29	39.82	38.78	38.20
85	43.26	34.01	41.18	40.23	39.28	39.59
86	41.76	41.40	39.02	38.20	39.42	39.96
87	37.06	35.95	39.98	40.00	43.36	39.27
88	41.01	37.56	36.95	39.71	37.97	38.64
89	34.97	38.36	36.30	38.48	34.24	36.47
90	38.38	38.94	40.96	36.13	35.98	38.08
91	39.41	30.78	37.66	37.31	42.04	37.44
92	39.83	35.88	30.20	45.07	40.06	38.21
93	36.25	39.56	34.53	40.69	37.03	37.61
94	45.64	40.66	44.51	40.50	39.43	42.15
95	37.63	44.77	38.31	36.53	38.41	39.13
96	39.78	33.34	43.42	43.63	38.77	39.79
97	41.48	37.39	38.62	43.83	34.26	39.12
98	37.68	40.66	38.93	40.94	37.54	39.15
99	39.72	32.61	32.62	40.35	38.65	36.79
100	39.25	41.06	41.17	38.30	38.24	39.60

Step 2: We compute the sample means for each of the 100 samples as shown in Table 9.

Step 3: We draw a histogram of the 100 sample means. See Figure 49.

Figure 49

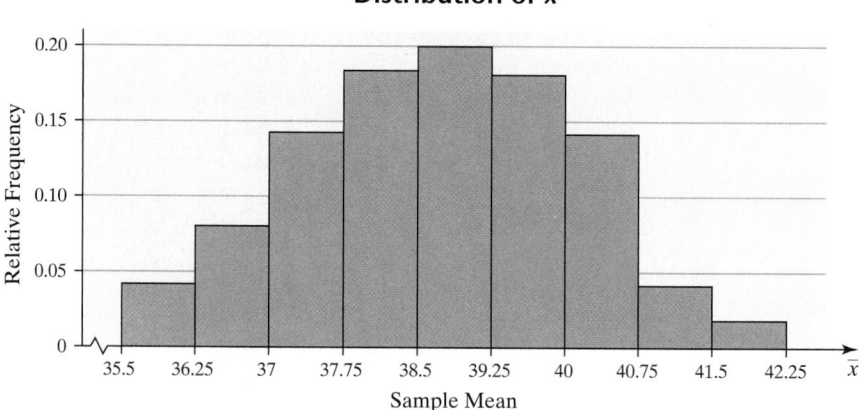

Distribution of $\bar{x}$

Step 4: The mean of the 100 sample means is 38.72, and the standard deviation is 1.408. ◀◀

If we refer to the results obtained in Example 1 from Section 7.1, we see that the histogram of the population data is normal, with mean $\mu = 38.72$ and $\sigma = 3.17$. The histogram in Figure 49 indicates that the distribution of sample means could also be normally distributed. In addition, the mean of the sample means is 38.72, but the standard deviation is only 1.374. We might conclude the following regarding the sampling distribution of $\bar{x}$:

1. It is normally distributed.

2. It has mean equal to the mean of the population.

3. It has standard deviation less than the standard deviation of the population.

A question that one might ask is, "What role does n, the sample size, play in the sampling distribution of $\bar{x}$?" Suppose the sample mean is computed for samples of size $n = 1$ through $n = 200$. That is, the sample mean is recomputed each time an additional individual is added to the sample. The sample mean is then plotted against the sample size in Figure 50.

Figure 50

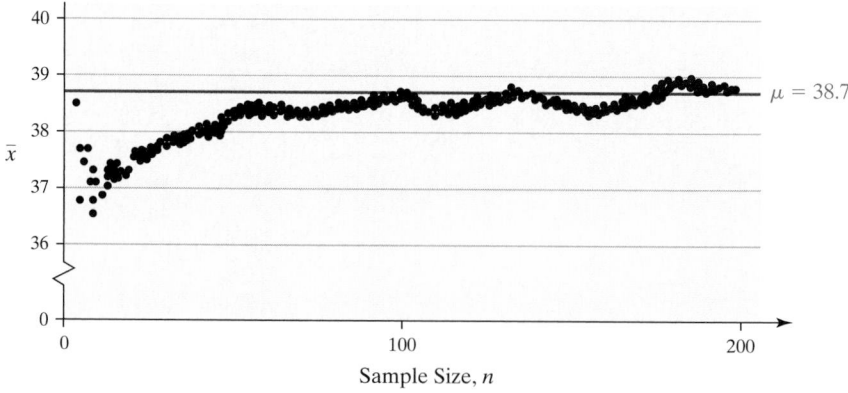

From the graph, we see that, as the sample size n increases, the sample mean gets closer to the population mean. This concept is known as the *Law of Large Numbers*.

Theorem

The Law of Large Numbers

As additional observations are added to the sample, the difference between the sample mean, $\bar{x}$, and the population mean μ approaches zero.

 In Your Own Words

As the sample size increases, the sample mean gets closer to the population mean.

So, according to the Law of Large Numbers, the more individuals we sample, the closer the sample mean gets to the population mean. This result implies that there is less variability in the distribution of the sample mean as the sample size increases. We demonstrate this result in the next example.

▶ **EXAMPLE 3**   **The Impact of Sample Size on Sampling Variability**

Problem: Repeat the problem in Example 2 with sample size $n = 15$.

Approach: The approach will be identical to that presented in Example 2, except we let $n = 15$ instead of $n = 5$.

Solution: Figure 51 shows the histogram of the sample means.

Figure 51

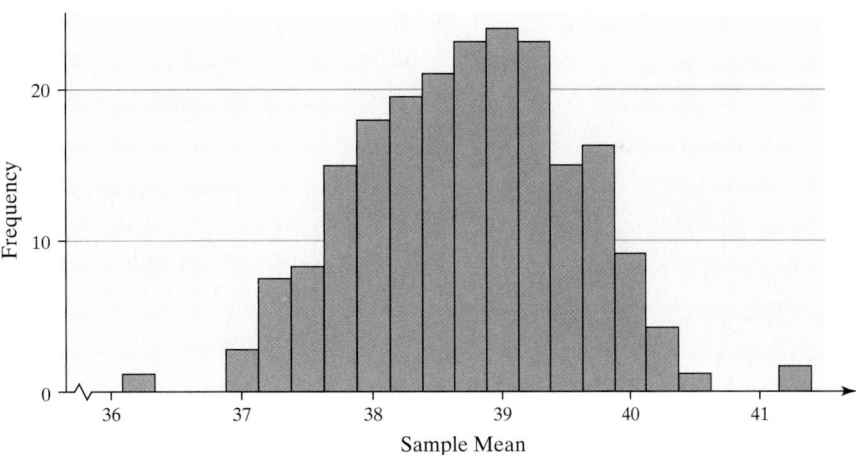

The histogram in Figure 51 is symmetric and bell shaped. This is an indication that the distribution of the sample mean is approximately normally distributed. The mean of the 200 sample means is 38.72 (just as in Example 2); however, the standard deviation is now 0.81.   ◀◀

From the results of Examples 2 and 3, we conclude that, as the sample size n increases, the standard deviation of the distribution of $\bar{x}$ decreases. Although the proof is beyond the scope of this text, we should be convinced that the following result is reasonable.

Theorem | **The Mean and Standard Deviation of the Sampling Distribution of $\bar{x}$**

Suppose that a simple random sample of size n is drawn from a population with mean μ and standard deviation σ. The sampling distribution of $\bar{x}$ will have mean $\mu_{\bar{x}} = \mu$ and standard deviation $\sigma_{\bar{x}} = \dfrac{\sigma}{\sqrt{n}}$.* The standard deviation of the sampling distribution of $\bar{x}$, $\sigma_{\bar{x}}$, is called the **standard error of the mean**.

In Your Own Words

Regardless of the distribution of the population, the sampling distribution of $\bar{x}$ will have a mean equal to the mean of the population and a standard deviation equal to the standard deviation of the population divided by the square root of the sample size!

For the population presented in Example 2, if we draw a simple random sample of size $n = 5$, the sampling distribution $\bar{x}$ will have mean $\mu_{\bar{x}} = 38.72$ and standard deviation

$$\sigma_{\bar{x}} = \frac{\sigma}{\sqrt{n}} = \frac{3.17}{\sqrt{5}}$$

NW *Now Work Problem 1.*

Now that we now know how to determine the mean and standard deviation for any sampling distribution of $\bar{x}$, we can concentrate on the shape. Refer back to Figures 49 and 51 from Examples 2 and 3. Recall that the population from which the sample was drawn was normal. The shapes of these histograms imply that the sampling distribution of $\bar{x}$ is normal. This leads us to believe that, if the population is normal, then the distribution of the sample mean is also normal.

Theorem | If a random variable X is normally distributed with mean μ and standard deviation σ, then the distribution of the sample mean, $\bar{x}$, is normally distributed with mean $\mu_{\bar{x}} = \mu$ and standard deviation $\sigma_{\bar{x}} = \dfrac{\sigma}{\sqrt{n}}$.

For example, the height of three-year-old females is a normal random variable with mean $\mu = 38.72$ and standard deviation $\sigma = 3.17$ inches. The distribution of the sample mean, $\bar{x}$, the mean height of a simple random sample of $n = 5$ three-year-old females, is normal with mean $\mu_{\bar{x}} = 38.72$ and standard deviation $\sigma_{\bar{x}} = \dfrac{3.17}{\sqrt{5}}$. See Figure 52.

Figure 52

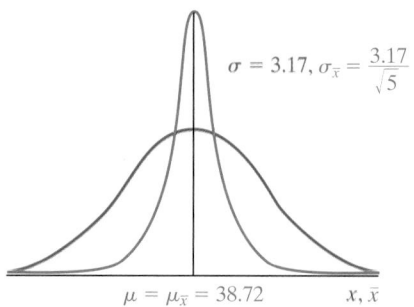

$$\sigma = 3.17, \sigma_{\bar{x}} = \frac{3.17}{\sqrt{5}}$$

$$\mu = \mu_{\bar{x}} = 38.72 \qquad x, \bar{x}$$

*Technically, $\sigma_{\bar{x}} = \sqrt{\dfrac{N-n}{N-1}} \cdot \dfrac{\sigma}{\sqrt{n}}$ for populations of finite size N. However, if the sample size is less than 5% of the population size $(n < 0.05N)$, the effect of $\sqrt{\dfrac{N-n}{N-1}}$ (the **finite population correction factor**) can be ignored without affecting the results.

▶ **EXAMPLE 4** **Describing the Distribution of the Sample Mean**

Problem: The height, X, of three-year-old females is normally distributed with mean $\mu = 38.72$ inches and standard deviation $\sigma = 3.17$ inches. Compute the probability that a simple random sample of size $n = 10$ results in a sample mean greater than 40 inches. That is, compute $P(\overline{x} > 40)$.

Approach: The random variable X is normally distributed, so the sampling distribution of $\overline{x}$ will also be normally distributed. The mean of the sampling distribution is $\mu_{\overline{x}} = \mu$, and its standard deviation is $\sigma_{\overline{x}} = \dfrac{\sigma}{\sqrt{n}}$. We convert the random variable $\overline{x} = 40$ to a Z-score and then find the area under the standard normal curve to the right of this Z-score.

Solution: The sample mean is normally distributed with mean $\mu_{\overline{x}} = 38.72$ inches and standard deviation $\sigma_{\overline{x}} = \dfrac{\sigma}{\sqrt{n}} = \dfrac{3.17}{\sqrt{10}} = 1.00$ inch.

Figure 53 displays the normal curve with the area we wish to compute shaded. We convert the random variable $\overline{x} = 40$ to a Z-score and obtain

$$Z = \frac{\overline{x} - \mu_{\overline{x}}}{\sigma_{\overline{x}}} = \frac{\overline{x} - \mu_{\overline{x}}}{\dfrac{\sigma}{\sqrt{n}}} = \frac{40 - 38.72}{1.00} = 1.28$$

The area to the right of $Z = 1.28$ is $1 - 0.8997 = 0.1003$.

Interpretation: The probability of obtaining a sample mean greater than 40 inches from a population whose mean is 38.72 inches is 0.1003. That is, $P(\overline{x} \geq 40) = 0.1003$. If we took 100 simple random samples of $n = 10$ from this population and if the population mean is 38.72, then about 10 of the samples will have a mean that is 40 or more. ◀◀

Figure 53

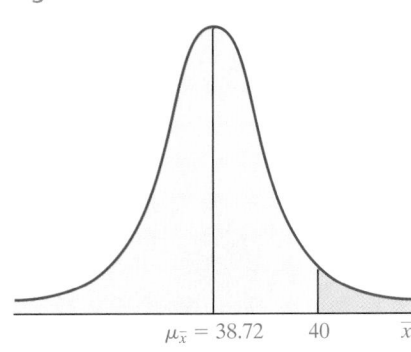

$\mu_{\overline{x}} = 38.72 \qquad 40 \qquad \overline{x}$

Note to Instructor
Emphasize the interpretation of the probabilities as a prelude to *P*-values.

NW *Now Work Problem 9.*

④ What if the population from which the sample is drawn is not normal?

▶ **EXAMPLE 5** **Sampling from a Population That Is Not Normal**

Figure 54

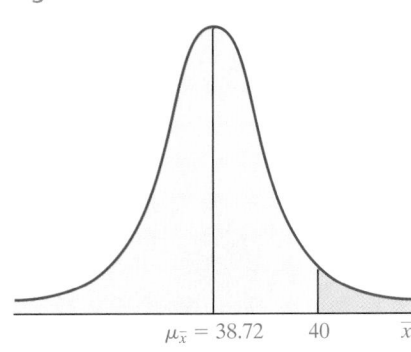

0   4   8   12   16   20   24   28
x

Problem: Figure 54 shows the graph of an *exponential density function* with mean and standard deviation equal to 10. The exponential distribution is used to model lifetimes of electronic components and to model the time required to serve a customer or repair a machine.

Clearly, the distribution is not normal. Approximate the sampling distribution of $\overline{x}$ by obtaining, through simulation, 300 random samples of size (a) $n = 3$, (b) $n = 12$, and (c) $n = 30$ from the probability distribution.

Approach:

Step 1: Use Minitab, Excel, or some other statistical software to obtain 300 random samples for each sample size.

Step 2: Compute the sample mean of each of the 300 random samples.

Step 3: Draw a histogram of the 300 sample means.

Solution:

Step 1: Using Minitab, we obtain 300 random samples of size (a) $n = 3$, (b) $n = 12$, and (c) $n = 30$. For example, in the first random sample of size $n = 30$, we obtained the following results:

9.2	20.0	17.0	2.4	2.6	19.9	21.2	5.7	8.1	10.8
1.2	22.3	18.4	4.2	9.9	41.8	4.2	1.2	10.8	2.1
11.3	17.9	28.0	12.1	3.0	0.5	4.5	14.2	5.0	11.4

Step 2: We compute the mean of each of the 300 random samples, using Minitab. For example, the sample mean of the first sample of size $n = 30$ is 11.36.

Step 3: Figure 55(a) displays the histogram of $\bar{x}$ that results from simulating 300 random samples of size $n = 3$ from an exponential distribution with $\mu = 10$ and $\sigma = 10$. Figure 55(b) displays the histogram of $\bar{x}$ that results from simulating 300 random samples of size $n = 12$, and Figure 55(c) displays the histogram of $\bar{x}$ that results from simulating 300 random samples of size $n = 30$.

Figure 55

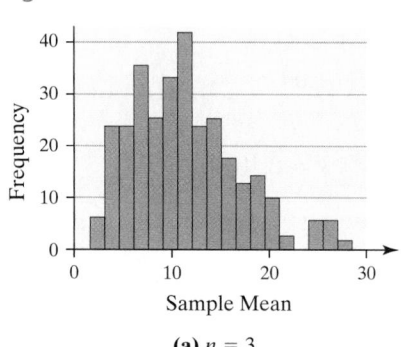

(a) $n = 3$

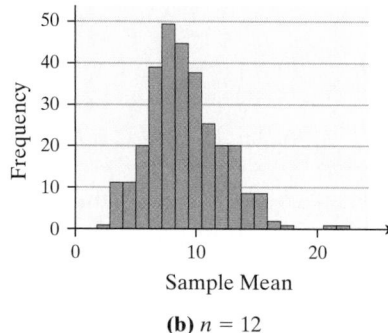

(b) $n = 12$

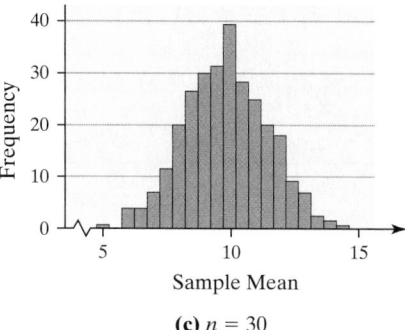

(c) $n = 30$

Notice that, as the sample size increases, the distribution of the sample mean becomes more normal, even though the population clearly is not normal! ◄◄

We formally state the results of Example 5 as the *Central Limit Theorem*.

Theorem

The Central Limit Theorem

Suppose a random variable X has population mean μ and standard deviation σ and that a random sample of size n is taken from this population. Then the sampling distribution of $\bar{x}$ becomes approximately normal as the sample size n increases. The mean of the distribution is $\mu_{\bar{x}} = \mu$ and the standard deviation is $\sigma_{\bar{x}} = \dfrac{\sigma}{\sqrt{n}}$.

So, if the random variable X is normally distributed, then the sampling distribution of $\bar{x}$ will be normal. If the sample size is large enough, then the sampling distribution of $\bar{x}$ will be approximately normal, *regardless of the distribution of X*. But how large does the sample size need to be before we can say that the sampling distribution of $\bar{x}$ is approximately normal? Statisticians agree that, if the sample size is 30 or more, the sampling distribution of $\bar{x}$ will be approximately normal.

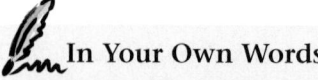

In Your Own Words

For any population, regardless of its shape, as the sample size increases, the shape of the distribution of the sample mean becomes more "normal."

▶ **EXAMPLE 6**

Caution

The Central Limit Theorem has to do only with the *shape* of the distribution of the sample mean—not with its center and spread! The mean of the distribution of $\overline{x}$ is μ and the standard deviation of $\overline{x}$ is $\dfrac{\sigma}{\sqrt{n}}$, regardless of the size of the sample, n.

Applying the Central Limit Theorem

Problem: According to the United States Department of Agriculture, the mean calorie intake of males 20–39 years old is $\mu = 2716$, with standard deviation $\sigma = 72.8$. Suppose a nutritionist conducts a simple random sample of $n = 35$ males between the ages of 20 and 39 years old and obtains a sample mean $\overline{x} = 2750$. What is the probability that a random sample of 35 males between the ages of 20 and 39 years old would result in a sample mean of 2750 or higher? Are the results of the survey unusual? Why?

Approach:

Step 1: We recognize that we are computing a probability regarding a sample mean, so we need to know the sampling distribution of $\overline{x}$. Because the population from which the sample is drawn is not known to be normal, the sample size must be greater than or equal to 30 in order to use the results of the Central Limit Theorem.

Step 2: Determine the mean and standard deviation of the sampling distribution of $\overline{x}$.

Step 3: Convert the sample mean to a Z-score.

Step 4: Use Table II to find the area under the normal curve.

Solution:

Step 1: Because the sample size is greater than 30 ($n = 35$), the Central Limit Theorem states that the sampling distribution of $\overline{x}$ is approximately normal.

Step 2: The mean of the sampling distribution of $\overline{x}$ will equal the mean of the population, so $\mu_{\overline{x}} = 2716$. The standard deviation of the sampling distribution of $\overline{x}$ will equal the standard deviation of the population divided by the square root of the sample size, so $\sigma_{\overline{x}} = \dfrac{\sigma}{\sqrt{n}} = \dfrac{72.8}{\sqrt{35}} = 12.3$.

Step 3: We convert $\overline{x} = 2750$ to a Z-score.

$$Z = \frac{2750 - 2716}{72.8/\sqrt{35}} = 2.76$$

Step 4: We wish to know the probability that a random sample of $n = 35$ from a population whose mean is 2716 results in a sample mean of at least 2750. That is, we wish to know $P(\overline{x} \geq 2750)$. See Figure 56.

Figure 56

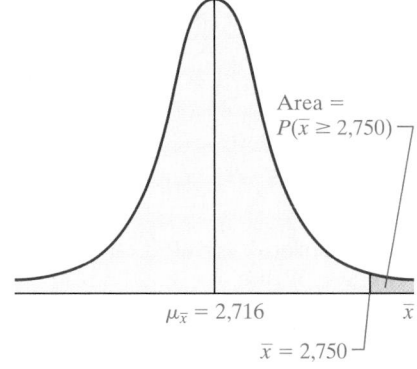

This probability is represented by the area under the standard normal curve to the right of $Z = 2.76$.

$$P(\overline{x} \geq 2750) = P(Z \geq 2.76) = 1 - 0.9971 = 0.0029$$

Interpretation: The probability that a random sample of 35 males between the ages of 20 and 39 will result in a sample mean of 2750 calories or higher if the population mean is 2716 calories is 0.0029. This means that less than 1 sample in 100 will result in a sample mean of 2750 calories or higher if the population mean is 2716 calories. We can conclude one of two things based upon this result.

1. The mean number of calories for males 20–39 years old is 2716, and we just happened to randomly select 35 individuals who, on average, consume more calories.

2. The mean number of calories consumed by 20–39-year-old males is higher than 2716 calories.

In statistical inference, we are inclined to accept the second possibility as the more reasonable choice. We recognize there is a possibility that our decision is incorrect.   ◄◄

 Now Work Problem 13.

7.5 Assess Your Understanding

Concepts and Vocabulary

1. Explain what a sampling distribution is.
2. What are the mean and standard deviation of the sampling distribution of $\bar{x}$, regardless of the distribution of the population from which the sample was drawn?
3. If a random sample of size $n = 20$ is taken from a population, what is required in order to say the sampling distribution of $\bar{x}$ is approximately normal?
4. State the Central Limit Theorem.
5. In order to cut the standard error of the mean in half, the sample size must be increased by a factor of _____.

6. Suppose a simple random sample of size $n = 10$ is obtained from a population that is normally distributed with $\mu = 30$ and $\sigma = 8$. What is the sampling distribution of $\bar{x}$?
7. Suppose a simple random sample of size $n = 40$ is obtained from a population with $\mu = 50$ and $\sigma = 4$. Does the parent population need to be normally distributed in order for the sampling distribution of $\bar{x}$ to be approximately normally distributed? Why? What is the sampling distribution of $\bar{x}$?

Exercises

• Skill Building

In Problems 1–4, determine $\mu_{\bar{x}}$ and $\sigma_{\bar{x}}$ from the given parameters of the population and the sample size.

1. $\mu = 50, \sigma = 6, n = 40$ $\mu_{\bar{x}} = 50, \sigma_{\bar{x}} = \dfrac{6}{\sqrt{40}}$

2. $\mu = 30, \sigma = 4, n = 34$ $\mu_{\bar{x}} = 30, \sigma_{\bar{x}} = \dfrac{4}{\sqrt{34}}$

3. $\mu = 100, \sigma = 12, n = 20$ $\mu_{\bar{x}} = 100, \sigma_{\bar{x}} = \dfrac{12}{\sqrt{20}}$

4. $\mu = 120, \sigma = 16, n = 10$ $\mu_{\bar{x}} = 120, \sigma_{\bar{x}} = \dfrac{16}{\sqrt{10}}$

5. Suppose a simple random sample of size $n = 40$ is obtained from a population with $\mu = 50$ and $\sigma = 6$.

   (a) Describe the sampling distribution of $\bar{x}$.
   (b) What is $P(\bar{x} > 51)$? 0.1459
   (c) What is $P(\bar{x} \le 48)$? 0.0175
   (d) What is $P(47.5 < \bar{x} < 51.2)$? 0.8928

   (a) Approximately normal, $\mu_{\bar{x}} = 50, \sigma_{\bar{x}} = \dfrac{6}{\sqrt{40}}$

6. Suppose a simple random sample of size $n = 34$ is obtained from a population with $\mu = 30$ and $\sigma = 4$.

   (a) Describe the sampling distribution of $\bar{x}$.
   (b) What is $P(\bar{x} > 30.2)$? 0.3853
   (c) What is $P(\bar{x} \le 30.6)$? 0.8091
   (d) What is $P(28.7 \le \bar{x} < 31.1)$? 0.9165

   (a) Approximately normal, $\mu_{\bar{x}} = 30, \sigma_{\bar{x}} = \dfrac{4}{\sqrt{34}}$

7. Suppose a simple random sample of size $n = 10$ is obtained from a population with $\mu = 105$ and $\sigma = 16$.

   (a) What must be true regarding the distribution of the population in order to compute probabilities regarding the sample mean? Describe the sampling distribution of $\bar{x}$. Normal

   (b) Assuming the requirements described in part (a) are satisfied, determine $P(\bar{x} > 103.2)$. 0.6390

   (c) Assuming the requirements described in part (a) are satisfied, determine $P(\bar{x} < 99.3)$. 0.1300

8. Suppose a simple random sample of size $n = 20$ is obtained from a population with $\mu = 105$ and $\sigma = 16$.

   (a) What must be true regarding the population in order to compute probabilities regarding the sample mean? Describe the sampling distribution of $\bar{x}$.

   (b) Assuming the requirements described in part (a) are satisfied, determine $P(\bar{x} > 103.2)$. 0.6926

   (c) Assuming the requirements described in part (a) are satisfied, determine $P(\bar{x} < 99.3)$. 0.0556

   (d) Compare the results obtained in parts (b) and (c) with the results obtained in parts (b) and (c) in Problem 7. What effect does increasing the sample size have on the probabilities? Why do you think this is the case?

• Applying the Concepts

9. **Serum Cholesterol** As reported by the U.S. National Center for Health Statistics, the mean serum high-density-lipoprotein (HDL) cholesterol of females 20–29 years old is $\mu = 53$. If serum HDL cholesterol is normally distributed with $\sigma = 13.4$, answer the following questions.

   (a) What is the probability a randomly selected female 20–29 years old will have a serum cholesterol above 60? 0.3007

   (b) What is the probability a random sample of 15 female 20–29-year-olds will have a mean serum cholesterol above 60? 0.0215

   (c) What is the probability that a random sample of 20 female 20–29-year-olds will have a mean serum cholesterol above 60? 0.0097

   (d) What effect does increasing the sample size have on the probability? Provide an explanation for this result.

   (e) What might you conclude if a random sample of 20 female 20–29-year-olds had a mean serum cholesterol above 60?

10. **ACT Math Scores** In 2000, as reported by ACT Research Service, the mean ACT Math score was $\mu = 20.7$. If ACT Math scores are normally distributed with $\sigma = 5$, answer the following questions.

    (a) What is the probability that a randomly selected student has an ACT Math score less than 18? 0.2946

    (b) What is the probability that a random sample of 10 ACT test takers had a mean math score of 18 or less? 0.0439

    (c) What is the probability that a random sample of 20 ACT test takers had a mean math score of 18 or less? 0.0079

    (d) What might you conclude if a random sample of 20 ACT test takers had a mean math score of 18 or less?

11. **Gestation Period** The length of human pregnancies is approximately normally distributed with mean $\mu = 266$ days and standard deviation $\sigma = 16$ days.

    (a) What is the probability a randomly selected pregnancy lasts less than 260 days? 0.3538

    (b) What is the probability that a random sample of 20 pregnancies have a mean gestation period of 260 days or less? 0.0468

    (c) What is the probability that a random sample of 50 pregnancies have a mean gestation period of 260 days or less? 0.0040

    (d) What might you conclude if a random sample of 50 pregnancies resulted in a mean gestation period of 260 days or less?

12. **Weather in Chicago** The high temperature in Chicago for the month of August is approximately normally distributed with mean $\mu = 80°$ F and standard deviation $\sigma = 8°$ F.

    (a) What is the probability that a randomly selected day in August has a high temperature less than $78°$ F? 0.4013

    (b) What is the probability that a random sample of 30 days in August has a mean high temperature less than $78°$ F? 0.0855

    (c) What is the probability that a random sample of 50 August days has a mean high temperature less than $78°$ F? 0.0385

13. **Insect Fragments** The Food and Drug Administration sets Food Defect Action Levels (FDALs) for some of the various foreign substances that inevitably end up in the food we eat and liquids we drink. For example, the FDAL for insect filth in peanut butter is 3 insect fragments (larvae, eggs, body parts, and so on) per 10 grams. A random sample of 50 ten-gram portions of peanut butter is obtained and results in a sample mean of 3.6 insect fragments per ten-gram portion.

    (a) Why is the sampling distribution of $\bar{x}$ approximately normal?

    (b) What is the mean and standard deviation of the sampling distribution of $\bar{x}$? [*Hint*: This is a Poisson process with $\mu = 3$ and $\sigma = \sqrt{3}$.]

    (c) Suppose a simple random sample of $n = 50$ ten-gram samples of peanut butter resulted in a sample mean of 3.6 insect fragments. What is the probability a simple random sample of 50 ten-gram portions results in a mean of at least 3.6 insect fragments? Is this result unusual? What might we conclude? 0.0072

    (b) $\mu_{\bar{x}} = 3,\ \sigma_{\bar{x}} = \dfrac{\sqrt{3}}{\sqrt{50}}$

14. **Burger King's Drive-Through** Suppose cars arrive at Burger King's drive-through at the rate of 20 cars every hour between 12:00 noon and 1:00 PM. A random sample of 40 one-hour time periods between 12:00 noon and 1:00 PM is selected and has 22.1 as the mean number of cars arriving.
    (a) Why is the sampling distribution of $\bar{x}$ approximately normal?
    (b) What is the mean and standard deviation of the sampling distribution of $\bar{x}$? [*Hint:* This is a Poisson process with $\mu = 20$ and $\sigma = \sqrt{20}$.]
    (c) What is the probability that a simple random sample of 40 one-hour time periods results in a mean of at least 22.1 cars? Is this result unusual? What might we conclude? 0.0015, Yes

15. **Winter Temperature** During the daytime in winter when nobody is at home, the mean household temperature is $67.6°$ F, with standard deviation $4.2°$ F, for households whose 1997 income was between $10,000 and $24,999, according to the Energy Information Administration. In a random sample of 50 households whose income was between $10,000 and $24,999 and for which nobody is home during the daytime, it was determined the average temperature was $68.3°$ F. What is the probability that a random sample of 50 households whose income is between $10,000 and $24,999 and for which nobody is home during the daytime results in an average household temperature of $68.3°$ F or higher? Is this result unusual? 0.1193, No

16. **Age of Refrigerator** According to the Energy Information Administration, the mean age of a refrigerator in a home owned by the occupant is 8.5 years, with standard deviation 6.6 years. A random sample of 50 homes owned by the occupant is conducted, and the average age of the refrigerator is found to be 5.7 years. What is the probability that a random sample of 50 homes owned by the occupant results in a mean age of refrigerator of 5.7 years or less? 0.0014

17. **Household Income** According to the Current Population Survey, the mean household income in the United States in 1997 was $45,127, with standard deviation $31,570.
    (a) What is the probability a random sample of 40 homes in Cook County, IL results in a sample mean household income less than $32,030? What might you conclude based on this result? 0.0043
    (b) The median household income in the United States in 1997 was $37,005. Given this information, do you think household income is a normally distributed random variable? Why? No, skewed right

18. **Household Size** According to the Energy Information Administration, the mean household size in the United States in 1997 was 2.6 people, with standard deviation

1.5 people. What is the probability that a random sample of 100 households results in a mean household size of 2.4 people or less? 0.0912

19. **Sampling Distributions** The following data represent the IQ scores based on the Stanford–Binet test of students in Sullivan's online College Algebra course in the Spring, 2001 semester.

    98   106   104   120   100   114

    (a) Compute the population mean, μ. $\mu = 107$
    (b) List all possible samples with size $n = 2$. There should be $_6C_2 = 15$ samples.
    (c) Construct a sampling distribution for the mean by listing the sample means and their corresponding probabilities.
    (d) Compute the mean of the sampling distribution.
    (e) Compute the probability that the sample mean will be within 5 IQ points of the population mean IQ.
    (f) Repeat parts (b) – (e) using samples of size $n = 3$. Comment on the effect of increasing the sample size.

20. **Sampling Distributions** The following data represent the ages of faculty members hired in the Mathematics Department at Joliet Junior College in the past 3 years.

    24   28   35   36   58   29

    (a) Compute the population mean, μ. $\mu = 35$
    (b) List all possible samples with size $n = 2$. There should be $_6C_2 = 15$ samples.
    (c) Construct a sampling distribution for the mean by listing the sample means and their corresponding probabilities.
    (d) Compute the mean of the sampling distribution.
    (e) Compute the probability that the sample mean will be within 5 years of the population mean age.
    (f) Repeat parts (b)–(e) using samples of size $n = 3$. Comment on the effect of increasing the sample size.

21. **Simulation** Scores on the Stanford–Binet IQ test are normally distributed with $\mu = 100$ and $\sigma = 16$.
    (a) Use Minitab, Excel, or some other statistical software to obtain 500 random samples of size $n = 20$.
    (b) Compute the sample mean of each of the 500 samples.
    (c) Draw a histogram of the 500 sample means. Comment on its shape.
    (d) What do you expect the mean and standard deviation of the sampling distribution of the mean to be?
    (e) Compute the mean and standard deviation of the 500 sample means. Are they close to the expected values?
    (f) Compute the probability that a random sample of 20 people results in a sample mean greater than 108.
    (g) What proportion of the 500 random samples had a sample mean IQ greater than 108? Is this result close to the theoretical value obtained in part (f)?

(14b) $\mu_{\bar{x}} = 20$, $\sigma_{\bar{x}} = \dfrac{\sqrt{20}}{\sqrt{40}}$

(d) $\mu_{\bar{x}} = 100$, $\sigma_{\bar{x}} = \dfrac{16}{\sqrt{20}}$ (f) 0.0127

22. **Simulation** The gestation period of humans is normally distributed with $\mu = 266$ days and $\sigma = 16$ days.
    (a) Use Minitab, Excel, or some other statistical software to obtain 500 random samples of size $n = 15$.
    (b) Compute the sample mean of each of the 500 samples.
    (c) Draw a histogram of the 500 sample means. Comment on its shape.
    (d) What do you expect the mean and standard deviation of the sampling distribution of the mean to be?
    (e) Compute the mean and standard deviation of the 500 sample means. Are they close to the expected values?
    (f) Compute the probability that a random sample of 15 people results in a sample mean greater than 270.
    (g) What proportion of the 500 random samples had a sample mean gestation period greater than 270? Is this result close to the theoretical value obtained in part (f)?

23. **Simulation** The exponential distribution is the distribution of the waiting time X until the occurrence of the first event in a Poisson process with parameter $\beta = 1/\lambda$. The probability density function of the exponential distribution is $y = \dfrac{1}{\beta}e^{-x/\beta}$, where β is both the mean

and standard deviation of the distribution. Suppose a certain intersection is especially dangerous, and accidents occur there at the rate $\lambda = 0.2$ accidents per day, so that $\beta = 1/0.2 = 5$ days between accidents. This implies we would expect to wait about 5 days before observing the first accident.
    (a) Use Minitab, Excel, or some other statistical software to randomly create 200 observations of the random variable X, the number of days between accidents.
    (b) Draw a histogram of the distribution of the random variable X. Is the exponential distribution symmetric and bell-shaped? According to this result, what sample size would be required to compute probabilities regarding the mean of the random variable X, the number of days between accidents.
    (c) Obtain 500 random samples with size 6 and obtain the sample means for each of the 500 samples.
    (d) Draw a histogram of the sample means. Is the sampling distribution of the mean normally distributed? Is the result what you expected?
    (e) Redo parts (c) and (d) for a sample of size $n = 40$.

(22d) $\mu_{\bar{x}} = 266,\ \sigma_{\bar{x}} = \dfrac{16}{\sqrt{15}}$ (22f) 0.1665

24. **Simulation** Let the random variable X represent the sum of the pips on two dice. The probability distribution of X is given below.

X	2	3	4	5	6	7	8	9	10	11	12
$P(X = x)$	0.0278	0.0556	0.0833	0.1111	0.1389	0.1666	0.1389	0.1111	0.0833	0.0556	0.0278

(a) Obtain 500 random samples of size $n = 6$ and obtain the sample means for each of the 500 samples.
(b) Draw a histogram of the sample means. Is the sampling distribution of the mean normally distributed? Did you expect it to be?
(c) Redo parts (a) and (b) with a sample of size $n = 40$.

7.6 The Normal Approximation to the Binomial Probability Distribution

Preparing for This Section Before getting started, review the following:

✓ Binomial probability distribution (Section 6.2, pp. 339–349)

Objective ① Approximate binomial probabilities by using the normal curve.

Note to Instructor
The material in this section is optional and can be omitted without loss of continuity.

 In Section 6.2, we discussed the binomial probability distribution. A probability experiment is said to be a binomial experiment if the following conditions are met.

Criteria for a Binomial Probability Experiment

A probability experiment is said to be a binomial experiment if all the following are true:
1. The experiment is performed n independent times. Each repetition of the experiment is called a **trial**. Independence means, that the outcome of one trial will not affect the outcome of the other trials.
2. For each trial, there are two mutually exclusive outcomes, success or failure.
3. The probability of success, p, is the same for each trial of the experiment.

The binomial probability formula can be used to compute probabilities of events in a binomial experiment. When there are a large number of trials of a binomial experiment, the binomial probability formula can be difficult to use. For example, suppose there are 500 trials of a binomial experiment and we wish to compute the probability of 400 or more successes. Using the binomial probability formula would require that we compute the following probabilities:

$$P(X \geq 400) = P(X = 400) + P(X = 401) + \dots + P(X = 500)$$

This would be time consuming to compute by hand! Fortunately, we have other means for approximating binomial probabilities, provided that certain conditions are met.

Recall the Exploration performed on page 348 in Section 6.2. In that Exploration, we discovered that, as the number of trials, n, in a binomial experiment increases, the probability histogram becomes more nearly symmetric and bell shaped. We restate the conclusion below.

Theorem   As the number of trials n in a binomial experiment increases, the probability distribution of the random variable X becomes more nearly symmetric and bell-shaped. As a general rule of thumb, if $np(1 - p) \geq 10$, then the probability distribution will be approximately symmetric and bell shaped.

Historical Note

The normal approximation to the binomial was discovered by Abraham de Moivre in 1733. With the advance of computing technology, its importance has been diminished.

Because of this result, we might be inclined to think that binomial probabilities could be approximated by the area under the normal curve, provided that $np(1 - p) \geq 10$. This intuition would be correct.

Theorem   **The Normal Approximation to the Binomial Probability Distribution**

If $np(1 - p) \geq 10$, then the binomial random variable X is approximately normally distributed with mean $\mu_X = np$ and standard deviation $\sigma_X = \sqrt{np(1 - p)}$.

Figure 57 shows a probability histogram for the binomial random variable X with $n = 40$ and $p = 0.5$ and a normal curve with $\mu_X = np = 40(0.5) = 20$ and standard deviation $\sigma_X = \sqrt{np(1 - p)} = \sqrt{40(0.5)(0.5)} = \sqrt{10}$.

Figure 57

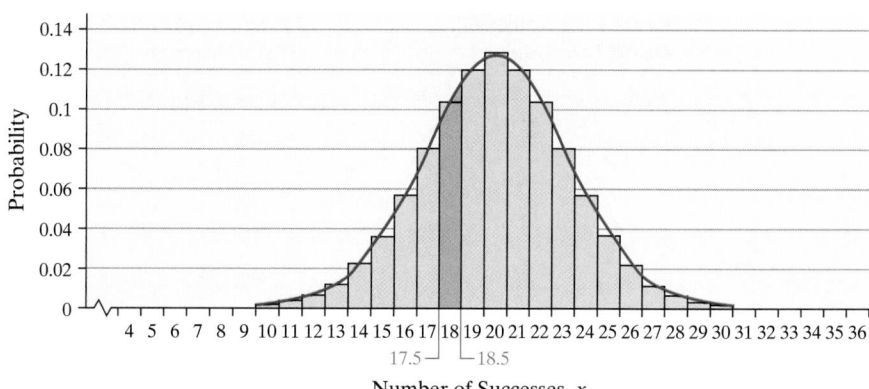

Binomial Histogram, n = 40, p = 0.5

We know from Section 6.2 that the area of the rectangle corresponding to $X = 18$ represents $P(X = 18)$. It should also be apparent that the width of each rectangle is one, so the rectangle extends from $X = 17.5$ to $X = 18.5$. The area under the normal curve from $X = 17.5$ to $X = 18.5$ is approximately equal to the area of the rectangle corresponding to $X = 18$. Therefore, the area under the normal curve between $X = 17.5$ and $X = 18.5$ is approximately equal to $P(X = 18)$ where X is a binomial random variable with $n = 40$ and $p = 0.5$. We add and subtract 0.5 from $X = 18$ as a **correction for continuity** because we are using a continuous density function to approximate a discrete probability.

Suppose we want to approximate $P(X \le 18)$. Figure 58 illustrates the situation.

> **Caution**
>
> Don't forget about the correction for continuity. It is needed because we are using a continuous density function to approximate the probability of a discrete random variable.

Figure 58

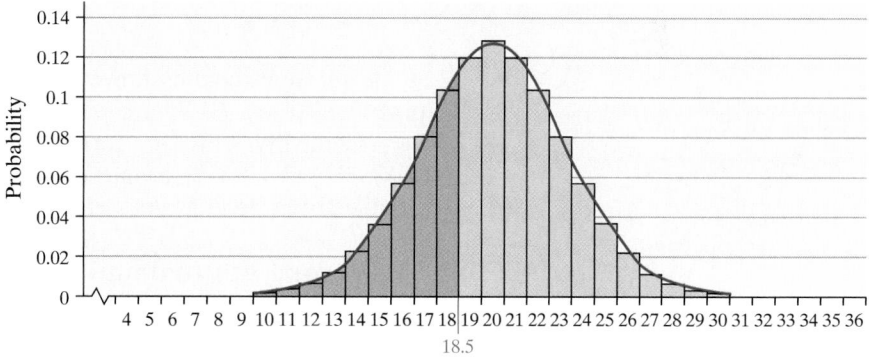

Binomial Histogram, n = 40, p = 0.5

In order to approximate $P(X \le 18)$, we compute the area under the normal curve for $X < 18.5$. Do you see why?

If we wanted to approximate $P(X \ge 18)$, we would compute $P(X \ge 17.5)$. Do you see why? Table 10 summarizes how to use the correction for continuity.

TABLE 10		
Exact Probability Using Binomial	**Approximate Probability Using Normal**	**Graphical Depiction**
$P(X = a)$	$P(a - 0.5 < X < a + 0.5)$	
$P(X \leq a)$	$P(X < a + 0.5)$	
$P(X \geq a)$	$P(X > a - 0.5)$	
$P(a \leq X \leq b)$	$P(a - 0.5 < X < b + 0.5)$	

A question remains, however. What do we do if the probability is of the form $P(X > a)$, $P(X < a)$ or $P(a < X < b)$? The solution is to rewrite the inequality in a form with $\leq$ or $\geq$. For example, $P(X > 4) = P(X \geq 5)$ and $P(X < 4) = P(X \leq 3)$ for binomial random variables, because the values of the random variables must be whole numbers.

▶ **EXAMPLE 1** **The Normal Approximation to a Binomial Random Variable**

Problem: According to the *Information Please* almanac, 6% of the human population has blood type O-negative. What is the probability that, in a simple random sample of 500, fewer than 25 have blood type O-negative?

Approach:

Step 1: We verify that this is a binomial experiment.
Step 2: Computing the probability by hand would be very tedious. Verify $np(1 - p) \geq 10$; then we will know that the condition for using the normal distribution to approximate the binomial distribution is met.
Step 3: Approximate $P(X < 25) = P(X \leq 24)$ by using the normal approximation to the binomial distribution.

Figure 59

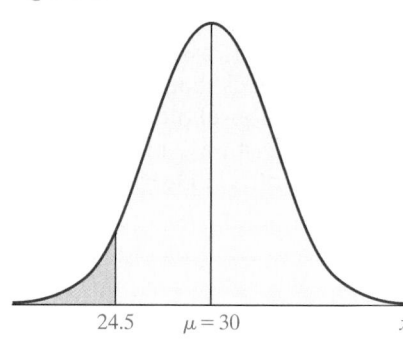

24.5 $\mu = 30$ x

Solution:

Step 1: There are 500 independent trials with each trial having a probability of success equal to 0.06. This is a binomial experiment.
Step 2: We verify $np(1 - p) \geq 10$:

$$np(1 - p) = 500(0.06)(0.94) = 28.2 \geq 10$$

We can use the normal distribution to approximate the binomial distribution.
Step 3: We wish to know the probability that fewer than 25 people in the sample have blood type O-negative—that is, we wish to know $P(X < 25) = P(X \leq 24)$. This is approximately equal to the area under the normal curve to the left of $X = 24.5$, with $\mu = np = 500(0.06) = 30$ and $\sigma = \sqrt{np(1 - p)} = \sqrt{500(0.06)(1 - 0.06)} = \sqrt{28.2} \approx 5.31$. See Figure 59.
   We convert $X = 24.5$ to a Z-score.

$$Z = \frac{24.5 - 30}{5.31} = -1.04$$

Figure 60

```
binomcdf(500,.06
,24)
        .1493809338
```

From Table II, we find the area to the left of $Z = -1.04$ is 0.1492. Therefore, the approximate probability that fewer than 25 people will have blood type O-negative is $0.1492 = 14.92\%$. ◀◀

   Using the *binomcdf(* command on a TI-83+ graphing calculator, we find that the exact probability is 0.1494. See Figure 60. The approximate result is close indeed!

NW *Now Work Problem 13.*

▶ **EXAMPLE 2**   **A Normal Approximation to the Binomial**

Problem: According to Nielsen Media Research, 75% of all United States households have cable television. Erica conducts a random sample of 1000 households in DuPage County and finds that 800 of them have cable. What might Erica conclude?

Approach: This is a binomial experiment with $n = 1000$ and $p = 0.75$. Erica needs to determine the probability of obtaining a random sample of at least 800 households with cable from a sample of size 1000 when assuming 75% of households have cable. Clearly, computing this via the binomial probability formula would be difficult, so Erica will compute the probability via the normal approximation to the binomial, since $np(1 - p) = 1000(0.75)(0.25) = 187.5 \geq 10$. We approximate $P(X \geq 800)$ by computing the area under the standard normal curve to the right of $X = 799.5$ with $\mu = np = 1000(0.75) = 750$ and $\sigma = \sqrt{np(1 - p)} = \sqrt{1000(0.75)(1 - 0.75)} = \sqrt{187.5} \approx 13.693$.

Figure 61

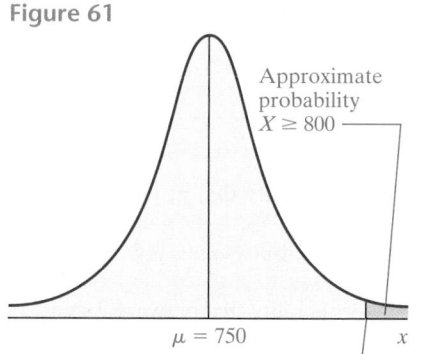

Approximate probability $X \geq 800$

$\mu = 750$ x

799.5

Solution: Figure 61 shows the area we wish to compute.
   We convert $X = 799.5$ to a Z-score.

$$Z = \frac{799.5 - 750}{13.693} = 3.61$$

The area under the standard normal curve to the right of $Z = 3.61$ is $1 - 0.9998 = 0.0002$. There is a 0.02% probability of obtaining 800 or more households with cable from a sample of 1000 households, assuming that the percentage of households with cable is 75%. This means that about 2 samples in every 10,000 samples will have 800 or more households with cable. Erica is not inclined to believe that her sample is one of the 2 in 10,000. She would rather believe that the proportion of households in DuPage County with cable is higher than 75%. ◄◄

NW *Now Work Problem 21.*

7.6 Assess Your Understanding

Concepts and Vocabulary

1. List the conditions required for a binomial experiment.
2. Under what circumstances can the normal distribution be used to approximate binomial probabilities?
3. Why must we use a correction for continuity when using the normal distribution to approximate binomial probabilities?

Exercises

• **Skill Building**

In Problems 1–8, a discrete random variable is given. Assume the probability of the random variable is going to be approximated via the normal distribution. Describe the area under the normal curve that will be computed. For example, if we wish to compute the probability of finding at least five defective items in a shipment, then we would approximate the probability by computing the area under the normal curve to the right of $X = 4.5$.

1. The probability that at least 40 households have a gas stove. Right of $X = 39.5$

2. The probability of no more than 20 people who want to see Roe versus Wade overturned. Left of $X = 20.5$

3. The probability that exactly eight defective parts are in the shipment. Between $X = 7.5$ and $X = 8.5$

4. The probability that exactly 12 students pass the course. Between $X = 11.5$ and $X = 12.5$

5. The probability that the number of people with blood type O-negative is between 18 and 24 inclusive.

6. The probability that the number of tornadoes that occur in the month of May is between 30 and 40 inclusive.

7. The probability that more than 20 people want to see the marriage tax penalty abolished. Right of $X = 20.5$

8. The probability that fewer than 40 households have a pet. Left of $X = 39.5$

5. Between $X = 17.5$ and $X = 24.5$ 6. Between $X = 29.5$ and $X = 40.5$

In Problems 9–12, compute $P(X = x)$ via the binomial probability formula. Then, determine whether the normal distribution can be used as an approximation for the binomial distribution. If the normal distribution can be used as an approximation for the binomial distribution, approximate $P(X = x)$ and compare the result to the exact probability.

9. $n = 60$, $p = 0.4$, $X = 20$ 0.0616; 0.0603

10. $n = 80$, $p = 0.15$, $X = 18$ 0.0221; 0.0216

11. $n = 75$, $p = 0.75$, $X = 60$ 0.0677; 0.0645

12. $n = 85$, $p = 0.8$, $X = 70$ 0.0970; 0.0932

• **Applying the Concepts**

13. **On-Time Flights** United Airlines flight 1832 from Chicago to Orlando is on time 80% of the time, according to United Airlines. Suppose 70 flights are randomly selected. Use the normal approximation to the binomial to
    (a) approximate the probability that exactly 60 flights are on time. 0.0584
    (b) approximate the probability that at least 60 flights are on time. 0.1478
    (c) approximate the probability that fewer than 50 flights are on time. 0.0261
    (d) approximate the probability that between 50 and 55 flights, inclusive, are on time. 0.4146

14. Smokers According to *Information Please* almanac, 80% of adult smokers started smoking before they were 18 years old. Suppose 100 smokers 18 years old or older are randomly selected. Use the normal approximation to the binomial to   *(c) 0.0043*

(a) approximate the probability that exactly 80 of them started smoking before they were 18 years old. *0.0995*

(b) approximate the probability that at least 80 of them started smoking before they were 18 years old. *0.5497*

(c) approximate the probability that fewer than 70 of them started smoking before they were 18 years old.

(d) approximate the probability that between 70 and 90 of them, inclusive, started smoking before they were 18 years old. *0.9913*

15. Operating Systems According to a survey conducted by StatMarket, 94% of computer users use Microsoft Windows as their operating system. Suppose 200 computer users are randomly selected. Use the normal approximation to the binomial to

(a) approximate the probability that exactly 180 of them use Microsoft Windows. *0.0071*

(b) approximate the probability that more than 180 of them use Microsoft Windows. *0.9872*

(c) approximate the probability that no more than 185 of them use Microsoft Windows. *0.2283*

(d) approximate the probability that between 160 and 180 of them, inclusive, use Microsoft Windows. *0.0128*

16. Murder by Firearm According to *Crime in the United States*, 1998, 65% of murders are committed with a firearm. Suppose 150 murders are randomly selected. Use the normal approximation to the binomial to

(a) approximate the probability that exactly 110 murders are committed with a firearm. *0.0070*

(b) approximate the probability that 100 or more murders are committed with a firearm. *0.3660*

(c) approximate the probability that 90 or fewer murders are committed with a firearm. *0.1154*

(d) approximate the probability that between 100 and 120 murders, inclusive, are committed with a firearm. *0.3660*

17. Migraine Sufferers In clinical trials and extended studies of a medication whose purpose is to reduce the pain associated with migraine headaches, 2% of the patients in the study experienced weight gain as a side effect. Suppose a random sample of 600 users of this medication is obtained. Use the normal approximation to the binomial to

(a) approximate the probability that exactly 20 will experience weight gain as a side effect. *0.0078*

(b) approximate the probability that 20 or fewer will experience weight gain as a side effect. *0.9934*

(c) approximate the probability that 22 or more patients will experience weight gain as a side effect. *0.0028*

(d) approximate the probability that between 20 and 30 patients, inclusive, will experience weight gain as a side effect. *0.0144*

(21a) 0.0088   (22a) 0.0004

18. Stomach Ulcers In clinical trials of a drug whose purpose is to treat acid reflux and stomach ulcers, 4.7% of the patients in the study experienced headaches as a side effect. Suppose a random sample of 300 users of this drug is obtained. Use the normal approximation to the binomial to

(a) approximate the probability that exactly 20 experienced headaches as a side effect. *0.0299*

(b) approximate the probability that fewer than 20 experienced headaches as a side effect. *0.9296*

(c) approximate the probability that more than 15 patients experienced headaches as a side effect. *0.3513*

(d) approximate the probability that between 10 and 25 patients, inclusive, experienced headaches as a side effect. *0.8943*

19. Softball Suppose a softball player safely reaches base 45% of the time. Assuming at-bats are independent events, use the normal approximation to the binomial to approximate the probability that, in the next 100 at bats,

(a) the player reaches base safely exactly 50 times. *0.0484*

(b) the player reaches base safely 60 or more times. *0.0018*

(c) the player reaches base safely 50 or fewer times.

(d) the player reaches base safely between 60 and 90 times, inclusive. *0.0018*   *(c) 0.8655*

20. Basketball Mark Price holds the record for percentage of free throws made in the National Basketball Association, at 90.4%. Assuming free throws are independent events, use the normal approximation to the binomial to approximate the probability that, in the next 200 free throws,   *(d) 0.6125*

(a) Mark Price makes exactly 190. *0.0084*

(b) Mark Price makes 180 or more. *0.6225*

(c) Mark Price makes fewer than 180. *0.3775*

(d) Mark Price makes between 180 and 190, inclusive.

21. Males Living at Home According to *Information Please* almanac, 59% of males between the ages of 18 and 24 lived at home in 1998. (Unmarried college students living in dorms are counted as living at home.) Suppose a survey is administered at a community college to 200 randomly selected male students between 18 and 24 years old and 135 of them responded they live at home.

(a) Approximate the probability that a survey would result in at least 135 of the respondents living at home under the assumption the true percentage is 59%.

(b) What might you conclude from this result?

22. Females Living at Home According to *Information Please* almanac, 48% of females between the ages of 18 and 24 live at home. (Unmarried college students living in dorms are counted as living at home.) Suppose a survey is administered at a community college to 200 randomly selected female students between 18 and 24 years old and 120 of them responded they live at home.

(a) Approximate the probability that a survey would result in at least 120 of the respondents living at home under the assumption the true percentage is 48%.

(b) What might you conclude from this result?

23. **Boys Are Preferred** In a Gallup poll conducted December 2–4, 2000, 42% of survey respondents said that, if they only had one child, they would prefer the child to be a boy. Suppose you conduct a survey of 150 randomly selected students on your campus and find that 80 of them would prefer a boy. *(b) Yes*

    (a) Approximate the probability that, in a random sample of 150 students, at least 80 would prefer a boy, assuming the true percentage is 42%. *0.0090*

    (b) Does this result contradict the Gallup poll? Explain.

24. **Liars** According to a *USA Today* "Snapshot," 3% of Americans surveyed lie frequently. Suppose you conduct a survey of 500 college students and find that 20 of them lie frequently.

    (a) Compute the probability that, in a random sample of 500 college students, at least 20 lie frequently, assuming the true percentage is 3%. *0.1191*

    (b) Does this result contradict the *USA Today* "Snapshot"? Explain. *No*

25. **Time to Graduate** According to a study done by ACT in 1997, 52.8% of students graduate from college in five years or less. Suppose you conduct a survey of 200 recent college graduates and find that 95 of them graduated in five years or less.

    (a) Compute the probability that, in a random sample of 200 recent college graduates, 95 or fewer graduated in five years or less, assuming the true percentage is 52.8%. *0.0763*

    (b) Does this result contradict the results of the study done by ACT? Explain. *No*

26. **Drunk-Driving Laws** In a Gallup poll conducted July 20–August 3, 2000, 72% of survey respondents said they would favor reducing the drunk-driving limit to 0.08% blood alcohol concentration (BAC). Survey respondents had to be 16 years old or older and a licensed driver. On October 3, 2000, President Bill Clinton signed into law a national BAC of 0.08% required to charge drunk drivers with a crime. Suppose you are a member of SADD (Students Against Drunk Driving) and conduct a survey of 200 students aged 16 years old or older who were licensed drivers, and 130 of them favored a drunk-driving limit of 0.08% BAC.

    (a) Compute the probability that, in a random sample of 200 students, 130 or fewer would favor a drunk-driving law of 0.08% BAC, assuming the true percentage is 72%. *0.0167*

    (b) Does this result contradict the results of the Gallup poll? Explain. *Yes*

CHAPTER 7 REVIEW

Summary

In this chapter, we introduced continuous random variables and, in particular, the normal probability density function. A continuous random variable is said to be normally distributed if a histogram of its values is symmetric and bell-shaped. In addition, we can draw normal probability plots that are based upon expected Z-scores. If these normal probability plots are approximately linear, then we say the distribution of the random variable is approximately normal. The area under the normal density function can be used to find theoretical proportions or probabilities for normal random variables. Also, we can find the value of a normal random variable that corresponds to a specific proportion, probability, or percentile.

In Section 7.5, we introduced what is arguably the most important theorem in inferential statistics, the Central Limit

Theorem. We discovered that, if X is a normal random variable or if the sample size is large ($n \geq 30$), the sampling distribution of $\bar{x}$ is approximately normally distributed. The mean of any sampling distribution of $\bar{x}$ is $\mu_{\bar{x}} = \mu$, and its standard deviation is $\sigma_{\bar{x}} = \dfrac{\sigma}{\sqrt{n}}$ (the standard error of the mean). We can compute a probability regarding the random variable $\bar{x}$ by measuring an area under the standard normal curve.

Finally, if X is a binomial random variable with $np(1 - p) \geq 10$, then we can use the area under the normal curve to approximate the probability of a binomial random variable. The parameters of the normal curve are $\mu_X = np$ and $\sigma_X = \sqrt{np(1 - p)}$, where n is the number of trials of the binomial experiment and p is the probability of success.

Formulas

Standardizing a Normal Random Variable

$$Z = \frac{X - \mu}{\sigma} \text{ or } Z = \frac{\bar{x} - \mu}{\dfrac{\sigma}{\sqrt{n}}}$$

Finding the Score
$$X = \mu + Z\sigma$$

Mean of Sampling Distribution of $\bar{x}$
$$\mu_{\bar{x}} = \mu$$

Standard Deviation of Sampling Distribution of $\bar{x}$
$$\sigma_{\bar{x}} = \frac{\sigma}{\sqrt{n}}$$

Vocabulary

Uniform probability distribution (p. 380)
Normal probability distribution (p. 382)
Probability density function (p. 381)
Inflection points (p. 383)
Normal probability density function
  (p. 383)

Standard normal distribution (p. 387)
Normal probability plot (p. 415)
Normal scores (p. 415)
Sampling distribution of the mean
  (p. 423)

The law of large numbers (p. 429)
Standard error of the mean (p. 430)
The Central Limit Theorem (p. 432)
Correction for continuity (p. 439)

Objectives

Section	You should be able to ...	Review Exercises
7.1	1 Understand the uniform probability distribution (p. 380)	37
	2 Graph a normal density curve (p. 382)	19–22
	3 State the properties of the normal curve (p. 384)	38
	4 Understand the role of area in the normal density function (p. 384)	1, 2
	5 Understand the relation between a normal random variable and a standard normal random variable in regards to area (p. 387)	3, 4
7.2	1 Find the area under the standard normal curve (p. 393)	5–8
	2 Find the Z-scores for given areas (p. 397)	13–18
	3 Interpret area under standard normal curve as a probability (p. 401)	9–12
7.3	1 Find and interpret area under a normal curve (p. 406)	19–22; 23(a)–(c); 24(a)–(c); 25(a)–(c); 26(a)–(d)
	2 Find the value of a normal random variable (p. 408)	23(d); 24(d), (e); 25(d), (e); 26(e), (f)
7.4	1 Draw normal probability plots to assess normality (p. 415)	29–32
7.5	1 Understand the concept of a sampling distribution (p. 422)	39
	2 Compute the mean and standard deviation of a sampling distribution of the mean (p. 428)	23(e), 24(f)
	3 Compute probabilities of a sample mean obtained from a normal population (p. 429)	23(f), (h); 24(g), (i); 25(f), (g); 26(g)
	4 Compute probabilities of a sample mean, utilizing the Central Limit Theorem (p. 431)	35, 36
7.6	1 Approximate binomial probabilities, using the normal curve (p. 437)	27, 28

Review Exercises

1.

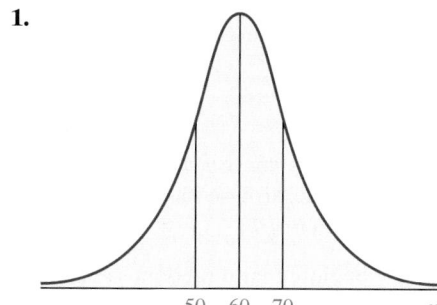

50   60   70 x

Use the preceding figure to answer the following questions:
(a) What is μ? 60
(b) What is σ? 10
(c) Suppose the area under the normal curve to the right of $X = 75$ is 0.0668. Provide two interpretations for this area.
(d) Suppose the area under the normal curve between $X = 50$ and $X = 75$ is 0.7745. Provide two interpretations for this area.

2.

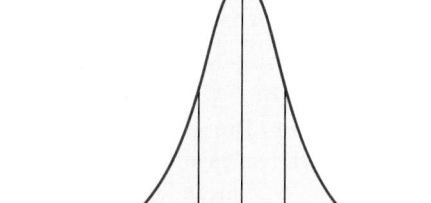

5   7   9 x

Use the preceding figure to answer the following questions:
(a) What is μ? 7
(b) What is σ? 2
(c) Suppose the area under the normal curve to the left of $X = 10$ is 0.9332. Provide two interpretations for this area.
(d) Suppose the area under the normal curve between $X = 5$ and $X = 8$ is 0.5328. Provide two interpretations for this area.

3. A random variable X is normally distributed with $\mu = 20$ and $\sigma = 4$.

   (a) Compute $Z_1 = \dfrac{X_1 - \mu}{\sigma}$ for $X_1 = 18$. -0.5

   (b) Compute $Z_2 = \dfrac{X_2 - \mu}{\sigma}$ for $X_2 = 21$. 0.25

   (c) The area under the normal curve between $X_1 = 18$ and $X_2 = 21$ is 0.2912. What is the area between Z_1 and Z_2? 0.2912

4. A random variable X is normally distributed with $\mu = 50$ and $\sigma = 8$.

   (a) Compute $Z_1 = \dfrac{X_1 - \mu}{\sigma}$ for $X_1 = 48$. -0.25

   (b) Compute $Z_2 = \dfrac{X_2 - \mu}{\sigma}$ for $X_2 = 60$. 1.25

   (c) The area under the normal curve between $X_1 = 48$ and $X_2 = 60$ is 0.4931. What is the area between Z_1 and Z_2? 0.4931

In Problems 5–8, draw a standard normal curve, and shade the area indicated. Then use Table II to find the area under the normal curve.

5. The area left of $Z = -1.04$ 0.1492

6. The area right of $Z = 2.04$ 0.0207

7. The area between $Z = -0.34$ and $Z = 1.03$ 0.4816

8. The area between $Z = 1.93$ and $Z = 3.93$ 0.0268

In Problems 9–12, find the indicated probability of the standard normal random variable Z.

9. $P(Z < 1.19)$ 0.8830

10. $P(Z \geq 1.61)$ 0.0537

11. $P(-1.21 < Z \leq 2.28)$ 0.8756

12. $P(0.21 < Z < 1.69)$ 0.3713

13. Find the Z-score such that the area to the left of the Z-score is 0.84. 0.99

14. Find the Z-score such that the area right of the Z-score is 0.483. 0.04

15. Find the Z-scores that separate the middle 92% of the data from the area in the tails of the standard normal distribution. $-1.75, 1.75$

16. Find the Z-scores that separate the middle 88% of the data from the area in the tails of the standard normal distribution. $-1.55, 1.55$

17. Find the value of $z_{0.20}$ 0.84

18. Find the value of $z_{0.04}$ 1.75

In Problems 19–22, draw the normal curve with the parameters indicated. Then find the probability of the random variable X. Shade the area that represents the probability.

19. $\mu = 50, \sigma = 6, P(X > 55)$ 0.2023

20. $\mu = 30, \sigma = 5, P(X \leq 23)$ 0.0808

21. $\mu = 70, \sigma = 10, P(65 < X < 85)$ 0.6247

22. $\mu = 20, \sigma = 3, P(22 \leq X \leq 27)$ 0.2427

---

23. Tire Wear Suppose Dunlop Tire manufactures tires having the property that the mileage the tire lasts follows a normal distribution with mean 70,000 miles and standard deviation 4400 miles.

   (a) What percent of the tires will last at least 75,000 miles? 0.1279

   (b) Suppose Dunlop warrants the tires for 60,000 miles. What percent of the tires will last 60,000 miles or less? 0.0115

   (c) What is the probability that a randomly selected Dunlop tire lasts between 65,000 and 80,000 miles? 0.8606

   (d) Suppose that Dunlop wants to warrant no more than 2% of its tires. What mileage should the company advertise as its warranty mileage? $60,964$ miles

   (e) Suppose that a quality-control engineer obtains a simple random sample of $n = 10$ tires. What is the sampling distribution of $\bar{x}$?

   (f) What is the probability that a random sample of 10 tires will result in a sample mean of at least 72,500 miles? 0.0362

   (g) Suppose that a quality-control engineer obtains a simple random sample of $n = 25$ tires. What is the sampling distribution of $\bar{x}$? What effect does increasing the sample size have on $\sigma_{\bar{x}}$?

   (h) What is the probability that a random sample of 25 tires will result in a sample mean of at least 72,500 miles? 0.0022

   (e) Normal; $\mu_{\bar{x}} = 70,000; \sigma_{\bar{x}} = \dfrac{4400}{\sqrt{10}}$

   (g) Normal; $\mu_{\bar{x}} = 70,000; \sigma_{\bar{x}} = \dfrac{4400}{\sqrt{25}}$

24. Talk Time on a Cell Phone Suppose the "talk time" in digital mode on a Motorola Timeport P8160 is normally distributed with mean 324 minutes and standard deviation 24 minutes.   *(c) 0.5808; (d) 344 minutes*
   (a) What proportion of the time will a fully charged battery last at least 300 minutes? *0.8413*
   (b) What proportion of the time will a fully charged battery last less than 340 minutes? *0.7475*
   (c) Suppose you charge the battery fully. What is the probability it will last between 310 and 350 minutes?
   (d) Determine the talk time that is in the top 20%.
   (e) Determine the talk time that makes up the middle 90% of talk time. *285–363 minutes*
   (f) Suppose that an engineer at Motorola obtains a simple random sample of $n = 15$ batteries. What is the sampling distribution of $\bar{x}$?
   (g) What is the probability that a random sample of $n = 15$ batteries results in a talk time of at least 330 minutes? *0.1665*
   (h) Suppose that an engineer at Motorola obtains a simple random sample of $n = 30$ batteries. What is the sampling distribution of $\bar{x}$? What effect does increasing the sample size have on $\sigma_{\bar{x}}$?
   (i) What is the probability that a random sample of $n = 30$ batteries results in a talk time of at least 330 minutes? *0.0855*

25. Serum Cholesterol As reported by the U.S. National Center for Health Statistics, the mean serum cholesterol of females 16–19 years old is $\mu = 171$. If serum cholesterol is normally distributed with $\sigma = 39.8$, answer the following.
   (a) Determine the proportion of 16–19-year-old females with a serum cholesterol above 180. *0.4105*
   (b) Determine the proportion of 16–19-year-old females with a serum cholesterol between 150 and 200. *0.4680*
   (c) Suppose a 16–19-year-old female is randomly selected. Determine the probability her serum cholesterol is below 140. *0.2180*
   (d) Determine the serum cholesterol that divides the bottom 10% from the top 90% of all serum cholesterol levels of 16–19-year-old females. *120*
   (e) According to the National Center for Health Statistics, the 25th percentile of serum cholesterol for 16–19-year-old females is 145. Is the 25th percentile on the normal curve close to the reported value of 145? *Yes, 144*
   (f) What is the probability that a random sample of eight females 16–19 years old has a mean serum cholesterol below 167? *0.3881*
   (g) What is the probability that a random sample of 20 females 16–19 years old has a mean serum cholesterol below 167? *0.3265*

(24f) Normal; $\mu_{\bar{x}} = 324$; $\sigma_{\bar{x}} = \dfrac{24}{\sqrt{15}}$

(24h) Normal; $\mu_{\bar{x}} = 324$; $\sigma_{\bar{x}} = \dfrac{24}{\sqrt{30}}$

26. Wechsler Intelligence Scale The Wechsler Intelligence Scale for Children is normally distributed with mean 100 and standard deviation 15.   *(a) 0.0478 (b) 0.2525*
   (a) What proportion of test takers will score above 125?
   (b) What proportion of test takers will score below 90?
   (c) What proportion of test takers will score between 110 and 140? *0.2487*
   (d) If a child is randomly selected, what is the probability that she scores above 150? *0.0004*
   (e) What intelligence score will place a child in the top 5% of all children? *125*
   (f) If "normal" intelligence is defined as scoring in the middle 95% of all test takers, figure out the scores that differentiate "normal" intelligence from "abnormal" intelligence. *71–129*
   (g) A random sample of 20 children was administered the Wechsler Intelligence Scale for Children, and their mean score was 110. Would it be unusual to obtain a random sample of 20 children whose mean score was 110 or higher? *Yes*

27. High Cholesterol According to the National Center for Health Statistics, 8% of 20–34-year-old females have high serum cholesterol. Suppose you conduct a random sample of 200 20–34-year-old females.
   (a) Verify that the conditions for using the normal distribution to approximate the binomial distribution are met.
   (b) Approximate the probability that exactly 15 have high serum cholesterol. Interpret this result. *0.1002*
   (c) Approximate the probability that more than 20 have high serum cholesterol. Interpret this result. *0.1204*
   (d) Approximate the probability that at least 15 have high serum cholesterol. Interpret this result. *0.6521*
   (e) Approximate the probability that fewer than 25 have high serum cholesterol. Interpret this result. *0.9866*
   (f) Approximate the probability that between 15 and 25, inclusive, have high serum cholesterol. Interpret this result. *0.6454*

28. America Reads According to a Gallup poll conducted September 10–14, 1999, 56% of Americans 18 years old or older stated they had read at least 6 books (fiction and nonfiction) within the past year. Suppose you conduct a random sample of 250 Americans 18 years old or older.
   (a) Verify that the conditions for using the normal distribution to approximate the binomial distribution are met.
   (b) Approximate the probability that exactly 125 read at least 6 books within the past year. Interpret this result. *0.0082*
   (c) Approximate the probability that fewer than 120 read at least 6 books within the past year. Interpret this result. *0.0045*
   (d) Approximate the probability that at least 140 read at least 6 books within the past year. Interpret this result. *0.5250*
   (e) Approximate the probability that between 100 and 120, inclusive, read at least 6 books within the past year. Interpret this result. *0.0065*

In Problems 29 and 30, a normal probability plot of a simple random sample of data from a population whose distribution is unknown was obtained. Given the normal probability plot, is there reason to believe the population is normally distributed?

29. Not normal

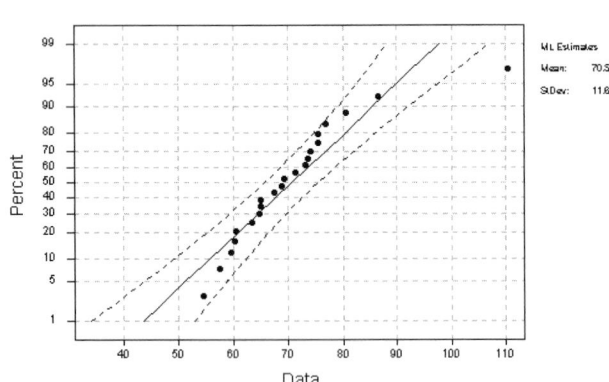

30. Normal

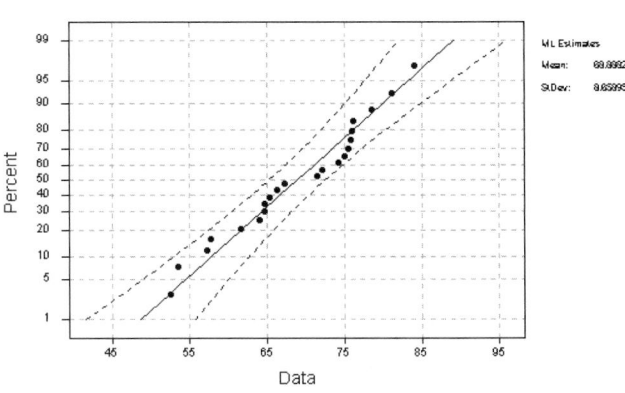

In Problems 31 and 32, assess the normality of the sample data.

31. Density of Earth In 1798, Henry Cavendish obtained 29 measurements of the density of Earth, using a torsion balance. The following data represent his estimates, represented as a multiple of the density of water:
Not normal

5.50	5.57	5.42	5.61	5.53
5.47	4.88	5.62	5.63	4.07
5.29	5.34	5.26	5.44	5.55
5.34	5.30	5.36	5.79	5.29
5.10	5.86	5.58	5.27	5.85
5.65	5.39			

Source: Stigler, S.M. "Do robust estimators work with real data?" *Annals of Statistics,* 5 (1977) p. 1055 - 1078

32. Life Expectancy The following data represent the life expectancy at birth in 1999 in a random sample of 20 countries: Normal

79.37	72.00	76.23	64.06	75.46
76.04	72.16	66.45	74.66	70.38
70.66	75.83	72.95	69.00	77.48
77.53	77.10	74.35	76.51	77.32

Source: U.S. Census Bureau

33. Birth Weight The following data represent the birth weights of babies for whom the period of gestation was 36 weeks:

Birth Weight	Frequency
0–499 grams	3
500–999 grams	61
1,000–1,499 grams	560
1,500–1,999 grams	5,031
2,000–2,499 grams	27,902
2,500–2,999 grams	59,394
3,000–3,499 grams	47,924
3,500–3,999 grams	17,873
4,000–4,499 grams	3,902
4,500–4,999 grams	679
5,000–5,499	102

Source: National Vital Statistics Report, Vol. 48, No. 3, March 28, 2000

(a) Construct a relative frequency distribution.
(b) Draw a relative frequency histogram. Does the distribution of baby's birth weight appear to be normal?
(c) Compute the mean and standard deviation of (the variable) baby's birth weight. $\mu = 2929.1, \sigma = 554.5$.
(d) Use the information obtained in part (c) to compute the theoretical proportion of birth weights in each class by finding the area under the normal curve.
(e) Are you convinced baby's birth weights are normally distributed?

34. Birth Weight The following data represent the birth weights of postterm babies for whom the period of gestation was 42 weeks or more:

Birth Weight	Frequency
0–499 grams	0
500–999 grams	23
1,000–1,499 grams	222
1,500–1,999 grams	805
2,000–2,499 grams	5338
2,500–2,999 grams	34,760
3,000–3,499 grams	106,916
3,500–3,999 grams	101,907
4,000–4,499 grams	35,252
4,500–4,999 grams	6,633
5,000–5,499	748

Source: National Vital Statistics Report, Vol. 48, No. 3, March 28, 2000

(a) Construct a relative frequency distribution.
(b) Draw a relative frequency histogram. Does the distribution of baby's birth weight appear to be normal?
(c) Compute the mean and standard deviation of (the variable) baby's birth weight. $\mu = 3499.7, \sigma = 513.6$.
(d) Use the information obtained in part (c) to compute the theoretical proportion of birth weights in each class by finding the area under the normal curve.
(e) Are you convinced baby's birth weights are normally distributed?

35. Energy Expenditures According to the Energy Information Association, the mean annual expenditure on electricity to run a refrigerator is $120, the standard deviation $17.
(a) Suppose a researcher for a consumer watchdog group obtains a simple random sample of $n = 100$ households. What is the sampling distribution of $\bar{x}$?
(b) What is the probability that a random sample of $n = 100$ households has a mean expenditure on electricity to run their refrigerators of $125 or more? *0.0016*

36. Driver Deaths According to the National Highway Traffic Safety Administration, the mean age of a driver involved in a fatal crash in 1999 was 39.4 years, the standard deviation 17.4 years.
(a) Suppose that a researcher for the National Highway Traffic Safety Administration obtains a simple random sample of $n = 50$ fatal crashes. What is the sampling distribution of $\bar{x}$?
(b) What is the probability that a random sample of $n = 50$ fatal crashes in 1999 would result in a driver's mean age less than 35 years old? *0.0369*

37. Suppose a continuous random variable X is uniformly distributed with $0 \leq X \leq 20$.
(a) Draw a graph of the uniform density function.
(b) What is $P(0 \leq X \leq 5)$? *0.25*
(c) What is $P(10 \leq X \leq 18)$? *0.4*

38. List the properties of the normal curve.

39. In your own words, explain what a sampling distribution is.

(35a) Normal; $\mu_{\bar{x}} = 120$; $\sigma_{\bar{x}} = \dfrac{17}{\sqrt{100}}$

(36a) Normal; $\mu_{\bar{x}} = 39.4$; $\sigma_{\bar{x}} = \dfrac{17.4}{\sqrt{50}}$

A Tale of Blood Chemistry and Health

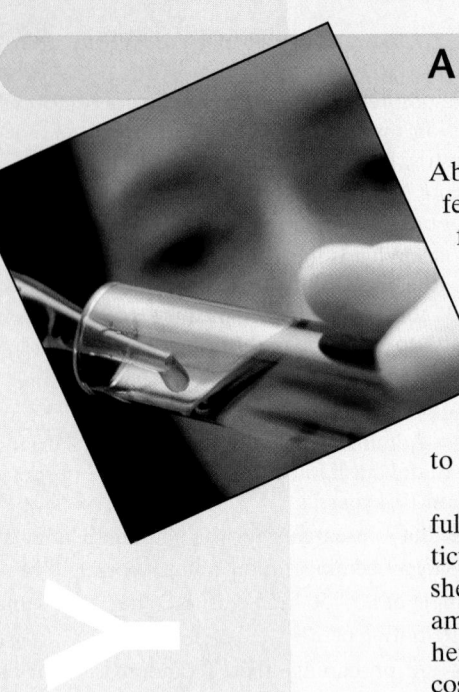

Abby Tudor recently turned 40 years old. Her knees ache, and she often feels short of breath during exercise. She is experiencing fatigue and often feels that she is going in slow motion. Periodic dizziness plagues her during most days. According to the drugstore machine, her blood pressure is elevated. Her family has a history of cardiac disease, with both of her parents having experienced heart attacks. Additionally, an aunt on her mother's side has diabetes. Hypothyroidism also runs throughout her immediate family. Abby is approximately 20 pounds overweight. She has tried various diet and exercise programs in an attempt to lose weight. Her results have been disappointing.

Upon the advice of her physician, she scheduled an appointment for a full physical exam, including a complete blood workup. Her doctor is particularly interested in the level of various blood components that might shed some light on Abby's reported symptoms. Specifically, he wants to examine her white blood cell count, red blood cell count, hemoglobin, and hematocrit figures for indications of infection or anemia. Her serum glucose level will provide information concerning the possibility of the onset of diabetes. Cholesterol and triglyceride levels will provide insight into potential cardiac problems. Additionally, the possibility of hypothyroidism will be investigated by examining Abby's serum TSH level.

As instructed, two weeks prior to her doctor's appointment, she reported to her HMO's lab for a blood test. She confirmed for the lab technician that she had fasted for the twelve hours immediately preceding the exam.

During her physical, Abby's doctor went over the blood test report with her. He expressed concern over some of the results, but Abby was not convinced that she had a problem. Additional blood tests were not a viable option because it takes a good deal of time to get a sample of readings and they are expensive. At the time of her doctor's appointment, she was unwilling to accept the offered prescriptions. She chose to do a little research before committing herself to any drug regimen.

Her research revealed that many medical measurements, such as cholesterol, are normally distributed in healthy populations. Unfortunately, the lab report did not provide the means and standard deviations necessary for Abby to calculate the various probabilities of interest. However, the report did provide the appropriate reference intervals. Assuming that the reference intervals represent the range of values for each blood component for a healthy adult population, it is possible to estimate the various means and standard deviations for this population. Abby estimated each mean by taking the midpoint of its reference interval. Using the Range Rule of Thumb ($\sigma \approx$ Range/4), standard deviations were estimated by dividing the reference interval range by four. The following table lists Abby's blood test results, as well as the mean and standard deviation of a number of blood test components for the population of normal healthy adults.

Blood Test Components for Healthy Adults and the Blood Test Results for Abby Tudor*

Abby's Blood Test Component	Unit	Mean	Standard Deviation	Abby's Result
White Blood Cell Count	10^3/uL	7.25	1.625	5.3
Red Blood Cell Count	10^6/uL	4.85	0.375	4.62
Hemoglobin	g/dL	14.75	1.125	14.6
Hematocrit	%	43.0	3.5	41.7
Glucose, Serum	mg/dL	87.0	11.0	95.0
Creatine, Serum	mg/dL	1.00	0.25	0.8
Sodium, Serum	mEq/L	141.5	3.25	143.0
Potassium, Serum	mEq/L	4.5	0.5	5.1
Chloride, Serum	mEq/L	102.5	3.25	100.0
Carbon Dioxide, Total	mEq/L	26.0	3.0	25.0
Calcium, Serum	mg/dL	9.55	0.525	10.1
Total Cholesterol	mg/dL	149.5	24.75	253.0
Triglycerides	mg/dL	99.5	49.75	150.0
HDL Cholesterol	mg/dL	92.5	28.75	42.0
LDL Cholesterol	mg/dL	64.5	32.25	181.0
LDL/HDL Ratio	Ratio	1.8	0.72	4.3
TSH, High Sensitivity, Serum	mcIU/mL	2.925	1.2875	3.15

For any blood component measurement that was below its population mean, Abby decided to calculate the probability that she would get a test value equal to the value obtained or less, given that she was a member of the healthy population. For example, her HDL cholesterol reading (42 mg/dL) was below the mean of the healthy population (92.5 mg/dL), so she calculated the following probability:

$$P(X \leq 42 \text{ mg/dL}).$$

Similarly, for any blood component measurement reading exceeding its population mean, Abby decided to calculate the probability that she would get a test value equal to the value obtained or more, given that she was a member of the healthy population. For example, her LDL cholesterol value (181 mg/dL) exceeds the mean of the healthy population (64.5 mg/dL), so she calculated the following probability:

$$P(X \geq 181 \text{ mg/dL}).$$

To help her interpret the calculated probabilities, Abby decided to be concerned about only those blood components that had a probability less than 0.025. By choosing this figure, she is acknowledging that it is unlikely that she could have such an extreme blood component reading and still be part of the healthy population.

1. The reference interval for HDL cholesterol is 35–150 mg/dL. Use this information to confirm the mean and standard deviation provided for this blood component.

2. Using Abby's criteria and the means and standard deviations provided in her blood test report, determine which blood components should be a cause of concern for Abby. Write up a summary report of your findings. Be sure to include a discussion concerning your assumptions and any limitations to your conclusions.

*Population means and standard deviations were estimated from the reference intervals derived from an actual blood test report provided by TA LabCorp, Tampa. Means were estimated by taking the midpoints of the reference intervals. Standard deviations were estimated by dividing the reference interval ranges by four. Test results attributed to Abby Tudor are actual results obtained from an anonymous patient.

Suppose that you are interested in starting your own club. In order to qualify for the club, the potential member must have intelligence that is in the top 2% of all people. The problem that you face is that you do not have a baseline for measuring what qualifies as a "top 2%" score. To gather this data, you must obtain a random sample of at least 25 "volunteers" to take an online intelligence test. There are many online intelligence tests, but you need to make sure that the test will supply scored exams. One suggested site is http://www.queendom.com/tests/iq/classical_iq_r2_access.html.

Once you have obtained your sample of at least 25 test scores, answer the following questions.

(a) What is the mean test score? What is the standard deviation test score?

(b) Do the sample data come from a population that is normally distributed? How do you know this?

(c) Assuming that the sample data come from a population that is normally distributed, determine the test score that would be required in order to join your club. That is, determine the test score that serves as a "cutoff" point for the top 2%. You can use this score to determine which potential members may join!

DECISIONS

More than 1 million skin cancers are expected to be diagnosed in the U.S. this year—almost half of all cancers diagnosed. The prevalence of skin cancer is attributable in part to a history of unprotected or under-protected sun exposure. Sunscreens have been shown to prevent certain types of lesions associated with skin cancer. They also protect skin against exposure to light that contributes to premature aging. As a result, sunscreen is now in moisturizers, lip balms, shampoos, hairstyling products, insect repellents, and makeup.

For a recent article, Consumer Reports (June 2001) tested 23 sunscreens and two moisturizers, all with a claimed sun-protection factor (SPF) of 15 or higher. SPF is defined as the degree to which a sunscreen protects the skin from UVB, the ultraviolet rays responsible for sunburn. (Some studies have shown that UVB, along with UVA, can increase the risk of skin cancers.) A person with untreated skin who can stay in the sun for 5 minutes before becoming sunburned should be able to stay in the sun for $15 \times 5 = 75$ minutes using a sunscreen rated at SPF15.

To test whether products met their SPF claims for UVB, we used a solar simulator—basically a sun lamp—to expose people to measured amounts of sunlight. First we determined the exposure time (in minutes) that caused each person's untreated skin to turn pink within 24 hours. Then we applied sunscreen to new areas of skin and made the same determination. To avoid potential sources of bias, samples of the sunscreens were applied to randomly assigned sites on the subjects' skin.

To determine the SPF rating of a sunscreen for a particular individual, the exposure time with sunscreen was divided by the exposure time without sunscreen. The following table contains the mean and standard deviation of the SPF measurements for two particular sunscreens.

Product	Mean	Std Dev
A	15.5	1.5
B	14.7	1.2

(a) In designing this experiment, why is it important to obtain the exposure time without sunscreen first, and then determine the exposure time with sunscreen for each person?

(b) Why is the random assignment of people and application sites to each treatment (the sunscreen) important?

(c) Calculate the percentage of SPF measurements that you would expect to be less than 15, the advertised level of protection for each of the products. (Assume that the SPF ratings are approximately normal.)

(d) Calculate the percentage of SPF measurements that you would expect to be greater than 17.5 for product A. Repeat this for product B.

(e) Calculate the percentage of SPF measurements that you would expect to fall between 14.5 and 15.5 for product A. Repeat this for product B.

(f) Which product appears to be superior, A or B? Support your conclusion.

Note to Readers: In many cases, our test protocol and analytical methods are more complicated than described in these examples. The data and discussions have been modified to make the material more appropriate for the audience.

Chapters 1–7 laid the groundwork for the remainder of the text. These chapters dealt with data collection (Chapter 1), descriptive statistics (Chapters 2–4), and probability (Chapters 5–7). We now discuss inferential statistics, the process of using information obtained in a sample and generalizing it to a population. There are two areas of inferential statistics: 1) estimation, in which sample data are used to estimate the value of unknown parameters such as μ or σ and 2) hypothesis testing, in which claims regarding a characteristic of the population are made and sample data are used to test the claim. In this chapter, we will discuss estimation of an unknown parameter and in the next chapter, we will discuss hypothesis testing.

We know from Section 7.5 that $\bar{x}$ is a random variable, and as such, has a distribution associated with it. We call this distribution the sampling distribution of the sample mean. The mean of the distribution of $\bar{x}$ is equal to the mean of the population, μ. The standard deviation of the distribution of $\bar{x}$ is $\dfrac{\sigma}{\sqrt{n}}$. Finally, we know that the distribution of the sample mean is normal if the population from which the sample was drawn is normal. And the sampling distribution of the sample mean becomes approximately normal as the sample size increases, regardless of the shape of the parent population. This result is known as the Central Limit Theorem. We use these results to help us in the estimation process.

Because the information that is collected from a sample is incomplete (the sample does not contain all the information in the population), we will assign probabilities to our estimates. These probabilities serve as a way of measuring what would happen if we estimated the value of the parameter many times and therefore provide a measure of confidence in our results.

Confidence Intervals about a Single Parameter

Outline

 For additional study help, go to www.prenhall.com/sullivanstats

Materials include

- Self-Graded Quizzes
- "Preparing for This Section" Quizzes
- STATLETs
- PowerPoint Downloads
- Step-by-Step Technology Guide
- Graphing Calculator Help

8.1 Confidence Intervals about a Population Mean, σ Known

Preparing for This Section   Before getting started, review the following:

✓ Simple random sampling (Section 1.2, pp. 15–17)

✓ Parameter versus statistic (Section 3.1, p. 112)

✓ Sampling error (Section 1.4, p. 30)

✓ z_α notation (Section 7.2, p. 401)

✓ Central Limit Theorem (Section 7.5, p. 432)

✓ Normal probability plots (Section 7.4, pp. 415–420)

Objectives

 Compute the point estimate of μ

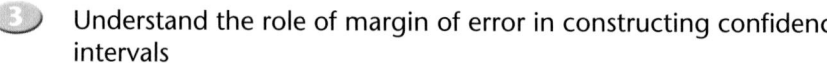 Compute confidence intervals about μ with σ known

 Understand the role of margin of error in constructing confidence intervals

 Determine sample size necessary for estimating the population mean

1 Point Estimates

If we do not have access to population data, then we cannot determine values of population parameters, such as μ or σ. Therefore, we use sample data to estimate the values of these parameters. These estimators are called *point estimators*.

Definition   A **point estimate** of a parameter is the value of a statistic that estimates the value of the parameter.

For example, the sample mean, $\bar{x}$, is a point estimate of the population mean, μ. The sample standard deviation, s, is a point estimate of the population standard deviation, σ.

For many parameters there is more than one point estimate. For example, we could use the sample median or mode as a point estimate of the population mean, μ. So the question becomes, which point estimate do I use if I want to estimate the value of the population mean? The answer is that we use the sample mean. There are three reasons for this:

1. The sample mean, $\bar{x}$, is an unbiased estimator of μ. A statistic is an **unbiased estimator** provided its expected value is equal to the value of the parameter. For example, if we took many samples of size n and computed the sample mean of each sample, then the mean of the sample means would equal μ. In other words, a statistic is unbiased if it does not systematically overestimate or underestimate the value of the parameter it estimates.

2. The sample mean provides more **consistent** estimates of the population mean. In other words, the larger your sample, the closer the sample mean gets to the population mean.

3. In repeated samples, a majority of the sample means will be "close" to the value of the population mean. This characteristic of the sample mean is called **efficiency**.

Caution

Appropriately obtaining individuals to participate in a survey or appropriate design of an experiment is vital for the statistical process to be valid. In other words, if data are carelessly or inappropriately collected, any statistical inference performed on the data is subject to scrutiny. For example, the results of Internet surveys should be looked upon with extreme skepticism.

Historical Note

It was R.A. Fisher who described the criteria of a good statistic.

Theorem	The sample mean, $\overline{x}$, is the **best point estimate** of the population mean, μ.

▶ **EXAMPLE 1**   **Computing a Point Estimate for μ**

Problem: Suppose we were in the market to purchase a used Corvette. We would like to estimate the population mean price of a three-year-old Chevy Corvette.

Approach: We estimate the population mean by obtaining a random sample of 15 used Corvettes listed in Table 1. The best point estimate of the population mean is the sample mean.

Solution: The sample mean is

$$\overline{x} = \frac{\$47{,}000 + \$32{,}750 + \cdots + \$43{,}785}{15} = \$38{,}247$$

The best point estimate of μ is \$38,247.   ◀◀

NW   *Now Work Problem 15(a).*

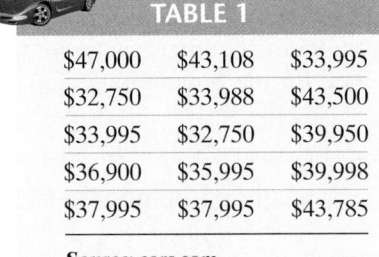

TABLE 1		
$47,000	$43,108	$33,995
$32,750	$33,988	$43,500
$33,995	$32,750	$39,950
$36,900	$35,995	$39,998
$37,995	$37,995	$43,785

Source: cars.com

② Confidence Intervals

While the sample mean obtained in Example 1 is considered the best point estimate of the population mean, we recognize that there is likely to be some sampling error. Remember that sampling error is the difference between the value of the statistic and the parameter. Sampling error occurs because the sample does not capture all the information that is in the population.

Perhaps the idea that the value of a statistic often does not equal the value of the parameter is best phrased by David Salsburg in this excerpt from his book, *The Lady Tasting Tea*:

> Never will we know if the value of a statistic for a particular set of data is correct. We can only say we used a procedure that produces a statistic that meets these criteria (unbiased, consistent and efficient).

Therefore, rather than reporting the value of the sample mean, it is preferable to report an interval around the sample mean along with a measure of our confidence that this interval contains the population mean. To help understand the idea of this interval, consider the following situation. Suppose that you were asked to guess the mean age of the students in your statistics class. After surveying five of the students, you might guess the mean age is 24 years. This would be a point estimate of μ, the mean age of all students in the class. We could also express our guess by producing a range of ages such as 24 years old give or take 2 years (the *margin of error*). Mathematically, we would write this 24 ± 2. Suppose further that you were asked how confident you were that the mean age was between 22 and 26. Your response might be "I am 80% confident that the mean age of students in my statistics class is between 22 and 26 years." If asked to construct an interval in which you were 99% confident, would your margin of error increase or decrease?

In statistics, we construct intervals for a population mean that center around a "guess" as well. The "guess" used in statistics is the sample mean. The margin of error depends upon the level of confidence, the standard deviation of the population, and the sample size.

Note to Instructor
Discuss reasons why the sample will probably not equal the population mean. Make sure the discussion addresses both sampling and non-sampling error (poorly worded questions, misinterpretation, false answers, and so on).

Definition

A **confidence interval estimate** of a parameter consists of an interval of numbers, along with a measure of the likelihood that the interval contains the unknown parameter. The **level of confidence** in a confidence interval is the proportion of intervals that will contain μ if a large number of repeated samples are obtained. The level of confidence is denoted $(1 - \alpha) \cdot 100\%$.

In Your Own Words

A confidence interval is a range of numbers, such as 22–30. The level of confidence represents our degree of confidence (expressed as a percent) that the interval contains the population mean.

For example, a 95% level of confidence ($\alpha = 0.05$) would mean that if 100 confidence intervals were constructed, each based on a different sample from the same population, we would expect 95 of the intervals to contain the population mean. The confidence interval for the population mean depends upon three factors:

1. The point estimate of the population mean,

2. Our level of confidence that the interval contains the population mean,

3. The standard deviation of the sample mean, $\sigma_{\bar{x}} = \dfrac{\sigma}{\sqrt{n}}$.

Because the sample mean is the best point estimate of the population mean, we expect the value of $\bar{x}$ to be close to μ; however, we do not know exactly how close $\bar{x}$ is to the unknown value of μ. The process of constructing a confidence interval relies on the fact that $\bar{x}$ is a random variable that is normally distributed with mean μ and standard deviation $\dfrac{\sigma}{\sqrt{n}}$, provided the population from which the sample is drawn is normal or the sample size is greater than or equal to 30.

While it is not reasonable to claim to know the population standard deviation without knowing the population mean, for ease of understanding the procedures in constructing confidence intervals, we will assume its value is known in this section. We will drop this assumption in the next section.

Because $\bar{x}$ is normally distributed, we know that 95% of all sample means should lie within 1.96 standard deviations of the population mean, μ, and 2.5% of the the sample means will lie in each tail. See Figure 1.

That is, 95% of all sample means are in the interval

$$\mu - 1.96 \cdot \frac{\sigma}{\sqrt{n}} < \bar{x} < \mu + 1.96 \cdot \frac{\sigma}{\sqrt{n}}$$

Figure 1

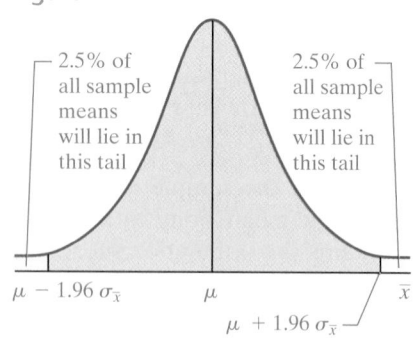

2.5% of all sample means will lie in this tail

2.5% of all sample means will lie in this tail

$\mu - 1.96\,\sigma_{\bar{x}}$ μ $\mu + 1.96\,\sigma_{\bar{x}}$ $\bar{x}$

With a little algebraic manipulation, we can rewrite this inequality with μ in the middle and obtain

$$\bar{x} - 1.96 \cdot \frac{\sigma}{\sqrt{n}} < \mu < \bar{x} + 1.96 \cdot \frac{\sigma}{\sqrt{n}}$$

This inequality means that 95% of the sample means will result in confidence intervals that contain the population mean. That is,

$$P\left(\bar{x} - 1.96 \cdot \frac{\sigma}{\sqrt{n}} < \mu < \bar{x} + 1.96 \cdot \frac{\sigma}{\sqrt{n}} \right) = 0.95$$

It is common to write the 95% confidence interval as

$$\bar{x} \pm 1.96 \cdot \frac{\sigma}{\sqrt{n}}$$

From this, we can see the confidence interval is of the form

Point estimate $\pm$ Margin of error

with the point estimate being the sample mean, $\bar{x}$, and the margin of error being $1.96 \cdot \dfrac{\sigma}{\sqrt{n}}$.

▶ **EXAMPLE 2** **Constructing 20 95% Confidence Intervals Based on 20 Samples**

Problem: It is known that scores on the Stanford–Binet IQ test are normally distributed with $\mu = 100$ and $\sigma = 16$. Use Minitab, Excel, or some other statistical software to simulate obtaining 20 simple random samples of size $n = 15$. Use these 20 different samples to construct 95% confidence intervals for the population mean, μ.

Approach:

Step 1: We will use Minitab to obtain 20 simple random samples of size 15 from a population that is normally distributed with mean $\mu = 100$ and $\sigma = 16$. We then compute the sample means of each of the 20 samples.
Step 2: Construct 95% confidence intervals by computing

$$\bar{x} - 1.96 \cdot \frac{\sigma}{\sqrt{n}} = \bar{x} - 1.96 \cdot \frac{16}{\sqrt{15}} \quad \text{and} \quad \bar{x} + 1.96 \cdot \frac{\sigma}{\sqrt{n}} = \bar{x} + 1.96 \cdot \frac{16}{\sqrt{15}}$$

for each sample mean.

Solution:

Step 1: Table 2 shows the 20 sample means obtained from Minitab.
Step 2: We construct the 20 confidence intervals for each of the 20 sample means and present the results in Table 3 on page 460.
 From the results presented in Table 3, we can see that 19 of the 20 (or 95%) samples resulted in 95% confidence intervals that contain the value of the population mean, 100. Notice that sample 3 does not result in a confidence interval that contains the population mean 100 (lower bound = $108.73 - 8.10 = 100.63$; upper bound = $108.73 + 8.10 = 116.83$). ◀◀

We can further see the results of Example 2 through Figure 2, in which we present the sampling distribution of $\bar{x}$, along with the 20 confidence intervals computed in Example 2. Notice that the interval corresponding to $\bar{x} = 108.73$ does not intersect $\mu = 100$.

Note: In this particular simulation exactly 95% of the samples resulted in intervals that contained μ. It will not always be the case that exactly 95% of the sample means result in intervals that contain μ when performing this simulation. It could easily have been the case that all the intervals contained μ or that 17 out of the 20 contained μ. The interpretation of the confidence interval remains: in a 95% confidence interval, if we obtain many samples of size n, the interval constructed will contain the population mean, μ, 95% of the time. Since we obtained only 20 samples, the exact percentage may be slightly different from 95%. ◀

TABLE 2

104.32	93.97	108.73	104.11	100.67
96.87	99.74	100.25	101.32	94.24
102.23	94.32	97.66	101.44	98.19
107.15	100.38	95.89	104.43	102.28

Figure 2

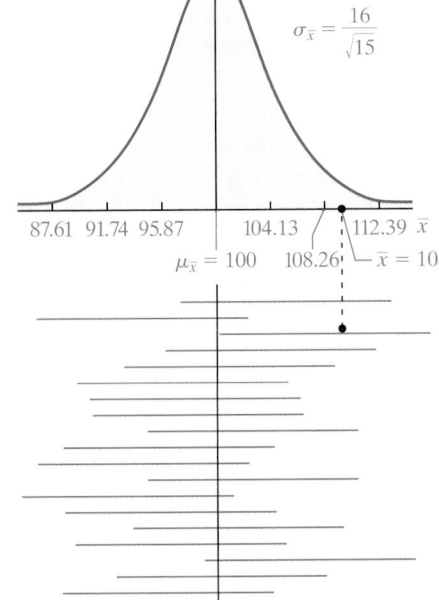

$\sigma_{\bar{x}} = \dfrac{16}{\sqrt{15}}$

87.61 91.74 95.87   104.13   112.39 $\bar{x}$
$\mu_{\bar{x}} = 100$ 108.26 $\bar{x} = 108.73$

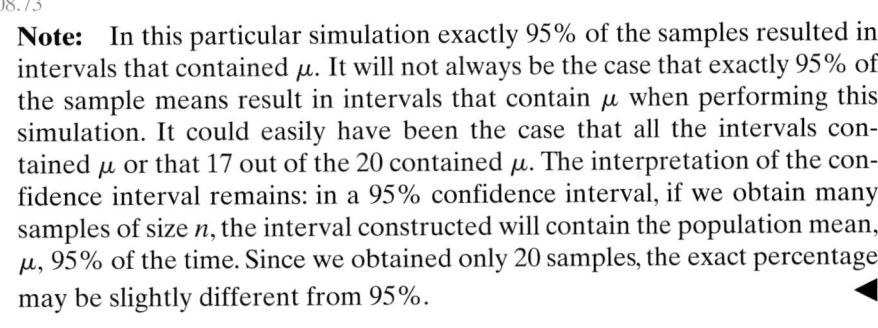

		TABLE 3		
Sample	Sample Mean	Margin of Error $1.96 \cdot \dfrac{\sigma}{\sqrt{n}} = 1.96 \cdot \dfrac{16}{\sqrt{15}} = 8.10$	Lower Bound $\bar{x} - 1.96 \cdot \dfrac{\sigma}{\sqrt{n}}$	Upper Bound $\bar{x} + 1.96 \cdot \dfrac{\sigma}{\sqrt{n}}$
1	104.32	8.10	$104.32 - 8.10 = 96.22$	$104.32 + 8.10 = 112.42$
2	93.97	8.10	$93.97 - 8.10 = 85.87$	$93.97 + 8.10 = 102.07$
3	108.73	8.10	$108.73 - 8.10 = 100.63$	$108.73 + 8.10 = 116.83$
4	104.11	8.10	96.01	112.21
5	100.67	8.10	92.57	108.77
6	96.87	8.10	88.77	104.97
7	99.74	8.10	91.64	107.84
8	100.25	8.10	92.15	108.35
9	101.32	8.10	93.22	109.42
10	94.24	8.10	86.14	102.34
11	102.23	8.10	94.13	110.33
12	94.32	8.10	86.22	102.42
13	97.66	8.10	89.56	105.76
14	101.44	8.10	93.34	109.54
15	98.19	8.10	90.09	106.29
16	107.15	8.10	99.05	115.25
17	100.38	8.10	92.28	108.48
18	95.89	8.10	87.79	103.99
19	104.43	8.10	96.33	112.53
20	102.28	8.10	94.18	110.38

Note to Instructor
Emphasize the relation between the area in the tail of the standard normal distribution and the critical value. Less area means a larger critical value, which implies a wider interval.

Of course, we might not always be interested in creating 95% confidence intervals. Therefore, we need a means for constructing any $(1 - \alpha) \cdot 100\%$ confidence interval. If we let $z_{\alpha/2}$ represent the Z-score that separates an area of $\alpha/2$ in the right tail from the rest of the distribution, we can construct a confidence interval for any level of confidence. Figure 3 demonstrates the idea. In general, a $(1 - \alpha) \cdot 100\%$ confidence interval will include the population mean, μ, for all sample means that lie within $z_{\alpha/2}$ standard deviations of the population mean, μ. The sample means that are in the tails will not have confidence intervals that include the population mean. The values of $\pm z_{\alpha/2}$ are called the **critical values** of the distribution.

Table 4 shows some of the more common critical values used in the construction of confidence intervals. The reader is encouraged to verify the results presented in the table.

Figure 3

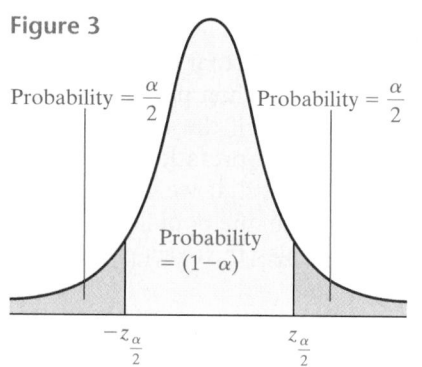

	TABLE 4	
Level of Confidence, $(1 - \alpha) \cdot 100\%$	Area in Each Tail, $\alpha/2$	Critical Value, $z_{\alpha/2}$
90%	0.05	1.645
95%	0.025	1.96
99%	0.005	2.575

In a 95% confidence interval, $\alpha = 0.05$, so that $z_{\alpha/2} = z_{0.05/2} = z_{0.025} = 1.96$. This means that any sample mean that lies within 1.96 standard deviations of the population mean will result in a confidence interval that contains μ and any sample mean that is more than 1.96 standard deviations from the population mean will result in a confidence interval that does not contain μ. This is an extremely important point. Whether a confidence interval contains μ depends solely upon the sample mean, $\overline{x}$. The population mean is a fixed value that either is or is not in the interval, and we do not know which of these possibilities is in fact true for any computed confidence interval. However, if repeated samples are taken, we do know that $(1 - \alpha) \cdot 100\%$ of the confidence intervals will contain the population mean. This result leads to the following interpretation of a confidence interval:

> **Interpretation of a Confidence Interval**
>
> A $(1 - \alpha) \cdot 100\%$ confidence interval means that if we obtained many simple random samples of size n from the population whose mean, μ, is unknown, then approximately $(1 - \alpha) \cdot 100\%$ of the intervals will contain μ.

For example, if we constructed a 90% confidence interval with a lower bound of 12 and an upper bound of 18, then we would interpret the interval as follows: "We are 90% confident that the population mean, μ, is between 12 and 18." Be sure that you understand that the level of confidence refers to the method, not the interval. So a 90% confidence interval means that the method will result in an interval that contains the population mean, μ, 90% of the time. It does not mean that there is a 90% probability that μ lies between 12 and 18.

We are now prepared to present a method for constructing a $(1 - \alpha) \cdot 100\%$ confidence interval about μ.

> **Constructing a $(1 - \alpha) \cdot 100\%$ Confidence Interval about μ, σ Known**
> Suppose a simple random sample of size n is taken from a population with unknown mean, μ, and known standard deviation σ. A $(1 - \alpha) \cdot 100\%$ confidence interval for μ is given by
>
> $$\text{Lower bound: } \overline{x} - z_{\alpha/2} \cdot \frac{\sigma}{\sqrt{n}} \qquad \text{Upper bound: } \overline{x} + z_{\alpha/2} \cdot \frac{\sigma}{\sqrt{n}}$$
>
> where $z_{\alpha/2}$ is the critical Z-value.
>
> **Note:** The size, n, of the sample must be greater than or equal to 30 or the population must be normally distributed.

When constructing a confidence interval about the population mean, we must verify that the sample either is large ($n \geq 30$) or comes from a population that is normally distributed. Fortunately, the procedures for constructing confidence intervals presented in this section are **robust**. This means that minor departures from normality will not seriously affect the results. Nevertheless, it is important that the requirements for constructing confidence intervals are verified. We shall follow the practice of verifying the normality assumption for small sample sizes by drawing a normal probability plot and checking for outliers by drawing a boxplot.

Because the construction of the confidence interval with σ known uses Z-scores, it is sometimes referred to as constructing a **Z-interval**.

Caution

A 95% confidence interval does not mean that there is a 95% probability that the interval contains μ. Remember, probability describes the likelihood of undetermined events. Therefore, it does not make sense to talk about the probability that the interval contains μ, since the population mean is a fixed value. Think of it this way: Suppose I flip a coin and obtain a head. If I ask you to determine the probability that the flip resulted in a head, it would not be 0.5, because the outcome has already been determined. Confidence intervals work the same way. Because μ is already determined, we do not say that there is a 95% probability that the interval contains μ.

▶ **EXAMPLE 3**   Constructing a Z-Interval

Problem: Remember that we are in the market to buy a three-year-old Chevy Corvette. In Example 1, we obtained a point estimate of $38,247 for the population mean. We now wish to construct a 90% confidence interval about the population mean, μ. Assume that the population standard deviation is known to be $4100.

Approach:

Step 1: We have a simple random sample of size $n = 15$. We need to verify that the data come from a population that is normally distributed with no outliers. We will verify normality by constructing a normal probability plot. We check for outliers by drawing a boxplot.

Step 2: Since we are constructing a 90% confidence interval, $\alpha = 0.10$. Therefore, we need to identify the value of $z_{\alpha/2} = z_{0.10/2} = z_{0.05}$. Recall, this is the Z-score such that the area under the standard normal curve to the right of $z_{0.05}$ is 0.05.

Step 3: We compute the lower and upper bounds on the interval with $\overline{x} = \$38,247$, $\sigma = \$4100$, and $n = 15$.

Step 4: We interpret the result by stating: "We are 90% confident that the mean price of all three-year-old Chevy Corvettes is somewhere between *lower bound* and *upper bound*."

Solution:

Step 1: A normal probability plot of the data in Table 1 (page 457) is provided in Figure 4(a). A boxplot is presented in Figure 4(b).

Figure 4   Normal Probability Plot for Price

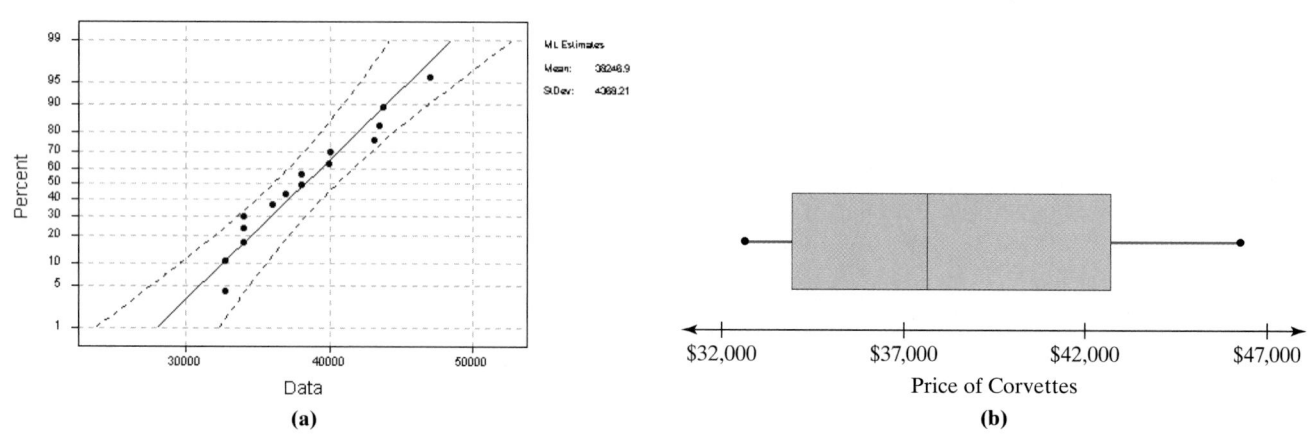

(a)   (b)

All the data values lie within the bounds on the normal probability plot, indicating that the data are roughly normal. The boxplot does not display any outliers. The requirements for computing the confidence interval are satisfied.

Step 2: We need to determine the value of $z_{0.05}$. We look in Table II for an area equal to 0.95 (remember the table gives areas left of the Z-scores). We have $z_{0.05} = 1.645$.

Step 3: We substitute into the formulas for the lower and upper bound of the confidence interval.

$$\text{Lower bound} = \bar{x} - z_{\alpha/2} \cdot \frac{\sigma}{\sqrt{n}} = \$38{,}247 - 1.645 \cdot \frac{\$4100}{\sqrt{15}} = \$38{,}247 - \$1741 = \$36{,}506$$

$$\text{Upper bound} = \bar{x} + z_{\alpha/2} \cdot \frac{\sigma}{\sqrt{n}} = \$38{,}247 + 1.645 \cdot \frac{\$4100}{\sqrt{15}} = \$38{,}247 + \$1741 = \$39{,}988$$

Step 4: We are 90% confident that the mean price of all three-year-old Chevy Corvettes is somewhere between $36,506 and $39,988. ◀◀

Using Technology: Statistical software and graphing calculators with advanced statistical features have the ability to construct confidence intervals with σ known. Figure 5 shows the results using Minitab.

Figure 5

Confidence Intervals

```
The assumed sigma = 4100

Variable            N    Mean   StDev   SeMean       90.0% CI
price              15   38247    4522     1059   (36506, 39988)
```

 *Now Work Problems 15(b), 15(c), and 15(d).*

The Role of the Margin of Error

Is there any way that we can reduce the width of the interval? The width of the interval is determined by the *margin of error*.

Definition

The Margin of Error

The margin of error, E, in a $(1 - \alpha) \cdot 100\%$ confidence interval in which σ is known is given by

$$E = z_{\alpha/2} \cdot \frac{\sigma}{\sqrt{n}}$$

where n is the sample size.

Note: We require the population from which the sample was drawn be normally distributed or the sample size n be greater than or equal to 30.

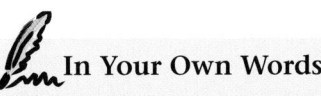**In Your Own Words**

The margin of error can be thought of as the "give or take" portion of the statement "The mean age of the class is 23, give or take 3 years."

As we look at the formula for obtaining the margin of error, we see that its value depends upon three quantities:

1. The level of confidence.
2. The standard deviation of the population.
3. The sample size, n.

We cannot control the standard deviation of the population, but we certainly can control the level of confidence and/or the sample size. Let's see how changing these values affect the margin of error.

▶ **EXAMPLE 4**   **The Role of the Level of Confidence in the Margin of Error**

Problem: For the problem of estimating the population mean price of all three-year-old Chevy Corvettes presented in Example 3, determine the effect of increasing the level of confidence on the confidence interval to 99%.

Approach: With a 99% level of confidence, we have $\alpha = 0.01$. So, to compute the margin of error, E, we simply determine the value of $z_{\alpha/2} = z_{0.01/2} = z_{0.005}$. We then substitute this value into the formula for the margin of error with $\sigma = \$4100$ and $n = 15$.

Solution: After consulting Table II, we determine $z_{0.005} = 2.575$. Substituting into the formula for margin of error, we obtain

$$E = z_{\alpha/2} \cdot \frac{\sigma}{\sqrt{n}} = 2.575 \cdot \frac{\$4100}{\sqrt{15}} = \$2726$$

In Your Own Words

As the level of confidence increases, the margin of error also increases.

Notice the margin of error has increased from \$1741 to \$2726 when the level of confidence increases from 90% to 99%. If we want to be more confident the interval contains the population mean, the width of the interval increases. ◀◀

▶ **EXAMPLE 5**   **The Role of Sample Size in the Margin of Error**

Problem: For the problem of estimating the population mean price of all three-year-old Chevy Corvettes presented in Example 3, determine the effect of increasing the sample size to $n = 25$. Leave the level of confidence at 90%.

Approach: We compute the margin of error with $n = 25$ instead of $n = 15$.

Solution: Substituting $z_{0.05} = 1.645$, $\sigma = \$4100$, and $n = 25$ into the formula for computing margin of error, we obtain

$$E = z_{\alpha/2} \cdot \frac{\sigma}{\sqrt{n}} = 1.645 \cdot \frac{\$4100}{\sqrt{25}} = \$1349$$

By increasing the sample size from $n = 15$ to $n = 25$., the margin of error, E, decreases from \$1741 to \$1349.

In Your Own Words

As the sample size increases, the margin of error decreases.

This result should not be very surprising. Remember the Law of Large Numbers states that as the sample size n increases, the sample mean approaches the value of the population mean. This outcome is supported by the smaller margin of error. ◀◀

NW *Now Work Problem 11.*

④ **Determining Sample Size**

Suppose we want to know the number of Corvettes that we should sample in order to estimate the price of a three-year-old Corvette within \$1500 with 95% confidence. If we solve the formula for the margin of error, E, for n, we obtain a formula for determining sample size:

$$E = z_{\alpha/2} \cdot \frac{\sigma}{\sqrt{n}}$$

$$E\sqrt{n} = z_{\alpha/2} \cdot \sigma \qquad \text{Multiply both sides by } \sqrt{n}.$$

$$\sqrt{n} = \frac{z_{\alpha/2} \cdot \sigma}{E} \qquad \text{Divide both sides by the margin of error, } E.$$

$$n = \left(\frac{z_{\alpha/2} \cdot \sigma}{E} \right)^2 \qquad \text{Square both sides.}$$

This gives us a formula for computing the sample size required to obtain a confidence interval for μ within a prescribed margin of error, E, and level of confidence, $(1 - \alpha) \cdot 100\%$.

Theorem

Determining the Sample Size n

The sample size required to estimate the population mean, μ, with a level of confidence $(1 - \alpha) \cdot 100\%$ with a specified margin of error, E, is given by

$$n = \left(\frac{z_{\alpha/2} \cdot \sigma}{E} \right)^2$$

where n is rounded up* to the nearest whole number.

Note to Instructor
Ask students to identify the reason we round up rather than round off.

When σ is unknown, it is common practice to conduct a preliminary survey in order to determine s and use it as an estimate of σ. When utilizing this approach, the size of the sample should be at least 30.

▶ **EXAMPLE 6**   **Determining Sample Size**

Problem: We will once again consider the problem of estimating the population mean price of a three-year-old Chevy Corvette. How large of a sample is required to estimate the mean price within $1000 with 90% confidence?

Approach: The sample size required can be obtained using the formula

$$n = \left(\frac{z_{\alpha/2} \cdot \sigma}{E} \right)^2$$

with $z_{\alpha/2} = z_{0.05} = 1.645$, $\sigma = \$4100$, and $E = \$1000$.

Solution: We substitute the values of z, σ, and E into the formula for determining sample size and obtain

$$n = \left(\frac{z_{\alpha/2} \cdot \sigma}{E} \right)^2 = \left(\frac{1.645 \cdot \$4100}{\$1000} \right)^2 = 6.7445^2 = 45.488$$

Caution

Don't forget to round up when determining sample size.

We round 45.488 up to 46. A sample size of $n = 46$ will result in an interval estimate of the population mean with a margin of error equal to $1000 with 90% confidence. This means that if we obtained 100 samples of size $n = 46$, we would expect about 90 of them to capture the population mean, while 10 would not.   ◄◄

NW *Now Work Problem 27.*

Some Final Thoughts

There are many requirements that must be satisfied in the implementation of any type of statistical inference. It is worthwhile to list the requirements for constructing a confidence interval about μ with σ known in a single location for quick reference.

*Rounding *up* is different than rounding *off*. We round 5.32 *up* to 6 and *off* to 5.

Requirements in the Construction of a Confidence Interval about μ, σ Known

1. The data obtained come from a simple random sample. In Chapter 1, we introduced other sampling techniques, such as stratified, cluster, and systematic. The techniques introduced in this section apply only to samples obtained through simple random sampling. Although methods do exist for constructing confidence intervals when using the other sampling methods, they are beyond the scope of this text. If the data are obtained from a suspect sampling method, such as voluntary response or convenience sampling, no methods exist for constructing confidence intervals. This is because the method of data collection itself is flawed. If data are collected in a flawed manner, any statistical inference performed on the data is useless!

2. The data are obtained from a population that is normally distributed, or the sample size, n, is greater than or equal to 30. We can use normal probability plots to help us judge whether the requirement of normality is satisfied. Remember, the techniques introduced in this section are robust. This means that minor departures from requirements will not have a severe effect on the results. However, we need to be aware that the sample mean is not resistant. This means that any outlier(s) in the data will affect the value of the sample mean and therefore affect the confidence interval. If data contain outliers, we should *not* use the methods introduced in this section.

3. The population standard deviation, σ, is assumed to be known. Clearly, it is unlikely that the population standard deviation is known when the population mean is not. We will drop this assumption in the next section.

8.1 Assess Your Understanding

Concepts and Vocabulary

1. What are the characteristics that an estimator of a parameter should have?
2. The construction of a confidence interval depends upon three factors. What are they?
3. Why does the margin of error increase as the level of confidence increases?
4. Why does the margin of error decrease as the sample size n increases?

5. Suppose a confidence interval has a lower bound of 10 and an upper bound of 18. What is the sample mean used to construct the interval? What is the margin of error?
6. When determining the sample size required to estimate μ, we always round the value of n up to the next whole number. Explain why we do so.

Exercises

• Basic Skills

In Problems 1–6, a simple random sample of size $n < 30$ has been obtained. From the normal probability plots and boxplots, judge whether a z-interval should be constructed.

1. No

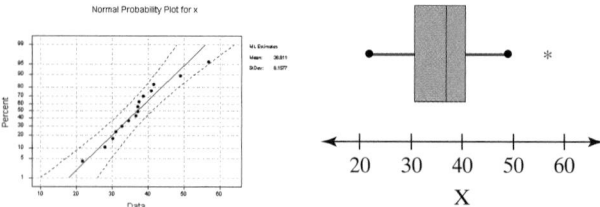

2. No

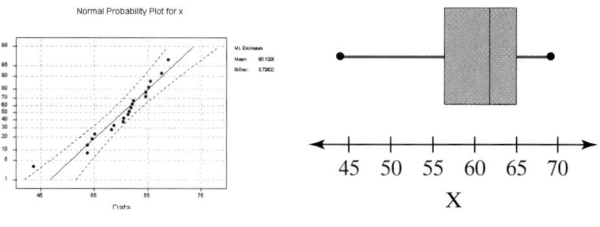

3. No

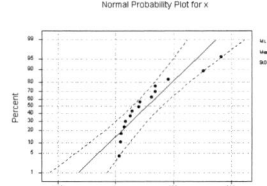

4. No

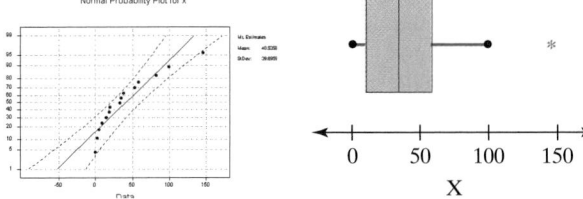

5. Yes

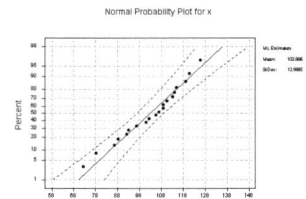

6. Yes

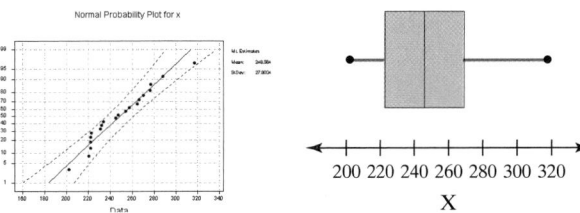

In Problems 7–10, compute the critical value $z_{\alpha/2}$ that corresponds to the given level of confidence.

7. 98% 2.33   **8.** 94% 1.88   **9.** 85% 1.44   **10.** 80% 1.28

---

11. A simple random sample of size n is drawn from a population whose population standard deviation, σ, is known to be 5.3. The sample mean, $\overline{x}$, is determined to be 34.2.   *(c)* (31.89, 36.51); increases

(a) Compute the 95% confidence interval if the sample size, n, is 35. (32.44, 35.96)

(b) Compute the 95% confidence interval if the sample size, n, is 50. How does increasing the sample size affect the margin of error, E? (32.73, 35.67); decreases

(c) Compute the 99% confidence interval if the sample size, n, is 35. Compare the results to those obtained in part (a). How does increasing the level of confidence affect the size of the margin of error, E?

(d) Can we compute a confidence interval based upon the information given if the sample size is $n = 15$? Why? If the sample size is $n = 15$, what must be true regarding the population from which the sample was drawn? Only if the population is normal

12. A simple random sample of size n is drawn from a population whose population standard deviation, σ, is known to be 3.8. The sample mean, $\overline{x}$, is determined to be 59.2.

(a) Compute the 90% confidence interval if the sample size, n, is 45. (58.27, 60.13)

(b) Compute the 90% confidence interval if the sample size, n, is 55. How does increasing the sample size affect the margin of error, E? (58.36, 60.04); decreases

(c) (57.88, 60.52); increases

(c) Compute the 98% confidence interval if the sample size, n, is 45. Compare the results to those obtained in part (a). How does increasing the level of confidence affect the size of the margin of error, E?

(d) Can we compute a confidence interval based upon the information given if the sample size is $n = 15$? Why? If the sample size is $n = 15$, what must be true regarding the population from which the sample was drawn? Only if the population is normal

13. A simple random sample of size n is drawn from a population that is normally distributed with population standard deviation, σ, known to be 13. The sample mean, $\overline{x}$, is found to be 108.   *(c)* (103.96, 112.04); decreases

(a) Compute the 96% confidence interval if the sample size, n, is 25. (102.66, 113.34)

(b) Compute the 96% confidence interval if the sample size, n, is 10. How does decreasing the sample size affect the margin of error, E? (99.56, 116.44); increases

(c) Compute the 88% confidence interval if the sample size, n, is 25. Compare the results to those obtained in part (a). How does decreasing the level of confidence affect the size of the margin of error, E?

(d) Could we have computed the confidence intervals in parts (a)–(c) if the population had not been normally distributed? Why? No

(e) Suppose an analysis of the sample data revealed three outliers greater than the mean. How would this affect the confidence interval?

14. A simple random sample of size n is drawn from a population that is normally distributed with population standard deviation, σ, known to be 17. The sample mean, $\overline{x}$, is found to be 123.

(a) Compute the 94% confidence interval if the sample size, n, is 20. (115.85, 130.15)

(b) Compute the 94% confidence interval if the sample size, n, is 12. How does decreasing the sample size affect the margin of error, E? (113.77, 132.23); increases

(c) Compute the 85% confidence interval if the sample size, n, is 20. Compare the results to those obtained in part (a). How does decreasing the level of confidence affect the size of the margin of error, E?

(d) Could we have computed the confidence intervals in parts (a)–(c) if the population had not been normally distributed? Why? No

(e) Suppose an analysis of the sample data revealed one outlier greater than the mean. How would this affect the confidence interval?

(c) (117.53, 128.47); decreases

• Applying the Concepts

15. Crash Test Results The Insurance Institute for Highway Safety routinely conducts crash tests on vehicles in order to determine the cost of repairs. In four crashes of a Chevy Cavalier at 5 miles per hour, the institute found the cost of repairs to be $225, $462, $729, and $753. Treat these data as a simple random sample of four crashes, and answer the following questions, assuming that $\sigma = \$220$.

(a) Use the data to compute a point estimate for the population mean cost of repairs on a Chevy Cavalier. $542.25

(b) Because the sample size is small, we must verify that cost is normally distributed and that the sample does not contain any outliers. The normal probability plot and boxplot are shown below. Are the conditions for constructing a z-interval satisfied? Yes

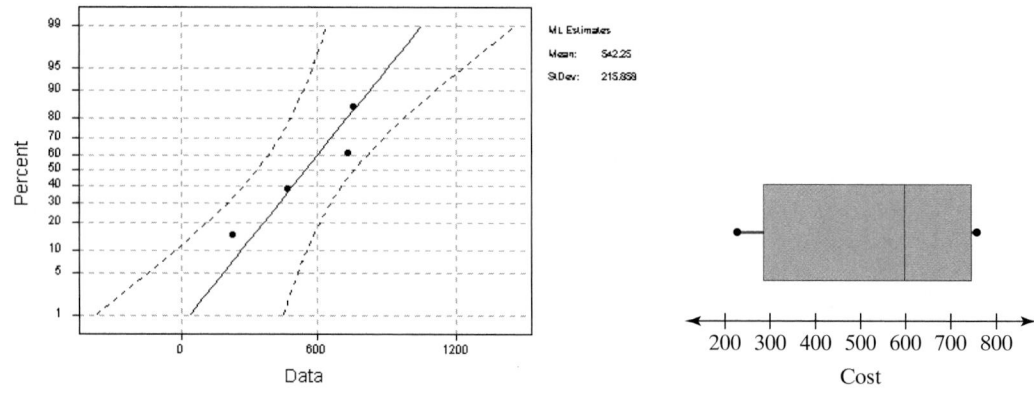

Normal Probability Plot for Cost

(c) ($326.65, $757.85)
(d) ($361.32, $723.18)

(c) Construct a 95% confidence interval for the cost of repairs. Interpret this interval.
(d) Construct a 90% confidence interval for the cost of repairs. Interpret this interval.

16. Flight Time A researcher for the FAA wants to estimate the average flight time (in minutes) from Albuquerque, New Mexico, to Dallas, Texas, for flights with American Airlines. He randomly selects 9 flights between the two cities and obtains the data shown. Assume that $\sigma = 8$ minutes.

117	95	109	103	111
91	100	99	106	

Source: United States Department of Transportation

(a) Use the data to compute a point estimate for the population mean flight time between Albuquerque and Dallas on an American Airlines flight. 103.4

(b) Because the sample size is small, we must verify that flight time is normally distributed and that the sample does not contain any outliers. The normal probability plot and boxplot are shown on page 469. Are the conditions for constructing a z-interval satisfied? Yes

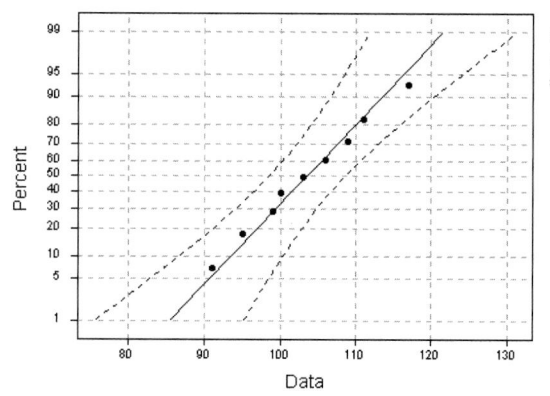

Normal Probability Plot for Flight Time

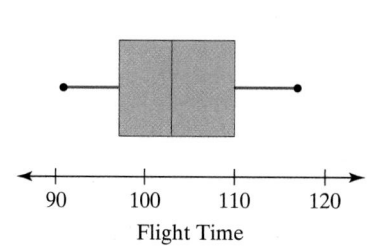

(c) (98.22, 108.67)
(d) (99.06, 107.83)

(c) Construct a 95% confidence interval for the flight time. Interpret this interval.
(d) Construct a 90% confidence interval for the flight time. Interpret this interval.

17. **Serum Cholesterol** As reported by the U.S. National Center for Health Statistics, the mean serum high density lipoprotein (HDL) cholesterol of females 20–29 years old is $\mu = 53$. Dr. Paul Oswiecmiski wants to estimate the mean serum HDL cholesterol of his 20–29-year-old female patients. He randomly selects 15 of his 20–29-year-old patients and obtains the data shown. Assume that $\sigma = 13.4$.

65	47	51	54	70
55	44	48	36	53
45	34	59	45	54

Source: Dr. Paul Oswiecmiski

(a) Use the data to compute a point estimate for the population mean serum HDL cholesterol in Dr. Oswiecmiski's patients. 50.67
(b) Because the sample size is small, we must verify that serum HDL cholesterol is normally distributed and that the sample does not contain any outliers. The normal probability plot and boxplot are shown below. Are the conditions for constructing a z-interval satisfied? Yes

Normal Probability Plot for Cholesterol

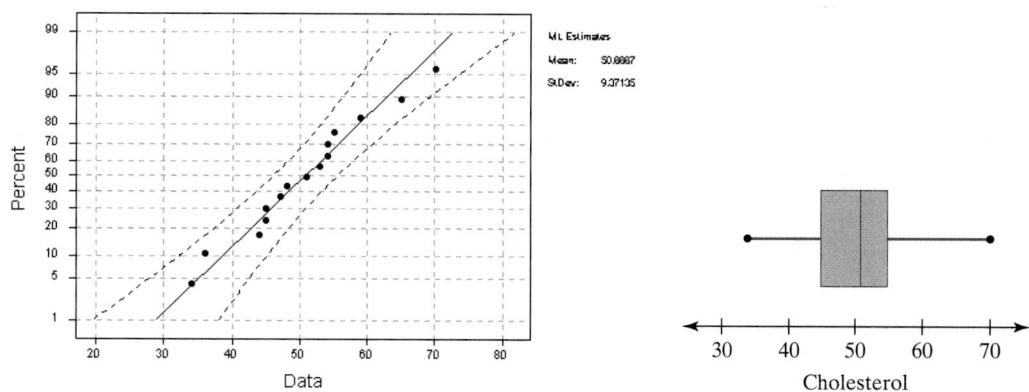

(c) Construct a 95% confidence interval for the mean serum HDL cholesterol for all of Dr. Oswiecmiski's 20–29-year-old female patients. Interpret this interval. (43.89, 57.45)
(d) Do Dr. Oswiecmiski's patients appear to have a serum HDL different from that of the general population? Why? No

18. **Serum Cholesterol** As reported by the U.S. National Center for Health Statistics, the mean serum high density lipoprotein (HDL) cholesterol of males 20–29 years old is $\mu = 47$. Dr. Paul Oswiecmiski wants to estimate the mean serum HDL cholesterol of his 20–29-year-old male patients. He randomly selects 15 of his 20–29-year-old male patients and obtains the data shown. Assume that $\sigma = 12.5$.

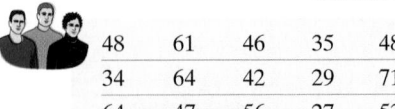

48	61	46	35	48
34	64	42	29	71
64	47	56	27	53

Source: Dr. Paul Oswiecmiski

(a) Use the data to compute a point estimate for the population mean serum HDL cholesterol in Dr. Oswiecmiski's patients. 48.33

(b) Because the sample size is small, we must verify that serum HDL cholesterol is normally distributed and that the sample does not contain any outliers. The normal probability plot and boxplot are shown below. Are the conditions for constructing a z-interval satisfied? Yes

Normal Probability Plot for Cholesterol

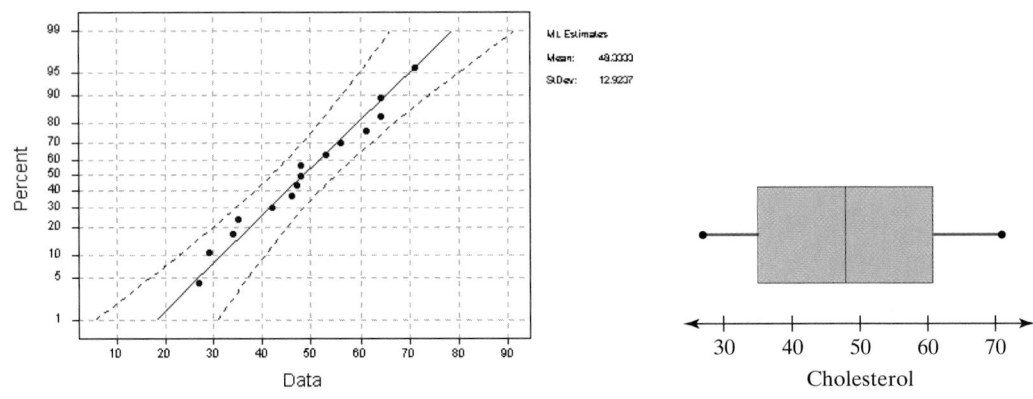

(c) Construct a 95% confidence interval for the mean serum HDL cholesterol for all of Dr. Oswiecmiski's 20–29-year-old male patients. Interpret this interval. (42.01, 54.66)

(d) Do Dr. Oswiecmiski's patients appear to have a serum HDL different from that of the general population? Why? No

19. **ACT Math Scores** In 2000, as reported by ACT Research Service, the mean ACT Math score was $\mu = 20.7$. Mrs. Teresa Gibson wants to estimate the mean ACT Math score of students in High School District 204. She obtains a simple random sample of 20 students who took the ACT in 2000, looks up their ACT Math scores, and obtains the results shown to the left. Assume that $\sigma = 5$.

24	23	16	26	25
22	18	25	26	17
28	27	23	21	23
20	25	21	19	30

(a) Use the data to compute a point estimate for the population mean ACT Math score in High School District 204. 22.95

(b) Because the sample size is small, we must verify that ACT scores are normally distributed and that the sample does not contain any outliers. The normal probability plot and boxplot are shown below. Are the conditions for constructing a z-interval satisfied? Yes

Normal Probability Plot for ACT Math

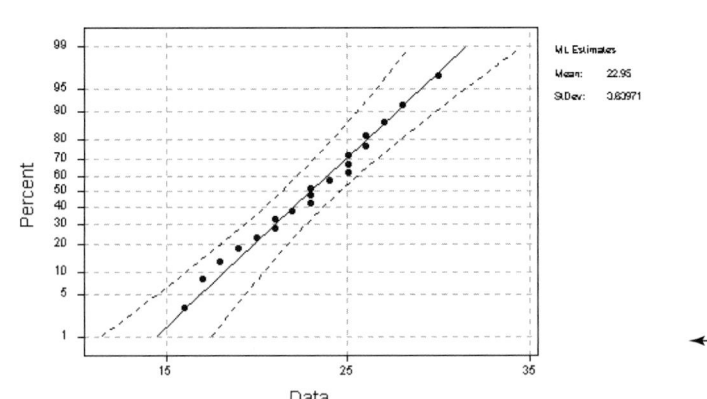

(c) Construct a 92% confidence interval for the mean ACT Math score for all students in District 204 who took the exam. Interpret this interval. (20.99, 24.91)

(d) Do Mrs. Gibson's students appear to have a mean ACT Math score different from that of the general population? Why? Yes

20. **ACT Science Scores** In 2000, as reported by ACT Research Service, the mean ACT Science score was $\mu = 21$. Mr. Matt Gibson is the chair of the science department in High School District 203. After speaking with his wife (Problem 19), he decides to estimate the mean ACT Science score of students in his district. He obtains a simple random sample of 20 students who took the ACT in 2000, looks up their ACT Science scores, and obtains the results shown to the left. Assume that $\sigma = 4.5$.

25	26	22	24	27
26	22	18	27	26
32	18	24	19	23
20	27	23	25	17

(a) Use the data to compute a point estimate for the population mean ACT science score in High School District 203. 23.55

(b) Because the sample size is small, we must verify that ACT scores are normally distributed and that the sample does not contain any outliers. The normal probability plot and boxplot are shown below. Are the conditions for constructing a z-interval satisfied? Yes

Normal Probability Plot for ACT Science

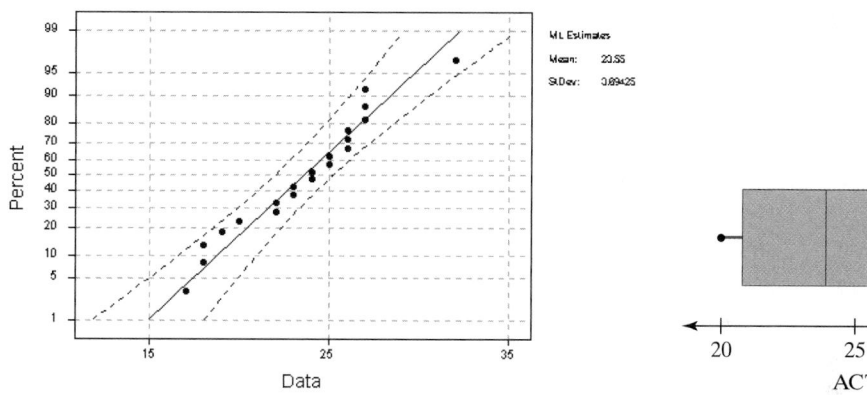

(c) Construct a 94% confidence interval for the mean ACT Science score for all students in District 203 who took the exam. Interpret this interval. (21.66, 25.44)

(d) Do Mr. Gibson's students appear to have a mean ACT Science score different from that of the general population? Why? Yes

21. **Gestation Period** The length of human pregnancies is approximately normally distributed with mean $\mu = 266$ days and standard deviation $\sigma = 16$ days. Dr. Margaret Oswiecmiski obtains a simple random sample of 10 of her patients and obtains the following results:

| 279 | 260 | 261 | 266 | 255 |
| 267 | 230 | 266 | 264 | 240 |

(a) Use the data to compute a point estimate for the population mean gestation period. 258.8

(b) Support the requirement that gestation period be normally distributed with no outliers by constructing a normal probability plot and boxplot.

(c) Construct a 90% confidence interval for the gestation period for all of Dr. Oswiecmiski's patients. Interpret this interval. (250.5, 267.1)

(d) Do Dr. Oswiecmiski's patients have a mean gestation period different from 266 days? Why? No

22. Weather in Chicago The high temperature in Chicago for the month of August is distributed approximately normally, with mean $\mu = 80°$ F and standard deviation $\sigma = 8°$ F. A random sample of 10 days in Chicago during August 2000 results in the following data:

| 77 | 81 | 72 | 86 | 76 |
| 81 | 73 | 92 | 75 | 87 |

(a) Use the data to compute a point estimate for the population mean high temperature in Chicago in August. *80.0°F*
(b) Support the requirement that high temperature be normally distributed with no outliers by constructing a normal probability plot and boxplot.
(c) Construct a 95% confidence interval for the high temperature in August in Chicago. Interpret this interval. *(75.04, 84.96)*
(d) Is there evidence that August, 2000 was normal? *Yes*

23. Volume of Philip Morris Stock The following data represent a random sample of the number of shares of Philip Morris stock traded for 35 days in 2000:

3.98	8.90	10.40	7.52	13.84
14.04	9.14	7.96	11.40	13.30
5.29	9.69	8.94	12.10	13.25
4.62	10.85	24.52	14.62	16.10
4.24	8.54	11.59	6.75	27.54
16.06	17.62	7.17	6.13	25.32
7.71	10.14	4.28	7.24	10.88

Source: http://finance.yahoo.com

The standard deviation of the number of shares traded in 2000 was $\sigma = 4.84$ million shares.

(a) Use the data to compute a point estimate for the population mean number of shares traded per day in 2000. *11.19 million shares*
(b) Construct a 90% confidence interval for the population mean number of shares traded per day in 2000. Interpret the confidence interval. *(9.84, 12.54)*
(c) A second random sample of 35 days in 2000 resulted in the following data:

15.22	7.58	5.16	5.76	11.78
10.14	5.24	21.71	8.08	9.14
6.55	5.80	9.19	18.21	6.66
9.31	6.58	10.49	10.54	7.95
6.11	5.29	7.40	3.05	2.93
5.45	13.07	7.15	10.31	6.81
5.57	11.59	7.89	10.91	7.28

Construct a 90% confidence interval for the population mean number of shares traded per day in 2000. Interpret the confidence interval. *(7.28, 9.97)*
(d) Explain why the confidence intervals obtained in parts (b) and (c) are different.

24. Volume of Harley Davidson Stock The following data represent a random sample of the number of shares of Harley Davidson stock traded for 40 days in 2000:

0.68	0.69	0.53	0.75	0.58
0.77	0.58	0.92	0.42	1.30
0.63	0.68	0.46	0.48	0.63
0.58	0.43	0.69	1.60	0.38
1.01	0.48	1.33	1.14	0.64
2.86	0.48	0.35	0.30	0.74
0.47	0.74	1.01	1.21	1.05
0.51	0.84	1.06	0.60	0.25

Source: http://finance.yahoo.com

The standard deviation of the number of shares traded in 2000 was $\sigma = 0.94$ million shares.

(a) Use the data to compute a point estimate for the population mean number of shares traded per day in 2000. *0.77 million shares*
(b) Construct a 95% confidence interval for the population mean number of shares traded per day in 2000. Interpret the confidence interval. *(0.48, 1.06)*
(c) A second random sample of 40 days in 2000 resulted in the following data:

1.30	0.36	0.91	0.43	0.67
0.47	0.69	0.80	0.35	0.67
0.82	0.82	0.84	0.61	0.49
0.49	1.30	0.56	0.50	0.85
0.57	0.56	0.66	0.77	0.42
0.56	1.62	2.86	0.79	2.95
0.70	0.87	1.36	0.37	0.63
0.95	0.64	0.76	0.84	0.72

Construct a 95% confidence interval for the population mean number of shares traded per day in 2000. Interpret the confidence interval. *(0.55, 1.13)*
(d) Explain why the confidence intervals obtained in parts (b) and (c) are different.

25. Miles on a Saturn A researcher is interested in approximating the mean number of miles on four-year-old Saturn SC1s. She finds a random sample of 33 such Saturn SC1s in the Chicagoland area and obtains the following results:

45,336	90,574	42,800	84,000	57,506
47,977	10,778	39,176	41,431	86,838
30,114	90,100	26,560	75,312	44,411
29,000	30,447	25,000	49,874	76,576
57,145	38,796	32,004	43,128	51,159
54,000	52,181	51,305	33,867	46,178
51,000	39,174	59,018		

Source: cars.com

(a) Obtain a point estimate of the population mean number of miles on a four-year-old Saturn SC1. 49,477.7
(b) Construct and interpret a 99% confidence interval for the population mean number of miles on a four-year-old Saturn SC1. Assume that $\sigma = 19,700$.
(c) Construct and interpret a 95% confidence interval for the population mean number of miles on a four-year-old Saturn SC1. Assume that $\sigma = 19,700$.
(d) What effect does decreasing the level of confidence have on the interval? *Decreases*
(e) Do the confidence intervals computed in parts (b) and (c) represent an interval estimate for the population mean number of miles on Saturn SC1s in the United States? Why? *No*

26. Miles on a Cavalier A researcher is interested in approximating the mean number of miles on three-year-old Chevy Cavaliers. She finds a random sample of 35 Cavaliers in the Orlando, Florida area and obtains the following results:

37,815	20,000	57,103	46,585	24,822
49,678	30,983	52,969	8,000	39,862
6,000	65,192	34,285	30,906	41,841
39,851	43,000	74,361	52,664	33,587
52,896	45,280	30,000	41,713	76,315
22,442	45,301	52,899	41,526	28,381
55,163	51,812	36,500	31,947	16,529

Source: cars.com

(a) Obtain a point estimate of the population mean number of miles on a three-year-old Cavalier.
(b) Construct and interpret a 99% confidence interval for the population mean number of miles on a three-year-old Cavalier. Assume that $\sigma = 16,100$.
(c) Construct and interpret a 95% confidence interval for the population mean number of miles on a three-year-old Cavalier. Assume that $\sigma = 16,100$.
(d) What effect does decreasing the level of confidence have on the width of the interval? *Decreases*

(25b) (40,644, 58,311) (25c) (42,756, 56,199)
(26a) 40,520.2 miles (26b) (33,510, 47,530) (26c) (35,186, 45,854)

(e) Do the confidence intervals computed in parts (b) and (c) represent an interval estimate for the population mean number of miles on Cavaliers in the United States? Why? *No*

27. Sample Size Dr. Paul Oswiecmiski wants to estimate the mean serum HDL cholesterol of all 20–29-year-old females. How many subjects would be needed in order to estimate the mean serum HDL cholesterol of all 20–29-year-old females within two points with 99% confidence, assuming that $\sigma = 13.4$? Suppose Dr. Oswiecmiski would be content with 95% confidence. How does the decrease in confidence affect the sample size required? *298; 173; decreases*

28. Sample Size Dr. Paul Oswiecmiski wants to estimate the mean serum HDL cholesterol of all 20–29-year-old males. How many subjects would be needed in order to estimate the mean serum HDL cholesterol of all 20–29-year-old males within 1.5 points with 90% confidence, assuming that $\sigma = 12.5$? Suppose Dr. Oswiecmiski would prefer 98% confidence. How does the increase in confidence affect the sample size required? *188; 378; increases*

29. How Often Do You Bathe? A Gallup poll conducted December 20–21, 1999 asked Americans how many times they bathe during the week. How many subjects would be needed in order to estimate the number of times Americans bathed during the week in 1999 within 0.5 with 95% confidence? Initial survey results indicate that $\sigma = 2.9$. *130*

30. How Much TV Do You Watch? A Gallup poll conducted December 20–21, 1999 asked Americans how many hours of TV they watch during the week. How many subjects would be needed in order to estimate the number of hours of TV Americans watched in 1999 during the week within 0.5 hours with 95% confidence? Initial survey results indicate that $\sigma = 1.8$. *50*

31. Miles on a Saturn A researcher wishes to estimate the mean number of miles on four-year-old Saturn SC1s.

(a) How many cars should be in a sample in order to estimate the mean number of miles within 1000 miles with 90% confidence, assuming that $\sigma = 19,700$? *1051*
(b) How many cars should be in a sample in order to estimate the mean number of miles within 500 miles with 90% confidence, assuming that $\sigma = 19,700$? *4201*
(c) What effect does increasing the required accuracy have on the sample size? Why is this the expected result? *Quadruples*

32. Miles on a Cavalier A researcher wishes to estimate the mean number of miles on three-year-old Chevy Cavaliers.

(a) How many cars should be in a sample in order to estimate the mean number of miles within 2000 miles with 98% confidence, assuming that $\sigma = 16,100$? *352*

(b) How many cars should be in a sample in order to estimate the mean number of miles within 1000 miles with 98% confidence, assuming that $\sigma = 16{,}100$? 1408

(c) What effect does increasing the required accuracy have on the sample size? Why is this the expected result? Quadruples

33. **Simulation** IQ scores as measured by the Stanford–Binet IQ test are normally distributed with $\mu = 100$ and $\sigma = 16$.

(a) Simulate obtaining 20 samples of size $n = 15$ from this population.

(b) Construct 95% confidence intervals for each of the 20 samples.

(c) How many of the intervals do you expect to include the population mean? How many actually contain the population mean?

34. **Simulation** Suppose the arrival of cars at Burger King's drive-through follows a Poisson process with $\mu = 4$ cars every 10 minutes.

(a) Simulate obtaining 30 samples of size $n = 40$ from this population.

(b) Construct 90% confidence intervals for each of the 30 samples. [*Hint:* $\sigma = \sqrt{\mu}$ in a Poisson process.]

(c) How many of the intervals do you expect to include the population mean? How many actually contain the population mean?

35. **The Effect of Nonnormal Data** The exponential probability distribution is a probability distribution that can be used to model time waiting in line or the lifetime of electronic components. Its density function with $\mu = 5$ is shown in the accompanying figure. Clearly, the distribution is skewed right.

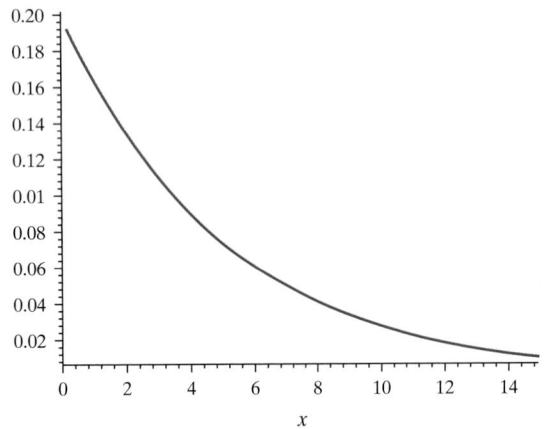

(a) Use Minitab or some other statistical software to generate 100 random samples of size $n = 6$ from a population that follows the exponential probability distribution with $\mu = 5$. (It turns out that σ also equals 5.)

(b) Use the 100 samples to determine 100 95% confidence intervals with $\sigma = 5$.

(c) How many of the intervals would we expect to contain $\mu = 5$? How many of the 100 intervals contain $\mu = 5$?

(d) What are the consequences of not having normal data when the sample size is small?

36. **The Effect of Outliers** Suppose the following small data set represents a simple random sample from a population whose mean is 50 and standard deviation is 10:

43	63	53	50	58	44
53	53	52	41	50	43

(a) A normal probability plot indicates the data are normally distributed with no outliers. Compute a 95% confidence interval for this data set, assuming $\sigma = 10$. (44.59, 55.91)

(b) Suppose the observation, 41, were inadvertently entered into the computer as 14. Verify that this observation is an outlier.

(c) Construct a 95% confidence interval on the data set with the outlier. What effect does the outlier have on the confidence interval? (42.34, 53.66)

(d) Consider the following data set, which represents a simple random sample of size 36 from a population whose mean is 50 and standard deviation is 10:

43	63	53	50	58	44
53	53	52	41	50	43
47	65	38	58	41	52
49	46	57	50	38	42
59	54	37	41	33	37
46	54	42	48	53	41

Verify that the sample mean for the large data set is the same as the sample mean for the small data set.

(e) Compute a 95% confidence interval for the large data set, assuming $\sigma = 10$. Compare the results to part (a). What effect does increasing the sample size have on the confidence interval?

(f) Suppose the last observation, 41, were inadvertently entered as 14. Verify that this observation is an outlier.

(g) Compute a 95% confidence interval for the large data set with the outlier, assuming $\sigma = 10$. Compare the results to part (g). What effect does an outlier have on a confidence interval when the data set is large? (44.07, 50.60)

37. By how many times does the sample size have to be increased to decrease the margin of error by a factor of $\frac{1}{2}$?

38. Suppose a certain population, A, has standard deviation $\sigma_A = 5$ and a second population, B, has standard deviation $\sigma_B = 10$. How many times larger than population A's does population B's sample size need to be, assuming the margin of error and level of confidence are the same? [*Hint:* Compute n_A / n_B.] 4 times

(36e) (44.82, 51.35); decreases width of interval

37. 4 times

Technology Step-by-Step
Confidence Intervals about μ, σ Known

TI-83 Plus   ***Step 1:*** If necessary, enter raw data in L1.

Step 2: Press STAT, highlight TESTS, and select `7: ZInterval`.

Step 3: If the data are raw, highlight DATA—make sure `List1` is set to L1 and `Freq` to 1. If summary statistics are known, highlight STATS and enter the summary statistics. Following σ:, enter the population standard deviation.

Step 4: Enter the confidence level following `C-Level:`.

Step 5: Highlight `Calculate`; press ENTER.

MINITAB   ***Step 1:*** Enter raw data in column C1.

Step 2: Select the <u>**Stat**</u> menu, highlight **Basic Statistics**, then highlight **1-Sample Z** ....

Step 3: Enter C1 in the cell marked "Variables". Select Confidence Interval, and enter a confidence level. In the cell marked "Sigma", enter the value of σ. Click OK.

Excel   ***Step 1:*** If necessary, enter raw data in column A.

Step 2: Load the PHStat Add-in.

Step 3: Select the **PHStat menu**, highlight **Confidence Intervals** ..., then highlight **Estimate for the mean, sigma known** ....

Step 4: Enter the value of σ and the confidence level. If the summary statistics are known, click "Sample statistics known" and enter the sample size and sample mean. If summary statistics are unknown, click "Sample statistics unknown". With the cursor in the "Sample cell range" cell, highlight the data in column A. Click OK.

8.2   Confidence Intervals about a Population Mean, σ Unknown

Preparing for This Section   Before getting started, review the following:

✓ Simple random sampling (Section 1.2, pp. 15–17)

✓ Parameter versus statistic (Section 3.1, p. 112)

✓ Degrees of freedom (Section 3.2, p. 136)

✓ Central Limit Theorem (Section 7.5, p. 432)

✓ Normal probability plots (Section 7.4, pp. 415–420)

Objectives   Know the properties of Student's t-distribution

 Determine t-values

 Construct confidence intervals about μ, σ unknown

Determine the method to use to compute an interval about μ

In Section 8.1, we made the assumption that the population standard deviation, σ, was known, while the population mean, μ, was unknown. In this section, we drop that assumption and compute confidence intervals about μ with the population standard deviation, σ, unknown.

Historical Note

William Sealy Gossett was born on June 13, 1876, in Canterbury, England. Gossett earned a degree in chemistry from New College in Oxford in 1899. He then got a job as a chemist for the Guinness Brewing Company. Gossett, along with other chemists, was asked to find a way to make the best beer at the cheapest cost. This allowed him to concentrate on statistics. In 1904, Gossett wrote a paper on the brewing of beer that included a discussion of standard errors. In July, 1905, Gossett met with Karl Pearson to learn about the theory of standard errors. Over the next few years, he developed his t-distribution. The Guinness Brewery did not allow its employees to publish, so Gossett published his research using the pen name Student. Gossett died October 16, 1937.

① Student's *t*-Distribution

In Section 8.1, we computed confidence intervals about a population mean, μ, on the assumption that the following conditions were met:

1. σ was known.
2. The population from which the sample was drawn followed a normal distribution or the sample size n was large ($n \geq 30$).
3. The sample was a simple random sample.

A $(1 - \alpha) \cdot 100\%$ confidence interval was then computed as

$$\bar{x} - z_{\alpha/2} \cdot \frac{\sigma}{\sqrt{n}} \quad \text{and} \quad \bar{x} + z_{\alpha/2} \cdot \frac{\sigma}{\sqrt{n}}$$

If σ is unknown, it seems reasonable to replace σ with s and proceed with the analysis. However, while it is true that $z = \dfrac{\bar{x} - \mu}{\sigma/\sqrt{n}}$ is normally distributed with mean 0 and standard deviation 1, we cannot replace σ with s and say that $z = \dfrac{\bar{x} - \mu}{s/\sqrt{n}}$ is normally distributed with mean 0 and standard deviation 1, because s, itself, is a random variable. Instead, $\dfrac{\bar{x} - \mu}{s/\sqrt{n}}$ follows **Student's *t*-distribution**, developed by William Gossett. Gossett was in charge of conducting experiments at the Guinness brewery in order to identify the best barley variety. At the time, the only available distribution was the standard normal distribution, but Gossett always performed experiments with small data sets and he did not know σ. This led Gossett to determine the sampling distribution of $\dfrac{\bar{x} - \mu}{s/\sqrt{n}}$. Gossett published his findings under the pen name *Student*.

Theorem

Student's *t*-Distribution

Suppose a simple random sample of size n is taken from a population. If the population from which the sample is drawn follows a normal distribution, then the distribution of

$$t = \frac{\bar{x} - \mu}{s/\sqrt{n}}$$

follows Student's *t*-distribution with $n - 1$ degrees of freedom,* where $\bar{x}$ is the sample mean and s is the sample standard deviation.

Note to Instructor
Consider the following to help students understand degrees of freedom: Suppose you have five pens of different colors and five students want to borrow a pen. The first four students have some freedom as to which pen to select; however, the last person has no freedom, but must choose the last available pen.

The interpretation of the *t*-statistic is the same as that of the *z*-score. The *t*-statistic represents the number of sample standard errors $\bar{x}$ is from the population mean, μ. It turns out that the shape of the *t*-distribution depends upon the sample size, n.

To help see how the *t*-distribution differs from the standard normal (or *z*-) distribution and the role the sample size n plays, we will go through the following exploration.

*The reader may wish to review the discussion of degrees of freedom in Section 3.2 on pp. 135–136.

EXPLORATION

(a) Obtain 1000 simple random samples of size $n = 5$ from a normal population with $\mu = 50$ and $\sigma = 10$.

(b) Calculate the sample mean and sample standard deviation for each of the samples.

(c) Compute $z = \dfrac{\overline{x} - \mu}{\sigma/\sqrt{n}}$ and $t = \dfrac{\overline{x} - \mu}{s/\sqrt{n}}$ for each sample.

(d) Draw histograms for both z and t.

Results   We use Minitab to obtain the 1000 simple random samples and compute the 1000 sample means and sample standard deviations. We then compute $z = \dfrac{\overline{x} - \mu}{\sigma/\sqrt{n}} = \dfrac{\overline{x} - 50}{10/\sqrt{5}}$ and $t = \dfrac{\overline{x} - \mu}{s/\sqrt{n}} = \dfrac{\overline{x} - 50}{s/\sqrt{5}}$ for each of the 1000 samples. Figure 6(a) shows the histogram for z, and Figure 6(b) shows the histogram for t.

Figure 6

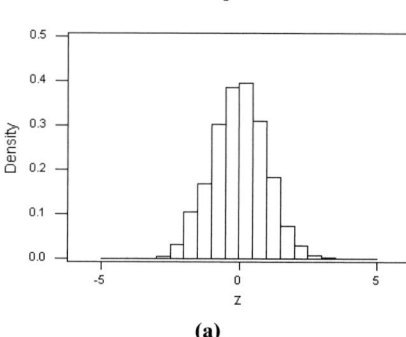

(a)   (b)

   We notice that the histogram in Figure 6(a) is symmetric and bell shaped, with the center of the distribution at 0 and virtually all the rectangles between -3 and 3. In other words, z follows a standard normal distribution. The distribution of t is also symmetric and bell shaped and has its center at 0, but the distribution of t has longer tails (i.e., t is more dispersed), so it is unlikely that t follows a standard normal distribution. The additional spread in the distribution of t can be attributed to the fact that we divide by $\dfrac{s}{\sqrt{n}}$ to find t instead of by $\dfrac{\sigma}{\sqrt{n}}$. Because the sample standard deviation is itself a random variable (rather than a constant such as σ), we have more dispersion in the distribution of t.   ◄◄

   We now introduce the properties of the t-distribution.

Properties of the t-Distribution

1. The t-distribution is different for different values of n, the sample size.

2. The t-distribution is centered at 0 and is symmetric about 0.

3. The area under the curve is 1. The area under the curve to the right of 0 equals the area under the curve to the left of 0 equals 1/2.

Figure 7

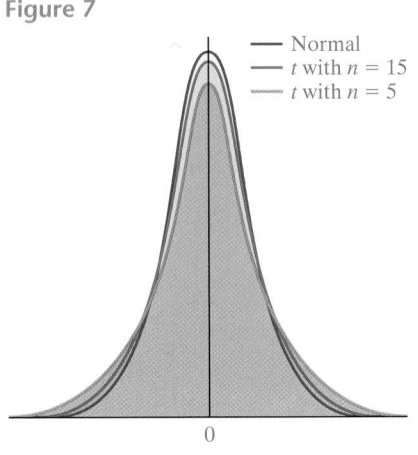

4. As t increases without bound, the graph approaches, but never equals, zero. As t decreases without bound, the graph approaches, but never equals, zero.

5. The area in the tails of the t-distribution is a little greater than the area in the tails of the standard normal distribution, because we are using s as an estimate of σ, thereby introducing further variability into the t-statistic.

6. As the sample size n increases, the density curve of t gets closer to the standard normal density curve. This result occurs because, as the sample size n increases, the values of s get closer to the values of σ, by the Law of Large Numbers.

In Figure 7, we show the t-distribution for the sample sizes $n = 5$ and $n = 15$. As a point of reference, we have also drawn the standard normal density curve.

Recall that the notation z_α is used to represent the z-score whose area under the normal curve to the right of z_α is α. Similarly, we let t_α represent the t-value such that the area under the t-distribution to the right of t_α is α. See Figure 8.

The shape of the t-distribution depends upon the sample size, n. Therefore, the value of t_α depends not only on α, but also on the degrees of freedom, $n - 1$. In Table III in Appendix A, the far left column gives the degrees of freedom. The top row represents the area under the t-distribution to the right of some t-value.

Figure 8

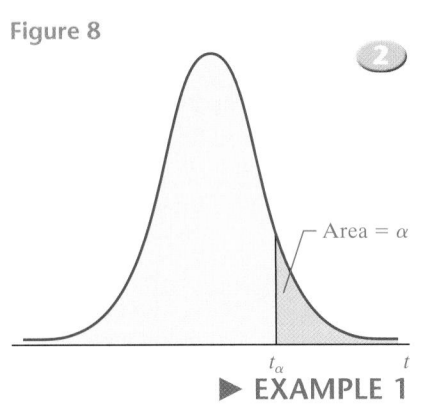

▶ **EXAMPLE 1** Finding t-Values

Problem: Find the t-value such that the area under the t-distribution to the right of the t-value is 0.10, assuming 15 degrees of freedom. That is, find $t_{0.10}$ with 15 degrees of freedom.

Approach: We will perform the following steps.

Step 1: Draw a t-distribution with the unknown t-value labeled. Shade the area under the curve to the right of the t-value, as in Figure 8.

Step 2: Find the row in Table III that corresponds to 15 degrees of freedom and the column that corresponds to an area in the right tail of 0.10. Identify where the row and column intersect. This is the unknown t-value.

Figure 9

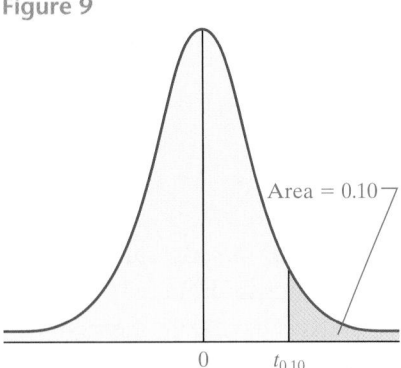

Solution:

Step 1: Figure 9 shows the graph of the t-distribution with 15 degrees of freedom. The unknown value of t is labeled, and the area under the curve to the right of t is shaded.

Step 2: A portion of Table III is reproduced in Figure 10. We have enclosed the row that represents 15 degrees of freedom and the column that represents the area 0.10 in the right tail. The point where the row and column intersect is the t-value we are seeking. The value of $t_{0.10}$ with 15 degrees of freedom is 1.341—that is, the area under the t-distribution to the right of $t = 1.341$ with 15 degrees of freedom is 0.10.

Figure 10

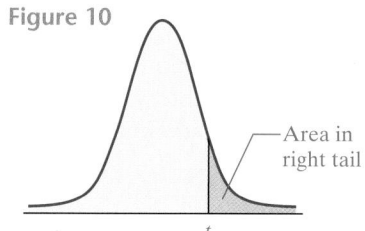

Area in right tail

						Area in Right Tail						
df	0.25	0.20	0.15	0.10	0.05	0.025	0.02	0.01	0.005	0.0025	0.001	0.0005
1	1.000	1.376	1.963	3.078	6.314	12.710	15.890	31.820	63.660	127.300	318.300	636.600
2	0.816	1.061	1.386	1.886	2.920	4.303	4.849	6.965	9.925	14.090	22.330	31.600
3	0.765	0.978	1.250	1.638	2.353	3.182	3.482	4.541	5.841	7.453	10.210	12.920
4	0.741	0.941	1.190	1.533	2.132	2.776	2.999	3.747	4.604	5.598	7.173	8.610
5	0.727	0.920	1.156	1.476	2.015	2.571	2.757	3.365	4.032	4.773	5.893	6.869
6	0.718	0.906	1.134	1.440	1.943	2.447	2.612	3.143	3.707	4.317	5.208	5.959
7	0.711	0.896	1.119	1.415	1.895	2.365	2.517	2.998	3.499	4.029	4.785	5.408
8	0.706	0.889	1.108	1.397	1.860	2.306	2.449	2.896	3.355	3.833	4.501	5.041
9	0.703	0.883	1.100	1.383	1.833	2.262	2.398	2.821	3.250	3.690	4.297	4.781
10	0.700	0.879	1.093	1.372	1.812	2.228	2.359	2.764	3.169	3.581	4.144	4.587
11	0.697	0.876	1.088	1.363	1.796	2.201	2.328	2.718	3.106	3.497	4.025	4.437
12	0.695	0.873	1.083	1.356	1.782	2.179	2.303	2.681	3.055	3.428	3.930	4.318
13	0.694	0.870	1.079	1.350	1.771	2.160	2.282	2.650	3.012	3.372	3.852	4.221
14	0.692	0.868	1.076	1.345	1.761	2.145	2.264	2.624	2.977	3.326	3.787	4.140
15	0.691	0.866	1.074	1.341	1.753	2.131	2.249	2.602	2.947	3.286	3.733	4.073
16	0.690	0.865	1.071	1.337	1.746	2.120	2.235	2.583	2.921	3.252	3.686	4.015
17	0.689	0.863	1.069	1.333	1.740	2.110	2.224	2.567	2.898	3.222	3.646	3.965
18	0.688	0.862	1.067	1.330	1.734	2.101	2.214	2.552	2.878	3.197	3.611	3.922

◄◄

Using Technology: The area under the t-distribution can also be computed by graphing calculators with advanced statistical features or by statistical software. Figure 11 shows the results from Minitab. Notice that Minitab asks for the area to the left of the unknown t-value because it uses the cumulative distribution. The area under the curve to the right of the unknown t-value is 0.10, so the area under the curve to the left must be 0.90.

Figure 11

Inverse Cumulative Distribution Function

Student's t distribution with 15 DF

```
P( X<= x)                    x
  0.9000                 1.3406
```

NW *Now Work Problem 1(a).*

If the degrees of freedom we desire are not available in Table III, we shall follow the practice of choosing the closest number of degrees of freedom available in the table. For example, if we have 43 degrees of freedom, we shall use 40 degrees of freedom from Table III. In addition, the last row of Table III provides the Z-values from the standard normal distribution. We shall use these values for situations where the degrees of freedom are substantially more than 1000. This is acceptable because the t-distribution starts to behave like the standard normal distribution as n increases.

③ Confidence Intervals

The construction of confidence intervals about μ with σ unknown follows the exact same logic as the construction of confidence intervals with σ known. The only difference is that we use s in place of σ and t in place of z.

> **Constructing a $(1 - \alpha) \cdot 100\%$ Confidence Interval about μ, σ Unknown**
>
> Suppose a simple random sample of size n is taken from a population with unknown mean μ and unknown standard deviation σ. A $(1 - \alpha) \cdot 100\%$ confidence interval for μ is given by
>
> $$\text{Lower bound: } \overline{x} - t_{\alpha/2} \cdot \frac{s}{\sqrt{n}} \quad \text{and} \quad \text{Upper bound: } \overline{x} + t_{\alpha/2} \cdot \frac{s}{\sqrt{n}} \quad \textbf{(1)}$$
>
> where $t_{\alpha/2}$ is computed with $n - 1$ degrees of freedom.
>
> **Note:** The interval is exact when the population is normally distributed; it is approximately correct for nonnormal populations, provided that n is large.

Notice that a confidence interval about μ with σ unknown can be computed for nonnormal populations even though Student's t-distribution required the population from which the sample was obtained to be normal. This is because the procedure for constructing the confidence interval is robust—that is, the procedure is accurate even despite moderate departures from the normality assumption. Notice that we said the procedure is accurate for *moderate* departures from normality. If a small data set has outliers, the results are compromised, because neither the sample mean, $\overline{x}$, nor the sample standard deviation, s, is resistant to outliers. Sample data should always be inspected for serious departures from normality and for outliers. This is easily done with normal probability plots and boxplots.

Because the interval uses the t-distribution, it is often referred to as the **t-interval**.

▶ **EXAMPLE 2** **Constructing a Confidence Interval about μ, σ Unknown**

Problem: Recall that, in Example 3 from Section 8.1, we computed a 90% confidence interval for the mean price of a three-year-old Chevy Corvette. We made the assumption that we knew σ to be $4100. Recompute the 90% confidence interval about the population mean with σ unknown. The data are displayed in Table 5.

TABLE 5		
$47,000	$43,108	$33,995
$32,750	$33,988	$43,500
$33,995	$32,750	$39,950
$36,900	$35,995	$39,998
$37,995	$37,995	$43,785

Approach:

Step 1: We draw a normal probability plot and boxplot to verify that there are no serious departures from normality and no outliers.

Step 2: Compute $\overline{x}$ and s.

Step 3: Look up the critical value $t_{\alpha/2}$ with $n - 1$ degrees of freedom.

Step 4: Compute the bounds on a $(1 - \alpha) \cdot 100\%$ confidence interval for μ, using the following:

$$\text{Lower bound: } \overline{x} - t_{\alpha/2} \cdot \frac{s}{\sqrt{n}} \qquad \text{Upper bound: } \overline{x} + t_{\alpha/2} \cdot \frac{s}{\sqrt{n}}$$

Step 5: We interpret the result by stating: "We are 90% confident that the mean price of all three-year-old Chevy Corvettes is somewhere between *lower bound* and *upper bound*."

Solution:

Step 1: We have already drawn the normal probability plot and boxplot in Example 3 from Section 8.1. The normal probability plot did not show any serious departures from normality and the boxplot did not indicate any outliers. We can proceed with the construction of the confidence interval.

Step 2: We compute $\bar{x}$ and s, using a calculator, and discover that $\bar{x} = \$38,247$ and $s = \$4522$.

Step 3: Because we wish to determine a 90% confidence interval, we have $\alpha = 0.10$. Therefore, we need to find $t_{0.10/2} = t_{0.05}$ with $15 - 1 = 14$ degrees of freedom. Referring to Table III, we find $t_{0.05} = 1.761$.

Step 4: Using Formula (1), we find the lower and upper bounds:

$$\text{Lower Bound: } \bar{x} - t_{\alpha/2} \cdot \frac{s}{\sqrt{n}} = 38,247 - 1.761 \cdot \frac{4522}{\sqrt{15}} = 38,247 - 2056 = 36,191$$

$$\text{Upper Bound: } \bar{x} + t_{\alpha/2} \cdot \frac{s}{\sqrt{n}} = 38,247 + 1.761 \cdot \frac{4522}{\sqrt{15}} = 38,247 + 2056 = 40,303$$

Step 5: We are 90% confident that the mean price of all three-year-old Chevy Corvettes is somewhere between \$36,191 and \$40,303.   ◄◄

Using Technology: Statistical software or graphing calculators with advanced statistical features can be used to construct confidence intervals with σ unknown. Figure 12 shows the results on a TI-83 Plus graphing calculator.

Figure 12

Lower Bound · Upper Bound

If we compare the confidence interval with σ unknown to the confidence interval with σ known (Example 3, Section 8.1), we notice the interval with σ unknown is wider. Why do you think this is the case?

NW *Now Work Problem 3.*

▶ **EXAMPLE 3**   **The Effect of Outliers**

Problem: The management of Disney World wanted to estimate the mean waiting time at the Dumbo ride. They randomly selected 15 riders and measured the amount of time the riders spent waiting in line. The results are in

Note to Instructor
Remind students that the mean and
standard deviation are not resistant.
This is why confidence intervals should
not be constructed from sample data
that have one or more outliers.

TABLE 6

30	29	34	41	37
16	18	30	24	25
29	16	80	19	30

Table 6. Figure 13 shows a normal probability plot and boxplot for the data in the table. Figure 13(a) demonstrates that the sample data could have come from a population that is normally distributed except for the single outlier. Figure 13(b) shows the outlier as well. Determine a 95% confidence interval for the mean waiting time at the Dumbo ride both with and without the outlier in the data set. Comment on the effect the outlier has on the confidence interval.

Figure 13 Normal Probability Plot for Wait Time

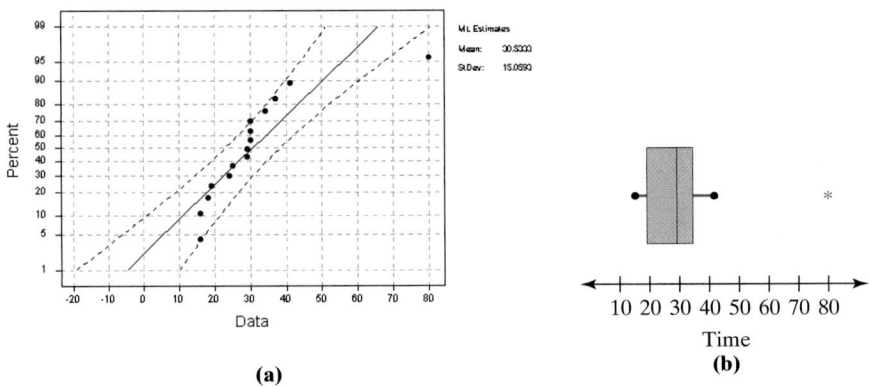

(a)

(b)

Approach: We will use Minitab to construct the confidence intervals.

Solution: Figure 14(a) shows confidence interval with the outlier included. Figure 14(b) shows the confidence interval with the outlier removed.

Figure 14

One-Sample T: Time(with outlier)

Variable	N	Mean	StDev	SE Mean	95.0% CI
Time	15	30.53	15.59	4.02	(21.90, 39.17)

(a)

One-Sample T: Time(without outlier)

Variable	N	Mean	StDev	SE Mean	95.0% CI
Time	14	27.00	7.75	2.07	(22.53, 31.47)

(b)

The 95% confidence interval with the outlier has a lower bound of 21.90 and an upper bound of 39.17. The 95% confidence interval with the outlier removed has a lower bound of 22.53 and an upper bound of 31.47. We notice a few things:

- With the outlier removed, the sample mean decreased, because the sample mean is not resistant.
- With the outlier removed, the sample standard deviation decreased, because the sample standard deviation is not resistant.
- With the outlier removed, the width of the interval decreased from $39.17 - 21.90 = 17.27$ to $31.47 - 22.53 = 8.94$. The confidence interval is nearly twice as wide when the outlier is included. ◀◀

What should we do if the assumptions required to compute a t-interval are not met? One option would be to increase the sample size beyond 30 observations. The other option is to use *nonparametric procedures*. **Nonparametric procedures** (Chapter 13) typically do not require an assumption of normality and the methods are resistant to outliers.

NW *Now Work Problem 25.*

④ **Choosing the Right Method**

It can seem difficult to choose the appropriate method for constructing confidence intervals. To help with the decision making, we provide the flowchart in Figure 15.

Figure 15

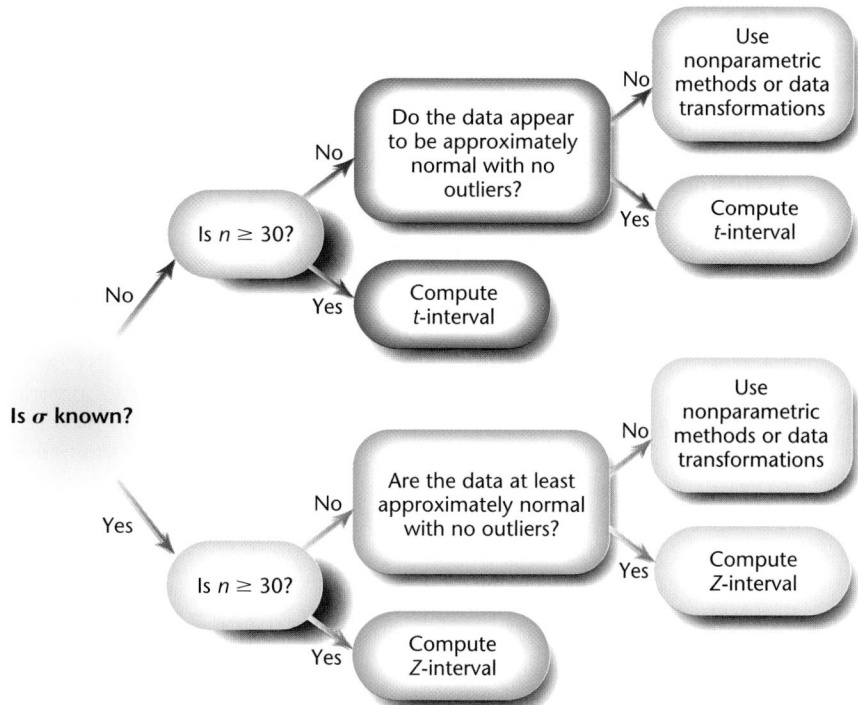

From the flowchart, the first step in choosing which method to use is to discover whether the population standard deviation, σ, is known. If it is known and the population is distributed at least approximately normally with no outliers, or if the sample size is large, compute the z-interval. If σ is unknown and the population is distributed at least approximately normally with no outliers, or if the sample size is large, compute the t-interval.

NW *Now Work Problem 21.*

8.2 Assess Your Understanding

Concepts and Vocabulary

1. Explain the circumstances under which a z-interval should be constructed. Under what circumstances should a t-interval be constructed? When can neither a z- nor a t-interval be constructed?
2. Explain why the t-distribution has less spread as the number of degrees of freedom increases.
3. The procedures for constructing a t-interval are robust. Explain what this means.
4. Consider Figures 6(a) and (b). Why are the t-values more dispersed than the z-values?
5. Discuss the similarities and differences between the standard normal distribution and the t-distribution.

Exercises

• **Basic Skills**

(c) −2.552

1. (a) Find the t-value such that the area in the right tail is 0.10 with 25 degrees of freedom. 1.316

   (b) Find the t-value such that the area in the right tail is 0.05 with 30 degrees of freedom. 1.697

   (c) Find the t-value such that the area left of the t-value is 0.01 with 18 degrees of freedom. [*Hint:* Use symmetry.]

   (d) Find the critical t-value that corresponds to 90% confidence. Assume 20 degrees of freedom. 1.725

2. (a) Find the t-value such that the area in the right tail is 0.02 with 19 degrees of freedom. 2.205

   (b) Find the t-value such that the area in the right tail is 0.10 with 32 degrees of freedom. 1.309

   (c) Find the t-value such that the area left of the t-value is 0.05 with 6 degrees of freedom. [*Hint:* Use symmetry.]

   (d) Find the critical t-value that corresponds to 95% confidence. Assume 16 degrees of freedom. 2.120

3. A simple random sample of size n is drawn from a population that is normally distributed. The sample mean, $\bar{x}$, is found to be 108, and the sample standard deviation, s, is found to be 10.

   (a) Construct the 96% confidence interval if the sample size, n, is 25. (103.7, 112.3)

   (b) Construct the 96% confidence interval if the sample size, n, is 10. How does decreasing the sample size affect the margin of error, E? (100.4, 115.6); increases

   (c) Construct the 90% confidence interval if the sample size, n, is 25. Compare the results to those obtained in part (a). How does decreasing the level of confidence affect the size of the margin of error, E?

   (d) Could we have computed the confidence intervals in parts (a)–(c) if the population had not been normally distributed? Why? No

4. A simple random sample of size n is drawn from a population that is normally distributed. The sample mean, $\bar{x}$, is found to be 50, and the sample standard deviation, s, is found to be 8.

   (a) Construct the 98% confidence interval if the sample size, n, is 20. (45.5, 54.5)

(2c) −1.943 (3c) (104.6, 111.4); decreases

(c) (46.3, 53.7); decreases

   (b) Construct the 98% confidence interval if the sample size, n, is 15. How does decreasing the sample size affect the margin of error, E? (44.6, 55.4); increases

   (c) Construct the 95% confidence interval if the sample size, n, is 20. Compare the results to those obtained in part (a). How does decreasing the level of confidence affect the size of the margin of error, E?

   (d) Could we have computed the confidence intervals in parts (a)–(c) if the population had not been normally distributed? Why? No

5. A simple random sample of size n is drawn. The sample mean, $\bar{x}$, is found to be 18.4, and the sample standard deviation, s, is found to be 4.5.

   (a) Construct the 95% confidence interval if the sample size, n, is 35. (16.85, 19.95)

   (b) Construct the 95% confidence interval if the sample size, n, is 50. How does increasing the sample size affect the margin of error, E? (17.12, 19.70); decreases

   (c) Construct the 99% confidence interval if the sample size, n, is 35. Compare the results to those obtained in part (a). How does increasing the level of confidence affect the size of the margin of error, E?

   (d) If the sample size is $n = 15$, what conditions must be satisfied in order to compute the confidence interval? Population must be normal.

6. A simple random sample of size n is drawn. The sample mean, $\bar{x}$, is found to be 35.1, and the sample standard deviation, s, is found to be 8.7.

   (a) Construct the 90% confidence interval if the sample size, n, is 40. (32.78, 37.42)

   (b) Construct the 90% confidence interval if the sample size, n, is 100. How does increasing the sample size affect the margin of error, E? (33.66, 36.55); decreases

   (c) Construct the 98% confidence interval if the sample size, n, is 40. Compare the results to those obtained in part (a). How does increasing the level of confidence affect the size of the margin of error, E?

   (d) If the sample size is $n = 18$, what conditions must be satisfied in order to compute the confidence interval? Population must be normal.

(5c) (16.33, 20.48); increases (6c) (31.76, 38.44); increases

• **Applying the Concepts**

(6.68, 7.13)

7. **How Often Do You Bathe?** A Gallup poll conducted December 20–21, 1999, asked 1031 randomly selected Americans, "How often do you bathe each week?" Results of the survey indicated that $\bar{x} = 6.9$ and $s = 2.8$. Construct a 99% confidence interval for the number of times Americans bathed each week in 1999. Interpret the interval.

8. **How Often Do You Bathe?** A Gallup poll conducted June 29–July 4, 1950, asked 1031 Americans, "How often do you bathe each week?" Results of the survey indicated that $\bar{x} = 3.7$ and $s = 2.3$.

   (a) Construct a 99% confidence interval for the number of times Americans bathed each week in 1950. Interpret the interval. (3.52, 3.88)

   (b) Compare these results to those of Problem 7. Were Americans bathing more in 1999 than in the 1950s?

9. **How Much TV Do You Watch?** A Gallup poll conducted December 20–21, 1999, asked 1031 Americans, "How much TV do you watch each week?" Results of the survey indicated that $\bar{x} = 3.4$ and $s = 1.8$ hours. Construct a 95% confidence interval for the number of hours of TV Americans watched each week in 1999. Interpret the interval. (3.29, 3.51)

10. **Rainfall in Chicago** For a simple random sample of 36 years, the mean amount of rainfall in Chicago during the month of April was 3.63 inches, with a standard deviation of 1.63 inches, according to data obtained from the Climate Diagnostics Center of the National Oceanic and Atmospheric Administration. Construct a 95% confidence interval for the mean amount of rainfall in Chicago during the month of April. Interpret the interval. (3.079, 4.182)

11. **Concentration of Dissolved Organic Carbon** The following data represent the concentration of organic carbon (mg/l) collected from organic soil:

22.74	29.8	27.1	16.51	6.51
8.81	5.29	20.46	14.9	33.67
30.91	14.86	15.91	15.35	9.72
19.8	14.86	8.09	17.9	18.3
5.2	11.9	14	7.4	17.5
10.3	11.4	5.3	15.72	20.46
16.87	15.42	22.49		

Source: Lisa Emili, Ph.D. Candidate, University of Waterloo

Construct a 99% confidence interval for the mean concentration of dissolved organic carbon collected from organic soil. Interpret the interval. (*Note:* $\bar{x} = 15.92$ mg/l and $s = 7.38$ mg/l.) (12.40, 19.44)

12. **Concentration of Dissolved Organic Carbon** The following data represent the concentration of organic carbon (mg/l) collected from mineral soil:

8.5	3.91	9.29	21	10.89
10.3	11.56	7	3.99	3.79
5.5	4.71	7.66	11.72	11.8
8.05	10.72	21.82	22.62	10.74
3.02	7.45	11.33	7.11	9.6
12.57	12.89	9.81	17.99	21.4
8.37	7.92	17.9	7.31	16.92
4.6	8.5	4.8	4.9	9.1
7.9	11.72	4.85	11.97	7.85
9.11	8.79			

Source: Lisa Emili, Ph.D. Candidate, University of Waterloo

(a) Construct a 99% confidence interval for the mean concentration of dissolved organic carbon collected from mineral soil. Interpret the interval. (*Note:* $\bar{x} = 10.03$ mg/l and $s = 4.98$ mg/l.) (8.078, 11.982)

(b) Compare the 99% confidence interval computed for organic soil (Problem 11) to the 99% confidence interval computed for mineral soil. Does there appear to be a difference between the concentration levels for the two soil types? Yes

13. **Wheat Pennies** "Wheat" pennies are pennies that were minted before 1954. The data to the left represent the weights (in grams) of a random sample of 15 wheat pennies:

3.01	3.06	3.13	3.00	3.05
3.07	3.02	2.98	3.04	3.02
3.06	3.03	3.07	3.04	2.96

(a) Because the sample size is small, we must verify that the weights of the pennies are normally distributed and that the sample does not contain any outliers. The normal probability plot and boxplot are shown in the accompanying diagrams. Are the conditions for constructing a *t*-interval satisfied? Yes

Normal Probability Plot for weight

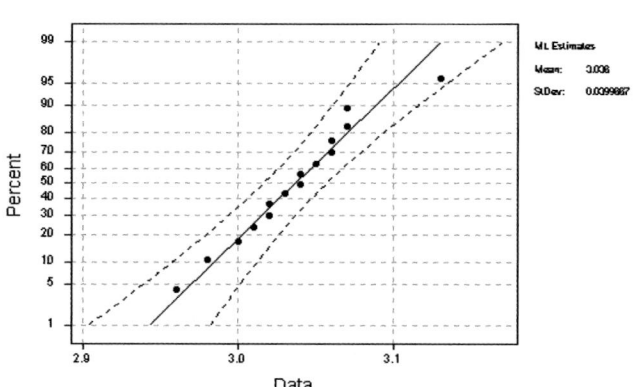

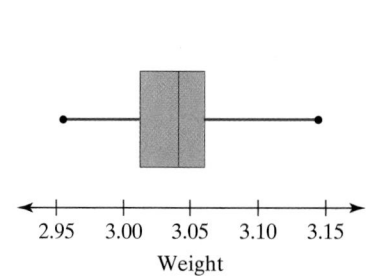

(b) Construct a 90% confidence interval for the weight of a "wheat" penny. (*Note:* $\bar{x} = 3.036$ grams and $s = 0.0414$ gram.) (3.017, 3.055)

(c) What could be done to increase the accuracy of the interval without changing the level of confidence? Increase sample size

14. **Miles on a Camaro** The following data represent the number of miles on a four-year-old Chevy Camaro:

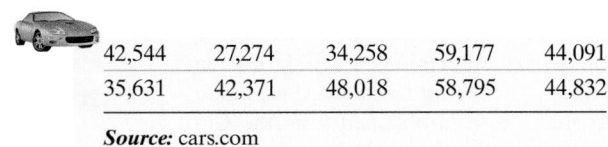

42,544	27,274	34,258	59,177	44,091
35,631	42,371	48,018	58,795	44,832

Source: cars.com

(a) Because the sample size is small, we must verify that the observations are normally distributed and that the sample does not contain any outliers. The accompanying diagrams show the normal probability plot and boxplot. Are the conditions for constructing a *t*-interval satisfied? Yes

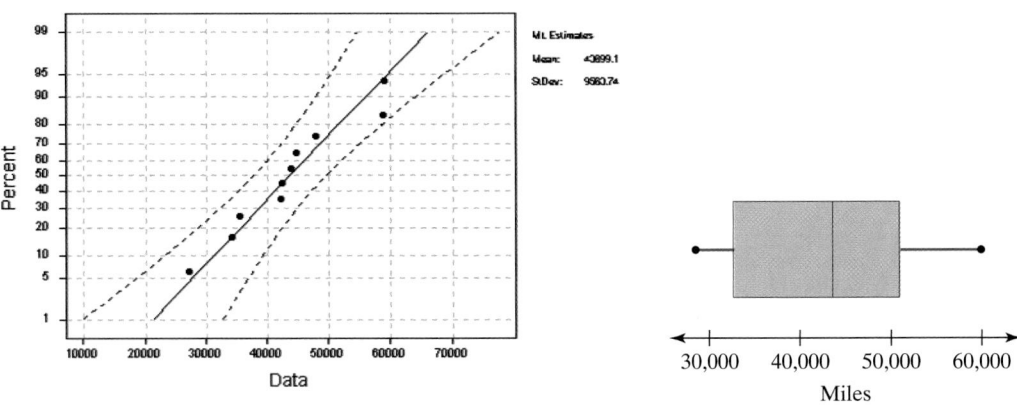

Normal Probability Plot for Miles

(b) Construct a 90% confidence interval for the number of miles on a four-year-old Camaro. Interpret the interval. (*Note:* $\bar{x} = 43,699.1$ miles and $s = 10,081.1$ miles.) (37,855, 49,543)

(c) Suppose you wanted more accuracy. What can be done to increase the accuracy of the interval without changing the level of confidence? Increase sample size

15. **Tensile Strength** Tensile strength is the maximum stress at which one can be reasonably certain failure will not occur. The following data represent tensile strength (in thousands of pounds per square inch) of a composite material to be used in an aircraft:

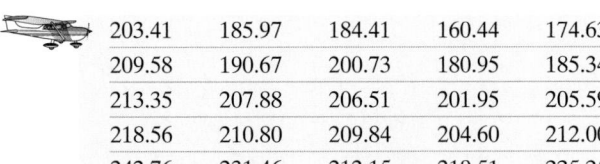

203.41	185.97	184.41	160.44	174.63
209.58	190.67	200.73	180.95	185.34
213.35	207.88	206.51	201.95	205.59
218.56	210.80	209.84	204.60	212.00
242.76	231.46	212.15	219.51	225.25

Source: Vangel, Mark G., "New Methods for One-sided Tolerance Limits for a One-way Balanced Random-Effects ANOVA Model.", *Technometrics*; May, 1992, Vol. 34, Issue 2, pp. 176 – 185.

(a) Because the sample size is small, we must verify that tensile strength is normally distributed and that the sample does not contain any outliers. The normal probability plot and boxplot are shown in the accompanying figures. Are the conditions for constructing a t-interval satisfied? Yes

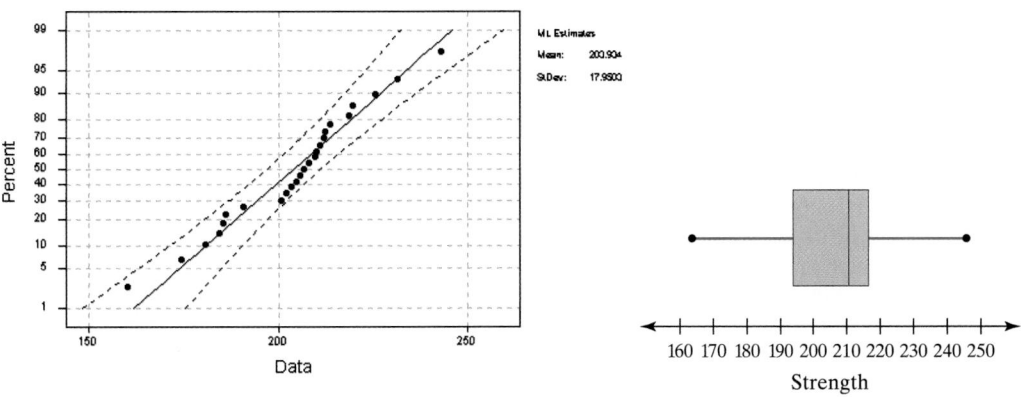

Normal Probability Plot for strength

(b) Construct a 95% confidence interval for the tensile strength of the composite material. (*Note*: $\bar{x} = 203.93$ thousand psi and $s = 18.32$ thousand psi.) (196.37, 211.49)

16. **Driving Distance** Dan wants to determine the average distance he hits a golf ball with a new driver he has just purchased. He goes to the driving range, uses a range finder to measure the length of each drive (in yards), and obtains the following data:

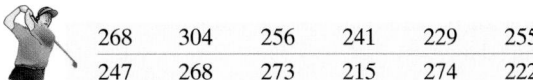

268	304	256	241	229	255
247	268	273	215	274	222

(a) Because the sample size is small, we must verify that driving distance is normally distributed and that the sample does not contain any outliers. The accompanying diagrams show the normal probability plot and boxplot. Are the conditions for constructing a t-interval satisfied? Yes

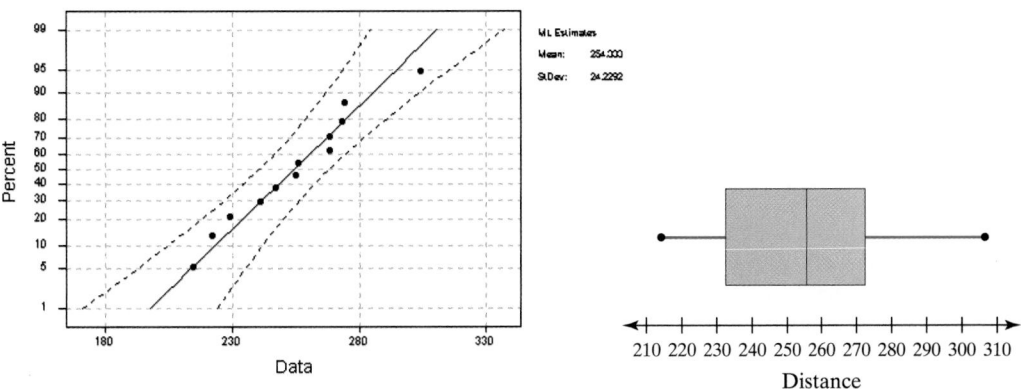

Normal Probability Plot for Distance

(b) Construct a 95% confidence interval for the driving distance. Interpret the interval. (*Note*: $\bar{x} = 254.3$ yards and $s = 25.3$ yards.) (238.2, 270.4)

17. Flight Time The following data represent the flight time (in minutes) of randomly selected flights from Denver, Colorado, to Chicago, Illinois, in June 2001 for American Airlines and United Airlines.

American Airlines	United Airlines
145 159 149 154 153	152 147 144 138 158
160 146 145 173 172	168 143 150 140 146

Source: United States Department of Transportation

(a) Verify that each airline's flight time is normally distributed with no outliers. Both are normal
(b) Compute a 95% confidence interval for the population mean of each airline.
(c) From the confidence intervals, does there appear to be any difference in the flight times? No

(b) AA: (148.2, 163.0); UA: (142.2, 155.03)

18. Red Blood Cell Mass The following data represent the red blood cell mass (in millimeters) of 15 rats in a flight group and 15 rats in a ground control group. The red blood cell mass was measured immediately after the flight group returned from space on the Spacelab Life Sciences 2.

Flight Group	Ground Control Group
8.59 8.64 6.87 7.89 7.00	8.65 6.99 7.62 7.33 7.14
8.80 6.39 7.54 7.43 7.21	8.40 8.55 9.88 9.66 7.44
9.79 6.85 8.23 8.03 9.30	8.58 9.14 11.78 8.70 9.94

Source: NASA Life Sciences Database

(a) Verify that each group's red blood cell mass is normally distributed with no outliers. Both are normal
(b) Compute a 95% confidence interval for the population mean of each group.
(c) From the confidence intervals, does there appear to be any difference in the red blood cell mass? No

(b) Flight: (7.359, 8.449); Control: (7.934, 9.373)

In Problems 19–24, construct a 95% z-interval or t-interval about the population mean, μ, whichever is appropriate. If neither can be constructed, state the reason.

19. Height of Males The heights of 20–29-year-old males are known to be normally distributed with $\sigma = 2.9$ inches. A simple random sample of $n = 15$ males 20–29 years old results in the following data: z-interval; (68.39, 71.32)

65.5	72.3	68.2	65.6	68.8
66.7	69.6	72.6	72.9	67.5
71.8	73.8	70.7	67.9	73.9

20. Gestation Period The gestation period of humans is normally distributed with $\sigma = 16$ days. A simple random sample of $n = 12$ live births results in the following data: z-interval; (258.7, 276.8)

266	270	277	278	258	275
261	260	270	269	252	277

21. Officer Friendly A police officer hides behind a billboard in order to catch speeders. The following data represent the number of minutes he needs to wait before first observing a car that is exceeding the speed limit by more than 10 miles per hour on 10 randomly selected days: Neither, nonnormal

1.0	5.4	0.8	14.1	0.5
0.9	3.9	0.4	1.0	3.9

22. Mutual Fund Performance The following data represent the three-year rate of return for a random sample of 15 large-cap growth mutual funds as of 8/26/2000: t-interval; (23.56, 32.39)

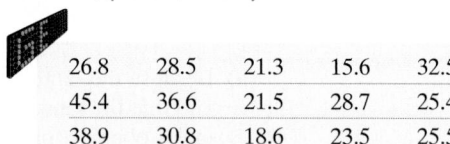

26.8	28.5	21.3	15.6	32.5
45.4	36.6	21.5	28.7	25.4
38.9	30.8	18.6	23.5	25.5

23. Pulse Fifteen randomly selected women were asked to work on the stair master for three minutes. After the three minutes, their pulses were measured and the following data were obtained: t-interval; (101.4, 117.3)

117	102	98	100	116
113	91	92	96	136
134	126	104	113	102

24. Law School Salaries A random sample of recent graduates of law school was conducted in which the graduates were asked to report their starting salary. The data, based upon results reported by the National Association for Law Placement, are as follows: Neither, nonnormal data

75,000	49,000	79,000	81,000	38,000
36,500	39,000	41,500	131,000	45,500
92,000	62,500	68,000	37,500	39,500

25. **The Effect of Outliers** The following data represent the asking price of a simple random sample of homes for sale in Houston, TX in February 2002:

149,900	154,900	155,500	270,000
259,000	270,000	166,000	229,000
153,000	177,500	185,000	875,000

(a) Construct a boxplot to identify the outlier.
(b) Construct a 99% confidence interval with the outlier included. ($73,258, $434,209)
(c) Construct a 99% confidence interval with the outlier removed. ($149,802, $244,707)
(d) Comment on the effect the outlier has on the confidence interval.

26. **The Effect of Outliers** The following data represent the age at which a simple random sample of Chicagoans died in February 2002:

67	78	60	73	90	59	68
86	75	99	80	73	18	39

Source: Chicago Tribune

(a) Construct a boxplot to identify the outlier.
(b) Construct a 90% confidence interval with the outlier included. (59.1, 78.7)
(c) Construct a 90% confidence interval with the outlier removed. (65.3, 80.4)
(d) Comment on the effect the outlier has on the confidence interval.

27. **Simulation** IQ scores based upon the Wechsler Intelligence Scale for Children (WIAT) are known to be normally distributed with $\mu = 100$ and $\sigma = 15$.
(a) Simulate obtaining 20 samples of size $n = 15$ from this population.

(b) Obtain the sample mean and standard deviation for each of the 20 samples.
(c) Construct 95% t-intervals for each of the 20 samples.
(d) How many of the intervals do you expect to include the population mean? How many actually contain the population mean?

28. **Simulation** Suppose the arrival of cars at Burger King's drive-through follows a Poisson process with $\mu = 4$ cars every 10 minutes.
(a) Simulate obtaining 30 samples of size $n = 35$ from this population.
(b) Obtain the sample mean and standard deviation for each of the 30 samples.
(c) Construct 90% t-intervals for each of the 30 samples.
(d) How many of the intervals do you expect to include the population mean? How many actually contain the population mean?

29. **The Effect of Nonnormal Data** The exponential distribution is used to model the time to failure for electronic components and time waiting in line. The figure in Problem 35 from Problem 8.1 shows that the density function for an exponential distribution with $\mu = 5$ is skewed right.
(a) Use Minitab or some other statistical software to generate 100 simple random samples of size $n = 6$ from a population that follows an exponential distribution with $\mu = 5$.
(b) Construct 95% confidence intervals for each of the 100 samples. Comment on the margin of error for each sample. What might cause the differences in the margin of error among the various samples?
(c) Use Minitab or some other statistical software to randomly generate 100 simple random samples of size $n = 36$ from a population that follows an exponential distribution with $\mu = 5$.
(d) Construct 95% confidence intervals for each of the 100 samples. Comment on the margin of error for each sample. What might cause the differences in the margin of error among the various samples?

Technology Step-by-Step
Confidence Intervals about μ, σ Unknown

TI-83 Plus **Step 1:** If necessary, enter raw data in L1.
Step 2: Press STAT, highlight TESTS, and select 8: TInterval.
Step 3: If the data are raw, highlight DATA—make sure List1 is set to L1 and Freq to 1. If summary statistics are known, highlight STATS and enter the summary statistics.
Step 4: Enter the confidence level following C-Level:.
Step 5: Highlight Calculate; press ENTER.

MINITAB **Step 1:** Enter raw data in column C1.
Step 2: Select the **Stat** menu, highlight **Basic Statistics**, then highlight **1-Sample t** . . . .

Step 3: Enter C1 in the cell marked "Variables." Select Confidence Interval, and enter a confidence level. Click OK.

Excel   *Step 1:* If necessary, enter raw data in column A.

Step 2: Load the PHStat Add-in.

Step 3: Select the **PHStat menu**, highlight **Confidence Intervals** . . . , then highlight **Estimate for the mean, sigma unknown** . . . .

Step 4: Enter the confidence level. If the summary statistics are known, click "Sample statistics known" and enter the sample size, sample mean, and sample standard deviation. If summary statistics are unknown, click "Sample statistics unknown." With the cursor in the "Sample cell range" cell, highlight the data in column A. Click OK.

8.3   Confidence Intervals about a Population Proportion

Preparing for This Section   Before getting started, review the following:

   ✓ Using the binomial probability distribution and the empirical rule to identify unusual results (Section 6.2, pp. 348–349).

Objectives   Obtain a point estimate for the population proportion

   Obtain and interpret a confidence interval for the population proportion

   Determine the sample size for estimating a population proportion

Probably the most frequently reported confidence interval is one involving the proportion of a population. Researchers are often interested in estimating the proportion of the population that has a certain characteristic. For example, in a poll conducted by the Gallup Organization in early January, 2001, a random sample of 1004 Americans resulted in 13% of the respondents stating that morality/dishonesty is the biggest problem facing America today. The poll had a margin of error of ± 3% with 95% confidence. Based upon discussions in Sections 8.1 and 8.2, we know that this means the pollsters are 95% confident the true proportion of Americans who believe morality/dishonesty is the biggest problem facing America today is somewhere between 10% and 16% (13% ± 3%).

     In this section, we will discuss the techniques for estimating the population proportion population, p. In addition, we present methods for determining the sample size required to estimate the population proportion.

In Your Own Words

The symbol ± is read "plus or minus." It means "to add and subtract the quantity following the ± symbol."

Point Estimate of the Population Proportion

Recall that a point estimate is an unbiased estimator of the parameter. The best point estimate is the one that has minimum variance among all unbiased estimators.

Theorem

In Your Own Words

$\hat{p}$ can be thought of as the probability that a randomly selected individual in the sample has a certain characteristic.

Point Estimate of a Population Proportion

Suppose a simple random sample of size n is obtained from a population in which each individual either does or does not have a certain characteristic. The best point estimate of p, denoted $\hat{p}$ (read "p-hat"), the proportion of the population with a certain characteristic, is given by

$$\hat{p} = \frac{x}{n} \qquad \text{(1)}$$

where x is the number of individuals in the sample with the specified characteristic.

▶ EXAMPLE 1   **Obtaining a Point Estimate of a Population Proportion**

Problem: In a poll conducted May 7–10, 2000, by ABC News, a simple random sample of 1068 American adults was asked, "Have you ever been shot at?" Of the 1068 adults, 96 responded yes. Obtain a point estimate for the population proportion of Americans who have been shot at.

Approach: The point estimate of the population proportion is $\hat{p} = \frac{x}{n}$, where $x = 96$ and $n = 1068$.

Solution: Substituting into Formula (1), we obtain $\hat{p} = \frac{x}{n} = \frac{96}{1068} = 0.090 = 9.0\%$. We estimate that 9.0% of Americans have been shot at. ◀◀

NW *Now Work Problem 7(a).*

② Confidence Intervals for the Population Proportion

The point estimate obtained in Example 1 is a single estimate of the unknown parameter, p. However, just as there is a sampling distribution associated with the sample mean, $\overline{x}$, there is a sampling distribution associated with $\hat{p}$. We recognize it is unlikely that the sample proportion will equal the population proportion (because of sampling and nonsampling error). Therefore, rather than reporting the value of the sample proportion alone, it is preferred to report an interval about the sample proportion.

Recall from Section 6.2 the distribution of X, the number of successes in n trials of a binomial experiment, is approximately normal, with mean $\mu = np$ and standard deviation $\sigma = \sqrt{np(1-p)}$, provided that $np(1-p) \geq 10$. If we standardize the binomial random variable X, we obtain

$$Z = \frac{x - \mu}{\sigma} = \frac{x - np}{\sqrt{np(1-p)}}$$

Divide the numerator and denominator of the standardized form by n, to obtain

$$Z = \frac{x - np}{\sqrt{np(1-p)}} = \frac{\dfrac{x - np}{n}}{\dfrac{\sqrt{np(1-p)}}{n}} = \frac{\dfrac{x}{n} - p}{\sqrt{\dfrac{p(1-p)}{n}}} = \frac{\hat{p} - p}{\sqrt{\dfrac{p(1-p)}{n}}}$$

and we have the following result:

Theorem

Sampling Distribution of $\hat{p}$

For a simple random sample of size n such that $n \leq 0.05N$ (that is, the sample size is no more than 5% of the population size), the sampling distribution of $\hat{p}$ is approximately normal with mean $\mu_{\hat{p}} = p$ and standard deviation

$$\sigma_{\hat{p}} = \sqrt{\frac{p(1-p)}{n}}, \text{ provided that } np(1-p) \geq 10.$$

We use the sampling distribution of $\hat{p}$ to construct a confidence interval about p.

> **Constructing a $(1 - \alpha) \cdot 100\%$ Confidence Interval for a Population Proportion**
>
> Suppose a simple random sample of size n is taken from a population. A $(1 - \alpha) \cdot 100\%$ confidence interval for p is given by the following quantities:
>
> $$\text{Lower bound: } \hat{p} - z_{\alpha/2} \cdot \sqrt{\frac{\hat{p}(1 - \hat{p})}{n}}$$
>
> $$\text{Upper bound: } \hat{p} + z_{\alpha/2} \cdot \sqrt{\frac{\hat{p}(1 - \hat{p})}{n}} \qquad \text{(2)}$$
>
> **Note:** It must be the case that $n\hat{p}(1 - \hat{p}) \geq 10$ to construct this interval.

Notice we use $\hat{p}$ in place of p in the standard deviation. This is because p is unknown and $\hat{p}$ is the best point estimate of p.

▶ **EXAMPLE 2** **Constructing a Confidence Interval for a Population Proportion**

Problem: In a poll conducted May 7–10, 2000, by ABC News, a simple random sample of 1068 American adults was asked, "Have you ever been shot at?" Of the 1068 adults, 96 responded yes. Obtain a 95% confidence interval about the population proportion, p.

Approach:

Step 1: Compute the value of $\hat{p}$.
Step 2: We can compute a 95% confidence interval about p provided that $n\hat{p}(1 - \hat{p}) \geq 10$.
Step 3: Determine the critical value, $z_{\alpha/2}$.
Step 4: Determine the lower and upper bounds of the confidence interval.

Solution:

Step 1: From Example 1, we have that $\hat{p} = 0.090$.
Step 2: $n\hat{p}(1 - \hat{p}) = 1068(0.09)(1 - 0.09) = 87.4692 \geq 10$. We can proceed to construct the confidence interval.
Step 3: Because we want a 95% confidence interval, we have $\alpha = 0.05$, so $z_{\alpha/2} = z_{0.05/2} = z_{0.025} = 1.96$.
Step 4: Substituting into Formula (2) with $n = 1068$, we obtain the lower and upper bounds of the confidence interval:

Lower bound:

$$\hat{p} - z_{\alpha/2} \cdot \sqrt{\frac{\hat{p}(1 - \hat{p})}{n}} = 0.090 - 1.96 \cdot \sqrt{\frac{0.090(1 - 0.090)}{1068}} = 0.090 - 0.017 = 0.073$$

Upper bound:

$$\hat{p} + z_{\alpha/2} \cdot \sqrt{\frac{\hat{p}(1 - \hat{p})}{n}} = 0.090 + 1.96 \cdot \sqrt{\frac{0.090(1 - 0.090)}{1068}} = 0.090 + 0.017 = 0.107$$

Given the results of the survey, we are 95% confident that the proportion of Americans who have been shot at is between 0.073 and 0.107.   ◀◀

Figure 16

Using Technology: Graphing calculators with advanced statistical features and statistical software can be used to construct confidence intervals about the population proportion. Figure 16 shows the results of Example 2 from a TI-83 Plus graphing calculator.

It is important to remember the correct interpretation of a confidence interval. The statement "95% confident" means that, if 1000 samples of size 1068 were taken, about 950 of the intervals would contain the parameter p and about 50 would not. Unfortunately, we cannot know whether the interval we computed in Example 2 is one of the 950 intervals that contains p or one of the 50 that does not contain p.

Often, polls will report their results by giving the value of $\hat{p}$ obtained from the sample data along with the margin of error, rather than reporting a confidence interval. In Example 2, ABC News might say "In a survey conducted May 7–10, 2000, 9% of adult Americans stated that they have been shot at. The survey results had a margin of error of 1.7%."

⬤ Caution

Beware of surveys that do not report a margin of error. Survey results should also report sample size, sampling technique, and the population that was being studied.

NW *Now Work Problems 7(b) and (c).*

③ Determining Sample Size

In Section 8.1, we introduced a method for determining the sample size n required to estimate the sample mean within a certain margin of error with a specified level of confidence. This formula was obtained by solving the margin of error, $E = z_{\alpha/2} \cdot \dfrac{\sigma}{\sqrt{n}}$, for n. We can follow the same approach to determine sample size when estimating a population proportion. In Formula (2), we notice that the margin of error, E, is given by

$E = z_{\alpha/2} \cdot \sqrt{\dfrac{\hat{p}(1 - \hat{p})}{n}}$. We solve the margin of error for n and obtain

$$n = \hat{p}(1 - \hat{p})\left(\frac{z_{\alpha/2}}{E}\right)^2$$

Figure 17

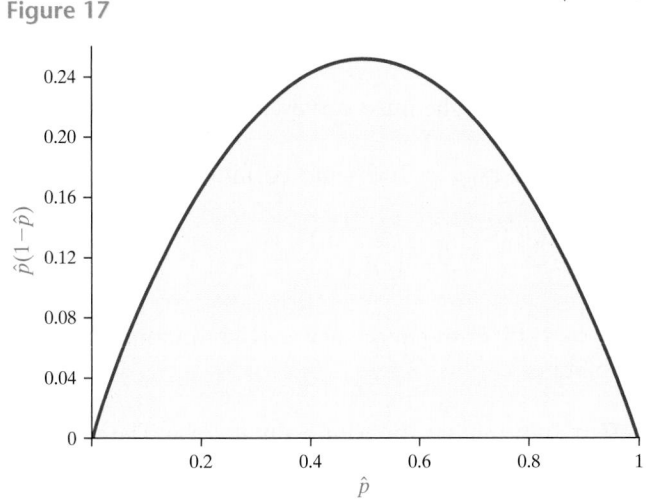

The problem with this formula is that it depends on $\hat{p}$. Moreover, $\hat{p} = \dfrac{x}{n}$ depends upon the sample size, n, which is what we are trying to determine in the first place! How do we resolve this issue? There are two possibilities: (1) We could use an estimate of p based upon a pilot study or an earlier study, or (2) we could let $\hat{p} = 0.5$ to maximize the value of $\hat{p}(1 - \hat{p})$ (as shown in Figure 17). By maximizing this value, we obtain the largest possible value of n for a given level of confidence and a given margin of error.

The disadvantage of the second option is that it could lead to a larger sample size than is necessary. Because of the time and expense of sampling, it is desirable to avoid too large a sample.

Note to Instructor
You might have students experiment with various values of $\hat{p}$ to see which one maximizes $\hat{p}(1 - \hat{p})$.

Theorem

In Your Own Words

There are two formulas for determining sample size when estimating the population proportion. Formula (3) requires a prior estimate of p; Formula (4) does not.

Sample Size for Estimating the Population Proportion p

The sample size required to obtain a $(1 - \alpha) \cdot 100\%$ confidence interval for p with a margin of error E is given by

$$n = \hat{p}(1 - \hat{p})\left(\frac{z_{\alpha/2}}{E}\right)^2 \tag{3}$$

(rounded up to the next integer) where $\hat{p}$ is a prior estimate of p. If a prior estimate of p is unavailable, the sample size required is

$$n = 0.25\left(\frac{z_{\alpha/2}}{E}\right)^2 \tag{4}$$

rounded up to the next integer.

▶ **EXAMPLE 3** **Determining Sample Size**

Problem: A sociologist wishes to estimate the percentage of the United States population living in poverty. What size sample should be obtained if she wishes the estimate to be within 2 percentage points with 99% confidence if

(a) she uses the 1999 estimate of 11.8% obtained from the Current Population Survey.

(b) she does not use any prior estimates.

Approach: In both cases, we have $E = 0.02^*$ (2% = 0.02) and $z_{\alpha/2} = z_{0.01/2} = z_{0.005} = 2.575$. To answer part (a), we let $\hat{p} = 0.118$ in Formula (3). To answer part (b), we use Formula (4).

Solution:

(a) Substituting $E = 0.02$, $z_{0.005} = 2.575$, and $\hat{p} = 0.118$ into Formula (3), we obtain

$$n = \hat{p}(1 - \hat{p})\left(\frac{z_{\alpha/2}}{E}\right)^2 = 0.118(1 - 0.118)\left(\frac{2.575}{0.02}\right)^2 = 1725.2$$

We round this value up to 1726, so she must survey 1726 randomly selected residents of the United States.

(b) Substituting $E = 0.02$ and $z_{0.005} = 2.575$ into Formula (4), we obtain

$$n = 0.25\left(\frac{z_{\alpha/2}}{E}\right)^2 = 0.25\left(\frac{2.575}{0.02}\right)^2 = 4144.1$$

We round this value up to 4145, so she must survey 4145 randomly selected residents of the United States. ◀◀

We can see the effect of not having a prior estimate of p: The required sample size more than doubled!

NW *Now Work Problem 15.*

*The margin of error should always be expressed as a decimal when using Formulas (3) and (4).

8.3 Assess Your Understanding

Concepts and Vocabulary

1. What is the best point estimate of a population proportion?

2. What are the requirements that must be satisfied in order to construct a confidence interval about a population proportion?

3. When determining the sample size required in order to obtain an estimate for a population proportion, is the researcher better off using a prior estimate of p or no prior estimate of p? Why? List some pros and cons for each scenario.

Exercises

- **Basic Skills**

In Problems 1–6, construct a confidence interval of the population proportion at the given level of confidence.

1. $x = 30, n = 150$, 90% confidence *(0.146, 0.254)*

2. $x = 80, n = 200$, 98% confidence *(0.319, 0.481)*

3. $x = 120, n = 500$, 99% confidence *(0.191, 0.289)*

4. $x = 400, n = 1200$, 95% confidence *(0.307, 0.360)*

5. $x = 860, n = 1100$, 94% confidence *(0.758, 0.805)*

6. $x = 540, n = 900$, 96% confidence *(0.566, 0.634)*

- **Applying the Concepts**

7. Lipitor The drug Lipitor is meant to lower cholesterol levels. In a clinical trial of 863 patients who received 10 mg doses of Lipitor daily, 47 reported a headache as a side effect.

(a) Obtain a point estimate for the population proportion of Lipitor users who will experience a headache as a side effect. *0.054*

(b) Verify that the requirements for constructing a confidence interval about $\hat{p}$ are satisfied.

(c) Construct a 90% confidence interval for the population proportion of Lipitor users who will report a headache as a side effect. *(0.042, 0.067)*

(d) Interpret the confidence interval.

8. Pepcid A study of 74 patients with ulcers was conducted in which they were prescribed 40 mg of Pepcid. After 8 weeks, 58 reported confirmed ulcer healing.

(a) Obtain a point estimate for the proportion of patients with ulcers receiving Pepcid who will have confirmed ulcer healing. *0.784*

(b) Verify that the requirements for constructing a confidence interval about $\hat{p}$ are satisfied.

(c) Construct a 99% confidence interval for the proportion of patients with ulcers receiving Pepcid who will have confirmed ulcer healing. *(0.661, 0.907)*

(d) Interpret the confidence interval.

9. Workplace Violence In a September 1999 poll conducted by the Gallup Organization, 230 of 1000 randomly selected adults aged 18 years or older stated that they knew someone capable of committing an act of violence in their workplace.

(a) Obtain a point estimate for the proportion of adults 18 years old or older who know someone capable of committing an act of violence in their workplace. *0.230*

(b) Verify that the requirements for constructing a confidence interval about $\hat{p}$ are satisfied.

(c) Construct a 98% confidence interval for the proportion of adults 18 years old or older who know someone capable of committing an act of violence in their workplace. *(0.199, 0.261)*

(d) Interpret the confidence interval.

10. Partial Birth Abortions In an October 2000 poll conducted by the Gallup Organization, 639 of 1014 randomly selected adults aged 18 years old or older stated they would support a law that would make it illegal to perform a specific abortion procedure conducted in the last six months of pregnancy known as a "partial birth abortion," except in cases necessary to save the life of the mother.

(a) Obtain a point estimate for the proportion of adults aged 18 years old or older who would support a law that would make it illegal to perform a specific abortion procedure conducted in the last six months of pregnancy known as a "partial birth abortion," except in cases necessary to save the life of the mother. *0.630*

(b) Verify that the requirements for constructing a confidence interval about $\hat{p}$ are satisfied.

(c) Construct a 95% confidence interval for the proportion of adults aged 18 years old or older who would favor such a law. *(0.600, 0.660)*

(d) Interpret the confidence interval.

11. **Breast-feeding** In a 1995 national survey conducted by the Centers for Disease Control, 5988 of 10,847 women who had a child between 1990 and 1993 indicated having breast-fed the baby.

 (a) Verify that the requirements for constructing a confidence interval about $\hat{p}$ are satisfied.

 (b) Construct a 90% confidence interval for the proportion of women who had a child between 1990 and 1993 who breast-fed their baby. Interpret this interval. (0.544, 0.560)

 (c) Construct a 99% confidence interval for the proportion of women who had a child between 1990 and 1993 who breast-fed their baby. Interpret this interval. (0.540, 0.564)

 (d) What is the effect of increasing the level of confidence on the width of the interval? Increases

12. **Child Safety Seats** In a Harris Poll conducted February 9, 2000, 1247 of 2208 randomly selected Americans said they judged that state laws governing child safety restraint in vehicles should be strengthened.

 (a) Verify that the requirements for constructing a confidence interval about $\hat{p}$ are satisfied.

 (b) Construct a 92% confidence interval for the proportion of Americans who judge that state laws governing child safety restraint in vehicles should be strengthened. Interpret this interval. (0.546, 0.583)

 (c) Construct a 96% confidence interval for the proportion of Americans who judge that state laws governing child safety restraint in vehicles should be strengthened. Interpret this interval. (0.543, 0.586)

 (d) What is the effect of increasing the level of confidence on the width of the interval? Increases

13. **Obesity** In a study conducted by the Centers for Disease Control in 1999, 1950 out of 10,485 randomly selected 30–39-year-old Americans were found to be obese.

 (a) Construct a 95% confidence interval, for the proportion of 30–39-year-old Americans who are obese, based upon the 1999 study. Interpret this interval. (0.179, 0.193)

 (b) When the same study was performed in 1998, 1937 out of 11,464 randomly selected 30–39-year-old Americans were found to be obese. On the basis of the 1998 study, construct a 95% confidence interval for the proportion of 30–39-year-old Americans who are obese. Interpret this interval. (0.162, 0.176)

 (c) Does it appear that the percentage of 30–39-year-old Americans who are obese increased from 1998 to 1999? Why? Yes

14. **Obesity** In a study conducted by the Centers for Disease Control in 1999, 3506 out of 17,020 randomly selected Americans with high school diplomas were found to be obese.

 (a) Construct a 95% confidence interval, for the proportion of Americans with high school diplomas who are obese, based upon the 1999 study. Interpret this interval. (0.200, 0.212)

 (b) When the same study was performed on Americans with 4 or more years of college, 2084 out of 14,572 were found to be obese. Construct a 95% confidence interval for the proportion of Americans with 4 or more years of college who are obese. Interpret this interval. (0.137, 0.149)

 (c) Does it appear that the percentage of Americans with high school diplomas who are obese is different from the percentage of Americans with 4 or more years of college who are obese? Why? Yes

15. **Child Care** A child psychologist wishes to estimate the percentage of fathers who watch their preschool-aged child when the mother works. What size sample should be obtained if she wishes the estimate to be within 3 percentage points with 99% confidence if

 (a) she uses a 1995 estimate obtained from the U.S. Census Bureau of 18.5%? 1111

 (b) she does not use any prior estimates? 1842

16. **Home Ownership** An urban economist wishes to estimate the percentage of Americans who own their house. What size sample should be obtained if he wishes the estimate to be within 2 percentage points with 90% confidence if

 (a) he uses an estimate of 67.5% from the fourth quarter of 2000 obtained from the U.S. Census Bureau? 1485

 (b) he does not use any prior estimates? 1692

17. **Affirmative Action** A sociologist wishes to conduct a poll in order to estimate the percentage of Americans who judge that affirmative action programs for minorities and women should be continued at some level. What size sample should be obtained if she wishes the estimate to be within 3 percentage points with 95% confidence if

 (a) she uses a 1999 estimate of 80% obtained from a Time/CNN poll? 683

 (b) she does not use any prior estimates? 1068

18. **Affirmative Action** A sociologist wishes to conduct a poll in order to estimate the percentage of Americans who judge that affirmative action programs should require businesses to hire a specific number or quota of minorities and women. What size sample should be obtained if she wishes the estimate to be within 4 percentage points with 90% confidence if

 (a) she uses a 1999 estimate of 37% obtained from a Time/CNN poll? 395

 (b) she does not use any prior estimates? 423

19. **Playing the Horses** A researcher wishes to conduct a poll in order to estimate the percentage of Americans aged 18 years old or older who placed a bet on a horse race last year. What size sample should be obtained if she wishes the estimate to be within 1.5 percentage points with 98% confidence if

 (a) she uses a 1998 estimate of 7% obtained from the National Gambling Impact Study Commission? 1566

 (b) she does not use any prior estimates? 6012

20. Credit Card Debt A school administrator is concerned about the amount of credit card debt college students have. She wishes to conduct a poll in order to estimate the percentage of full-time college students who have credit card debt of $2000 or more. What size sample should be obtained if she wishes the estimate to be within 2.5 percentage points with 94% confidence, if

(a) a pilot study indicates the percentage is 34%? 1269
(b) no prior estimates are used? 1414

21. The Death Penalty In a Harris Poll conducted in July, 2000, 64% of the people polled answered yes to the following question: "Do you believe in capital punishment, that is the death penalty, or are you opposed to it?" The margin of error in the poll was ±3% = ±0.03, and the estimate was made with 95% confidence. How many people were surveyed? 984

22. Own a Gun? In a Harris Poll conducted in May, 2000, 39% of the people polled answered "yes" to the following question: "Do you happen to have in your home or garage any guns or revolvers?" The margin of error in the poll was ±3% = ±0.03 and the estimate was made with 95% confidence. How many people were surveyed? 1016

23. Simulation The following exercise is meant to illustrate the normality of the distribution of the sample proportion, $\hat{p}$.

(a) Using Minitab or some other statistical spreadsheet, randomly generate 2000 samples of size 765 from a population with $p = 0.3$. Store the number of successes in a column called x.
(b) Determine $\hat{p}$ for each of the 2000 samples by computing $x/765$. Store each $\hat{p}$ in a column called *phat*.
(c) Draw a histogram of the 2000 estimates of p. Comment on the shape of the distribution.
(d) Compute the mean and standard deviation of the sampling distribution of $\hat{p}$ in the simulation.
(e) Compute the theoretical mean and standard deviation of the sampling distribution of $\hat{p}$. Compare the theoretical results to the results of the simulation. Are they close?
(f) Compute the confidence interval for each of the 2000 samples. How many of the intervals do you expect to contain p? How many actually contain p?

24. The 2000 Presidential Election The Gallup Organization conducted a poll of 2350 likely voters just prior to the 2000 presidential election. The results of the survey indicated that George W. Bush would receive 48% of the popular vote and Al Gore would receive 46% of the popular vote. The margin of error was reported to be 2%. The Gallup Organization reported that the race was too close to call. Use the concept of a confidence interval to explain what this means.

25. Finite Population Correction Factor In this section, we assumed that the sample size was less than 5% of the size of the population. When sampling from a finite population in which $n > 0.05N$ without replacement, the standard deviation of the distribution of $\hat{p}$ is given by

$$s_{\hat{p}} = \sqrt{\frac{\hat{p}(1-\hat{p})}{n-1} \cdot \left(\frac{N-n}{N}\right)}$$

where N is the size of the population. Suppose a survey is conducted at a college having an enrollment of 6,502 students. The student council wants to estimate the percentage of students in favor of establishing a student union. In a random sample of 500 students, it was determined that 410 were in favor of establishing a student union.

(a) Obtain a point estimate of the proportion of students at the college in favor of establishing a student union.
(b) Calculate the standard deviation of the sampling distribution of $\hat{p}$. 0.017
(c) Obtain a 95% confidence interval for the proportion of students in favor of establishing a student union. Interpret the interval. (0.787, 0.853)

(a) 0.82

Technology Step-by-Step
Confidence Intervals about p

TI-83 Plus   **Step 1:** Press STAT, highlight TESTS, and select `A:1-PropZInt..`
Step 2: Enter the values of x and n.
Step 3: Enter the confidence level following `C-Level:`
Step 4: Highlight `Calculate`; press ENTER.

MINITAB   **Step 1:** If you have raw data, enter the data in column C1.
Step 2: Select the **Stat** menu, highlight **Basic Statistics**, then highlight **1 Proportion** . . . .
Step 3: Enter C1 in the cell marked "Sample in Columns" if you have raw data. If you have summary statistics, click "Summarized data" and enter the number of trials, n, and the number of successes, x.
Step 4: Hit the Options button. Select a Confidence Level. Click "Use test based on a normal distribution" (provided that the assumptions stated are satisfied). Click OK twice.

> *Excel* **Step 1:** Load the PHStat Add-in.
> **Step 2:** Select the **PHStat menu**, highlight **Confidence Intervals . . .** , then highlight **Estimate for the proportion . . . .**
> **Step 3:** Enter the confidence level. Enter the sample size, n, and the number of successes, x. Click OK.

8.4 Confidence Intervals about a Population Standard Deviation

Objectives Find critical values for the chi-square distribution

 Construct confidence intervals about the population variance and standard deviation

Note to Instructor
This section can be omitted without loss of continuity, except that you might need to refer to Objective 1 from this section when covering Section 11.1.

In this section, we discuss methods for estimating a population variance or standard deviation. Just as we discovered the sampling distribution of $\bar{x}$ and $\hat{p}$, we must find the sampling distribution of s^2, the point estimate of σ^2. We then construct intervals about the point estimate of σ^2, using this sampling distribution.

Why might we be interested in obtaining estimates of σ^2? Many production processes not only require accuracy on average (the mean), they also require consistency. Consider a filling machine (such as a coffee machine) that consistently over- and underfills cups, but, on average, fills correctly. Certainly, customers are not happy if the machine underfills their cups, and they might be dissatisfied even if it overfills, because of spilling. A machine that consistently delivers the correct amount of liquid is desired. As another example, consider a mutual fund that claims an average rate of return of 12% per year over the past 20 years. An investor might prefer consistent year-to-year returns near 12% to returns that fluctuated wildly yet resulted in a mean return of 12%. Both these situations illustrate the importance of measuring variability, the topic of this section.

The Chi-Square Distribution

We begin by exploring the sampling distribution of s^2 through a simulation. Suppose we obtain 2000 samples of size $n = 10$ from a population that is known to be normally distributed with mean 100 and standard deviation 15. We then compute the sample variance of each of the 2000 samples. Next, we compute $\dfrac{(n - 1)s^2}{\sigma^2} = \dfrac{9s^2}{15^2}$ for each sample. We then draw a histogram of these values as shown in Figure 18.

Figure 18

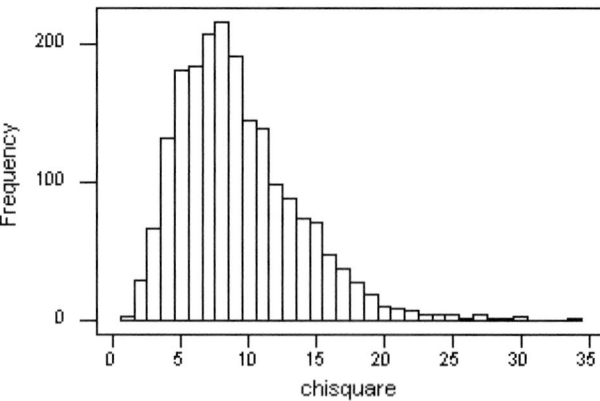
Chi-Square Distribution

The histogram represents the sampling distribution of $(n - 1)s^2/\sigma^2$. Clearly, the histogram does not imply that the sampling distribution of $(n - 1)s^2/\sigma^2$ is normal. Rather, the histogram appears to be skewed right as indicated by the extended right tail of the histogram.

Theorem

Chi-Square Distribution

If a simple random sample of size n is obtained from a normally distributed population with mean μ and standard deviation σ, then

$$\chi^2 = \frac{(n - 1)s^2}{\sigma^2}$$

has a chi-square distribution with $n - 1$ degrees of freedom.

The symbol χ^2, chi-square, is pronounced "kigh-square" (to rhyme with "sky-square"). We can find critical values of the chi-square distribution in Table IV in Appendix A of the text. Before discussing how to read Table IV, we introduce characteristics of the chi-square distribution.

Characteristics of the Chi-Square Distribution

1. It is not symmetric.
2. The shape of the chi-square distribution depends upon the degrees of freedom, just as with Student's t-distribution.
3. As the number of degrees of freedom increases, the chi-square distribution becomes more nearly symmetric. See Figure 19.
4. The values of χ^2 are nonnegative—that is, values of χ^2 are always greater than or equal to 0.

Figure 19

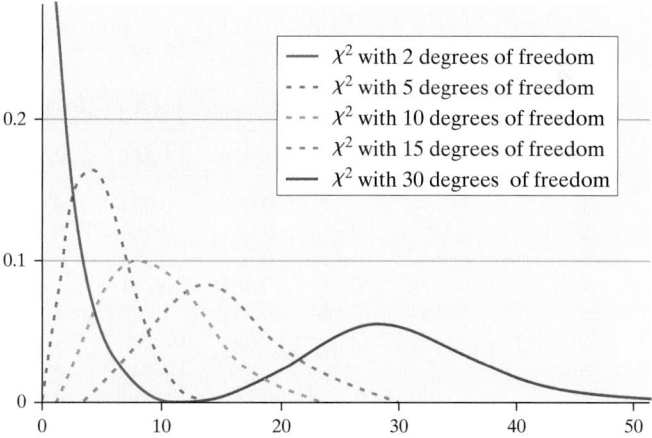

Because the χ^2 distribution is not symmetric, we cannot construct a confidence interval for σ^2 by computing "point estimate±margin of error". Instead, we must determine the left and right bounds by using different critical values.

Table IV is structured similarly to Table III for the t-distribution. The left column represents the degrees of freedom, and the top row represents the area under the chi-square distribution to the right of the critical value. We shall use the notation χ^2_α to denote the critical χ^2-value such that the area under the chi-square distribution to the right of χ^2_α is α.

▶ **EXAMPLE 1** Finding Critical Values for the Chi-Square Distribution

Problem: Find the critical values that separate the middle 90% of the chi-square distribution from the 5% area in each tail, assuming 15 degrees of freedom.

Approach: We shall perform the following steps to obtain the critical values.

Step 1: Draw a chi-square distribution with the critical values and area labeled.
Step 2: Use Table IV to find the critical values.

Solution:

Step 1: Figure 20 shows the chi-square distribution with 15 degrees of freedom and the unknown critical values labeled. The area to the right of the right critical value is 0.05. We denote this critical value $\chi^2_{0.05}$. The area to the right of the left critical value is $1 - 0.05 = 0.95$. We denote this critical value $\chi^2_{0.95}$.

Figure 20

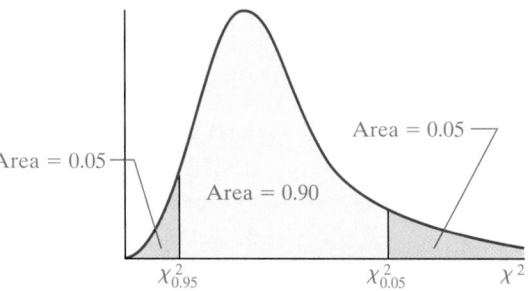

Step 2: Figure 21 shows a partial representation of Table IV. The row containing 15 degrees of freedom is boxed. The columns corresponding to an area to the right of 0.95 and 0.05 are also boxed. The critical values are $\chi^2_{0.95} = 7.261$ and $\chi^2_{0.05} = 24.996$.

Figure 21

Degrees of Freedom	Area to the Right of the Critical Value									
	0.995	0.99	0.975	0.95	0.90	0.10	0.05	0.025	0.01	0.005
1	—	—	0.001	0.004	0.016	2.706	3.841	5.024	6.635	7.879
2	0.010	0.020	0.051	0.103	0.211	4.605	5.991	7.378	9.210	10.597
3	0.072	0.115	0.216	0.352	0.584	6.251	7.815	9.348	11.345	12.838
4	0.207	0.297	0.484	0.711	1.064	7.779	9.488	11.143	13.277	14.860
5	0.412	0.554	0.831	1.145	1.610	9.236	11.071	12.833	15.086	16.750
6	0.676	0.872	1.237	1.635	2.204	10.645	12.592	14.449	16.812	18.548
7	0.989	1.239	1.690	2.167	2.833	12.017	14.067	16.013	18.475	20.278
8	1.344	1.646	2.180	2.733	3.490	13.362	15.507	17.535	20.090	21.955
9	1.735	2.088	2.700	3.325	4.168	14.684	16.919	19.023	21.666	23.589
10	2.156	2.558	3.247	3.940	4.865	15.987	18.307	20.483	23.209	25.188
11	2.603	3.053	3.816	4.575	5.578	17.275	19.675	21.920	24.725	26.757
12	3.074	3.571	4.404	5.226	6.304	18.549	21.026	23.337	26.217	28.299
13	3.565	4.107	5.009	5.892	7.042	19.812	22.362	24.736	27.688	29.819
14	4.075	4.660	5.629	6.571	7.790	21.064	23.685	26.119	29.141	31.319
15	4.601	5.229	6.262	7.261	8.547	22.307	24.996	27.488	30.578	32.801
16	5.142	5.812	6.908	7.962	9.312	23.542	26.296	28.845	32.000	34.267
17	5.697	6.408	7.564	8.672	10.085	24.769	27.587	30.191	33.409	35.718
18	6.365	7.215	8.231	9.288	10.265	25.200	28.601	31.595	24.265	36.456

◀◀

In studying Table IV, we notice that the degrees of freedom are numbered 1–30 inclusive, then 40, 50, 60, ..., 100. If the number of degrees of freedom is not found in the table, we shall follow the practice of choosing the degrees of freedom closest to that desired. If the degrees of freedom is exactly between two values, find the mean of the values. For example, to find the critical value corresponding to 75 degrees of freedom, compute the mean of the critical values corresponding to 70 and 80 degrees of freedom.

NW *Now Work Problem 1.*

❷ Confidence Interval for a Population Variance and Standard Deviation

The sample variance, s^2, is the best point estimate of the population variance, σ^2. We use the sample standard deviation as the point estimate of σ.*

We now must develop a method for constructing a confidence interval for the population variance. Suppose that we take a simple random sample of size n from a population that is normally distributed with mean μ and standard deviation σ; then $\chi^2 = \dfrac{(n-1)s^2}{\sigma^2}$ follows a chi-square distribution with $n - 1$ degrees of freedom. Therefore, $(1 - \alpha) \cdot 100\%$ of the values of χ^2 will lie between $\chi^2_{1-\alpha/2}$ and $\chi^2_{\alpha/2}$. Figure 22 illustrates the situation.

Figure 22

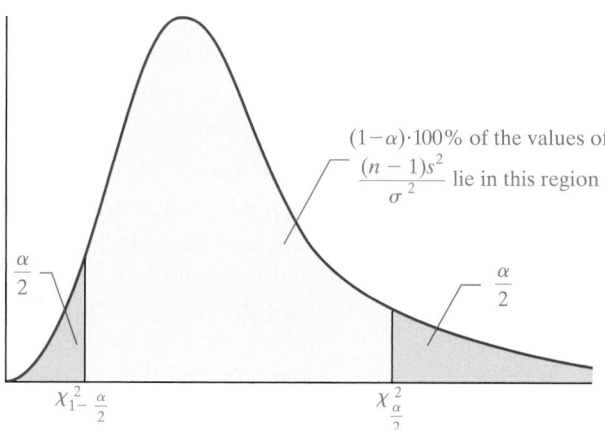

We say that $(1 - \alpha) \cdot 100\%$ of the values of $\dfrac{(n-1)s^2}{\sigma^2}$ lie within the interval defined by the inequality

$$\chi^2_{1-\alpha/2} < \frac{(n-1)s^2}{\sigma^2} < \chi^2_{\alpha/2}$$

If we rewrite this inequality with σ^2 in the center, we will have the formula for a $(1 - \alpha) \cdot 100\%$ confidence interval about σ^2:

$$\frac{(n-1)s^2}{\chi^2_{\alpha/2}} < \sigma^2 < \frac{(n-1)s^2}{\chi^2_{1-\alpha/2}}$$

We now have a formula for computing a $(1 - \alpha) \cdot 100\%$ confidence interval about σ^2.

Caution

A confidence interval about the population variance or standard deviation is not of the form "point estimate±margin of error."

---

*Although the sample standard deviation is a biased estimator of σ, it is common practice to use s as the estimator of σ.

A $(1 - \alpha) \cdot 100\%$ Confidence Interval about σ^2

If a simple random sample of size n is taken from a normal population with mean μ and standard deviation σ, then a $(1 - \alpha) \cdot 100\%$ confidence interval about σ^2 is given by

$$\text{Lower bound: } \frac{(n - 1)s^2}{\chi^2_{\alpha/2}} \qquad \text{Upper bound: } \frac{(n - 1)s^2}{\chi^2_{1-\alpha/2}} \qquad \textbf{(1)}$$

▶ **EXAMPLE 2**   **Constructing a Confidence Interval about a Population Variance and Standard Deviation**

Problem: Recall that, in Example 2 from Section 8.2, we constructed a 90% confidence interval for the mean price of a three-year-old Chevy Corvette. Now construct a 90% confidence interval about the population variance and standard deviation. The data are displayed in Table 7.

TABLE 7

$47,000	$32,750	$35,995
$32,750	$33,995	$39,998
$33,995	$43,500	$37,995
$43,108	$39,950	$37,995
$33,988	$36,900	$43,785

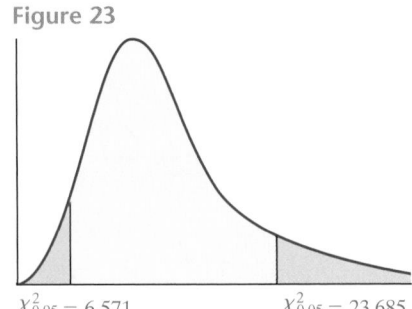

Approach: We will perform the following steps to construct the confidence interval:

Step 1: Check to see whether it is reasonable to conclude that the data come from a normally distributed population.

Step 2: Compute the sample variance.

Step 3: Determine the critical values.

Step 4: Use Formula (1) to construct the confidence interval for the population variance.

Step 5: Compute the square root of the lower and upper bound to obtain the confidence interval for the population standard deviation.

Solution:

Step 1: In Figure 4 from Section 8.1, we constructed a normal probability plot and boxplot. These graphs indicated that the price of Corvettes is normally distributed.

Step 2: From Example 2 in Section 8.2, we calculated the sample standard deviation to be $4,522. The sample variance is $4,522^2$.

Step 3: For 90% confidence, we have $\alpha = 0.10$. Using Table IV with $15 - 1 = 14$ degrees of freedom, we find the left critical value to be $\chi^2_{1-\alpha/2} = \chi^2_{1-0.10/2} = \chi^2_{0.95} = 6.571$. We find the right critical value to be $\chi^2_{\alpha/2} = \chi^2_{0.10/2} = \chi^2_{0.05} = 23.685$. See Figure 23.

Figure 23

$\chi^2_{0.95} = 6.571$ $\chi^2_{0.05} = 23.685$

Step 4: Substitute these values into Formula (1), yielding

$$\text{Lower bound: } \frac{(n - 1)s^2}{\chi^2_{\alpha/2}} = \frac{14(4522)^2}{23.685} = 12{,}086{,}923$$

$$\text{Upper bound: } \frac{(n - 1)s^2}{\chi^2_{1-\alpha/2}} = \frac{14(4522)^2}{6.571} = 43{,}567{,}003$$

Step 5: Taking the square root of each part,* we obtain

Lower bound: $3477   Upper bound: $6601

We are 90% confident that the population standard deviation of the price of a three-year-old Chevy Corvette is between $3477 and $6601.   ◀◀

*Be sure to take the square root of the *unrounded* values.

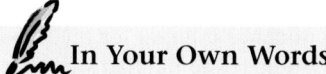
In Your Own Words

To determine a confidence interval for the population standard deviation, first determine the confidence interval about the population variance. Then take the square root of each side of the inequality.

The formula presented for constructing the confidence interval about a population variance requires that the data come from a normal distribution. Confidence intervals for the population mean and population proportion are robust (i.e., not sensitive to moderate departures from normality), but the intervals computed for population variance are not robust. Therefore, it is vital that the requirement of normality be verified before proceeding.

NW *Now Work Problem 7.*

8.4 Assess Your Understanding

Concepts and Vocabulary

1. State the characteristics of the chi-square distribution.

2. What does the distribution of the parent population have to be in order to construct a confidence interval about a population standard deviation?

Exercises

• **Basic Skills**

In Problems 1–4, find the critical values $\chi^2_{1-\alpha/2}$ and $\chi^2_{\alpha/2}$ for the given level of confidence and sample size.

1. 90% confidence; $n = 20$ 10.117; 30.144
NW

2. 95% confidence, $n = 25$ 12.401; 39.364

3. 98% confidence, $n = 23$ 9.542; 40.289

4. 99% confidence, $n = 14$ 3.565; 29.819

5. A simple random sample of size n is drawn from a population that is known to be normally distributed. The sample variance, s^2, is determined to be 12.6.
   (a) Construct the 90% confidence interval for σ^2 if the sample size, n, is 20. (7.95, 23.66)
   (b) Construct the 90% confidence interval for σ^2 if the sample size, n, is 30. How does increasing the sample size affect the width of the interval?
   (c) Construct the 98% confidence interval for σ^2 if the sample size, n, is 20. Compare the results with those obtained in part (a). How does increasing the level of confidence affect the confidence interval?
   (6.61, 31.36); increases
   (b) (8.59, 20.63); decreases

6. A simple random sample of size n is drawn from a population that is known to be normally distributed. The sample variance, s^2, is determined to be 19.8.
   (a) Construct the 95% confidence interval for σ^2 if the sample size, n, is 10. (9.37, 66.00)
   (b) Construct the 95% confidence interval for σ^2 if the sample size, n, is 25. How does increasing the sample size affect the width of the interval?
   (c) Construct the 99% confidence interval for σ^2 if the sample size, n, is 10. Compare the results with those obtained in part (a). How does increasing the level of confidence affect the confidence interval?
   (7.55, 102.71); increases
   (b) (12.07, 38.32); decreases

• **Applying the Concepts**

7. **Wheat Pennies** "Wheat" pennies are pennies that
NW were minted before 1954. The following data represent the weights (in grams) of a random sample of 15 wheat pennies:

3.01	3.06	3.13	3.00	3.05
3.07	3.02	2.98	3.04	3.02
3.06	3.03	3.07	3.04	2.96

In Problem 13 from Section 8.2, it was verified that the data are normally distributed and that $s = 0.0414$ gram. Construct a 95% confidence interval for the population standard deviation of the weight of a wheat penny. Interpret the interval. (0.0303, 0.0653)

8. **Miles on a Camaro** The following data represent the number of miles on a four-year-old Chevy Camaro:

42,544	27,274	34,258	59,177	44,091
35,631	42,371	48,018	58,795	44,832

Source: cars.com

In Problem 14 from Section 8.2, it was verified that the data are normally distributed and that $s = 10,081.1$ miles. Construct a 95% confidence interval for the population standard deviation of the number of miles on a four-year-old Camaro. Interpret the interval. (6934.09, 18,405.49)

9. **Tensile Strength** Tensile strength is the maximum stress at which one can be reasonably certain failure will not occur. The following data represent tensile strength (in thousands of pounds per square inch) of a composite material to be used in an aircraft:

203.41	185.97	184.41	160.44	174.63
209.58	190.67	200.73	180.95	185.34
213.35	207.88	206.51	201.95	205.59
218.56	210.80	209.84	204.60	212.00
242.76	231.46	212.15	219.51	225.25

Source: Vangel, Mark G., "New Methods for One-sided Tolerance Limits for a One-way Balanced Random-Effects ANOVA Model.", *Technometrics*; May, 1992, Vol. 34, Issue 2, pp. 176 – 185.

In Problem 15 from Section 8.2, it was verified that the data are normally distributed and that $s = 18.320$ thousand psi. Construct a 99% confidence interval for the population standard deviation of the tensile strength. Interpret the interval. (13.297, 28.545)

10. **Driving Distance** Dan wants to determine the variability in the distance he hits a golf ball with a new driver he just purchased. He goes to the driving range, uses a range finder to measure the length of each drive (in yards), and obtains the following data:

268	304	256	241	229	255
247	268	273	215	274	222

In Problem 16 from Section 8.2, it was verified that the data are normally distributed and that $s = 25.3$ yards. Construct a 99% confidence interval for the population standard deviation of the length of drive. Interpret the interval. (16.2, 52.0)

11. **Peanuts** A jar of peanuts is supposed to have 16 ounces of peanuts. The filling machine inevitably experiences fluctuations in filling, so a quality-control manager randomly samples 12 jars of peanuts from the storage facility and measures their contents. She obtains the following data:

15.94	15.74	16.21	15.36	15.84	15.84
15.52	16.16	15.78	15.51	16.28	16.53

(a) Verify that the data are normally distributed by constructing a normal probability plot.
(b) Determine the sample standard deviation. 0.349

(c) Construct a 90% confidence interval for the population standard deviation of the number of ounces of peanuts. (0.261, 0.541)
(d) Suppose the quality-control manager wants the machine to have a population standard deviation below 0.20 ounces. Does the confidence interval validate this desire? No

12. **Investment Risk** Investors not only desire a high return on their money, but they would also like the rate of return to be stable from month to month. An investment manager invests with the goal of reducing volatility (month-to-month fluctuations in the rate of return). The following data represent the rate of return (in percent) for his mutual fund for the past 12 months:

13.8	15.9	10.0	12.4	11.3	6.6
9.6	12.4	10.3	8.7	14.9	6.7

(c) (2.11, 5.06)

(a) Verify that the data are normally distributed by constructing a normal probability plot.
(b) Determine the sample standard deviation. 2.979
(c) Construct a 95% confidence interval for the population standard deviation of the rate of return.
(d) Suppose the investment manager wants to have a population standard deviation for the rate of return below 6%. Does the confidence interval validate this desire? Yes

13. **Flight Time** The following data represent the flight time (in minutes) of randomly selected flights from Denver, Colorado, to Chicago, Illinois, in June 2001 for American Airlines and United Airlines:

American Airlines	United Airlines
145 159 149 154 153	152 147 144 138 158
160 146 145 173 172	168 143 150 140 146

Source: United States Department of Transportation

In Problem 17 from Section 8.2, we verified that each airline's flight time is normally distributed with no outliers.

(a) Compute a 95% confidence interval for the population standard deviation of flight time for each airline. AA: (7.2, 19.0); UA: (6.2, 16.4)
(b) From the confidence intervals, does there appear to be any difference in the variability of flight times? No

14. Red Blood Cell Mass The following data represent the red blood cell mass (in millimeters) of 15 rats in a flight group and 15 rats in a ground control group:

Flight Group	Ground Control Group
8.59 8.64 6.87 7.89 7.00	8.65 6.99 7.62 7.33 7.14
8.80 6.39 7.54 7.43 7.21	8.40 8.55 9.88 9.66 7.44
9.79 6.85 8.23 8.03 9.30	8.58 9.14 11.78 8.70 9.94

Source: NASA Life Sciences Database

The red blood cell mass was measured immediately after the flight group returned from space on the Spacelab Life Sciences 2. In Problem 18 from Section 8.2, we verified that each group's red blood cell mass is normally distributed with no outliers.

(a) Flight: (0.757, 1.437); Control: (0.999, 1.896)
(a) Compute a 90% confidence interval for the population standard deviation of red blood cell mass for each group.
(b) From the confidence intervals, does there appear to be any difference in the variability of red blood cell mass? No

15. Critical Values Sir R. A. Fisher, a famous statistician, showed that the critical values of a chi-square distribution can be approximated via the standard normal distribution

$$\chi_k^2 = \frac{(z_k + \sqrt{2v - 1})^2}{2}$$

where v is the degrees of freedom. Use Fisher's approximation to find $\chi_{0.975}^2$ and $\chi_{0.025}^2$ with 100 degrees of freedom. Compare the results with those found in Table IV. 73.772; 129.070

Technology Step-by-Step
Confidence Intervals about σ

TI-83 Plus   The TI-83 Plus does not construct confidence intervals about σ.

MINITAB   **Step 1:** Enter raw data in column C1.

Step 2: Select the **Stat** menu, highlight **Basic Statistics**, then highlight **Display Descriptive Statistics** . . . .

Step 3: Enter C1 in the cell marked "Variables." Click **Graphs** . . . .

Step 4: Check the Graphical summary box. Enter the Confidence level desired. Click OK twice. The confidence interval for sigma is reported in the output.

Excel   Excel does not construct confidence intervals about σ.

CHAPTER 8 REVIEW

Summary

In this chapter, we discussed estimation methods. We estimated the values of the parameters μ, p, and σ. We started by estimating the population mean under the assumption that the population standard deviation was known. This assumption allowed us to construct a confidence interval about μ by utilizing the standard normal distribution. In order to construct the interval, we required either that the population from which the sample was drawn be normal or that the sample size, n, be greater than or equal to 30. In addition, the sampling method had to be simple random sampling. With these requirements satisfied, the $(1 - \alpha) \cdot 100\%$ confidence interval about μ is $\bar{x} \pm z_{\alpha/2} \cdot \frac{\sigma}{\sqrt{n}}$. We have $(1 - \alpha) \cdot 100\%$ confidence that the unknown value of μ lies within the interval.

In Section 8.2, we dropped the assumption that the population standard deviation be known. With σ unknown, the sampling distribution of $t = \frac{\bar{x} - \mu}{s/\sqrt{n}}$ follows Student's t-distribution with $n - 1$ degrees of freedom. We use the t-distribution to construct the confidence interval about μ. In order to construct this interval, either the population from which the sample was drawn must be normal or the sample size must be large. In addition, the sampling method must be simple random sampling. With these requirements satisfied, the $(1 - \alpha) \cdot 100\%$ confidence interval about μ is $\bar{x} \pm t_{\alpha/2} \cdot \frac{s}{\sqrt{n}}$, where $t_{\alpha/2}$ has $n - 1$ degrees of freedom. This means that the procedure results in an interval that contains μ, the population mean, $(1 - \alpha) \cdot 100\%$ of the time.

In Section 8.3, a confidence interval regarding the population proportion, p, was constructed. This confidence interval is constructed about the binomial parameter p. Provided that the sample is obtained via simple random sampling and that $n\hat{p}(1 - \hat{p}) \geq 10$, the $(1 - \alpha) \cdot 100\%$ confidence interval about p is $\hat{p} \pm z_{\alpha/2} \cdot \sqrt{\dfrac{\hat{p}(1 - \hat{p})}{n}}$. We have $(1 - \alpha) \cdot 100\%$ confidence that the unknown value of p lies within the interval.

Finally, we introduced a method for estimating the population standard deviation. In order to perform this estimation, the population from which the sample is drawn must be normal and the sampling method must be simple random sampling. If these requirements are satisfied, then $\chi^2 = \dfrac{(n - 1)s^2}{\sigma^2}$ follows the chi-square distribution with $n - 1$ degrees of freedom. The $(1 - \alpha) \cdot 100\%$ confidence interval about σ^2 is $\dfrac{(n - 1)s^2}{\chi^2_{\alpha/2}} < \sigma^2 < \dfrac{(n - 1)s^2}{\chi^2_{1-\alpha/2}}$.

To construct the $(1 - \alpha) \cdot 100\%$ about σ, we take the square root of each part of the inequality and obtain $\sqrt{\dfrac{(n - 1)s^2}{\chi^2_{\alpha/2}}} < \sigma < \sqrt{\dfrac{(n - 1)s^2}{\chi^2_{1-\alpha/2}}}$. We have $(1 - \alpha) \cdot 100\%$ confidence that the unknown value of σ lies within the interval.

Formulas

Confidence Intervals

- A $(1 - \alpha) \cdot 100\%$ confidence interval about μ with σ known is $\bar{x} \pm z_{\alpha/2} \cdot \dfrac{\sigma}{\sqrt{n}}$, provided that the population from which the sample was drawn is normal or that the sample size is large ($n \geq 30$).

- A $(1 - \alpha) \cdot 100\%$ confidence interval about μ with σ unknown is $\bar{x} \pm t_{\alpha/2} \cdot \dfrac{s}{\sqrt{n}}$ where $t_{\alpha/2}$ has $n - 1$ degrees of freedom, provided that the population from which the sample was drawn is normal or that the sample size is large ($n \geq 30$).

- A $(1 - \alpha) \cdot 100\%$ confidence interval about p is $\hat{p} \pm z_{\alpha/2} \cdot \sqrt{\dfrac{\hat{p}(1 - \hat{p})}{n}}$, provided that $n\hat{p}(1 - \hat{p}) \geq 10$.

- A $(1 - \alpha) \cdot 100\%$ confidence interval about σ^2 is $\dfrac{(n - 1)s^2}{\chi^2_{\alpha/2}} < \sigma^2 < \dfrac{(n - 1)s^2}{\chi^2_{1-\alpha/2}}$ where χ^2 has $n - 1$ degrees of freedom, provided that the population from which the sample was drawn is normal.

Sample Size

- To estimate the population mean within a margin of error E at a $(1 - \alpha) \cdot 100\%$ level of confidence requires a sample of size $n = \left(\dfrac{z_{\alpha/2} \cdot \sigma}{E}\right)^2$ (rounded up to the next integer).

- To estimate the population proportion within a margin of error E at a $(1 - \alpha) \cdot 100\%$ level of confidence requires a sample of size $n = \hat{p}(1 - \hat{p})\left(\dfrac{z_{\alpha/2}}{E}\right)^2$ (rounded up to the next integer), where $\hat{p}$ is a prior estimate of the population proportion.

- To estimate the population proportion within a margin of error E at a $(1 - \alpha) \cdot 100\%$ level of confidence requires a sample of size $n = 0.25\left(\dfrac{z_{\alpha/2}}{E}\right)^2$ (rounded up to the next integer) when no prior estimate is available.

Vocabulary

Point estimate (p. 456)	Level of confidence (p. 458)	Margin of error (p. 463)
Consistent (p. 456)	Critical values (p. 460)	Student's t-distribution (p. 476)
Efficiency (p. 456)	Robust (p. 461)	t-interval (p. 480)
Unbiased estimator (p. 456)	z-interval (p. 461)	Chi-square distribution (p. 499)
Confidence interval estimate (p. 458)		

Objectives

Section	You should be able to . . .	Review Exercises
8.1	1 Compute the point estimate of μ (p. 456)	9(b); 10(b); 13(a); 14(a)
	2 Compute confidence intervals about μ with σ known (p. 457)	5; 6(a)–(c); 7(b), (c); 8(b),(c); 9(c),(d); 10(c), (d)
	3 Understand the role of margin of error in constructing confidence intervals (p. 463)	5; 6(a)–(c)
	4 Find the sample size necessary for estimating the population mean (p. 464)	7(d); 8(d)

8.2	1 Know the properties of Student's t-distribution (p. 476)	21–23
	2 Determine t-values (p. 478)	1,2
	3 Construct confidence intervals about μ, σ unknown (p. 480)	11(b),(c); 12(b),(c); 13(c),(d); 14(c),(d); 15; 16
	4 Determine the method to use to compute an interval about μ (p. 483)	5–16
8.3	1 Obtain a point estimate for the population proportion (p. 490)	17(a); 18(a)
	2 Obtain and interpret a confidence interval for the population proportion (p. 491)	17(b); 18(b)
	3 Determine the sample size for estimating a population proportion (p. 493)	17(c),(d); 18(c),(d)
8.4	1 Find critical values for the chi-square distribution (p. 498)	3,4
	2 Construct confidence intervals about the population variance and standard deviation (p. 501)	6(d);13(e);14(e);19;20

Exercises

In Problems 1 and 2, find the critical t-value for constructing a confidence interval about a population mean at the given level of confidence for the given sample size, n.

1. 99% confidence; $n = 18$ 2.898

2. 90% confidence; $n = 27$ 1.706

In Problems 3 and 4, find the critical values $\chi^2_{1-\alpha/2}$ and $\chi^2_{\alpha/2}$ required to construct a confidence interval about σ for the given level of confidence and sample size.

3. 95% confidence; $n = 22$ 10.283, 35.479

4. 99% confidence; $n = 12$ 2.603, 26.757

---

5. A simple random sample of size n is drawn from a population that is known to be normally distributed. The sample mean, $\bar{x}$, is determined to be 54.8. (50.94, 58.66)

(a) Construct the 90% confidence interval about the population mean if the population standard deviation, σ, is known to be 10.5 and the sample size, n, is 20.

(b) Construct the 90% confidence interval about the population mean if the population standard deviation, σ, is known to be 10.5 and the sample size, n, is 30. How does increasing the sample size affect the width of the interval? (51.65, 57.95); Decreases

(c) Construct the 99% confidence interval about the population mean if the population standard deviation, σ, is known to be 10.5 and the sample size, n, is 20. Compare the results to those obtained in part (a). How does increasing the level of confidence affect the confidence interval? (48.75, 60.85); increases width

6. A simple random sample of size n is drawn from a population that is known to be normally distributed. The sample mean, $\bar{x}$, is determined to be 104.3 and the sample standard deviation, s, is determined to be 15.9.

(a) Construct the 90% confidence interval about the population mean if the sample size, n, is 15. (97.07, 111.53)

(b) Construct the 90% confidence interval about the population mean if the sample size, n, is 25. How does increasing the sample size affect the width of the interval? (98.86, 109.74); decreases

(c) Construct the 95% confidence interval about the population mean if the sample size, n, is 15. Compare the results to those obtained in part (a). How does increasing the level of confidence affect the confidence interval? (95.50, 113.11); increases width

(d) Construct the 90% confidence interval about the population standard deviation if the sample size, n, is 15. (12.22, 23.21)

7. Tire Wear Suppose Dunlop wishes to estimate the mean mileage for its SP4000 tire. In a random sample of 35 tires, the sample mean mileage was $\bar{x} = 62{,}450$ miles.

(a) Why can we say that the sampling distribution of $\bar{x}$ is approximately normal? Large sample

(b) Construct a 90% confidence interval for the mean mileage for all SP4000 tires, assuming that $\sigma = 4400$ miles. Interpret this interval.

(c) Construct a 95% confidence interval for the mean mileage for all SP4000 tires, assuming that $\sigma = 4400$ miles. Interpret this interval.

(d) How many tires would Dunlop need in order to estimate the mean mileage for all SP4000 tires within 3000 miles with 99% confidence? 15

(7b) (61,227, 63,673) (7c) (60,992, 63,908)

8. **Talk Time on a Cell Phone** Suppose Motorola wishes to estimate the mean "talk time" for its Timeport P8160 digital phone before the battery must be recharged. In a random sample of 40 phones, the sample mean talk time was 315 minutes.
   (a) Why can we say that the sampling distribution of $\bar{x}$ is approximately normal? Large sample
   (b) Construct a 94% confidence interval for the mean "talk time" for all Timeport P8160 digital phones, assuming that $\sigma = 24$ minutes. (307.9, 322.1)
   (c) Construct a 98% confidence interval for the mean "talk time" for all Timeport P8160 digital phones, assuming that $\sigma = 24$ minutes. (306.2, 323.8)
   (d) How many phones would Motorola need in order to estimate the mean "talk time" for all Timeport P8160 phones within 10 minutes with 95% confidence? 23

9. **Math Achievement** The following data represent the mathematics achievement test scores for a random sample of 15 students who had just completed high school in Canada and in the United States, according to data obtained from the International Association for the Evaluation of Education Achievement study in 1998:

Canada				
558	556	594	592	458
600	468	554	614	500
637	511	557	531	526

United States				
583	402	510	432	500
531	410	469	459	450
465	483	553	446	559

   (a) Verify that the scores for each country are normally distributed with no outliers.
   (b) Obtain a point estimate for the population mean score of each country. C: 550.4; U.S.: 483.5
   (c) Construct a 99% confidence interval for the population mean achievement score of Canada, assuming that $\sigma = 62.6$. (508.8, 592.0)
   (d) Construct a 99% confidence interval for the population mean achievement score of the United States, assuming that $\sigma = 71.5$. (435.9, 531.0)
   (e) Does it appear to be the case that Canadians scored higher than Americans on the exam? Why? No

(11a) Normal, $\mu_{\bar{x}} = 2.27, \sigma_{\bar{x}} = \dfrac{1.22}{\sqrt{60}}$

10. **Math Achievement** The following data represent the mathematics achievement test scores for a random sample of 15 male and female students who had just completed high school in the United States, according to data obtained from the International Association for the Evaluation of Education Achievement study in 1998:

Male				
488	350	547	488	474
471	443	385	477	452
418	388	441	463	412

Female				
433	389	520	479	454
563	411	458	398	337
418	492	442	494	514

   (a) Verify that the scores for each gender are normally distributed with no outliers.
   (b) Obtain a point estimate for the population mean score of each gender. M: 446.5; F: 453.5
   (c) Construct a 95% confidence interval for the population mean achievement score of males, assuming that $\sigma = 64.8$. (413.7, 479.3)
   (d) Construct a 95% confidence interval for the population mean achievement score of females, assuming that $\sigma = 56.9$. (424.7, 482.3)
   (e) Does there appear to be any difference between the scores of males and those of females? Why? No

11. **Family Size** A random sample of 60 married couples who have been married seven years, were asked the number of children they have. The results of the survey are as follows:

0	0	0	3	3	3	1	3	2	2	3	1
3	2	4	0	3	3	3	1	0	2	3	3
1	4	2	3	1	3	3	5	0	2	3	0
4	4	2	2	3	2	2	2	2	3	4	3
2	2	1	4	3	2	4	2	1	2	3	2

   Note: $\bar{x} = 2.27, s = 1.22$.
   (a) What is the sampling distribution of $\bar{x}$? In other words, what is the shape, mean, and standard deviation of the distribution of $\bar{x}$? Why?
   (b) Compute a 95% confidence interval for the mean number of children of all couples who have been married 7 years. Interpret this interval. (1.95, 2.58)
   (c) Compute a 99% confidence interval for the mean number of children of all couples who have been married 7 years. Interpret this interval. (1.85, 2.69)

12. **Waiting in Line** The following data represent the number of cars that arrive at McDonald's drive-through between 11:50 A.M. and 12:00 noon for a random sample of Wednesdays:

Note: $\bar{x}$ = 4.08, s = 2.12.

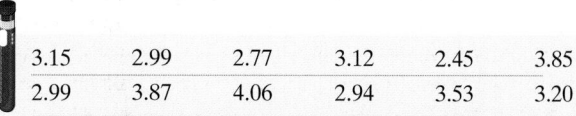

1	7	3	8	2	3	8	2	6	3
6	5	6	4	3	4	3	8	1	2
5	3	6	3	3	4	3	2	1	2
4	4	9	3	5	2	3	5	5	5
2	5	6	1	7	1	5	3	8	4

(a) What is the sampling distribution of $\bar{x}$? In other words, what is the shape, mean and standard deviation of the distribution of $\bar{x}$? Why?

(b) Compute a 90% confidence interval for the mean number of cars waiting in line between 11:50 A.M. and 12:00 noon on Wednesdays. Interpret this interval. (3.58, 4.58)

(c) Compute a 95% confidence interval for the mean number of cars waiting in line between 11:50 A.M. and 12:00 noon on Wednesdays. Interpret this interval. (3.48, 4.68)

(a) Normal, $\mu_{\bar{x}}$ = 4.08, $\sigma_{\bar{x}} = \dfrac{2.12}{\sqrt{50}}$

---

13. **Blood Plasma** In a study of aerobic activity, the blood plasma volume (in liters) of 12 women was measured, and the following data were obtained:

| 3.15 | 2.99 | 2.77 | 3.12 | 2.45 | 3.85 |
| 2.99 | 3.87 | 4.06 | 2.94 | 3.53 | 3.20 |

Source: *Journal of Applied Physiology* 65, 6 (December, 1988), p. 361 from *Hogg and Tanis Probability and Statistical Inference* 6/e.

(a) Use the data to compute a point estimate for the population mean and population standard deviation. $\bar{x}$ = 3.243, s = 0.487

(b) Because the sample size is small, we must verify that blood plasma is normally distributed and that the data do not contain any outliers. The figures below show the normal probability plot and boxplot. Are the conditions for constructing a confidence interval about μ satisfied? Yes

Normal Probability Plot for Blood Plasma

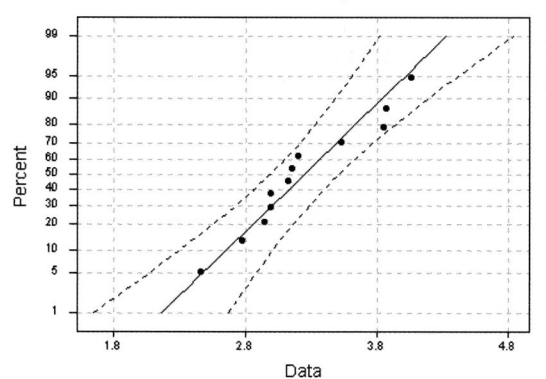

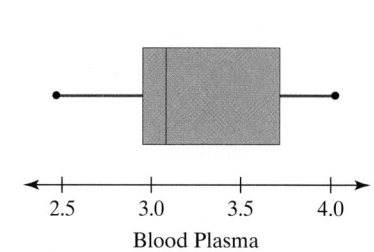

(c) Construct a 95% confidence interval for the mean blood plasma volume for all women. Interpret this interval. (2.934, 3.553)

(d) Construct a 99% confidence interval for the mean blood plasma volume for all women. Interpret this interval. (2.807, 3.680)

(e) Construct a 99% confidence interval for the population standard deviation of blood plasma volume. Interpret this interval. (0.312, 1.001)

14. **Water Clarity** The campus at Joliet Junior College has a lake. A Secchi dish is used to measure the water clarity of the lake's water by lowering the dish into the water and measuring the distance below water until the dish is no longer visible. The following measurements (in inches) were taken on the lake at various points in time over the course of a year:

82	64	62	66	68	43
38	26	68	56	54	66

Source: Virginia Piekarski, Joliet Junior College

(a) Use the data to compute a point estimate for the population mean and population standard deviation. $\bar{x} = 57.8$, $s = 15.4$

(b) Because the sample size is small, we must verify that the data are normally distributed and do not contain any outliers. The figures below show the normal probability plot and boxplot. Are the conditions for constructing a confidence interval about μ satisfied? Yes

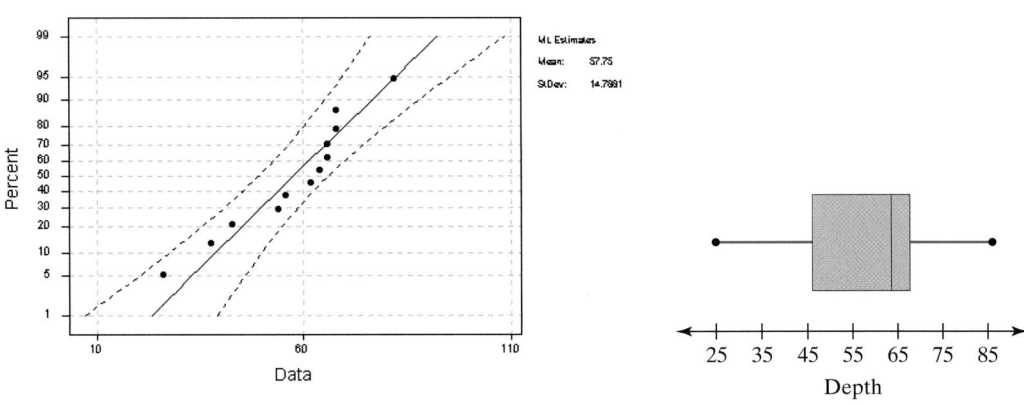

Normal Probability Plot for Depth

ML Estimates
Mean: 57.75
StDev: 14.7691

(c) Construct a 95% confidence interval for the mean Secchi disk measurement. Interpret this interval. (47.9, 67.6)

(d) Construct a 99% confidence interval for the mean Secchi disk measurement. Interpret this interval. (43.9, 71.6)

(e) Construct a 95% confidence interval for the population standard deviation Secchi disk measurement. Interpret this interval. (10.9, 26.2)

---

15. **Math Achievement** Redo Problems 9(c)–(e), assuming that σ is unknown.

16. **Math Achievement** Redo Problems 10(c)–(e), assuming that σ is unknown.

17. **Hypertension** In a random sample of 678 adult males 20–34 years of age, it was determined that 58 of them have hypertension (high blood pressure) [from data obtained from the Centers for Disease Control].

(a) Obtain a point estimate for the proportion of adult males 20–34 years of age who have hypertension.

(b) Construct a 95% confidence interval for the proportion of adult males 20–34 years of age who have hypertension. Interpret the confidence interval. (0.064, 0.107)

15. Canada: (510.3, 590.5) U.S.: (441.3, 525.6)
16. Male: (418.9, 474.0); Female: (420.9, 486.0)
(17a) 0.086

(c) Suppose you wish to conduct your own study to determine the proportion of adult males 20–34 years old who have hypertension. What sample size would be needed for the estimate to be within 3 percentage points with 95% confidence if you use the point estimate obtained in part (a)? 336

(d) Suppose you wish to conduct your own study to determine the proportion of adult males 20–34 years old who have hypertension. What sample size would be needed for the estimate to be within 3 percentage points with 95% confidence if you don't have a prior estimate? 1068

18. **Carbon Monoxide** From a random sample of 1201 Americans, it was discovered that 1139 of them lived in neighborhoods with acceptable levels of carbon monoxide [from data obtained from the Environmental Protection Agency].

(a) Obtain a point estimate for the proportion of Americans who live in neighborhoods with acceptable levels of carbon monoxide. 0.948

(b) Construct a 99% confidence interval for the proportion of Americans who live in neighborhoods with acceptable levels of carbon monoxide. (0.932, 0.965)

(c) Suppose you wish to conduct your own study to determine the proportion of Americans who live in neighborhoods with acceptable levels of carbon monoxide. What sample size would be needed for the estimate to be within 1.5 percentage points with 90% confidence if you use the estimate obtained in part (a)? 593

(d) Suppose you wish to conduct your own study to determine the proportion of Americans who live in neighborhoods with acceptable levels of carbon monoxide. What sample size would be needed for the estimate to be within 1.5 percentage points with 90% confidence if you don't have a prior estimate? 3007

19. **Math Achievement** Use the data in Problem 9 to answer these questions:

(a) Compute the 95% confidence interval for the population standard deviation test score of Canadians.

(b) Compute the 95% confidence interval for the population standard deviation test score of Americans.

(c) Does it appear to be the case that the test scores of Canadians are more dispersed than the test scores of Americans? No

20. **Math Achievement** Use the data in Problem 10 to answer these questions:

(a) Compute the 95% confidence interval for the population standard deviation test score of males.

(b) Compute the 95% confidence interval for the population standard deviation test score of females.

(c) Does it appear to be the case that the test scores of males are more dispersed than the test scores of females? No

21. The area under the t-distribution with 18 degrees of freedom to the right of $t = 1.56$ is 0.0681. What is the area under the t-distribution with 18 degrees of freedom to the left of $t = -1.56$? Why? 0.0681

22. Which is larger, the area under the t-distribution with 10 degrees of freedom to the right of $t = 2.32$ or the area under the standard normal distribution to the right of $z = 2.32$? Why? t-distribution

23. State the properties of Student's t-distribution.

(19a) (38.2, 82.4); (b) (40.1, 86.4)
(20a) (36.4, 78.5); (b) (43.0, 92.6)

The Search for a Fire-Safe Cigarette

In the United States, approximately 1000 deaths and 3000 serious injuries result annually from fires caused by dropped or discarded cigarettes. The dollar value of the property lost in these fires is staggering. Over one-fifth of all deadly fires have cigarettes as their ignition source! Cigarettes are the single largest cause of these life-consuming blazes.

The National Fire Protection Agency describes the cigarette fire mortality rate among young children as moderate, and that for children between the ages of 10 and 17 is considered low. For adults, the cigarette fire mortality rate steadily increases with age, peaking above age 85. The elderly smoker who uses sedating medications or alcohol is particularly imperiled. (Source: *The Fire-Safe Cigarette: the Search for a Standard*. http://www.burnfoundation.org/firesafecig.html)

Recently, the United States National Institute of Standards and Technology (NIST) conducted a study to assess the risk of fire from a dropped or discarded cigarette. Two types of cigarettes, designated 529 and 531, were chosen for their experiment. Both cigarettes were purchased in the same geographical region and were advertised as being 100 mm long and 25 mm in circumference. Each brand used expanded, flue-cured tobacco. Cigarette 529 was wrapped with low-air-permeability paper; cigarette 531 was wrapped with paper of conventional air permeability.

The study's response variables were binary (e.g., full-length burn or not, and substrate ignition or not), so a binomial probability distribution was used to perform the analysis. Specifically, the NIST study relied upon confidence intervals of binomial (population) proportions. The report noted that there were some limitations concerning the use of these confidence intervals. Specifically, the text mentioned that the distribution of a binomial proportion is approximately normal if the sample size is sufficiently large. Furthermore, the sample size necessary for the appropriate use of the normal approximation depends directly upon the value of the proportion. That is, if the proportion is near zero or one, a very large sample size is needed for the normal approximation to work well. For outcomes where the normal approximation were not appropriate, the researchers used other, more computationally intensive methods.

One phase of the study dealt with the relative ignition strengths of cigarettes 529 and 531. The number of successful full-length burns was counted for each brand of cigarettes for different numbers of original filter paper substrate layers. The results for tests conducted in 1993 and 2000 are presented in the following table:

	1993				2000		
Cigarette	3 Layers	10 Layers	15 Layers		3 Layers	10 Layers	15 Layers
529	22/32	0/32	0/32		18/48	0/48	
531	32/32	30/32	28/32			44/48	38/48

Relative Ignition Strengths of Cigarettes 529 and 531 (Number of Full-Length Burns/Number of Trials)[*]

Where appropriate, for each sample year, calculate the 95% confidence interval for the proportion of full-length burns for the various combinations of cigarette and number of original filter paper substrate layers. State conclusions based on your findings concerning the relative ignition strengths of cigarettes 529 and 531. If you could repeat this experiment, how large a sample would you need to ensure that the use of the normal distribution was appropriate for all the various combinations?

Another phase of the study addressed the ignition propensities of conventionally wrapped and banded ("modified product") cigarettes. The Mock-up Ignition Method, developed under the Fire-Safe Cigarette Act of 1990, was followed during this test. The Mock-up method measures whether a cigarette transfers enough heat to a fabric/foam substrate (simulated piece of furniture) to cause ignition. Substrate materials were formed by placing a fabric on a piece of non-fire-retarded foam. To ensure adequate contact between layers, a metal rim was placed on top of the substrate. An ignition was declared when the char advanced 10 mm away from the burning cigarette. Lit cigarettes of each type were exposed to four different substrate materials, with the number of ignitions being recorded for each scenario. The results of this experiment are presented in the following table:

Ignition Propensities of Conventional and Banded Cigarettes of the Same Brand, Measured with of the Mock-up Ignition Method (Number of Ignitions/Number of Trials)*

	Substrate			
Cigarette	Duck #10	Duck #6	Duck #4	Ivory Cotton
Conventional	64/64	64/64	12/64	64/64
Banded	24/64	32/64	2/64	38/64

Where appropriate, calculate the 95% confidence interval for the proportion of each substrate that was ignited by conventional and banded cigarettes. State conclusions based on your findings regarding the ignition propensities of conventional and banded cigarettes. If you could repeat this experiment, how large a sample would you need to ensure that the use of the normal distribution was appropriate for each scenario?

Write a final report detailing your findings. Include in this document a discussion concerning any assumptions made.

---

*Richard G. Gann, *et al. Relative Ignition Propensity of Test Market Cigarettes*. National Institute of Standards and Technology, Technical Note 1436, January 2001. Web address: http://www.bfrl.nist.gov/pdf/cigaretterpt.pdf. The original data contained in this report were doubled to ensure that some of the binomial proportions would satisfy the normal approximation requirements.

One of the most difficult decisions that a person needs to make is choosing a major field of study. This decision plays a major role in the career path of an individual. The purpose of this project is to help you make a more informed decision regarding your major.

You are to randomly select people who have recently graduated in the major that you have chosen or randomly select individuals who have recently secured a job in a career that you are considering. If you have not yet chosen a major, select one that interests you. Create a survey that will allow you to make a more informed decision regarding your major field of study. Some suggested sample questions follow:

(a) What was your major in college?

(b) On average, how many hours do you work?

(c) Approximately how many weeks did it take you to find your job?

(d) What was your starting annual salary?

(e) Are you satisfied or dissatisfied with your career?

(f) Do you feel you have job security?

Administer the survey. Be sure to explain the purpose of the survey and make it look professional. Because it is important that we obtain accurate results, make sure that the surveys are completed anonymously. We will treat the randomly selected individuals as a simple random sample.

Estimate the unknown parameter for each of the questions asked. For example, in question (b) given above, estimate the population mean number of hours worked. In question (e), estimate the proportion of individuals satisfied with their career. Then construct 95% confidence intervals about each parameter. Write a report detailing your findings.

Consumer Reports' specialized auto-test facility is the largest, most sophisticated consumer-based auto-testing facility in the world. Located on 327 acres in East Haddam, Conn., the facility is staffed by a team of experienced engineers and test personnel who buy and test more than 40 new cars, SUVs, minivans, and light trucks each year. For each of these vehicles, Consumer Reports conducts more than 46 individual tests, ranging from emergency handling, acceleration, and braking to fuel-economy measurements, noise-level evaluations, and bumper-impact tests.

© 2001 by Consumers Union of U.S., Inc., Yonkers, NY 10703-1057, a nonprofit organization. Reprinted with permission from CONSUMER REPORTS® for educational purposes only. No commercial use or photocopying permitted. To learn more about Consumers Union, log onto www.ConsumerReports.org <http://www.ConsumerReports.org>.

In addition to testing vehicles, Consumer Reports also tests tires. Our tire evaluations include dry and wet braking from 60 mph, braking on ice, snow traction on a flat surface, snow traction on a snow hill, emergency handling, routine cornering, ride comfort, rolling resistance, and noise. All the test data are recorded using an optical instrument that provides precise speed and distance measurements.

The following table contains the dry brake stopping distance data for one brand of tires recently tested (November 2001):

Measurement	Distance
1	131.8
2	123.2
3	132.9
4	139.8
5	140.3
6	128.3
7	129.3
8	129.5
9	134.0

(a) A normal probability plot of the dry brake distance data is shown below. What does this plot suggest about the distribution of the brake data?

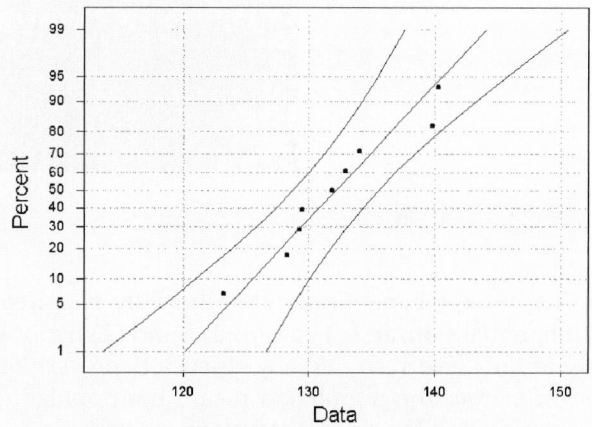

(b) Does the data set contain any outliers?

(c) Use this data to construct a 95% confidence interval for the mean dry braking distance for this brand of tires. Write a statement that explains the meaning of this confidence interval to the readers of Consumer Reports magazine.

Note to Readers: In many cases, our test protocol and analytical methods are more complicated than described in these examples. The data and discussions have been modified to make the material more appropriate for the audience.

Putting It All Together

In Chapter 8, we mentioned that there are two areas of inferential statistics: (1) estimation and (2) hypothesis testing. We have already discussed procedures for estimating the population mean, the population proportion and the population standard deviation.

We now focus our attention on hypothesis testing. Hypothesis testing is used to test claims regarding a characteristic of one or more populations. In this chapter, we will test claims regarding a single population parameter. The claims that we test regard the population mean, the population proportion and the population standard deviation.

Hypothesis Testing

Outline

 For additional study help, go to www.prenhall.com/sullivanstats

Materials include

- Self-Graded Quizzes
- "Preparing for This Section" Quizzes
- STATLETs
- PowerPoint Downloads
- Step-by-Step Technology Guide
- Graphing Calculator Help

9.1 The Language of Hypothesis Testing

Preparing for This Section Before getting started, review the following:

✓ Simple random sampling (Section 1.2, pp. 15–17)

✓ Parameter versus statistic (Section 3.1, p. 112)

✓ Table 8 (Section 6.2, p. 343)

✓ Central Limit Theorem (Section 7.5, p. 432)

Objectives Determine the null and alternative hypotheses from a claim

 Understand Type I and Type II errors

 Understand the probability of making Type I and Type II errors

 State conclusions to hypothesis tests

Let's begin with an example that introduces the idea behind hypothesis testing.

▶ **EXAMPLE 1** Illustrating Hypothesis Testing

Note to Instructor
Before starting this section, divide your students into groups. Each group should then define the following (along with the symbolic representation): population mean, sample mean, population standard deviation, sample standard deviation, and standard error of the mean.

Problem: According to the National Center for Chronic Disease Prevention and Health Promotion, 73.8% of females between the ages of 18 and 29 years exercise. Kathleen believes that more women between the ages of 18 and 29 years are now exercising, so she obtains a simple random sample of 1000 women and finds that 750 of them are exercising. Is this evidence that the percent of women between the ages of 18 and 29 who are exercising has increased? What if Kathleen's sample resulted in 920 women exercising?

Approach: Here is the situation Kathleen faces. If 73.8% of 18–29-year-old females exercise, then she would expect 738 of the 1000 respondents in the sample to exercise. The question that Kathleen needs to answer is: "How likely is it to obtain a sample of 750 out of 1000 women exercising from a population when the percentage of women who exercise is 73.8%? How likely is a sample that has 920 women exercising?"

Solution: The result of 750 women who exercise is close to what we would expect, so Kathleen is not inclined to believe that the percentage of women exercising has increased. However, the likelihood of obtaining a sample of 920 women who exercise is extremely low if the actual percentage of women who exercise is 73.8%. For the case of obtaining a sample of 920 women who exercise, Kathleen can conclude one of two things: either the proportion of women who exercise is 73.8% and her sample just happens to include a lot of women who exercise or the proportion of women who exercise has increased. Provided the sampling was performed in a correct fashion, Kathleen is more inclined to believe that the percentage of women who exercise has increased. ◀◀

 Example 1 presents the basic premise behind hypothesis testing: A claim is made, information is collected, and this information is used to test the claim. The steps in conducting a hypothesis test are presented next.

Note to Instructor
Emphasize that "supporting" a claim is different from proving that a claim is true.

Steps in Hypothesis Testing

1. A claim is made.

2. Evidence (sample data) is collected in order to test the claim.

3. The data are analyzed in order to support or refute the claim.

In this section, we introduce the language of hypothesis testing. Sections 9.2–9.5 discuss the formal process of testing a hypothesis.

Definition   A **hypothesis** is a statement or claim regarding a characteristic of one or more populations.

In Your Own Words

In this chapter, we will focus on hypothesis testing regarding a single population parameter. The characteristic we test regards the population mean, proportion, or standard deviation.

In this chapter, we look at hypotheses regarding a single population parameter. The following are examples of claims regarding a characteristic of a single population.

(A) According to a Gallup poll conducted in 1995, 74% of Americans felt that men were more aggressive than women. A researcher claims the percentage of Americans that feel men are more aggressive than women is different today (a claim regarding a population proportion).

(B) The packaging on a lightbulb states that the bulb will last 500 hours under normal use. A consumer advocate would like to know if the mean lifetime of a bulb is less than 500 hours (a claim regarding the population mean).

(C) The standard deviation rate of return for a certain class of mutual funds is 0.08. A mutual fund manager claims the standard deviation rate of return for his fund is less than 0.08 (a claim regarding the population standard deviation).

Caution

If population data are available, there is no need for inferential statistics.

We test these types of claims using sample data because it is usually impossible or impractical to gain access to the entire population.

Consider the lightbulb manufacturer mentioned in situation B. The packaging states that the lightbulb lasts 500 hours. The consumer advocate would like to know if the manufacturer is misleading the public, so he wants to know if there is evidence to support the claim that the mean lifetime of the bulb is less than 500 hours. To test the claim, the researcher might obtain a random sample of 49 lightbulbs. Suppose he determines the mean length of time before they burned out is 476 hours. Is this result enough evidence to conclude that the bulb's life is less than 500 hours? If we give the manufacturer the benefit of the doubt, then the mean lifetime of the bulb would be $\mu_{\bar{x}} = 500$. Let's assume that the standard deviation lifetime of the bulb is $\sigma = 42$ hours, so that the standard deviation of $\bar{x}$ is $\sigma_{\bar{x}} = \dfrac{42}{\sqrt{49}} = 6$. In addition, by the Central Limit Theorem we know the distribution of the sample mean is approximately normal (because the sample size is greater than 30). From Figure 1, we can see the sampling distribution of $\bar{x}$ with the observed sample mean of 476 hours labeled.

The sample mean of 476 is so far from the claimed mean that we have reason to believe that the manufacturer's claim is probably not true. The consumer advocate would conclude that the population mean is likely some value less than 500 hours.

Figure 1

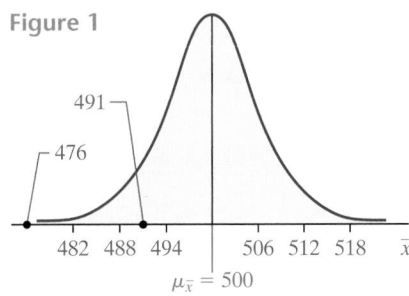

Note to Instructor
Consider introducing the concept of hypothesis testing using this informal approach. Draw a normal curve with the mean, one, two, and three standard errors from the mean labeled (as in Figure 1). Ask students whether a sample mean that is one standard error from the mean is "too far". What about three standard errors? Be sure to emphasize that "too far" is expressed in terms of standard errors.

Suppose that instead of getting a sample mean of 476 hours, the consumer advocate got a sample mean of 491 hours. Would this result be unusual if the bulb does, in fact, have a mean lifetime of 500 hours? Again, we label the observed sample mean on the distribution in Figure 1. This result could very easily occur by chance when the population mean is 500 hours. We have no reason to believe the mean lifetime of the bulb is less than 500 hours.

From the two situations just presented, it is clear from Figure 1 that 476 hours is "too far" from the claimed mean, while 491 hours is "close enough" for us to believe that the population mean could be 500 hours. This raises an interesting question. How far from the presumed mean of 500 hours can our sample mean (evidence) be before we reject the idea that the bulb lasts 500 hours? To answer to this question requires *hypothesis testing*.

Definition

Hypothesis testing is a procedure, based on sample evidence and probability, used to test claims regarding a characteristic of one or more populations.

Hypothesis testing is based upon two types of hypotheses.

Definitions

The **null hypothesis**, denoted H_0 (read "H-naught"), is a statement to be tested. The null hypothesis is assumed true until evidence indicates otherwise. In this chapter, it will be a statement regarding the value of a population parameter.

The **alternative hypothesis**, denoted H_1 (read "H-one"), is a claim to be tested. We are trying to find evidence for the alternative hypothesis. In this chapter, it will be a claim regarding the value of a population parameter.

In Your Own Words

The null hypothesis is a statement of "status quo" or "no difference" and always contains a statement of equality. The null hypothesis is assumed to be true until we have evidence to the contrary. The claim that we seek evidence for always becomes the alternative hypothesis.

For the lightbulb manufacturer the consumer advocate wishes to test the claim that the mean lifetime of the bulb is less than 500 hours. Because we are trying to obtain evidence for this claim, it is expressed as the alternative hypothesis using the notation $H_1: \mu < 500$. The statement made by the manufacturer is that the bulb lasts 500 hours. We express the statement to be tested using the notation $H_0: \mu = 500$.

In this chapter, there are three ways to set up the null and alternative hypotheses.

1. Equal hypothesis versus not equal hypothesis **(two-tailed test)**
   H_0: parameter $=$ some value
   H_1: parameter $\neq$ some value

2. Equal versus less than **(left-tailed test)**
   H_0: parameter $=$ some value
   H_1: parameter $<$ some value

3. Equal versus greater than **(right-tailed test)**
   H_0: parameter $=$ some value
   H_1: parameter $>$ some value

Left- and right-tailed tests are collectively referred to as **one-tailed tests**. Notice that in the left-tailed test the direction of the inequality in the alternative hypothesis points to the left ($<$), while in the right-tailed test the direction of the inequality in the alternative hypothesis points to the right

($>$). Notice that in all three tests the null hypothesis contains a statement of equality. The statement of equality comes from existing information.

Refer to the three claims made on page 519. In Situation A, the null hypothesis would be H_o: $p = 0.74$. This is a statement of "status quo" or "no difference."* It means that American opinions have not changed from 1995. In Situation B, the null hypothesis is H_o: $\mu = 500$. This is a statement of "no difference" between the population mean and the lifetime stated on the label. In Situation C, the null hypothesis is H_o: $\sigma = 0.08$. This is a statement of "no difference" between the population standard deviation rate of return of the manager's mutual fund and all mutual funds.

The wording of the claim, which is dictated by the researcher before any data are collected, determines the structure of the alternative hypothesis (two-tailed, left-tailed, or right-tailed). For example, the label on a can of soda states that the can contains 12 ounces of liquid. A consumer advocate would be concerned only if the mean contents are less than 12 ounces, so the alternative hypothesis would be H_1: $\mu < 12$. However, a quality-control engineer for the soda manufacturer would be concerned if there is too little or too much soda in the can, so the alternative hypothesis would be H_1: $\mu \neq 12$. In both cases, however, the null hypothesis is a statement of no difference between the manufacturer's assertion on the label and the actual mean contents of the can. So the null hypothesis is H_o: $\mu = 12$.

▶ **EXAMPLE 2**

Forming Hypotheses

Problem: For each of the following claims, determine the null and alternative hypotheses. State whether the test is two-tailed, left-tailed, or right-tailed.

(a) The Medco pharmaceutical company has just developed a new antibiotic for children. In competing antibiotics, 2% of children who take the drug experience headaches as a side effect. A researcher for the Food and Drug Administration wishes to test the claim that the percentage of children taking the new antibody who experience headaches as a side effect is more than 2%.

(b) The "blue book" value of a used three-year-old Chevy Corvette is $37,500. Grant wishes to test the claim that the mean price of a used three-year-old Chevy Corvette in his neighborhood is different from $37,500.

(c) The standard deviation of the contents in a 64-ounce bottle of detergent using an old filling machine was known to be 0.23 ounces. The company just purchased a new filling machine and wants to test the claim that the new filling machine fills the bottles with a standard deviation less than 0.23 ounces.

Approach: In each of these cases we must first identify the parameter about which the claim is made and the "status quo." We then assess the direction of the claim (greater than, less than, or not equal to) to help us form the alternative hypothesis.

Solution:

(a) The claim is regarding a population proportion, p. If the new drug is no different from current drugs on the market, then the proportion of individuals taking the new drug who experience a headache will be

*The Latin phrase *status quo* means "the existing state or condition."

In Your Own Words

Look for key phrases in the claim. For example, "more than" means >; "different from" means ≠; "less than" means <; and so on.

 *Now Work Problem 9(a).*

0.02, so that the null hypothesis is H_o: $p = 0.02$. The phrase "more than" is represented symbolically as $>$, so the claim is $p > 0.02$. Therefore, the alternative hypothesis is H_1: $p > 0.02$. This is a right-tailed test because the alternative hypothesis contains a $>$ symbol.

(b) The claim is regarding a population mean, μ. If the mean price of a three-year-old Corvette in Grant's neighborhood is no different from the blue book price, then the population mean in Grant's neighborhood will be \$37,500, so that the null hypothesis is H_o: $\mu = 37{,}500$. Grant wishes to test the claim that the mean price is different from \$37,500, so that the alternative hypothesis is H_1: $\mu \neq 37{,}500$. This is a two-tailed test because the alternative hypothesis contains a $\neq$ symbol.

(c) The claim is regarding a population standard deviation, σ. If the new machine is no different from the old machine, then the standard deviation amount in the bottles filled by the new machine will be 0.23 ounces, so that the null hypothesis is H_o: $\sigma = 0.23$. The phrase "less than" is represented symbolically by $<$, so the claim is $\sigma < 0.23$ ounces and the alternative hypothesis is H_1: $\sigma < 0.23$. This is a left-tailed test because the alternative hypothesis contains a $<$ symbol. ◄◄

② Type I and Type II Errors

As stated earlier, we use sample data to determine whether to reject or not reject the null hypothesis. Because the decision to reject or not reject the null hypothesis is based upon incomplete (i.e., sample) information, there is always the possibility of making an incorrect decision. In fact, there are four possible outcomes from hypothesis testing.

In Your Own Words

When you are testing a hypothesis, there is always the possibility that your conclusion will be wrong. To make matters worse, you won't know whether you are wrong or not!

> **Four Outcomes from Hypothesis Testing**
>
> 1. We reject H_o when in fact H_1 is true. This decision would be correct.
> 2. We do not reject H_o when in fact H_o is true. This decision would be correct.
> 3. We reject H_o when in fact H_o is true. This decision would be incorrect. This type of error is called a **Type I error**.
> 4. We do not reject H_o when in fact H_1 is true. This decision would be incorrect. This type of error is called a **Type II error**.

Note to Instructor
Discuss the idea of a "false positive" or "false negative" as it relates to Type I and Type II errors.

Figure 2 illustrates the two types of errors that can be made in hypothesis testing.

Figure 2

Conclusion		Reality	
		H_o Is True	H_1 Is True
	Do Not Reject H_o	Correct Conclusion	Type II Error
	Reject H_o	Type I Error	Correct Conclusion

We illustrate the idea of Type I and Type II errors by looking at hypothesis testing from the point of view of a criminal trial. In any trial, the defendant is assumed to be innocent. (We give the defendant the benefit of the doubt.) The district attorney must present evidence proving that the defendant is guilty. Because we are seeking evidence for guilt, it becomes the alternative hypothesis. The null hypothesis is innocence, so the hypotheses for a trial would be written:

H_0: the defendant is innocent
H_1: the defendant is guilty

The trial is the process whereby information (sample data) is obtained. The jury then analyzes the data (the deliberations). Finally, the jury either rejects the null hypothesis and the defendant is considered guilty or does not reject the null hypothesis and declares the defendant not guilty. Note that the defendant is never declared innocent. That is, we never say that the null hypothesis is true. Using this analogy, the two correct decisions would be to conclude that an innocent person is not guilty or conclude that a guilty person is guilty. The two incorrect decisions would be to convict an innocent person (a Type I error) or to let a guilty person go free (a Type II error). It is helpful to think in this way when trying to remember the difference between a Type I and a Type II error.

In Your Own Words

A Type I error is like putting an innocent person in jail. A Type II error is like letting a guilty person go free.

▶ **EXAMPLE 3** **Type I and Type II Errors**

Problem: The Medco pharmaceutical company has just developed a new antibiotic. In competing antibiotics, 2% of children who take the drug experience headaches as a side effect. A researcher for the Food and Drug Administration claims that the percentage of children taking the new antibody who experience a headache as a side effect is more than 2%. To test this claim, we conduct a hypothesis test with H_0: $p = 0.02$ and H_1: $p > 0.02$. Provide statements explaining what it would mean to make (a) a Type I error and (b) a Type II error.

Approach: A Type I error would occur if the null hypothesis is rejected when, in reality, the null hypothesis is true. A Type II error would occur if the null hypothesis is not rejected when, in reality, the alternative hypothesis is true.

Solution:

(a) We would make a Type I error if the sample evidence leads us to believe that $p > 0.02$ (i.e., we reject the null hypothesis) when, in fact, the proportion of children who experience a headache is not greater than 0.02.

(b) We would make a Type II error if we do not reject the null hypothesis that the proportion of children experiencing a headache is equal to 0.02 when, in fact, the proportion of children who experience a headache is more than 0.02. For example, the sample evidence led the researcher to believe $p = 0.02$ when in fact the true proportion is $p = 0.023$. ◀◀

 *Now Work Problems 9(b) and 9(c).*

3 **The Level of Significance**

Recall that we never know whether a confidence interval contains the unknown parameter. In addition, we never know whether the outcome of a hypothesis test results in an error or not. However, just as we place a level of confidence in the construction of a confidence interval, we can determine the probability of making errors. The following notation is commonplace:

$$\alpha = P(\text{Type I error}) = P(\text{rejecting } H_o \text{ when } H_o \text{ is true})$$

$$\beta = P(\text{Type II error}) = P(\text{not rejecting } H_o \text{ when } H_1 \text{ is true})$$

The symbol β is the Greek letter beta (pronounced "BAY tah"). The probability of making a Type I error, α, is chosen by the researcher *before* the sample data are collected. This probability is referred to as the *level of significance*.

Definition   The **level of significance**, α, is the probability of making a Type I error.

The choice of the level of significance will depend upon the consequences of making a Type I error. If the consequences are severe, then the level of significance should be small (say, $\alpha = 0.01$). However, if the consequences of making a Type I error are not severe, then a higher level of significance can be chosen (say $\alpha = 0.05$ or $\alpha = 0.10$).

Why is the level of significance not always set at $\alpha = 0.01$? By reducing the probability of making a Type I error, you increase the probability of making a Type II error, β. Using our court analogy, a jury is instructed that the prosecution must provide proof of guilt "beyond all reasonable doubt." This implies that we are choosing to make α small so that the probability we will send an innocent person to jail is very small. The consequence of the small α, however, is a large β, which means many guilty defendants would go free. For now, we will be content with recognizing the inverse relation between α and β (as one goes up the other goes down).

In Your Own Words

As the probability of a Type I error increases, the probability of a Type II error decreases, and vice versa.

Caution

We never "accept" the null hypothesis, because, without having access to the entire population, we don't know the exact value of the parameter stated in the null. Rather, we say that we do not reject the null hypothesis. This is just like the court system. We never declare a defendant innocent, but rather say the defendant is not guilty.

④ Writing the Conclusion

Once the decision to reject or not reject the null hypothesis is made, the researcher must state his or her conclusion. It is important to recognize that we never *accept* the null hypothesis. Again, the court system analogy helps to illustrate the idea. The null hypothesis is H_o: innocent. When the evidence presented to the jury is not enough to convict beyond all reasonable doubt, the jury comes back with a verdict of not guilty. Notice that the verdict does not state that the null hypothesis of innocence is true; it simply states that there is not enough evidence to support guilt. This is a huge difference. Being told that you are not guilty is very different from being told that you are innocent!

This means that sample evidence can never prove the null hypothesis to be true. When we do not reject the null hypothesis, we are saying that the evidence indicates that the null hypothesis *could* be true.

▶ **EXAMPLE 4**   **Stating the Conclusion**

Problem: The Medco pharmaceutical company has just developed a new antibiotic. In competing antibiotics, 2% of children who take the drug experience a headache as a side effect. A researcher for the Food and Drug Administration claims that the percentage of children taking the new antibody who experience a headache as a side effect is more than 2%. From Example 2(a) we know the null hypothesis is $H_o: p = 0.02$ and the alternative hypothesis is $H_1: p > 0.02$.

(a) Suppose the sample evidence indicates that the null hypothesis is rejected. State the conclusion.
(b) Suppose the sample evidence indicates that the null hypothesis is not rejected. State the conclusion.

Approach: When the null hypothesis is rejected, we say that there is sufficient evidence to support the claim. When the null hypothesis is not rejected, we say that there is not sufficient evidence to support the claim. We never say that the null hypothesis is true!

Solution:

(a) The claim is that the percentage of children taking the new antibody who experience a headache as a side effect is more than 2%. Because the null hypothesis ($p = 0.02$) is rejected, we conclude there is sufficient evidence to support the claim that the proportion of children who experience a headache as a side effect is more than 0.02.
(b) Because the null hypothesis is not rejected, we conclude that there is not sufficient evidence to support the claim that the proportion of children who experience a headache as a side effect is more than 0.02. ◀◀

NW *Now Work Problem 17.*

9.1 Assess Your Understanding

Concepts and Vocabulary

1. Explain what it means to make a Type I error. Explain what it means to make a Type II error.
2. Suppose the consequences of making a Type I error are severe. Would you choose the level of significance, α, to equal 0.01, 0.05 or 0.10? Why?
3. What happens to the probability of making a Type II error, β, as the level of significance, α, decreases? Why is this result intuitive?
4. If a hypothesis is tested at the $\alpha = 0.05$ level of significance, what is the probability of making a Type I error?
5. The following is a quotation from Sir Ronald A. Fisher, a famous statistician.

"For the logical fallacy of believing that a hypothesis has been proved true, merely because it is not contradicted by the available facts, has no more right to insinuate itself in statistics than in other kinds of scientific reasoning ... It would, therefore, add greatly to the clarity with which the tests of significance are regarded if it were generally understood that tests of significance, when used accurately, are capable of rejecting or invalidating hypotheses, in so far as they are contradicted by the data: but that they are never capable of establishing them as certainly true ... "

In your own words, explain what this quotation means.

Exercises

- **Basic Skills**

In Problems 1–6, a null and alternative hypothesis are given. Determine whether the hypothesis test is left-tailed, right-tailed, or two-tailed. What parameter is being tested?

1. $H_0: \mu = 5$ right-tailed, μ
    $H_1: \mu > 5$

2. $H_0: p = 0.2$ left-tailed, p
    $H_1: p < 0.2$

3. $H_0: \sigma = 4.2$ two-tailed, σ
    $H_1: \sigma \neq 4.2$

4. $H_0: p = 0.76$ right-tailed, p
    $H_1: p > 0.76$

5. $H_0: \mu = 120$ left-tailed, μ
    $H_1: \mu < 120$

6. $H_0: \sigma = 7.8$ two-tailed, σ
    $H_1: \sigma \neq 7.8$

For each claim in Problems 7–14, (a) determine the null and alternative hypotheses, (b) explain what it would mean to make a Type I error, and (c) explain what it would mean to make a Type II error.

7. **Farm Rents** According to the United States Department of Agriculture, the mean farm rent in Indiana was $89.00 per acre in 1995. A researcher for the USDA claims that the mean rent has decreased since then.

8. **Acid Rain** In 2000, the mean pH of rain in Gunnison County, Colorado, was 5.01, according to the National Atmospheric Deposition Program. A researcher claims that the level of acidity in the rain has increased. (This would mean that the pH has decreased.)

9. **Health Insurance** According to the United States Census Bureau, 16.3% of Americans did not have health insurance coverage in 1998. A politician claims that this percentage has decreased since 1998.
   (NW)

10. **Protein** According to the United States Department of Agriculture, 78.2% of females between the ages of 12 and 19 years get the USDA's recommended daily allowance of protein. A nutritionist believes that the percentage of 12-to-19-year-old females at her boarding school who get the USDA's recommended daily allowance of protein is above 78.2%.

11. **Energy Expenditures** According to the United States Energy Information Administration, the mean expenditure for residential energy consumption (electricity, natural gas, etc.) was $1338 in 1997. An economist claims that the mean expenditure for residential energy is different today. $H_o: \mu = 1338$; $H_1: \mu \neq 1338$

12. **Death Row** According to the U.S. Department of Justice, the mean age of a death row inmate in 1980 was 36.7 years. A district attorney believes the mean age of a death row inmate is different today. $H_o: \mu = 36.7$; $H_1: \mu \neq 36.7$

13. **Stock Market Returns** During the past forty years, the standard deviation monthly rate of return for stocks has been 4.2 percent. A stock analyst claims the standard deviation monthly rate of return is higher today. $H_o: \sigma = 4.2$; $H_1: \sigma > 4.2$

14. **SAT Verbal Scores** In 2001, the standard deviation SAT verbal score for males was 111. A teacher claims the standard deviation SAT verbal score for male students enrolled at her school is less than 111. $H_o: \sigma = 111$; $H_1: \sigma < 111$

7. $H_o: \mu = 89$; $H_1: \mu < 89$ 8. $H_o: \mu = 5.01$; $H_1: \mu < 5.01$ 9. $H_o: p = 0.163$; $H_1: p < 0.163$ 10. $H_o: p = 0.782$; $H_1: p > 0.782$

In Problems 15–26, state the conclusion based upon the results of the test.

15. For the claim made in Problem 7, suppose the null hypothesis is rejected.

16. For the claim made in Problem 8, suppose the null hypothesis is not rejected.

17. For the claim made in Problem 9, suppose the null hypothesis is not rejected.
    (NW)

18. For the claim made in Problem 10, suppose the null hypothesis is rejected.

19. For the claim made in Problem 11, suppose the null hypothesis is not rejected.

20. For the claim made in Problem 12, suppose the null hypothesis is not rejected.

21. For the claim made in Problem 13, suppose the null hypothesis is rejected.

22. For the claim made in Problem 14, suppose the null hypothesis is not rejected.

23. For the claim made in Problem 7, suppose the null hypothesis is not rejected.

24. For the claim made in Problem 8, suppose the null hypothesis is rejected.

25. For the claim made in Problem 9, suppose the null hypothesis is rejected.

26. For the claim made in Problem 10, suppose the null hypothesis is not rejected.

• Applying the Concepts

27. **Potato Consumption** According to the Statistical Abstract of the United States, the mean per capita consumption of potatoes in 1999 was 48.3 pounds. A researcher believes that potato consumption has risen since then.
    (a) Determine the null and alternative hypotheses.
    (b) Suppose sample data indicate that the null hypothesis should be rejected. State the conclusion of the researcher.
    (c) Suppose, in reality, the mean per capita consumption of potatoes is 48.3 pounds. Was a Type I or Type II error committed? If we tested this hypothesis at the $\alpha = 0.05$ level of significance, what is the probability of committing a Type I error? Type I error; 0.05

    (d) If we wanted to decrease the probability of making a Type II error, would we need to increase or decrease the level of significance, α? Increase

28. **Test Preparation** The mean score on the SAT I Math exam is 505. A test preparatory company claims that the mean scores of students who take their course is higher than the mean of 505.
    (a) Determine the null and alternative hypotheses.
    (b) Suppose sample data indicate that the null hypothesis should not be rejected. State the conclusion of the company.
    (c) Suppose, in reality, the mean score of students taking the preparatory course is 507. Was a Type I or Type

(27a) $H_o: \mu = 48.3$; $H_1: \mu > 48.3$ (28a) $H_o: \mu = 505$; $H_1: \mu > 505$

II error committed? If we tested this hypothesis at the $\alpha = 0.01$ level of significance, what is the probability of committing a Type I error? Type II error; 0.01

(d) If we wanted to decrease the probability of making a Type II error, would we need to increase or decrease the level of significance, α? Increase

29. **Traffic Fatalities** In 1998, the proportion of traffic fatalities in which the driver had a blood alcohol content (BAC) of 0.08% or higher was 0.38. After a strong advertising campaign, a member of MADD claims that the proportion of traffic fatalities in which the driver had a BAC of 0.08% or higher has decreased from the 1998 level.

(a) Determine the null and alternative hypotheses.

(b) Suppose sample data indicate that the null hypothesis should not be rejected. State the conclusion of the member of MADD.

(c) Suppose, in reality, the proportion of traffic fatalities in which the driver had a blood alcohol content (BAC) of 0.08% or higher was 0.36. Was a Type I or Type II error committed? Type II error

30. **Internet Usage** According to the Statistical Abstract of the United States, in 2000 10.7% of Americans over 65 years of age utilized the Internet. A researcher believes the proportion of Americans over 65 years of age who utilize the Internet is higher than 10.7% today.

(a) Determine the null and alternative hypotheses.

(b) Suppose sample data indicate that the null hypothesis should be rejected. State the conclusion of the researcher.

(c) Suppose, in reality, the percentage of Americans over 65 years of age who utilize the Internet is still 10.7%. Was a Type I or Type II error committed? Type I error

31. **Consumer Reports** The following is an excerpt from a *Consumer Reports* article from February, 2001.

> The *Platinum Gasaver* makes some impressive claims. The device, $188 for two, is guaranteed to increase gas mileage by 22 percent, says the

manufacturer, National Fuelsaver. Further, the company quotes "the government" as concluding, "Independent testing shows greater fuel savings with *Gasaver* than the 22 percent claimed by the developer." Readers have told us they want to know more about it.

> The Environmental Protection Agency (EPA), after its lab tests of the *Platinum Gasaver*, concluded in 1991, "Users of the device would not be expected to realize either an emission or fuel economy benefit." The Federal Trade Commission says, "No government agency endorses gas-saving products for cars."

Determine the null and alternative hypotheses that the EPA used in order to draw the conclusion stated in the second paragraph.

32. **Prolong Engine Treatment** The manufacturer of Prolong Engine Treatment claims that if you add one 12-ounce bottle of their $20 product, your engine will be protected from excessive wear. In fact, an infomercial claims that a woman drove four hours without oil, thanks to Prolong. *Consumer Reports* magazine tested two engines in which they added Prolong to the motor oil, ran the engines, drained the oil, and then determined the time until the engines seized.

(a) Determine the null and alternative hypotheses *Consumer Reports* will test. $H_o: \mu = 4$; $H_1: \mu < 4$

(b) Both engines took exactly 13 minutes to seize. What conclusion might Consumer Reports draw based upon this evidence? Prolong's claim not true

33. Refer to the claim made in Problem 8. Researchers must choose the level of significance based upon the consequences of making a Type I error. Explain what it would mean to make a Type I error for this hypothesis. Explain what it would mean to make a Type II error. In your opinion, which error is more serious? Why? On the basis of your answer decide on a level of significance, α. Be sure to support your opinion.

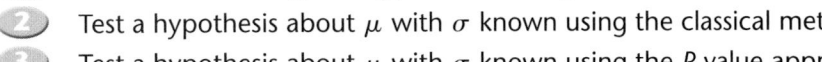

(29a) $H_o: p = 0.38$; $H_1: p < 0.38$ (30a) $H_o: p = 0.107$; $H_1: p > 0.107$ 31. $H_o: \mu = 0$; $H_1: \mu > 0$ where μ is the mean increase

9.2   Testing a Hypothesis about μ, σ Known

Preparing for This Section   Before getting started, review the following:

- ✓ Central Limit Theorem (Section 7.5, pp. 423–434)
- ✓ Computing normal probabilities (Section 7.3, pp. 406–408)
- ✓ Using probabilities to identify unusual events (Section 5.1, p. 263)
- ✓ z_α notation (Section 7.2, p. 401)

Objectives   **①**   Understand the logic of hypothesis testing

②   Test a hypothesis about μ with σ known using the classical method

③   Test a hypothesis about μ with σ known using the P-value approach

④   Test a hypothesis about μ with σ known using confidence intervals

We are now in a position to present methods for conducting hypothesis tests. In this section, we will present three approaches to testing hypotheses about a population mean, μ, with σ known. The first method is often referred to as the classical (or traditional) method, the second method is the more modern *P*-value approach and the third method utilizes confidence intervals. As with constructing confidence intervals, it is not likely that we know the population standard deviation without knowing the population mean, but for ease of understanding the procedures of hypothesis testing, we will assume that the value of the population standard deviation is known in this section.

① The Logic of Hypothesis Testing

In order to test hypotheses regarding the population mean, we need certain requirements to be satisfied.

- A simple random sample is obtained;
- The population from which the sample is drawn is normally distributed or the sample size is large ($n \geq 30$);
- The population standard deviation, σ, is known.

If these requirements are met, then the distribution of $\bar{x}$ is normal with mean μ and standard deviation $\frac{\sigma}{\sqrt{n}}$.

Remember that in hypothesis testing, the null hypothesis must always contain a statement of equality and the null hypothesis is assumed true. In testing a population mean, there are three ways to structure the hypothesis test:

Two-Tailed	Left-Tailed	Right-Tailed
$H_0: \mu = \mu_0$	$H_0: \mu = \mu_0$	$H_0: \mu = \mu_0$
$H_1: \mu \neq \mu_0$	$H_1: \mu < \mu_0$	$H_1: \mu > \mu_0$

Note: μ_0 is the assumed value of the population mean.

Suppose we work in the quality control department of Ruffles Potato Chips. The quality control manager wants us to verify that the filling machine is calibrated correctly. We wish to determine if the mean amount of chips in a bag is different from 12.5 ounces (the company would be concerned if there are too many or too few chips in the bag). Experience indicates that the population standard deviation is 0.15 ounce. The null and alternative hypotheses are given by

$$H_0: \mu = 12.5 \qquad \text{versus} \qquad H_1: \mu \neq 12.5$$

In order to test the claim, we take a simple random sample of size $n = 40$ bags from the warehouse. If the sample mean is significantly different from 12.5 ounces, we have evidence that the null hypothesis is not true. What do we mean by significantly different? A common criterion is to reject H_0 if the sample mean is too many standard deviations away from the assumed (or "status quo") population mean, μ_0. For example, our criterion might be

Historical Note

to reject the null hypothesis if the sample mean is more than two standard deviations away from 12.5, the hypothesized mean.

Recall that $Z = \dfrac{\overline{x} - \mu_o}{\sigma/\sqrt{n}}$ represents the number of standard deviations that $\overline{x}$ is from the population mean, μ_o. Suppose our simple random sample of 40 bags results in sample mean weight of $\overline{x} = 12.43$ ounces. Then, under the assumption that the null hypothesis is true, we have

$$Z = \frac{\overline{x} - \mu_o}{\sigma/\sqrt{n}} = \frac{12.43 - 12.5}{0.15/\sqrt{40}} = -2.95$$

The sample mean is 2.95 standard deviations below the hypothesized mean. Because the sample mean is more than 2 standard deviations (i.e. "too far") from the hypothesized population mean, we will reject the null hypothesis and conclude that there is sufficient evidence to refute the claim that the machine is filling the bag with 12.5 ounces of potato chips. This conclusion would lead the quality control engineer to shut down and recalibrate the filling machine.

Why does this criterion make sense? The area under the standard normal curve to the left of $Z = -2$ is 0.0228 and the area under the standard normal curve to the right of $Z = 2$ is 0.0228. Therefore, the area under the standard normal curve between $Z = -2$ and $Z = 2$ is 0.9544 as shown in Figure 3.

That is, if the null hypothesis is true, then 95.44% of all sample means should lie within $2\sigma_{\overline{x}} = 2 \cdot \dfrac{\sigma}{\sqrt{n}} = 2 \cdot \dfrac{0.15}{\sqrt{40}} = 0.047$ ounces of the hypothesized mean of 12.5 ounces as shown in Figure 4.

Caution

We always test hypotheses assuming that the null hypothesis is true.

Figure 3

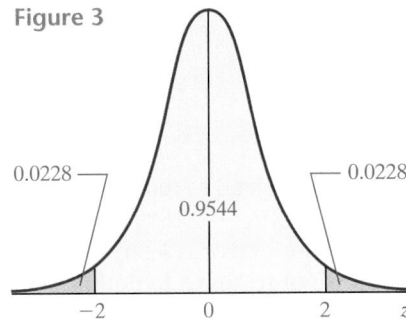

Figure 4

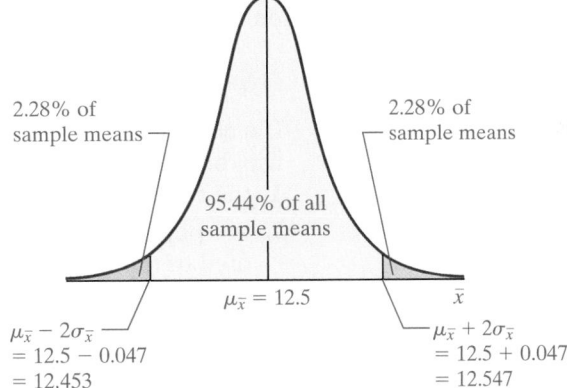

Referring to Figure 4, we see that only 2.28% of the sample means are less than 2 standard deviations below the hypothesized mean and 2.28% of the sample means are more than 2 standard deviations above the hypothesized mean (indicated by the shaded region in green in Figure 4). If the null hypothesis is true, sample means in this range will occur in only 2.28% + 2.28% = 4.56% of samples. Recall that we stated in Chapter 5 that events that occur less than 5% of the time are considered unusual. Therefore, if a sample mean lies in the green region, we are inclined to believe that it came from a population whose mean does not equal 12.5 rather than believe that the population mean does equal 12.5 and our sample just happened to result in an unusual outcome (a bunch of under- or over-filled bags).

Figure 5 further illustrates the situation. The sample mean of 12.43 is too far from the assumed population mean of 12.5. Therefore, we reject the null hypothesis that $\mu = 12.5$ and conclude that the sample came from a population with some population mean different from 12.5 ounces, as indicated by the distribution in blue. We don't know what the population mean weight of the bags is, but we have evidence that it is not 12.5 ounces.

Figure 5

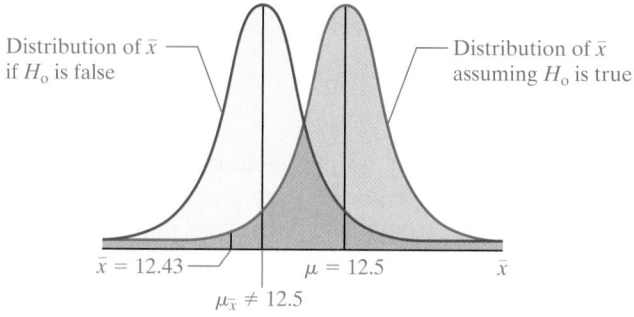

Distribution of $\bar{x}$ if H_o is false

Distribution of $\bar{x}$ assuming H_o is true

$\bar{x} = 12.43$ $\mu = 12.5$ $\bar{x}$

$\mu_{\bar{x}} \neq 12.5$

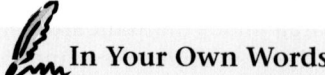

In Your Own Words

If the sample mean is too many standard deviations from the mean stated in the null hypothesis, then we reject the null hypothesis.

Notice that our criterion for rejecting the null will lead to making a Type I error (rejecting the null when the null is true) $2.28\% + 2.28\% = 4.56\%$ of the time. That is, the probability of making a Type I error is 4.56%.

The previous discussion presents the premise of testing a hypothesis:

If the sample data result in a statistic that is not likely under the assumption that the null hypothesis is true, we reject the null hypothesis.

 ## The Classical Method of Testing a Hypothesis

We now formalize the procedure for testing a claim regarding the population mean when the population standard deviation, σ, is known.

> **Hypothesis Test Regarding μ with σ Known**
>
> If a claim is made regarding the population mean with σ known, we can use the following steps to test the claim provided:
> **1.** the sample is obtained using simple random sampling,
> **2.** the population from which the sample is drawn is normally distributed or the sample size, n, is large ($n \geq 30$).
>
> **Step 1:** A claim is made regarding the population mean. The claim is used to determine the null and alternative hypotheses. Again, the hypotheses can be structured in one of three ways:
>
> | Two-Tailed | Left-Tailed | Right-Tailed |
> |---|---|---|
> | $H_o: \mu = \mu_o$ | $H_o: \mu = \mu_o$ | $H_o: \mu = \mu_o$ |
> | $H_1: \mu \neq \mu_o$ | $H_1: \mu < \mu_o$ | $H_1: \mu > \mu_o$ |
>
> *Note:* μ_o is the assumed or "status quo" value of the population mean.
>
> **Step 2:** Select a level of significance α based upon the seriousness of making a Type I error. The level of significance is used to determine the *critical value*. The **critical value** represents the maximum number of standard deviations the sample mean can be from μ_o before the null hypothesis is rejected. For example, the critical value in the left-tailed test is $-z_\alpha$. The shaded region(s) represents the *critical (or rejection) region(s)*.

The **critical region** or **rejection region** is the set of all values such that the null hypothesis is rejected.

Two-Tailed	Left-Tailed	Right-Tailed

Step 3: Provided the population from which the sample is drawn is normal or the sample size is large ($n \geq 30$) and the population standard deviation, σ, is known, the distribution of the sample mean, $\bar{x}$, is normal with mean μ_{o} and standard deviation $\frac{\sigma}{\sqrt{n}}$. Therefore,

$$Z = \frac{\bar{x} - \mu_{o}}{\sigma / \sqrt{n}}$$

represents the number of standard deviations the sample mean is from the assumed mean, μ_{o}. This value is called the **test statistic**.

Step 4: Compare the critical value with the test statistic:

Two-Tailed	Left-Tailed	Right-Tailed
If $Z < -z_{\alpha/2}$ or $Z > z_{\alpha/2}$ reject the null hypothesis	If $Z < -z_{\alpha}$ reject the null hypothesis	If $Z > z_{\alpha}$ reject the null hypothesis

Step 5: State the conclusion.

The procedure presented requires that the data come from a population that is normally distributed or that the sample size be large ($n \geq 30$). The procedure is **robust**, which means that minor departures from normality will not adversely affect the results of the test. However, for small samples, if the data have outliers, the procedure should not be used.

For small samples, we will verify that the data come from a population that is normal by constructing normal probability plots (to assess normality) and boxplots (to determine whether there are outliers). If the normal probability plot indicates that the data are not normally distributed or the boxplot reveals outliers, nonparametric tests should be performed, as discussed in Chapter 13, Section 3.

▶ EXAMPLE 1   The Classical Method of Hypothesis Testing

Problem: According to the U.S. Federal Highway Administration, the mean number of miles driven annually in 1990 was 10,300. Patricia believes that people are driving more today than in 1990. She obtains a simple random

TABLE 1		
8,777	19,187	12,022
16,759	7,294	10,163
9,021	12,682	16,747
16,733	15,331	5,347
13,798	13,235	11,302
6,929	17,576	9,455
16,306	8,266	

sample of 20 people and asks them to disclose the number of miles they drove last year. The results of the survey are presented in Table 1. Assuming $\sigma = 3500$ miles, test Patricia's claim at the $\alpha = 0.1$ level of significance.

Approach: Before we can perform the hypothesis test, we must verify that the data come from a population that is approximately normally distributed with no outliers because the sample size, n, is less than 30. We will construct a normal probability plot and boxplot to verify these assumptions. We then proceed to follow Steps 1–5.

Solution: Figure 6 displays the normal probability plot and boxplot.

Figure 6

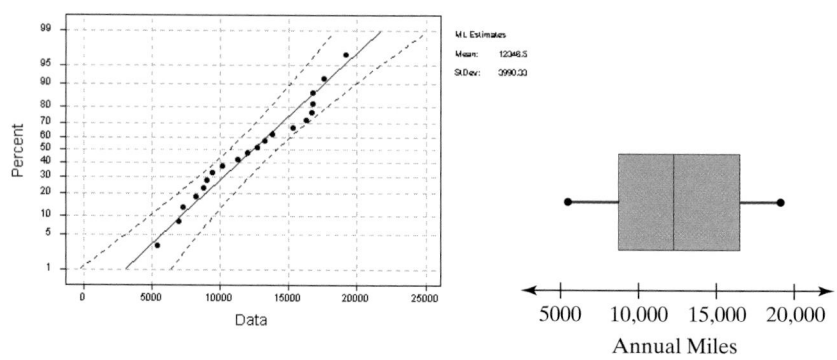

Normal Probability Plot for Annual Miles

The normal probability plot indicates that the data could come from a population that is normal. The boxplot does not show any outliers. We can proceed to perform the hypothesis test.

Step 1: Patricia claims people are driving more than 10,300 miles annually. This claim can be written $\mu > 10,300$. This is a right-tailed test and we have

$$H_o: \mu = 10,300 \qquad \text{versus} \qquad H_1: \mu > 10,300$$

Step 2: Because Patricia is performing a right-tailed test, we determine the critical value at the $\alpha = 0.1$ level of significance to be $z_{0.1} = 1.28$. The critical region is displayed in Figure 7.

Step 3: Patricia computes the sample mean, $\bar{x}$, to be 12,346.5 miles. The test statistic is

$$Z = \frac{\bar{x} - \mu_o}{\sigma/\sqrt{n}} = \frac{12,346.5 - 10,300}{3500/\sqrt{20}} = 2.61$$

Figure 7

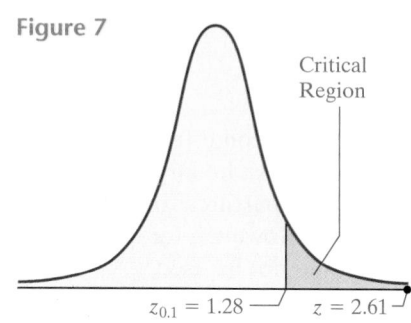

Critical Region

$z_{0.1} = 1.28$ $z = 2.61$

The sample mean of 12,346.5 miles is 2.61 standard deviations above the assumed mean of 10,300 miles.

Step 4: Because the test statistic $Z = 2.61$ is more than the critical value of $z_{0.1} = 1.28$, we reject the null hypothesis. That is, the value of the test statistic falls within the critical region so we reject H_o. We label this point in Figure 7.

Step 5: There is sufficient evidence at the $\alpha = 0.1$ level of significance to support Patricia's claim that the mean number of miles people are driving is greater than 10,300 miles per year. ◄◄

NW *Now Work Problem 9.*

We now present a two-tailed hypothesis test.

► EXAMPLE 2

The Classical Method of Hypothesis Testing

TABLE 2

$47,000	$32,750	$35,995
$32,750	$33,995	$39,998
$33,995	$43,500	$37,995
$43,108	$39,950	$37,995
$33,988	$36,900	$43,785

Source: cars.com

Note to Instructor
Ask students how this problem would change if Grant thought the mean price of a Corvette was more than $37,500.

Problem: Grant is in the market to buy a three-year-old Chevy Corvette. Before shopping for the car, he wants to determine what he should expect to pay. According to the "blue book," the mean price of a three-year-old Chevy Corvette is $37,500. Grant thinks the mean price is different from $37,500 in his neighborhood. After visiting 15 neighborhood dealers on-line, Grant obtains the data shown in Table 2.

Assuming $\sigma = \$4100$, use these data to test Grant's claim that the mean price of a Corvette is different from $37,500 at the $\alpha = 0.1$ level of significance.

Approach: Because the sample size, n, is less than 30, we must verify that the data come from a population that is approximately normal with no outliers. We will construct a normal probability plot and boxplot to verify these requirements. We then proceed to follow Steps 1–5.

Solution: A normal probability plot and boxplot were drawn for this data in Figure 4 of Section 8.1. They indicate that the price of used Corvettes is approximately normal with no outliers.

Step 1: Grant claims the price of a three-year-old Corvette is different from $37,500. This claim can be written $\mu \neq 37,500$ and so we have a two-tailed test. The null and alternative hypotheses are:

$$H_o: \mu = 37,500 \quad \text{versus} \quad H_1: \mu \neq 37,500.$$

Step 2: Because Grant is performing a two-tailed test, we determine the critical values at the $\alpha = 0.1$ level of significance to be $-z_{0.1/2} = -z_{0.05} = -1.645$ and $z_{0.1/2} = z_{0.05} = 1.645$. The critical regions are displayed in Figure 8.

Figure 8

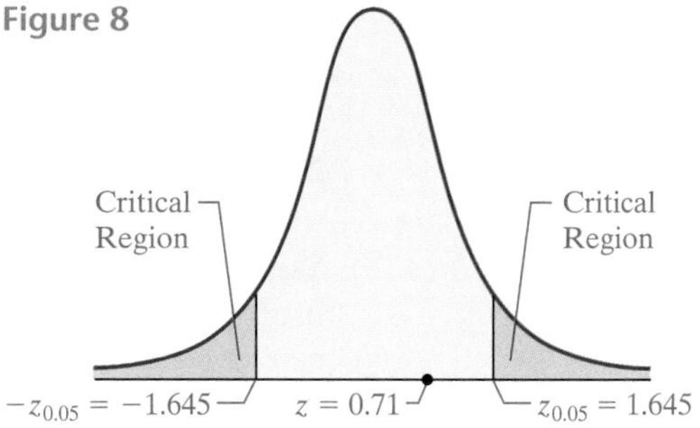

Critical Region — Critical Region
$-z_{0.05} = -1.645$ $z = 0.71$ $z_{0.05} = 1.645$

Caution
In Example 2, we see that the test statistic $Z = 0.71$ is not far enough from the "status quo" value of the population mean, $37,500. Therefore, we do not have enough evidence to reject the null hypothesis. However, this does not mean we are accepting the null hypothesis that the mean price of a three-year old Corvette is $37,500. We simply are saying we don't have enough evidence to say it is not $37,500. Be sure you understand the difference between these two comments.

Step 3: Grant computes the sample mean, $\overline{x}$, to be $38,246.9. The test statistic is

$$Z = \frac{\overline{x} - \mu_o}{\sigma/\sqrt{n}} = \frac{38,246.9 - 37,500}{4100/\sqrt{15}} = 0.71$$

The sample mean of $38,246.9 is 0.71 standard deviations above the assumed mean of $37,500.

Step 4: Because the test statistic $Z = 0.71$ is less than $z_{0.05} = 1.645$ and greater than $-z_{0.05} = -1.645$, we do not reject the null hypothesis. That is, the value of the test statistic does not fall within the critical regions. We label this point in Figure 8.

Step 5: There is not sufficient evidence at the $\alpha = 0.1$ level of significance to support Grant's claim that the mean price of a three-year-old Corvette is different from \$37,500. ◄◄

NW *Now Work Problem 15.*

③ Testing a Hypothesis about μ with σ Known Using *P*-Values

A second approach to testing hypotheses is with *P*-values.

Definition

A ***P*-value** is the probability of observing a sample statistic as extreme or more extreme than the one observed under the assumption that the null hypothesis is true.

Note to Instructor
Stress to students that the interpretation of P-values is the same for all hypothesis tests. Therefore, they are more versatile.

Recall our criterion for rejecting the null hypothesis. If the sample mean is too far away from the hypothesized value of the population mean, we reject the null hypothesis. Using the classical approach, "too far away" means too many standard deviations from the mean. The *P*-value is the likelihood or probability that a sample will result in a sample mean such as the one obtained if the null hypothesis is true. A small *P*-value implies that the sample mean is unlikely if the null hypothesis is true and would be considered as evidence against the null hypothesis.

The following procedures can be used to compute *P*-values when testing a hypothesis about a population mean with σ known.

Computing *P*-Values

If a claim is made regarding the population mean with σ known, we can use the following steps to compute the *P*-value, provided that
1. the sample is obtained using simple random sampling, and
2. the population from which the sample is drawn is normally distributed or the sample size, n, is large ($n \geq 30$).

Step 1: A claim is made regarding the population mean. The claim is used to determine the null and alternative hypotheses. The hypotheses can be structured in one of three ways:

Two-Tailed	Left-Tailed	Right-Tailed
$H_0: \mu = \mu_0$	$H_0: \mu = \mu_0$	$H_0: \mu = \mu_0$
$H_1: \mu \neq \mu_0$	$H_1: \mu < \mu_0$	$H_1: \mu > \mu_0$

Note: μ_0 is the assumed value of the population mean.

Decide on a level of significance, α, depending upon the seriousness of making a Type I error.

Step 2: Compute the test statistic, $Z_0 = \dfrac{\overline{x} - \mu_0}{\sigma/\sqrt{n}}$.

Step 3: Determine the P-value:

Two-Tailed	Left-Tailed	Right-Tailed

P-value $= P(Z < -|Z_o|$ or $Z > |Z_o|)$
     $= 2P(Z > |Z_o|)$

P-value $= P(Z < Z_o)$

P-value $= P(Z > Z_o)$

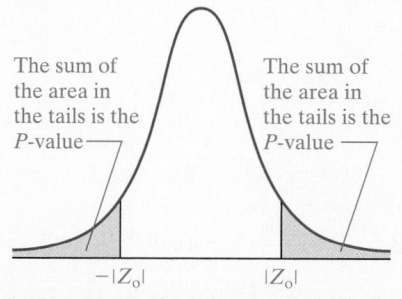

The sum of the area in the tails is the P-value

The sum of the area in the tails is the P-value

$-|Z_o|$ $|Z_o|$

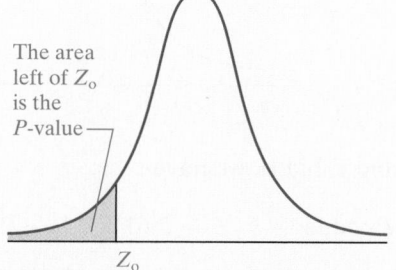

The area left of Z_o is the P-value

Z_o

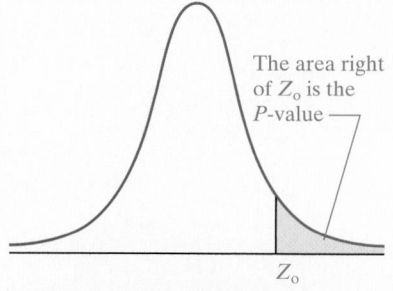

The area right of Z_o is the P-value

Z_o

Interpretation: The P-value is the probability of obtaining a sample mean that is more than $|Z_o|$ standard deviations from the hypothesized mean, μ_o.

Interpretation: The P-value is the probability of obtaining a sample mean of $\bar{x}$ or smaller under the assumption that H_o is true. In other words, it is the probability of obtaining a sample mean that is more than Z_o standard deviations to the left of μ_o.

Interpretation: The P-value is the probability of obtaining a sample mean of $\bar{x}$ or larger under the assumption that H_o is true. In other words, it is the probability of obtaining a sample mean that is more than Z_o standard deviations to the right of μ_o.

Step 4: Reject the null hypothesis if the P-value is less than the level of significance, α.

Step 5: State the conclusion.

▶ **EXAMPLE 3**   Computing the P-Value of a Right-Tailed Test

Problem: Using the data from Example 1, test Patricia's claim using the P-value approach at the $\alpha = 0.01$ level of significance.

Approach: We will follow the Steps just presented. Remember, we've already confirmed in Example 1 that the data come from a population that is approximately normal with no outliers.

Solution:

Step 1: Patricia claims that people are driving more than 10,300 miles annually. This claim can be written $\mu > 10,300$. We have

$$H_o: \mu = 10,300 \qquad \text{versus} \qquad H_1: \mu > 10,300$$

This is a right-tailed test.

Step 2: From Example 1, we have $\bar{x} = 12,346$, $\sigma = 3500$ and $n = 20$. We compute the test statistic, Z_o:

$$Z_o = \frac{\bar{x} - \mu_o}{\sigma/\sqrt{n}} = \frac{12,346.5 - 10,300}{3500/\sqrt{20}} = 2.61$$

Step 3: Because we are performing a right-tailed test, P-value $= P(Z > Z_o) = P(Z > 2.61)$. That is, we need to determine the area under the standard normal curve to the right of $Z = 2.61$ as shown in Figure 9.

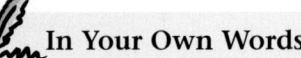

In Your Own Words

For this test (a right-tailed test), the P-value is the area under the standard normal curve to the right of Z = 2.61.

Figure 9

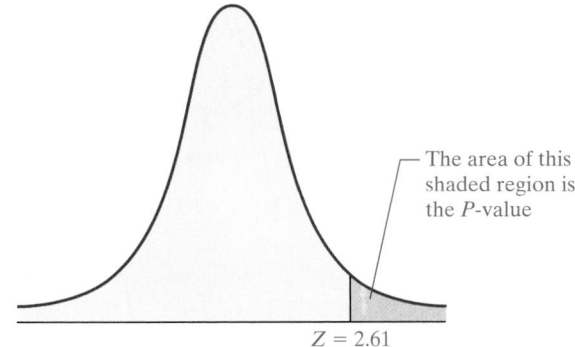

The area of this shaded region is the P-value

$Z = 2.61$

Using Table II, we have

$$P\text{-value} = P(Z > 2.61) = 1 - P(Z \le 2.61) = 1 - 0.9955 = 0.0045$$

In Your Own Words

If P-value $< \alpha$, then reject the null hypothesis.

The probability of obtaining a sample mean of 12,346.5 or higher from a population whose mean is 10,300 is 0.0045. So less than 1 sample in 100 will result in a sample mean of 12,346.5 (or higher) from a population whose mean is 10,300 (if the null hypothesis is true).

Step 4: If the P-value is less than the level of significance, we reject the null hypothesis. Because $0.0045 < 0.01$, we reject the null hypothesis.

Step 5: There is evidence to support the claim that the annual number of miles driven is higher than the 1990 level of 10,300 miles at the $\alpha = 0.01$ level of significance. ◀◀

NW *Now Work Problem 19.*

▶ **EXAMPLE 4** **Computing the P-Value of a Two-Tailed Test**

Problem: Use the data in Table 2 from Example 2 to test Grant's claim that the mean price of a three-year-old Corvette is different from $37,500 at the $\alpha = 0.1$ level of significance using the P-value approach.

Approach: Before we can perform the hypothesis test, we must verify that the data come from a population that is approximately normally distributed with no outliers. The normal probability plot and boxplot constructed in Figure 4 from Section 8.1 verified these requirements. We follow Steps 1–5 on pages 534–535 to test the hypothesis.

Solution:

Step 1: Grant claims that the price of a three-year-old Corvette is different from $37,500. This claim can be written $\mu \ne 37,500$. We have

$$H_o: \mu = 37,500 \qquad \text{versus} \qquad H_1: \mu \ne 37,500$$

This is a two-tailed test.

Step 2: From Example 2, we have $\bar{x} = 38,246.9$, $\sigma = 4100$, and $n = 15$. We compute the test statistic, Z_o:

$$Z_o = \frac{\bar{x} - \mu_o}{\sigma/\sqrt{n}} = \frac{38,246.9 - 37,500}{4100/\sqrt{15}} = 0.71$$

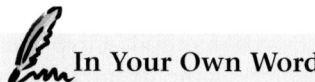

In Your Own Words

To find the P-value for a two-tailed test, first determine whether the test statistic, Z_o, is positive or negative. If Z_o is negative, determine the area under the standard normal curve to the left of Z_o, and then multiply this area by two. If Z_o is positive, find the area under the standard normal curve to the right of Z_o and then double this value.

Step 3: Because we are performing a two-tailed test, P-value = $2P(Z > |Z_0|) = 2P(Z > 0.71)$. That is, we need to determine the area under the standard normal curve to the right of $Z = 0.71$ and the left of $Z = -0.71$, as shown in Figure 10.

Figure 10

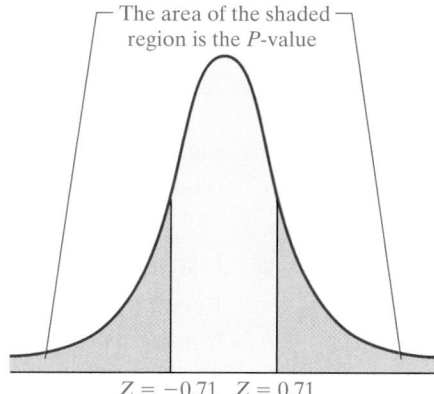

The area of the shaded region is the P-value

$Z = -0.71$ $Z = 0.71$

Using Table II, we have

$$P\text{-value} = P(Z < -0.71) + P(Z > 0.71) = 2P(Z > 0.71) =$$
$$2(1 - P(Z \le 0.71)) = 2(1 - 0.7611) = 2(0.2389) = 0.4778$$

The probability of obtaining a sample mean more than 0.71 standard deviation away from the assumed mean of 37,500 is 0.4778. This means that about 48 samples in 100 will result in a sample mean at least 0.71 standard deviation from \$37,500.

Step 4: If the P-value is greater than the level of significance, we do not reject the null hypothesis. Because $0.4778 > 0.1$, we do not reject the null hypothesis.

Step 5: The sample evidence does not support the claim that the price of a three-year-old Corvette is different from \$37,500 at the $\alpha = 0.1$ level of significance. ◄◄

Using Technology: Statistical software and graphing calculators with advanced statistical features can be used to test hypotheses regarding a population mean with σ known. The output usually reports a P-value, and the user is expected to decide whether to reject the null hypothesis based upon the reported P-value. For example, Figure 11 shows the output for the hypothesis tested in Example 4 from a TI-83 Plus graphing calculator. The results differ from the "by hand" solution due to rounding.

Figure 11

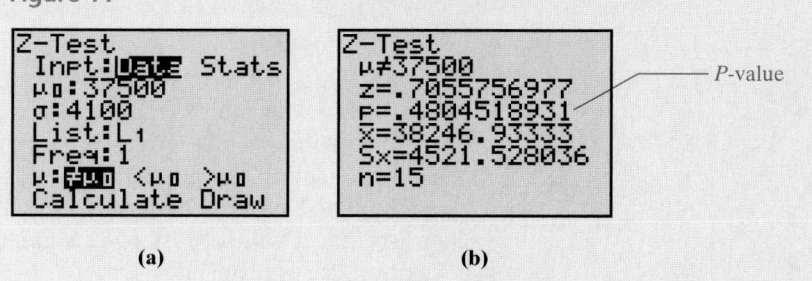

(a)   (b)

NW *Now Work Problem 7.*

One advantage of using P-values over the classical method in hypothesis testing is that P-values provide information regarding the strength of the evidence. In Example 1, we rejected the null hypothesis, but did not learn anything about the strength of the evidence against the null hypothesis. Example 3 tested the same claim using P-values. The P-value was 0.0045. This result not only led us to reject the null hypothesis, but also indicates the strength of the evidence against the null hypothesis: Less than 1 sample in 100 would give us the sample mean that we got if the null hypothesis, $H_o: \mu = 10,300$, were true.

Another advantage of P-values is that they are interpreted the same way, regardless of the type of hypothesis test being performed. If P-value $< \alpha$, reject the null hypothesis.

④ Using Confidence Intervals to Test Hypotheses

Recall the level of confidence in a confidence interval is a probability that represents the percentage of intervals that will contain μ if repeated samples are obtained. The level of confidence is denoted $(1 - \alpha) \cdot 100\%$. We can use confidence intervals to test $H_o: \mu = \mu_o$ versus $H_1: \mu \neq \mu_o$ using the following criterion.

> **When testing $H_o: \mu = \mu_o$ versus $H_1: \mu \neq \mu_o$, if a $(1 - \alpha) \cdot 100\%$ confidence interval contains μ_o, we do not reject the null hypothesis. However, if the confidence interval does not contain μ_o, we have evidence that supports the claim stated in the alternative hypothesis and conclude $\mu \neq \mu_o$ at the level of significance, α.**

▶ **EXAMPLE 5**   **Using a Confidence Interval to Test a Hypothesis**

Problem: Test the hypothesis presented in Example 2 at the $\alpha = 0.1$ level of significance by constructing a 90% confidence interval about μ, the population mean price of a three-year-old Chevy Corvette.

Approach: We construct the 90% confidence interval. If the interval contains the "status quo" mean of $37,500$, we do not reject the null hypothesis.

Solution: From the results of Example 3 from Section 8.1, we were 90% confident that the price of a three-year-old Chevy Corvette is between $36,506 and $39,988. Because this interval contains the hypothesized value of the mean, $37,500$, we do not reject the null hypothesis. We conclude that there is not sufficient evidence to support Grant's claim that the mean price of a three-year-old Chevy Corvette is different from $37,500 at the $\alpha = 0.1$ level of significance.   ◀◀

NW *Now Work Problem 27.*

One of the more difficult aspects of hypothesis testing is identifying the appropriate procedure to use. In this section, you should notice that all the problems involve testing a population mean where σ is known. In the next section, we test hypotheses about a population mean where σ is unknown. You are encouraged to carefully read the problems in this section so that it will be easy to recognize when procedures presented in the section are appropriate.

9.2 Assess Your Understanding

Concepts and Vocabulary

1. State the requirements that must be satisfied in order to test a claim regarding a population mean with σ known.

2. Determine the critical value for a right-tailed test regarding a population mean with σ known at the $\alpha = 0.01$ level of significance. $Z = 2.33$

3. Determine the critical value for a two-tailed test regarding a population mean with σ known at the $\alpha = 0.05$ level of significance. $Z = \pm 1.96$

4. The procedures for testing a claim regarding a population mean with σ known are robust. What does this mean?

5. Explain what a P-value is. What is the criterion for rejecting the null hypothesis using the P-value approach?

6. Suppose that we are testing the hypotheses $H_0: \mu = \mu_0$ versus $H_1: \mu < \mu_0$ and we find the P-value to be 0.23. Explain what this means. Would you reject H_0? Why?

7. Suppose that we are testing the hypotheses $H_0: \mu = \mu_0$ versus $H_1: \mu \neq \mu_0$ and we find the P-value to be 0.02. Explain what this means. Would you reject H_0? Why?

8. Discuss the advantages and disadvantages of using the classical approach to hypothesis testing. Discuss the advantages and disadvantages of using the P-value approach to hypothesis testing.

Exercises

- **Basic Skills**

1. In order to test $H_0: \mu = 50$ versus $H_1: \mu < 50$, a random sample of size $n = 24$ is obtained from a population that is known to be normally distributed with $\sigma = 12$.
   (a) If the sample mean is determined to be $\bar{x} = 47.1$, compute the test statistic. $Z = -1.18$
   (b) If the researcher decides to test this hypothesis at the $\alpha = 0.05$ level of significance, determine the critical value. $-Z_{0.05} = -1.645$
   (c) Draw a normal curve that depicts the critical region.
   (d) Will the researcher reject the null hypothesis? Why? No

2. In order to test $H_0: \mu = 40$ versus $H_1: \mu > 40$, a random sample of size $n = 25$ is obtained from a population that is known to be normally distributed with $\sigma = 6$.
   (a) If the sample mean is determined to be $\bar{x} = 42.3$, compute the test statistic. $Z = 1.92$
   (b) If the researcher decides to test this hypothesis at the $\alpha = 0.1$ level of significance, determine the critical value. $Z_{0.1} = 1.28$
   (c) Draw a normal curve that depicts the critical region.
   (d) Will the researcher reject the null hypothesis? Why? Yes

3. In order to test $H_0: \mu = 100$ versus $H_1: \mu \neq 100$ a random sample of size $n = 23$ is obtained from a population that is known to be normally distributed with $\sigma = 7$.
   (a) If the sample mean is determined to be $\bar{x} = 104.8$, compute the test statistic. $Z = 3.29$
   (b) If the researcher decides to test this hypothesis at the $\alpha = 0.01$ level of significance, determine the critical values. $-Z_{0.005} = -2.575$; $Z_{0.005} = 2.575$
   (c) Draw a normal curve that depicts the critical regions.
   (d) Will the researcher reject the null hypothesis? Why? Yes

4. In order to test $H_0: \mu = 80$ versus $H_1: \mu < 80$, a random sample of size $n = 22$ is obtained from a population that is known to be normally distributed with $\sigma = 11$.
   (a) If the sample mean is determined to be $\bar{x} = 76.9$, compute the test statistic. $Z = -1.32$
   (b) If the researcher decides to test this hypothesis at the $\alpha = 0.02$ level of significance, determine the critical value. $-Z_{0.02} = -2.05$
   (c) Draw a normal curve that depicts the critical region.
   (d) Will the researcher reject the null hypothesis? Why? No

5. In order to test $H_0: \mu = 20$ versus $H_1: \mu < 20$, a random sample of size $n = 18$ is obtained from a population that is known to be normally distributed with $\sigma = 3$.
   (a) If the sample mean is determined to be $\bar{x} = 18.3$, compute and interpret the P-value. 0.0081
   (b) If the researcher decides to test this hypothesis at the $\alpha = 0.05$ level of significance, will the researcher reject the null hypothesis? Why? Yes

6. In order to test $H_0: \mu = 4.5$ versus $H_1: \mu > 4.5$, a random sample of size $n = 13$ is obtained from a population that is known to be normally distributed with $\sigma = 1.2$.
   (a) If the sample mean is determined to be $\bar{x} = 4.9$, compute and interpret the P-value. 0.1147
   (b) If the researcher decides to test this hypothesis at the $\alpha = 0.1$ level of significance, will the researcher reject the null hypothesis? Why? No

7. In order to test $H_0: \mu = 105$ versus $H_1: \mu \neq 105$, a random sample of size $n = 35$ is obtained from a population whose standard deviation is known to be $\sigma = 12$.
   (a) Does the population need to be normally distributed in order to compute the P-value? No

(b) If the sample mean is determined to be $\bar{x} = 101.2$, compute and interpret the *P*-value. *0.0610*

(c) If the researcher decides to test this hypothesis at the $\alpha = 0.02$ level of significance, will the researcher reject the null hypothesis? Why? *No*

8. In order to test $H_0: \mu = 45$ versus $H_1: \mu \neq 45$, a random sample of size $n = 40$ is obtained from a population whose standard deviation is known to be $\sigma = 8$.

(a) Does the population need to be normally distributed in order to compute the *P*-value? *No*

(b) If the sample mean is determined to be $\bar{x} = 48.3$, compute and interpret the *P*-value. *0.0091*

(c) If the researcher decides to test this hypothesis at the $\alpha = 0.05$ level of significance, will the researcher reject the null hypothesis? Why? *Yes*

• **Applying the Concepts**

9. **Are Mothers Getting Older?** A researcher claims that the average age of a woman before she has her first child is greater than the 1990 mean age of 26.4 years, on the basis of data obtained from the *National Vital Statistics Report*, Vol. 48, No. 14. She obtains a simple random sample of 40 women who gave birth to their first child in 1999 and finds the sample mean age to be 27.1 years. Assume that the population standard deviation is 6.4 years. Test the researcher's claim, using the classical approach at the $\alpha = 0.05$ level of significance.

10. **Miles per Gallon** The Environmental Protection Agency publishes data regarding the miles per gallon of all cars. A researcher claims that fuel additives increase the miles per gallon of cars driven under highway driving conditions. The mean miles per gallon of all large cars manufactured in 1999 without the fuel additive is 25.1, on the basis of data obtained from the EPA. The researcher obtains a simple random sample of 35 large cars manufactured in 1999 and adds a fuel additive. The sample mean is determined to be 26.8 miles per gallon. Assume that the population standard deviation is 3.9. Test the researcher's claim, using the classical approach at the $\alpha = 0.05$ level of significance.

11. **SAT Exam Scores** A school administrator claims that students whose first language learned is not English score worse on the verbal portion of the SAT exam than students whose first language is English. The mean SAT verbal score of students whose first language is English is 516, on the basis of data obtained from the College Board. Suppose a simple random sample of 20 students whose first language learned was not English results in a sample mean SAT verbal score of 458. SAT verbal scores are normally distributed with a population standard deviation of 119.

(a) Why is it necessary for SAT verbal scores to be normally distributed in order to test the claim using the methods of this section? *Small sample*

(b) Test the researcher's claim using the classical approach at the $\alpha = 0.10$ level of significance.

12. **SAT Exam Scores** A school administrator claims that students whose first language learned is not English do not score differently on the SAT math portion of the SAT exam from students whose first language is English. The mean SAT math score of students whose first language is English is 516, on the basis of data obtained from the College Board. Suppose a simple random sample of 20 students whose first language learned was not English results in a sample mean SAT math score of 518. SAT math scores are normally distributed with a population standard deviation of 109.

(a) Why is it necessary for SAT math scores to be normally distributed in order to test the claim using the methods of this section? *Small sample*

(b) Test the researcher's claim using the classical approach at the $\alpha = 0.10$ level of significance.

13. **Acid Rain** In 1990, the mean pH level of the rain in Pierce County, Washington, was 5.03. A biologist claims that the acidity of rain has increased. (This would mean that the pH level of the rain has decreased.) From a random sample of 19 rain dates in 2000, she obtains the following data:

5.08	4.66	4.70	4.87
4.78	5.00	4.50	4.73
4.79	4.65	4.91	5.07
5.03	4.78	4.77	4.60
4.73	5.05	4.70	

Source: National Atmospheric Deposition Program

9. $Z = 0.69$; do not reject H_o 10. $Z = 2.58$; reject H_o (11b) $Z = -2.18$; reject H_o (12b) $Z = 0.08$; do not reject H_o

(a) Because the sample size is small, she must verify that pH level is normally distributed and the sample does not contain any outliers. The normal probability plot and boxplot are shown below. Are the conditions for testing the hypothesis satisfied? Yes

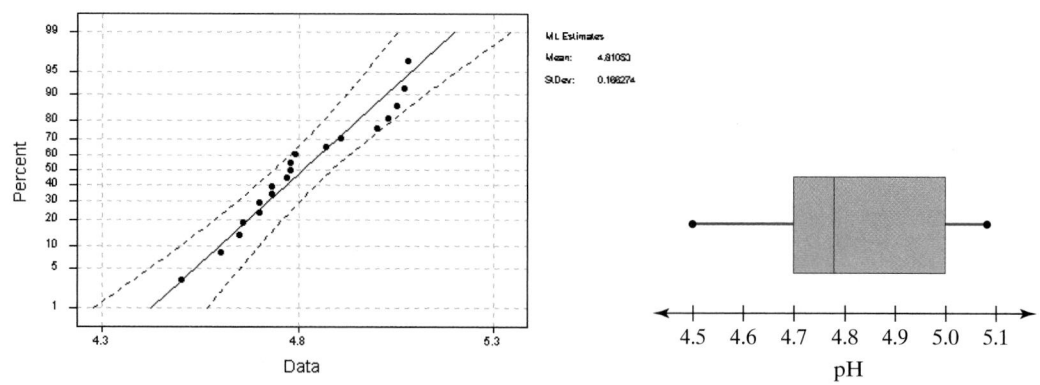

Normal Probability Plot for pH

(b) Test the hypothesis, assuming that $\sigma = 0.2$ at the $\alpha = 0.01$ level of significance. Reject H_o

14. **Age of the Bride** A sociologist claims that the mean age at which women marry in Memphis, Tennessee, is greater than the mean age of 25.0 throughout the United States, on the basis of data from the *Monthly Vital Statistics Report* published by the Centers for Disease Control. Based upon a random sample of 20 recently filed marriage certificates, she obtains the ages shown in the table on the right.

40	23	30	24	31
29	28	24	35	34
24	21	46	29	31
29	29	21	33	39

Source: The Commercial Appeal, June 30, 2001

(a) Because the sample size is small, she must verify that age at marriage is normally distributed and the sample does not contain any outliers. The normal probability plot and boxplot are as shown below. Are the conditions for testing the hypothesis satisfied? Yes

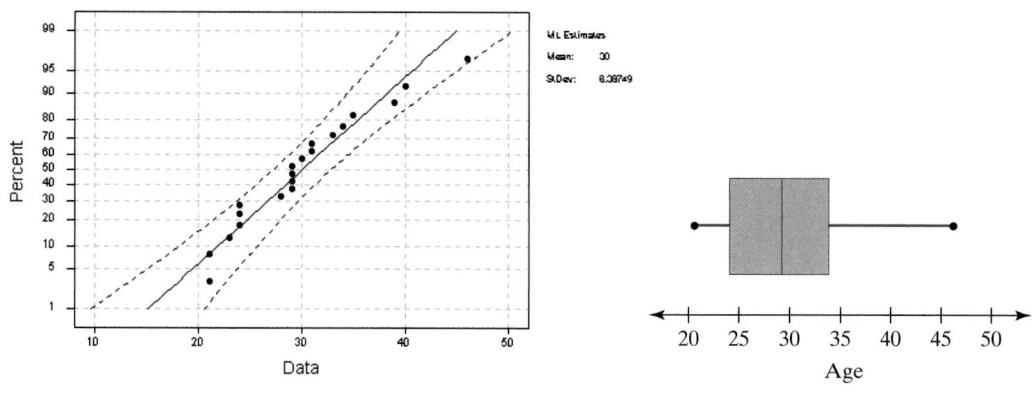

Normal Probability Plot for Age

(b) Test the hypothesis, assuming that $\sigma = 6.2$ at the $\alpha = 0.05$ level of significance. Reject H_o

15. **Filling Bottles** A certain brand of apple juice is supposed to have 64 ounces of juice. Because the filling machine is not precise, the exact amount of juice varies from bottle to bottle. The quality control manager wishes to verify that the mean amount of juice in each bottle is 64 ounces, so she can be sure that the machine is not over- or under-filling. She randomly samples 22 bottles of juice and measures the content. She obtains the data on the right.

63.97	63.87	64.03	63.95	63.95	64.02
64.01	63.90	64.00	64.01	63.92	63.94
63.90	64.05	63.90	64.01	63.91	63.92
63.93	63.97	63.93	63.98		

(a) Because the sample size is small, she must verify that the amount of juice is normally distributed and the sample does not contain any outliers. The normal probability plot and boxplot are shown below. Are the conditions for testing the hypothesis satisfied? Yes

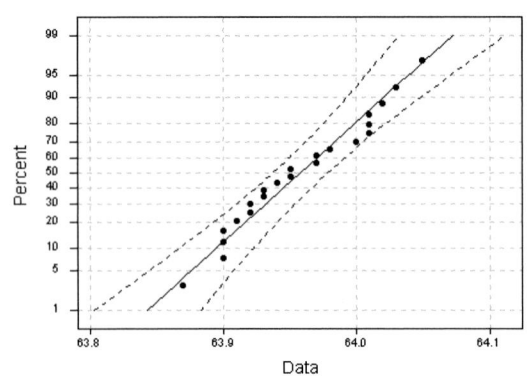

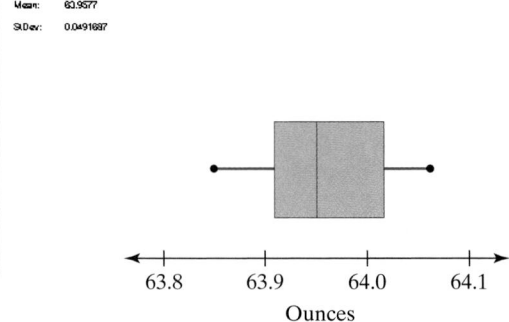

(b) Test the hypothesis, assuming that $\sigma = 0.06$ at the $\alpha = 0.1$ level of significance. Reject H_o
(c) Should the assembly line be shut down so that the machine can be recalibrated? Yes

16. **Price of Gasoline** In February of 2001, an executive of a major oil company claimed that the mean price of regular unleaded gasoline in Cook County, Illinois, was exactly $1.56. A member of the county board feels that the mean price is different from $1.56. He randomly sampled 20 gas stations and obtained the data on the right.

1.52	1.61	1.55	1.58	1.66
1.51	1.58	1.55	1.58	1.61
1.58	1.59	1.57	1.53	1.59
1.56	1.61	1.57	1.65	1.53

(a) Because the sample size is small, he must verify that the price of gasoline is normally distributed and the sample does not contain any outliers. The normal probability plot and boxplot are shown below. Are the conditions for testing the hypothesis satisfied? Yes

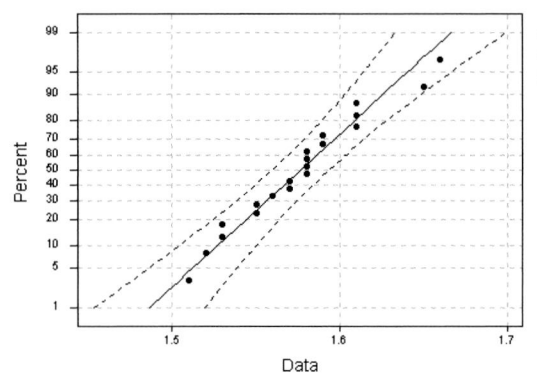

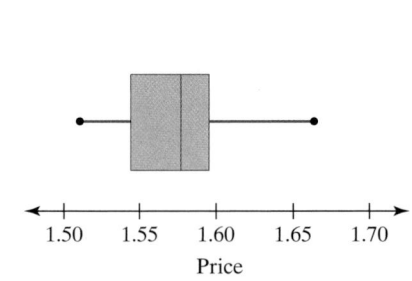

(b) Test the hypothesis, assuming that $\sigma = 0.05$ at the $\alpha = 0.1$ level of significance. Do not reject H_o

17. Are Cars Younger? Suppose you have just been hired by Ford Motor Company. Management asks you to test the claim that cars are younger today versus 1995. According to the Nationwide Personal Transportation Survey conducted by the U.S. Department of Transportation, the mean age of a car in 1995 was 8.33 years. Based upon a random sample of 18 automobile owners, you obtain the ages as shown in the data on the right.

8	12	1	2	13	3
5	9	12	6	5	6
10	7	10	11	6	10

(a) Because the sample size is small, you must verify that the data are normally distributed with no outliers by drawing a normal probability plot and boxplot. Based on the following graphs, can you perform a hypothesis test? Yes

Normal Probability Plot for Age

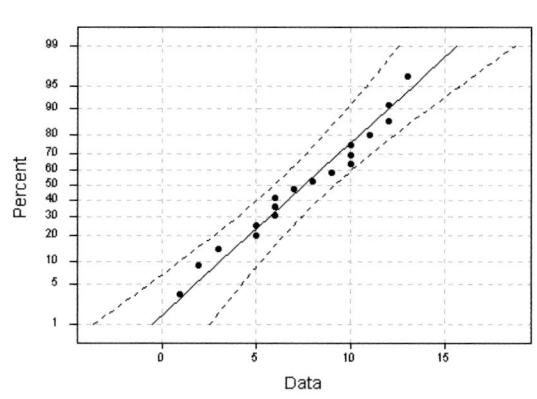

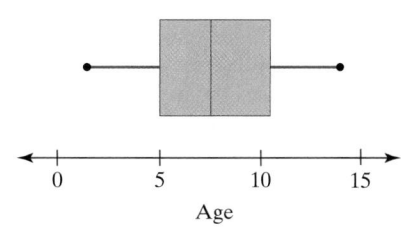

(b) Test the hypothesis, assuming that $\sigma = 3.8$ years at the $\alpha = 0.1$ level of significance. Do not reject H_o

18. It's a Hot One! Recently, a friend of mine claimed that the summer of 2000 in Houston, Texas was hotter than usual. To test his claim, I went to AccuWeather.com and randomly selected 12 days in the summer of 2000. I then recorded the departure from normal, with positive values indicating above-normal temperatures and negative values indicating below-normal temperatures, as shown in the data on the right.

+4	−1	0	+2
+2	+4	−1	−3
−1	0	+2	+4

Source: AccuWeather.com

(a) Because the sample size is small, I must verify that the temperature departure is normally distributed and the sample does not contain any outliers. The normal probability plot and boxplot are shown below. Are the conditions for testing the hypothesis satisfied? Yes

Normal Probability Plot for Departure

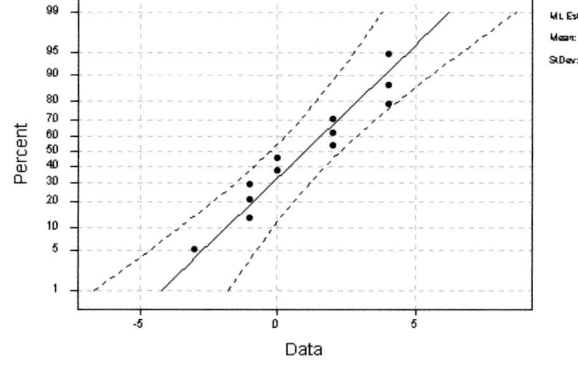

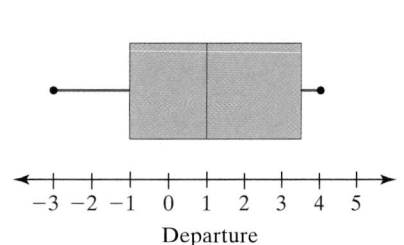

(b) Test the hypothesis, assuming that $\sigma = 1.8$ at the $\alpha = 0.05$ level of significance. Reject H_o

19. **Farm Size** In 1990, the average farm size in Kansas was 694 acres, according to data obtained from the U.S. Department of Agriculture. A researcher claims that farm sizes are larger now due to consolidation of farms. She obtains a random sample of 40 farms and determines the mean size to be 731 acres. Assume that $\sigma = 212$ acres. Test the researcher's claim, using the P-value approach at the $\alpha = 0.05$ level of significance.

20. **Oil Output** An energy official claims that the oil output per well in the United States has declined from the 1998 level of 11.1 barrels per day. He randomly samples 50 wells throughout the United States and determines the mean output to be 10.7 barrels per day. Assume that $\sigma = 1.3$ barrels. Test the researcher's claim using the P-value approach at the $\alpha = 0.05$ level of significance.

21. **Cellular Phone Bills** The mean monthly cellular telephone bill in 1999 was $40.24, according to the Cellular Telecommunications Industry Association. A researcher at CTIA claims that the average monthly bill has increased since then. She conducts a survey of 49 cellular phone users and determines the mean bill to be $45.15. Assume that $\sigma = \$21.20$. Test the researcher's claim, using the P-value approach at the $\alpha = 0.1$ level of significance.

22. **Length of a Cellular Phone Call** The mean length of a cellular telephone call in 1999 was 2.38 minutes, according to the Cellular Telecommunications Industry Association. A researcher at CTIA claims the average length of a phone call has increased since then. She conducts a survey of 49 cellular phone users and determines the mean length to be 2.48 minutes. Assume that $\sigma = 1.8$ minutes. Test the researcher's claim, using the P-value approach at the $\alpha = 0.01$ level of significance.

23. **Volume of Dell Computer Stock** The average daily volume of Dell Computer stock in 2000 was $\mu = 31.8$ million shares, with a standard deviation of $\sigma = 14.8$ million shares, according to Yahoo!Finance. A stock analyst claims that the stock volume in 2001 is different from the 2000 level. Based on a random sample of 35 trading days in 2001, he finds the sample mean to be 39.2 million shares. Test the analyst's claim, using the P-value approach at the $\alpha = 0.05$ level of significance.

24. **Volume of Motorola Stock** The average daily volume of Motorola stock in 2000 was $\mu = 11.4$ million shares, with a standard deviation of $\sigma = 8.3$ million shares, according to Yahoo!Finance. A stock analyst claims the stock volume in 2001 is different from the 2000 level. Based on a random sample of 35 trading days in 2001, he finds the sample mean to be 15.0 million shares. Test the analyst's claim, using the P-value approach at the $\alpha = 0.05$ level of significance.

25. **Using Confidence Intervals to Test Hypotheses** Test the claim made in Problem 15 by constructing a 95% confidence interval. $(63.93, 63.98)$; reject H_o

26. **Using Confidence Intervals to Test Hypotheses** Test the claim made in Problem 16 by constructing a 95% confidence interval. $(1.555, 1.598)$; do not reject H_o

27. **Using Confidence Intervals to Test Hypotheses** Test the claim made in Problem 23 by constructing a 90% confidence interval. $(35.1, 43.3)$; reject H_o

28. **Using Confidence Intervals to Test Hypotheses** Test the claim made in Problem 24 by constructing a 90% confidence interval. $(12.69, 17.31)$; reject H_o

29. **Statistical Significance versus Practical Significance** A math teacher claims that she has developed a review course that increases the scores of students on the math portion of the SAT exam. Based on data from the College Board, SAT scores are normally distributed with $\mu = 514$ and $\sigma = 113$. The teacher obtains a random sample of 1800 students, puts them through the review class, and finds that the mean SAT math score of the 1800 students is 518.

    (a) State the null and alternative hypotheses.
    (b) Test the claim at the $\alpha = 0.10$ level of significance. Is a mean SAT math score of 518 significantly higher than 514? Reject H_o
    (c) Do you think that a mean SAT math score of 518 versus 514 will affect the decision of a school admissions administrator? In other words, does the increase in the score have any practical significance?
    (d) Test the claim at the $\alpha = 0.10$ level of significance with $n = 400$ students. Assume that the sample mean is still 518. Is a sample mean of 518 significantly more than 514? Conclude that large sample sizes cause P-values to shrink substantially, all other things being the same. Do not reject H_o

30. **Simulation** Simulate drawing 50 simple random samples of size $n = 20$ from a population that is normally distributed with mean 80 and standard deviation 7.

    (a) Test the null hypothesis $H_o: \mu = 80$ versus the alternative hypothesis $H_1: \mu \neq 80$.
    (b) Suppose we were testing this hypothesis at the $\alpha = 0.1$ level of significance. How many of the 50 samples would you expect to result in a Type I error?
    (c) Count the number of samples that lead to a rejection of the null hypothesis. Is it close to the expected value determined in part (b)?
    (d) Describe how we know that a rejection of the null hypothesis results in making a Type I error in this situation.

19. P-value $= 0.1348$; do not reject H_o 20. P-value $= 0.0148$; reject H_o 21. P-value $= 0.0525$; reject H_o
22. P-value $= 0.3487$; do not reject H_o 23. P-value $= 0.0031$; reject H_o (24) P-value $= 0.0031$; reject H_o
(29a) $H_o: \mu = 514$ vs. $H_1: \mu > 514$

31. Simulation Simulate drawing 40 simple random samples of size $n = 35$ from a population that is exponentially distributed with mean 8 and standard deviation $\sqrt{8}$.

(a) Test the null hypothesis $H_o: \mu = 8$ versus the alternative hypothesis $H_1: \mu \neq 8$.

(b) Suppose we were testing this hypothesis at the $\alpha = 0.05$ level of significance. How many of the 40 samples would you expect to result in a Type I error?

(c) Count the number of samples that lead to a rejection of the null hypothesis. Is it close to the expected value determined in part (b)?

(d) Describe how we know that a rejection of the null hypothesis results in making a Type I error in this situation.

32. Suppose a chemical company has developed a catalyst that is meant to reduce reaction time in a chemical process. For a certain chemical process, reaction time is known to be 150 seconds. The researchers conducted an experiment with the catalyst 40 times and measured reaction time. The researchers reported that the catalysts reduced reaction time with a P-value of 0.02.

(a) Identify the null and alternative hypotheses.

(b) Explain what this result means. Do you believe that the catalyst is effective?

(32a) $H_o: \mu = 150$ vs $H_1: \mu < 150$

Technology Step-by-Step
Hypothesis Tests Regarding μ, σ Known

TI-83 Plus   **Step 1:** If necessary, enter raw data in L1.

Step 2: Press STAT, highlight TESTS, and select `1:Z-Test`.

Step 3: If the data are raw, highlight DATA; make sure that List1 is set to L1 and Freq is set to 1. If summary statistics are known, highlight STATS and enter the summary statistics. Following σ, enter the population standard deviation. For the value of μ_o, enter the value of the mean stated in the null hypothesis.

Step 4: Select the direction of the alternative hypothesis.

Step 5: Highlight Calculate and press ENTER. The TI-83 gives the P-value.

MINITAB   **Step 1:** Enter raw data in column C1.

Step 2: Select the **Stat** menu, highlight **Basic Statistics**, and then highlight **1-Sample Z** . . .

Step 3: Enter C1 in the cell marked "Variables." Select "Test Mean" and enter the value of the mean stated in the null hypothesis. In the cell marked "Alternative," select the direction of the alternative hypothesis. In the cell marked "Sigma," enter the value of σ. Click OK.

Excel   **Step 1:** If necessary, enter raw data in column A.

Step 2: Load the PHStat Add-in.

Step 3: Select the **PHStat** menu, highlight **One Sample Tests** . . . , and then highlight **Z Test for the mean, sigma known** . . . .

Step 4: Enter the value of the null hypothesis, the level of significance, α, and the value of σ. If the summary statistics are known, click "Sample statistics known" and enter the sample size and sample mean. If summary statistics are unknown, click "Sample statistics unknown." With the cursor in the "Sample cell range" cell, highlight the data in column A. Click the option corresponding to the desired test (two-tail, upper (right) tail, or lower (left) tail). Click OK.

9.3 Testing a Hypothesis about μ, σ Unknown

Preparing for This Section   Before getting started, review the following:

    ✓ Central Limit Theorem (Section 7.5, p. 432)

    ✓ The t-distribution (Section 8.2, pp. 476–479)

    ✓ Using probabilities to identify unusual events (Section 5.1, p. 263)

Objectives   ①   Test hypotheses about μ, σ unknown, using the classical approach

         ②   Test hypotheses about μ, σ unknown, using the P-value approach

In Section 9.2, we assumed that the population standard deviation, σ, was known when testing claims regarding the population mean. We now introduce procedures for testing claims regarding a population mean when σ is not known. The only difference from the situation where σ is known is that we must use the t-distribution rather than the z-distribution.

 In Your Own Words

When σ is known, use z; when σ is unknown use t.

We cannot replace σ with s and say that $z = \dfrac{\overline{x} - \mu}{s/\sqrt{n}}$ is normally distributed with mean 0 and standard deviation 1. Instead, $t = \dfrac{\overline{x} - \mu}{s/\sqrt{n}}$ follows

Student's t-distribution with $n - 1$ degrees of freedom. First, let's review the properties of the t-distribution.

> **Properties of the t-Distribution**
>
> **1.** The t-distribution is different for different values of n, the sample size.
>
> **2.** The t-distribution is centered at 0 and is symmetric about 0.
>
> **3.** The area under the curve is 1. Because of the symmetry, the area under the curve to the right of 0 equals the area under the curve to the left of 0 equals $\frac{1}{2}$.
>
> **4.** As t increases without bound, the graph approaches, but never equals, zero. As t decreases without bound the graph approaches, but never equals, zero.
>
> **5.** The area in the tails of the t-distribution is a little greater than the area in the tails of the standard normal distribution because using s as an estimate of σ introduces more variability to the t-statistic.
>
> **6.** As the sample size n increases, the density curve of t gets closer to the standard normal density curve. This result occurs because, as the sample size n increases, the values of s get closer to the values of σ, by the Law of Large Numbers.

① **Testing a Hypothesis about μ, σ Unknown, Using the Classical Approach**

The classical approach to testing a hypothesis about μ with σ unknown follows the exact same logic as testing a hypotheses about μ with σ known. The only difference is that the **test statistic** is

$$t = \frac{\overline{x} - \mu_{\text{o}}}{s/\sqrt{n}},$$

and the **critical value** will be found from Table III.

Hypothesis Test Regarding μ with σ Unknown

If a claim is made regarding the population mean with σ unknown, we can use the following steps to test the claim, provided that
1. the sample is obtained using simple random sampling, and
2. the population from which the sample is drawn is normally distributed or the sample size, n, is large ($n \geq 30$).

Step 1: A claim is made regarding the population mean. The claim is used to determine the null and alternative hypotheses. The hypotheses can be structured in one of three ways:

Two-Tailed	Left-Tailed	Right-Tailed
$H_0: \mu = \mu_0$	$H_0: \mu = \mu_0$	$H_0: \mu = \mu_0$
$H_1: \mu \neq \mu_0$	$H_1: \mu < \mu_0$	$H_1: \mu > \mu_0$

Note: μ_0 is the assumed value of the population mean.

Step 2: Select a level of significance, α, to reflect the seriousness of making a Type I error. The level of significance is used to determine the critical value. For example, the critical value in the left-tailed test is $-t_\alpha$ with $n - 1$ degrees of freedom. The shaded region(s) represent(s) the critical region.

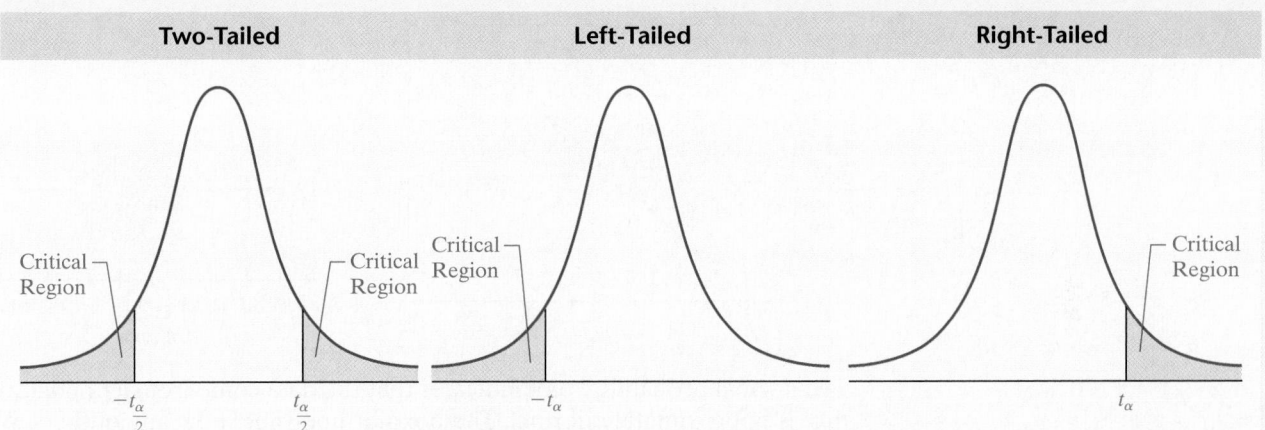

Step 3: Compute the test statistic $t = \dfrac{\overline{x} - \mu_0}{s/\sqrt{n}}$, which follows Student's t-distribution with $n - 1$ degrees of freedom.

Step 4: Compare the critical value with the test statistic:

Two-Tailed	Left-Tailed	Right-Tailed
If $t < -t_{\alpha/2}$ or $t > t_{\alpha/2}$, reject the null hypothesis	If $t < -t_\alpha$, reject the null hypothesis	If $t > t_\alpha$, reject the null hypothesis

Step 5: State the conclusion.

Notice that the procedure just presented requires either that the population from which the sample was drawn be normal or that the sample size be large ($n \geq 30$). The procedure is robust, so minor departures from normality will not adversely affect the results of the test; however, if the data include outliers, the procedure should not be used. Just as we did for hypothesis tests with σ known, we will verify this assumption by constructing normal probability plots (to assess normality) and boxplots (to discover whether there are outliers). If the normal probability plot indicates that the data do not come from a normal population or if the boxplot reveals outliers, nonparametric tests should be performed, as discussed in Section 13.3.

▶ **EXAMPLE 1** **Caffeine Intake of 20–29-Year-Old Females**

TABLE 3		
140.4	145.8	148.3
169.8	147.9	130.0
161.1	164.3	130.5
174.3	181.1	105.8
168.1	160.3	154.1
117.3	103.4	127.8
164.6	154.5	

Problem: In a study conducted by the U.S. Department of Agriculture, it was found that the mean daily caffeine intake of 20–29-year-old females in 1996 was 142.8 milligrams. A nutritionist claims that the mean daily caffeine intake has increased since then. She obtains a simple random sample of 20 females between 20 and 29 years of age and determines their daily caffeine intakes. The results are presented in Table 3. Test the nutritionist's claim at the $\alpha = 0.05$ level of significance.

Approach: Before we can perform the hypothesis test, we must verify that the data come from a population that is distributed approximately normally, with no outliers. We will construct a normal probability plot and boxplot to verify these requirements. We then proceed to follow Steps 1–5.

Solution: Figure 12 displays the normal probability plot and boxplot.

Figure 12

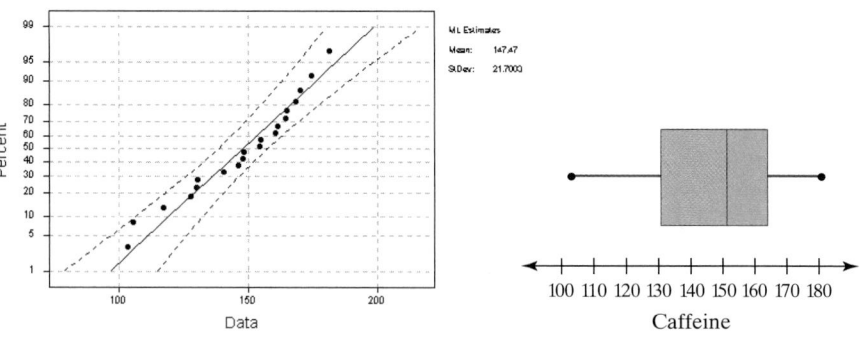

The normal probability plot indicates that the data come from a population that is approximately normal. The boxplot does not show any outliers. We can proceed to perform the hypothesis test.

Step 1: The nutritionist claims that 20–29-year-old females are consuming more than 142.8 mg of caffeine. This claim can be written $\mu > 142.8$. We have

$$H_0: \mu = 142.8 \qquad \text{versus} \qquad H_1: \mu > 142.8.$$

This is a right-tailed test.

Step 2: Because the nutritionist is performing a right-tailed test, we determine the critical t-value at the $\alpha = 0.05$ level of significance with $n - 1 = 20 - 1 = 19$ degrees of freedom to be $t_{0.05} = 1.729$. The critical region is displayed in Figure 13.

Step 3: The nutritionist computes the sample mean, $\bar{x}$, to be 147.47 mg and the sample standard deviation, s, to be 22.26 mg. Because the data are distributed approximately normally, the test statistic is

$$t = \frac{\bar{x} - \mu_0}{s/\sqrt{n}} = \frac{147.47 - 142.8}{22.26/\sqrt{20}} = 0.938$$

Figure 13

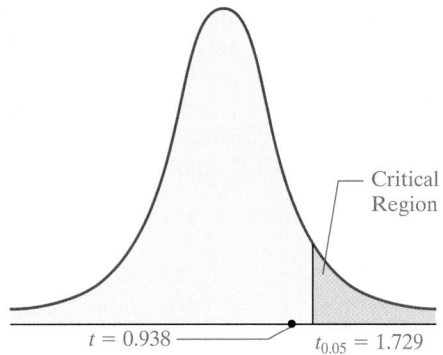

$t = 0.938$ $t_{0.05} = 1.729$

The sample mean, 147.47 mg, is 0.938 sample standard deviation above the hypothesized mean, 142.8 mg.

Step 4: Because the test statistic $t = 0.938$ is less than the critical value $t_{0.05} = 1.729$, the nutritionist does not reject the null hypothesis. That is, the value of the test statistic does not fall within the critical region, so we do not reject H_o. We label this point in Figure 13.

Step 5: There is not sufficient evidence to support the nutritionist's claim that the mean number of milligrams of caffeine has increased from the 1996 level of 142.8 mg at the $\alpha = 0.05$ level of significance. ◄◄

 Now Work Problem 3.

② Testing a Hypothesis about μ, σ Unknown, Using P-Values

We can also test hypotheses about a population mean with the population standard deviation unknown by using P-values. Recall that a P-value is the probability of observing a sample statistic as extreme or more extreme than the one observed, under the assumption that the null hypothesis is true. If the P-value is small, we have evidence against the null hypothesis. Because the t-distribution table (Table III) provides only t-values that correspond to certain areas, we cannot use the table to compute exact P-values.

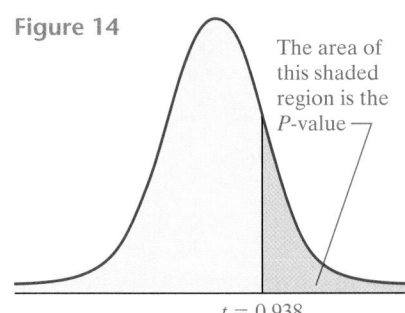

In Your Own Words

When σ is unknown, exact P-values can be found only via technology.

However, we can use the table to calculate lower and upper bounds on the P-value. In order to find exact P-values, we need to use statistical software or a graphing calculator with advanced statistical features.

▶ **EXAMPLE 2**   Approximating a P-Value

Problem: Using the data from Example 1, test the nutritionist's claim, using the P-value approach at the $\alpha = 0.05$ level of significance.

Approach: Because this is a right-tailed test, the P-value is the area under the t-distribution with $20 - 1 = 19$ degrees of freedom to the right of the test statistic.

Figure 14

Solution: The test statistic is $t = 0.938$. Because we are performing a right-tailed test, P-value $= P(t > t_0) = P(t > 0.938)$, with 19 degrees of freedom—that is, we need to find the area under the t-distribution to the right of $t = 0.938$, as shown in Figure 14.

Using Table III, we find the row that corresponds to 19 degrees of freedom. The test statistic, $t = 0.938$, lies between 0.861 and 1.066. The value of 0.861 has 0.20 as the area under the t-distribution to the right. The area under the t-distribution with 19 degrees of freedom to the right of $t = 1.066$ is 0.15. See Figure 15.

Figure 15

					Area in Right Tail							
df	0.25	0.20	0.15	0.10	0.05	0.025	0.02	0.01	0.005	0.0025	0.001	0.0005
1	1.000	1.376	1.963	3.078	6.314	12.71	15.89	31.82	63.66	127.3	318.3	636.6
2	0.816	1.061	1.386	1.886	2.920	4.303	4.849	6.965	9.925	14.09	22.33	31.60
3	0.765	0.978	1.250	1.638	2.353	3.182	3.482	4.541	5.841	7.453	10.21	12.92
4	0.741	0.941	1.190	1.533	2.132	2.776	2.999	3.747	4.604	5.598	7.173	8.610
5	0.727	0.920	1.156	1.476	2.015	2.571	2.757	3.365	4.032	4.773	5.893	6.869
6	0.718	0.906	1.134	1.440	1.943	2.447	2.612	3.143	3.707	4.317	5.208	5.959
7	0.711	0.896	1.119	1.415	1.895	2.365	2.517	2.998	3.499	4.029	4.785	5.408
8	0.706	0.889	1.108	1.397	1.860	2.306	2.449	2.896	3.355	3.833	4.501	5.041
9	0.703	0.883	1.100	1.383	1.833	2.262	2.398	2.821	3.250	3.690	4.297	4.781
10	0.700	0.879	1.093	1.372	1.812	2.228	2.359	2.764	3.169	3.581	4.144	4.587
11	0.697	0.876	1.088	1.363	1.796	2.201	2.328	2.718	3.106	3.497	4.025	4.437
12	0.695	0.873	1.083	1.356	1.782	2.179	2.303	2.681	3.055	3.428	3.930	4.318
13	0.694	0.870	1.079	1.350	1.771	2.160	2.282	2.650	3.012	3.372	3.852	4.221
14	0.692	0.868	1.076	1.345	1.761	2.145	2.264	2.624	2.977	3.326	3.787	4.140
15	0.691	0.866	1.074	1.341	1.753	2.131	2.249	2.602	2.947	3.286	3.733	4.073
16	0.690	0.865	1.071	1.337	1.746	2.120	2.235	2.583	2.921	3.252	3.686	4.015
17	0.689	0.863	1.069	1.333	1.740	2.110	2.224	2.567	2.898	3.222	3.646	3.965
18	0.688	0.862	1.067	1.330	1.734	2.101	2.214	2.552	2.878	3.197	3.611	3.922
19	0.688	0.861	1.066	1.328	1.729	2.093	2.205	2.539	2.861	3.174	3.579	3.883
20	0.687	0.860	1.064	1.325	1.725	2.086	2.197	2.528	2.845	3.153	3.552	3.850

Because $t = 0.938$ is between 0.861 and 1.066, we know that the P-value is between 0.15 and 0.20. We will present the P-value as follows:

$$0.15 < P\text{-value} < 0.20$$

Because the P-value is greater than the level of significance, $\alpha = 0.05$, we do not reject the null hypothesis. There is not sufficient evidence to support the nutritionist's claim. ◄◄

Suppose we desire a more accurate result. We can use a graphing calculator with advanced statistical features or statistical software to obtain the P-value. Figure 16(a) shows the results obtained from a TI-83 Plus graphing calculator by using the calculate option; Figure 16(b) shows the results from using the draw option. The P-value is about 0.18.

Figure 16

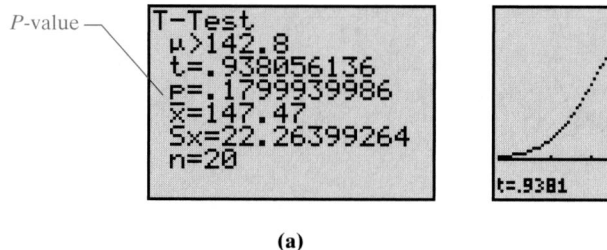

(a)   (b)

NW *Now Work Problem 5.*

Sections 9.2 and 9.3 discussed performing hypothesis tests about a population mean. The main criterion for choosing which test to use is whether the population standard deviation, σ, is known. Provided that the population from which the sample is drawn is normal or that the sample size is large,

- if σ is known, use the z-test procedures from Section 9.2;
- if σ is unknown, use the t-test procedures from Section 9.3.

In Section 9.4, we will discuss testing hypotheses about a population proportion; Section 9.5 will present methods for testing hypotheses about a population variance or standard deviation.

9.3 Assess Your Understanding

Concepts and Vocabulary

1. State the requirements that must be satisfied in order to test a claim about a population mean with σ unknown.
2. Determine the critical value for a right-tailed test of a population mean with σ unknown at the $\alpha = 0.01$ level of significance with 15 degrees of freedom.
3. Determine the critical value for a two-tailed test of a population mean with σ unknown at the $\alpha = 0.05$ level of significance with 12 degrees of freedom.
4. Determine the critical value for a left-tailed test of a population mean with σ unknown at the $\alpha = 0.05$ level of significance with 19 degrees of freedom.

Exercises

(1a) $t = -1.379$ (2a) $t = 2.674$ (3a) $t = 2.502$ (4a) $t = -1.711$ (5a) $t = -1.677$
(5c) P-value $= 0.0559$ (6a) $t = 1.109$ (6c) P-value $= 0.1445$

• Basic Skills

1. In order to test $H_0: \mu = 50$ versus $H_1: \mu < 50$, a simple random sample of size $n = 24$ is obtained from a population that is known to be normally distributed.
   (a) If $\bar{x} = 47.1$ and $s = 10.3$, compute the test statistic.
   (b) If the researcher decides to test this hypothesis at the $\alpha = 0.05$ level of significance, determine the critical value. $-t_{0.05} = -1.714$
   (c) Draw a t-distribution that depicts the critical region.
   (d) Will the researcher reject the null hypothesis? Why? No

2. In order to test $H_0: \mu = 40$ versus $H_1: \mu > 40$, a simple random sample of size $n = 25$ is obtained from a population that is known to be normally distributed.
   (a) If $\bar{x} = 42.3$ and $s = 4.3$, compute the test statistic.
   (b) If the researcher decides to test this hypothesis at the $\alpha = 0.1$ level of significance, determine the critical value. $t_{0.1} = 1.318$
   (c) Draw a t-distribution that depicts the critical region.
   (d) Will the researcher reject the null hypothesis? Why? Yes

3. In order to test $H_0: \mu = 100$ versus $H_1: \mu \neq 100$, a simple random sample of size $n = 23$ is obtained from a population that is known to be normally distributed.
   (a) If $\bar{x} = 104.8$ and $s = 9.2$, compute the test statistic.
   (b) If the researcher decides to test this hypothesis at the $\alpha = 0.01$ level of significance, determine the critical values. $-t_{0.005} = -2.819$; $t_{0.005} = 2.819$
   (c) Draw a t-distribution that depicts the critical region.
   (d) Will the researcher reject the null hypothesis? Why? No

4. In order to test $H_0: \mu = 80$ versus $H_1: \mu < 80$, a simple random sample of size $n = 22$ is obtained from a population that is known to be normally distributed.
   (a) If $\bar{x} = 76.9$ and $s = 8.5$, compute the test statistic.
   (b) If the researcher decides to test this hypothesis at the $\alpha = 0.02$ level of significance, determine the critical value. $-t_{0.02} = -2.189$
   (c) Draw a t-distribution that depicts the critical region.
   (d) Will the researcher reject the null hypothesis? Why? No

5. In order to test $H_0: \mu = 20$ versus $H_1: \mu < 20$, a simple random sample of size $n = 18$ is obtained from a population that is known to be normally distributed.
   (a) If $\bar{x} = 18.3$ and $s = 4.3$, compute the test statistic.
   (b) Draw a t-distribution with the area that represents the P-value shaded.
   (c) Approximate and interpret the P-value.
   (d) If the researcher decides to test this hypothesis at the $\alpha = 0.05$ level of significance, will the researcher reject the null hypothesis? Why? No

6. In order to test $H_0: \mu = 4.5$ versus $H_1: \mu > 4.5$, a simple random sample of size $n = 13$ is obtained from a population that is known to be normally distributed.
   (a) If $\bar{x} = 4.9$ and $s = 1.3$, compute the test statistic.
   (b) Draw a t-distribution with the area that represents the P-value shaded.
   (c) Approximate and interpret the P-value.
   (d) If the researcher decides to test this hypothesis at the $\alpha = 0.1$ level of significance, will the researcher reject the null hypothesis? Why? No

7. In order to test $H_0: \mu = 105$ versus $H_1: \mu \neq 105$, a simple random sample of size $n = 35$ is obtained.
   (a) Does the population need to be normally distributed in order to test this hypothesis by using the methods presented in this section? No
   (b) If $\bar{x} = 101.9$ and $s = 5.9$, compute the test statistic.
   (c) Draw a t-distribution with the area that represents the P-value shaded.
   (d) Determine and interpret the P-value.
   (e) If the researcher decides to test this hypothesis at the $\alpha = 0.01$ level of significance, will the researcher reject the null hypothesis? Why? Yes

8. In order to test $H_0: \mu = 45$ versus $H_1: \mu \neq 45$, a simple random sample of size $n = 40$ is obtained.
   (a) Does the population need to be normally distributed in order to test this hypothesis by using the methods presented in this section?
   (b) If $\bar{x} = 48.3$ and $s = 8.5$, compute the test statistic.
   (c) Draw a t-distribution with the area that represents the P-value shaded.
   (d) Determine and interpret the P-value.
   (e) If the researcher decides to test this hypothesis at the $\alpha = 0.01$ level of significance, will the researcher reject the null hypothesis? Why? No

• **Applying the Concepts**

9. **Effects of Alcohol on the Brain** In a study published in the *American Journal of Psychiatry* [157:737–744, May 2000], researchers wanted to measure the effect of alcohol on the development of the hippocampal region in adolescents. The hippocampus is the portion of the brain responsible for long-term memory storage. The researchers randomly selected 12 adolescents with adolescent-onset alcohol use disorders. They wanted to test the claim that the hippocampal volumes in the alcoholic adolescents were less than the normal volume of 9.02 cm^3. An analysis of the sample data revealed that the hippocampal volume is approximately normal with $\bar{x} = 8.10$ and $s = 0.7$.
   (a) Test the researchers' claim at the $\alpha = 0.01$ level of significance, using the classical approach.
   (b) Approximate and interpret the P-value.

10. **Vitamin A Supplements** In an experiment meant to investigate the effect of Vitamin A supplements on serum retinol levels in low-birth-weight babies, 65 low-birth-weight infants were administered 25,000 IU of vitamin A. ["Effect of Vitamin A Supplementation on Morbidity of Low-Birth-Weight Neonates, *South African Medical Journal*, July 2000, 90(7), pp. 730–736] The sample mean serum retinol level of the infants administered the Vitamin A was determined to be 45.77, with a sample standard deviation equal to 17.07.

   (a) Why is it not necessary to verify that the data are normally distributed in order to perform inference on the sample mean? Large sample size
   (b) At the $\alpha = 0.01$ level of significance, test the claim that vitamin A increased the serum retinol level above 12.88 micrograms/dl, the mean level of serum retinol for all low-birth-weight babies, using the classical approach. $t = 15.534$; reject H_0
   (c) Determine and interpret the P-value.

11. **Getting Enough Fiber?** A nutritionist claims that the mean daily consumption of fiber for 20–39-year-old males is less than 20 grams per day. (The National Cancer Institute recommends that individuals consume 20–30 grams per day.) In a survey of 457 males who were 20–39 years old, conducted by the U.S. Department of Agriculture, it was found that the mean daily intake of fiber was 19.1 grams, with standard deviation 9.1 grams.
   (a) Using the classical approach, decide whether there is enough evidence to support the nutritionist's claim at the $\alpha = 0.01$ level of significance.
   (b) Determine and interpret the P-value.

12. **Too Much Sodium?** A nutritionist claims that the mean daily consumption of sodium for 20–39-year-old females is more than 2750 mg. (The USDA recommended daily allowance of sodium is 2400 mg.) In a survey conducted by the United States Department of Agriculture of 490 females who were 20–39 years old, it was found that the mean daily intake of sodium was 2919 milligrams, with a standard deviation of 1350 milligrams.
   (a) Using the classical approach, decide whether there is sufficient evidence to support the nutritionist's claim at the $\alpha = 0.05$ level of significance. $t = 2.771$
   (b) Determine and interpret the P-value.

13. **Normal Temperature** Carl Reinhold August Wunderlich said that the mean temperature of humans is $98.6°$ F. Researchers Philip Mackowiak, Steven Wasserman, and Myron Levine [*JAMA*, Sep 23–30 1992; 268(12):1578–80] felt that the mean temperature of humans is less than $98.6°$ F. They measured the temperature of 148 healthy adults 1–4 times daily for three days, obtaining 700 measurements. The sample data resulted in a sample mean of $98.2°$ F and a sample standard deviation of $0.7°$ F.
   (a) Using the classical approach, judge whether there is evidence to support the researchers' claim at the $\alpha = 0.01$ level of significance. $t = -15.119$; reject H_0
   (b) Determine and interpret the P-value.

14. **Normal Temperature** Carl Reinhold August Wunderlich said that the mean temperature of humans is $98.6°$ F. Researchers Philip Mackowiak, Steven Wasserman, and Myron Levine [*JAMA*, Sep 23–30 1992; 268(12):1578–80] measured the temperatures of 26 females 1–4 times daily for three days to get a total of 123 measurements. The sample data yielded a sample

(7b) $t = -3.108$ (7d) P-value $= 0.0038$ (8b) $t = 2.455$ (8d) P-value $= 0.0186$ (9a) $t = -4.553$; reject H_0
(9b) P-value $= 0.0004$ (10c) P-value < 0.0001 (11a) $t = -2.114$; do not reject   (11b) P-value $= 0.0175$
(12b) P-value $= 0.0029$ (13b) P-value < 0.0001

mean of 98.4° F and a sample standard deviation of 0.7° F. *(b) P-value = 0.0001*

(a) Using the classical approach, judge whether there is evidence to support the claim that the normal temperature of women is less than 98.6°F at the $\alpha = 0.01$ level of significance. *t = −3.169; reject H₀*

(b) Determine and interpret the *P*-value.

15. Age of Death-Row Inmates In 1989, the average age of an inmate on death row was 36.2 years of age, according to data obtained from the U.S. Department of Justice. A sociologist wants to test the claim that the average age of a death-row inmate has changed since then. She randomly selects 32 death-row inmates and finds that their mean age is 38.9, with a standard deviation of 9.6.

(a) Using the classical approach, test the sociologist's claim at the $\alpha = 0.05$ level of significance.

(b) Determine and interpret the *P*-value.

16. Energy Consumption In 1997, the average household expenditure for energy was $1338, according to data obtained from the U.S. Energy Information Administration. An economist wanted to know whether this amount has changed significantly from its 1997 level. In a random sample of 35 households, he found the mean expenditure (in 1997 dollars) for energy during the most recent year to be $1423, with standard deviation $321.

(a) Using the classical approach, test the economist's claim that the mean expenditure has changed significantly from the 1997 level at the $\alpha = 0.05$ level of significance. *t = 1.567; do not reject H₀*

(b) Determine and interpret the *P*-value.

17. Cholesterol A dietician maintains that the total cholesterol for 40–49-year-old males is high. Anyone with total cholesterol above 200 is considered to have high cholesterol. She conducts a random sample of 40 males between the ages of 40 and 49 years and finds that their mean total cholesterol is 211, with a standard deviation of 39.2 (data obtained from the Centers for Disease Control).

(a) Using the classical approach, test the dietician's claim that the total cholesterol of males 40–49 years old is more than 200 at the $\alpha = 0.05$ level of significance.

(b) Determine and interpret the *P*-value.

18. LDL Cholesterol A person's low-density lipoprotein (LDL) cholesterol is the so-called "bad" cholesterol, because it contributes to the build-up of plaque in the person's arteries. This plaque restricts blood flow to the heart or brain. If blood flow is restricted to the heart, a heart attack results. If blood flow is restricted to the brain, a stroke results. A dietician claims that the LDL cholesterol for 40–49-year-old females is more than 130. (The American Heart Association states that individuals with an LDL cholesterol higher than 130 are at an increased risk of heart attack or stroke.) In a random sample of 35 females between the ages of 40 and 49 years, it was found that their mean LDL was 147, with a standard deviation of 31.9 (based upon data obtained from the Centers for Disease Control).

(a) Using the classical approach, test the dietician's claim that the mean LDL cholesterol is more than 130 mg at the $\alpha = 0.01$ level of significance.

(b) Determine and interpret the *P*-value.

19. Conforming Golf Balls The United States Golf Association requires that golf balls have a mean diameter that is 1.68 inches. An engineer for the USGA wishes to discover whether Maxfli XS golf balls have a mean diameter different from 1.68 inches. A random sample of Maxfli XS golf balls was selected; their diameters are shown in the table on the right.

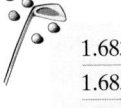

1.683	1.677	1.681
1.685	1.678	1.686
1.684	1.684	1.673
1.685	1.682	1.674

Source: Michael McCraith, Joliet Junior College

(a) Because the sample size is small, he must verify that the diameter is normally distributed and the sample does not contain any outliers. The normal probability plot and boxplot are shown below. Are the conditions for testing the hypothesis satisfied? *Yes*

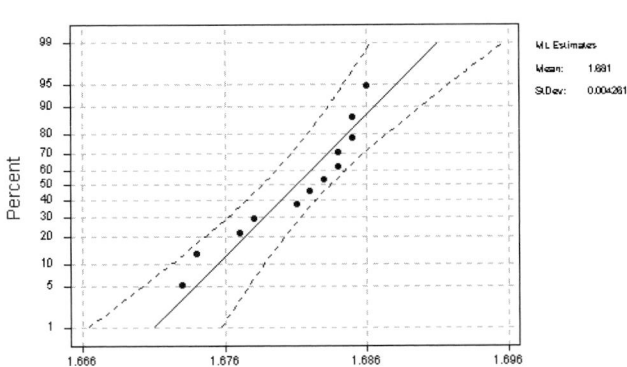

Normal Probability Plot for Diameter

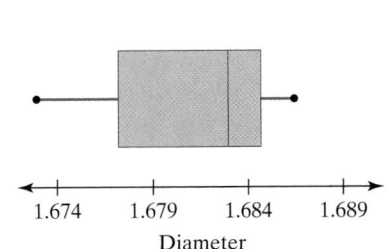

(15a) *t = 1.591; do not reject H₀* (15b) *P-value = 0.0609* (16b) *P-value = 0.1265* (17a) *t = 1.775; reject H₀*
(17b) *P-value = 0.0419* (18a) *t = 3.153; reject H₀* (18b) *P-value = 0.0017*

(b) Using the classical approach, test the claim that the golf balls have a mean diameter that is different from 1.68 inches at the $\alpha = 0.05$ level of significance. $t = 0.78$; do not reject

(c) Determine and interpret the P-value. P-value $= 0.45$

20. **Conforming Golf Balls** The USGA requires that golf balls have a weight that is less than 1.62 ounces. An engineer for the USGA wants to test the claim that Maxfli XS golf balls have a mean weight less than 1.62 ounces. He obtains a random sample of 12 Maxfli XS golf balls; their weights are in the table on the right.

1.614	1.619	1.614
1.614	1.610	1.610
1.621	1.612	1.615
1.621	1.602	1.617

Source: Michael McCraith, Joliet Junior College

(a) Because the sample size is small, he must verify that weight is normally distributed and that the sample does not contain any outliers. The normal probability plot and boxplot are shown below. Are the conditions for testing the hypothesis satisfied? Yes

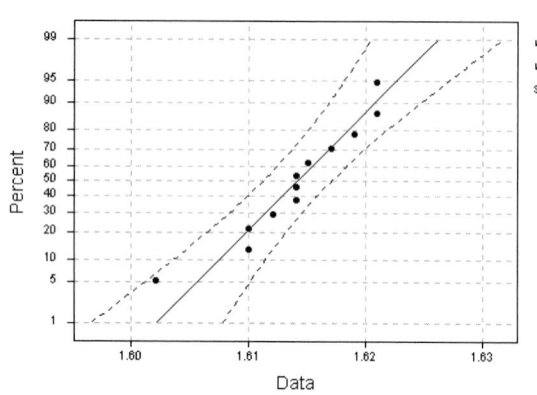

Normal Probability Plot for Weight

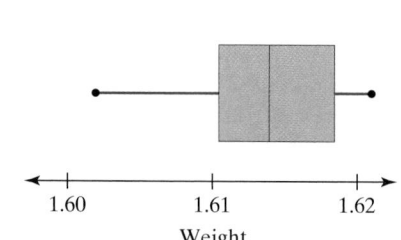

Weight

(b) Using the classical approach, decide whether the golf balls meet Maxfli's standard at the $\alpha = 0.1$ level of significance. $t = -3.84$; reject H_o

(c) Determine and interpret the P-value. P-value $= 0.0014$

21. **Calibrating a pH Meter** An engineer wants to measure the bias in a pH meter. She uses the meter to measure the pH in 14 neutral substances (pH $= 7.0$) and obtains the data on the right.

7.01	7.04	6.97	7.00	6.99	6.97	7.04
7.04	7.01	7.00	6.99	7.04	7.07	6.97

(a) Because the sample size is small, she must verify that pH is normally distributed and the sample does not contain any outliers. The normal probability plot and boxplot are shown below. Are the conditions for testing the hypothesis satisfied? Yes

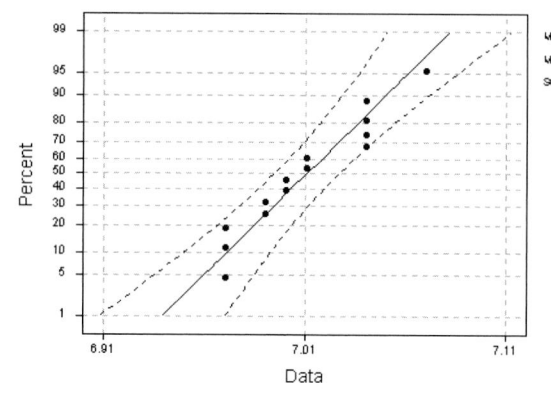

Normal Probability Plot for pH

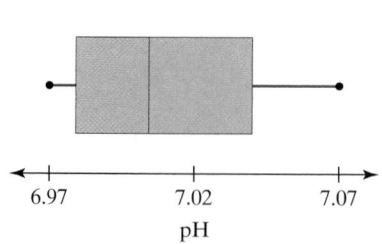

pH

(b) $t = 1.18$; do not reject H_o (b) Using the classical approach, is there sufficient evidence to support the claim that the pH meter is not correctly calibrated at the $\alpha = 0.05$ level of significance?
(c) Determine and interpret the P-value. P-value $= 0.26$

22. **Medication in a Tablet** A drug states that the mean amount of Naproxen Sodium, the active ingredient in reducing pain, in a tablet is 220 mg. A pharmacist randomly selects 17 tablets and measures the amount of Naproxen Sodium in each of them. She obtains the following data:

219.9	219.9	224.9	218.1	224.5
222.5	221.8	219.5	220.3	221.6
221.3	222.9	226.3	218.5	218.1
222.5	218.3			

(a) Because the sample size is small, she must verify that the amount of Naproxen Sodium in the tablet is normally distributed and the sample does not contain any outliers. The normal probability plot and boxplot are shown below. Are the conditions for testing the hypothesis satisfied? Yes

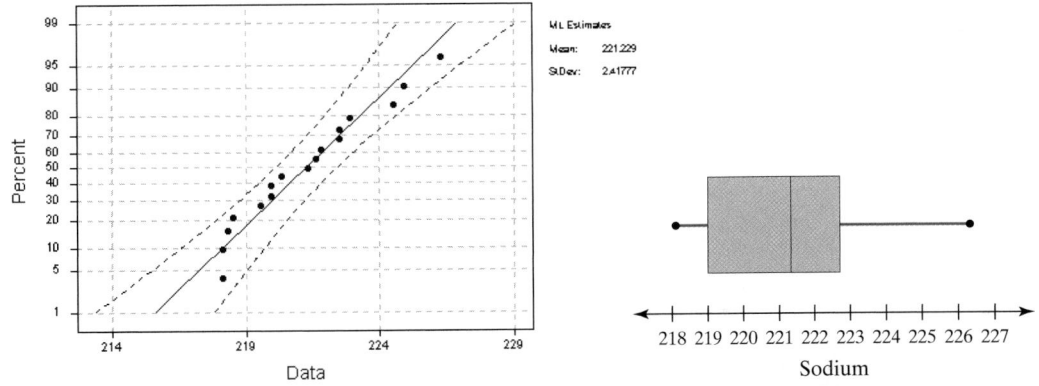

(b) Using the classical approach, is there sufficient evidence to support the claim that the amount of Naproxen Sodium is different from 220 mg at the $\alpha = 0.01$ level of significance? $t = 2.03$; do not reject H_o
(c) Determine and interpret the P-value. P-value $= 0.059$

23. **A Bat's Range** In order to catch flying insects, bats emit high-frequency sounds and then determine the time until they hear an echo. When an insect is detected, the bat can determine the location of the insect by the time it takes the echo to return. Suppose the researchers want to test the claim that the bat's range is more than 35 cm. They collect the following data regarding the detection distance (in centimeters) of 11 bats:

62	52	68	23	34	45
27	42	83	56	40	

Source: Griffen, Donald R.; Webster, Frederick A.; and Michael, Charles R. "The Echolocation of Flying Insects by Bats." *Animal Behavior*, 8 (1960), p. 148.

(a) Verify that the detection distance of bats is normally distributed, and check for outliers by drawing a normal probability plot and boxplot.
(b) Test the researchers' claim at the $\alpha = 0.05$ level of significance. $t = 2.451$; Reject H_o
(c) Determine and interpret the P-value. P-value $= 0.017$

24. P/E Ratio A stock analyst believes that the price-to-earnings (P/E) ratio of companies listed on the Standard and Poor's 500 (S&P 500) Index is less than its December 1, 2000 level of 22.0, in response to economic uncertainty. The P/E ratio is the price an investor is willing to pay for $1 of earnings. For example, a P/E of 23 means the investor pays $23 for each $1 of earnings. A higher P/E is an indication of investor optimism; lower P/Es are generally assigned to companies with lower earnings growth. In order to test his claim, he randomly samples 14 companies listed on the S&P 500 and calculates their P/E ratios. He obtains the following data:

Company	P/E Ratio	Company	P/E Ratio
Boeing	25.1	Dow Chemical	13.7
General Motors	7.8	Citigroup	18.5
Halliburton	35.8	Merck and Co.	26.8
Norfolk Southern	25.6	Sara Lee	11.9
Agilent Technologies	22.5	Harley-Davidson	37.4
Old Kent Financial	20.0	Circuit City	14.5
Cendent	15.0	Minnesota Mining and Manufacturing	23.8

Source: Checkfree Corporation

(a) Verify that P/E ratios are normally distributed, and check for outliers by drawing a normal probability plot and boxplot.
(b) Test the analyst's claim at the $\alpha = 0.05$ level of significance. *t = −0.30; do not reject H_o*
(c) Determine and interpret the *P*-value. *P-value = 0.39*

25. Benign Prostatic Hyperplasia Benign prostatic hyperplasia is a common cause of urinary outflow obstruction in aging males. The efficacy of Cardura (doxazosin mesylate) was measured in clinical trials of 173 patients with benign prostatic hyperplasia. Researchers wanted to discover whether Cardura significantly increased the urinary flow rate. It was found that an average increase of 0.8 mL/sec was obtained. This was said to be significant with a *P*-value less than 0.01. State the null and alternative hypotheses of the researchers and interpret the *P*-value.

26. Systolic Blood Pressure of Surgical Patients A nursing student maintained that the mean systolic blood pressure of her male patients on the surgical floor was less than 130 mm Hg. She randomly selected 19 male surgical patients and collected the systolic blood pressures shown on the right.

116	150	140	148	105
118	128	112	124	128
140	112	126	130	120
90	134	112	142	

Source: Lora McGuire, Nursing Instructor, Joliet Junior College

(a) Because the sample size is small, she must verify that the systolic blood pressure is normally distributed and the sample does not contain any outliers. The normal probability plot and boxplot are shown below. Are the conditions for testing the hypothesis satisfied? *Yes*

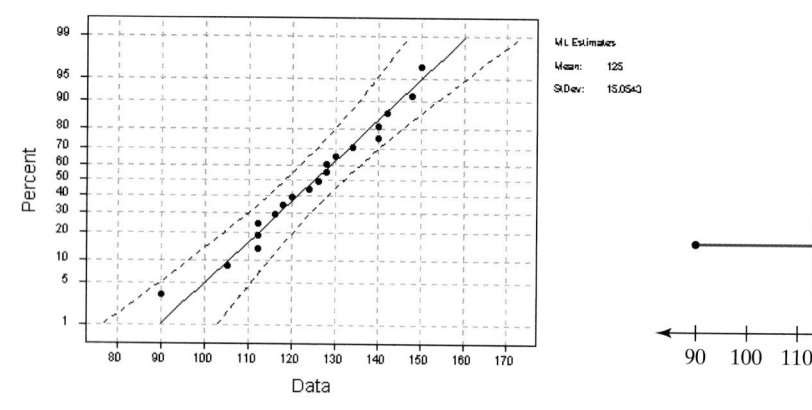

(b) The student enters the data into Minitab and obtains the following results:

T-Test of the Mean

```
Test of mu = 130.00 vs mu < 130.00

Variable           N    Mean   StDev   SE Mean      T      P
Systolic          19     125   15.47      3.55  -1.41  0.088
```

What are the null and alternative hypotheses? Identify the P-value. Will the nursing student reject the null hypothesis at the α = 0.05 level of significance? State her conclusion. H_o: μ = 130 vs. H_1: μ < 130; do not reject H_o

27. **Temperature of Surgical Patients** A nursing student suspects that the mean temperature of surgical patients is above the normal temperature, 98.2°F. (See Problem 13.) She randomly selects 32 surgical patients and obtains the temperatures shown on the right.
    (a) What are the null and alternative hypotheses of the student?
    (b) The student enters the data into Minitab and obtains the following results: (a) H_o: μ = 98.2 vs H_1: μ > 98.2

97.4	98.6	98.2	98.2	98.4	98.6
99.8	97.7	97.8	98.9	97.8	97.8
96.7	97.8	98.3	98.5	98.0	98.7
96.8	98.6	98.4	97.4	99.1	98.7
97.8	99.2	99.2	98.1	98.6	98.4
99.2	98.6				

Source: Lora McGuire, Nursing Instructor, Joliet Junior College

T-Test of the Mean

```
Test of mu = 98.200 vs mu > 98.200

Variable           N     Mean   StDev   SE Mean     T      P
Temperat          32   98.291   0.689     0.122  0.74   0.23
```

What is the P-value of the test? State the nursing student's conclusion. P-value = 0.23; do not reject H_o

28. **Soybeans** The average yield per acre of soybeans on farms in Iowa in 1999 was 45 bushels, according to data obtained from the U.S. Department of Agriculture. A farmer in Iowa claims the yield is higher this year. He randomly samples 15 acres on his farm and determines the mean yield to be 48.7 bushels, with a standard deviation of 2.48 bushels. He computes the P-value to be less than 0.0001 and concludes that the U.S. Department of Agriculture was wrong. Why should his conclusions be looked upon with skepticism?

29. **Simulation** Simulate drawing 40 simple random samples of size n = 20 from a population that is normally distribution with mean 50 and standard deviation 10.
    (a) Test the null hypothesis H_0: μ = 50 versus the alternative hypothesis H_1: μ ≠ 50 for each of the 40 samples using a t-test.
    (b) Suppose we were testing this hypothesis at the α = 0.05 level of significance. How many of the 40 samples would you expect to result in a Type I error?
    (c) Count the number of samples that lead to a rejection of the null hypothesis. Is it close to the expected value determined in part (b)?
    (d) Describe why we know a rejection of the null hypothesis results in making a Type I error in this situation.

Technology Step-by-Step
Hypothesis Tests Regarding μ, σ Unknown

TI-83 Plus   **Step 1:** If necessary, enter raw data in L1.

Step 2: Press STAT, highlight TESTS, and select 2:T-Test.

Step 3: If the data are raw, highlight DATA; make sure that List1 is set to L1 and Freq is set to 1. If summary statistics are known, highlight STATS and enter the summary statistics. For the value of μ_0, enter the value of the mean stated in the null hypothesis.

Step 4: Select the direction of the alternative hypothesis.

Step 5: Highlight **Calculate** and press ENTER. The TI-83 gives the P-value.

MINITAB **Step 1:** Enter raw data in column C1.

Step 2: Select the **Stat** menu, highlight **Basic Statistics**, then highlight **1-Sample t**....

Step 3: Enter C1 in the cell marked "Variables." Select "Test Mean," and enter the value of the mean stated in the null hypothesis. In the cell marked "Alternative," select the direction of the alternative hypothesis. Click OK.

Excel **Step 1:** If necessary, enter raw data in column A.

Step 2: Load the PHStat Add-in.

Step 3: Select the **PHStat menu**, highlight **One Sample Tests**..., and then highlight **t Test for the mean, sigma unknown**....

Step 4: Enter the value of the null hypothesis and the level of significance, α. If the summary statistics are known, click "Sample statistics known" and enter the sample size, sample mean, and sample standard deviation. If summary statistics are unknown, click "Sample statistics unknown." With the cursor in the "Sample cell range" cell, highlight the data in column A. Click the option corresponding to the desired test (two-tail, upper (right) tail, or lower (left) tail). Click OK.

9.4 Testing a Hypothesis about a Population Proportion

Preparing for This Section Before getting started, review the following:

 ✓ Binomial probability distribution (Section 6.2, pp. 339–351)

 ✓ Confidence intervals about a population proportion (Section 8.3, pp. 490–493)

Objectives ① Test a hypothesis about a population proportion using the classical method

 ② Test a hypothesis about a population proportion using the *P*-value approach

 ③ Test a hypothesis about a population proportion on a small sample

① Recall that the best point estimate of p, the proportion of the population with a certain characteristic, is given by

$$\hat{p} = \frac{x}{n}$$

where x is the number of individuals in the sample with the specified characteristic and n is the sample size. Recall, from Section 8.3, that the sampling distribution of $\hat{p}$ is approximately normal, with mean $\mu_{\hat{p}} = p$ and standard deviation $\sigma_{\hat{p}} = \sqrt{\dfrac{p(1-p)}{n}}$, provided that $np(1-p) \geq 10.$*

---

*The sample must be a simple random sample with $n \leq 0.05N$ (i.e., the sample size is no more than 5% of the population size).

Caution

When determining the standard error for the sampling distribution of $\hat{p}$, use the assumed value of the population proportion, p_o.

The classical approach to testing a hypothesis about the population proportion, p, follows the exact same logic as the testing of hypotheses about a population mean with σ known. The only difference is that the **test statistic** is

$$Z = \frac{\hat{p} - p_o}{\sqrt{\dfrac{p_o(1 - p_o)}{n}}}$$

where p_o is the assumed value of the population proportion.

The careful reader will notice that we are using p_o in computing the standard error rather than $\hat{p}$ (as we did in computing confidence intervals about p). This is because, when we test a hypothesis, the null hypothesis is always assumed true. Therefore, we are assuming that the population proportion is p_o.

Hypothesis Test Regarding a Population Proportion, p

If a claim is made regarding the population proportion, we can use the following steps to test the claim, provided that
1. the sample is obtained via simple random sampling, and
2. $np_o(1 - p_o) \geq 10$ with $n \leq 0.05N$ (the sample size, n, is no more than 5% of the population size, N).

Step 1: A claim is made regarding the population proportion. The claim is used to determine the null and alternative hypotheses. The hypotheses can be structured in one of three ways:

Two-Tailed	Left-Tailed	Right-Tailed
$H_o: p = p_o$	$H_o: p = p_o$	$H_o: p = p_o$
$H_1: p \neq p_o$	$H_1: p < p_o$	$H_1: p > p_o$

Note: p_o is the assumed value of the population proportion.

Step 2: Select a level of significance, α, to reflect the seriousness of making a Type I error. The level of significance is used to determine the critical value. The critical value represents the maximum number of standard deviations the sample proportion can be from p_o before the null hypothesis is rejected. For example, the critical value in the left-tailed test is $-z_\alpha$. The shaded region(s) represent(s) the critical region. The critical region is the set of all values such that the null hypothesis is rejected.

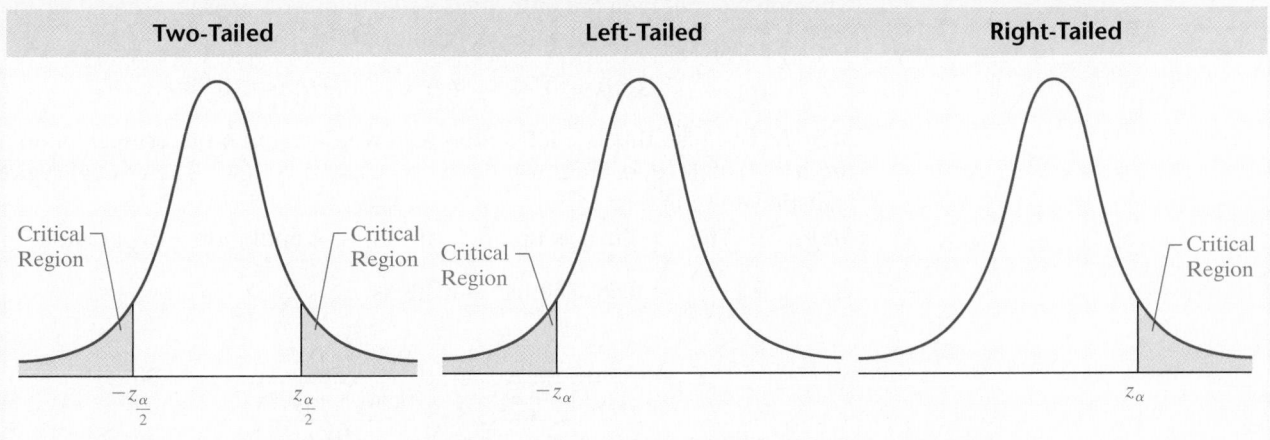

Step 3: Compute the test statistic:

$$Z = \frac{\hat{p} - p_o}{\sqrt{\dfrac{p_o(1 - p_o)}{n}}}$$

Step 4: Compare the critical value with the test statistic.

Two-Tailed	Left-Tailed	Right-Tailed
If $Z < -z_{\alpha/2}$ or $Z > z_{\alpha/2}$, reject the null hypothesis.	If $Z < -z_\alpha$, reject the null hypothesis.	If $Z > z_\alpha$, reject the null hypothesis.

Step 5: State the conclusion.

▶ **EXAMPLE 1**   **Who Are Thought to Be More Aggressive, Men or Women?**

Problem: In 1995, 74% of Americans felt that men were more aggressive than women. In a poll conducted by the Gallup Organization from December 2–4, 2000, a simple random sample of 1026 Americans 18 years old or older resulted in 698 respondents stating that men were more aggressive than women. Is there significant evidence to indicate that the proportion of Americans who believe that men are more aggressive than women has decreased from the level reported in 1995 at the $\alpha = 0.05$ level of significance?

> 🚦 **Caution**
>
> Always verify the requirements before conducting a hypothesis test.

Approach: We must verify the requirements to perform the hypothesis test—namely, the sample must be a simple random sample and $np_o(1 - p_o) \geq 10$. In addition, the sample size cannot be more than 5% of the population size. Then, we follow Steps 1–5 listed on pages 559–560.

Solution: We are testing the claim that the proportion of Americans 18 years old or older who believe that men are more aggressive than women is less than 0.74—that is, $p < 0.74$. The sample is a simple random sample. Also, $np_o(1 - p_o) = (1,026)(0.74)(0.26) = 197.4 > 10$. Because there are over 19 million Americans 18 years old or older, the sample size is less than 5% of the population size. The requirements are satisfied, so we now proceed to follow Steps 1–5.

Step 1: The claim is that the proportion of Americans 18 years old or older who believe that men are more aggressive than women is less than 0.74; that is, $p < 0.74$. This is a left-tailed hypothesis with

$$H_o: p = 0.74 \qquad \text{versus} \qquad H_1: p < 0.74$$

Step 2: Because this is a left-tailed test, we determine the critical value at the $\alpha = 0.05$ level of significance to be $-z_{0.05} = -1.645$. The critical region is displayed in Figure 17.

Step 3: The point estimate of the population proportion is $\hat{p} = \dfrac{x}{n} = \dfrac{698}{1026} = 0.68$. The test statistic is

$$Z = \frac{\hat{p} - p_o}{\sqrt{\dfrac{p_o(1 - p_o)}{n}}} = \frac{0.68 - 0.74}{\sqrt{\dfrac{0.74(1 - 0.74)}{1026}}} = -4.38$$

Figure 17

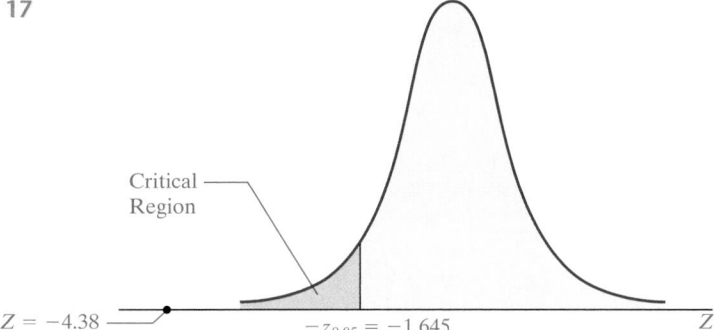

$$Z = -4.38$$ Critical Region $-z_{0.05} = -1.645$ Z

The sample proportion of 0.68 is 4.38 standard deviations below the hypothesized proportion of 0.74.

Step 4: Because the test statistic $Z = -4.38$ is less than the critical value of $-z_{0.05} = -1.645$, we reject the null hypothesis. That is, the value of the test statistic falls within the critical region, so we reject H_o. We label this point in Figure 17.

Step 5: There is sufficient evidence to support the claim that the proportion of Americans 18 years old or older who believe that men are more aggressive than women is less than the proportion reported in 1995 at the $\alpha = 0.05$ level of significance. ◄◄

 Now Work Problem 1(a).

② *P*-values

Recall that a *P*-value is the probability of observing a sample statistic as extreme or more extreme than the one observed, under the assumption that the null hypothesis is true. Our criterion for rejecting the null hypothesis by using *P*-values is as follows:

> **Reject the null hypothesis if the *P*-value is less than the level of significance. That is, we reject H_o if *P*-value $< \alpha$.**

The procedures that follow can be used to compute *P*-values when testing a hypothesis about a population proportion.

Computing *P*-Values

If a claim is made regarding the population proportion, we can use the following steps to compute the *P*-value, provided that

1. the sample is obtained by using simple random sampling, and

2. $np_o(1 - p_o) \geq 10$ with $n \leq 0.05N$ (the sample size is no more than 5% of the population size).

Step 1: A claim is made regarding the population proportion. The claim is used to determine the null and alternative hypotheses. The hypotheses can be structured in one of three ways:

Two-Tailed	Left-Tailed	Right-Tailed
$H_o: p = p_o$	$H_o: p = p_o$	$H_o: p = p_o$
$H_1: p \neq p_o$	$H_1: p < p_o$	$H_1: p > p_o$

Note: p_o is the assumed value of the population proportion.

Step 2: Compute the test statistic $Z_o = \dfrac{\hat{p} - p_o}{\sqrt{\dfrac{p_o(1 - p_o)}{n}}}$.

Step 3: Compute the *P*-value.

Two-Tailed	**Left-Tailed**	**Right-Tailed**

P-value = $P(Z < -|Z_o| \text{ or } Z > |Z_o|)$

$= 2P(Z > |Z_o|) = 2P(Z < -|Z_o|)$

P-value = $P(Z < Z_o)$

P-value = $P(Z > Z_o)$

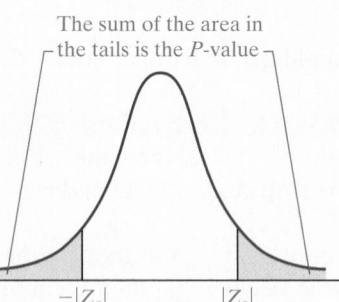

The sum of the area in the tails is the *P*-value

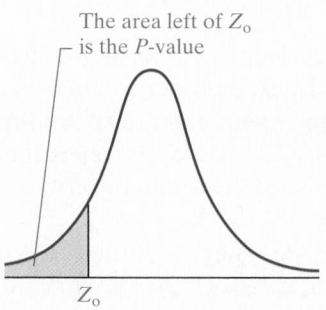

The area left of Z_o is the *P*-value

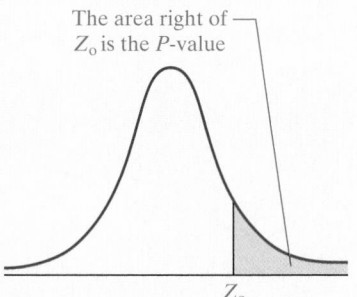

The area right of Z_o is the *P*-value

Interpretation: The *P*-value is the probability of obtaining a sample proportion that is more than $|Z_o|$ standard deviations from the hypothesized proportion, p_o.

Interpretation: The *P*-value is the probability of obtaining a sample proportion of $\hat{p}$ or smaller, under the assumption that H_o is true. In otherwords, it is the probability of obtaining a sample proportion that is more than Z_o standard deviations to the left of p_o.

Interpretation: The *P*-value is the probability of obtaining a sample proportion of $\hat{p}$ or larger, under the assumption that H_o is true. In other words, it is the probability of obtaining a sample proportion that is more than Z_o standard deviations to the right of p_o.

Step 4: Reject the null hypothesis if the *P*-value is less than the level of significance, α.

Step 5: State the conclusion.

▶ **EXAMPLE 2**   **Side Effects of Prevnar**

Problem: The drug Prevnar is a vaccine meant to prevent meningitis. (It also helps control ear infections.) It is typically administered to infants. In clinical trials, the vaccine was administered to 710 randomly sampled infants between 12 and 15 months of age. Of the 710 infants, 121 experienced a decrease in appetite. Is there significant evidence to conclude that the proportion of infants who receive Prevnar and experience a decrease in appetite is different from 0.135, the proportion of children who experience a decrease in appetite in competing medications? Test using the *P*-value approach at the $\alpha = 0.01$ level of significance.

Approach: We must verify the requirements to perform the hypothesis test—namely, the sample must be a simple random sample with $np_o(1 - p_o) \geq 10$ and the sample size cannot be more than 5% of the population. Then, we follow Steps 1–5, as laid out previously.

Solution: We are testing the claim that the proportion of infants who experience a decrease in appetite is different from 0.135—that is, $p \neq 0.135$. The sample is a simple random sample. Also, $np_o(1 - p_o) =$

$(710)(0.135)(1 - 0.135) = 82.9 > 10$. Because there are about 1 million babies between 12 and 15 months of age, the sample size is less than 5% of the population size. The requirements are satisfied, so we now proceed to follow Steps 1–5.

Step 1: We are testing the claim that $p \neq 0.135$. This is a two-tailed test.

$$H_o: p = 0.135 \qquad \text{versus} \qquad H_1: p \neq 0.135$$

Step 2: The point estimate of the population proportion is $\hat{p} = \dfrac{x}{n} = \dfrac{121}{710} = 0.170$. The test statistic is

Figure 18

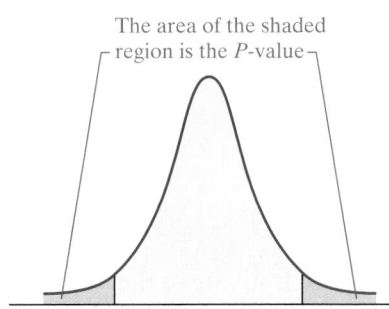

The area of the shaded region is the P-value

$Z = -2.73$ $\qquad$ $Z = 2.73$

$$Z_o = \frac{\hat{p} - p_o}{\sqrt{\dfrac{p_o(1 - p_o)}{n}}} = \frac{0.170 - 0.135}{\sqrt{\dfrac{0.135(1 - 0.135)}{710}}} = 2.73$$

The sample proportion, 0.170, is 2.73 standard deviations above the hypothesized proportion, 0.135.

Step 3: Because we are performing a two-tailed test, P-value $= 2P(Z < -|Z_o|) = 2P(Z < -2.73)$. That is, we need to determine the area under the standard normal curve to the left of $Z = -2.73$ and to the right of $Z = 2.73$ as shown in Figure 18.

Using Table II, we have

$$P\text{-value} = P(Z < -2.73) + P(Z > 2.73) = 2P(Z < -2.73) = 2(0.0032) = 0.0064$$

The probability of obtaining a sample proportion more than 2.73 standard deviations away from the hypothesized proportion, 0.135, is 0.0064. This means that less than 1 sample in 100 will result in a sample proportion more than 2.73 standard deviations from the hypothesized proportion of 0.135.

Step 4: Because the P-value is less than the level of significance $(0.0064 < 0.01)$, we reject the null hypothesis.

Step 5: The sample evidence supports the claim that the proportion of infants who experienced a decrease in appetite when receiving Prevnar is different from 0.135, the proportion of children who experienced a decrease in appetite in competing medications, at the $\alpha = 0.01$ level of significance. ◄◄

NW *Now Work Problem 1(b).*

Using Technology: We can obtain the results of Example 2 using a graphing calculator with advanced statistical capabilities or statistical software. Figure 19 shows the results from Minitab.

Figure 19 **Test and CI for One Proportion**

```
Test of p = 0.135 vs p not = 0.135

Sample   X     N   Sample p      99.0% CI         Z-Value  P-Value
1       121   710  0.170423  (0.134075, 0.206770)   2.76    0.006
```

③ Small-Sample Hypothesis Tests

Note to Instructor
This section is optional and may be skipped without loss of continuity.

In order for the sampling distribution of $\hat{p}$ to be approximately normal, we require that $np(1 - p)$ be at least 10. What if this requirement is not satisfied? In Section 6.2, we used the binomial probability formula to identify unusual events. We stated that an event was unusual if the probability of observing the event was less than 0.05. This criterion is based on the *P*-value approach to testing hypotheses; the probability that we computed was the *P*-value. We use this same approach to test hypotheses regarding a population proportion for small samples.

▶ **EXAMPLE 3** **Hypothesis Test for a Population Proportion—Small Sample Size**

Problem: According to the United States Department of Agriculture, 48.9% of males between 20 and 39 years of age consume the minimum daily requirement of calcium. After an aggressive "got milk" advertising campaign, the USDA conducts a survey of 35 randomly selected males between the ages of 20 and 39 and finds that 21 of them consume the recommended daily allowance of calcium. At the $\alpha = 0.10$ level of significance, is there evidence to conclude that the percentage of males between the ages of 20 and 39 who consume the recommended daily allowance of calcium has increased?

Approach: We use the following steps.

Step 1: Determine the null and alternative hypotheses.

Step 2: Check whether $np_o(1 - p_o)$ is greater than or equal to 10, where p_o is the proportion stated in the null hypothesis. If it is, then the sampling distribution of $\hat{p}$ is approximately normal and we can use the steps presented on pages 561–562. Otherwise, we use Steps 3 and 4, presented next.

Step 3: Compute the *P*-value. For right-tailed tests, the *P*-value is the probability of obtaining *x* or more successes. For left-tailed tests, the *P*-value is the probability of obtaining *x* or fewer successes.* The *P*-value is always computed with the proportion given in the null hypothesis. Remember, we assume that the null is true until we have evidence to the contrary.

Step 4: If the *P*-value is less than the level of significance, α, then reject the null hypothesis.

Solution:

Step 1: The "status quo" or "no change" proportion of 20–39-year-old males who consume the minimum daily requirement of calcium is 0.489. We wish to know whether the advertising campaign helped to increase this proportion. Therefore,

$$H_o: p = 0.489 \qquad \text{and} \qquad H_1: p > 0.489.$$

Step 2: From the null hypothesis, we have $p_o = 0.489$. There were $n = 35$ individuals surveyed, so $np_o(1 - p_o) = 35(0.489)(1 - 0.489) = 8.75$. Because $np_o(1 - p_o) < 10$, the sampling distribution of $\hat{p}$ is not approximately normal.

Step 3: Let the random variable *X* represent the number of individuals who consume the daily requirement of calcium. We have $x = 21$ successes in $n = 35$ trials, so $\hat{p} = \dfrac{21}{35} = 0.6$. We want to judge whether the larger proportion is due to the population proportion's having increased or to sam-

---

*We shall not address *P*-values for two-tailed hypothesis tests. For those who are interested, the *P*-value would be 2 times the probability of obtaining *x* or more successes if $\hat{p} > p$ and 2 times the probability of obtaining *x* or fewer successes if $\hat{p} < p$.

Figure 20

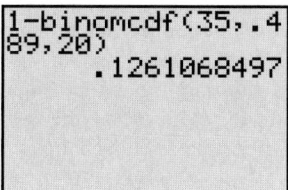

```
1-binomcdf(35,.4
89,20)
        .1261068497
```

pling error. We obtained $x = 21$ successes in the survey and this is a right tailed test, so the *P*-value will be $P(X \geq 21)$.

$$\text{P-value} = P(X \geq 21) = 1 - P(X < 21) = 1 - P(X \leq 20).$$

We will compute this *P*-value by using statistical software or a graphing calculator with advanced statistical features, with $n = 35$ and $p = 0.489$. Figure 20 shows the results using a TI-83 Plus graphing calculator.

The *P*-value is 0.1261. Minitab will compute exact *P*-values via this approach as well.

Step 4: The *P*-value is greater than the level of significance $(0.1261 > 0.10)$, so we do not reject H_o. There is not significant evidence (at the $\alpha = 0.1$ level of significance) to conclude that the proportion of 20–39-year-old males who consume the recommended daily allowance of calcium has increased. ◄◄

NW *Now Work Problem 23.*

9.4 Assess Your Understanding

Concepts and Vocabulary

1. State the assumptions required in order to test a hypothesis about a population proportion.

2. A poll that was conducted by CNN, *USA Today*, and Gallup reported the following results: "According to the most recent CNN/USA *Today*/Gallup poll, conducted June 28–July 1, a majority of Americans (52%)

approve of the job Bush is doing as president, ..." The poll results were obtained by conducting simple random sample of 1014 adults aged 18 years old or older, with a margin of error of ± 3 percentage points. State what is wrong with the conclusions presented by the pollsters.

Exercises

• **Basic Skills**

In Problems 1–6, test the hypothesis, using (a) the Classical Approach and then (b) the P-value approach. Be sure to verify the requirements of the test.

1. $H_o: p = 0.3$ versus $H_1: p > 0.3$
NW $n = 200; x = 75; \alpha = 0.05$ *P-value = 0.0103*

2. $H_o: p = 0.6$ versus $H_1: p < 0.6$
$n = 250; x = 124; \alpha = 0.01$ *P-value = 0.0004*

3. $H_o: p = 0.55$ versus $H_1: p < 0.55$
$n = 150; x = 78; \alpha = 0.1$ *P-value = 0.2301*

4. $H_o: p = 0.25$ versus $H_1: p < 0.25$
$n = 400; x = 96; \alpha = 0.1$ *P-value = 0.3221*

5. $H_o: p = 0.9$ versus $H_1: p \neq 0.9$
$n = 500; x = 440; \alpha = 0.05$ *P-value = 0.1360*

6. $H_o: p = 0.4$ versus $H_1: p \neq 0.4$
$n = 1000; x = 420; \alpha = 0.01$ *P-value = 0.1967*

• **Applying the Concepts**

In Problems 7–22, test the hypothesis, using (a) the Classical Approach and then (b) the P-value approach. Be sure to verify the requirements of the test. 7. $H_o: p = 0.47$ vs $H_1: p < 0.47$; P-value < 0.0001   8. $H_o: p = 0.47$ vs $H_1: p > 0.47$; P-value < 0.0001

7. Gun Control? In a survey conducted by the Gallup Organization between August 29 and September 5, 2000, 395 of 1012 adults aged 18 years or older said they had a gun in the house. In 1990, 47% of households had a gun. Is there significant evidence to support the claim that the proportion of households that have a gun has decreased since 1990 at the $\alpha = 0.05$ level of significance?

8. Teenagers and the Death Penalty In a survey conducted by the Gallup Organization in October of 2000, 320 of 500 teenagers between the ages of 13 and 17 years said that they favor life imprisonment without the possibility of parole for convicted murderers instead of the death penalty.

Suppose that it is known that 47% of adults prefer life imprisonment. Is there significant evidence to support the claim that a higher proportion of teenagers support life imprisonment at the $\alpha = 0.1$ level of significance?

9. Lipitor The drug Lipitor is meant to reduce total cholesterol and LDL-cholesterol. In clinical trials, 19 out of 863 patients taking 10 mg of Lipitor daily complained of flulike symptoms. Suppose that it is known that 1.9% of patients taking competing drugs complain of flulike symptoms. Is there significant evidence to support the claim that more than 1.9% of Lipitor users experience flulike symptoms as a side effect at the $\alpha = 0.01$ level of significance? $H_o: p = 0.019$ vs $H_1: p > 0.019$; P-value = 0.2582

10. **Pepcid** Pepcid is a drug that can be used to heal duodenal ulcers. Suppose the manufacturer of Pepcid claims that more than 80% of patients are healed after taking 40 mg of Pepcid every night for eight weeks. In clinical trials, 148 of 178 patients suffering from duodenal ulcers were healed after eight weeks. Test the manufacturer's claim at the $\alpha = 0.01$ level of significance.

11. **Low Birth Weight** According to the U.S. Census Bureau, 7.1% of all births to nonsmoking mothers are of low birth weight (< 5 lbs., 8 oz.). An obstetrician wanted to know whether mothers between the ages of 35 and 39 years old gave birth to a higher percentage of low-birth-weight babies. She randomly selected 240 births where the mother was 35–39 years old and found that 22 of them gave birth to low-birth-weight babies. Is there significant evidence to support the claim that mothers between 35 and 39 years old have a higher percentage of low-birth-weight babies at the $\alpha = 0.01$ level of significance?

12. **Exercise** A personal trainer wanted to know whether the proportion of males 30 to 44 years old who do not exercise has decreased from 24.9%, the proportion in 1998 (data obtained from the U.S. National Center for Chronic Disease Prevention and Health Promotion). He randomly selects 150 males between the ages of 30 and 44 years and finds that 28 of them do not exercise. Is there significant evidence that the proportion of males 30 to 44 years old who do not exercise has decreased at the $\alpha = 0.05$ level of significance?

13. **Parents at Home** In 1989, 33% of Americans felt that one parent should stay home to raise the children. In a poll conducted by the Gallup Organization in 2001, 416 of 1015 American adults 18 years of age or older believed that one parent should stay home to raise the children. Is there significant evidence to conclude that the percentage of Americans who believe that one parent should stay home to raise the children has increased at the $\alpha = 0.05$ level of significance?

14. **Own a PC?** According to the Energy Information Administration, 42.1% of households in the United States owned a personal computer in 1998. An economist wants to discover whether this percentage has changed significantly since then. She randomly selects 320 households throughout the United States and finds that 154 of them own a personal computer. Is there sufficient evidence to conclude the percentage of households that own a personal computer is significantly different from the percentage in 1998, at the $\alpha = 0.1$ level of significance?

15. **Free Throws** Shaquille O'Neal makes 43.8% of his free throws. His coach sends him to a free-throw specialist in order to improve his free-throw shooting. After five days with the specialist, his coach randomly selects 80 free throw attempts of Shaq and finds that he makes 39 of them. Is there significant evidence at the $\alpha = 0.05$ level of significance that Shaq's free throwing has improved?

16. **Living Alone?** In 1990, 39% of males aged 15 years of age and older lived alone, according to the U.S. Census Bureau. A sociologist tests whether this percentage is different today by conducting a random sample of 400 males aged 15 years of age and older and finds that 164 are living alone. Is there significant evidence at the $\alpha = 0.10$ level of significance to support belief in a change?

17. **The Environment** In 1990, 58% of Americans 18 years old and older reported they have a great deal of concern regarding air pollution. On February 20, 2001, the Gallup Organization released results of a poll in which 592 of 1004 Americans 18 years old or older stated that they have a great deal of concern regarding the level of air pollution in America. Is there evidence at the $\alpha = 0.05$ level of significance to conclude that the proportion of 2001 Americans having a great deal of concern about the level of air pollution in America is significantly different from the 1990 proportion?

18. **Pathological Gamblers** Pathological gambling is an impulse-control disorder. The American Psychiatry Association lists 10 characteristics that diagnose the disorder in its DSM-IV manual. The National Gambling Impact Study Commission randomly selected 2417 adults and found that 35 were pathological gamblers. Is there evidence to support the claim that more than 1% of the adult population are pathological gamblers at the $\alpha = 0.05$ level of significance?

19. **Teachers Using the Internet** According to the U.S. Department of Education's Office of Educational Technology, 85% of teachers used the Internet to teach in 2000. An educator claims that that percentage has increased from its 2000 level. She randomly samples 340 teachers and discovers that 302 of them have used the Internet in their teaching. Is there significant evidence to support the claim that the percentage of teachers using the Internet in their teaching has increased, at the $\alpha = 0.1$ level of significance?

20. **Does the Internet Affect Watching TV?** A researcher at Neilsen Media Research wanted to determine the impact that the Internet had on households' watching of television. In a study conducted in May, 1999, it was determined that 57.8% of all television households had the television on during "prime time" [*Source*: Neilsen Media Research]. In a random sample of 1025 television and Internet households, 575 had the television on during "prime time." Is there evidence to support the claim that a lower proportion of television and Internet households have the television on during prime time than do television households, at the $\alpha = 0.1$ level of significance?

21. **Talk to the Animals** In a survey conducted by the American Animal Hospital Association, 37% of respondents stated that they talk to their pets on the answering machine or telephone. A veterinarian found this result hard to believe, so he randomly selected 150 pet owners

12. $H_o: p = 0.249$ vs $H_1: p < 0.249$; P-value $= 0.0387$ 13. $H_o: p = 0.33$ vs $H_1: p > 0.33$; P-value < 0.0001

14. $H_o: p = 0.421$ vs $H_1: p \neq 0.421$; P-value $= 0.0290$ 15. $H_o: p = 0.438$ vs $H_1: p > 0.438$; P-value $= 0.1861$

16. $H_o: p = 0.39$ vs $H_1: p \neq 0.39$, P-value $= 0.4122$ 17. $H_o: p = 0.58$ vs $H_1: p \neq 0.58$; P-value $= 0.5359$

and discovered that 54 of them spoke to their pet on the answering machine or telephone. Test the veterinarian's claim that less than 37% of pet owners speak to their pets on the answering machine or telephone, at the $\alpha = 0.05$ level of significance.

22. **Eating Salad** According to a survey conducted by the Association of Dressings and Sauces (this is an actual association!), 85% of American adults eat salad at least once a week. A nutritionist suspects that the percentage is higher than this. She conducts a survey of 200 American adults and finds that 171 of them eat salad at least once a week. Is there sufficient evidence to support the nutritionist's claim at the $\alpha = 0.10$ level of significance?

23. **Small-Sample Hypothesis Test** In 1997, 4% of mothers smoked more than 21 cigarettes during their pregnancy. An obstetrician believes that the percentage of mothers who smoke 21 cigarettes or more is less than 4% today. She randomly selects 120 pregnant mothers and finds that 3 of them smoked 21 or more cigarettes during pregnancy. Test the researcher's claim at the $\alpha = 0.05$ level of significance. P-value = 0.2887

24. **Small-Sample Hypothesis Test** According to the United States Census Bureau, in 2000, 3.2% of Americans worked at home. An economist believes that the percentage of Americans working at home has increased since then. He randomly selects 150 working Americans and finds that 8 of them work at home. Test the economist's claim at the $\alpha = 0.05$ level of significance.

25. **Small-Sample Hypothesis Test** According to the United States Census Bureau, in 2000, 9.6% of Californians had a travel time to work of more than 60 minutes. An urban economist believes that the percentage of Californians who have a travel time to work of more than 60 minutes has increased since then. She randomly selects 80 working Californians and finds that 13 of them have a travel time to work that is more than 60 minutes. Test the urban economist's claim at the $\alpha = 0.1$ level of significance.

26. **Small-Sample Hypothesis Test** According to the United States Census Bureau, in 2000, 1.5% of males living in Colorado were teachers. A researcher believes that this percentage has decreased since then. She randomly selects 500 males living in Colorado and finds that 3 of them are teachers. Test the researcher's claim at the $\alpha = 0.1$ level of significance. P-value = 0.0578

Technology Step-by-Step
Hypothesis Tests Regarding a Population Proportion

TI-83 Plus
Step 1: Press STAT, highlight TESTS, and select 5:1-PropZTest.
Step 2: For the value of p_0, enter the "status quo" value of the population proportion.
Step 3: Enter the number of successes, x, and the sample size, n.
Step 4: Select the direction of the alternative hypothesis.
Step 5: Highlight **Calculate** or **Draw**, and press ENTER. The TI-83 gives the P-value.

MINITAB
Step 1: Select the **Stat** menu, highlight **Basic Statistics**, then highlight **1-Proportion**.
Step 2: Select "Summarized data."
Step 3: Enter the number of trials, n, and the number of successes, x.
Step 4: Click Options. Enter the "status quo" value of the population proportion in the cell "Test proportion." Enter the direction of the alternative hypothesis. If $np_0(1 - p_0) \geq 10$, then check the box marked "Use test and interval based on normal distribution." Click OK twice.

Excel
Step 1: Load the PHStat Add-in.
Step 2: Select the **PHStat menu**, highlight **One Sample Tests . . .**, then highlight **Z Test for proportion**.
Step 3: Enter the value of the null hypothesis, the level of significance, α, the number of successes, x, and the number of trials, n. Click the option corresponding to the desired test (two-tail, upper (right) tail, or lower (left) tail). Click OK.

---

18. H_0: $p = 0.01$ vs H_1: $p > 0.01$; P-value = 0.0134   19. H_0: $p = 0.85$ vs H_1: $p > 0.85$; P-value = 0.0242
20. H_0: $p = 0.578$ vs H_1: $p < 0.578$; P-value = 0.1349   21. H_0: $p = 0.37$ vs H_1: $p < 0.37$; P-value = 0.3999
22. H_0: $p = 0.85$ vs H_1: $p > 0.85$; P-value = 0.4215   24. P-value = 0.1099   25. P-value = 0.0410

9.5 Testing a Hypothesis about σ

Preparing for This Section   Before getting started, review the following:

✓ Confidence intervals about a population standard deviation (Section 8.4, pp. 498–503)

Objectives Test a claim about a population standard deviation using the classical approach.

 Test a claim about a population standard deviation using the P-value approach.

Note to Instructor
This section is optional and may be skipped without loss of continuity.

In this section, we discuss methods for testing hypotheses regarding a population variance or standard deviation.

Why might we be interested in testing hypotheses regarding σ^2 or σ? Many production processes not only require accuracy on average (the mean), they also require consistency. Consider a filling machine (such as a coffee machine) that consistently over- and underfills cups, but, on average, fills correctly. Certainly, customers are not happy if the machine underfills their cups, and they might be dissatisfied even if it overfills, because of spilling. A machine that *consistently* delivers the correct amount of liquid is desired. As another example, consider a mutual fund that invests in the stock market. An investor would prefer consistent year-to-year returns near 12% rather than returns that fluctuate wildly, yet result in a mean return of 12%. Both these situations illustrate the importance of measuring variability. The main idea is that the standard deviation and the variance are measures of consistency. The less consistent the values of a variable, the higher the standard deviation of the variable.

We begin by reviewing the chi-square distribution.

Theorem   **Chi-Square Distribution**

If a simple random sample of size n is obtained from a normally distributed population with mean μ and standard deviation σ, then

$$\chi^2 = \frac{(n-1)s^2}{\sigma^2}$$

has a chi-square distribution with $n - 1$ degrees of freedom.

Remember, the symbol χ^2 is pronounced "kigh-square." You can find critical values of the chi-square distribution in Table IV in Appendix A of the text.

Characteristics of the Chi-Square Distribution

1. It is not symmetric.
2. The shape of the chi-square distribution depends upon the degrees of freedom, just as with Student's t-distribution.
3. As the number of degrees of freedom increases, the chi-square distribution becomes more nearly symmetric, as is illustrated in Figure 21.
4. The values of χ^2 are nonnegative—that is, the values of χ^2 are greater than or equal to 0.

Figure 21
Chi-Square Distributions

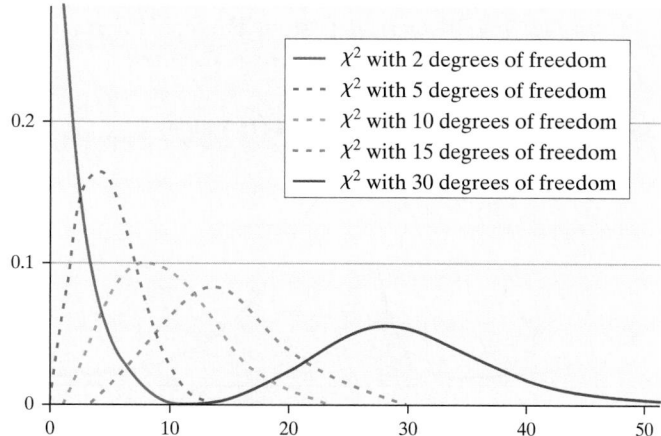

Recall that Table IV is structured similarly to Table III (for the t-distribution). The left column represents the degrees of freedom and the top row represents the area under the chi-square distribution to the right of the critical value. We use the notation χ_α^2 to denote the critical χ^2-value such that the area under the chi-square distribution to the right of χ_α^2 is α. For example, the area under the chi-square distribution to the right of $\chi_{0.10}^2$ is 0.10.

We now present the classical approach to testing a hypothesis regarding a population variance or standard deviation.

Hypothesis Test Regarding a Population Variance or Standard Deviation

If a claim is made regarding the population variance or standard deviation, we can use the following steps to test the claim, provided that

1. the sample is obtained using simple random sampling, and

2. the population is normally distributed.

Step 1: A claim is made regarding the population variance or standard deviation. The claim is used to determine the null and alternative hypotheses. We present the three cases for a claim regarding a population standard deviation:

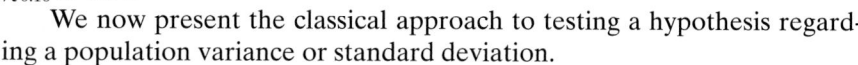

Two-Tailed	Left-Tailed	Right-Tailed
$H_0: \sigma = \sigma_0$	$H_0: \sigma = \sigma_0$	$H_0: \sigma = \sigma_0$
$H_1: \sigma \neq \sigma_0$	$H_1: \sigma < \sigma_0$	$H_1: \sigma > \sigma_0$

Note: σ_0 is the assumed value of the population standard deviation.

Step 2: Select a level of significance α based upon the seriousness of making a Type I error. The level of significance is used to determine the critical value. For example, the critical value in the left-tailed test is $\chi_{1-\alpha}^2$ with $n - 1$ degrees of freedom. The shaded region(s) represents the critical region. The critical region is the set of all values such that the null hypothesis is rejected.

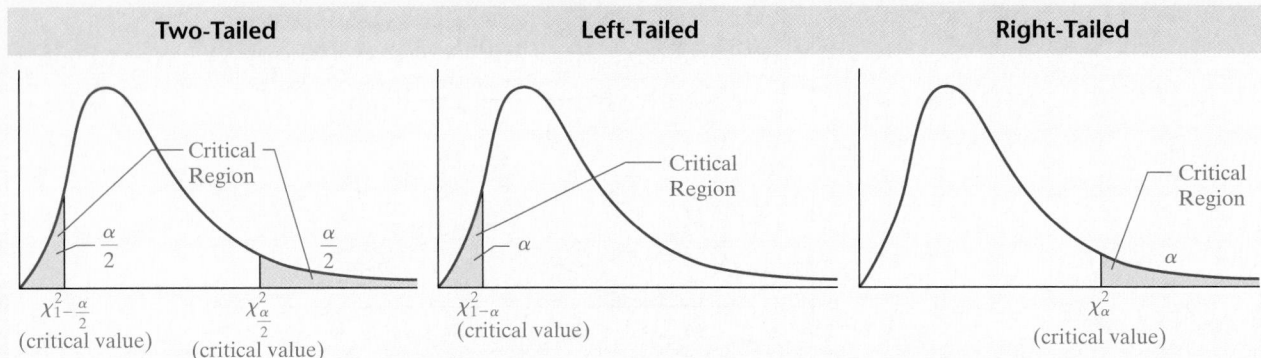

| Two-Tailed | Left-Tailed | Right-Tailed |

Step 3: Compute the **test statistic**

$$\chi^2 = \frac{(n-1)s^2}{\sigma_o^2}$$

Step 4: Compare the critical value with the test statistic.

Two-Tailed	Left-Tailed	Right-Tailed
If $\chi^2 < \chi^2_{1-\alpha/2}$ or $\chi^2 > \chi^2_{\alpha/2}$, reject the null hypothesis.	If $\chi^2 < \chi^2_{1-\alpha}$, reject the null hypothesis.	If $\chi^2 > \chi^2_{\alpha}$, reject the null hypothesis.

Step 5: State the conclusion.

Caution

The procedures in this section are not robust.

The methods presented for testing a hypothesis regarding a population variance or standard deviation are not robust. Therefore, if analysis of the data indicates that the variable is not normally distributed, then the procedures presented in this section are not valid. Again, always be sure to verify the requirements are satisfied before proceeding with the test!

▶ **EXAMPLE 1**   **Testing a Hypothesis about a Population Standard Deviation**

TABLE 4

8,777	19,187	12,022
16,759	7,294	10,163
9,021	12,682	16,747
16,733	15,331	5,347
13,798	13,235	11,302
6,929	17,576	9,455
16,306	8,266	

Problem: Recall, from Example 1 in Section 9.2, that Patricia claimed that people are driving more today than in 1990. In testing this claim, she assumed that the population standard deviation was known to be 3500 miles. Test the claim that the population standard deviation is greater than 3500 miles at the $\alpha = 0.05$ level of significance. For convenience, the data are reproduced in Table 4.

Approach: Before we can perform the hypothesis test, we must verify that the data come from a population that is normally distributed. We will construct a normal probability plot to verify this requirement. We then proceed to follow Steps 1–5.

Solution: A normal probability plot was drawn in Figure 6 of Section 9.2. This plot indicates that the number of miles driven comes from a population that is normally distributed.

Figure 22

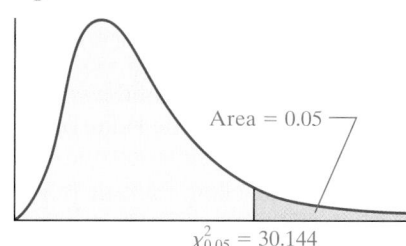

Area = 0.05

$\chi^2_{0.05} = 30.144$

Caution

The test statistic requires s^2 and σ^2, so be careful if the problem gives s or σ.

NW *Now Work Problem 7.*

Step 1: The claim is that the population standard deviation is greater than 3500. This claim can be written $\sigma > 3500$. We have

$$H_o: \sigma = 3500 \qquad \text{versus} \qquad H_1: \sigma > 3500$$

This is a right-tailed test.

Step 2: Because this is a right-tailed test, we determine the critical value at the $\alpha = 0.05$ level of significance with $n - 1 = 20 - 1 = 19$ degrees of freedom to be $\chi^2_{0.05} = 30.144$. The critical region is displayed in Figure 22.

Step 3: We compute the sample standard deviation to be 4094. The test statistic is

$$\chi^2 = \frac{(n-1)s^2}{\sigma_o^2} = \frac{(19)(4094)^2}{3500^2} = 25.996$$

Step 4: Because the test statistic is less than $\chi^2_{0.05} = 30.144$, we do not reject the null hypothesis. That is, the value of the test statistic does not fall within the critical region.

Step 5: There is not sufficient evidence to support the claim that the population standard deviation is greater than 3500 miles at the $\alpha = 0.05$ level of significance.   ◄◄

The next example illustrates a two-tailed test about a population standard deviation.

▶ **EXAMPLE 2**   **Testing a Hypothesis about a Population Standard Deviation**

TABLE 5		
$47,000	$32,750	$35,995
$32,750	$33,995	$39,998
$33,995	$43,500	$37,995
$43,108	$39,950	$37,995
$33,988	$36,900	$43,785

Source: cars.com

Problem: Recall, in Example 2 from Section 9.2, that Grant is in the market to buy a three-year-old Chevy Corvette. In that example, we assumed that $\sigma = \$4100$. Test the claim that σ is different from $4100 at the $\alpha = 0.05$ level of significance. For convenience, the data are reproduced in Table 5.

Approach: Before we can perform the hypothesis test, we must verify that the data come from a population that is normally distributed. We draw a normal probability plot to verify this requirement. We then proceed to follow Steps 1–5.

Solution: A normal probability plot was drawn in Figure 4 of Section 8.1. This plot indicates that the price of used Corvettes is normally distributed.

Step 1: The claim is that $\sigma \neq \$4100$. We have

$$H_o: \sigma = \$4100 \qquad \text{versus} \qquad H_1: \sigma \neq \$4100$$

This is a two-tailed test.

Step 2: Because this is a two-tailed test, we determine the critical values at the $\alpha = 0.05$ level of significance with $n - 1 = 15 - 1 = 14$ degrees of freedom to be $\chi^2_{1-0.05/2} = \chi^2_{0.975} = 5.629$ and $\chi^2_{0.05/2} = \chi^2_{0.025} = 26.119$. The critical regions are displayed in Figure 23.

Figure 23

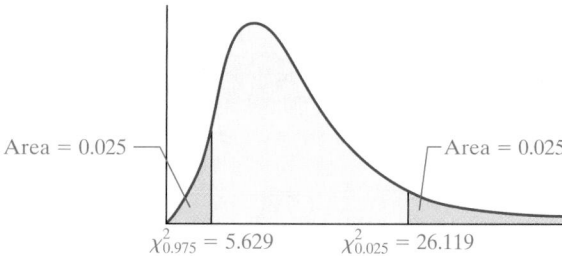

Area = 0.025

Area = 0.025

$\chi^2_{0.975} = 5.629$ $\chi^2_{0.025} = 26.119$

Step 3: We compute the sample standard deviation to be $4522. The test statistic is

$$\chi^2 = \frac{(n-1)s^2}{\sigma_o^2} = \frac{(14)(4522)^2}{4100^2} = 17.030$$

Step 4: Because the test statistic is greater than $\chi^2_{0.975} = 5.629$ and less than $\chi^2_{0.025} = 26.119$, we do not reject the null hypothesis. That is, the value of the test statistic does not fall within the critical regions.

Step 5: There is not sufficient evidence to support the claim that the population standard deviation is different from $4100 at the $\alpha = 0.05$ level of significance. ◄◄

② P-Values

Because the chi-square distribution table (Table IV) only provides critical values that correspond to certain areas, we cannot use the table to compute exact P-values. However, we can approximate P-values.

► **EXAMPLE 3**   **Approximating the P-Value**

Problem: Approximate the P-value for the hypothesis test in Example 1.

Approach: The P-value will be the area under the chi-square distribution with $n - 1 = 20 - 1 = 19$ degrees of freedom to the right of the test statistic (because this is a right-tailed test).

Solution: In referring to Table IV, we look at the row corresponding to 19 degrees of freedom. The area under the chi-square distribution to the right of 27.204 is 0.10. The test statistic obtained in Example 1 is 25.996. The area under the chi-square distribution to the right of 25.996 must be greater than 0.10, so the P-value is greater than 0.10. Figure 24 illustrates this result. Since the P-value is greater than the level of significance ($\alpha = 0.05$ in Example 1), we do not reject the null hypothesis. There is not sufficient evidence at the $\alpha = 0.05$ level of significance to support the claim that the population standard deviation is greater than 3500 miles. ◄◄

Figure 24

Area = 0.10

$\chi^2 = 25.996$ $\chi^2_{0.10} = 27.204$

Using Techology: Exact P-values can be calculated via technology by finding the area under the chi-square distribution. For example, Figure 25 shows the results of finding the area under the chi-square distribution to the right of $\chi^2 = 25.996$ with 19 degrees of freedom by using a TI-83 Plus graphing calculator.
The exact P-value is 0.13.

Figure 25 P-value = 0.13

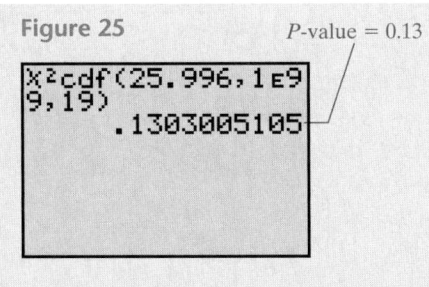

```
χ²cdf(25.996,1ᴇ9
9,19)
        .1303005105
```

9.5 Assess Your Understanding

Concepts and Vocabulary

1. State the requirements to test a claim regarding a population standard deviation.

2. Determine the critical value for a right-tailed test of a population standard deviation with 18 degrees of freedom at the $\alpha = 0.05$ level of significance.

Exercises

• Basic Skills

1. In order to test H_0: $\sigma = 50$ versus H_1: $\sigma < 50$, a random sample of size $n = 24$ is obtained from a population that is known to be normally distributed.
   (a) If the sample standard deviation is determined to be $s = 47.2$, compute the test statistic. $\chi^2 = 20.496$
   (b) If the researcher decides to test this hypothesis at the $\alpha = 0.05$ level of significance, determine the critical value. $\chi^2_{0.95} = 13.091$
   (c) Draw a chi-square distribution that depicts the critical region.
   (d) Will the researcher reject the null hypothesis? Why? No

2. In order to test H_0: $\sigma = 35$ versus H_1: $\sigma > 35$, a random sample of size $n = 15$ is obtained from a population that is known to be normally distributed.
   (a) If the sample standard deviation is determined to be $s = 37.4$, compute the test statistic. $\chi^2 = 15.986$
   (b) If the researcher decides to test this hypothesis at the $\alpha = 0.01$ level of significance, determine the critical value. $\chi^2_{0.01} = 29.141$
   (c) Draw a chi-square distribution that depicts the critical region.
   (d) Will the researcher reject the null hypothesis? Why? No

3. In order to test H_0: $\sigma = 1.8$ versus H_1: $\sigma > 1.8$, a random sample of size $n = 18$ is obtained from a population that is known to be normally distributed.
   (a) If the sample standard deviation is determined to be $s = 2.4$, compute the test statistic. $\chi^2 = 30.222$
   (b) If the researcher decides to test this hypothesis at the $\alpha = 0.10$ level of significance, determine the critical value. $\chi^2_{0.1} = 24.769$
   (c) Draw a chi-square distribution that depicts the critical region.
   (d) Will the researcher reject the null hypothesis? Why? Yes

4. In order to test H_0: $\sigma = 0.35$ versus H_1: $\sigma < 0.35$, a random sample of size $n = 41$ is obtained from a population that is known to be normally distributed.
   (a) If the sample standard deviation is determined to be $s = 0.23$, compute the test statistic. $\chi^2 = 17.273$
   (b) If the researcher decides to test this hypothesis at the $\alpha = 0.01$ level of significance, determine the critical value. $\chi^2_{0.99} = 22.164$
   (c) Draw a chi-square distribution that depicts the critical region.
   (d) Will the researcher reject the null hypothesis? Why? Yes

5. In order to test H_0: $\sigma = 4.3$ versus H_1: $\sigma \neq 4.3$, a random sample of size $n = 12$ is obtained from a population that is known to be normally distributed.
   (a) If the sample standard deviation is determined to be $s = 4.8$, compute the test statistic. $\chi^2 = 13.707$
   (b) If the researcher decides to test this hypothesis at the $\alpha = 0.05$ level of significance, determine the critical values. $\chi^2_{0.975} = 3.816$; $\chi^2_{0.025} = 21.920$
   (c) Draw a chi-square distribution that depicts the critical regions.
   (d) Will the researcher reject the null hypothesis? Why? No

6. In order to test H_0: $\sigma = 1.2$ versus H_1: $\sigma \neq 1.2$, a random sample of size $n = 22$ is obtained from a population that is known to be normally distributed.
   (a) If the sample standard deviation is determined to be $s = 0.8$, compute the test statistic. $\chi^2 = 9.333$
   (b) If the researcher decides to test this hypothesis at the $\alpha = 0.10$ level of significance, determine the critical values. $\chi^2_{0.95} = 11.591$; $\chi^2_{0.05} = 32.671$
   (c) Draw a chi-square distribution that depicts the critical regions.
   (d) Will the researcher reject the null hypothesis? Why? Yes

• Applying the Concepts

7. **Mutual Fund Risk** One measure of the risk of a mutual fund is the standard deviation of its rate of return. Suppose a mutual fund qualifies as having moderate risk if the standard deviation of its monthly rate of return is less than 4 percent. A mutual-fund manager claims that his fund has moderate risk. A mutual-fund rating agency does not believe this claim and randomly selects 25 months and determines the rate of return for the fund. The standard deviation of the rate of return is computed to be 3.01 percent. Is there sufficient evidence to support the claim that the fund has moderate risk at the $\alpha = 0.05$ level of significance? A normal probability plot indicates that the monthly rates of return are normally distributed. Reject H_0

8. **Filling Machine** A machine fills bottles with 64 fluid ounces of liquid. The quality-control manager determines that the fill levels are normally distributed with a mean of 64 ounces and a standard deviation of 0.42 ounces. He has an engineer recalibrate the machine in an attempt to lower the standard deviation. After the recalibration, the quality-control manager randomly selects 19 bottles from the line and determines that the standard deviation is 0.38 ounces. Is there significant evidence for the manager to conclude that the standard deviation has decreased at the $\alpha = 0.01$ level of significance? Do not reject H_0

9. Acid Rain In Problem 13 from Section 9.2, we tested a hypothesis regarding the mean amount of acidity in rain in Pierce County, Washington. To test the hypothesis, we verified that the data are normally distributed and assumed that $\sigma = 0.2$. Test this assumption at the $\alpha = 0.05$ level of significance, given that $s = 0.1708$. *Do not reject* H_o

5.08	4.66	4.70	4.87
4.78	5.00	4.50	4.73
4.79	4.65	4.91	5.07
5.03	4.78	4.77	4.60
4.73	5.05	4.70	

Source: National Atmospheric Deposition Program

10. Age of the Bride In Problem 14 from Section 9.2, we tested a hypothesis regarding the mean age at which women marry in Memphis, Tennessee. To test this hypothesis, we verified that the data are normally distributed and assumed that $\sigma = 6.2$ years. Test this assumption at the $\alpha = 0.05$ level of significance, given that $s = 6.553$. *Do not reject* H_o

40	23	30	24	31
29	28	24	35	34
24	21	46	29	31
29	29	21	33	39

Source: The Commercial Appeal, June 30, 2001

11. Conforming Golf Balls In Problem 19 from Section 9.3, we verified that Maxfli XS golf balls conformed to the USGA requirements for mean diameter. Suppose the USGA also requires that the standard deviation of the diameter of a golf ball must be less than 0.004 inch. Determine whether these balls conform to this requirement at the $\alpha = 0.01$ level of significance. (*Note*: In Problem 19 from Section 9.3, we verified that the data are normally distributed.) *Do not reject* H_o

1.683	1.677	1.681
1.685	1.678	1.686
1.684	1.684	1.673
1.685	1.682	1.674

Source: Michael McCraith, Joliet Junior College

12. Conforming Golf Balls In Problem 20 from Section 9.3, we verified that Maxfli XS golf balls conformed to USGA requirements for mean weight. Suppose the USGA also requires that the standard deviation of the weight of a golf ball must be less than 0.005 ounce.

Determine whether these balls conform to this requirement at the $\alpha = 0.01$ level of significance. (*Note*: In Problem 20 from Section 9.3, we verified that the data are normally distributed.) *Do not reject* H_o

1.614	1.619	1.614
1.614	1.610	1.610
1.621	1.612	1.615
1.621	1.602	1.617

Source: Michael McCraith, Joliet Junior College

13. An Inconsistent Player We often hear sports announcers say, "I wonder which player will show up to play today." This is the announcer's way of saying that the player is inconsistent—that his or her performance varies dramatically from game to game. Suppose the standard deviation of the number of points scored by shooting guards in the NBA is 8.3. A random sample of 25 games played by Allen Iverson of the Philadelphia 76ers results in a sample standard deviation of 6.7 points. Assuming that a normal probability plot indicates that the points scored are approximately normally distributed, test the claim that Allen Iverson is more consistent than other shooting guards in the NBA at the $\alpha = 0.10$ level of significance. *Reject* H_o

14. Waiting in Line One aspect of queuing theory is to study waiting time in lines. Suppose a fast-food chain is trying to determine whether it should switch from having four cash registers with four separate lines to four cash registers with a single line. It has been determined that the mean wait time in both lines is equal; however, the chain is uncertain about which line has less variability in wait time. From experience, the chain knows that the wait times in the four separate lines are normally distributed with $\sigma = 1.2$ minutes. In a study, the chain reconfigured five restaurants to have a single line and measured the wait times for 50 randomly selected customers. The sample standard deviation was determined to be $s = 0.84$ minutes. Test the claim that the variability in wait time is less for a single line than for multiple lines at the $\alpha = 0.05$ level of significance. *Reject* H_o

15. Heights of Baseball Players Data obtained from the National Center for Health Statistics show that men between the ages of 20 and 29 have a mean height of 69.3 inches, with a standard deviation of 2.9 inches. A baseball analyst claims that the standard deviation of heights of major-league baseball players is less than 2.9 inches. The heights (in inches) of 20 randomly selected players are shown on the top of page 575.

(a) Verify that the data are normally distributed by drawing a normal probability plot.
(b) Compute the sample standard deviation.
(c) Test the claim at the $\alpha = 0.01$ level of significance.

(15b) *s = 2.059 inches*   (15c) *Do not reject* H_o

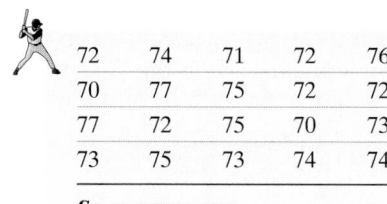

72	74	71	72	76
70	77	75	72	72
77	72	75	70	73
73	75	73	74	74

Source: espn.com

16. *P*-Values Determine the *P*-value of the hypothesis test in Problem 8. P-value = 0.3199

17. *P*-Values Determine the *P*-value of the hypothesis test in Problem 7. P-value = 0.0446

9.6   The Probability of a Type II Error; the Power of the Test

Preparing for This Section   Before getting started, review the following:

✓ Computing normal probabilities (Section 7.3, pp. 406–408).

Objectives ① Determine the probability of making a Type II error
② Compute the power of the test

Note to Instructor
This section is optional and may be skipped without loss of continuity.

① Probability of a Type II Error

It can be shown that α, β, and the sample size n are related. Once two of the three values are chosen, the third can be determined. It is common for researchers to choose a level of α and the sample size n so that β is then determined. In order to minimize the value of β for a given level of α, the researcher should choose n to be as large as time, money, and other resources allow. We shall present only the procedure for computing the probability of making a Type II error for tests regarding the population mean, assuming the population standard deviation is known.

Recall, from Section 9.1, that β is the probability of making a Type II error—that is, β is the probability of not rejecting the null hypothesis when the alternative hypothesis is true. The probability of making a Type II error depends upon the level of significance, α, and on the sample size. In order to compute the probability of making a Type II error, a specific value of the parameter that is in the alternative hypothesis must be given. Consider Example 1 from Section 9.2, where we tested

$$H_o: \mu = 10,300$$

$$H_1: \mu > 10,300$$

We tested this hypothesis at the $\alpha = 0.1$ level of significance by obtaining a random sample of size $n = 20$ with the population standard deviation, σ, assumed to be 3500 miles. The alternative hypothesis is true for any μ greater than 10,300. For example, the probability of a Type II error, given that the true population mean is $\mu = 10,700$, would be computed as follows:

$$P(\text{Type II error}) = P(\text{do not reject } H_o \text{ given that } H_1 \text{ is true})$$

$$= P(\text{do not reject } H_o \text{ given that } \mu = 10,700)$$

To compute this probability, we need to determine the criterion for not rejecting the null hypothesis. For example, if we are testing the foregoing

Figure 26

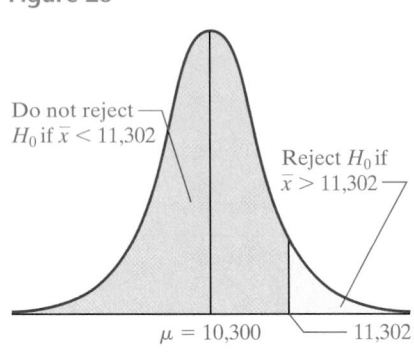

Do not reject H_0 if $\bar{x} < 11{,}302$

Reject H_0 if $\bar{x} > 11{,}302$

$\mu = 10{,}300$ $11{,}302$

hypothesis, we would reject H_o if $Z > z_{0.1} = 1.28$. We can write this rejection criterion in terms of a sample mean. Using the Z-score, we will reject H_o if

$$Z = \frac{\bar{x} - 10{,}300}{3500/\sqrt{20}} > 1.28$$

Solving this inequality for the sample mean, we would reject H_o if

$$\bar{x} > 10{,}300 + 1.28\left(\frac{3500}{\sqrt{20}}\right) = 11{,}302$$

We will *not* reject the null hypothesis if $\bar{x} < 11{,}302$. Figure 26 shows the "reject" and "do not reject" regions.

Suppose that the population mean is 10,700. Then

$$\begin{aligned}
P(\text{Type II error}) &= P(\text{do not reject } H_o \text{ given that } H_1 \text{ is true}) \\
&= P(\text{do not reject } H_o \text{ given that } \mu = 10{,}700) \\
&= P(\text{sample mean is less than 11,302 given that } \mu = 10{,}700) \\
&= P\left(Z < \frac{11{,}302 - 10{,}700}{3500/\sqrt{20}}\right) \\
&= P(Z < 0.77) \\
&= 0.7794
\end{aligned}$$

The probability of committing a Type II error is 0.7794 if the population mean is 10,700. Figure 27 helps to illustrate the concept.

Figure 27

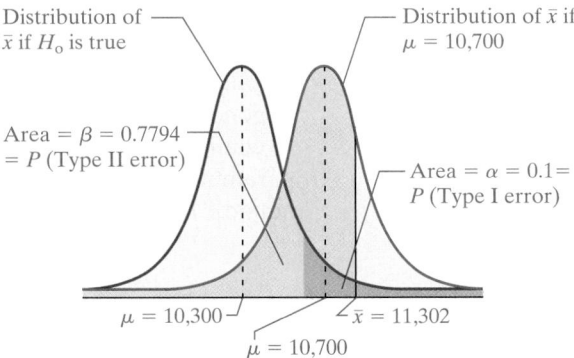

Distribution of $\bar{x}$ if H_o is true

Distribution of $\bar{x}$ if $\mu = 10{,}700$

Area $= \beta = 0.7794$ $= P$ (Type II error)

Area $= \alpha = 0.1 =$ P (Type I error)

$\mu = 10{,}300$ $\bar{x} = 11{,}302$

$\mu = 10{,}700$

Because there are an infinite number of values more than 10,300, there are an infinite number of Type II error probabilities.

We summarize the procedure for computing the probability of making a Type II error with the steps that follow.

The Probability of a Type II Error

Step 1: Determine the sample mean that separates the rejection region from the nonrejection region.

Two-Tailed Test $(H_1: \mu \neq \mu_o)$	Right-Tailed Test $(H_1: \mu > \mu_o)$	Left-Tailed Test $(H_1: \mu < \mu_o)$
$\overline{x}_L = \mu_o - z_{\alpha/2} \cdot \dfrac{\sigma}{\sqrt{n}}$	$\overline{x} = \mu_o + z_\alpha \cdot \dfrac{\sigma}{\sqrt{n}}$	$\overline{x} = \mu_o - z_\alpha \cdot \dfrac{\sigma}{\sqrt{n}}$
$\overline{x}_U = \mu_o + z_{\alpha/2} \cdot \dfrac{\sigma}{\sqrt{n}}$		

Note: z is the critical value, μ_o is the assumed value of the population mean, σ is the population standard deviation, and n is the sample size.

Step 2: Draw a normal curve whose mean is a particular value from the alternative hypothesis, with the sample mean(s) found in Step 1 labeled.

Step 3:

Two-Tailed Test $(H_1: \mu \neq \mu_o)$	Right-Tailed Test $(H_1: \mu > \mu_o)$	Left-Tailed Test $(H_1: \mu < \mu_o)$
Find the area under the normal curve drawn in Step 2 between $\overline{x}_L$ and $\overline{x}_U$ found in Step 1. This area represents β, the probability of not rejecting the null hypothesis when the alternative hypothesis is true.	Find the area under the normal curve drawn in Step 2 to the left of the sample mean, $\overline{x}$, found in Step 1. This area represents β, the probability of not rejecting the null hypothesis when the alternative hypothesis is true.	Find the area under the normal curve drawn in Step 2 to the right of the sample mean, $\overline{x}$, found in Step 1. This area represents β, the probability of not rejecting the null hypothesis when the alternative hypothesis is true.

▶ **Example 1**   **Computing the Probability of a Type II Error**

Problem: In Example 1 from Section 9.2, we tested $H_o: \mu = 10{,}300$ versus $H_1: \mu > 10{,}300$ for a random sample of size $n = 20$, with the population standard deviation, σ, assumed to be 3500 miles at the $\alpha = 0.1$ level of significance. Compute the probability of a Type II error, given that the population mean is $\mu = 10{,}500$.

Approach: We follow the preceding Steps 1–3.

Solution:

Step 1: We first determine $z_{0.1}$ to be 1.28. We let $Z = 1.28$, $\mu_o = 10{,}300$, $\sigma = 3500$, and $n = 20$ to find the sample mean that separates the rejection region from the non-rejection region:

$$1.28 = \frac{\overline{x} - 10{,}300}{3500/\sqrt{20}}$$

Now solve for the sample mean, $\overline{x}$:

$$1.28 \cdot \frac{3500}{\sqrt{20}} = \overline{x} - 10{,}300; \quad \text{Multiply both sides by } \frac{3500}{\sqrt{20}}.$$

$$\overline{x} = 10{,}300 + 1.28 \cdot \frac{3500}{\sqrt{20}} \approx 11{,}302. \quad \text{Add 10,300 to both sides and simplify.}$$

For any sample mean less than 11,302, we do not reject the null hypothesis.
Step 2: Figure 28 on page 578 shows the normal curve with $\mu = 10{,}500$. The sample mean found in Step 1, $\overline{x} = 11{,}302$, is also labeled.

Figure 28

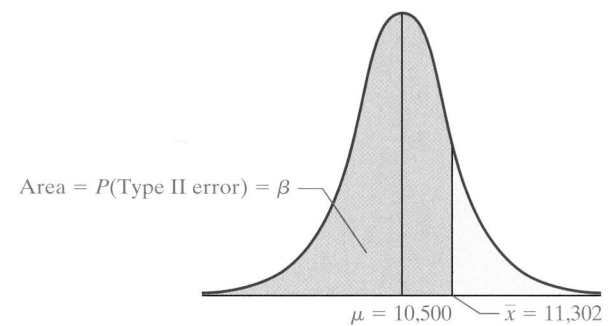

Step 3: Because this is a right-tailed test, the area to the left of $\overline{x} = 11{,}302$ represents β, the probability of a Type II error.

$$P(\text{Type II error}) = P(\overline{x} < 11{,}302 \text{ given that } \mu = 10{,}500)$$

$$= P\left(Z < \frac{11{,}302 - 10{,}500}{3500/\sqrt{20}} \right) = P(Z < 1.02) = 0.8461$$

There is a 0.8461 probability of making a Type II error if the true population mean is 10,500. ◄◄

NW *Now Work Problem 9.*

Notice that, as the population mean gets closer to the hypothesized mean, the probability of making a Type II error increases.

② The Power of the Test

The complement of β, $1 - \beta$, is the probability of rejecting the null hypothesis when the alternative hypothesis is true. The value of $1 - \beta$ is referred to as the **power of the test**. The higher the power of the test, the more likely the test will reject the null when the alternative hypothesis is true.

► **EXAMPLE 2** Computing the Power of the Test

Problem: Compute the power of the test for the situation in Example 1.

In Your Own Words

The power of the test is the probability of correctly rejecting H_o.

Approach: The power of the test is $1 - \beta$. We computed β in Example 1 to be 0.8461 when the true population mean is 10,500.

Solution: The power of the test is $1 - 0.8461 = 0.1539$. There is a 0.1539 probability of rejecting the null hypothesis if the true population mean is 10,500 miles. ◄◄

In Table 6, we show the probability of making a Type II error and the power of the test for a number of different values of the population mean greater than 10,300. Notice that, the closer the population mean gets to the hypothesized value of 10,300, the larger the probability of a Type II error becomes. This should not be surprising. When the true population mean is close to the population mean stated in the null hypothesis, there is a high probability that we will not reject the null hypothesis and will make a Type II error.

We can use the values of μ and their corresponding powers to construct a *power curve*. A **power curve** is a graph that shows the power of the test against values of the population mean that make the null hypothesis false. Figure 29 shows the power curve for the values in Table 6.

	TABLE 6	
Value of μ	Probability of Making a Type II Error, β	Power, $1 - \beta$
10,301	0.8996	0.1004
10,400	0.8473	0.1527
10,700	0.7794	0.2206
11,000	0.6550	0.3450
11,500	0.4001	0.5999
12,000	0.1862	0.8138
12,500	0.0629	0.9371

Figure 29

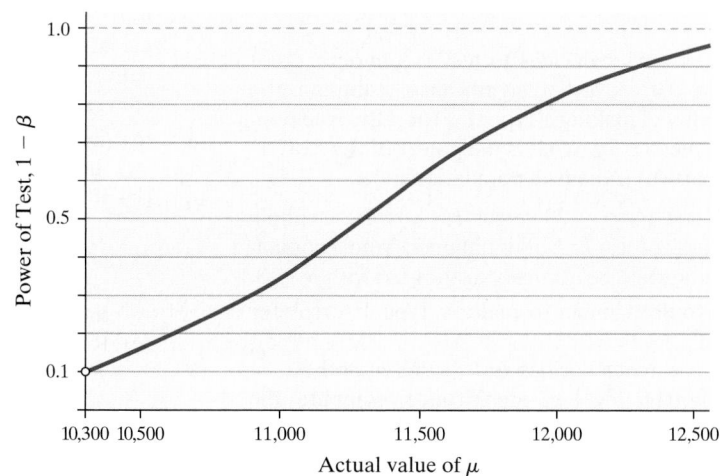

Figure 29 shows that, as the true mean gets farther from the hypothesized mean, the power of test approaches 1.

9.6 Assess Your Understanding

Concepts and Vocabulary

1. Explain what it means to make a Type II error.
2. Explain the term "power of the test."

3. What happens to the power of the test as the true mean gets closer to the hypothesized value of the mean? Why is this result reasonable?

Exercises

• Basic Skills

1. In order to test $H_0: \mu = 50$ versus $H_1: \mu < 50$, a simple random sample of size $n = 24$ is obtained from a population that is known to be normally distributed with $\sigma = 12$.

   (a) What would it mean to make a Type II error for this test?

   (b) If the researcher decides to test this hypothesis at the $\alpha = 0.05$ level of significance, compute the probability of making a Type II error if the true population mean is 48. What is the power of the test? *0.7964; 0.2036*

   (c) Redo part (b) if the true population mean is 49.2. *0.9064; 0.0936*

2. In order to test $H_0: \mu = 40$ versus $H_1: \mu > 40$, a simple random sample of size $n = 25$ is obtained from a population that is known to be normally distributed with $\sigma = 6$.

   (a) What would it mean to make a Type II error for this test?

   (b) If the researcher decides to test this hypothesis at the $\alpha = 0.05$ level of significance, compute the probability of making a Type II error if the true population mean is 42. What is the power of the test? *0.4914; 0.5086*

   (c) Redo part (b) if the true population mean is 40.6. *0.8739; 0.1261*

3. In order to test $H_0: \mu = 100$ versus $H_1: \mu \neq 100$, a simple random sample of size $n = 23$ is obtained from a population that is known to be normally distributed with $\sigma = 7$.

   (a) What would it mean to make a Type II error for this test?

   (b) If the researcher decides to test this hypothesis at the $\alpha = 0.01$ level of significance, compute the probability of making a Type II error if the true population mean is 103. What is the power of the test?

   (c) Redo part (b) if the true population mean is 101.4.

4. In order to test $H_0: \mu = 80$ versus $H_1: \mu < 80$, a simple random sample of size $n = 22$ is obtained from a population that is known to be normally distributed with $\sigma = 11$.

   (a) What would it mean to make a Type II error for this test?

   (b) If the researcher decides to test this hypothesis at the $\alpha = 0.01$ level of significance, compute the probability of making a Type II error if the true population mean is 79. What is the power of the test?

   (c) Redo part (b) if the true population mean is 77.5.

5. In order to test $H_0: \mu = 20$ versus $H_1: \mu < 20$, a simple random sample of size $n = 18$ is obtained from a population that is known to be normally distributed with $\sigma = 3$.

   (a) What would it mean to make a Type II error for this test?

   (b) If the researcher decides to test this hypothesis at the $\alpha = 0.05$ level of significance, compute the probability of making a Type II error if the true population mean is 17.4. What is the power of the test?

   (c) Redo part (b) if the true population mean is 19.2.

6. In order to test $H_0: \mu = 4.5$ versus $H_1: \mu > 4.5$, a simple random sample of size $n = 13$ is obtained from a population that is known to be normally distributed with $\sigma = 1.2$.

   (a) What would it mean to make a Type II error for this test?

   (b) If the researcher decides to test this hypothesis at the $\alpha = 0.05$ level of significance, compute the probability of making a Type II error if the true population mean is 4.7. What is the power of the test?

   (c) Redo part (b) if the true population mean is 5.4.

7. In order to test $H_0: \mu = 105$ versus $H_1: \mu \neq 105$, a simple random sample of size $n = 35$ is obtained from a population whose standard deviation is known to be $\sigma = 12$.

   (a) What would it mean to make a Type II error for this test?

   (b) If the researcher decides to test this hypothesis at the $\alpha = 0.1$ level of significance, compute the probability of making a Type II error if the true population mean is 101.8. What is the power of the test?

   (c) Redo part (b) if the true population mean is 103.1.

8. In order to test $H_0: \mu = 45$ versus $H_1: \mu \neq 45$, a simple random sample of size $n = 40$ is obtained from a population whose standard deviation is known to be $\sigma = 8$.

   (a) What would it mean to make a Type II error for this test?

   (b) If the researcher decides to test this hypothesis at the $\alpha = 0.1$ level of significance, compute the probability of making a Type II error if the true population mean is 46.2. What is the power of the test?

   (c) Redo part (b) if the true population mean is 48.3. *0.1674; 0.8326*

• Applying the Concepts

9. **Are Mothers Getting Older?** A researcher maintains that the average age of a woman before she has her first child is greater than the 1990 average age, 26.4 years, obtained from data in the *National Vital Statistics Report*, Vol. 48, No. 14. She obtains a simple random sample of 40 women who recently gave birth to their first child. Assume that the population standard deviation is 6.4 years.

   (a) What would it mean to make a Type II error for this test?

   (b) If the researcher decides to test this hypothesis at the $\alpha = 0.05$ level of significance, compute the probability of making a Type II error if the true population mean is 26.9 years. What is the power of the test? *0.8742; 0.1258*

   (c) Redo part (b) if the true population mean is 27.5 years. *0.7100; 0.2900*

10. **Miles per Gallon** The Environmental Protection Agency publishes data regarding the number of miles per gallon achieved by all cars. A researcher maintains that fuel additives increase the miles per gallon of cars driven under highway driving conditions. The mean number of miles per gallon of all large cars manufactured in 1999 and not using the fuel additive is 25.1, according to data obtained from the EPA. The researcher obtains a simple random sample of 35 large cars manufactured in 1999 and adds a fuel additive. Assume the population standard deviation is 3.9.

   (a) What would it mean to make a Type II error for this test?

   (b) If the researcher decides to test this hypothesis at the $\alpha = 0.1$ level of significance, compute the probability of making a Type II error if the true population mean is 25.7. What is the power of the test?

   (c) Redo part (b) if the true population mean is 26.4.

11. **SAT Exam Scores** A school administrator states that students whose first language learned is not English score worse on the verbal portion of the SAT exam than students whose first language is English. The mean SAT verbal score of students whose first language is English is 516, according to data obtained from the College Board. Suppose the administrator obtains a simple random sample of 20 students whose first language learned was not English. SAT verbal scores are normally distributed with a population standard deviation of 119.

(3b) 0.6987; 0.3013 (3c) 0.9468; 0.0532 (4b) 0.9714; 0.0286 (4c) 0.8966; 0.1034 (5b) 0.0209; 0.9791
(5c) 0.6947; 0.3053 (6b) 0.8535; 0.1465 (6c) 0.1465; 0.8535 (7b) 0.5269; 0.4731 (7c) 0.7562; 0.2438
(8b) 0.7519; 0.2481 (10b) 0.6421; 0.3579 (10c) 0.2427; 0.7573

(a) What would it mean to make a Type II error for this test?

(b) If the researcher decides to test this hypothesis at the $\alpha = 0.01$ level of significance, compute the probability of making a Type II error if the true population mean is 500. What is the power of the test?

(c) Redo part (b) if the true population mean is 480.

12. SAT Exam Scores A school administrator states that students whose first language learned is not English do not score differently on the math portion of the SAT exam from students whose first language is English. The mean SAT math score of students whose first language is English is 516, according to data obtained from the College Board. Suppose the researcher obtains a simple random sample of 20 students whose first language learned was not English. SAT math scores are normally distributed with a population standard deviation of 109.

(a) What would it mean to make a Type II error for this test?

(b) If the researcher decides to test this hypothesis at the $\alpha = 0.05$ level of significance, compute the probability of making a Type II error if the true population mean is 505. What is the power of the test?

(c) Redo part (b) if the true population mean is 475.

13. The Effect of α Redo Problem 1(b) with $\alpha = 0.01$. What effect does lowering α have on the power of the test?

14. The Effect of α Redo Problem 2(b) with $\alpha = 0.1$. What effect does increasing α have on the power of the test?

15. Probability of a Type II Error in Tests on Proportion Suppose we wish to test H_0: $p = 0.75$ versus H_1: $p < 0.75$. In this problem, we compute the power of the test for proportions.

(a) Suppose the researcher decides to test this hypothesis at the $\alpha = 0.05$ level of significance by conducting a simple random sample of $n = 500$ people. Compute the probability of making a Type II error if the true population proportion is 0.70. (*Hint*: The hypothesized mean is $p_0 = 0.75$ and the standard deviation is $\sqrt{\dfrac{p_0(1 - p_0)}{n}}$.) *0.1899*

(b) What is the power of the test? *0.8101*

16. Probability of a Type II Error in Tests on Proportion Suppose we wish to test H_0: $p = 0.35$ versus H_1: $p > 0.35$. In this problem, we compute the power of the test for proportions.

(a) Suppose the researcher decides to test this hypothesis at the $\alpha = 0.05$ level of significance by conducting a simple random sample of $n = 700$ people. Compute the probability of making a Type II error if the true population proportion is 0.39. (*Hint*: The hypothesized mean is $p_0 = 0.35$ and the standard deviation is $\sqrt{\dfrac{p_0(1 - p_0)}{n}}$.) *0.2938*

(b) What is the power of the test? *0.7062*

CHAPTER 9 REVIEW

Summary

In this chapter, we discussed testing claims by using hypothesis testing. A claim is made regarding a population parameter, which leads to a null and an alternative hypothesis. The null hypothesis is assumed true. We collect sample data, which are used to test the veracity of the claim. Given the sample data, we either reject or do not reject the null hypothesis. In performing a hypothesis test, there is always the possibility of making a Type I error—rejecting the null hypothesis when it is true—or of making a Type II error—not rejecting the null hypothesis when it is false. The probability of making a Type I error is equal to the level of significance, α, of the test.

We discussed four types of hypothesis tests in this chapter. First, we performed tests about a population mean with σ known. Second, we performed tests about a population mean with σ unknown. In both of these cases, we required that either the sample size be large (i.e. $n \geq 30$) or the population be approximately normal with no outliers. For small sample sizes, we verified the normality of the data by using normal probability plots. Boxplots were used to check for outliers. The third test we performed regarded claims about a population proportion. In order to perform these tests, we required a large sample size, so that $np(1 - p) \geq 10$, yet the sample size could be no more than 5% of the population size. Finally, we performed tests regarding a population standard deviation (or variance). These tests require that the population from which the sample is drawn be normally distributed. This test is not robust, so deviation from the requirement of normality was not allowed. All four hypothesis tests were performed by using classical methods and the P-value approach. The P-value approach to testing hypotheses has appeal, because the rejection rule is always to reject the null hypothesis if the P-value is less than the level of significance, α.

In order to assist in the choosing of the appropriate test to perform, we provide the flowchart in Figure 30 on page 582.

Notes:

- In testing claims about the population mean, if the sample size is not large or the population is not normally distributed, use the nonparametric methods discussed in Section 13.3.

- In testing claims about the population proportion, if $np_0(1 - p_0) < 10$, use the binomial probability formula to test the claim.

(11b) *0.9581; 0.0419*   (11c) *0.8357; 0.1643*   (12b) *0.9264; 0.0736*
(12c) *0.6093; 0.3907*   13. *0.9351; 0.0649*   14. *0.3495; 0.6505*

Figure 30

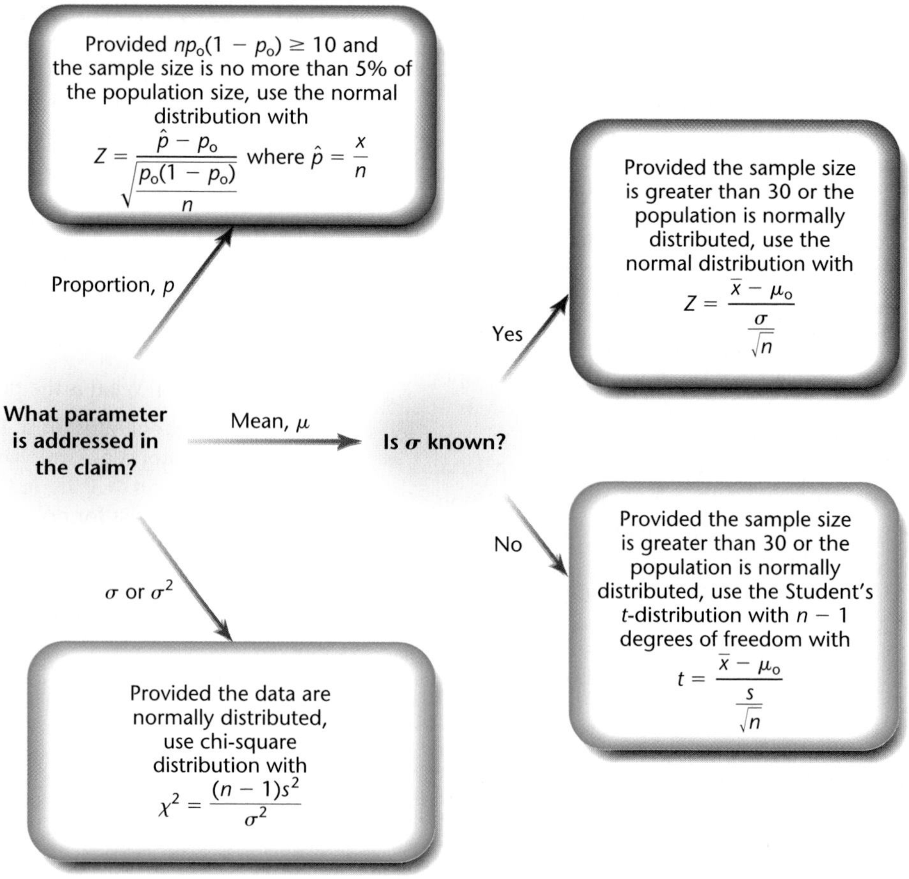

Provided $np_o(1 - p_o) \geq 10$ and the sample size is no more than 5% of the population size, use the normal distribution with

$$Z = \frac{\hat{p} - p_o}{\sqrt{\dfrac{p_o(1 - p_o)}{n}}} \text{ where } \hat{p} = \frac{x}{n}$$

Provided the sample size is greater than 30 or the population is normally distributed, use the normal distribution with

$$Z = \frac{\bar{x} - \mu_o}{\dfrac{\sigma}{\sqrt{n}}}$$

Proportion, p

Yes

What parameter is addressed in the claim?   Mean, μ Is σ known?

No

Provided the sample size is greater than 30 or the population is normally distributed, use the Student's t-distribution with $n - 1$ degrees of freedom with

$$t = \frac{\bar{x} - \mu_o}{\dfrac{s}{\sqrt{n}}}$$

σ or σ^2

Provided the data are normally distributed, use chi-square distribution with

$$\chi^2 = \frac{(n - 1)s^2}{\sigma^2}$$

We concluded the section by learning how to compute the probability of making a Type II error and the power of the test. The power of the test is the probability of rejecting the null hypothesis when the alternative hypothesis is true. The closer the true value of the population mean is to the hypothesized value of the population mean, the lower the power of the test.

Formulas

Test Statistics

- $z = \dfrac{\bar{x} - \mu_o}{\sigma/\sqrt{n}}$ follows the standard normal distribution if the population from which the sample was drawn is normal or if the sample size is large ($n \geq 30$).

- $t = \dfrac{\bar{x} - \mu_o}{s/\sqrt{n}}$ follows Student's t-distribution with $n - 1$ degrees of freedom if the population from which the sample was drawn is normal or if the sample size is large ($n \geq 30$).

- $z = \dfrac{\hat{p} - p_o}{\sqrt{\dfrac{p_o(1 - p_o)}{n}}}$ follows the standard normal distribution if $np_o(1 - p_o) \geq 10$ and $n \leq 0.05N$.

- $\chi^2 = \dfrac{(n - 1)s^2}{\sigma_o^2}$ follows the χ^2-distribution with $n - 1$ degrees of freedom if the population from which the sample was drawn is normal.

Type I/Type II Errors

- $\alpha = P(\text{Type I Error}) = P(\text{rejecting } H_o \text{ when } H_o \text{ is true})$
- $\beta = P(\text{Type II Error}) = P(\text{not rejecting } H_o \text{ when } H_1 \text{ is true})$

Vocabulary

Hypothesis (p. 519)
Hypothesis testing (p. 520)
Null hypothesis (p. 520)
Alternative hypothesis (p. 520)
Two-tailed test (p. 520)
Left-tailed test (p. 520)

Right-tailed test (p. 520)
Type I error (p. 522)
Type II error (p. 522)
Level of significance (p. 524)
Critical value (p. 530)
Critical region (p. 531)

Test statistic (p. 531)
Robust (p. 531)
P-value (p. 534)
Power of the test (p. 578)
Power curve (p. 578)

Objectives

Section	You Should Be Able to ...	Review Exercises
9.1	1 Determine the null and alternative hypotheses from a claim (p. 518)	1, 2
	2 Understand Type I and Type II errors (p. 522)	1, 2, 17(a), (b); 18(a), (b)
	3 Understand the probability of making Type I and Type II errors (p. 523)	1–4, 17(c), 18(c)
	4 State conclusions to hypothesis tests (p. 524)	1, 2
9.2	1 Understand the logic of hypothesis testing (p. 528)	29
	2 Test a hypothesis about μ with σ known using the classical method (p. 530)	5, 6, 15, 16, 19, 20
	3 Test a hypothesis about μ with σ known using the *P*-value approach (p. 534)	5, 6, 15, 16, 19, 20
	4 Test a hypothesis about μ with σ known using confidence intervals (p. 538)	6(f)
9.3	1 Test hypotheses about μ, σ unknown, using the classical approach (p. 546)	7, 8, 13, 14, 17, 18
	2 Test hypotheses about μ, σ unknown, using the *P*-value approach (p. 549)	7, 8, 13, 14, 17, 18
9.4	1 Test a hypothesis about a population proportion using the classical method (p. 558)	9, 10, 21, 22
	2 Test a hypothesis about a population proportion using the *P*-value approach (p. 561)	9, 10, 21, 22
	3 Test a hypothesis about a population proportion on a small sample (p. 563)	27, 28
9.5	1 Test a claim about a population standard deviation using the classical approach (p. 569)	11, 12, 23, 24
	2 Test a claim about a population standard deviation using the *P*-value approach (p. 572)	11, 12, 23, 24
9.6	1 Determine the probability of making a Type II error (p. 575)	25, 26
	2 Compute the power of the test (p. 578)	25, 26

Review Exercises

For each claim in Problems 1 and 2, (a) determine the null and alternative hypotheses, (b) explain what it would mean to make a Type I error, (c) explain what it would mean to make a Type II error, (d) state the conclusion that would be drawn if the null hypothesis is not rejected, and (e) state the conclusion that would be reached if the null hypothesis is rejected.

1. Charitable Contributions A government economist maintains that the mean charitable contribution in 2002 was more than $1100 per household.

2. Online Shopping According to shop.org, 17.6% of all computer hardware/software purchases in 1999 were made online. A researcher claims the proportion of computer hardware/software purchases in 2000 is more than 0.176.

3. Suppose a test is conducted at the $\alpha = 0.05$ level of significance. What is the probability of a Type I error?

4. Suppose β is computed to be 0.113. What is the probability of a Type II error? What is the power of the test? How would you interpret the power of the test?

5. In order to test $H_0: \mu = 30$ versus $H_1: \mu < 30$, a simple random sample of size $n = 12$ is obtained from a population that is known to be normally distributed with $\sigma = 4.5$.
 (a) If the sample mean is determined to be $\bar{x} = 28.6$, compute the test statistic. $Z = -1.08$
 (b) If the researcher decides to test this hypothesis at the $\alpha = 0.05$ level of significance, determine the critical value. $-Z_{0.05} = -1.645$
 (c) Draw a normal curve that depicts the rejection region.
 (d) Will the researcher reject the null hypothesis? Why? No
 (e) What is the *P*-value? 0.1406

6. In order to test $H_o: \mu = 65$ versus $H_1: \mu \neq 65$, a simple random sample of size $n = 23$ is obtained from a population that is known to be normally distributed with $\sigma = 12.3$.
   (a) If the sample mean is determined to be $\bar{x} = 70.6$, compute the test statistic. $Z = 2.18$
   (b) If the researcher decides to test this hypothesis at the $\alpha = 0.1$ level of significance, determine the critical values. $-Z_{0.05} = -1.645$; $Z_{0.05} = 1.645$
   (c) Draw a normal curve that depicts the rejection region.
   (d) Will the researcher reject the null hypothesis? Why? Yes
   (e) What is the P-value? 0.0290
   (f) Test the claim by constructing a 90% confidence interval. (66.38, 74.82)

7. In order to test $H_o: \mu = 8$ versus $H_1: \mu \neq 8$, a simple random sample of size $n = 15$ is obtained from a population that is known to be normally distributed. (e) 0.154
   (a) If $\bar{x} = 7.3$ and $s = 1.8$, compute the test statistic. $t = -1.506$

(b) If the researcher decides to test this hypothesis at the $\alpha = 0.02$ level of significance, determine the critical values. $-t_{0.01} = -2.624$; $t_{0.01} = 2.624$
(c) Draw a t-distribution that depicts the rejection region.
(d) Will the researcher reject the null hypothesis? Why?
(e) Determine the P-value. 0.154

8. In order to test $H_o: \mu = 3.9$ versus $H_1: \mu < 3.9$, a simple random sample of size $n = 25$ is obtained from a population that is known to be normally distributed.
   (a) If $\bar{x} = 3.5$ and $s = 0.9$, compute the test statistic.
   (b) If the researcher decides to test this hypothesis at the $\alpha = 0.05$ level of significance, determine the critical value. $-t_{0.05} = -1.711$
   (c) Draw a t-distribution that depicts the rejection region.
   (d) Will the researcher reject the null hypothesis? Why? Yes
   (e) Determine the P-value. 0.0180

(7d) No   (8a) $t = -2.222$

In Problems 9 and 10, test the hypothesis at the $\alpha = 0.05$ level of significance, using (a) the Classical Approach and (b) the P-value approach. Be sure to verify the requirements of the test.

9. $H_o: p = 0.6$ versus $H_1: p > 0.6$
   $n = 250$; $x = 165$; $\alpha = 0.05$

10. $H_o: p = 0.35$ versus $H_1: p \neq 0.35$
    $n = 420$; $x = 138$; $\alpha = 0.01$

---

11. In order to test $H_o: \sigma = 5.2$ versus $H_1: \sigma \neq 5.2$, a simple random sample of size $n = 18$ is obtained from a population that is known to be normally distributed.
    (a) If the sample standard deviation is determined to be $s = 4.9$, compute the test statistic. $\chi^2 = 15.095$
    (b) If the researcher decides to test this hypothesis at the $\alpha = 0.05$ level of significance, determine the critical values. $\chi^2_{0.975} = 7.564$; $\chi^2_{0.025} = 30.191$
    (c) Draw a chi-square distribution that depicts the rejection region.
    (d) Will the researcher reject the null hypothesis? Why? No

12. In order to test $H_o: \sigma = 15.7$ versus $H_1: \sigma > 15.7$, a simple random sample of size $n = 25$ is obtained from a population that is known to be normally distributed.
    (a) If the sample standard deviation is determined to be $s = 16.5$, compute the test statistic. $\chi^2 = 26.508$
    (b) If the researcher decides to test this hypothesis at the $\alpha = 0.1$ level of significance, determine the critical value. $\chi^2_{0.1} = 33.196$
    (c) Draw a chi-square distribution that depicts the rejection region.
    (d) Will the researcher reject the null hypothesis? Why? No

13. **Hotel/Motel Costs** According to the American Hotel and Motel Association, the average price of a room was $78.62 per night in 1998. A lodging analyst believes that this value has changed from its 1998 level. He conducts a

simple random sample of 50 hotels and motels and determines the mean price to be $80.04 and the standard deviation to be $10.83. Test the analyst's claim at the $\alpha = 0.05$ level of significance. Do not reject H_o

14. **Net Worth** A household's net worth is defined as all household assets minus any debt. The mean household net worth where the head of household has a high school diploma was $157.8 thousand in 1998, according to the Federal Reserve Bulletin. A government economist claims that the mean household net worth where the head of household has a high school diploma is higher today. She obtains a simple random sample of 100 households and determines the mean net worth to be $165.2 thousand, with a standard deviation of $43.1 thousand (both in 1998 dollars). Test the analyst's claim at the $\alpha = 0.05$ level of signficance. Reject H_o

15. **SAT Math Scores** A mathematics instructor wanted to know whether use of a calculator improves SAT math scores. In 2000, the SAT math scores of students who used a calculator once or twice weekly were normally distributed, with a mean of 474 and a standard deviation 103. In a random sample of 50 students who use a calculator every day, the mean score was 539. Is there significant evidence to support the claim that students who use a calculator "frequently" score better on the SAT math portion than those who use a calculator "infrequently"? Test at the $\alpha = 0.01$ level of significance. Reject H_o

16. Birth Weight An obstetrician wants to determine whether a new diet significantly increases the birth weight of babies. In 1998, birth weights of full-term babies (gestation period of 37–41 weeks) were normally distributed, with mean 7.53 pounds and standard deviation 1.15 pounds, according to the National Vital Statistics Report, Vol. 48, No. 3. The obstetrician randomly selects 50 recently pregnant mothers and persuades them to partake of this new diet. The obstetrician then records the birth weights of the babies and obtains a mean of 7.79 pounds. Is there significant evidence to support the claim that the new diet increases the birth weights of newborns at the $\alpha = 0.01$ level of significance? Do not reject H_o

17. High Cholesterol A nutritionist maintains that 20–39-year-old males consume too much cholesterol. The USDA-recommended daily allowance of cholesterol is 300 mg. In a survey conducted by the U.S. Department of Agriculture of 404 20–39-year-old males, it was determined the mean daily cholesterol intake was 326 milligrams, with standard deviation 342 milligrams.

(a) Is there evidence to support the nutritionist's claim at the $\alpha = 0.05$ level of significance? No
(b) What would it mean for the nutritionist to make a Type I error? A Type II error?
(c) What is the probability the nutritionist will make a Type I error? 0.05

18. Sodium A nutritionist claims that 20–39-year-old females consume too much sodium. The USDA-recommended daily allowance of sodium is 2400 mg. In a survey conducted by the U.S. Department of Agriculture of 257 20–39-year-old females, it was determined the mean daily sodium intake was 2919 milligrams and the standard deviation was 906 milligrams.

(a) Is there evidence to support the nutritionist's claim at the $\alpha = 0.10$ level of significance? Yes
(b) What would it mean for the nutritionist to make a Type I error? A Type II error?
(c) What is the probability the nutritionist will make a Type I error? 0.1

19. Acid Rain In 1990, the mean pH level of the rain in Barnstable County, Massachussetts was 4.61. A biologist fears that the acidity of rain has increased (in other words that the pH level of the rain has decreased). She draws a random sample of 25 rain dates in 2000 and obtains the following data:

4.80	4.27	4.09	4.55	5.08	4.34	4.08
4.36	4.82	4.70	4.40	4.73	4.62	4.48
4.28	4.28	4.48	4.72	4.12	4.00	4.93
4.91	4.32	4.63	4.03			

Source: National Atmospheric Deposition Program

(a) Because the sample size is small, she must verify pH level is normally distributed and the sample does not contain any outliers. The normal probability plot and boxplot are shown below. Are the conditions for testing the hypothesis satisfied? Yes

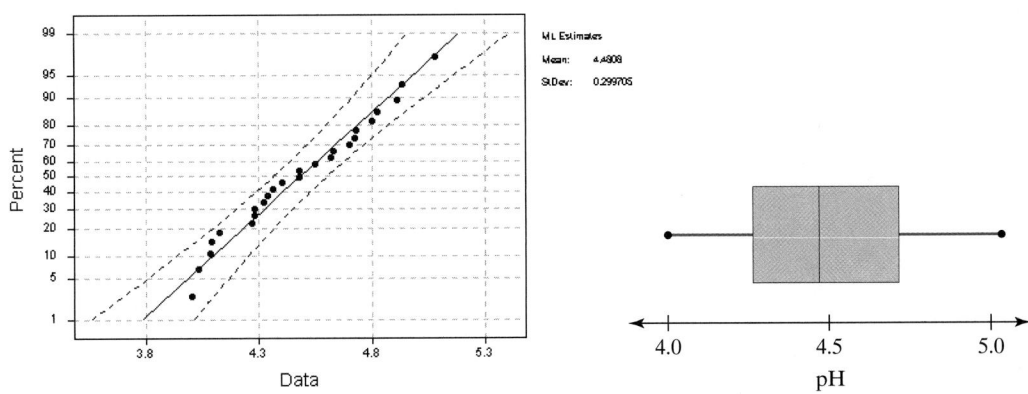

(b) Test the claim, assuming $\sigma = 0.26$, at the $\alpha = 0.01$ level of significance. Reject H_o
(c) Compute and interpret the P-value. 0.0065

20. **Hemoglobin** A medical researcher maintains that the mean hemoglobin reading of surgical patients is different from 14.0 grams per deciliter. She randomly selects nine surgical patients and obtains the following data:

14.6	12.8	8.9	9.0	9.9
10.7	13.0	12.0	13.0	

Source: Lora McGuire, Nursing Instructor, Joliet Junior College

(a) Because the sample size is small, she must verify that hemoglobin is normally distributed and the sample does not contain any outliers. The normal probability plot and boxplot are shown below. Are the conditions for testing the hypothesis satisfied? Yes

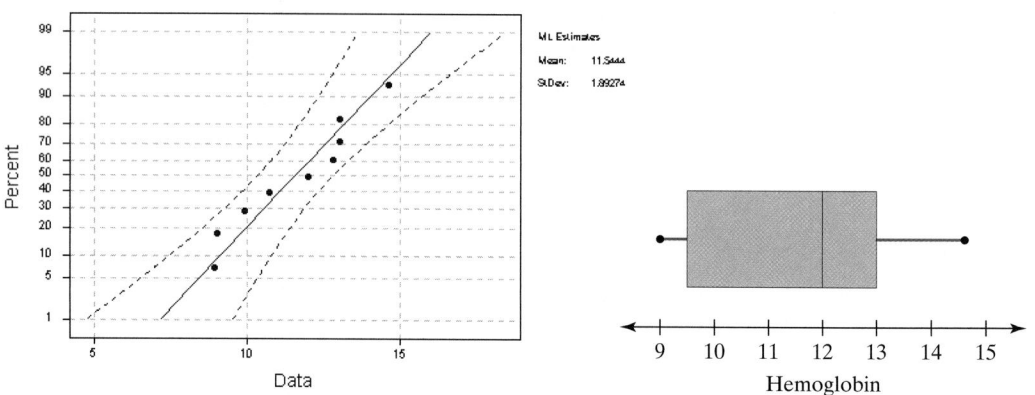

(b) Test the claim, assuming that $\sigma = 2.001$ at the $\alpha = 0.01$ level of significance. Reject H_o

(c) Compute and interpret the P-value. 0.0002

---

21. **Tuberculosis** According to the Center for Disease Control, 56% of all tuberculosis cases in 1999 were of foreign-born residents of the United States. A researcher believes that this proportion has increased from its 1999 level. She obtains a simple random sample of 300 tuberculosis cases in the United States and determines that 170 of them are foreign-born. Is there sufficient evidence to support the claim that the percentage of cases of tuberculosis of foreign-born residents has increased at the $\alpha = 0.01$ level of significance? No, do not reject H_o

22. **Phone Purchases** In 1997, 39.4% of females ordered merchandise or services by phone in the last 12 months. A market research analyst feels that the percentage of females ordering merchandise or services by phone has declined from the 1997 level, because of Internet purchases. She obtains a random sample of 500 females and determines that 191 of them have ordered merchandise or services by phone in the last 12 months. Test the researcher's claim that the percentage of females ordering merchandise or services by phone has decreased from its 1997 proportion at the $\alpha = 0.10$ level of significance. Do not reject H_o

23. **SAT Math Scores** A researcher believes there is more variability in SAT math scores for students living in low-income households than for students living in high-income households. According to the College Board, SAT math scores of students living in households with a household income above $50,000 per year are normally distributed, with a standard deviation of 104. In a random sample of 23 students who live in households with an income below $30,000 per year, it was determined their SAT math scores had a standard deviation of 112. Test the researcher's claim that students in low-income households have a higher standard deviation on their SATs than do students in high-income households, at the $\alpha = 0.10$ level of significance. *Do not reject H_o*

24. **Birth Weights** An obstetrician maintains that preterm babies (gestation period less than 37 weeks) have a higher variability in birth weight than do full-term babies (gestation period 37–41 weeks). According to the *National Vital Statistics Report*, Vol. 48, No. 3, the birth weights of full-term babies are normally distributed, with standard deviation 505.6 grams. A random sample of 41 preterm babies results in a standard deviation equal to 840 grams. Test the researcher's claim that the variability in the birth weight of preterm babies is more than the variability in birth weight of full term babies, at the $\alpha = 0.01$ level of significance. *Reject H_o*

25. **SAT Math Scores** Refer to Problem 15. Suppose the true mean SAT math score of students who use a calculator every day is 510.
    (a) What is the probability of a Type II error? *0.4438*
    (b) What is the power of the test? *0.5562*

26. **Birth Weight** Refer to Problem 16. Suppose the true mean weight of babies whose mothers partake of the new diet is 7.59 pounds.
    (a) What is the probability of a Type II error? *0.9754*
    (b) What is the power of the test? *0.0246*

27. **Prestigious Occupation** In 1997, 49% of Americans believed that being a teacher was a prestigious occupation. A researcher wanted to know whether this percentage had risen since then. She surveys 40 randomly selected Americans and finds that 22 of them felt that being a teacher was a prestigious occupation. Is this evidence to support the claim that the proportion of Americans who believe that being a teacher is a prestigious occupation has increased at the $\alpha = 0.05$ level of significance? *No*

28. **Leisure Activities** In 1999, 27% of Americans stated that reading was their favorite leisure-time activity. A researcher wants to know whether this percentage has declined since then. He surveys 35 Americans and finds that 4 of them consider reading to be their favorite leisure-time activity. Is this evidence to support the claim that the proportion of Americans who consider reading to be their favorite leisure-time activity has decreased at the $\alpha = 0.05$ level of significance? *Yes*

29. In your own words, explain the procedure for testing a hypothesis about a population mean when assuming the population standard deviation is known.

Approximately eight miles north of Salisbury, Wiltshire, England, stands a large circular stone monument surrounded by an earthwork. This prehistoric structure is known throughout the world as Stonehenge. Its name is derived from the old English word *hengen*, referring to something hung up. In the case of the monument, this name refers to the large horizontal lintel stones. The monument consists of an outer ring of Sarsen stones, surrounding two inner circles of bluestones. The first and third circles are adorned with the familiar stone lintels. The Sarsen stones show signs of having been carefully shaped, suggesting a Mycenaean Greece and Minoan Crete influence. The entire structure is surrounded by a ditch and bank. Just inside the bank are 56 pits, named the Aubrey Holes, after their discoverer. These holes appear to have been filled shortly after their excavation.

Stonehenge is a mysterious, magnificent monument, which popularly has been associated with the Druids. However, there is no direct evidence supporting this connection. Recently, it has been discovered that a number of the stone alignments are associated with important solar and lunar risings and settings, suggesting that the site served as some sort of massive astronomical calendar. If this conclusion is accurate, then it seems likely that the monument might have been used as a temple for sky worshipers, although the exact nature of their religion is unknown.

Corinn Dillion is interested in dating the construction of the structure. Excavations at the site uncovered a number of unshed antlers, antler tines, and animal bones. Carbon-14 dating methods were used to estimate the ages of the Stonehenge artifacts. Carbon-14 is one of three carbon isotopes found in the Earth's atmosphere. Carbon-12 makes up 99% of all the carbon dioxide in the air. Virtually all of the remaining one percent is composed of Carbon-13. By far, the rarest form of carbon isotope found in the atmosphere is Carbon-14. The ratio of Carbon-14 to Carbon-12 remains constant in living organisms. However, once the organism dies, the amount of Carbon-14 in the remains of the organism begins to decline, because it is radioactive, with half-life 5730 years (the "Cambridge half-life"). So, the decay of Carbon-14 into ordinary nitrogen makes possible a reliable estimate about the time of death of the organism. The counted Carbon-14 decay events are known to be normally distributed.

Dillion's team used two different Carbon-14 dating methods to arrive at age estimates for the numerous Stonehenge artifacts. The Liquid Scintillation Counting (LSC) method utilizes benzene, acetylene, ethanol, methanol, or a similar chemical. Unlike the LSC method, the Accelerator Mass Spectrometry (AMS) technique offers direct Carbon-14 isotope counting. The AMS method's greatest advantage is that it requires only milligram-sized samples for testing. The AMS method was used only on recovered artifacts that were of extremely small size.

Stonehenge's main ditch was dug in a series of segments. Excavations at the base of the ditch uncovered a number of antlers, which bore signs of heavy use. These antlers could have been used by the builders as picks or rakes. The fact that no primary silt was discovered beneath the antlers suggests that they were buried in the ditch shortly after its completion. Another researcher, Phillip Corbin, using an archaeological markings approach, had previously claimed that the mean date for the construction of the ditch was 2950 B.C. A sample of nine age estimates from unshed antlers excavated from the ditch produced a mean of 3033.1 B.C., with standard deviation 66.9 years. Assume that the ages are normally distributed with no obvious outliers. At an $\alpha = 0.05$ significance level, is there any reason to dispute Corbin's claim?

Four animal bone samples were discovered in the ditch terminals. These bones bore signs of attempts at artificial preservation and might have been in use for a substantial period of time prior to their being placed at Stonehenge. When dated, these bones had mean age 3187.5 B.C. and standard deviation 67.4 years. Assume that the ages are normally distributed with no obvious outliers. Use an $\alpha = 0.05$ significance level to test the claim that the population mean age of the site is different from 2950 B.C.

In the center of the monument are two concentric circles of igneous rock pillars, called bluestones. The construction of these circles was never completed. These circles are known as the Bluestone Circle and the Bluestone Horseshoe. The stones in these two formations were transported to the site from the Prescelly Mountains in Pembrokeshire, southwest Wales. Excavation at the center of the monument revealed an antler, an antler tine, and an animal bone. Each of these artifacts was submitted for dating. It was determined that this sample of three artifacts had mean age 2193.3 B.C, with a standard deviation of 104.1 years. Assume that the ages are normally distributed with no obvious outliers. Use an $\alpha = 0.05$ significance level to test the claim that the population mean age of the Bluestone formations is different from Corbin's declared mean age of the ditch, that is, 2950 B.C.

Finally, three additional antler samples were uncovered at the Y and Z holes. These holes are part of a formation of concentric circles 11 meters and 3.7 meters, respectively, outside of the Sarsen Circle. The sample mean age of these antlers is 1671.7 B.C. with a standard deviation of 99.7 years. Assume that the ages are normally distributed with no obvious outliers. Use an $\alpha = 0.05$ significance level to test whether the population mean age of the Y and Z holes is different from Corbin's stated mean age of the ditch—that is, 2950 B.C.

From your analysis, does it appear that the mean ages of the artifacts for the ditch, the ditch terminals, the Bluestones, and the Y and Z holes dated by Dillion are consistent with Corbin's claimed mean age of 2950 B.C. for the construction of the ditch? Can you use the results from your hypothesis tests to infer the likely construction order of the various Stonehenge structures? Explain.

Using Dillion's data, construct a 95% confidence interval for the population mean ages of the various sites. Do these confidence intervals support Corbin's claim? Can you use these confidence intervals to infer the likely construction order of the various Stonehenge structures? Explain.

Which statistical technique, hypothesis testing or confidence intervals, is more useful in assessing the age and likely construction order of the Stonehenge structures? Explain.

Discuss the limitations and assumptions of your analysis. Is there any additional information that you would like to have before publishing your findings? Would another statistical procedure be more useful in analyzing these data? If so, which one? Explain. Write a report to Corinn Dillion detailing your analysis.

Source: This fictional account is based upon information obtained from *Archaeometry and Stonehenge* (http://www.eng_h.gov.uk/stoneh). The means and standard deviations used throughout this case study were constructed by calculating the statistics from the midpoint of the calibrated date range supplied for each artifact.

Many of the consumer products that we purchase have labels that describe the net weight of the contents. For example, the net weight of a candy bar might be listed as 4 ounces. Choose any consumer product that reports the net weight of the contents on the packaging.

(a) Obtain a random sample of size 8 or more of the consumer product. We will treat the random purchases as a simple random sample. Weigh the contents.

(b) If your sample size is less than 30, verify that the population from which the sampling was drawn is normal and that the sample does not contain any outliers.

(c) As the consumer, you are concerned only with situations in which you are getting "ripped off." Determine the null and alternative hypotheses from the point of view of the consumer.

(d) Test the claim that the consumer is getting "ripped off" at the $\alpha = 0.05$ level of significance. Are you getting "ripped off"? What makes you say so?

(e) Suppose you are the quality-control manager. How would you structure the alternative hypothesis? Test this claim at the $\alpha = 0.05$ level of significance. Is there anything wrong with the manufacturing process? What makes you say so?

DECISIONS

Consumer Reports®
Eyeglass Lenses

Eyeglasses are part medical device and part fashion statement, a marriage that has always made them a tough buy. Aside from the thousands of different frames the consumer has to choose from, there are various lens materials and coatings that can add to the durability, and the cost, of a pair of eyeglasses. One manufacturer even goes so far as to claim that its lenses are "the most scratch-resistant plastic lenses ever made." With a claim like that, we had to test the lenses (June 2001).

One test involved tumbling the lenses in a drum containing scrub pads of grit of varying size and hardness. Afterward, readings of the lenses' haze were taken on a spectrometer to determine how scratched they had become. To evaluate their scratch resistance, we measured the difference between the haze reading before and after tumbling.

The graphic illustrates the difference between an uncoated lens (on the left) and the manufacturer's "scratch-resistant" lens (on the right).

The following table contains the haze measurements both before and after the scratch resistance test for this manufacturer. Haze difference is measured by subtracting the before score from the after score; in other words haze difference is computed as "After"−"Before".

(a) Suppose it is known that the closest competitor to the manufacturer's lens has a mean haze difference of 1.0. Do the data support the manufacturer's scratch resistance claim?

(b) Write the null and alternative hypotheses, letting μ_{hdiff} represent the mean haze difference for the manufacturer's lens.

(c) We used Minitab (release 13.1) to perform a one-sample t-test. The results are shown below.

Using the Minitab output, answer the following questions:

1. What is the value of the test statistic?

2. What is the P-value of the test?

3. What is the conclusion of this test? Write a paragraph for the readers of Consumer Reports magazine that explains your findings.

Note to Readers: In many cases, our test protocol and analytical methods are more complicated than described in these examples. The data and discussions have been modified to make the material more appropriate for the audience.

Before	After	Difference
0.18	0.72	0.54
0.16	0.85	0.69
0.20	0.71	0.51
0.17	0.42	0.25
0.21	0.76	0.55
0.21	0.51	0.30

One-Sample T: Difference

```
Test of mu = 1 vs mu < 1

Variable            N              Mean      StDev     SE Mean
Difference          6           0.4733     0.1665      0.0680

Variable        95.0%     Upper Bound         T           P
Difference                     0.6103     -7.75       0.000
```

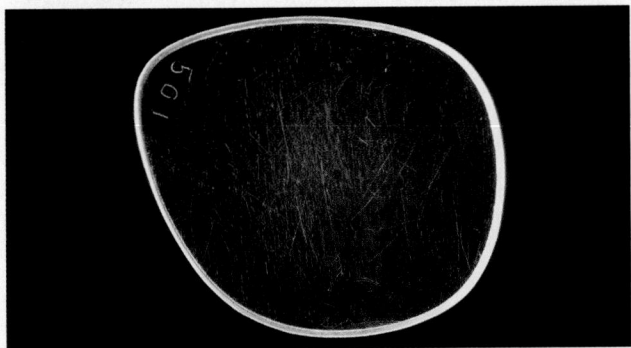

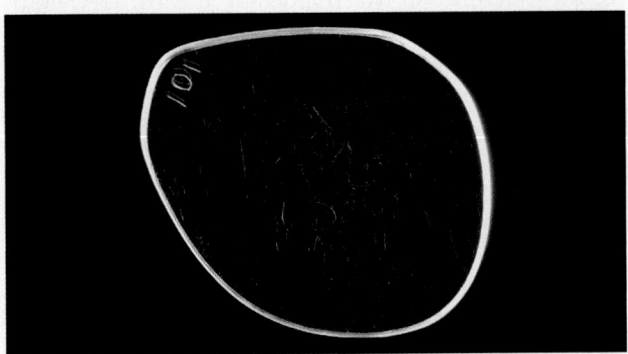

In Chapters 8 and 9 we discussed inferences regarding a single population parameter such as μ or p. The inferential methods presented in these chapters will be modified slightly in this chapter so that we can compare two population parameters.

The first two sections of this chapter deal with testing for the difference of two population means. The methods presented in this chapter can be used to determine whether a certain treatment results in significantly different sample statistics. From a design-of-experiments point of view, the methods presented in Section 10.1 are used to handle matched-pairs designs (Section 1.5, page 40) with a quantitative-response variable. For example, we might want to know whether married couples have similar IQs. To test this theory, we could randomly select 20 married couples and determine the difference in their IQs.

Section 10.2 presents inferential methods used to handle completely randomized designs when there is

a single treatment that has two levels (Section 1.5, pages 36–37) and the response variable is quantitative. For example, we might randomly divide 100 volunteers that have a common cold into two groups–a control group and an experimental group. The control group would receive a placebo and the experimental group would receive a predetermined amount of some experimental drug. The response variable might be the time until the cold symptoms go away.

Section 10.3 discusses the difference between two population proportions. Again, we can use a completely randomized design to compare two population proportions. However, rather than having a quantitative response variable, we would have a binomial response variable. That is, either the experimental unit has a characteristic or it does not.

Finally, Section 10.4 presents a discussion for comparing two population standard deviations.

Inferences on Two Samples

Outline

For additional study help, go to
www.prenhall.com/sullivanstats

Materials include

• Self-Graded Quizzes

• "Preparing for This Section" Quizzes

• STATLETs

• PowerPoint Downloads

• Step-by-Step Technology Guide

• Graphing Calculator Help

10.1 Inference about Two Means: Dependent Samples

Preparing for This Section Before getting started, review the following:

- ✓ Matched-pairs design (Section 1.5, pp. 40–41)
- ✓ Confidence intervals about μ, σ unknown (Section 8.2, pp. 475–481)
- ✓ Hypothesis tests about μ, σ unknown (Section 9.3, pp. 546–551)
- ✓ Type I and Type II errors (Section 9.1, pp. 522–523)

Objectives   Distinguish between independent and dependent sampling

 Test claims made regarding matched-pairs data

 Construct confidence intervals about the population mean difference of matched-pairs data

 Independent versus Dependent Sampling

In order to perform inference on the difference of two population means, we must first determine whether the data come from an independent or dependent sample. A sampling method is **independent** when the individuals selected for one sample do not dictate which individuals are to be in a second sample. A sampling method is **dependent** when the individuals selected to be in one sample are used to determine the individuals to be in the second sample. For example, if we are conducting a study that compares the IQs of husbands and wives, then once a husband is selected to be in the study, his wife is automatically matched with him. Dependent samples are often referred to as **matched-pairs** samples.

> **In Your Own Words**
>
> If the individuals in two samples are somehow related (husband–wife, siblings, similar characteristics, or even the same person), then the sampling is dependent.

▶ **EXAMPLE 1** **Distinguishing between Independent and Dependent Sampling**

Problem: For each of the following experiments, determine whether the sampling method is independent or dependent.

(a) Researcher Steven J. Sperber, MD, and his associates wanted to determine the effectiveness of a new medication* in the treatment of discomfort associated with the common cold. They randomly divided 430 subjects into two groups: Group 1 received the new medication and Group 2 received a placebo. The goal of the study was to determine whether the mean symptom assessment scores of the individuals receiving the treatment (Group 1) was less than that of the control group (Group 2).

(b) In an experiment conducted in a biology class, Professor Andy Neill measured the time required for students to catch a falling meter stick using their dominant hand and nondominant hand for 21 students. The goal of the study was to determine whether the reaction time in an individual's dominant hand is different from the reaction time in the nondominant hand.

---

*The medication was a combination of pseudoephedrine and acetaminophen. The study is published in the *Archives of Family Medicine* 9(2000): 979–985.

Approach: We must determine whether the individuals in one group were used to determine the individuals that were in the other group. If so, the sampling method is dependent; if not, the sampling method is independent.

Solution:

(a) The sampling method is independent because the individuals in the treatment group were not used to determine which individuals are in the control group.

(b) The sampling method is dependent because the individuals are related. The measurements for the dominant and nondominant hand are on the same individual. ◄◄

NW *Now Work Problem 1.*

In this section, we will discuss inference on the difference of two means for dependent sampling. Section 10.2 addresses inference when the sampling is independent.

② Hypothesis Tests

The approach to analyzing matched-pairs data is very similar to that presented in constructing a confidence interval or testing a claim regarding a population mean with the population standard deviation unknown. Recall that if the population from which the sample was drawn is normally distributed or the sample size is large ($n \geq 30$), we said that

$$t = \frac{\bar{x} - \mu}{s / \sqrt{n}}$$

In Your Own Words

Statistical inference methods on matched-pairs data use the same methods as inference on a single population mean with σ unknown, except that the "differences" are analyzed.

follows Student's *t*-distribution with $n - 1$ degrees of freedom.

When analyzing matched-pairs data, we compute the difference in each matched pair and then perform inference on the differenced data using the methods of Section 8.2 or 9.3.

> **Testing a Claim Regarding the Difference of Two Means Using a Matched-Pairs Design**
>
> If a claim is made regarding the mean difference of matched-pairs data, we can use the following steps to test the claim, provided that
> **1.** the sample is obtained using simple random sampling;
> **2.** the sample data are matched-pairs;
> **3.** the differences are normally distributed or the sample size, n, is large ($n \geq 30$).
>
> **Step 1:** A claim is made regarding the mean difference from matched-pairs data. The claim is used to determine the null and alternative hypotheses. The hypotheses can be structured in one of three ways, where μ_d is the claimed mean difference of the matched-pairs data.

Note to Instructor
Ask students to explain the differences in the meaning of the following symbols:

$\mu,\ \mu_{\bar{x}},\ \mu_o,\ \mu_d$

Two-Tailed	Left-Tailed	Right-Tailed
$H_0: \mu_d = 0$	$H_0: \mu_d = 0$	$H_0: \mu_d = 0$
$H_1: \mu_d \neq 0$	$H_1: \mu_d < 0$	$H_1: \mu_d > 0$

Step 2: Choose a level of significance α based upon the seriousness of making a Type I error and determine the critical value with $n - 1$ degrees of freedom.

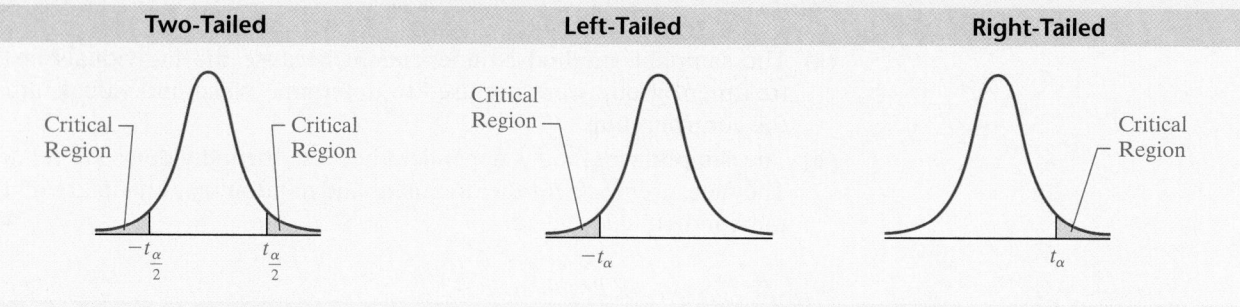

| Two-Tailed | Left-Tailed | Right-Tailed |

Step 3: Compute the **test statistic** $t = \dfrac{\overline{d} - 0}{s_d \big/ \sqrt{n}} = \dfrac{\overline{d}}{s_d \big/ \sqrt{n}}$ which

approximately follows Student's t-distribution with $n - 1$ degrees of freedom. The values of $\overline{d}$ and s_d are the mean and standard deviation of the differenced data.

Step 4: Compare the critical value with the test statistic, using the guidelines shown below.

Two-Tailed	Left-Tailed	Right-Tailed
If $t < -t_{\alpha/2}$ or $t > t_{\alpha/2}$, reject the null hypothesis	If $t < -t_{\alpha}$, reject the null hypothesis	If $t > t_{\alpha}$, reject the null hypothesis

Step 5: State the conclusion.

The procedures just presented require either that the differenced data be normally distributed or that the sample size be large. The procedure is **robust**, which means that minor departures from normality will not adversely affect the results of the test. If the data have outliers, however, the procedure should not be used. We will verify the assumption that the data come from a population that is normally distributed by constructing normal probability plots. We use boxplots to determine whether there are outliers. If the normal probability plot indicates that the differenced data are not normally distributed or the boxplot reveals outliers, nonparametric tests should be performed as discussed in Chapter 13, Section 4.

▶ **EXAMPLE 2** **Testing a Claim Regarding Matched-Pairs Data**

Problem: Professor Andy Neill measured the time (in seconds) required to catch a falling meter stick for 12 randomly selected students' dominant hand and nondominant hand. Professor Neill claims that the reaction time in an individual's dominant hand is less than the reaction time in their nondominant hand. Test the claim at the $\alpha = 0.05$ level of significance. The data obtained are presented in Table 1.

TABLE 1		
Student	Dominant Hand, X_1	Nondominant Hand, X_2
1	0.177	0.179
2	0.210	0.202
3	0.186	0.208
4	0.189	0.184
5	0.198	0.215
6	0.194	0.193
7	0.160	0.194
8	0.163	0.160
9	0.166	0.209
10	0.152	0.164
11	0.190	0.210
12	0.172	0.197

Source: Professor Andy Neill, Joliet Junior College

Note to Instructor
Remind students of some of the key phrases in the claim that help them to determine whether the test is right tailed, left tailed, or two tailed. Examples include "less than," "more than," "no different."

Approach: This is a matched-pairs sample because the variable is measured on the same subject for both the dominant and nondominant hand. We compute the difference between the dominant time and the nondominant time, $X_1 - X_2$, for each student. If the reaction time in the dominant hand is less than the reaction time in the nondominant hand, we would expect the values of $X_1 - X_2$ to be negative. Before we perform the hypothesis test, we must verify that the differenced data is approximately normally distributed with no outliers because the sample size is small. We will construct a normal probability plot and boxplot of the differenced data to verify these requirements. We then proceed to follow Steps 1–5.

Note to Instructor
Emphasize the importance of constructing a table such as Table 2. Not only does it help organize the information, but also it can be used to help students "see" the direction of the alternative hypothesis.

Solution: We compute the differences as $d_i = X_1 - X_2 =$ time of dominant hand for ith student minus time of nondominant hand for ith student. We expect these differences to be negative, so we wish to test the claim that $\mu_d < 0$. Table 2 displays the differences.

TABLE 2			
Student	Dominant Hand, X_1	Nondominant Hand, X_2	Difference, d_i
1	0.177	0.179	$0.177 - 0.179 = -0.002$
2	0.210	0.202	$0.210 - 0.202 = 0.008$
3	0.186	0.208	-0.022
4	0.189	0.184	0.005
5	0.198	0.215	-0.017
6	0.194	0.193	0.001
7	0.160	0.194	-0.034
8	0.163	0.160	0.003
9	0.166	0.209	-0.043
10	0.152	0.164	-0.012
11	0.190	0.210	-0.020
12	0.172	0.197	-0.025
			$\sum d_i = -0.158$

We compute the mean and standard deviation of the differences and obtain $\bar{d} = -0.0132$ rounded to four decimal places and $s_d = 0.0164$ rounded to four decimal places. Before we proceed with the test of the hypothesis, we must verify that the data are approximately normal with no outliers. Figure 1 shows the normal probability plot and boxplot of the differenced data.

Figure 1

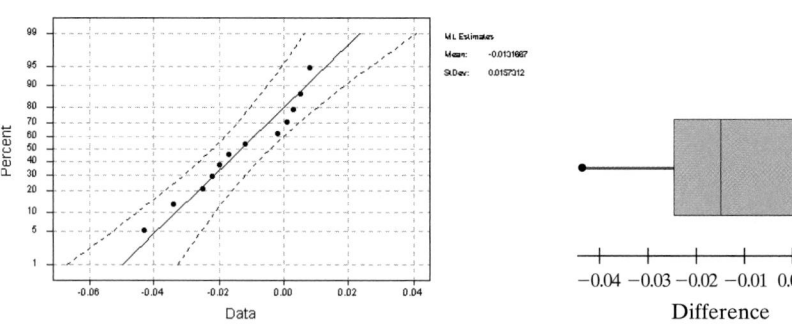

Normal Probability Plot for Difference

> **Caution**
>
> The way that we define the difference determines the direction of the alternative hypothesis in one-tailed tests. In Example 1, we expect $X_1 < X_2$, so the difference $X_1 - X_2$ is expected to be negative. Therefore, the alternative hypothesis is $H_1: \mu_d < 0$, and we have a left-tailed test. However, if we computed the differences as $X_2 - X_1$, then we'd expect the differences to be positive, and we'd have a right-tailed test!

The normal probability plot is roughly linear and the boxplot does not indicate any outliers. We can proceed with the hypothesis test.

Step 1: Professor Neill claims that the reaction time in the dominant hand is less than the reaction time in the nondominant hand. We express this claim as $\mu_d < 0$. We have

$$H_o: \mu_d = 0 \qquad \text{versus} \qquad H_1: \mu_d < 0$$

This test is left tailed.

Step 2: Because the professor is performing a left-tailed test, we determine the critical t-value at the $\alpha = 0.05$ level of significance with $n - 1 = 12 - 1 = 11$ degrees of freedom to be $-t_{0.05} = -1.796$. The critical region is displayed in Figure 2.

Step 3: The sample mean difference, $\bar{d}$, is -0.0132 second, and the sample standard deviation, s_d, is 0.0164 second. Because the data are approximately normally distributed, the test statistic is

Figure 2

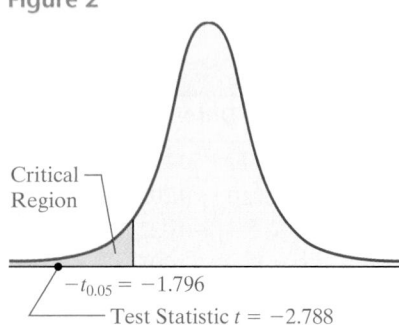

Critical Region

$-t_{0.05} = -1.796$

Test Statistic $t = -2.788$

$$t = \frac{\bar{d} - 0}{s_d / \sqrt{n}} = \frac{-0.0132 - 0}{0.0164 / \sqrt{12}} = -2.788$$

The sample mean difference of -0.0132 second is 2.788 sample standard deviations below the assumed mean difference of 0 seconds.

Step 4: Because the test statistic $t = -2.788$ is less than the critical value $-t_{0.05} = -1.796$, Professor Neill rejects the null hypothesis. We label the test statistic in Figure 2.

Step 5: There is sufficient evidence at the $\alpha = 0.05$ level of significance to support Professor Neill's claim that the reaction time in the dominant hand is less than the reaction time in the nondominant hand. ◄◄

Using Technology: We can test Professor Neill's claim using statistical software or a graphing calculator with advanced statistical features. For example, using Minitab we obtain the results displayed in Figure 3.

Figure 3

Paired T-Test and Confidence Interval

```
Paired T for Dominant - Non-dominant

                 N        Mean       StDev     SE Mean
Dominant        12      0.17975     0.01752    0.00506
Non-domi        12      0.19292     0.01799    0.00519
Difference      12     -0.01317     0.01643    0.00474

95% CI for mean difference: (-0.02361, -0.00273)
T-Test of mean difference = 0 (vs < 0): T-Value = -2.78 P-Value = 0.009
```

Notice the P-value is 0.009. We interpret this by saying that there is a 0.009 probability of obtaining a sample mean difference of -0.01317 or less from a population whose mean difference is 0. At the $\alpha = 0.05$ level of significance there is sufficient evidence to reject the null hypothesis because the P-value is less than α. We conclude that an individual's dominant hand has a faster reaction time than the nondominant hand.

NW *Now Work Problem 11(a).*

③ Confidence Intervals

We can also create a confidence interval for the mean difference, μ_d, using the sample mean difference, $\overline{d}$, the sample standard deviation difference, s_d, the sample size, and $t_{\alpha/2}$. Remember, the format for a confidence interval about a population mean is of the following form:

$$\text{Point estimate} \pm \text{Margin of error}$$

Based on the preceding formula we compute the confidence interval about μ_d as follows:

Confidence Interval for Matched-Pairs Data

A $(1 - \alpha) \cdot 100\%$ confidence interval for μ_d is given by

$$\text{Lower Bound: } \overline{d} - t_{\alpha/2} \cdot \frac{s_d}{\sqrt{n}} \qquad \text{Upper Bound: } \overline{d} + t_{\alpha/2} \cdot \frac{s_d}{\sqrt{n}} \qquad \textbf{(1)}$$

The critical value $t_{\alpha/2}$ is determined using $n - 1$ degrees of freedom. The values of $\overline{d}$ and s_d are the mean and standard deviation of the differenced data.

Note: The interval is exact when the population is normally distributed and approximately correct for nonnormal populations, provided that n is large.

▶ **EXAMPLE 3** **Constructing a Confidence Interval for Matched-Pairs Data**

Problem: Using the data from Table 2, construct a 95% confidence interval estimate of the mean difference, μ_d.

Approach:

Step 1: Compute the differenced data. Because the sample size is small, we must verify that the differenced data are approximately normal with no outliers.

Step 2: Compute the sample mean difference, $\bar{d}$, and the sample standard deviation difference, s_d.

Step 3: Determine the critical value, $t_{\alpha/2}$, with $\alpha = 0.05$ and $n - 1$ degrees of freedom.

Step 4: Use Formula (1) to determine the lower and upper bounds.

Step 5: Interpret the results.

Solution:

Step 1: We computed the differenced data and verified that they are approximately normally distributed with no outliers in Example 2.

Step 2: We computed the sample mean difference, $\bar{d}$, to be -0.0132 and sample standard deviation of the difference, s_d, to be 0.0164 in Example 2.

Step 3: Using Table III with $\alpha = 0.05$ and $12 - 1 = 11$ degrees of freedom, we find $t_{\alpha/2} = t_{0.025} = 2.201$.

Step 4: Substituting into Formula (1), we find

$$\text{Lower Bound: } \bar{d} - t_{\alpha/2} \cdot \frac{s_d}{\sqrt{n}} = -0.0132 - 2.201 \cdot \frac{0.0164}{\sqrt{12}} = -0.0236$$

$$\text{Upper Bound: } \bar{d} + t_{\alpha/2} \cdot \frac{s_d}{\sqrt{n}} = -0.0132 + 2.201 \cdot \frac{0.0164}{\sqrt{12}} = -0.0028$$

Step 5: We are 95% confident that the mean difference between the dominant hand's reaction time and the nondominant hand's reaction time is between -0.0236 and -0.0028 seconds. In other words, we are 95% confident that the dominant hand has a mean reaction time that is somewhere between 0.0028 seconds and 0.0236 seconds faster than the nondominant hand. Notice that the confidence interval does not contain zero. This evidence supports the claim that the reaction time of a person's dominant hand is different from the reaction time of the nondominant hand. ◀◀

We can see that the results of Example 3 agree with the 95% confidence interval determined by Minitab in Figure 3.

NW *Now Work Problem 11(b).*

10.1 Assess Your Understanding

Concepts and Vocabulary

1. Explain the difference between independent and dependent sampling.
2. Suppose a researcher claims the mean from population 1 is less than the mean from population 2 in matched-pairs data. How would you define μ_d? How would you determine d_i?

3. What are the assumptions that must be satisfied in order to test a claim regarding the difference of two means with dependent sampling?

Exercises

• Skill Building

In Problems 1–6, determine whether the sampling is dependent or independent.

1. A sociologist wishes to compare the annual salaries of married couples. She obtains a random sample of 50 married couples in which both spouses work and determines each spouse's annual salary. Dependent

2. A researcher wishes to determine the effects of alcohol on people's reaction times to a stimulus. She randomly divides 100 people aged 21 or older into two groups. Group 1 (the treatment group) is asked to drink 3 ounces of alcohol while group 2 drinks a placebo. Both drinks taste the same, so the individuals in the study do not know which group they belong to. Thirty minutes after consuming the drink, the subjects in each group perform a series of tests meant to measure reaction time. Independent

3. An educator wants to determine whether a new curriculum significantly improves standardized test scores for third-grade students. She randomly divides 80 third-graders into two groups. Group 1 (the treatment group) is taught using the new curriculum, while group 2 (the control group) is taught using the traditional curriculum. At the end of the school year, both groups are given the standardized test with the mean scores compared. Independent

4. A psychologist wants to know whether subjects respond faster to a go/no go stimulus or a choice stimulus. With the go/no go stimulus, subjects must respond to a particular stimulus by pressing a button and disregard other stimuli. In the choice stimulus, the subjects respond differently depending on the stimulus. She randomly selects 20 subjects and each subject is presented a series of go/no go stimuli and choice stimuli. The mean reaction time to each stimulus is compared. Dependent

5. A study was conducted by researchers designed "to determine the genetic and nongenetic factors to structural brain abnormalities on schizophrenia." The researchers examined the brains of 29 twin patients diagnosed with schizophrenia and compared them with 29 healthy twins. The whole brain volumes of the two groups were compared. Independent

   Source: "Volumes of Brain Structures in Twins Discordant for Schizophrenia," William F.C. Baare, et al., *Archives of General Psychiatry* **58**: (2000) 33–40

6. An agricultural researcher wanted to determine whether there were any significant differences in the plowing method used on crop yield. He divided a parcel of land that had uniform soil quality into 30 subplots. He then randomly selected 15 of the plots to be chisele plowed and 15 plots to be fall plowed. He recorded the crop yield at the end of the growing season, to determine whether there was a significant difference in the mean crop yield. Independent

In Problems 7 and 8, assume that the paired data came from a population that is normally distributed.

7.

Observation	1	2	3	4	5	6	7
X_1	7.6	7.6	7.4	5.7	8.3	6.6	5.6
X_2	8.1	6.6	10.7	9.4	7.8	9.0	8.5

(a) Determine $d_i = X_1 - X_2$ for each pair of data.
(b) Compute $\bar{d}$ and s_d. $\bar{d} = -1.614$; $s_d = 1.915$
(c) Test the claim that $\mu_d < 0$ at the $\alpha = 0.05$ level of significance. Reject H_o
(d) $(-3.39, 0.16)$ (d) Compute a 95% confidence interval about the population mean difference $\mu_d = \mu_1 - \mu_2$.

8.

Observation	1	2	3	4	5	6	7	8
X_1	19.4	18.3	22.1	20.7	19.2	11.8	20.1	18.6
X_2	19.8	16.8	21.1	22.0	21.5	18.7	15.0	23.9

(a) Determine $d_i = X_1 - X_2$ for each pair of data.
(b) Compute $\bar{d}$ and s_d. $\bar{d} = -1.075$; $s_d = 3.833$
(c) Test the claim that $\mu_d \neq 0$ at the $\alpha = 0.01$ level of significance. Do not reject H_o
(d) Compute a 99% confidence interval about the population mean difference $\mu_d = \mu_1 - \mu_2$.
   $(-5.82, 3.67)$

• **Applying the Concepts**

9. **Muzzle Velocity** The following data represent the muzzle velocity (in feet per second) of rounds fired from a 155 mm gun. For each round, two measurements of the velocity were recorded using two different measuring devices, with the following data obtained:

Observation	1	2	3	4	5	6	7	8	9	10	11	12
A	793.8	793.1	792.4	794.0	791.4	792.4	791.7	792.3	789.6	794.4	790.9	793.5
B	793.2	793.3	792.6	793.8	791.6	791.6	791.6	792.4	788.5	794.7	791.3	793.5

Source: Christenson, Ronald and Blackwood, Larry, "Tests for Precision and Accuracy of Multiple Measuring Devices," *Technometrics*, Nov. 93, Vol 35, Issue 4, pp. 411–421.

(a) Why is this matched-pairs data?

(b) Test the claim that there is a difference in the measurement of the muzzle velocity between device A and device B at the $\alpha = 0.01$ level of significance. *Note:* A normal probability plot and boxplot of the data indicate that the differences are approximately normally distributed with no outliers. Do not reject H_o

(c) Construct a 99% confidence interval about the population mean difference. Interpret your results. $(-0.309, 0.542)$

(d) Draw a boxplot of the differenced data. Does this visual evidence support the results obtained in part (b)?

10. **The Effects of Exercise** A physical therapist wishes to determine whether an exercise program increases flexibility. He measures the flexibility (in inches) of 12 randomly selected subjects both before and after an intensive eight-week training program and obtains the following data:

Subject	1	2	3	4	5	6	7	8	9	10	11	12
Before	18.5	21.5	16.5	21	20	15	19.75	15.75	18	22	15	20.5
After	19.25	21.75	16.5	20.5	22.25	16	19.5	17	19.25	19.5	16.5	20

Source: Michael McCraith, Joliet Junior College

(a) Why is this matched-pairs data?

(b) Test the claim that the flexibility before the exercise program is less than the flexibility after the exercise program at the $\alpha = 0.02$ level of significance. *Note:* A normal probability plot and boxplot of the data indicate that the differences are approximately normally distributed with no outliers. Do not reject H_o

(c) Construct a 95% confidence interval about the population mean difference. Interpret your results. $(-0.419, 1.169)$

(d) Draw a boxplot of the differenced data. Does this visual evidence support the results obtained in part (b)?

11. **Reaction Time** In an experiment conducted on-line at the University of Mississippi, study participants are asked to react to a stimulus. In one experiment, the participant must press a key on seeing a blue screen. Reaction time (in seconds) to press the key is measured. The same person is then asked to press a key on seeing a red screen, again with reaction time measured. The results for six randomly sampled study participants are as follows:

Participant Number	1	2	3	4	5	6
Reaction Time to Blue	0.582	0.481	0.841	0.267	0.685	0.45
Reaction Time to Red	0.408	0.407	0.542	0.402	0.456	0.533

Source: PsychExperiments at the University of Mississippi

(a) Test the claim that the reaction time to the blue stimulus is different from the reaction time to the red stimulus at the $\alpha = 0.01$ level of significance. *Note*: A normal probability plot and boxplot of the data indicate that the differences are approximately normally distributed with no outliers. Do not reject H_o

(b) Construct a 98% confidence interval about the population mean difference. Interpret your results. $(-0.3316, 0.1456)$

(c) Draw a boxplot of the differenced data. Does this visual evidence support the results obtained in part (a)?

12. **Rat's Hemoglobin.** Hemoglobin helps the red blood cells transport oxygen and remove carbon dioxide. Researchers at NASA wanted to determine the effects of space flight on a rat's hemoglobin. The following data represent the hemoglobin (in grams per deciliter) at lift-off minus 3 days (H-L3) and immediately upon the return (H-R0) for 12 randomly selected rats sent to space on the Spacelab Sciences 1 flight.

Rat #	1	2	3	4	5	6	7	8	9	10	11	12
H-L3	15.2	16.1	15.3	16.4	15.7	14.7	14.3	14.5	15.2	16.1	15.1	15.8
H-R0	15.8	16.5	16.7	15.7	16.9	13.1	16.4	16.5	16.0	16.8	17.6	16.9

Source: NASA Life Sciences Data Archive

(a) Test the claim that the hemoglobin levels at lift-off minus 3 days are less than the hemoglobin levels upon return at the $\alpha = 0.05$ level of significance. *Note*: A normal probability plot and boxplot of the data indicate that the differences are approximately normally distributed with no outliers. Reject H_o

(b) Construct a 90% confidence interval about the population mean difference. Interpret your results. $(0.27, 1.48)$

(c) Draw a boxplot of the differenced data. Does this visual evidence support the results obtained in part (a)?

13. **Secchi Disk** A Secchi disk is an eight-inch diameter weighted disk that is painted black and white and attached to a rope. The disk is lowered into water and the depth (in inches) at which it is no longer visible is recorded. The measurement is an indication of water clarity. A environmental biologist is interested in determining whether the water clarity of the lake at Joliet Junior College is improving. She takes measurements at the same location on the same dates during the course of a year and repeats the measurements on the same dates five years later. She obtains the following results:

Observation	1	2	3	4	5	6	7	8
Date	5/11	6/7	6/24	7/8	7/27	8/31	9/30	10/12
Initial Depth	38	58	65	74	56	36	56	52
Depth 5 Years Later	52	60	72	72	54	48	58	60

Source: Virginia Piekarski, Joliet Junior College

(a) Test the claim that the clarity of the lake is improving at the $\alpha = 0.05$ level of significance. *Note*: A normal probability plot and boxplot of the data indicate that the differences are approximately normally distributed with no outliers. Reject H_o

(b) Construct a 95% confidence interval about the population mean difference. Interpret your results. $(0.04, 10.21)$

14. **The Effect of Aspirin on Blood Clotting** Blood clotting occurs due to a sequence of chemical reactions. The protein thrombin initiates blood clotting by working with another protein, prothrombin. It is common to measure an individual's blood clotting time through prothrombin time—the time between the start of the thrombin–prothrombin reaction and the formation of the clot. Researchers wanted to study the effect of aspirin on prothrombin time. They randomly selected 12 subjects and measured the prothrombin time (in seconds), first without taking aspirin and again three hours after taking two aspirin tablets. They obtained the following data:

Subject	1	2	3	4	5	6	7	8	9	10	11	12
With Aspirin	12.3	12.0	12.0	13.0	13.0	12.5	11.3	11.8	11.5	11.0	11.0	11.3
Without Aspirin	12.0	12.3	12.5	12.0	13.0	12.5	10.3	11.3	11.5	11.5	11.0	11.5

Source: Yochem, Donald and Roach, Darrell. "Aspirin: Effect of Thrombus Formation Time and Prothrombin Time of Human Subjects." *Angiology,* **22** (1971), pp. 70–76.

(a) Test the claim that aspirin affects the time it takes for a clot to form at the $\alpha = 0.05$ level of significance. *Note:* A normal probability plot and boxplot of the data indicate that the differences are approximately normally distributed with no outliers. *Do not reject* H_o

(b) Construct a 90% confidence interval about the population mean difference. Interpret your results. $(-0.37, 0.16)$

15. **Car Repairs** The Insurance Institute for Highway Safety regularly tests cars for various safety factors. In one such test, the institute tests the bumpers in 5-mph crashes. The following data represent the cost of repair (in dollars) after four different 5-mph crashes on a 2000 Dodge Neon and a 2000 Honda Civic:

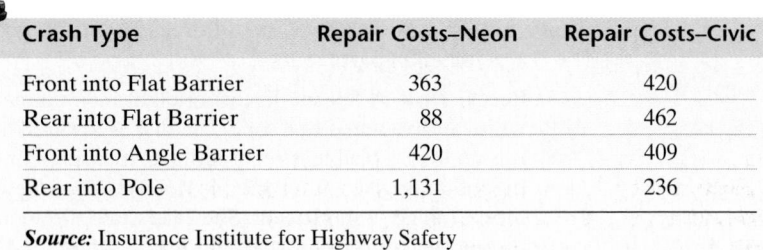

Crash Type	Repair Costs–Neon	Repair Costs–Civic
Front into Flat Barrier	363	420
Rear into Flat Barrier	88	462
Front into Angle Barrier	420	409
Rear into Pole	1,131	236

Source: Insurance Institute for Highway Safety

(a) Test the claim that the repair costs differ at the $\alpha = 0.05$ level of significance. *Note:* A normal probability plot and boxplot of the data indicate that the differences are approximately normally distributed with no outliers. *Do not reject* H_o

(b) Construct a 90% confidence interval about the population mean difference. Interpret your results. $(-759, 521)$

16. **Improving SAT Math Scores** A test preparation company claims that its SAT preparation course improves SAT math scores. The company administers the SAT to 12 randomly selected students and determines their scores. The same students then participate in the course. Upon completion, they retake the SAT. The results are presented in the following table:

Before	436	431	270	463	528	377	397	413	525	323	413	292
After	443	429	287	501	522	380	402	450	548	349	403	303

(a) Test the claim that the preparatory course improves SAT math scores at the $\alpha = 0.1$ level of significance. *Note:* A normal probability plot and boxplot of the data indicate that the differences are approximately normally distributed with no outliers. *Reject* H_o

(b) Construct a 95% confidence interval about the population mean difference. Interpret your results. $(2.28, 22.56)$

17. **Car Rentals** The following data represent the daily rental for a compact automobile charged by two car rental companies, Thrifty and Hertz, in 10 locations:

City	Thrifty	Hertz	City	Thrifty	Hertz
Chicago	21.81	18.99	Seattle	21.96	22.99
Los Angeles	29.89	48.99	Pittsburgh	20.90	19.99
Houston	17.90	19.99	Phoenix	47.75	36.99
Orlando	27.98	35.99	New Orleans	33.81	26.99
Boston	24.61	25.60	Minneapolis	33.49	20.99

Source: Yahoo! Travel

(a) Test the claim that Thrifty is less expensive than Hertz at the $\alpha = 0.1$ level of significance. *Note*: A normal probability plot and boxplot of the data indicate that the differences are approximately normally distributed with no outliers. *Do not reject H_o*

(b) Construct a 90% confidence interval about the population mean difference. Interpret your results. $(-5.08, 5.59)$

18. **Thermocouples** A thermocouple is a temperature sensor used to measure the temperature inside furnaces. A researcher wanted to know whether two thermocouples were measuring the temperature the same. He wrapped the thermocouples together, placed them in an oven and recorded the temperature (in °C) reported by the thermocouple. He did this 9 times and obtained the following data:

Thermocouple 1	326.06	326.08	326.05	326.03	326.00	326.00	325.97	326.07	326.11
Thermocouple 2	326.03	326.06	326.02	326.01	325.99	325.99	325.95	326.03	326.08

Source: Christenson, Ronald and Blackwood, Larry, "Tests for Precision and Accuracy of Multiple Measuring Devices," *Technometrics*, Nov. 93, Vol 35, Issue 4, pp. 411–421.

(a) Test the claim that there is a difference in the mean temperature at the $\alpha = 0.05$ level of significance. *Note*: A normal probability plot and boxplot of the data indicate that the differences are approximately normally distributed with no outliers. *Reject H_o*

(b) Construct a 90% confidence interval about the population mean difference. Interpret your results. $(0.017, 0.030)$

19. **Rat's Red Blood Cell Count** Researchers at NASA wanted to determine the effects of space flight on a rat's red blood cell count (RBC). The following data represent the red blood cell count at lift-off minus three days (RBC-L3) and immediately upon the return (RBC-R0) of 27 rats sent to space on the Spacelab Sciences 1 flight:

Rat #	RBC-L3	RBC-R0	Rat #	RBC-L3	RBC-R0	Rat #	RBC-L3	RBC-R0	Rat #	RBC-L3	RBC-R0
112	7.53	8.16	136	7.95	9.55	79	7.79	8.52	156	7.27	9.11
145	7.79	9.15	127	8.44	9.38	47	8.24	8.59	128	8.23	9.81
15	7.84	9.09	153	6.70	9.66	109	7.69	7.29	99	14.50	9.86
142	6.86	8.42	97	6.95	8.83	13	7.23	8.93	90	7.73	9.90
45	7.93	8.96	94	6.73	8.46	74	7.83	8.64	82	7.31	7.64
150	7.48	9.25	124	7.21	9.04	126	8.09	9.65	55	7.84	9.54
162	7.94	7.40	117	6.95	9.48	157	8.27	8.76			

Source: NASA Life Sciences Data Archive

The researchers used Minitab to test the claim that the red blood cell count three days prior to lift-off was different from the red blood cell count upon their return. The results are as follows:

Paired T-Test and Confidence Interval
```
Paired T for RBC-L3 — RBC-R0
```

	N	Mean	StDev	SE Mean
RBC-L3	27	7.864	1.414	0.272
RBC-R0	27	8.929	0.715	0.138
Difference	27	−1.065	1.397	0.269

```
95% CI for mean difference: (−1.618, −0.512)
T-Test of mean difference = 0 (vs not = 0): T-Value = −3.96 P-Value = 0.001
```

(a) State the null and alternative hypotheses. $H_o: \mu_d = 0$ vs $H_1: \mu_d \neq 0$
(b) What requirements must be satisfied in order to test the claim?
(c) Does it appear that the flight to space affected the red blood cell count of the rats at the $\alpha = 0.05$ level of significance? Why? Yes

20. Reaction Time Experiment Researchers at the University of Mississippi wanted to determine the reaction time (in seconds) of students to different stimuli. In the data that follow, the reaction time for subjects was measured after they received a simple stimulus and a go/no go stimulus. The simple stimulus presented an auditory cue and the time from when the cue was given to when the student reacted was measured. The go/no go stimulus required the student to respond to a particular stimulus and not to respond to other stimuli. Again, the reaction time was measured, with the following results:

Subject Number	Simple	Go/No Go	Subject Number	Simple	Go/No Go	Subject Number	Simple	Go/No Go
1	0.22	0.375	7	0.255	0.442	12	0.498	0.565
2	0.338	0.652	8	0.198	0.347	13	0.262	0.402
3	0.266	0.467	9	0.352	0.698	14	0.62	0.643
4	0.381	0.651	10	0.259	0.488	15	0.3	0.351
5	0.885	1.246	11	0.2	0.281	16	0.424	0.38
6	0.25	0.654						

Source: PsychExperiments at The University of Mississippi

The researchers used Minitab to test the claim that the simple stimulus had a lower reaction time than the go/no go stimulus. The results of the analysis are as follows:

Paired T-Test and Confidence Interval
```
Paired T for Simple — Go/No Go
```

	N	Mean	StDev	SE Mean
Simple	16	0.3567	0.1815	0.0454
Go/No Go	16	0.5401	0.2312	0.0578
Difference	16	−0.1834	0.1308	0.0327

```
95% CI for mean difference: (−0.2531, −0.1137)
T-Test of mean difference = 0 (vs < 0): T-Value = −5.61 P-Value = 0.000
```

(a) State the null and alternative hypotheses. $H_o: \mu_d = 0$ vs $H_1: \mu_d < 0$
(b) What requirements must be satisfied in order to test the claim?
(c) Does it appear that the reaction time to the simple stimulus is less than the reaction time to the go/no go stimulus at the $\alpha = 0.05$ level of significance? Why? Yes

Technology Step-by-Step
Two-sample *T*-tests, Dependent Sampling

TI-83 Plus   **Hypothesis Tests**

Step 1: If necessary, enter raw data in L1 and L2. Let L3 = L1 − L2 (or L2 − L1), depending upon how the alternative hypothesis was defined.

Step 2: Press STAT, highlight TESTS, and select 2:T-Test.

Step 3: If the data are raw, highlight Data making sure that List is set to L3 with frequency set to 1. If summary statistics are known, highlight Stats and enter the summary statistics.

Step 4: Highlight the appropriate relation between μ_1 and μ_2 in the alternative hypothesis.

Step 5: Highlight Calculate or Draw and press ENTER. Calculate gives the test statistic and *P*-value. Draw will draw the *t*-distribution with the *P*-value shaded.

Confidence Intervals

Follow the same steps as those given for hypothesis tests, except select 8: TInterval Also, select a confidence level (such as 95% = 0.95).

MINITAB   *Step 1:* Enter raw data in columns C1 and C2.

Step 2: Select the **Stat** menu, highlight **Basic Statistics**, and then highlight **Paired-t . . .**

Step 3: Enter C1 in the cell marked "First Sample" and enter C2 in the cell marked "Second Sample." Under OPTIONS, select the direction of the alternative hypothesis and select a confidence level. Click OK.

Excel   *Step 1:* Enter raw data in columns A and B.

Step 2: Select the **Tools** menu, highlight **Data Analysis . . .**

Step 3: Select "*t*-test: Paired Two-Sample for Means." With the cursor in the "Variable 1 Range" cell, highlight the data in column A. With the cursor in the "Variable 2 Range" cell, highlight the data in column B. Enter the hypothesized difference in the means (usually 0) and a value for alpha. Click OK.

10.2   Inference about Two Means: Independent Samples

Preparing for This Section   Before getting started, review the following:

✓ Design of experiments (Section 1.5, pp. 35–38)

✓ Confidence intervals about μ, σ unknown (Section 8.2, pp. 475–481)

✓ Hypothesis tests about μ, σ unknown (Section 9.3, pp. 546–551)

✓ Type I and Type II errors (Section 9.1, pp. 522–523)

Objectives   Perform hypothesis tests regarding the difference of two means

Construct confidence intervals regarding the difference of two means

Note to Instructor
Students should be familiar with the concept of hypothesis testing by now, so the pace can be a little quicker.

We now turn our attention to inferential methods for comparing means from two independent samples. For example, suppose we wish to know whether a new experimental drug relieves symptoms attributable to the

Note to Instructor
The computations in this section become quite tedious. You might consider emphasizing technology solutions. This allows for more emphasis on the P-value approach to hypothesis testing.

common cold. The response variable might be the time until the cold symptoms go away. If the drug is effective, then the mean time until the cold symptoms go away should be less for individuals taking the drug than for those not taking the drug. If we let μ_1 represent the mean time until cold symptoms go away for the individuals taking the drug, and μ_2 represent the mean time until cold symptoms go away for individuals taking a placebo, the null and alternative hypotheses will be

$$H_0: \mu_1 = \mu_2 \quad \text{versus} \quad H_1: \mu_1 < \mu_2$$

or equivalently,

$$H_0: \mu_1 - \mu_2 = 0 \quad \text{versus} \quad H_1: \mu_1 - \mu_2 < 0$$

To test this claim, we might randomly divide 500 volunteers who have a common cold into two groups—an experimental group (Group 1) and a control group (Group 2). The control group would receive a placebo and the experimental group would receive a predetermined amount of the experimental drug. Next, determine the time until the cold symptoms go away. Compute $\overline{x}_1$, the sample mean time until cold symptoms go away in the experimental group, and $\overline{x}_2$, the sample mean time until cold symptoms go away in the control group. Now, we would determine whether the difference in the sample means, $\overline{x}_1 - \overline{x}_2$, was significantly different from 0—the assumed difference stated in the null hypothesis. To do this, we need to know the sampling distribution of $\overline{x}_1 - \overline{x}_2$.

Theorem

Sampling Distribution of the Difference of Two Means: Independent Samples with Population Standard Deviations Known

Suppose a simple random sample of size n_1 is taken from a population with mean μ_1 and standard deviation σ_1. In addition, a simple random sample of size n_2 is taken from a second population with mean μ_2 and standard deviation σ_2. If the two populations are normally distributed or the sample sizes are sufficiently large ($n_1 \geq 30$ and $n_2 \geq 30$), then the sampling distribution of $\overline{x}_1 - \overline{x}_2$ is normally distributed with mean $\mu_1 - \mu_2$ and standard deviation $\sigma_{\overline{x}_1 - \overline{x}_2} = \sqrt{\dfrac{\sigma_1^2}{n_1} + \dfrac{\sigma_2^2}{n_2}}$. The standardized version of $\overline{x}_1 - \overline{x}_2$ is then written as

$$Z = \frac{(\overline{x}_1 - \overline{x}_2) - (\mu_1 - \mu_2)}{\sqrt{\dfrac{\sigma_1^2}{n_1} + \dfrac{\sigma_2^2}{n_2}}}$$

which has the standard normal distribution.

Knowing the sampling distribution of $\overline{x}_1 - \overline{x}_2$, we can use the methods introduced in Sections 8.1 and 9.2 to construct confidence intervals and perform hypothesis tests regarding claims about μ_1 and μ_2 with σ_1 and σ_2 known. Unfortunately, it is unreasonable to expect to know information regarding σ_1 and σ_2 without knowing information regarding the population means. Therefore, we must develop a sampling distribution for the difference of two means when the population standard deviations are unknown.

The comparison of two means with unequal (and unknown) population variances is known as the "Behrens–Fisher problem." While an exact method for performing inference on the equality of two means with unequal population standard deviations does not exist, an approximate solution is available. The approach that we use is known as **Welch's approximate *t***, in honor of English statistician Bernard Lewis Welch (1911–1989).

Theorem

Sampling Distribution of the Difference of Two Means: Independent Samples with Population Standard Deviations Unknown (Welch's *t*)

Suppose a simple random sample of size n_1 is taken from a population with unknown mean μ_1 and unknown standard deviation σ_1. In addition, a simple random sample of size n_2 is taken from a second population with unknown mean μ_2 and unknown standard deviation σ_2. If the two populations are normally distributed or the sample sizes are sufficiently large $(n_1 \geq 30$ and $n_2 \geq 30)$, then

$$t = \frac{(\overline{x}_1 - \overline{x}_2) - (\mu_1 - \mu_2)}{\sqrt{\dfrac{s_1^2}{n_1} + \dfrac{s_2^2}{n_2}}} \qquad (1)$$

approximately follows Student's *t*-distribution with the smaller of $n_1 - 1$ or $n_2 - 1$ degrees of freedom where $\overline{x}_1$ is the sample mean, and s_1 is the sample standard deviation from population 1; $\overline{x}_2$ is the sample mean and s_2 is the sample standard deviation from population 2.

① Inference on the Difference of Two Means with Unknown Population Variances

Now that we know the approximate sampling distribution of $\overline{x}_1 - \overline{x}_2$ with the population standard deviations unknown, we can introduce a procedure that can be used to test claims regarding two population means.

Hypothesis Test Regarding the Difference of Two Means with σ Unknown

If a claim is made regarding two population means, μ_1 and μ_2, with unknown population standard deviations, we can use the following steps to test the claim, provided that

1. the samples are obtained using simple random sampling;

2. the samples are independent;

3. the populations from which the samples are drawn are normally distributed or the sample sizes are large $(n_1 \geq 30$ and $n_2 \geq 30)$.

Step 1: A claim is made regarding two population means. The claim is used to determine the null and alternative hypotheses. The hypotheses are structured in one of three ways, as shown below.

Two-Tailed	Left-Tailed	Right-Tailed
$H_o: \mu_1 = \mu_2$	$H_o: \mu_1 = \mu_2$	$H_o: \mu_1 = \mu_2$
$H_1: \mu_1 \neq \mu_2$	$H_1: \mu_1 < \mu_2$	$H_1: \mu_1 > \mu_2$

Note: μ_1 is the population mean for population 1, and μ_2 is the population mean for population 2.

Step 2: Decide on a level of significance α based upon the seriousness of making a Type I error. The critical value is determined using the smaller of $n_1 - 1$ and $n_2 - 1$ degrees of freedom. For example, the critical value in the left-tailed test is $-t_\alpha$, with the smaller of $n_1 - 1$ or $n_2 - 1$ degrees of freedom. The shaded regions represent the critical region as shown:

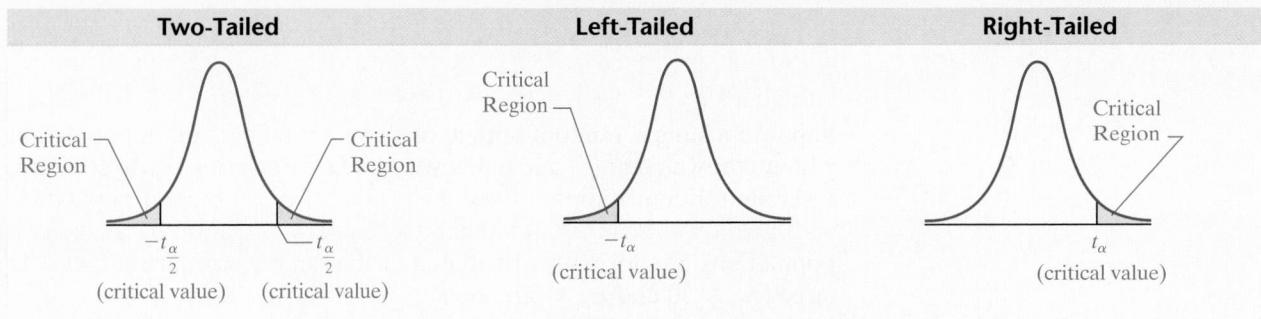

Step 3: Compute the **test statistic** $t = \dfrac{(\bar{x}_1 - \bar{x}_2) - (\mu_1 - \mu_2)}{\sqrt{\dfrac{s_1^2}{n_1} + \dfrac{s_2^2}{n_2}}}$, which

approximately follows Student's t-distribution.

Step 4: Compare the critical value with the test statistic, as shown:

Two-tailed	Left-tailed	Right-tailed
If $t < -t_{\alpha/2}$ or $t > t_{\alpha/2}$, reject the null hypothesis	If $t < -t_\alpha$, reject the null hypothesis	If $t > t_\alpha$, reject the null hypothesis

Step 5: State the conclusion.

The procedure just presented requires a normal distribution of each population or a large sample size. The procedure is robust, so minor departures from normality will not adversely affect the results of the test. If the data have outliers, however, the procedure should not be used. We will verify these requirements by constructing normal probability plots (to assess normality) and boxplots (to determine whether there are outliers). If the normal probability plot indicates that the data came from a population that is not normally distributed or the boxplot reveals outliers, nonparametric tests should be performed as discussed in Chapter 13, Section 5.

▶ EXAMPLE 1   **Testing a Claim Regarding Two Means**

Problem: In the Spacelab Life Sciences 2 payload, 14 male rats were sent to space. Upon their return, the red blood cell mass (in milliliters) of the rats was determined. A control group of 14 male rats was held under the same conditions (except for space flight) as the space rats and their red blood cell mass was also determined when the space rats returned. The project, led by Dr. Paul X. Callahan, resulted in the data listed in Table 3.

Test the claim that the flight animals have a different red blood cell mass from the control animals at the $\alpha = 0.05$ level of significance.

TABLE 3							
Flight				**Control**			
8.59	8.64	7.43	7.21	8.65	6.99	8.40	9.66
6.87	7.89	9.79	6.85	7.62	7.44	8.55	8.70
7.00	8.80	9.30	8.03	7.33	8.58	9.88	9.94
6.39	7.54			7.14	9.14		

Source: NASA Life Sciences Data Archive

Approach: We verify that each of the samples comes from a population that is approximately normal with no outliers by drawing normal probability plots and boxplots. The boxplots will be drawn on the same graph so that we can visually compare the two populations. We then follow Steps 1–5, listed on pages 609–610.

Solution: Figure 4 shows normal probability plots of the data, which indicate that the data could come from populations that are normal. On the basis of the boxplots, it would seem that there is not much difference in the red blood cell mass of the two populations, although the flight group might have a slightly lower red blood cell mass.

Figure 4

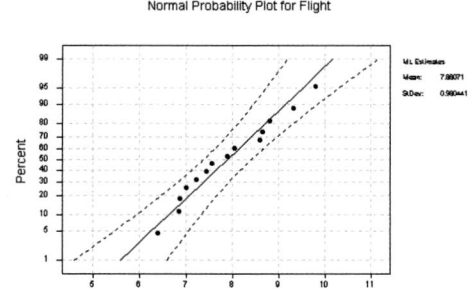

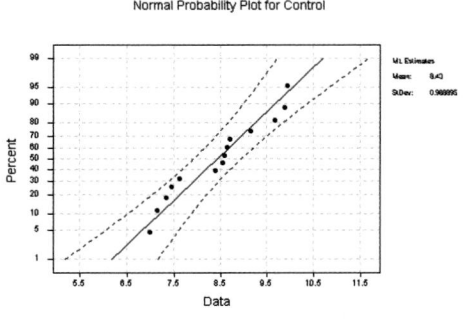

Red Blood Cell Mass

Step 1: The claim is that the flight animals have a different red blood cell mass from the control animals. Let μ_1 represent the mean red blood cell mass of the flight animals and μ_2 represent the mean red blood cell mass of the control animals. Then the claim can be expressed as $\mu_1 \neq \mu_2$, and we have the hypotheses

$$H_o: \mu_1 = \mu_2$$

versus

$$H_1: \mu_1 \neq \mu_2$$

which can be written as

$$H_o: \mu_1 - \mu_2 = 0$$

versus

$$H_1: \mu_1 - \mu_2 \neq 0$$

Figure 5

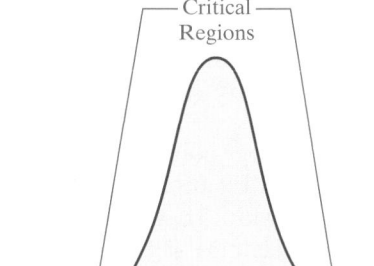

Step 2: We have a two-tailed test with $\alpha = 0.05$. Since the sample size of the experimental group and control group are both 14, we have $n_1 - 1 = 14 - 1 = 13$ degrees of freedom. The critical values are $t_{\alpha/2} = t_{0.05/2} = t_{0.025} = 2.160$ and $-t_{0.025} = -2.160$. The critical regions are displayed in Figure 5.

TABLE 4		
	Flight Animals	Control Animals
Sample Size	$n_1 = 14$	$n_2 = 14$
Sample Mean	$\bar{x}_1 = 7.881$	$\bar{x}_2 = 8.430$
Sample Standard Deviation	$s_1 = 1.017$	$s_2 = 1.005$

Step 3: We compute the sample statistics for each population and obtain the results shown in Table 4.

Compute the test statistic as follows:

$$t = \frac{(\bar{x}_1 - \bar{x}_2) - (\mu_1 - \mu_2)}{\sqrt{\frac{s_1^2}{n_1} + \frac{s_2^2}{n_2}}} = \frac{(7.881 - 8.430) - 0}{\sqrt{\frac{1.017^2}{14} + \frac{1.005^2}{14}}}$$

$$= \frac{-0.549}{0.3821288115} = -1.437$$

Step 4: We compare the test statistic with the critical values. Because the test statistic, $t = -1.437$, lies between the critical values of -2.160 and 2.160, we do not reject the null hypothesis. That is, the test statistic does not lie within the critical regions, so we do not reject H_o. We label this point in Figure 5.

Step 5: There is not sufficient evidence at the $\alpha = 0.05$ level of significance to support the claim that there is a significant difference in red blood cell mass between the flight animals and the control animals. ◀◀

The degrees of freedom used to determine the critical value(s) presented in Example 1 are conservative. Results that are more accurate can be obtained by using the following degrees of freedom:

$$df = \frac{\left(\frac{s_1^2}{n_1} + \frac{s_2^2}{n_2}\right)^2}{\frac{\left(\frac{s_1^2}{n_1}\right)^2}{n_1 - 1} + \frac{\left(\frac{s_2^2}{n_2}\right)^2}{n_2 - 1}}. \tag{2}$$

When using Formula (2) to compute degrees of freedom, round down to the nearest integer in order to use Table III. For hand inference, it is recommended that we employ the conservative approach of using the smaller of $n_1 - 1$ or $n_2 - 1$ as the degrees of freedom, to ease computational difficulty. However, computer software will use Formula (2) when computing the degrees of freedom, for increased precision in determining the critical t.

Figure 6

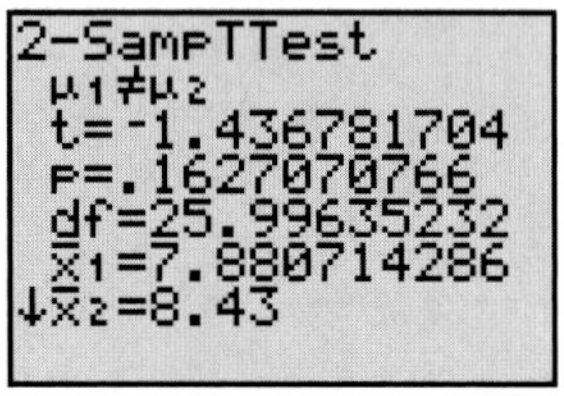

```
2-SampTTest
μ1≠μ2
t=-1.436781704
p=.1627070766
df=25.99635232
x̄1=7.880714286
↓x̄2=8.43
```

🚦 **Caution**

The degrees of freedom in "by hand" solutions will not equal the degrees of freedom in "technology" solutions unless you use Formula (2) to compute degrees of freedom.

Using Technology: Statistical spreadsheets and graphing calculators with advanced statistical functions can be used to compare two means. Figure 6 shows the results of Example 1 using a TI-83 Plus graphing calculator. The P-value is reported as 0.1627. Because the P-value is greater than the level of significance, $\alpha = 0.05$, we do not reject the null hypothesis. There is not sufficient evidence to support the claim that the mean red blood cell mass of flight animals is different from the mean red blood cell mass of control animals.

Notice that the degrees of freedom in the technology solution is 25.996 versus 13 in the conservative solution done by hand in Example 1. With the lower degrees of freedom, the critical t is larger (2.160 with 13 degrees of freedom versus 2.056 with approximately 26 degrees of freedom). The larger critical value increases the number of standard deviations the difference in the sample means must be from the hypothesized mean difference before the null hypothesis is rejected. Therefore, in using the smaller of $n_1 - 1$ or $n_2 - 1$ degrees of freedom, we need more substantial evidence to reject the null hypothesis. This requirement decreases the probability of a Type I error (rejecting the null when the null is true) below the actual level of α chosen by the researcher. This is what we mean when we say that the method of using the lesser of $n_1 - 1$ and $n_2 - 1$ as a proxy for degrees of freedom is conservative compared with using Formula (2) on page 612.

 Now Work Problem 7(a).

②   Constructing a confidence interval about the difference of two means is simply an extension of the results presented in Section 8.2.

> **Constructing a $(1 - \alpha) \cdot 100\%$ Confidence Interval about the Difference of Two Means**
>
> Suppose a simple random sample of size n_1 is taken from a population with unknown mean μ_1 and unknown standard deviation σ_1. In addition, a simple random sample of size n_2 is taken from a population with unknown mean μ_2 and unknown standard deviation σ_2. If the two populations are normally distributed or the sample sizes are sufficiently large ($n_1 \geq 30$ and $n_2 \geq 30$), then a $(1 - \alpha) \cdot 100\%$ confidence interval about $\mu_1 - \mu_2$ is given by
>
> $$\text{Lower Bound: } (\overline{x}_1 - \overline{x}_2) - t_{\alpha/2} \cdot \sqrt{\frac{s_1^2}{n_1} + \frac{s_2^2}{n_2}}$$
>
> and
>
> $$\text{Upper Bound: } (\overline{x}_1 - \overline{x}_2) + t_{\alpha/2} \cdot \sqrt{\frac{s_1^2}{n_1} + \frac{s_2^2}{n_2}} \tag{3}$$
>
> where $t_{\alpha/2}$ is computed using the smaller of $n_1 - 1$ or $n_2 - 1$ degrees of freedom or Formula (2).

▶ **EXAMPLE 2**   **Constructing a Confidence Interval about the Difference of Two Means**

Problem: Construct a 95% confidence interval about $\mu_1 - \mu_2$, using the data presented in Table 3.

Approach: A normal probability plot and boxplot (Figure 4) indicate that the data are approximately normal with no outliers. We compute the confidence interval with $\alpha = 0.05$ using Formula (3).

Solution: We have already found the sample statistics in Example 1. In addition, we found $t_{\alpha/2} = t_{0.025}$ with 13 degrees of freedom to be 2.160. Substituting into Formula (3), we obtain the following results:

Lower Bound:

$$(\overline{x}_1 - \overline{x}_2) - t_{\alpha/2} \cdot \sqrt{\frac{s_1^2}{n_1} + \frac{s_2^2}{n_2}} = (7.881 - 8.430) - 2.160 \cdot \sqrt{\frac{1.017^2}{14} + \frac{1.005^2}{14}} = -0.549 - 0.825 = -1.374$$

Upper Bound:

$$(\overline{x}_1 - \overline{x}_2) + t_{\alpha/2} \cdot \sqrt{\frac{s_1^2}{n_1} + \frac{s_2^2}{n_2}} = (7.881 - 8.430) + 2.160 \cdot \sqrt{\frac{1.017^2}{14} + \frac{1.005^2}{14}} = -0.549 + 0.825 = 0.276$$

Interpretation: We are 95% confident that the mean difference between the red blood cell mass of the flight animals and control animals is between −1.374 ml and 0.276 ml. Because the confidence interval contains zero, there is not sufficient evidence to support the claim that there is a difference in the red blood cell mass of the flight group and the control group.

◄◄

 *Now Work Problem 7(b).*

 **Caution**

We would use the pooled two-sample *t*-test when the two samples come from populations that have the same variance. "Pooling" refers to finding a weighted average of the two sample variances from the independent samples. It is difficult to verify that two sample variances might be equal, so we will always use Welch's *t* when comparing two means.

What about the Pooled Two-Sample *t*-tests?

Perhaps you noticed that statistical software and graphing calculators with advanced statistical features provide an option for two types of two-sample *t* tests: one that assumes equal population variances (pooling) and one that does not assume equal population variances. Welch's *t*-statistic does not assume that the population variances are equal and can be used whether the population variances are equal or not. The test that assumes equal population variances is referred to as the *pooled t-statistic*.

The **pooled *t*-statistic** is computed by finding a weighted average of the sample variances and uses this average in the computation of the test statistic. The advantage of this test statistic is that it exactly follows Student's *t*-distribution with $n_1 + n_2 - 2$ degrees of freedom. The disadvantage of the test statistic is that it requires that the population variances be equal. How is this requirement to be verified? While a test for determining the equality of variances does exist (*F*-test, Section 10.4), the test *requires* that each population be normally distributed. However, the *F*-test is not robust. Any minor departures from normality will make the results of the *F*-test unreliable. It has been recommended by numerous statisticians* that a preliminary *F*-test to check the requirement of equality of variance not be performed. In fact, George Box once said "To make preliminary tests on variances is rather like putting to sea in a rowing boat to find out whether conditions are sufficiently calm for an ocean liner to leave port!"

Because the formal *F*-test for testing the equality of variances is so volatile, we shall be content in using Welch's *t*. This test is more conservative than the pooled *t*. The price that must be paid for the conservative approach is that the probability of a Type II error is higher in Welch's *t* than in the pooled *t* when the population variances are equal. However, the two tests typically provide the same conclusion, even if the assumption of equal population standard deviations seems reasonable.

10.2 Assess Your Understanding

Concepts and Vocabulary

1. What are the requirements that need to be satisfied in order to test a hypothesis regarding the difference of two means with σ unknown?

2. Explain why using the smaller of $n_1 - 1$ or $n_2 - 1$ degrees of freedom to determine the critical *t* instead of Formula (2) is conservative.

*Moser and Stevens, "Homogeneity of Variance in the Two-Sample Means Test," *The American Statistician*, Vol. 46, No. 1.

Exercises

• Skill Building

In Problems 1–6, assume that the populations are normally distributed.

1. (a) Test the claim that $\mu_1 \neq \mu_2$ at the $\alpha = 0.05$ level of significance for the given sample data. Do not reject H_o
   (b) Construct a 95% confidence interval about $\mu_1 - \mu_2$.*

	Sample for Population 1	Sample for Population 2
n	15	15
$\overline{x}$	15.3	14.2
s	3.2	3.5

2. (a) Test the claim that $\mu_1 \neq \mu_2$ at the $\alpha = 0.05$ level of significance for the given sample data. Reject H_o
   (b) Construct a 95% confidence interval about $\mu_1 - \mu_2$.

	Sample for Population 1	Sample for Population 2
n	20	20
$\overline{x}$	111	104
s	8.6	9.2

3. (a) Test the claim that $\mu_1 > \mu_2$ at the $\alpha = 0.1$ level of significance for the given sample data. Reject H_o
   (b) Construct a 90% confidence interval about $\mu_1 - \mu_2$.

	Sample for Population 1	Sample for Population 2
n	25	18
$\overline{x}$	50.2	42.0
s	6.4	9.9

4. (a) Test the claim that $\mu_1 < \mu_2$ at the $\alpha = 0.05$ level of significance for the given sample data. Reject H_o
   (b) Construct a 95% confidence interval about $\mu_1 - \mu_2$.

	Sample for Population 1	Sample for Population 2
n	40	32
$\overline{x}$	94.2	115.2
s	15.9	23.0

5. (a) Test the claim that $\mu_1 < \mu_2$ at the $\alpha = 0.02$ level of significance for the given sample data. Reject H_o
   (b) Construct a 90% confidence interval about $\mu_1 - \mu_2$. $(-16.65, -4.95)$

	Sample for Population 1	Sample for Population 2
n	32	25
$\overline{x}$	103.4	114.2
s	12.3	13.2

6. (a) Test the claim that $\mu_1 > \mu_2$ at the $\alpha = 0.05$ level of significance for the given sample data. Do not reject H_o
   (b) Construct a 95% confidence interval about $\mu_1 - \mu_2$. $(-1.60, 5.80)$

	Sample for Population 1	Sample for Population 2
n	23	13
$\overline{x}$	43.1	41.0
s	4.5	5.1

• Applying the Concepts

7. **Treating Acute Bipolar Mania** In a study published in the *Archives of General Psychiatry* entitled "Efficacy of Olanzapine in Acute Bipolar Mania," (Vol. 57, No. 9, pp. 841–849), researchers conducted a randomized, double-blind study to measure the effects of the drug olanzapine on patients diagnosed with bipolar disorder. A total of 115 patients with a DSM-IV diagnosis of bipolar disorder were randomly divided into two groups. Group 1 ($n = 55$) received 5 to 20 mg per day of olanzapine, while Group 2 ($n = 60$) received a placebo. The effectiveness of the drug was measured using the Young–Mania Rating Scale total score with the net improvement in the score recorded. The results are presented in the table to the right.

	Treatment Group	Control Group
n	55	60
Mean improvement	14.8	8.1
Sample standard deviation	12.5	12.7

(a) Test the claim that the treatment group experienced a larger mean improvement than the control group at the $\alpha = 0.01$ level of significance. Reject H_o
(b) Construct a 95% confidence interval about $\mu_1 - \mu_2$ and interpret the results. $(1.98, 11.42)$

* The confidence intervals in the back of the text were computed using the smaller of $n_1 - 1$ or $n_2 - 1$ degrees of freedom. These intervals will be wider than those obtained using technology.

(1b) $(-1.53, 3.73)$
(2b) $(1.1, 12.9)$

(3b) $(3.57, 12.83)$
(4b) $(-30.75, -11.25)$

8. **Treating the Common Cold** Researcher Steven J. Sperber, MD, and his associates wanted to determine the efficacy (effectiveness) of a new medication in the treatment of discomfort associated with the common cold. They published their results in the *Archives of Family Medicines (2000): 979–985.* In their study, they randomly divided 430 subjects into two groups: Group 1 ($n = 216$) received the new medication and Group 2 ($n = 214$) received a placebo. The goal of the study was to determine whether the reduction in the mean symptom assessment score of the individuals receiving the treatment group (Group 1) was more than that of the control group (Group 2). In Group 1, the mean reduction in the symptom assessment scores was 1.30, with a standard deviation of 0.88; in Group 2, participants had a mean reduction in the symptom assessment score of 0.93, with a standard deviation of 0.88.

(a) Test the claim that subjects in Group 1 had a larger reduction in the symptom assessment score than the subjects in Group 2 at the $\alpha = 0.05$ level of significance.

(b) Construct a 95% confidence interval about $\mu_1 - \mu_2$ and interpret the results. (0.202, 0.538)

9. **Concrete Strength** An engineer wanted to know whether the strength of two different concrete mix designs differed significantly. He randomly selected 9 cylinders, measuring 6 inches in diameter and 12 inches in height, into which mixture 67-0-301 was poured. After 28 days, he measured the strength (in pounds per square inch) of the cylinder. He also randomly selected 10 cylinders of mixture 67-0-400 and performed the same test. The results are as follows:

Mixture 67-0-301			Mixture 67-0-400			
3960	4090	3100	4070	4890	5020	4330
3830	3200	3780	4640	5220	4190	3730
4080	4040	2940	4120	4620		

(a) Is it reasonable to use Welch's *t*-test? Why? *Note:* Normal probability plots indicate that the data are approximately normal and boxplots indicate that there are no outliers. Yes

(b) Test the claim that mixture 67-0-400 is stronger than mixture 67-0-301 at the $\alpha = 0.05$ level of significance.

(c) Construct a 90% confidence interval about $\mu_{400} - \mu_{301}$ and interpret the results. (416, 1212)

(d) Draw boxplots of each data set using the same scale. Does this visual evidence support the results obtained in part (b)?

(8a) Reject H_o
(9b) Reject H_o

10. **Measuring Reaction Time** Researchers at the University of Mississippi wanted to determine the whether the reaction time (in seconds) of males differed from that of females to a go/no go stimulus. The researchers randomly selected 20 females and 15 males to participate in the study. The go/no go stimulus required the student to respond to a particular stimulus and not to respond to other stimuli. The data are courtesy of PsychExperiments at the University of Mississippi. The results are as follows:

Female Students							Male Students				
0.588	0.652	0.442	0.293	0.380	0.434	0.613	0.375	0.256	0.427	0.373	0.224
0.340	0.636	0.391	0.367	0.403	0.443	0.274	0.654	0.563	0.405	0.488	0.477
0.377	0.646	0.403	0.377	0.617	0.481		0.374	0.465	0.402	0.337	0.655

(a) Is it reasonable to use Welch's *t*-test? Why? *Note:* Normal probability plots indicate that the data are approximately normal and boxplots indicate that there are no outliers. Yes

(b) Test the claim that there is no difference in the reaction time of males and females at the $\alpha = 0.05$ level of significance. Do not reject H_o

(c) (−0.0483, 0.1006)

(c) Construct a 90% confidence interval about $\mu_f - \mu_m$ and interpret the results.

(d) Draw boxplots of each data set using the same scale. Does this visual evidence support the results obtained in part (b)?

11. **Bacteria in Carpeting** Researchers wanted to determine whether carpeted rooms contained more bacteria than uncarpeted rooms. To determine the amount of bacteria in a room, researchers pumped the air from the room over a Petri dish at the rate of one cubic foot per minute for eight carpeted rooms and eight uncarpeted rooms. Colonies of bacteria were allowed to form in the 16 Petri dishes. The results are presented in the table to the right.

(a) Verify that the data are approximately normally distributed with no outliers.

Carpeted Rooms (Bacteria/cubic foot)		Uncarpeted Rooms (Bacteria/cubic foot)	
11.8	10.8	12.1	12.0
8.2	10.1	8.3	11.1
7.1	14.6	3.8	10.1
13.0	14.0	7.2	13.7

Source: Walter, William G., and Stober, Angie, "Microbial Air Sampling in a Carpeted Hospital." *Journal of Environmental Health*, **30** (1968), p. 405.

(b) Test the claim that carpeted rooms have more bacteria than uncarpeted rooms at the $\alpha = 0.05$ level of significance. Do not reject H_o

(c) Construct a 95% confidence interval about $\mu_{carpet} - \mu_{uncarpet}$ and interpret the results.

12. **Visual versus Textual Learners** Researchers wanted to know whether there was a difference in comprehension among students learning a computer program based on the style of the text. They randomly divided 36 students into two groups of 18 each. The researchers verified that the 36 students were similar in terms of educational level, age, and so on. Group 1 individuals learned the software using a visual manual (*multimodal instruction*), while Group 2 individuals learned the software using a textual manual (*unimodal instruction*). The following data represent scores the students received on an exam given to them after they studied from the manuals.

Visual Manual		Textual Manual	
51.08	60.35	64.55	56.54
57.03	76.60	57.60	39.91
44.85	70.77	68.59	65.31
75.21	70.15	50.75	51.95
56.87	47.60	49.63	49.07
75.28	46.59	43.58	48.83
57.07	81.23	57.40	72.40
80.30	67.30	49.48	42.01
52.20	60.82	49.57	61.16

Source: Based on "Multimodal Versus Unimodal Instruction in a Complex Learning Context" by Mark Gellevij, et. al., *Journal of Experimental Education*, 2002, 70(3), pp. 215–239.

(a) Verify that the data are approximately normally distributed with no outliers.

(b) Test the claim that there is a difference in test scores at the $\alpha = 0.05$ level of significance. Reject H_o

(c) Construct a 95% confidence interval about $\mu_{visual} - \mu_{textual}$ and interpret the results.

13. **Cost of Housing** An urban economist wanted to determine whether the mean price of a home in Lemont is less than the mean price of a home in Naperville. A random sample of homes sold in each neighborhood results in the following statistics, where the means and standard deviations are in thousands of dollars:

Lemont	Naperville
$n_1 = 44$	$n_2 = 32$
$\bar{x}_1 = 253.6$	$\bar{x}_2 = 310.3$
$s_1 = 106.9$	$s_2 = 153.9$

Source: County's Recorders Office

(a) Test the claim that housing is less expensive in Lemont than in Naperville at the $\alpha = 0.05$ level of significance. Reject H_o

(b) Construct a 90% confidence interval about $\mu_{Lemont} - \mu_{Naperville}$ and interpret the results.

(c) Why do you think it is necessary to have large sample sizes to test this hypothesis?

14. **Debt** Erica Egizio, mathematics instructor at Joliet Junior College, claims that college women have more credit card debt than college men. She conducts a random sample of 38 college men and 32 college women, determines their credit card debt, and obtains the following statistics:

Men	Women
$n_1 = 38$	$n_2 = 32$
$\bar{x}_1 = 435$	$\bar{x}_2 = 781$
$s_1 = 1026$	$s_2 = 1489$

(a) Test the claim that college women have more credit card debt than college men at the $\alpha = 0.05$ level of significance. Do not reject H_o

(b) Construct a 90% confidence interval about $\mu_{women} - \mu_{men}$ and interpret the results.

15. **Hormone Replacement Therapy** Coronary heart disease is the leading cause of death among older women. In observational studies, the number of deaths due to coronary heart disease has been reduced in postmenopausal women who take hormone replacement therapy. Low levels of serum high-density lipoprotein (HDL) cholesterol is considered to be one of the risk factors predictive of death from coronary heart disease. Researchers at the Washington University School of Medicine claimed that serum HDL increases when patients participate in hormone replacement therapy. The researchers randomly divided 59 sedentary women 75 years of age or older into two groups. The 30 patients in Group 1 (the experimental group) received nine months of oral therapy with conjugated estrogens, 0.625 milligrams per day, plus trimonthly medroxyprogesterone acetate, 5 milligrams per day for 13 days. The 29 patients in Group 2 (the control group) received nine months of oral therapy with a placebo. At the conclusion of the treatment, the patient's serum HDL was recorded. The experiment was double-blind. The following results were obtained, where the means and standard deviations are in mg/dL:

	Experimental Group	Control Group
Sample size	$n_1 = 30$	$n_2 = 29$
Mean increase in HDL	$\bar{x}_1 = 8.1$	$\bar{x}_2 = 2.4$
Sample standard deviation	$s_1 = 10.5$	$s_2 = 4.3$

Source: Ellen F. Binder, et al., "Effects of Hormone Replacement Therapy on Serum Lipids in Elderly Women." *Annals of Internal Medicine* 134 (May 2001): pp. 754–760

(a) What type of experimental design is this? What is the treatment? How many levels does the treatment have?

(b) Test the claim that the treatment group had a larger mean increase in serum HDL levels than the control group at the $\alpha = 0.01$ level of significance (serum HDL is normally distributed). Reject H_o

(c) Construct a 95% confidence interval about $\mu_1 - \mu_2$ and interpret the results. (1.45, 9.95)

16. **SAT Test Scores** A researcher wanted to know whether students who do not plan to apply for financial aid score better on the SAT I math test than those who do plan to apply for financial aid. She obtains a random sample of 35 students who do not plan to apply for financial aid and a random sample of 39 students who do plan to apply for financial aid and obtains the following results:

Do Not Plan to Apply for Financial Aid	Plan to Apply for Financial Aid
$n_1 = 35$	$n_2 = 38$
$\overline{x}_1 = 546.6$	$\overline{x}_2 = 497.1$
$s_1 = 123.1$	$s_2 = 119.4$

(a) Test the claim that students who do not apply for financial aid score higher on the SAT math I examthan students who do apply for financial aid at the $\alpha = 0.01$ level of significance. Do not reject H_o

(b) Construct a 98% confidence interval about $\mu_{\text{do not}} - \mu_{\text{do}}$ and interpret the results. $(-20.44, 119.44)$

---

17. **Comparing Step Pulses** A physical therapist wanted to know whether the mean step pulse of men was less than the mean step pulse of women. She randomly selected 51 men and 70 women to participate in the study. Each subject was required to step up and down onto a six-inch platform for three minutes. The pulse of each subject (in beats per minute) was then recorded. After the data were entered into Minitab, the following results were obtained:

Two Sample T-Test and Confidence Interval

Two sample T for Men vs Women

	N	Mean	StDev	SE Mean
Men	51	112.3	11.3	1.6
Women	70	118.3	14.2	1.7

95% CI for mu Men $-$ mu Women: $(-10.7, -1.5)$
T-Test mu Men $=$ mu Women (vs $<$):T $= -2.61$ P $= 0.0051$ DF $= 118$

(a) State the null and alternative hypotheses. H_o: $\mu_{\text{men}} = \mu_{\text{women}}$ vs H_1: $\mu_{\text{men}} < \mu_{\text{women}}$

(b) Identify the P-value and state the researcher's conclusion if the level of significance was $\alpha = 0.01$. 0.0051

(c) What is the 95% confidence interval for the mean difference in pulse rates of men versus women? Interpret this interval. $(-10.7, -1.5)$

18. **Comparing Flexibility** A physical therapist claims that women are more flexible than men. She measures the flexibility of 31 randomly selected women and 45 randomly selected men by determining the number of inches subjects could reach while sitting on the floor with their legs straight out and back perpendicular to the ground. The more flexible an individual is, the higher the measured flexibility would be. After entering the data into Minitab, she obtained the following results:

Two Sample T-Test and Confidence Interval

Two sample T for Men vs Women

	N	Mean	StDev	SE Mean
Men	45	18.64	3.29	0.49
Women	31	20.99	2.07	0.37

95% CI for mu Men $-$ mu Women: $(-3.58, -1.12)$
T-Test mu Men $=$ mu Women (vs $<$):T $= -3.82$ P $= 0.0001$ DF $= 73$

(a) State the null and alternative hypotheses. H_o: $\mu_{\text{men}} = \mu_{\text{women}}$ vs H_1: $\mu_{\text{men}} < \mu_{\text{women}}$

(b) Identify the P-value and state the researcher's conclusion if the level of significance was $\alpha = 0.01$. 0.0001

(c) What is the 95% confidence interval for the mean difference in flexibility of men versus women? Interpret this interval. $(-3.58, -1.12)$

Technology Step-by-Step
Two-sample T-tests, Independent Sampling

TI-83 Plus

Hypothesis Tests

Step 1: If necessary, enter raw data in L1 and L2.

Step 2: Press STAT, highlight TESTS, and select `4:2-SampTTest`...

Step 3: If the data are raw, highlight Data, making sure that List1 is set to L1 and List2 is set to L2 with frequencies set to 1. If summary statistics are known, highlight Stats and enter the summary statistics.

Step 4: Highlight the appropriate relation between μ_1 and μ_2 in the alternative hypothesis. Set Pooled to NO.

Step 5: Highlight Calculate or Draw and press ENTER. Calculate gives the test statistic and *P*-value. Draw will draw the *t*-distribution with the *P*-value shaded.

Confidence Intervals

Follow the same steps as those given for hypothesis tests, except select `0:2-SampTInt`. Also, select a confidence level (such as 95% = 0.95).

MINITAB

Step 1: Enter raw data in columns C1 and C2.

Step 2: Select the **Stat** menu, highlight **Basic Statistics**, then highlight **2-Sample t**...

Step 3: Select "Samples in different columns." Enter C1 in the cell marked "First" and enter C2 in the cell marked "Second." Select the direction of the alternative hypothesis and select a confidence level. Click OK.

Excel

Step 1: Enter raw data in columns A and B.

Step 2: Select the **Tools menu**, highlight **Data Analysis**...

Step 3: Select "*t*-test: Two-Sample Assuming Unequal Variances." With the cursor in the "Variable 1 Range" cell, highlight the data in column A. Enter the hypothesized difference in the means (usually 0) and a value for alpha. Click OK.

10.3 Inference about Two Population Proportions

Preparing for This Section Before getting started, review the following:

- ✓ Confidence intervals about a population proportion (Section 8.3, pp. 490–493)
- ✓ Hypothesis tests about a population proportion (Section 9.4, pp. 558–565)

Objectives Conduct hypothesis tests on the difference between two population proportions

 Construct confidence intervals for the difference between two population proportions

Determine sample size for the difference between two population proportions

In Sections 8.3 and 9.4, we discussed inference regarding a single population proportion. We will now discuss inferential methods for comparing two population proportions. For example, in clinical trials of the drug Nasonex, a drug that is meant to relieve allergy symptoms, 26% of patients receiving 200 mcg of Nasonex reported a headache as a side effect while 22% of patients receiving a placebo reported a headache as a side effect. Researchers might want to determine whether the proportion of patients receiving the treatment and complaining of headaches is significantly higher than the proportion of patients receiving the placebo and complaining of headaches.

In order to test claims about two population proportions, we must first determine the sampling distribution of the difference of two proportions. Recall that the point estimate of a population proportion, p, is given by $\hat{p} = \dfrac{x}{n}$ where x is the number of the n individuals in the sample that have a specific characteristic. In addition, we recall that the sampling distribution of $\hat{p}$ is approximately normal with mean $\mu_{\hat{p}} = p$ and standard deviation $\sigma_{\hat{p}} = \sqrt{\dfrac{p(1-p)}{n}}$, provided that $np(1-p) \geq 10$, so that

$$Z = \frac{\hat{p} - p}{\sqrt{\dfrac{p(1-p)}{n}}}$$

is approximately normal with mean 0 and standard deviation 1. Using this information along with the idea of independent sampling from two populations, we obtain the sampling distribution of the difference between two proportions:

Theorem

Sampling Distribution of the Difference between Two Proportions

Suppose a simple random sample of size n_1 is taken from a population where x_1 of the individuals have a specified characteristic and a simple random sample of size n_2 is independently taken from a different population where x_2 of the individuals have a specified characteristic. The sampling distribution of $\hat{p}_1 - \hat{p}_2$ is approximately normal, with mean $\mu_{\hat{p}_1 - \hat{p}_2} = p_1 - p_2$ and standard deviation $\sigma_{\hat{p}_1 - \hat{p}_2} = \sqrt{\dfrac{p_1(1-p_1)}{n_1} + \dfrac{p_2(1-p_2)}{n_2}}$, provided that $n_1\hat{p}_1(1-\hat{p}_1) \geq 10$ and $n_2\hat{p}_2(1-\hat{p}_2) \geq 10$ where $\hat{p}_1 = \dfrac{x_1}{n_1}$ and $\hat{p}_2 = \dfrac{x_2}{n_2}$. The standardized version of $\hat{p}_1 - \hat{p}_2$ is then written as

$$Z = \frac{(\hat{p}_1 - \hat{p}_2) - (p_1 - p_2)}{\sqrt{\dfrac{p_1(1-p_1)}{n_1} + \dfrac{p_2(1-p_2)}{n_2}}}$$

which has an approximate standard normal distribution.

① Testing a Claim Regarding Two Population Proportions

Now that we know the approximate sampling distribution of $\hat{p}_1 - \hat{p}_2$, we can introduce a procedure that can be used to test claims regarding two population proportions. However, we must first consider the test statistic. It would seem logical that the test statistic for the difference of two population proportions would be

$$Z = \frac{(\hat{p}_1 - \hat{p}_2) - (p_1 - p_2)}{\sqrt{\dfrac{p_1(1 - p_1)}{n_1} + \dfrac{p_2(1 - p_2)}{n_2}}} \qquad (1)$$

However, whenever we test a hypothesis, the null hypothesis is assumed true. When comparing two population proportions, the null hypothesis will always be H_0: $p_1 = p_2$. Because the null hypothesis is assumed to be true, the test assumes $p_1 = p_2$, so that $p_1 - p_2 = 0$ and $p_1 = p_2 = p$ where p is the common population proportion. If we substitute the common value of p into Equation (1), we obtain

$$Z = \frac{(\hat{p}_1 - \hat{p}_2) - (p_1 - p_2)}{\sqrt{\dfrac{p_1(1 - p_1)}{n_1} + \dfrac{p_2(1 - p_2)}{n_2}}} = \frac{\hat{p}_1 - \hat{p}_2 - 0}{\sqrt{\dfrac{p(1 - p)}{n_1} + \dfrac{p(1 - p)}{n_2}}} = \frac{\hat{p}_1 - \hat{p}_2}{\sqrt{p(1 - p)}\sqrt{\dfrac{1}{n_1} + \dfrac{1}{n_2}}} \qquad (2)$$

We need a point estimate of p because it is unknown. The best point estimate of p is called the **pooled estimate of p**, denoted $\hat{p}$, where

$$\hat{p} = \frac{x_1 + x_2}{n_1 + n_2}$$

Substituting the pooled estimate of p into Equation (2), we obtain

$$Z = \frac{\hat{p}_1 - \hat{p}_2}{\sigma_{\hat{p}_1 - \hat{p}_2}} = \frac{\hat{p}_1 - \hat{p}_2}{\sqrt{\hat{p}(1 - \hat{p})}\sqrt{\dfrac{1}{n_1} + \dfrac{1}{n_2}}}$$

This test statistic will be used to test claims regarding two population proportions. We now present the steps necessary to test claims regarding two population proportions.

Hypothesis Test Regarding the Difference between Two Population Proportions

If a claim is made regarding the two population proportions, p_1 and p_2, we can use the steps that follow to test the claim, provided that
1. the samples are independently obtained using simple random sampling,
2. $n_1\hat{p}_1(1 - \hat{p}_1) \geq 10$ and $n_2\hat{p}_2(1 - \hat{p}_2) \geq 10$,
3. $n_1 \leq 0.05N_1$ and $n_2 \leq 0.05N_2$ (the sample size is no more than 5% of the population size); this requirement ensures the independence necessary for a binomial experiment.

Step 1: A claim is made regarding two population proportions. The claim is used to determine the null and alternative hypotheses. The hypotheses can be structured in one of three ways, as shown below:

Two-Tailed	Left-Tailed	Right-Tailed
H_0: $p_1 = p_2$	H_0: $p_1 = p_2$	H_0: $p_1 = p_2$
H_1: $p_1 \neq p_2$	H_1: $p_1 < p_2$	H_1: $p_1 > p_2$

Note: p_1 is the population proportion for population 1, and p_2 is the assumed value of the population proportion for population 2.

Step 2: Select a level of significance α based upon the seriousness of making a Type I error. The level of significance is used to determine the critical value. For example, the critical value in the left-tailed test is $-z_\alpha$.

The shaded region(s) represents the critical region.

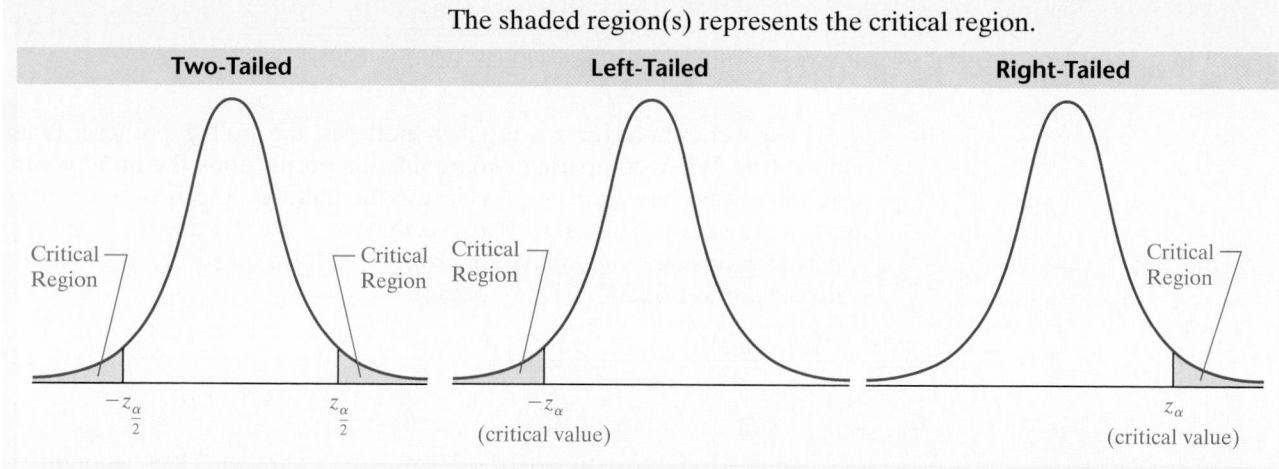

Step 3: Compute the **test statistic** $Z = \dfrac{\hat{p}_1 - \hat{p}_2}{\sqrt{\hat{p}(1 - \hat{p})}\sqrt{\dfrac{1}{n_1} + \dfrac{1}{n_2}}}$ where $\hat{p} = \dfrac{x_1 + x_2}{n_1 + n_2}$.

Step 4: Compare the critical value with the test statistic.

Two-Tailed	Left-Tailed	Right-Tailed
If $Z < -z_{\alpha/2}$ or $Z > z_{\alpha/2}$, reject the null hypothesis	If $Z < -z_\alpha$, reject the null hypothesis	If $Z > z_\alpha$, reject the null hypothesis

Step 5: State the conclusion.

▶ **EXAMPLE 1** **Testing a Claim Regarding Two Population Proportions**

Problem: In clinical trials of Nasonex, 3774 adult and adolescent allergy patients (patients 12 years and older) were randomly divided into two groups. The patients in Group 1 (experimental group) received 200 mcg of Nasonex, while the patients in Group 2 (control group) received a placebo. Of the 2103 patients in the experimental group, 547 reported headaches as side effect. Of the 1671 patients in the control group, 368 reported headaches as a side effect. Is there significant evidence to support the claim that the proportion of Nasonex users that experienced headaches as a side effect is greater than the proportion in the control group at the $\alpha = 0.05$ level of significance?

Approach: We must verify the requirements to perform the hypothesis test. That is, the sample must be a simple random sample and $n_1 \hat{p}_1(1 - \hat{p}_1) \geq 10$ and $n_2 \hat{p}_2(1 - \hat{p}_2) \geq 10$. In addition, the sample size cannot be more than 5% of the population. Then we follow the preceding Steps 1–5.

Solution: First we verify that the requirements are satisfied:

1. The samples are independently obtained using simple random sampling.

2. We have $x_1 = 547$, $n_1 = 2103$, $x_2 = 368$, and $n_2 = 1671$, so that $\hat{p}_1 = \dfrac{x_1}{n_1} = \dfrac{547}{2103} = 0.26$ and $\hat{p}_2 = \dfrac{x_2}{n_2} = \dfrac{368}{1671} = 0.22$. Therefore,

$$n_1\hat{p}_1(1 - \hat{p}_1) = 2103(0.26)(1 - 0.26) = 404.6172 \geq 10$$

$$n_2\hat{p}_2(1 - \hat{p}_2) = 1671(0.22)(1 - 0.22) = 286.7436 \geq 10$$

3. There are over 10 million Americans who are 12 years old or older who are allergy sufferers, so the sample sizes are less than 5% of the population size.

All three requirements are satisfied, so we now proceed to follow Steps 1–5.

Step 1: The claim is that the proportion of patients taking Nasonex who experience a headache is greater than the proportion of patients taking the placebo who experience a headache. Letting p_1 represent the population proportion of patients taking Nasonex who experience a headache and p_2 represent the population proportion of patients taking the placebo who experience a headache, we can express the claim as $p_1 > p_2$. This is a right-tailed hypothesis with

$$H_o\!: p_1 = p_2 \qquad \text{versus} \qquad H_1\!: p_1 > p_2$$

or equivalently,

$$H_o\!: p_1 - p_2 = 0 \qquad \text{versus} \qquad H_1\!: p_1 - p_2 > 0$$

Step 2: Because this is a right-tailed test, we determine the critical value at the $\alpha = 0.05$ level of significance to be $z_{0.05} = 1.645$. The critical region is displayed in Figure 7.

Figure 7

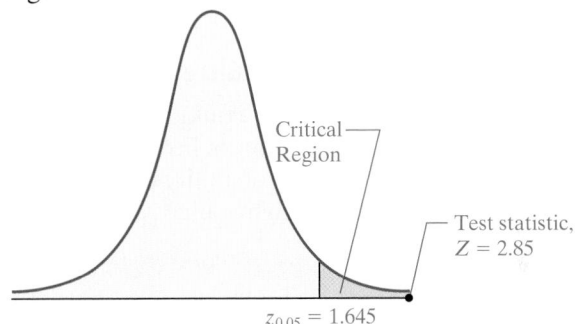

Critical Region

Test statistic, $Z = 2.85$

$z_{0.05} = 1.645$

Step 3: From verifying that requirement 2 was satisfied we have that
$\hat{p}_1 = \dfrac{x_1}{n_1} = \dfrac{547}{2103} = 0.26$ and $\hat{p}_2 = \dfrac{x_2}{n_2} = \dfrac{368}{1671} = 0.22.$
To find the test statistic, we first must compute the pooled estimate of p,

$$\hat{p} = \frac{x_1 + x_2}{n_1 + n_2} = \frac{547 + 368}{2103 + 1671} = 0.242$$

The test statistic is

$$Z = \frac{\hat{p}_1 - \hat{p}_2}{\sqrt{\hat{p}(1 - \hat{p})}\sqrt{\dfrac{1}{n_1} + \dfrac{1}{n_2}}} = \frac{0.26 - 0.22}{\sqrt{0.242(1 - 0.242)}\sqrt{\dfrac{1}{2103} + \dfrac{1}{1671}}} = \frac{0.04}{0.0140357419} = 2.85$$

The sample difference in proportions is 2.85 standard deviations above the assumed difference of 0.

Step 4: Because the test statistic $Z = 2.85$ is greater than the critical value of $z_{0.05} = 1.645$, we reject the null hypothesis. That is, the value of the test statistic falls within the critical region so we reject H_o. We label this point in Figure 7.

Step 5: There is sufficient evidence at the $\alpha = 0.05$ level of significance to support the claim that the proportion of individuals 12 years and older taking 200 mcg of Nasonex who experience headaches is greater than the proportion of individuals 12 years and older taking a placebo who experience headaches. ◄◄

In looking back at the results of Example 1, we notice that the proportion of individuals taking 200 mcg of Nasonex who experience headaches is *statistically significantly* greater than the proportion of individuals 12 years and older taking a placebo who experience headaches. However, we need to ask ourselves a pressing question. Would a mother not give her child an allergy medication because 26% of patients experienced a headache taking the medication versus 22% who experienced a headache taking a placebo? Most mothers would be willing to accept the additional "risk" of a headache in order to relieve her child's allergy symptoms. While the difference of 4% is statistically significant, it does not have any *practical significance*.

Definition

Practical significance refers to the idea that small differences in statistics can be statistically significant, while not large enough to have any functional value.

Caution

In any statistical study, be sure to consider practical significance. Many statistically significant results can be produced simply by increasing the sample size.

When performing significance tests with large samples, small differences between the null hypothesis and the sample statistics will result in a statistically significant difference. Be sure to ask yourself whether the difference has any practical significance.

P-Values

We could also test the hypothesis of Example 1 by using the *P*-value approach. From Step 4, we have the test statistic $Z = 2.85$. The *P*-value is the probability of obtaining a test statistic $Z = 2.85$ or higher (because this is a right-tailed test). Consulting Table II, we find that

$$P\text{-value} = P(Z \geq 2.85) = 1 - P(Z < 2.85) = 1 - 0.9978 = 0.0022$$

Because the *P*-value is less than the level of significance, $\alpha = 0.05$, we reject the null hypothesis.

Using Technology: We could also test the claim presented in Example 1 using statistical software or a graphing calculator with advanced statistical features. Figure 8 shows the results of Example 1, using Minitab.

Figure 8

Test and Confidence Interval for Two Proportions

```
Sample        X        N  Sample p
1           547     2103  0.260105
2           368     1671  0.220227


Estimate for p(1) - p(2): 0.0398772
95% CI for p(1) - p(2): (0.0125583, 0.0671961)
Test for p(1) - p(2) = 0 (vs > 0): Z = 2.84  P-Value = 0.002
```

Notice that the test statistic is $Z = 2.84$. The discrepancy between the output of Minitab and the solution presented in Example 1 is due simply to rounding. The *P*-value presented by Minitab is 0.002, which agrees with the *P*-value we obtained.

NW   *Now Work Problem 11(a).*

② **Confidence Intervals for the Difference between Two Population Proportions**

The sampling distribution of the difference of two proportions, $\hat{p}_1 - \hat{p}_2$, can also be used to construct confidence intervals for the difference of two proportions.

Constructing a $(1 - \alpha) \cdot 100\%$ Confidence Interval for the Difference between Two Population Proportions

To construct a $(1 - \alpha) \cdot 100\%$ confidence interval for the difference between two population proportions, the following requirements must be satisfied:
1. the samples are obtained independently, using simple random sampling,
2. $n_1 \hat{p}_1 (1 - \hat{p}_1) \geq 10$ and $n_2 \hat{p}_2 (1 - \hat{p}_2) \geq 10$,
3. $n_1 \leq 0.05 N_1$ and $n_2 \leq 0.05 N_2$ (the sample size is no more than 5% of the population size); this ensures the independence necessary for a binomial experiment.

Provided that these requirements are met, a $(1 - \alpha) \cdot 100\%$ confidence interval for $p_1 - p_2$ is given by

$$\text{Lower Bound: } (\hat{p}_1 - \hat{p}_2) - z_{\alpha/2} \cdot \sqrt{\frac{\hat{p}_1(1 - \hat{p}_1)}{n_1} + \frac{\hat{p}_2(1 - \hat{p}_2)}{n_2}}$$

$$\text{Upper Bound: } (\hat{p}_1 - \hat{p}_2) + z_{\alpha/2} \cdot \sqrt{\frac{\hat{p}_1(1 - \hat{p}_1)}{n_1} + \frac{\hat{p}_2(1 - \hat{p}_2)}{n_2}} \quad \textbf{(3)}$$

Notice that we do not pool the sample proportions. This is because we are not making any assumptions regarding their equality as we did in hypothesis testing.

▶ **EXAMPLE 2**   **Constructing a Confidence Interval for the Difference between Two Population Proportions**

Problem: In clinical trials of Nasonex, 750 randomly selected pediatric patients (ages 3 to 11 years old) were randomly divided into two groups. The patients in Group 1 (experimental group) received 100 mcg of Nasonex, while the patients in Group 2 (control group) received a placebo. Of the 374 patients in the experimental group, 64 reported headaches as side effect. Of the 376 patients in the control group, 68 reported headaches as a side effect. Construct a 90% confidence interval for the difference between the two population proportions, $p_1 - p_2$.

Approach: We can compute a 90% confidence interval about $p_1 - p_2$, provided that the requirements stated above are satisfied. We then construct the interval by using Formula (3).

Solution:

Step 1: We need to verify the requirements for constructing a confidence interval about the difference between two population proportions. (1) The samples were randomly divided into two groups. (2) For the experimental group

(Group 1), we have $n_1 = 374$ and $x_1 = 64$, so that $\hat{p}_1 = \dfrac{x_1}{n_1} = \dfrac{64}{374} = 0.171$.

For the control group (Group 2), we have $n_2 = 376$ and $x_2 = 68$, so that $\hat{p}_2 = \dfrac{x_2}{n_2} = \dfrac{68}{376} = 0.181$. Therefore,

$$n_1 \hat{p}_1 (1 - \hat{p}_1) = 374(0.171)(1 - 0.171) = 53.02 \geq 10$$

$$n_2 \hat{p}_2 (1 - \hat{p}_2) = 376(0.181)(1 - 0.181) = 55.74 \geq 10$$

(3) The samples were independently obtained and the sample sizes are less than 5% of the population size. (There are over 20 million children between the ages of 3 and 11 in the United States.)

Step 2: Because we want a 90% confidence interval, we have $\alpha = 0.10$, so $z_{\alpha/2} = z_{0.05} = 1.645$.

Step 3: Substituting into Formula (3) with $\hat{p}_1 = 0.171$, $n_1 = 374$, $\hat{p}_2 = 0.181$, and $n_2 = 376$, we obtain the lower and upper bounds on the confidence interval:

Lower Bound:

$$(\hat{p}_1 - \hat{p}_2) - z_{\alpha/2} \cdot \sqrt{\frac{\hat{p}_1(1 - \hat{p}_1)}{n_1} + \frac{\hat{p}_2(1 - \hat{p}_2)}{n_2}}$$

$$= (0.171 - 0.181) - 1.645 \cdot \sqrt{\frac{0.171(1 - 0.171)}{374} + \frac{0.181(1 - 0.181)}{376}}$$

$$= -0.010 - 0.046 = -0.056$$

Upper Bound:

$$(\hat{p}_1 - \hat{p}_2) + z_{\alpha/2} \cdot \sqrt{\frac{\hat{p}_1(1 - \hat{p}_1)}{n_1} + \frac{\hat{p}_2(1 - \hat{p}_2)}{n_2}}$$

$$= (0.171 - 0.181) + 1.645 \cdot \sqrt{\frac{0.171(1 - 0.171)}{374} + \frac{0.181(1 - 0.181)}{376}}$$

$$= -0.010 + 0.046 = 0.036$$

Based upon the results of the study, we are 90% confident that the difference between the proportion of headaches in the experimental group and the control group is between −0.056 and 0.036. Because the confidence interval contains 0, there is no evidence to support the claim that the proportion of patients complaining of headaches who receive Nasonex is different from those who do not receive Nasonex at the $\alpha = 0.1$ level of significance. ◄◄

Figure 9

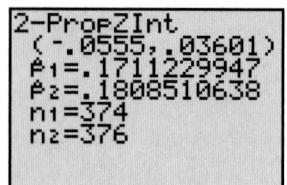

NW *Now Work Problem 11(b).*

Using Technology: Graphing calculators with advanced statistical features and statistical spreadsheets can be used to construct confidence intervals about the difference between two population proportions. Figure 9 shows the results using a TI-83 Plus graphing calculator.

Determining Sample Sizes

In Section 8.3, we introduced a method for determining the sample size n required to estimate a single population proportion within a specified margin of error, E, with a specified level of confidence. This formula was obtained by solving the margin of error, $E = z_{\alpha/2} \cdot \sqrt{\dfrac{\hat{p}(1 - \hat{p})}{n}}$, for n. We can follow the same approach to determine the sample size when we estimate two population proportions. Notice that the margin of error, E, in Formula (3) is given by

$E = z_{\alpha/2} \cdot \sqrt{\dfrac{\hat{p}_1(1 - \hat{p}_1)}{n_1} + \dfrac{\hat{p}_2(1 - \hat{p}_2)}{n_2}}$. Assuming that $n_1 = n_2 = n$, we can solve this expression for $n = n_1 = n_2$ and obtain the following result:

Theorem

> **Sample Size for Estimating $p_1 - p_2$**
>
> The sample size required to obtain a $(1 - \alpha) \cdot 100\%$ confidence interval with a margin of error, E, is given by
>
> $$n = n_1 = n_2 = [\hat{p}_1(1 - \hat{p}_1) + \hat{p}_2(1 - \hat{p}_2)]\left(\frac{z_{\alpha/2}}{E}\right)^2 \qquad (4)$$
>
> rounded up to the next integer if prior estimates of p_1 and p_2, $\hat{p}_1$ and $\hat{p}_2$, are available. If prior estimates of p_1 and p_2 are unavailable, the sample size is
>
> $$n = n_1 = n_2 = 0.5\left(\frac{z_{\alpha/2}}{E}\right)^2 \qquad (5)$$
>
> rounded up to the next integer.

▶ **EXAMPLE 3   Determining Sample Size**

Problem: A nutritionist wishes to estimate the difference between the proportion of males and females that consume the USDA's recommended daily intake of calcium. What sample size should be obtained if she wishes the estimate to be within 3 percentage points with 95% confidence, assuming that

(a) she uses the results of the USDA's 1994–1996 Diet and Health Knowledge Survey, according to which 51.1% of males and 75.2% of females consume the USDA's recommended daily intake of calcium,

(b) she does not use any prior estimates.

Approach: We have $E = 0.03*$ and $z_{\alpha/2} = z_{0.05/2} = z_{0.025} = 1.96$. To answer part (a), we let $\hat{p}_1 = 0.511$ (for males) and $\hat{p}_2 = 0.752$ (for females) in Formula (4). To answer part (b), we use Formula (5).

Solution:

(a) Substituting $E = 0.03$, $z_{0.025} = 1.96$, $\hat{p}_1 = 0.511$, and $\hat{p}_2 = 0.752$ into Formula (4), we obtain

$$n_1 = n_2 = [\hat{p}_1(1 - \hat{p}_1) + \hat{p}_2(1 - \hat{p}_2)]\left(\frac{z_{\alpha/2}}{E}\right)^2 = [0.511(1 - 0.511) + 0.752(1 - 0.752)]\left(\frac{1.96}{0.03}\right)^2$$

$$= 1862.642444$$

*The margin of error should always be expressed as a decimal when using Formulas (4) and (5).

We round this value up to 1863. The nutritionist must survey 1863 randomly selected males and 1863 randomly selected females.

(b) Substituting $E = 0.03$ and $z_{0.025} = 1.96$ into Formula (5), we obtain

$$n_1 = n_2 = 0.5\left(\frac{z_{\alpha/2}}{E}\right)^2 = 0.5\left(\frac{1.96}{0.03}\right)^2 = 2134.222222$$

We round this value up to 2135. The nutritionist must survey 2135 randomly selected males and 2135 randomly selected females. ◀◀

NW *Now Work Problem 17.*

We can see that having prior estimates of the population proportions reduces the number of individuals that need to be surveyed.

10.3 Assess Your Understanding

Concepts and Vocabulary

1. Explain why we determine a pooled estimate of the population proportion when computing $\sigma_{\hat{p}_1 - \hat{p}_2}$.

2. State the requirements that must be satisfied in order to test a claim regarding two population proportions.

3. Describe the difference between statistical significance and practical significance.

Exercises

• Skill Building

In Problems 1–4, test the claim at the $\alpha = 0.05$ level of significance by determining (a) the null and alternative hypotheses, (b) the test statistic, (c) the critical value, and (d) the P-value. Assume the samples were obtained independently using simple random sampling.

1. Claim $p_1 > p_2$. Sample data:
   $x_1 = 368, n_1 = 541, x_2 = 351, n_2 = 593$

2. Claim $p_1 < p_2$. Sample data:
   $x_1 = 109, n_1 = 475, x_2 = 78, n_2 = 325$

3. Claim $p_1 \neq p_2$. Sample data:
   $x_1 = 28, n_1 = 254, x_2 = 36, n_2 = 301$

4. Claim $p_1 \neq p_2$. Sample data:
   $x_1 = 804, n_1 = 874, x_2 = 902, n_2 = 954$

In Problems 5–8, construct a confidence interval for $p_1 - p_2$ at the given level of confidence.

5. $x_1 = 368, n_1 = 541, x_2 = 421, n_2 = 593$,
   90% confidence $(0.04, 0.14)$

6. $x_1 = 109, n_1 = 475, x_2 = 78, n_2 = 325$,
   99% confidence $(-0.09, 0.07)$

7. $x_1 = 28, n_1 = 254, x_2 = 36, n_2 = 301$,
   95% confidence $(-0.06, 0.04)$

8. $x_1 = 804, n_1 = 874, x_2 = 892, n_2 = 954$,
   95% confidence $(-0.04, 0.01)$

• Applying the Concepts

9. **Prevnar** The drug Prevnar is a vaccine meant to prevent certain types of bacterial meningitis. It is typically administered to infants starting around two months of age. In randomized, double-blind clinical trials of Prevnar, infants were randomly divided into two groups. Subjects in Group 1 received Prevnar while subjects in Group 2 received a control vaccine. After the first dose, 107 of 710 subjects in the experimental group (Group 1) experienced fever as a side effect. After the first dose, 67 of 611 of the subjects in the control group (Group 2) experienced fever as a side effect.

   (a) Test the claim that a higher proportion of subjects in Group 1 experienced fever as a side effect than subjects in Group 2 at the $\alpha = 0.05$ level of significance, using both the classical approach and P-value approach. Reject H_o; P-value = 0.0139

(b) Construct a 90% confidence interval for the difference between the two population proportions, $p_1 - p_2$. (0.01, 0.07)

10. **Prevnar** The drug Prevnar is a vaccine meant to prevent certain types of bacterial meningitis. It is typically administered to infants starting around two months of age. In randomized, double-blind clinical trials of Prevnar, infants were randomly divided into two groups. Subjects in Group 1 received Prevnar, while subjects in Group 2 received a control vaccine. After the second dose, 137 of 452 subjects in the experimental group (Group 1) experienced drowsiness as a side effect. After the second dose, 31 of 99 subjects in the control group (Group 2) experienced drowsiness as a side effect.

(a) Test the claim that a different proportion of subjects in Group 1 experienced drowsiness as a side effect than subjects in Group 2 at the $\alpha = 0.05$ level of significance, using both the classical approach and P-value approach. Do not reject H_o; P-value = 0.8443

(b) Construct a 99% confidence interval for the difference between the two population proportions, $p_1 - p_2$. (−0.14, 0.12)

11. **Too Much Cholesterol in Your Diet?** A nutritionist claims that the proportion of individuals who have at most an eighth-grade education and consume more than the USDA's recommended daily allowance of 300 mg of cholesterol is higher than the proportion of individuals who have at least some college and consume too much cholesterol. In interviews with 320 individuals who have at most an eighth-grade education, she determined that 114 of them consumed too much cholesterol. In interviews with 350 individuals with at least some college, she determined that 112 of them too much cholesterol per day. (Based upon data obtained from the USDA's 1994–1996 Diet and Health Knowledge Survey.)

(a) Test the claim that the proportion of individuals with at most an eighth-grade education who consume too much cholesterol is higher than the proportion of individuals who have at least some college and consume too much cholesterol at the $\alpha = 0.1$ level of significance, using both the classical approach and P-value approach. Do not reject H_o

(b) Construct a 95% confidence interval for the difference between the two population proportions, $p_8 - p_c$. (−0.04, 0.11)

12. **Consumption of Saturated Fat** A nutritionist claims that the proportion of females who consume too much saturated fat is lower than the proportion of males who consume too much saturated fat. In interviews with 513 randomly selected females, she determines that 300 consume too much saturated fat. In interviews with 564 randomly selected males, she determines that 391 consume too much saturated fat, based upon data obtained from the USDA's 1994–1996 Diet and Health Knowledge Survey.

(a) Test the claim that a lower proportion of females than males consume too much saturated fat at the $\alpha = 0.05$ level of significance, using both the classical approach and P-value approach. Reject H_o

(b) Construct a 95% confidence interval for the difference between the two population proportions, $p_f - p_m$. (−0.17, −0.05)

13. **Percentage of Americans Who Smoke on the Decline?** On November 13–15, 2000, the Gallup Organization surveyed 1028 adults and found that 257 of them had smoked at least one cigarette in the past week. In 1990, they also asked 1028 adults the same question and determined that 278 adults had smoked at least one cigarette in the past week.

(a) Test the claim that the proportion of adults who had smoked at least one cigarette in the past week decreased from its 1990 level at the $\alpha = 0.05$ level of significance, using both the classical approach and P-value approach. Do not reject H_o

(b) Construct a 95% confidence interval for the difference between the two population proportions, $p_{2000} - p_{1990}$. (−0.05, 0.01)

14. **Life on Mars?** On March 19–21, 1999, the Gallup Organization surveyed 535 adults aged 18 years old or older and asked, "Do you think there is life of some form on other planets in the universe or not?" Of the 535 individuals surveyed, 326 responded "Yes." When the same question was asked on September 3–5, 1996, 385 of the 535 individuals surveyed responded "Yes."

(a) Test the claim that the proportion of adults who believe that there is life on other planets has decreased since September, 1996 at the $\alpha = 0.10$ level of significance, using both the classical approach and P-value approach. Reject H_o

(b) Construct a 90% confidence interval for the difference between the two population proportions, $p_{1996} - p_{2000}$. (−0.16, −0.06)

15. **The Salk Vaccine** On April 12, 1955, Dr. Jonas Salk released the results of clinical trials for his vaccine to prevent polio. In these clinical trials, 400,000 children were randomly divided in two groups. The subjects in Group 1 (the experimental group) were given the vaccine, while the subjects in Group 2 (the control group) were given a placebo. Of the 200,000 children in the experimental group, 33 developed polio. Of the 200,000 children in the control group, 115 developed polio.

(a) Test the claim that the proportion of subjects in the experimental group who contracted polio is less than the percentage of subjects in the control group who contracted polio at the $\alpha = 0.01$ level of significance, using both the classical approach and P-value approach. Reject H_o

(b) Construct a 90% confidence interval for the difference between the two population proportions, $p_1 - p_2$. (−0.0005, −0.0003)

16. **Child Safety** In 1977, the Gallup Organization asked the following question of 275 randomly selected parents who have children in Grades K–12: "Thinking about your oldest child, when he or she is at school, do you fear for his or her physical safety?" Of the 275 parents, 66 responded that they did fear for their child's safety. The same question was asked of 275 randomly selected parents in August of 2001, with 88 responding that they feared for their child's safety.

    (a) Test the claim that the proportion of parents that fear for their child's safety has increased from 1977 at the $\alpha = 0.05$ level of significance, using both the classical approach and the P-value approach. Reject H_o

    (b) Construct a 95% confidence interval for the difference between the two population proportions, $p_1 - p_2$. (0.01, 0.15)

    (c) Why do you think that Gallup required the parents to think only of their oldest child?

17. **Determining Sample Size** A physical therapist wants to determine the difference in the proportion of men and women that participate in regular sustained physical activity. What sample size should be obtained if she wishes the estimate to be within three percentage points with 95% confidence, assuming that

    (a) she uses the 1998 estimates of 21.9% male and 19.7% female from the U.S. National Center for Chronic Disease Prevention and Health Promotion? 1406

    (b) she does not use any prior estimates? 2135

18. **Determining Sample Size** An educator wants to determine the difference between the proportion of males and females that have completed four or more years of college. What sample size should be obtained if she wishes the estimate to be within two percentage points with 90% confidence, assuming that

    (a) she uses the 1999 estimates of 27.5% male and 23.1% female from the U.S. Census Bureau? 2551

    (b) she does not use any prior estimates? 3383

19. **Pepcid** In clinical trials of Pepcid, subjects were randomly divided into two groups. The 89 subjects in Group 1 received 40 mg of Pepcid during the evening hours, while 84 subjects received 20 mg of Pepcid twice a day. Of the 89 subjects in Group 1, 62 were healed after four weeks. Of the 84 subjects in Group 2, 56 were healed after four weeks. In order to test the claim that the proportion healed is different, the researchers entered the data into the Minitab statistical software and obtained the following results:

    ### Test and Confidence Interval for Two Proportions

    ```
    Sample       X       N  Sample p
    1           62      89  0.696629
    2           56      84  0.666667


    Estimate for p(1) — p(2): 0.0299625
    95% CI for p(1) — p(2): (−0.108906, 0.0168831)
    Test for p(1) — p(2) = 0 (vs not = 0): Z = 0.42 P-Value = 0.672
    ```

    What conclusion can be drawn from the clinical trials?

20. **Accupril** Accupril, a medication supplied by Pfizer Pharmaceuticals, is meant to control hypertension. In clinical trials of Accupril, 2142 subjects were divided into two groups. The 1563 subjects in Group 1 (the experimental group), received Accupril. The 579 subjects in Group 2 (the control group), received a placebo. Of the 1563 subjects in the experimental group, 61 experienced dizziness as a side effect. Of the 579 subjects in the control group, 15 experienced dizziness as a side effect. In order to test the claim that the proportion experiencing dizziness in the experimental group is greater than that in the control group, the researchers entered the data into Minitab statistical software and obtained the following results:

    ### Test and Confidence Interval for Two Proportions

    ```
    Sample       X       N  Sample p
    1           61    1563  0.039028
    2           15     579  0.025907


    Estimate for p(1) — p(2): 0.0131208
    95% CI for p(1) — p(2): (−0.00299150, 0.0292330)
    Test for p(1) — p(2) = 0 (vs > 0): Z = 1.46 P-Value = 0.072
    ```

    What conclusion can be drawn from the clinical trials?

21. Treating Apnea An individual with apnea stops breathing while sleeping. In a randomized, double-blind study to evaluate the efficacy of caffeine citrate for treatment of apnea, infants with six or more episodes of apnea were administered 10 mg/kg of caffeine citrate intravenously, followed by 2.5 mg/kg/day for up to 10 days or a placebo. ("Caffeine Citrate for the Treatment of Apnea in Prematurity: A Double-blind, Placebo Controlled Study," *Pharmacotherapy*, June 2000, 20(6): 644–652). With successful treatment defined as a 50% or more reduction in apnea episodes, it was determined that caffeine citrate was significantly more effective than the placebo in reducing apnea episodes by at least 50% in six days with the *P*-value less than 0.05. State any conclusions, using this *P*-value.

Technology Step-by-Step
Inference about Two Population Proportions

TI-83 Plus **Hypothesis Tests**

Step 1: Press STAT, highlight TESTS, and select `6:2-PropZTest`...

Step 2: Enter the values of x_1, n_1, x_2, and n_2.

Step 3: Highlight the appropriate relation between p_1 and p_2 in the alternative hypothesis.

Step 4: Highlight Calculate or Draw and press ENTER. Calculate gives the test statistic and *P*-value. Draw will draw the *Z*-distribution with the *P*-value shaded.

Confidence Intervals

Follow the same steps as those given for hypothesis tests, except select `B:2-PropZInt`... Also, select a confidence level (such as 95% = 0.95).

MINITAB *Step 1:* Select the **Stat** menu, highlight **Basic Statistics**, then highlight **2 Proportions**...

Step 2: Click the Summarized Data Option. Enter the number of trials, n_1, and the number of successes, x_1. Enter the number of trials, n_2, and the number of successes, x_2.

Step 3: Under OPTIONS, select the direction of the alternative hypothesis and select a confidence level. Click OK.

Excel *Step 1:* Load the PHStat add-in.

Step 2: Select the **PHStat** menu. Highlight **Two-Sample Tests**, then highlight **Z Test for Differences in Two Proportions**...

Step 3: Enter the hypothesized difference in the two proportions (ususally 0). Enter the level of significance, α. For the Population 1 sample, enter the number of success, x_1, and the sample size, n_1. For the Population 2 sample, enter the number of success, x_2, and the sample size, n_2. Select the appropriate test option. Click OK.

10.4 Inference about Two Population Standard Deviations

Objectives Find critical values of the *F*-distribution

 Test claims regarding two population standard deviations

Note to Instructor
This section is optional and may be skipped without loss of continuity.

 In this section, we discuss methods for comparing two population standard deviations (or variances). For example, we might be interested in testing the claim that the rate of return for Cisco Systems stock is more volatile than

General Electric (GE) stock. If Cisco Systems stock is more volatile than GE, then the standard deviation rate of return on Cisco Systems would be higher than the standard deviation rate of return on GE. In order to test claims regarding population standard deviations, we use Fisher's F-distribution, named in honor of Sir Ronald A. Fisher. Certain requirements must be satisfied to test claims regarding two population standard deviations.

Requirements for Testing Claims Regarding Two Population Standard Deviations

1. The samples are independent simple random samples.
2. The populations from which the samples are drawn are normally distributed.

⬤
⬤
⬤ **Caution**

If the populations from which the samples are drawn are not normal, do not use the inferential procedures discussed in this section.

The second requirement is critical. The procedures introduced in this section are **not robust**. That is, any departures from normality will adversely affect the results of the test and make them unreliable. One reason for this outcome is that the standard deviation is not a good measure of spread in nonsymmetric distributions. This is because the standard deviation is not resistant to extreme values. Populations that are skewed will have extreme values that inflate the value of the standard deviation. Therefore, whenever performing inference regarding two population standard deviations, we must verify the requirement of the normality of the population using normal probability plots.

We shall use the following notation when describing the two populations:

Notation Used when Comparing Two Population Standard Deviations

σ_1^2: Variance for population 1.
σ_2^2: Variance for population 2.
s_1^2: Sample variance for population 1.
s_2^2: Sample variance for population 2.
n_1: Sample size for population 1.
n_2: Sample size for population 2.

Before we can perform statistical inference regarding two population standard deviations, we need to know the sampling distribution of the test statistic. In comparing two population standard deviations, the test statistic follows Fisher's F-distribution.

Theorem

Fisher's F-distribution

If $\sigma_1^2 = \sigma_2^2$ and s_1^2 and s_2^2 are sample variances from independent simple random samples of size n_1 and n_2, respectively, drawn from normal populations, then

$$F = \frac{s_1^2}{s_2^2}$$

follows the F-distribution with $n_1 - 1$ degrees of freedom in the numerator and $n_2 - 1$ degrees of freedom in the denominator.

We can find critical values of the F-distribution using Table V in Appendix A. Before discussing how to read Table V, we present characteristics of the F-distribution.

Characteristics of the *F*-distribution

1. It is not symmetric. The *F*-distribution is skewed right.

2. The shape of the *F*-distribution depends upon the degrees of freedom in the numerator and denominator. See Figure 10. This is similar to the χ^2 distribution and Student's *t*-distribution, whose shapes depend upon their degrees of freedom.

3. The total area under the curve is 1.

4. The values of *F* are always greater than or equal to zero.

Figure 10
F-Distributions

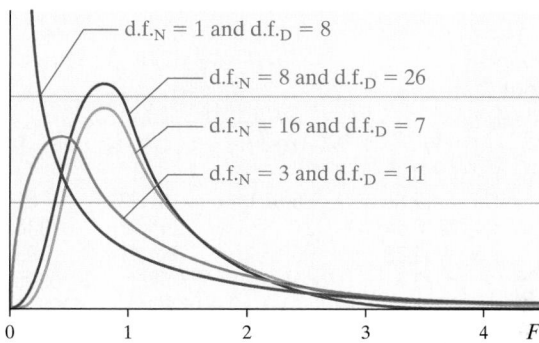

Table V is structured differently than the *t*- or χ^2 distribution. The row across the top provides the degrees of freedom in the numerator, while the column on the left provides the degrees of freedom in the denominator. Corresponding to the degrees of freedom in the numerator and denominator, we have various areas (0.1, 0.05, 0.025, 0.01, 0.001) in the right tail of the *F*-distribution. The body of the table provides the critical *F* values. We shall use the notation

$$F_{\alpha, n_1-1, n_2-1}$$

where $n_1 - 1$ is the degrees of freedom in the numerator and $n_2 - 1$ is the degrees of freedom in the denominator and α is the area to the right of F_{α, n_1-1, n_2-1}. To determine the critical value that has an area of α to the left, we use the following property:

$$F_{1-\alpha, n_1-1, n_2-1} = \frac{1}{F_{\alpha, n_2-1, n_1-1}}$$

So, to find the critical *F* that has an area of $\alpha = 0.05$ to the left with 12 degrees of freedom in the numerator and 20 degrees of freedom in the denominator, find the critical *F* that has an area of $\alpha = 0.05$ to the right with 20 degrees of freedom in the numerator and 12 degrees of freedom in the denominator, and compute its reciprocal.

▶ **EXAMPLE 1**   **Finding Critical Values for the *F*-distribution**

Problem: Find the critical *F*-value

(a) for a right-tailed test with $\alpha = 0.05$, degrees of freedom in the numerator = 10 and degrees of freedom in the denominator = 7.

(b) for a two-tailed test with $\alpha = 0.05$, degrees of freedom in the numerator = 15 and degrees of freedom in the denominator = 20.

Figure 11

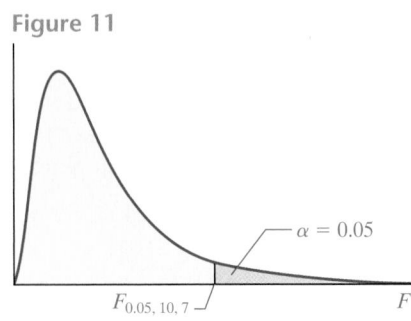

$\alpha = 0.05$

$F_{0.05,\,10,\,7}$ F

Approach: We shall perform the following steps to obtain the critical values:

Step 1: Draw an *F*-distribution with the critical value and area labeled.

Step 2: Use Table V to find the critical value.

Solution:

(a) *Step 1:* Figure 11 shows the *F*-distribution with 10 degrees of freedom in the numerator and 7 degrees of freedom in the denominator. The area to the right of the unknown critical value is 0.05. We denote this critical value $F_{0.05,\,10,\,7}$.

Figure 12

	Area to the Right of Critical Value	Degrees of Freedom in the Numerator							
		9	10	15	20	30	60	120	1000
1	0.100	59.86	60.19	61.22	61.74	62.26	62.79	63.06	63.30
	0.050	240.54	241.88	245.95	248.01	250.10	252.20	253.25	254.19
	0.025	963.28	968.63	984.87	993.10	1001.4	1009.8	1014	1017.7
	0.010	6022.5	6055.8	6157.3	6208.7	6260.6	6313	6339.4	6362.7
	0.001	602284	605621	615764	620908	626099	631337	633972	636301
2	0.100	9.38	9.39	9.42	9.44	9.16	9.47	9.48	9.49
	0.050	19.38	19.40	19.43	19.45	19.46	19.48	19.49	19.49
	0.025	39.39	39.40	39.43	39.45	39.46	39.48	39.49	39.50
	0.010	99.39	99.40	99.43	99.45	99.47	99.48	99.49	99.50
	0.001	999.39	999.40	999.43	999.45	999.47	999.48	999.49	999.50
3	0.100	5.24	5.23	5.20	5.18	5.17	5.15	5.14	5.13
	0.050	8.81	8.79	8.70	8.66	8.62	8.57	8.55	8.53
	0.025	14.47	14.42	14.25	14.17	14.08	13.99	13.95	13.91
	0.010	27.35	27.23	26.87	26.69	26.50	26.32	26.22	26.14
	0.001	129.86	129.25	127.37	126.42	125.45	124.47	123.97	123.53
4	0.100	3.94	3.92	3.87	3.84	3.82	3.79	3.78	3.76
	0.050	6.00	5.96	5.86	5.80	5.75	5.69	5.66	5.63
	0.025	8.90	8.84	8.66	8.56	8.46	8.36	8.31	8.26
	0.010	14.66	14.55	14.20	14.02	13.84	13.65	13.56	13.47
	0.001	48.47	48.05	46.76	46.10	45.43	44.75	44.40	44.09
5	0.100	3.32	3.30	3.24	3.21	3.17	3.14	3.12	3.11
	0.050	4.77	4.74	4.62	4.56	4.50	4.43	4.40	4.37
	0.025	6.68	6.62	6.43	6.33	6.23	6.12	6.07	6.02
	0.010	10.16	10.05	9.72	9.55	9.38	9.20	9.11	9.03
	0.001	27.24	26.92	25.91	25.39	24.87	24.33	24.06	23.82
6	0.100	2.96	2.94	2.87	2.84	2.80	2.76	2.74	2.72
	0.050	4.10	4.06	3.94	3.87	3.81	3.74	3.70	3.67
	0.025	5.52	5.46	5.27	5.17	5.07	4.96	4.90	4.86
	0.010	7.98	7.87	7.56	7.40	7.23	7.06	6.97	6.89
	0.001	18.69	18.41	17.56	17.12	16.67	16.21	15.98	15.77
7	0.100	2.72	2.70	2.63	2.59	2.56	2.51	2.49	2.47
	0.050	3.68	3.64	3.51	3.44	3.38	3.30	3.27	3.23
	0.025	4.82	4.76	4.57	4.47	4.36	4.25	4.20	4.15
	0.010	6.72	6.62	6.31	6.16	5.99	5.82	5.74	5.66
	0.001	14.33	14.08	13.32	12.93	12.53	12.12	11.91	11.72
8	0.100	2.56	2.54	2.46	2.42	2.38	2.34	2.32	2.30
	0.050	3.39	3.35	3.22	3.15	3.08	3.01	2.97	2.93
	0.025	4.36	4.30	4.10	4.00	3.89	3.78	3.73	3.68
	0.010	5.91	5.81	5.52	5.36	5.20	5.03	4.95	4.87
	0.001	11.77	11.54	10.84	10.48	10.11	9.73	9.53	9.36

Degrees of Freedom in the Denominator

Step 2: Figure 12 shows a partial representation of Table V. We box the column corresponding to 10 degrees of freedom (the numerator degrees of freedom) and the row corresponding to 7 degrees of freedom (the denominator degrees of freedom) with $\alpha = 0.05$. The critical value is $F_{0.05, \, 10, \, 7} = 3.64$.

(b) Step 1: Figure 13 shows the F-distribution with 15 degrees of freedom in the numerator and 20 degrees of freedom in the denominator. The area to the right of the right critical value is $\alpha/2 = 0.025$. We denote this critical value $F_{0.025, \, 15, \, 20}$. The area to the right of the left critical value is $1 - \alpha/2 = 0.975$. We denote this critical value $F_{0.975, \, 15, \, 20}$.

Figure 13

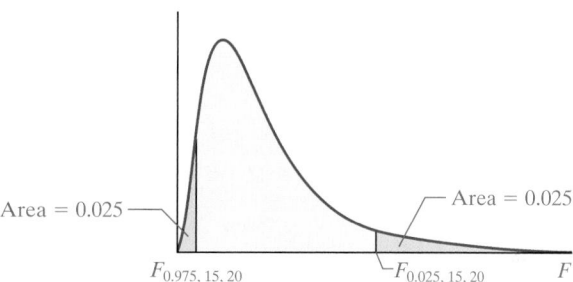

Area = 0.025

Area = 0.025

$F_{0.975, \, 15, \, 20}$

$F_{0.025, \, 15, \, 20}$

F

Step 2: We refer to Table V. To find the right critical value, identify the column that represents 15 degrees of freedom (the numerator degrees of freedom) and the row that represents 20 degrees of freedom (the denominator degrees of freedom) with $\alpha/2 = 0.025$. The right critical value is $F_{0.025, \, 15, \, 20} = 2.57$. To find the left critical value, we use the fact that $F_{1-\alpha, n_1-1, n_2-1} = \dfrac{1}{F_{\alpha, n_2-1, n_1-1}}$. Therefore, we use Table V and find that $F_{0.025, \, 20, \, 15} = 2.76$. So the left critical value is

$$F_{0.975, 15, 20} = \frac{1}{F_{0.025, 20, 15}} = \frac{1}{2.76} = 0.36. \qquad \blacktriangleleft\blacktriangleleft$$

In studying Table V, we notice that some values of the degrees of freedom for either the numerator or denominator are not in the table. If the number of degrees of freedom is not found in the table, we shall follow the practice of choosing the degrees of freedom closest to that desired. If the degrees of freedom is exactly between two values, find the mean of the values. For example, to find the critical value corresponding to 35 degrees of freedom in the numerator, compute the mean of the critical values corresponding to 30 and 40 degrees of freedom in the numerator.

NW *Now Work Problem 1.*

② Hypothesis Tests on Two Population Standard Deviations

Now that we know the approximate sampling distribution of $\dfrac{s_1^2}{s_2^2}$ and we know how to find critical values in the F-distribution, we can introduce a procedure that can be used to test claims regarding two population standard deviations (or variances).

Hypothesis Test Regarding Two Population Standard Deviations

If a claim is made regarding two population standard deviations, σ_1 and σ_2, we can use the following steps to test the claim provided:

1. The sample is obtained using simple random sampling.
2. The sample data are independent.
3. The populations from which the samples are drawn are normally distributed.

Step 1: A claim is made regarding two population standard deviations. The claim is used to determine the null and alternative hypotheses. The hypotheses can be structured in one of three ways, as shown below.

Two-Tailed	Left-Tailed	Right-Tailed
$H_0: \sigma_1 = \sigma_2$	$H_0: \sigma_1 = \sigma_2$	$H_0: \sigma_1 = \sigma_2$
$H_1: \sigma_1 \neq \sigma_2$	$H_1: \sigma_1 < \sigma_2$	$H_1: \sigma_1 > \sigma_2$

Note: σ_1 is the population standard deviation for population 1, and σ_2 is the population standard deviation for population 2.

Step 2: Choose a level of significance α based upon the seriousness of making a Type I error. The level of significance is used to determine the critical value. The critical value is determined using the degrees of freedom in the numerator $n_1 - 1$ and the degrees of freedom in the denominator $n_2 - 1$. For example, the critical value in the right-tailed test is F_{α, n_1-1, n_2-1} with the $n_1 - 1$ degrees of freedom in the numerator and $n_2 - 1$ degrees of freedom in the denominator. The shaded regions represent the critical region, as shown.

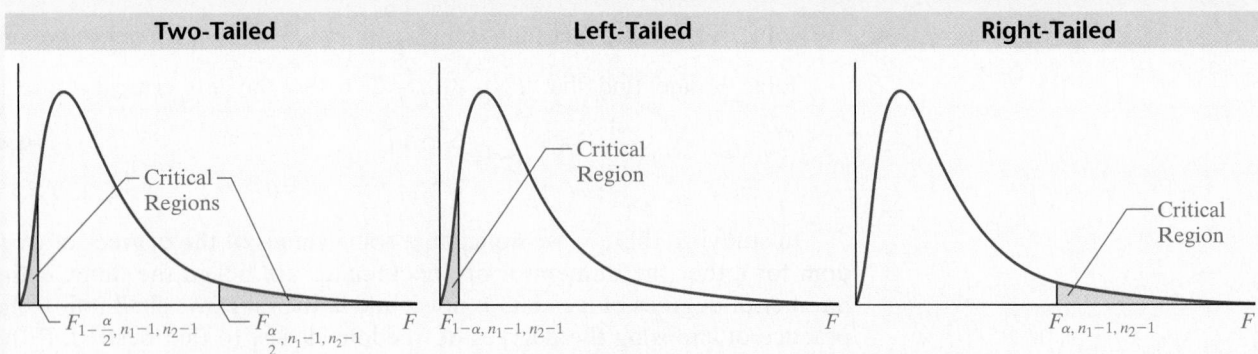

Step 3: Compute the **test statistic** $F = \dfrac{s_1^2}{s_2^2}$, which follows Fisher's F-distribution.

Step 4: Compare the critical value with the test statistic, as shown.

Two-Tailed	Left-Tailed	Right-Tailed
If $F < F_{1-\alpha/2, n_1-1, n_2-1}$ or $F > F_{\alpha/2, n_1-1, n_2-1}$, reject the null hypothesis	If $F < F_{1-\alpha, n_1-1, n_2-1}$, reject the null hypothesis	If $F > F_{\alpha, n_1-1, n_2-1}$, reject the null hypothesis

Step 5: State the conclusion.

Notice that the procedure just presented requires that the data be normally distributed. Because the procedure is **not robust**, minor departures from normality will adversely affect the results of the test. Therefore, the test should be used only when the assumption of normality has been verified. We will verify this assumption by constructing normal probability plots.

▶ **EXAMPLE 2**

Caution

The test for equality of population standard deviations is not robust. Thus, any departures from normality destroy the results of the test.

Testing a Claim Regarding Two Population Standard Deviations

Problem: An investor believes that Cisco Systems is a more volatile stock than General Electric. The volatility of a stock is measured by the standard deviation rate of return on the stock. The data in Table 5 represent the monthly rate of return between 1990 and 2001 for 10 randomly selected months for Cisco Systems stock and 14 randomly selected months for General Electric stock.

TABLE 5			
Monthly Rate of Return For Cisco Systems Stock (%)		**Monthly Rate of Return For General Electric Stock (%)**	
1.93	31.11	1.15	−1.92
11.64	4.87	4.68	−2.32
23.13	−5.56	3.23	−5.19
5.18	8.91	0.98	4.80
−7.60	9.72	−0.55	5.29
		−5.88	9.00
		−3.26	−0.60

Source: Yahoo! Finance

Test the investor's claim that Cisco Systems stock is more volatile than General Electric stock at the $\alpha = 0.05$ level of significance.

Approach: First we need to verify that both variables are normally distributed by constructing normal probability plots. We then follow Steps 1–5 to test the claim.

Solution: Figure 14(a) shows the normal probability plot for Cisco Systems, while Figure 14(b) shows the normal probability plot for General Electric.

Figure 14

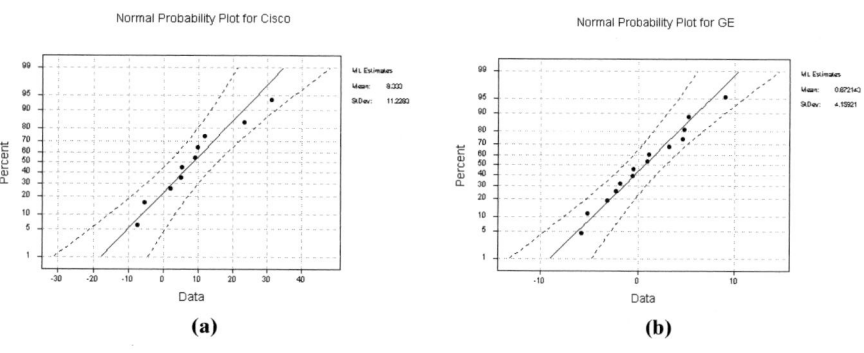

(a)   (b)

Both normal probability plots are linear, so the data come from a population that is normally distributed. We now proceed to follow Steps 1–5.

Step 1: The investor claims that Cisco Systems is a more volatile stock than General Electric. The standard deviation of the rate of return is a measure of a stock price's volatility. If we let σ_1 represent the standard deviation of the rate of return for Cisco Systems and σ_2 represent the standard deviation of the rate of return for General Electric, this claim can be written $\sigma_1 > \sigma_2$. We have

$$H_o: \sigma_1 = \sigma_2 \qquad \text{versus} \qquad H_1: \sigma_1 > \sigma_2$$

This is a right-tailed test.

Step 2: Because the investor is performing a right-tailed test, we look up the critical value at the $\alpha = 0.05$ level of significance with $n_1 - 1 = 10 - 1 = 9$ degrees of freedom in the numerator and $n_2 - 1 = 14 - 1 = 13$ degrees of freedom in the numerator and find it to be $F_{0.05,9,13} \approx 2.80$ (using 12 degrees of freedom in the denominator, because that is closest). The critical region is displayed in Figure 15.

Step 3: We compute the sample standard deviation of the rate of return for Cisco Systems, s_1, to be 11.84 percent and the sample standard deviation of the rate of return for General Electric, s_2, to be 4.32 percent. Because the data are normally distributed, the test statistic is

$$F = \frac{s_1^2}{s_2^2} = \frac{11.84^2}{4.32^2} = 7.51$$

Step 4: Because the test statistic $F = 7.51$ is greater than $F_{0.05,9,13} \approx 2.80$, we reject the null hypothesis. That is, the value of the test statistic falls within the critical region.

Step 5: There is sufficient evidence to support the investor's claim that Cisco Systems stock is more volatile than General Electric stock. Investors would use this result to demand a higher rate of return on investments in Cisco Systems. ◀◀

Figure 15

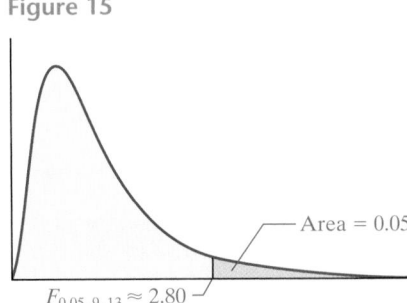

Area = 0.05

$F_{0.05,\,9,\,13} \approx 2.80$

NW *Now Work Problem 17.*

▶ **EXAMPLE 3** **Testing a Claim Regarding Two Population Standard Deviations**

Problem: In the Spacelab Life Sciences 2 payload, 14 male rats were sent to space. Upon their return, the red blood cell mass (in milliliters) of the rats was determined. A control group of 14 male rats was held under the same conditions (except for spaceflight) as the space rats, and their red blood cell mass was likewise determined when the space rats returned. The project was led by Dr. Paul X. Callahan. The data in Table 6 were obtained.

TABLE 6			
Flight		**Control**	
8.59	8.64	8.65	6.99
6.87	7.89	7.62	7.44
7.00	8.80	7.33	8.58
6.39	7.54	7.14	9.14
7.43	7.21	8.40	9.66
9.79	6.85	8.55	8.70
9.30	8.03	9.88	9.94

Source: NASA, Life Sciences Data Archive

Test the claim that the standard deviation of the red blood cell mass in the flight animals is different from the standard deviation of the red blood cell mass in the control animals at the $\alpha = 0.05$ level of significance.

Approach: We have already verified the data are normally distributed, in Example 1 from Section 10.2. See Figure 4.

Step 1: The claim is that the standard deviation of the red blood cell mass in the flight animals is different from the standard deviation of the red blood cell mass in the control animals. If we let σ_1 represent the standard deviation of the red blood cell mass for the flight animals and σ_2 represent the standard deviation of the red blood cell mass for the control animals, this claim can be written $\sigma_1 \neq \sigma_2$. We have

$$H_0: \sigma_1 = \sigma_2 \qquad \text{versus} \qquad H_1: \sigma_1 \neq \sigma_2$$

This is a two-tailed test.

Step 2: Because the researcher is performing a two-tailed test, we look up the critical values at the $\alpha = 0.05$ level of significance with $n_1 - 1 = 14 - 1 = 13$ degrees of freedom in the numerator and $n_2 - 1 = 14 - 1 = 13$ degrees of freedom in the numerator and find them to be $F_{0.025,13,13} \approx 3.28$ (using 12 degrees of freedom in the numerator and denominator, because that is closest) and $F_{0.975,13,13} \approx \dfrac{1}{F_{0.025,13,13}} = \dfrac{1}{3.28} = 0.30$. The critical regions are displayed in Figure 16.

Figure 16

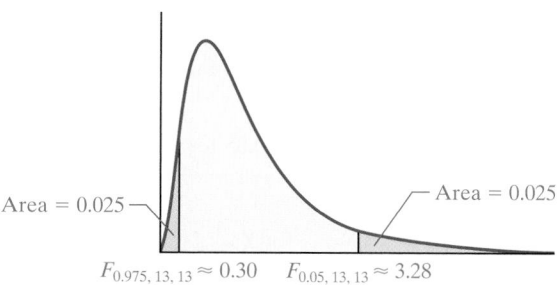

Area = 0.025

Area = 0.025

$F_{0.975,\,13,\,13} \approx 0.30 \qquad F_{0.05,\,13,\,13} \approx 3.28$

Step 3: In Example 1 from Section 10.2, we computed the sample standard deviation of the red blood cell mass for the experimental group, s_1, to be 1.017 and the sample standard deviation of the red blood cell mass for the control group, s_2, to be 1.005. Because the data are normally distributed, the test statistic is

$$F = \frac{s_1^2}{s_2^2} = \frac{1.017^2}{1.005^2} = 1.024$$

Step 4: Because the test statistic, $F = 1.024$, lies between the critical values 0.30 and 3.28, we do not reject the null hypothesis. That is, the value of the test statistic does not fall within the critical region.

Step 5: There is not sufficient evidence to support the claim that the standard deviation of the red blood cell mass in the experimental group is significantly different from the standard deviation of the red blood cell mass in the control group. ◄◄

10.4 Assess Your Understanding

Concepts and Vocabulary

1. Is the test for comparing two population standard deviations robust? Why is the assumption of normality so important in order to perform the test presented in this section?

2. State the assumptions that must be satisfied in order to compare two population standard deviations.

Exercises

• **Skill Building**

1. Find the critical value for a right-tailed test with $\alpha = 0.05$, degrees of freedom in the numerator = 9, and degrees of freedom in the denominator = 10. *3.02*

2. Find the critical value for a right-tailed test with $\alpha = 0.01$, degrees of freedom in the numerator = 20, and degrees of freedom in the denominator = 25. *2.70*

3. Find the critical values for a two-tailed test with $\alpha = 0.05$, degrees of freedom in the numerator = 6, and degrees of freedom in the denominator = 8. *0.18, 4.65*

4. Find the critical values for a two-tailed test with $\alpha = 0.02$, degrees of freedom in the numerator = 5, and degrees of freedom in the denominator = 7. *0.10, 7.46*

5. Find the critical value for a left-tailed test with $\alpha = 0.10$, degrees of freedom in the numerator = 25, and degrees of freedom in the denominator = 20. *0.58*

6. Find the critical value for a left-tailed test with $\alpha = 0.01$, degrees of freedom in the numerator = 15, and degrees of freedom in the denominator = 20. *0.30*

7. Find the critical value for a right-tailed test with $\alpha = 0.05$, degrees of freedom in the numerator = 45, and degrees of freedom in the denominator = 15. *2.19*

8. Find the critical value for a right-tailed test with $\alpha = 0.01$, degrees of freedom in the numerator = 55, and degrees of freedom in the denominator = 50. *1.93*

In Problems 9–14 assume the populations are normally distributed.

9. Test the claim that $\sigma_1 \neq \sigma_2$ at the $\alpha = 0.05$ level of significance for the given sample data. *Do not reject H_o*

	Sample for Population 1	Sample for Population 2
n	16	16
s	3.2	3.5

10. Test the claim that $\sigma_1 \neq \sigma_2$ at the $\alpha = 0.1$ level of significance for the given sample data. *Do not reject H_o*

	Sample for Population 1	Sample for Population 2
n	21	21
s	8.6	9.2

11. Test the claim that $\sigma_1 > \sigma_2$ at the $\alpha = 0.01$ level of significance for the given sample data. *Do not reject H_o*

	Sample for Population 1	Sample for Population 2
n	26	19
s	9.9	6.4

12. Test the claim that $\sigma_1 < \sigma_2$ at the $\alpha = 0.05$ level of significance for the given sample data. *Reject H_o*

	Sample for Population 1	Sample for Population 2
n	21	26
s	15.9	23.0

13. Test the claim that $\sigma_1 < \sigma_2$ at the $\alpha = 0.1$ level of significance for the given sample data. *Reject H_o*

	Sample for Population 1	Sample for Population 2
n	51	26
s	8.3	13.2

14. Test the claim that $\sigma_1 > \sigma_2$ at the $\alpha = 0.05$ level of significance for the given sample data. *Do not reject H_o*

	Sample for Population 1	Sample for Population 2
n	23	13
s	7.5	5.1

• **Applying the Concepts**

15. **Treating Acute Bipolar Mania** In a study published in the *Archives of General Psychiatry* entitled "Efficacy of Olanzapine in Acute Bipolar Mania" (Vol. 57, No. 9, pp. 841–849), researchers conducted a randomized, double-blind study to measure the effects of the drug olanzapine on patients diagnosed with bipolar disorder. One hundred fifteen patients with a DSM-IV diagnosis of bipolar disorder were randomly divided into two groups. Group 1 ($n = 55$) received 5 to 20 mg per day of olanzapine, while Group 2 ($n = 60$) received a placebo. The effectiveness of the drug was measured by the Young–Mania Rating Scale total score, with the net improvement in the score recorded. The results are presented in the following table:

	Treatment Group	Control Group
n	55	60
Mean improvement	14.8	8.1
Sample standard deviation	12.5	12.7

Assuming that the data are normally distributed, test the claim that the standard deviation in the treatment group is different from the standard deviation in the control group at the $\alpha = 0.05$ level of significance. Do not reject H_o

16. **Treating the Common Cold** Researcher Steven J. Sperber, MD, and his associates wanted to determine the efficacy (effectiveness) of pseudoephedrine and acetaminophen in the treatment of discomfort associated with the common cold. They published their results in the *Archives of Family Medicine 2000* 9: 979–985. In their study, they randomly divided 430 subjects into two groups: Group 1 ($n = 216$) received pseudoephedrine and acetaminophen; Group 2 ($n = 214$) received a placebo. The goal of the study was to discover whether the mean symptom assessment score of the individuals receiving the treatment (Group 1) was less than that of the control group (Group 2). In Group 1, the mean reduction in the symptom assessment scores was 1.30, with a standard deviation of 0.88; in Group 2, participants had a mean reduction in the symptom assessment score of 0.93, with a standard deviation of 0.88. Assuming that the data are normally distributed, test the claim that the standard deviation of the symptom assessment score of the subjects in Group 1 is different from the standard deviation of the symptom assessment score for the subjects in Group 2 at the $\alpha = 0.05$ level of significance. Do not reject H_o

17. **Vitamin A Supplements in Low-Birth-Weight Babies** Low-birth-weight babies are at increased risk of respiratory infections in the first few months of life and have low liver stores of vitamin A. In a randomized, double-blind experiment, 130 low-birth-weight babies were randomly divided into two groups. Subjects in Group 1 (the treatment group, $n_1 = 65$) were given 25,000 IU of vitamin A on study days 1, 4, and 8, where study day 1 was between 36 and 60 hours after delivery. Subjects in Group 2 (the control group, $n_2 = 65$) were given a placebo. The treatment group had a mean serum retinol concentration 45.77 micrograms/dl, with a standard deviation of 17.07 micrograms/dl. The control group had a mean serum retinol concentration of 12.88 micrograms/dl, with a standard deviation of 6.48 micrograms/dl. Test the claim that the treatment group had a higher standard deviation for serum retinol concentration than did the control group at the $\alpha = 0.01$ level of significance. It is known that serum retinol concentration is normally distributed. Reject H_o

18. **SAT Test Scores** A researcher wants to know whether students who do not plan to apply for financial aid had more variability on the SAT I math test than those who do plan to do so. She obtains a random sample of 35 students who do not plan to apply for financial aid and a random sample of 38 students who do plan to apply for financial aid and obtains the following results:

Do Not Plan to Apply for Financial Aid	Plan to Apply for Financial Aid
$n_1 = 35$	$n_2 = 38$
$s_1 = 123.1$	$s_2 = 119.4$

Test the claim that students who do not plan to apply for financial aid have a higher standard deviation on the SAT math I exam than do students who do plan to apply for financial aid at the $\alpha = 0.01$ level of significance. SAT math I exam scores are known to be normally distributed. Do not reject H_o

19. **Waiting Time in Line** McDonald's executives want to experiment with redesigning its restaurants so that the customers form one line leading to four registers to place orders rather than four lines leading to four separate registers. They redesign 30 randomly selected restaurants with the single line. In addition, they randomly select 30 restaurants with the four-line configuration to participate in the study. At each restaurant, an employee monitors the wait time (in minutes) of randomly selected patrons. The following data are collected:

Single Line			
1.2	2.1	1.7	2.8
1.9	2.1	2.4	3.0
2.1	2.3	1.9	2.9
2.7	2.0	2.9	2.3
2.8	1.1	3.1	1.8

Multiple Lines			
1.1	1.6	2.9	4.6
3.8	2.9	2.8	2.9
4.3	2.3	2.0	2.6
1.3	1.3	2.0	2.7
2.0	3.2	2.3	0.9

(a) Test the claim that the standard deviation for wait time in the single line is less than the standard deviation for wait time in the multiple lines at the $\alpha = 0.05$ level of significance. *Note*: Normal probability plots indicate the data are normally distributed. Reject H_o

(b) Draw boxplots of each set of data to confirm the results of part (a) visually.

20. **Filling Machines** A quality-control engineer wants to find out whether a new machine that fills bottles with liquid has less variability than the machine currently in use. The engineer calibrates each machine to fill bottles with 16 ounces of a liquid. After running each machine for 5 hours, she randomly selects 15 filled bottles from each machine and measures their contents. She obtains the following results:

Old Machine		
16.01	16.04	15.96
16.00	16.07	15.89
16.04	16.05	15.91
16.10	16.01	16.00
15.92	16.16	15.92

New Machine		
16.02	15.96	16.05
15.95	15.99	16.02
16.00	15.97	16.03
16.06	16.05	15.94
16.08	15.96	15.95

(a) Test the claim that the standard deviation of fill in the new machine is less than the standard deviation of fill in the old machine at the $\alpha = 0.05$ level of significance. *Note*: Normal probability plots indicate the data are normally distributed. Do not reject H_o

(b) Draw boxplots of each set of data to confirm the results of part (a) visually.

21. **Systolic Blood Pressure** A nurse was interested in discovering whether men have more variability in their systolic blood pressure than women. She randomly selects 20 males and 17 females from the surgical floor of her hospital and records their systolic blood pressures. The data, courtesy of Lora McGuire, nursing instructor, Joliet Junior College, are as follows:

Females			
140	124	126	106
126	132	126	140
136	120	110	122
118	130	118	114
140			

Males			
112	134	118	112
140	105	134	128
148	95	124	140
120	130	150	112
126	116	128	142

(a) Given the following normal probability plots, comment on whether the requirement of normality required for the F-test is satisfied, and justify your answer: Satisfied

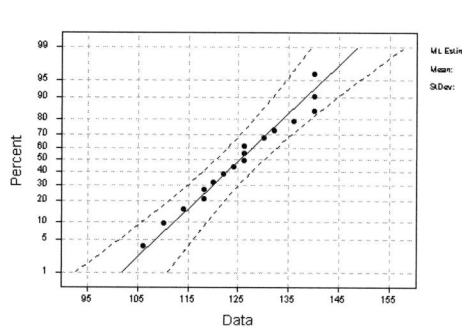

Normal Probability Plot for Female

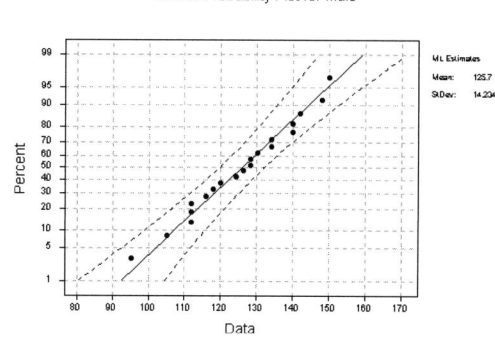

Normal Probability Plot for Male

(b) The nursing student enters the data into Minitab to test the claim that males have a higher standard deviation of systolic blood pressure than females at the $\alpha = 0.05$ level of significance. She obtains a P-value of 0.169. What should the nursing student conclude? Do not reject H_o

(c) Compute the test statistic, and use Table V in the back of the text to verify that the P-value computed is correct.

22. **Measuring Reaction Time** Researchers at the University of Mississippi wanted to discover whether the standard deviation for reaction time to a go/no go stimulus of males differed from that of females. The researchers randomly selected 20 females and 15 males to participate in the study. The go/no go stimulus required the student to respond to a particular stimulus and not to respond to other stimuli. The data, courtesy of PsychExperiments at the University of Mississippi (http://www.olemiss.edu/psychexps), are as follows:

Female Students						
0.588	0.403	0.293	0.377	0.613	0.377	0.391
0.367	0.442	0.274	0.434	0.403	0.636	0.481
0.652	0.443	0.380	0.646	0.340	0.617	

Male Students						
0.375	0.477	0.374	0.465	0.402	0.337	0.655
0.488	0.427	0.373	0.224	0.654	0.563	0.405
0.256						

```
2-SampFTest
 σ1≠σ2
F=.9674532069
p=.9276177898
Sx1=.122578986
Sx2=.124623815
↓x̄1=.45785
```

Normal probability plots indicate the requirement of normality is satisfied. The output to the left is from a TI-83 Plus.

(a) Use the results to test the claim that there is no difference between the standard deviations in reaction time of males and females at the $\alpha = 0.05$ level of significance. Do not reject H_o

(b) Draw boxplots of each data set, using the same scale. Does this visual evidence support the results obtained in part (a)?

Technology Step-by-Step
Comparing Two Population Standard Deviations

TI-83 Plus **Hypothesis Tests**

Step 1: If necessary, enter raw data in L1 and L2.

Step 2: Press STAT, highlight TESTS, and select `D:2-SampleFTest`.

Step 3: If the data are raw, highlight DATA—make sure List1 is set to L1 and List2 is set to L2, with frequencies set to 1. If summary statistics are known, highlight STATS and enter the summary statistics.

Step 4: Highlight the appropriate relation between σ_1 and σ_2 in the alternative hypothesis.

Step 5: Highlight Calculate or Draw and press ENTER. Calculate gives the test statistic and *P*-value. Draw will draw the *F*-distribution with the *P*-value shaded.

MINITAB *Step 1:* Enter data in column C1 and subscripts (usually 1 and 2) in C2 so as to identify the population of the data in C1.

Step 2: Select the **Stat** menu, highlight **ANOVA**, then highlight **Homogeneity of Variance . . . .**

Step 3: Enter C1 in the cell marked "Response," enter C2 in the cell marked "Factors." Select the confidence level. Click OK.

Excel *Step 1:* Enter raw data in columns A and B.

Step 2: Select the **Tools** menu; highlight **Data Analysis . . . .**

Step 3: Select "*F*-test Two-Sample for Variances." With the cursor in the "Variable 1 Range" cell, highlight the data in column A. With the cursor in the "Variable 2 Range" cell, highlight the data in column B. Enter a value for alpha. Click OK.

CHAPTER 10 REVIEW

Summary

This chapter discussed performing statistical inference by comparing two population parameters. We began with a discussion regarding the comparison of two population means. In order to determine the method to use, we must know whether the sampling was dependent or independent. A sampling method is independent when the choice of individuals for one sample does not dictate which individuals are to be in a second sample. A sampling method is dependent when the individuals selected to be in one sample are used to determine the individuals to be in the second sample. For dependent sampling, we use the paired *t*-test to perform statistical inference. For independent sampling, we use Welch's two-sample *t*. For both tests, the population must be normally distributed or the sample sizes must be large.

Section 10.3 dealt with statistical inference for comparing two population proportions. In order to perform these tests, $n\hat{p}(1 - \hat{p})$ must be greater than or equal to 10 for each population; then distribution of $\hat{p}_1 - \hat{p}_2$ is approximately normal, with mean $p_1 - p_2$ and standard deviation $\sqrt{\dfrac{p_1(1 - p_1)}{n_1} + \dfrac{p_2(1 - p_2)}{n_2}}$.

We wrapped up the chapter with a discussion on inference for comparing two population standard deviations. We use the *F*-test, but require that both populations be normally distributed. This test is not robust, so if the data show any departures from normality, the test should not be used.

In order to help determine which test to use, we include the flowchart in Figure 17.

Figure 17

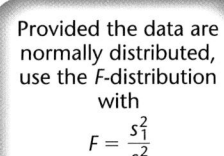

Provided the data are normally distributed, use the F-distribution with

$$F = \frac{s_1^2}{s_2^2}$$

σ or σ^2 ← **What parameters are addressed in the claim?** → Proportion, p

Provided $n\hat{p}(1 - \hat{p}) \geq 10$ for each sample and the sample size is no more than 5% of the population size, use the normal distribution with

$$Z = \frac{\hat{p}_1 - \hat{p}_2}{\sqrt{\hat{p}(1 - \hat{p})}\sqrt{\frac{1}{n_1} + \frac{1}{n_2}}} \quad \text{where } \hat{p} = \frac{x_1 + x_2}{n_1 + n_2}$$

Mean, μ

Dependent or independent sampling? ← Independent →

Provided each sample size is greater than 30 or each population is normally distributed, use Student's t-distribution

$$t = \frac{(\bar{x}_1 - \bar{x}_2) - (\mu_1 - \mu_2)}{\sqrt{\frac{s_1^2}{n_1} + \frac{s_2^2}{n_2}}}$$

Dependent

Provided each sample size is greater than 30 or the population is normally distributed, use Student's t-distribution with $n - 1$ degrees of freedom with

$$t = \frac{\bar{d} - \mu_d}{s_d / \sqrt{n}}$$

Formulas

- Test statistic for matched-pairs data:

$$t = \frac{\bar{d}}{s_d / \sqrt{n}},$$

where $\bar{d}$ is the mean and s_d is the standard deviation of the differenced data

- Confidence interval for matched-pairs data:

$$\text{Lower Bound: } \bar{d} - t_{\alpha/2} \cdot \frac{s_d}{\sqrt{n}}$$

$$\text{Upper Bound: } \bar{d} + t_{\alpha/2} \cdot \frac{s_d}{\sqrt{n}}$$

- Test statistic comparing two means (independent sampling):

$$t = \frac{(\bar{x}_1 - \bar{x}_2) - (\mu_1 - \mu_2)}{\sqrt{\frac{s_1^2}{n_1} + \frac{s_2^2}{n_2}}}$$

- Confidence interval for the difference of two means (independent samples):

$$\text{Lower Bound: } (\bar{x}_1 - \bar{x}_2) - t_{\alpha/2} \cdot \sqrt{\frac{s_1^2}{n_1} + \frac{s_2^2}{n_2}}$$

$$\text{Upper Bound: } (\bar{x}_1 - \bar{x}_2) + t_{\alpha/2} \cdot \sqrt{\frac{s_1^2}{n_1} + \frac{s_2^2}{n_2}}$$

- Test statistic comparing two population proportions:

$$Z = \frac{\hat{p}_1 - \hat{p}_2}{\sqrt{\hat{p}(1 - \hat{p})}\sqrt{\frac{1}{n_1} + \frac{1}{n_2}}},$$

where $\hat{p} = \frac{x_1 + x_2}{n_1 + n_2}$.

- Confidence interval for the difference of two proportions:

$$\text{Lower Bound: } (\hat{p}_1 - \hat{p}_2) - z_{\alpha/2} \cdot \sqrt{\frac{\hat{p}_1(1 - \hat{p}_1)}{n_1} + \frac{\hat{p}_2(1 - \hat{p}_2)}{n_2}}$$

$$\text{Upper Bound: } (\hat{p}_1 - \hat{p}_2) + z_{\alpha/2} \cdot \sqrt{\frac{\hat{p}_1(1 - \hat{p}_1)}{n_1} + \frac{\hat{p}_2(1 - \hat{p}_2)}{n_2}}$$

- Sample Size for Estimating $p_1 - p_2$

$$n = n_1 = n_2 = [\hat{p}_1(1 - \hat{p}_1) + \hat{p}_2(1 - \hat{p}_2)]\left(\frac{z_{\alpha/2}}{E}\right)^2$$

$$n = n_1 = n_2 = 0.5\left(\frac{z_{\alpha/2}}{E}\right)^2$$

- Finding a critical F for the left tail:

$$F_{1-\alpha, n_1-1, n_2-1} = \frac{1}{F_{\alpha, n_2-1, n_1-1}}$$

- Test statistic for comparing two population standard deviations:

$$F = \frac{s_1^2}{s_2^2}$$

Vocabulary

Dependent sampling (p. 594)
Independent sampling (p. 594)
Matched-pairs (p. 594)

Welch's approximate t (p. 609)
Pooled t-statistic (p. 614)
Pooled estimate of p (p. 621)

Practical significance (p. 624)
F distribution (p. 632)

Objectives

Section	You should be able to …	Review Exercises
10.1	1 Distinguish between independent and dependent sampling (p. 594)	1–4
	2 Test claims made regarding matched-pairs data (p. 595)	7(c), 8(c), 18(b)
	3 Construct confidence intervals about the population mean difference of matched-pairs data (p. 599)	7(d), 8(d), 18(c)
10.2	1 Perform hypothesis tests regarding the difference of two means (p. 609)	9(a), 10(a), 11(a), 12(a), 15(b), 16(b), 17(b), 25(a)
	2 Construct confidence intervals regarding the difference of two means (p. 613)	9(b), 10(b), 11(b), 12(b), 15(c), 16(c), 17(c), 25(b)
10.3	1 Conduct hypothesis tests on the difference between two population proportions (p. 620)	13, 14, 19(a), 20(a)
	2 Construct confidence intervals for the difference between two population proportions (p. 625)	19(b), 20(b)
	3 Determine the sample size for the difference between two population proportions (p. 627)	21, 22
10.4	1 Find critical values of the F-distribution (p. 631)	5, 6
	2 Test claims regarding two population standard deviations (p. 635)	9(c), 10(c), 11(c), 12(c), 23, 24, 25(c)

Review Exercises

In Problems 1–4, determine whether the sampling is dependent or independent.

1. A researcher wants to know whether the mean length of stay in for-profit hospitals is different from the mean length of stay in not-for-profit hospitals. He randomly selected 20 individuals in the for-profit hospital and matched them with 20 individuals in the not-for-profit hospital by diagnosis. Dependent

2. An urban economist believes that commute times to work in the South are less than commute times to work in the Midwest. He randomly selects 40 employed individuals in the South and 45 employed individuals in the Midwest and determines their commute times. Independent

3. A stock analyst wants to know whether there is a difference between the mean rate of return from energy stocks and that from financial stocks. He randomly selects 13 energy stocks and computes the rate of return for the past year. He randomly selects 13 financial stocks and computes the rate of return for the past year. Independent

4. A prison warden wants to know whether men receive longer sentences for crimes than women. He randomly samples 30 men and matches them with 30 women by type of crime committed and records their lengths of sentence. Dependent

---

In Problems 5 and 6, find the critical F-value.

5. (a) for a right-tailed test with $\alpha = 0.05$, degrees of freedom in the numerator = 8, and degrees of freedom in the denominator = 9. 3.23

(b) for a two-tailed test with $\alpha = 0.05$, degrees of freedom in the numerator = 10, and degrees of freedom in the denominator = 5. 0.24; 6.62

6. (a) for a right-tailed test with $\alpha = 0.1$, degrees of freedom in the numerator = 20, and degrees of freedom in the denominator = 12. 2.06

(b) for a left-tailed test with $\alpha = 0.1$, degrees of freedom in the numerator = 12, and degrees of freedom in the denominator = 20. 0.49

In Problems 7 and 8, assume that the paired data came from a population that is normally distributed.

7.

Observation	1	2	3	4	5	6
X_1	34.2	32.1	39.5	41.8	45.1	38.4
X_2	34.9	31.5	39.5	41.9	45.5	38.8

   (a) Compute $d_i = X_1 - X_2$ for each pair of data.
   (b) Compute $\bar{d}$ and s_d. $\bar{d} = -0.167, s_d = 0.450$
   (c) Test the claim that $\mu_d < 0$ at the $\alpha = 0.05$ level of significance. *Do not reject H_o*
   (d) Compute a 98% confidence interval about the population mean difference μ_d. $(-0.79, 0.45)$

8.

Observation	1	2	3	4	5	6	7
X_1	18.5	21.8	19.4	22.9	18.3	20.2	23.1
X_2	18.3	22.3	19.2	22.3	18.9	20.7	23.9

   (a) Compute $d_i = X_1 - X_2$ for each pair of data.
   (b) Compute $\bar{d}$ and s_d. $\bar{d} = -0.2, s_d = 0.526$
   (c) Test the claim that $\mu_d \neq 0$ at the $\alpha = 0.01$ level of significance. *Do not reject H_o*
   (d) Compute a 95% confidence interval about the population mean difference μ_d. $(-0.69, 0.29)$

In Problems 9–12, assume that the populations are normally distributed and that independent sampling occurred.

9. (a) Test the claim that $\mu_1 \neq \mu_2$ at the $\alpha = 0.1$ level of significance for the given sample data. *Reject H_o*
   (b) Construct a 90% confidence interval about $\mu_1 - \mu_2$.
   (c) Test the claim that $\sigma_1 \neq \sigma_2$ at the $\alpha = 0.05$ level of significance for the given sample data. *Do not reject H_o*

	Sample for Population 1	Sample for Population 2
n	13	8
$\bar{x}$	32.4	28.2
s	4.5	3.8

10. (a) Test the claim that $\mu_1 \neq \mu_2$ at the $\alpha = 0.05$ level of significance for the given sample data. *Reject H_o*
   (b) Construct a 95% confidence interval about $\mu_1 - \mu_2$.
   (c) Test the claim that $\sigma_1 > \sigma_2$ at the $\alpha = 0.1$ level of significance for the given sample data. *Reject H_o*

	Sample for Population 1	Sample for Population 2
n	24	27
$\bar{x}$	104.2	110.4
s	12.3	8.7

11. (a) Test the claim that $\mu_1 > \mu_2$ at the $\alpha = 0.01$ level of significance for the given sample data. *Do not reject H_o*
   (b) Construct a 90% confidence interval about $\mu_1 - \mu_2$.
   (c) Test the claim that $\sigma_1 < \sigma_2$ at the $\alpha = 0.01$ level of significance for the given sample data. *Do not reject H_o*

	Sample for Population 1	Sample for Population 2
n	45	41
$\bar{x}$	48.2	45.2
s	8.4	10.3

12. (a) Test the claim that $\mu_1 < \mu_2$ at the $\alpha = 0.05$ level of significance for the given sample data. *Do not reject H_o*
   (b) Construct a 99% confidence interval about $\mu_1 - \mu_2$.
   (c) Test the claim that $\sigma_1 \neq \sigma_2$ at the $\alpha = 0.05$ level of significance for the given sample data. *Do not reject H_o*

	Sample for Population 1	Sample for Population 2
n	13	8
$\bar{x}$	96.6	98.3
s	3.2	2.5

In Problems 13 and 14, test the claim at the $\alpha = 0.05$ level of significance by (a) determining the null and alternative hypotheses, (b) computing the test statistic, (c) computing the critical value, and (d) computing the P-value. Assume that the samples were obtained independently via simple random sampling.

13. Claim $p_1 \neq p_2$. Sample data:
$x_1 = 451, n_1 = 555, x_2 = 510, n_2 = 600$

14. Claim $p_1 < p_2$. Sample data:
$x_1 = 156, n_1 = 650, x_2 = 138, n_2 = 540$

(9b) $(0.73, 7.67)$
(10b) $(-12.44, 0.04)$

(11b) $(-0.43, 6.43)$
(12b) $(-6.08, 2.68)$

15. **Measuring Reaction Time** Researchers at the University of Mississippi wanted to discover whether the reaction time of males to a "choice" stimulus differed from that of females. The researchers randomly selected 16 females and 12 males to participate in the study. The "choice" stimulus required the student to respond differently, depending upon the stimulus. The data are courtesy of PsychExperiments at the University of Mississippi. The results are as follows:

Female Students						
0.474	0.436	0.398	0.633	0.831	0.887	0.711
0.743	0.48	0.561	0.596	0.725	0.905	0.338
0.538	0.531					

Male Students					
0.541	1.05	0.577	0.849	0.464	0.626
0.659	0.88	0.752	0.544	0.675	0.393

(a) Is it reasonable to use Welch's t-test? Why? *Note*: Normal probability plots indicate that the data are approximately normal, and boxplots indicate that there are no outliers. Yes
(b) Test the claim that there is no difference in the reaction time of males and females at the $\alpha = 0.05$ level of significance. Do not reject H_o
(c) Construct a 95% confidence interval about $\mu_F - \mu_M$ and interpret the results. $(-0.21, 0.09)$
(d) Draw boxplots of each data set, using the same scale. Does this visual evidence support the results obtained in part (b)?

16. **Acid Rain** A researcher wants to know whether the acidity of rain (pH) near Houston, Texas, is significantly different from that near Chicago, Illinois. He randomly selects 12 rain dates in Texas and 14 rain dates in Illinois and obtains the following data:

Texas					
4.69	5.10	5.22	4.46	4.93	4.65
5.22	4.76	4.25	5.14	4.11	4.71

Illinois						
4.40	4.69	4.22	4.64	4.54	4.35	4.69
4.40	4.75	4.63	4.45	4.49	4.36	4.52

Source: National Atmospheric Deposition Program

(a) Is it reasonable to use Welch's t-test? Why?
(b) Test the claim that there is no difference between the acidity of rain in Houston and that in Chicago at the $\alpha = 0.05$ level of significance. Reject H_o
(c) Construct a 95% confidence interval about $\mu_T - \mu_I$ and interpret the results. $(0.009, 0.513)$
(d) Draw boxplots of each data set, using the same scale. Does this visual evidence support the results obtained in part (b)?

17. **Pennies** Prior to 1982, all pennies were 95% copper and 5% zinc (except in 1943, when pennies were of zinc-coated steel so that copper could be used for the war effort). There are two types of pennies that have this composition. "Wheat" pennies have a wheat emblem on the back and were minted from 1909 to 1958. The modern penny (1959–1982) has the Lincoln Memorial on the back. The following data represent the weight (in grams) of a random sample of "wheat" and "modern" pennies:

Wheat Pennies							
3.01	3.02	3.04	3.04	3.00	3.00	3.02	3.03
3.02	3.06	3.02	2.96	3.02	3.05	3.07	3.01
3.07	2.98	3.00	3.02	3.07	3.06		

Modern Pennies						
3.03	3.11	3.05	3.04	3.08	3.01	3.10
3.08	3.08	3.04	3.10	3.09	3.06	3.03
3.03	3.05	3.00	3.02	3.05		

(a) Is this dependent or independent sampling? Why? (a) Independent
(b) Test the claim that the weight of wheat pennies is less than the weight of modern pennies at the $\alpha = 0.05$ level of significance. *Note*: A normal probability plot indicates that the data are approximately normal, and a boxplot does not indicate any outliers. Reject H_o
(c) Construct a 95% confidence interval about $\mu_m - \mu_w$. Interpret the result. $(0.009, 0.050)$
(d) Why is the result obtained in part (b) reasonable?

18. **Pulse** A physical therapist wants to check on whether a new exercise program reduces the pulse rate of subjects. She randomly selects 10 women to participate in the study. Each subject is asked to step up and down on a 6-inch step for 3 minutes. Their pulses (in beats per minute) are then recorded. After a 10-week training program, the pulse is again measured, using the same technique. The results are presented in the table on page 649.

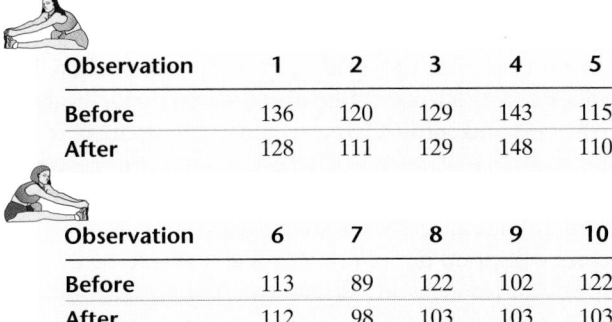

Observation	1	2	3	4	5
Before	136	120	129	143	115
After	128	111	129	148	110

Observation	6	7	8	9	10
Before	113	89	122	102	122
After	112	98	103	103	103

(a) Is this dependent or independent sampling? Why?

(b) Test the claim that the pulse before exercising is greater than the pulse after exercising at the $\alpha = 0.05$ level of significance. *Note*: A normal probability plot indicates that the data are approximately normal, and a boxplot does not indicate any outliers. Do not reject H_o

(c) Construct a 99% confidence interval about the population mean difference. Interpret the result.

19. **Treatment for Osteoporosis** Osteoporosis is a condition in which people experience decreased bone mass and an increase in the risk of bone fracture. Actonel is a drug that helps combat osteoporosis in postmenopausal women. In clinical trials, 1374 postmenopausal women were randomly divided into experimental and control groups. The subjects in the experimental group were administered 5 mg of Actonel, while the subjects in the control group were administered a placebo. The number of women who experienced a bone fracture over the course of one year was recorded. Of the 696 women in the experimental group, 27 experienced a fracture during the course of the year. Of the 678 women in the control group, 49 experienced a fracture during the course of the year.

(a) Test the claim that a lower proportion of women in the experimental group experienced a bone fracture than the women in the control group at the $\alpha = 0.01$ level of significance. Reject H_o

(b) Construct a 95% confidence interval for the difference between the two population proportions, $p_{exp} - p_{control}$. (−0.06, −0.01)

(c) What type of experimental design is this? What is the treatment? How many levels does it have?

20. **Zoloft** Zoloft is a drug that is used to treat obsessive–compulsive disorder (OCD). In randomized, double-blind clinical trials, 926 patients diagnosed with OCD were randomly divided into two groups. Subjects in Group 1 (experimental group) received 200 mg per day of Zoloft, while subjects in Group 2 (control group) received a placebo. Of the 553 subjects in the experimental group, 77 experienced dry mouth as a side effect. Of the 373 subjects in the control group, 34 experienced dry mouth as a side effect.

(a) Test the claim that a higher proportion of the subjects in the experimental group experienced dry mouth than did the subjects in the control group at the $\alpha = 0.05$ level of significance. Reject H_o

(b) Construct a 90% confidence interval for the difference between the two population proportions, $p_1 - p_2$. (0.01, 0.08)

21. **Determining Sample Size** A nutritionist wants to estimate the difference between the percentage of men and women who have high cholesterol. What sample size should be obtained if she wishes the estimate to be within 2 percentage points with 90% confidence, assuming

(a) that she uses the 1994 estimates of 18.8% male and 20.5% female from the National Center for Health Statistics? 2136

(b) that she does not use any prior estimates? 3383

22. **Determining Sample Size** A researcher wants to estimate the difference between the percentage of individuals without a high school diploma who smoke and the percentage of individuals with bachelors degrees who smoke. What sample size should be obtained if she wishes the estimate to be within 4 percentage points with 95% confidence, assuming

(a) that she uses the 1999 estimates of 32.2% of those without a high school diploma and 11.1% of those with a bachelors degree, from the National Center for Health Statistics? 762

(b) that she does not use any prior estimates? 1201

23. **Reaction Time** Using the data from Problem 15, test the claim that the standard deviation of reaction time in male students is more than that in female students at the $\alpha = 0.05$ level of significance. Do not reject H_o

24. **Acid Rain** Using the data from Problem 16, test the claim that the standard deviation of acidity in the rain near Houston, Texas, is different from that near Chicago, Illinois, at the $\alpha = 0.05$ level of significance. Reject H_o

25. Explain when the matched-pairs t should be used instead of Welch's t in comparing two population means. What are some advantages in designing a matched-pairs experiment versus using Welch's t?

(18a) Dependent (18c) (−5.02, 14.22)
(19c) Completely randomized design; drug; 2

CASE STUDY

Dr. Penelope Nicholls is interested in exploring a possible connection between high plasma homocysteine (a toxic amino acid created by the body as it metabolizes protein) levels and cardiac hypertrophy (enlargement of the heart) in humans. She realizes that, because there are many complex relationships among human characteristics, it will be difficult to answer her research question unambiguously because there is a significant risk that confounding factors will cloud her inferences. She wants to be as sure as possible that any differences in cardiac hypertrophy are due to high plasma homocysteine levels and not to other hidden factors. Consequently, she needs to design her experiment carefully, so that she controls lurking variables to the extent possible. Therefore, she decides to design a two-sample experiment with independent sampling—one of the groups will be the experimental group, the other a control group. Knowing that there are many factors that can affect the degree of cardiac hypertrophy (the response variable), Dr. Nicholls controls these factors by randomly assigning the experimental units to the experimental or control group. She hopes the randomization will result in both groups having similar characteristics. By controlling the data collection environment and procedures, she also hopes to minimize any situational contaminants within her experimental design.

In her preliminary literature review, Dr. Nicholls uncovered an article in which the authors hypothesized that there might be a relationship between high plasma homocysteine levels in patients with end-stage renal disease (ESRD) and cardiac hypertrophy. As her assistant, she has asked you to review this article and to write a brief report detailing your findings.

Upon reading the article, you discover that the authors employed a nonrandom process to select a control and an ESRD group. The researchers enlisted 75 stable ESRD patients into their study. All of these patients were on hemodialysis for between 6 and 312 months. The control group was composed of 57 nonuremic members. Nonuremic subjects were chosen so as to eliminate any intergroup differences in terms of mean blood pressure (BP) and gender. Any individuals taking vitamins and any individuals with any type of specified heart-related ailments were excluded from the study. In an effort to minimize situational contaminants, all physical and biochemical measurements were made after an overnight fast. The results of the clinical characteristics and the biochemical findings for the control and ESRD groups are reproduced in the following tables.

Clinical Characteristics (Mean $\pm$ Standard Deviation)		
Parameters	**Controls** ($n = 57$)	**ESRD Subjects** ($n = 75$)
Age (years)	49.2 ± 14.7	57.3 ± 15.1
Sex (M/F ratio)	1.4 ± 0.50	1.4 ± 0.50
Body Surface Area (m2)	1.85 ± 0.25	1.67 ± 0.20
Body Mass Index (kg/m2)	26.0 ± 4.70	23.7 ± 3.90
Systolic BP (mmHg)	145.0 ± 15.5	148.8 ± 29.7
Diastolic BP (mmHg)	85.0 ± 14.8	80.2 ± 14.3
Mean BP (mmHg)	104.5 ± 14.2	103.6 ± 17.4
Pulse Pressure (mmHg)	59.4 ± 15.5	68.6 ± 24.3
Heart Rate (beats/min)	63.0 ± 8.0	70.0 ± 9.0

Biological Findings (Mean $\pm$ Standard Deviation)		
Parameters	Controls ($n = 57$)	ESRD Subjects ($n = 75$)
Total Cholesterol (mmol/L)	5.28 ± 1.04	4.91 ± 1.06
HDL Cholesterol (mmol/L)	1.38 ± 0.39	1.07 ± 0.38
Triglycerides (mmol/L)	1.39 ± 0.63	1.90 ± 1.02
Serum Albumin (g/L)	44.7 ± 2.60	39.9 ± 3.00
Plasma Fibrinogen (g/L)	3.21 ± 0.78	4.75 ± 1.04
Plasma Creatinine (mmol/L)	0.10 ± 0.01	0.90 ± 0.13
Blood Urea (mmol/L)	6.10 ± 1.20	24.3 ± 2.00
Calcium (mmol/L)	2.46 ± 0.08	2.45 ± 0.12
Phosphates (mmol/L)	1.03 ± 0.21	1.88 ± 0.38

Source: Jacques Blacher, et al. "Association between Plasma Homocysteine Concentrations and Cardiac Hypertrophy in End-Stage Renal Disease." *Journal of Nephrology* 12, 4 (July–August, 1999): 248–255. Article available at http://www.sin_italia.org/jnonline/vol12n4/blacher/blacher.htm

Which type of sampling method, independent or dependent, was used in this experiment? Explain.

Using the appropriate hypothesis-testing procedure, ascertain whether the control and ESRD groups have equivalent population means for each of the various clinical and biochemical parameters. Dr. Nicholls requires that you indicate those parameters that have P-values less than 0.05 and those less than 0.01.

Detail any assumptions, and the rationale behind making them, that you made while carrying out your analysis. Is there any additional information that you would like to have? Explain. Are there any additional statistical procedures that you think might be useful for analyzing these data? Explain.

Based on your findings, does it appear that the control and ESRD groups have similar initial clinical characteristics and biochemical findings? Does it appear that the authors of this article were successful in reducing the likelihood that a confounding effect would obscure their results?

Even though Dr. Nicholls does not wish to restrict her research to patients with end-stage renal disease, how might the information presented for this research assist her in designing her own experiment?

Write a report for Dr. Nicholls that outlines all of your findings and recommendations.

Suppose that you have just received an inheritance of $10,000 and you decide that you should invest the money rather than blow it on frivolous items. You have decided that you will invest the money in one of two types of mutual funds. The first type you are considering follows a "large value" approach to investing. This means that the mutual fund invests only in large, established companies that are considered to be a good bargain. The second type of mutual fund you are considering follows a "large growth" approach to investing. This means that the mutual fund invests in large companies that are experiencing solid sales growth.

In order to make an informed decision, you decide to research the rate of return of the past three years for each of these types of mutual funds. The mutual fund must have a Morningstar rating of four or five stars. The Morningstar mutual-fund rating system ranks mutual funds, using one to five stars. The stars divide the mutual-fund performance into quintiles—that is, a mutual fund with a one-star rating is in the bottom 20% of mutual funds in its category, a mutual fund with a two-star rating has an investment performance between the 21st and 40th percentile, and so on. These data can be found at www.morningstar.com or http://screen.yahoo.com/funds.html.

(a) Obtain a simple random sample of at least 15 mutual funds for each investment category. Determine the three-year rate of return for each of the funds.

(b) Verify that the three-year rates of return come from a population that is normally distributed. Also, verify that the data have no outliers. If the data do not come from a population that is normally distributed, you'll have to increase the sample size so that the Central Limit Theorem can be used.

(c) Construct a boxplot for the rate of return of each fund category, using the same scale. Which investment category, if any, seems superior?

(d) Obtain a 95% confidence interval for the difference between the mean rates of return. Interpret the interval.

(e) Write a report that details which investment category seems to be superior.

For a recent article, Consumer Reports (December 2001) was interested in comparing a name brand paper towel with a new version packaged in a box. The towels in the box, which cost nearly twice as much as the traditional roll, are marketed for their convenience. Given the difference in cost, one might wonder if the boxed version performs better than the traditional roll. To help answer this question, technicians at Consumers Union subjected both types of towels to 5 physical tests: absorption time in water, absorption time in oil, absorption capacity in water, absorption capacity in oil, and wet strength. For brevity, we will discuss only the results of the absorption time in water test.

The absorption time in water was defined as the amount of time necessary for a single sheet to absorb a predetermined amount of water. In order to compare the absorption times of the two types of towels, we tested six randomly selected sheets of paper towels. To avoid potential sources of bias, the individual sheets were taken from different samples of the products and the tests were conducted in a randomly chosen order.

The claim being tested is that the water absorption time for the boxed version is less than the water absorption time for the traditional roll.

(a) Write the null and alternative hypotheses, letting μ_{box} represent the mean absorption time for the

boxed version and μ_{roll} represent the mean absorption time for the roll version.

(b) Normal probability plots of the water absorption times for the two products are shown below. Based on the normal probability plots, is it reasonable to conduct a two-sample hypothesis test?

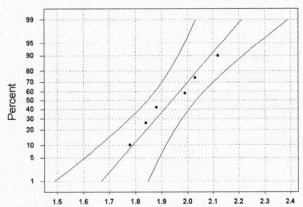 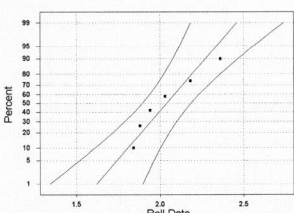

(c) A boxplot of the water absorption times for the two products is shown below.

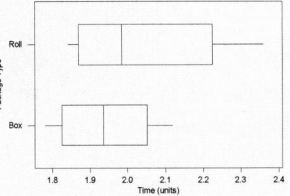

Does the data set have any outliers? Based on the boxplots, do you think that the absorption times for the boxed version are lower than the absorption times for the roll?

(d) To test the claim, we used Minitab (release 13.1) to perform a two-sample t-test. The results are shown below.

Using the Minitab output, determine the value of the test statistic. What is the P-value of the test?

Although they are not discussed here, the other physical tests provided similar results. Write an article that states your conclusion and any recommendations that you would make regarding the purchase of the two products.

Two-Sample T-Test and CI: Absorption Time In Water, CU

```
Two-sample  T  for Absorption  Time  In Water

CU-Text       N          Mean    StDev    SE Mean
Box           6        0.9717   0.0538      0.022
Roll          6        1.0200   0.0942      0.038

Difference = mu (Box) - mu (Roll)
Estimate for difference: -0.0483
95% upper bound for difference: 0.0320
T-Test of difference = 0 (vs <): T-Value = -1.09 P-Value = 0.150 DF = 10
Both use Pooled StDev = 0.0767
```

Note to Readers: In many cases, our test protocol and analytical methods are more complicated than described in these examples. The data and discussions have been modified to make the material more appropriate for the audience.

Putting It All Together

In Chapters 8–10, we introduced statistical methods that can be used to test claims regarding a population parameter such as μ or σ.

Often, however, rather than being interested in testing a claim regarding a parameter of a probability distribution, we are interested in testing a claim regarding the entire probability distribution. For example, we might wish to test the claim that the distribution of colors in a bag of plain M&M candies is 30% brown, 20% yellow, 20% red, 10% orange, 10% blue, and 10% green. We introduce methods for testing claims such as this in Section 11.1.

Remember way back to Section 4.1 where we introduced the correlation coefficient? The correlation coefficient is a measure of strength of linear relation between two quantitative variables. In Section 11.2, we introduce methods that can be used to get a feel for the strength of relation between two qualitative variables for population data.

In Section 11.3, we discuss a method that can be used to determine whether two variables are independent based on a sample. If they are not independent, then we can say that the value of one variable impacts the value of the other variable, so the variables are somehow related. We conclude Section 11.3 by introducing tests for homogeneity. This procedure is used to compare proportions from two or more populations. It is an extension of the two-sample z-test for proportions discussed in Section 10.3.

Chi-Square Procedures

Outline

 For additional study help, go to www.prenhall.com/sullivanstats

Materials include

- Self-Graded Quizzes
- "Preparing for This Section" Quizzes
- STATLETs
- PowerPoint Downloads
- Step-by-Step Technology Guide
- Graphing Calculator Help

11.1 Chi-Square Goodness-of-Fit Test

Preparing for This Section   Before getting started, review the following:

Note to Instructor
If you have not introduced the chi-square distribution, be sure to cover it now.

✓ Chi-square distribution (Section 8.4, pp. 498–501)

✓ Expected value (Section 6.1, pp. 333–334)

✓ Mean of a binomial random variable (Section 6.2, pp. 345–346)

✓ Mutually exclusive (Section 5.2, pp. 276–278)

Objectives   Perform a chi-square goodness-of-fit test

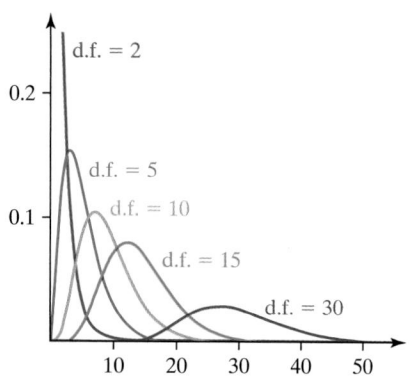

Figure 1
Chi-square distributions

In this section, we present a procedure that can be used to test claims regarding a probability distribution. For example, we might want to test the claim that the distribution of plain M&M candies in a bag is 30% brown, 20% yellow, 20% red, 10% orange, 10% blue, and 10% green. Or we might want to test the claim that the number of hits a player gets in his next four at-bats follows a binomial distribution with $n = 4$ and $p = 0.298$.

The methods used to test these types of claims utilize the chi-square distribution, introduced in Section 8.4. Recall the following properties of the chi-square distribution.

> **Characteristics of the Chi-Square Distribution**
>
> **1.** It is not symmetric.
> **2.** The shape of the chi-square distribution depends upon the degrees of freedom, just like Student's t-distribution.
> **3.** As the number of degrees of freedom increases, the chi-square distribution becomes more symmetric, as illustrated in Figure 1.
> **4.** The values χ^2 are nonnegative. That is, the values of χ^2 are greater than or equal to 0.

The critical values of the chi-square distribution can be found in Table IV.

Goodness-of-Fit Tests

We begin with a definition.

Definition   A **goodness-of-fit test** is an inferential procedure used to determine whether a frequency distribution follows a claimed distribution.

As an example, we might want to test the claim that a die is fair, or the probability that each outcome is 1/6 when the die is cast. We express this claim as

$$H_o: p_1 = p_2 = p_3 = p_4 = p_5 = p_6 = 1/6$$

Here's another example: According to the U.S. Bureau of the Census, in 1999, 19.6% of the population of the United States resided in the Northeast, 23.0% resided in the Midwest, 35.4% resided in the South, and 22.0% resided in the West. We might want to test the claim that the distribution of U.S. residents is the same today as it was in 1999. Remember, the null hypothesis is a statement of "no change," so for this claim, the null hypothesis is

H_o: The distribution of residents in the United States is the same today as it was in 1999.

The idea behind testing these types of claims is to compare the actual number of observations for each category of data with the number of observations we would expect if the null hypothesis were true. If a significant difference between the observed counts and expected counts exists, we have evidence against the null hypothesis.

The method for obtaining the expected counts is an extension of the expected value of a binomial random variable. Recall that the mean (and therefore expected value) of a binomial random variable with n independent trials and probability of success, p, is given by $E = \mu = np$.

Theorem	**Expected Counts**

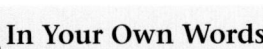
In Your Own Words

The expected count for each category is the number of trials of the experiment times the probability of success in the category.

Suppose there are n independent trials of an experiment with $k \geq 3$ mutually exclusive possible outcomes. Let p_1 represent the probability of observing the first outcome and E_1 represent the expected count of the first outcome, p_2 represent the probability of observing the second outcome and E_2 represent the expected count of the second outcome, and so on. The expected counts for each possible outcome are given by

$$E_i = \mu_i = np_i \quad \text{for} \quad i = 1, 2, \ldots, k.$$

▶ **EXAMPLE 1**   **Finding Expected Counts**

Problem: An urban economist wishes to determine whether the distribution of residents in the United States is the same today as it was in 1999. That year, 19.6% of the population of the United States resided in the Northeast, 23.0% resided in the Midwest, 35.4% resided in the South, and 22.0% resided in the West (based upon data obtained from the Census Bureau). If the economist randomly selects 2000 households in the United States, compute the expected number of households in each region, assuming that the distribution of households did not change from 1999.

Approach:

Step 1: Determine the probabilities for each outcome.
Step 2: There are $n = 2000$ trials (the 2000 households surveyed) of the experiment. We expect $np_{\text{northeast}}$ of the households surveyed to reside in the Northeast, np_{midwest} of the households to reside in the Midwest, and so on.

Solution:

Step 1: The probabilities are the relative frequencies from the 1999 distribution: $p_{\text{northeast}} = 0.196$, $p_{\text{midwest}} = 0.23$, $p_{\text{south}} = 0.354$, and $p_{\text{west}} = 0.22$.
Step 2: The expected counts for each of the locations within the United States are as follows:

Expected count of Northeast: $np_{\text{northeast}} = 2000(0.196) = 392$
Expected count of Midwest: $np_{\text{midwest}} = 2000(0.23) = 460$
Expected count of South: $np_{\text{south}} = 2000(0.354) = 708$
Expected count of West: $np_{\text{west}} = 2000(0.22) = 440$

Of the 2000 households surveyed, we expect 392 households in the Northeast, 460 households in the Midwest, 708 households in the South, and 440 households in the West if the distribution of residents of the United States is the same today as it was in 1999.   ◀◀

Historical Note

The goodness-of-fit test was invented by Karl Pearson (the Pearson of correlation coefficient fame). Pearson believed that statistics should be done by determining the distribution of a random variable. Such a determination could be made only by looking at large amounts of data. This philosophy caused Pearson to "butt heads" with Ronald Fisher, because Fisher believed in analyzing small samples.

 *Now Work Problem 1.*

To test a claim, we compare the observed counts with the expected counts. If the observed counts are significantly different from the expected counts, we have evidence against the null hypothesis. We need a test statistic and sampling distribution in order to test the claim.

Theorem

Test Statistic for Goodness-of-Fit Tests

Let O_i represent the observed counts of category i, E_i represent the expected counts of category i, k represent the number of categories, and n represent the number of independent trials of an experiment. Then the formula

$$\chi^2 = \sum \frac{(O_i - E_i)^2}{E_i} \qquad i = 1, 2, \ldots, k$$

approximately follows the chi-square distribution with $k - 1$ degrees of freedom, provided that (1) all expected frequencies are greater than or equal to 1 (all $E_i \geq 1$) and (2) no more than 20% of the expected frequencies are less than 5. *Note*: $E_i = np_i$ for $i = 1, 2, \ldots, k$.

> **Caution**
>
> Goodness-of-fit tests are used to test a claim regarding the distribution of a variable based on a single population. If you wish to compare two or more populations, you must use tests for homogeneity presented in Section 11.3.

From Example 1, there were $k = 4$ categories (Northeast, Midwest, South, and West). For the Northeast, the expected frequency, E, is 392.

Now that we know the distribution of goodness-of-fit tests, we can present a method for testing claims regarding the distribution of a random variable.

The Chi-Square Goodness-of-Fit Test

If a claim is made regarding a distribution, we can use the steps that follow to test the claim, provided that
1. the data are randomly selected,
2. all expected frequencies are greater than or equal to 1,
3. no more than 20% of the expected frequencies are less than 5.

> **Caution**
>
> If requirements (2) or (3) are not satisfied, one option is to combine two of the low frequency categories into a single category.

Step 1: A claim is made regarding a distribution. The claim is used to determine the null and alternative hypotheses:

H_0: The random variable follows the claimed distribution.

H_1: The random variable does not follow the claimed distribution.

Step 2: Calculate the expected frequencies for each of the k categories. The expected frequencies are np_i for $i = 1, 2, \ldots, k$, where n is the number of trials and p_i is the probability of the ith category, assuming that the null hypothesis is true.

Step 3: Verify that the requirements for the goodness-of-fit test are satisfied:
1. All expected frequencies are greater than or equal to 1 (all $E_i \geq 1$),
2. No more than 20% of the expected frequencies are less than 5.

Step 4: Select a level of significance α based upon the seriousness of making a Type I error. The level of significance is used to determine the critical value. All chi-square goodness-of-fit tests are right-tailed tests, so the critical value is χ_α^2 with $k - 1$ degrees of freedom. The shaded region represents the critical region. See Figure 2.

Figure 2

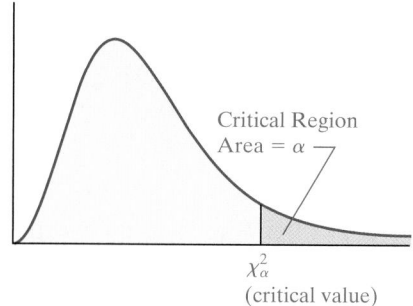

Critical Region
Area = α

χ_α^2
(critical value)

Step 5: Compute the **test statistic**:

$$\chi^2 = \sum \frac{(O_i - E_i)^2}{E_i}$$

Step 6: Compare the critical value with the test statistic. If $\chi^2 > \chi^2_\alpha$, reject the null hypothesis.

Step 7: State the conclusion.

▶ **EXAMPLE 2** Testing a Claim Using the Goodness-of-Fit Test

TABLE 1

Region	Frequency
Northeast	365
Midwest	404
South	752
West	479

Problem: An urban economist wishes to test the claim that the distribution of United States residents in the United States is different today than it was in 1999. In 1999, 19.6% of the population of the United States resided in the Northeast, 23.0% resided in the Midwest, 35.4% resided in the South, and 22.0% resided in the West (based upon data obtained from the Census Bureau). The economist randomly selects 2000 households in the United States and obtains the frequency distribution shown in Table 1.

Test the claim that the distribution of residents in the United States is different today from the distribution in 1999 at the $\alpha = 0.05$ level of significance.

Approach: We follow Steps 1–7 on pages 658–659.

Solution: The requirement that the data be randomly selected is satisfied.

Step 1: The claim is that the distribution of residents is the same today as it was in 1999. This claim will be the null hypothesis:

H_o: The distribution of residents of the United States is the same today as it was in 1999.

H_1: The distribution of residents of the United States is different today from what it was in 1999.

In Your Own Words

Remember, the null hypothesis is always the statement of "no change." Therefore, the null hypothesis is that there is no change in the distribution from 1999.

Step 2: We compute the expected counts for each category, assuming that the null hypothesis is true. We did this computation in Example 1; Table 2 shows the results.

TABLE 2		
Region	Frequency (Observed Count)	Expected Frequency
Northeast	365	2000(0.196) = 392
Midwest	404	2000(0.230) = 460
South	752	2000(0.354) = 708
West	479	2000(0.220) = 440

Step 3: Since all the expected counts are greater than 5, the requirements for the goodness-of-fit test are satisfied.

Step 4: There are $k = 4$ possible outcomes, so we find the critical value by using $4 - 1 = 3$ degrees of freedom. We consult Table IV and identify the column corresponding to $\alpha = 0.05$ with 3 degrees of freedom. The critical value is $\chi^2_{0.05} = 7.815$.

Step 5: The test statistic is

$$\chi^2 = \sum \frac{(O_i - E_i)^2}{E_i} = \frac{(365 - 392)^2}{392} + \frac{(404 - 460)^2}{460} + \frac{(752 - 708)^2}{708} + \frac{(479 - 440)^2}{440} = 14.868$$

Step 6: Because the test statistic, 14.868, is greater than the critical value, 7.815, we reject the null hypothesis. See Figure 3.

Figure 3

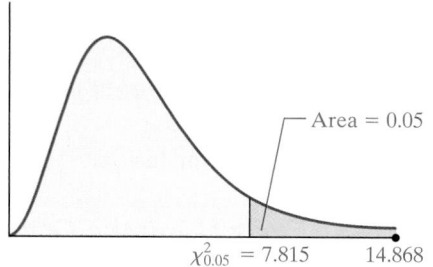

$$\chi^2_{0.05} = 7.815 \qquad 14.868$$

Step 7: There is sufficient evidence at the $\alpha = 0.05$ level of significance to support the claim that the distribution of United States residents is different from the distribution in 1999. ◀◀

If we compare the observed and expected counts, we notice that the Northeast and Midwest regions of the United States have observed counts lower than expected, while the South and West regions of the United States have observed counts higher than expected. So we might conclude that residents of the United States are moving to southern and western locations.

NW *Now Work Problem 7.*

In the next example, each of the k categories is equally likely.

▶ **EXAMPLE 3**

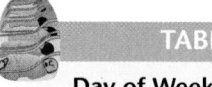

TABLE 3	
Day of Week	**Frequency**
Sunday	57
Monday	78
Tuesday	74
Wednesday	76
Thursday	71
Friday	81
Saturday	63

Testing a Claim Using a Goodness-of-Fit Test

Problem: An obstetrician wants to know whether the proportion of children born each day of the week is the same. She randomly selects 500 birth records and obtains the data shown in Table 3 (based on data obtained from *Vital Statistics of the United States,* 1997, Volume 1).

Is there reason to believe that the day on which a child is born occurs with equal frequency at the $\alpha = 0.01$ level of significance?

Approach: We follow Steps 1–7 presented on pages 658–659.

Solution: We notice that the data were randomly selected.

Step 1: We will assume that the day on which a child is born occurs with equal frequency. If we let 1 represent Sunday, 2 represent Monday, and so on, we can express this claim as $p_1 = p_2 = \ldots = p_7 = 1/7$. Thus, we have

$$H_o: p_1 = p_2 = p_3 = p_4 = p_5 = p_6 = p_7 = 1/7$$

H_1: At least one of the proportions is different from the others.

Step 2: In Table 4, we compute the expected counts for each category (day of the week), assuming that the null hypothesis is true.

Step 3: Since all the expected counts for each category are greater than 5 ($500/7 \approx 71.43$), the requirements of the goodness-of-fit test are satisfied.

Step 4: There are $k = 7$ categories, so we find the critical value using $7 - 1 = 6$ degrees of freedom. We consult Table IV and identify the column corresponding to $\alpha = 0.01$ with 6 degrees of freedom. The critical value is $\chi^2_{0.01} = 16.812$.

TABLE 4			
Day of the Week	Frequency (Observed Count)	Theoretical Probability	Expected Count
Sunday	57	1/7	500(1/7) = 500/7
Monday	78	1/7	500/7
Tuesday	74	1/7	500/7
Wednesday	76	1/7	500/7
Thursday	71	1/7	500/7
Friday	81	1/7	500/7
Saturday	63	1/7	500/7

Figure 4

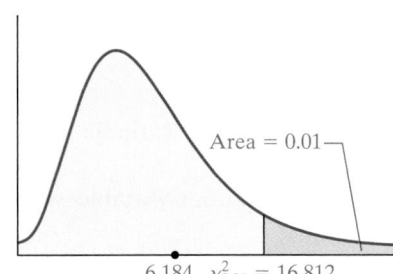

Area = 0.01

6.184 $\chi^2_{0.01} = 16.812$

Step 5: The test statistic is

$$\chi^2 = \frac{(57 - 500/7)^2}{500/7} + \frac{(78 - 500/7)^2}{500/7} + \frac{(74 - 500/7)^2}{500/7} +$$

$$\frac{(76 - 500/7)^2}{500/7} + \frac{(71 - 500/7)^2}{500/7} + \frac{(81 - 500/7)^2}{500/7} + \frac{(63 - 500/7)^2}{500/7} = 6.184$$

Step 6: Because the test statistic, 6.184, is less than the critical value, 16.812, we do not reject the null hypothesis. See Figure 4.

Step 7: There is evidence at the $\alpha = 0.01$ level of significance to support the belief that the day on which a child is born occurs with equal frequency.

◄◄

 Now Work Problem 13.

P-Values

We used the classical approach to test claims in this section, but we could also use the *P*-value approach. We cannot obtain exact *P*-values by hand, but statistical software will provide *P*-values based upon the value of the test statistic and the degrees of freedom. We can compute the *P*-value of the hypothesis tested in Example 3, using the χ^2-cdf command on a TI-83 Plus graphing calculator. See Figure 5. The area under the chi-square distribution to the right of 6.184 with 6 degrees of freedom is 0.403, so the *P*-value is 0.403. See Figure 6. The *P*-value is greater than the level of significance, so we do not reject the null hypothesis.

Caution

To find exact *P*-values, we must use technology.

Figure 5

Figure 6

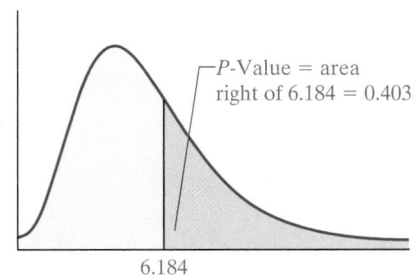

P-Value = area right of 6.184 = 0.403

6.184

Goodness-of-Fit tests can also be used to test the claim that a random variable *X* follows a certain distribution, such as the binomial probability distribution.

▶ EXAMPLE 4

Testing a Claim That a Random Variable Follows a Binomial Distribution

TABLE 5	
Number of Made Free Throws	**Frequency**
0	10
1	52
2	67
3	56
4	15

Problem: It is known that a basketball player makes 60% of her free throws. Suppose we conduct an experiment in which the player shoots four free throws. We repeat this experiment 200 times and obtain the data presented in Table 5.

Is there evidence to support the belief that the random variable X, the number of made free throws in four attempts, is a binomial random variable with $p = 0.6$ at the $\alpha = 0.05$ level of significance?

Approach: We will follow Steps 1–7 on pages 658–659.

Solution:

Step 1: We assume that the random variable X is a binomial random variable with $p = 0.6$. This will be the null hypothesis:

H_0: The random variable X is a binomial random variable with $n = 4$ and $p = 0.6$.

H_1: The random variable X is not a binomial random variable with $n = 4$ and $p = 0.6$.

Step 2: We compute the expected counts for each possible outcome, assuming that the null hypothesis is true. This is done using the binomial probability formula with $n = 4$ and $p = 0.6$ for $X = 0, 1, 2, 3,$ and 4:

$$P(0 \text{ made free throws}) = P(X = 0) = p_0 = {}_4C_0 (0.6)^0 (0.4)^4 = 0.0256$$

$$P(1 \text{ made free throw}) = P(X = 1) = p_1 = {}_4C_1 (0.6)^1 (0.4)^3 = 0.1536$$

$$P(2 \text{ made free throws}) = P(X = 2) = p_2 = {}_4C_2 (0.6)^2 (0.4)^2 = 0.3456$$

$$P(3 \text{ made free throws}) = P(X = 3) = p_3 = {}_4C_3 (0.6)^3 (0.4)^1 = 0.3456$$

$$P(4 \text{ made free throws}) = P(X = 4) = p_4 = {}_4C_4 (0.6)^4 (0.4)^0 = 0.1296$$

The expected counts for each of the possible outcomes are as follows:

Expected Count of 0 Made Free Throws: $np_0 = 200(0.0256) = 5.12$
Expected Count of 1 Made Free Throw: $np_1 = 200(0.1536) = 30.72$
Expected Count of 2 Made Free Throws: $np_2 = 200(0.3456) = 69.12$
Expected Count of 3 Made Free Throws: $np_3 = 200(0.3456) = 69.12$
Expected Count of 4 Made Free Throws: $np_4 = 200(0.1296) = 25.92$

So, in 200 trials of the experiment, we expect the player to make 0 free throws about 5 times, 1 free throw about 31 times, 2 free throws about 69 times, 3 free throws about 69 times and all 4 free throws about 26 times. The observed and expected counts are presented in Table 6.

TABLE 6			
Number of Made Free Throws	Frequency (Observed Count)	Theoretical Probability	Expected Count
0	10	0.0256	$200(0.0256) = 5.12$
1	52	0.1536	$200(0.1536) = 30.72$
2	67	0.3456	$200(0.3456) = 69.12$
3	56	0.3456	69.12
4	15	0.1296	25.92

Step 3: Since all the expected counts are greater than 5, the requirements of the goodness-of-fit test are satisfied.

Step 4: There are $k = 5$ possible outcomes, so we find the critical value using $5 - 1 = 4$ degrees of freedom. We consult Table IV and identify the column corresponding to $\alpha = 0.05$ with 4 degrees of freedom. The critical value is $\chi^2_{0.05} = 9.488$.

Step 5: The test statistic is

$$\chi^2 = \frac{(10 - 5.12)^2}{5.12} + \frac{(52 - 30.72)^2}{30.72} + \frac{(67 - 69.12)^2}{69.12} +$$
$$\frac{(56 - 69.12)^2}{69.12} + \frac{(15 - 25.92)^2}{25.92} = 26.55$$

Step 6: Because the test statistic, 26.55, is greater than the critical value, 9.488, we reject the null hypothesis. See Figure 7.

Figure 7

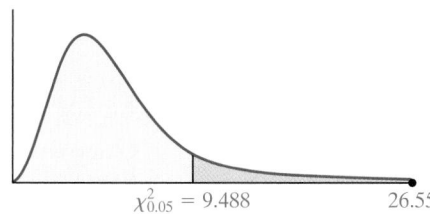

$\chi^2_{0.05} = 9.488$ 26.55

Caution

We are rejecting the claim that the random variable X follows a binomial distribution with n = 4 and p = 0.6. It might be that p is different from 0.6, but it also might be that X does not follow a binomial distribution because the shots are not independent. We do not know which of these applies to the results of Example 4.

Step 7: There is sufficient evidence at the $\alpha = 0.05$ level of significance to reject the claim that the random variable X follows a binomial distribution with $n = 4$ and $p = 0.6$. ◄◄

In Example 4, we are rejecting the claim that the data follow a binomial distribution with $p = 0.6$. This result could occur because one of the requirements of a binomial experiment (such as independent trials) is violated. It could also result because the claimed value of p, the probability of success, is different from 0.6.

NW *Now Work Problem 15.*

11.1 Assess Your Understanding

Concepts and Vocabulary

1. Why is "Goodness-of-Fit" a good choice for the title of the procedures used in this section?
2. Explain why chi-square goodness-of-fit tests are always right tailed.
3. State the assumptions that must be satisfied in order to perform a goodness-of-fit test.

Exercises

• Skill Building

In Problems 1 and 2, determine the expected counts for each outcome.

1. **NW**

$n = 500$				
p_i	0.2	0.1	0.45	0.25
Expected Counts	100	50	225	125

2. | $n = 700$ | | | | |
   |---|---|---|---|---|
   | p_i | 0.15 | 0.3 | 0.35 | 0.20 |
   | Expected Counts | 105 | 210 | 245 | 140 |

In Problems 3–6, (a) determine the χ^2 test statistic, (b) determine the degrees of freedom, (c) determine the critical value using $\alpha = 0.05$, and (d) test the hypothesis at the $\alpha = 0.05$ level of significance.

3. $H_0: p_A = p_B = p_C = p_D = \frac{1}{4}$. Do not reject H_0
   H_1: At least one of the proportions is different from the others.

Outcome	A	B	C	D
Observed	30	20	28	22
Expected	25	25	25	25

4. $H_0: p_A = p_B = p_C = p_D = p_E = 1/5$.
   H_1: At least one of the proportions is different from the others. Do not reject H_0

Outcome	A	B	C	D	E
Observed	38	45	41	33	43
Expected	40	40	40	40	40

5. H_0: The random variable X is binomial with $n = 4$, $p = 0.8$.
   H_1: The random variable X is not binomial with $n = 4$, $p = 0.8$. Reject H_0

X	0	1	2	3	4
Observed	1	38	132	440	389
Expected	1.6	25.6	153.6	409.6	409.6

6. H_0: The random variable X is binomial with $n = 4$, $p = 0.3$.
   H_1: The random variable X is not binomial with $n = 4$, $p = 0.3$. Reject H_0

X	0	1	2	3	4
Observed	260	400	280	50	10
Expected	240.1	411.6	264.6	75.6	8.1

• Applying the Concepts

7. **Plain M&Ms** According to the manufacturer of **NW** M&Ms, 30% of the plain M&Ms in a bag should be brown, 20% yellow, 20% red, 10% orange, 10% blue, and 10% green. A student wanted to determine whether a randomly selected bag of plain M&Ms had contents that followed this distribution. He counted the number of M&Ms that were each color and obtained the results shown to the right.

   Test the claim that plain M&Ms follow the distribution stated by M&M/Mars at the $\alpha = 0.05$ level of significance by following Steps 1–7 on pages 658–659. Do not reject H_0

Color	Frequency
Brown	125
Yellow	77
Red	90
Blue	31
Orange	42
Green	35

8. **Peanut M&Ms** According to the manufacturer of M&Ms, 20% of the peanut M&Ms in a bag should be brown, 20% yellow, 20% red, 20% blue, 10% orange, and 10% green. A student wanted to determine whether a randomly selected bag of peanut M&Ms had contents that followed this distribution. He counted the number of M&Ms that were each color and obtained the results shown to the right. *Do not reject H_o*

Color	Frequency	Color	Frequency
Brown	67	Blue	85
Yellow	84	Orange	40
Red	85	Green	39

Test the claim that peanut M&Ms follow the distribution stated by M&M/Mars at the $\alpha = 0.05$ level of significance by following Steps 1–7 on pages 658–659.

9. **Pedestrian Deaths versus Bicycle Deaths** A researcher wanted to determine whether the distribution of pedestrian deaths by time of day differed significantly from the distribution of bicycle deaths by time of day. The distribution of pedestrian deaths by time of day is as follows:

Time of Day	Midnight–3 am	3 am–6 am	6 am–9 am	9 am–Noon	Noon–3 pm	3 pm–6 pm	6 pm–9 pm	9 pm–Midnight
Relative Frequency	0.112	0.071	0.092	0.061	0.061	0.123	0.255	0.225

Source: Bureau of Transportation Statistics

To test his claim, the researcher randomly selected 400 bicycle deaths, recorded the time of the accident, and obtained the following data:

Time of Day	Midnight–3 am	3 am–6 am	6 am–9 am	9 am–Noon	Noon–3 pm	3 pm–6 pm	6 pm–9 pm	9 pm–Midnight
Frequency	19	20	42	34	39	98	101	47

At the $\alpha = 0.05$ level of significance, follow Steps 1–7 on pages 658–659 to test the claim that the distribution of the number of deaths on a bicycle is different from the distribution of the number of pedestrian deaths. *Reject H_o*

10. **Are Mothers Getting Older?** A sociologist wanted to determine whether the age distribution at which women have babies is changing. The U.S. Census Bureau provided her with the following data, which represent the relative frequency of total births by age in 1990:

Age of Mother	Relative Frequency	Age of Mother	Relative Frequency
15–19	0.086	30–34	0.228
20–24	0.265	35–39	0.096
25–29	0.305	40–44	0.020

A recent random sample of 500 births yielded the following frequencies:

Age of Mother	Frequency	Age of Mother	Frequency
15–19	58	30–34	131
20–24	105	35–39	69
25–29	128	40–44	9

Test the claim that the distribution of age of mothers is different today from what it was in 1990 at the $\alpha = 0.05$ level of significance by following Steps 1–7 on pages 658–659. *Reject H_o*

11. **Are Some Months Busier than Others?** A researcher wants to know whether the distribution of birth month is uniform. The following data, based upon results obtained from *Vital Statistics of the United States*, 1997, Volume 1, represent the distribution of months in which 500 randomly selected children were born:

Month	Frequency	Month	Frequency
Jan.	52	July	44
Feb.	35	Aug.	34
March	44	Sep.	36
April	42	Oct.	46
May	42	Nov.	48
June	36	Dec.	41

Is there reason to believe that each birth month occurs with equal frequency at the $\alpha = 0.05$ level of significance? *Do not reject H_o*

12. **Bicycle Deaths** A researcher wanted to determine whether bicycle deaths were uniformly distributed over the days of the week. She randomly selected 200 deaths that involved a bicycle, recorded the day of the week on which the death occurred, and obtained the following results (the data are based upon information obtained from the Insurance Institute for Highway Safety):

Reject H_o

Day of the Week	Frequency	Day of the Week	Frequency
Sunday	16	Thursday	34
Monday	35	Friday	41
Tuesday	16	Saturday	30
Wednesday	28		

Is there reason to believe that the day of the week on which a fatality occurs on a bicycle occurs with equal frequency at the $\alpha = 0.05$ level of significance?

13. **Pedestrian Deaths** A researcher wanted to determine whether pedestrian deaths were uniformly distributed over the days of the week. She randomly selected 300 pedestrian deaths, recorded the day of the week on which the death occurred, and obtained the following results (the data are based upon information obtained from the Insurance Institute for Highway Safety):

Reject H_o

Day of the Week	Frequency	Day of the Week	Frequency
Sunday	39	Thursday	41
Monday	40	Friday	49
Tuesday	30	Saturday	61
Wednesday	40		

Test the belief that the day of the week on which a fatality occurs involving a pedestrian occurs with equal frequency at the $\alpha = 0.05$ level of significance. *Reject H_o*

14. **Is the Die Loaded?** A player in a craps game suspects that one of the die being used in the game is loaded. A loaded die is one in which not all of the possibilities (1, 2, 3, 4, 5 and 6) are equally likely. The player throws the die 400 times, records the outcome after each throw, and obtains the following results: (a) *Do not reject H_o*

Outcome	Frequency	Outcome	Frequency
One	62	Four	62
Two	76	Five	57
Three	76	Six	67

(a) Is there evidence to support the claim that the die is loaded at the $\alpha = 0.01$ level of significance?
(b) Why do you think the player might test the claim at the $\alpha = 0.01$ level of significance, rather than, say, the $\alpha = 0.1$ level of significance?

15. **Testing the Random-Number Generator** Statistical spreadsheets and graphing calculators with advanced statistical features have random-number generators that create random numbers conforming to a specified distribution.

(a) Use the random-number generator to create a list of 500 randomly selected integers numbered 1–5.
(b) What proportion of the numbers generated should be 1? 2? 3? 4? 5?
(c) Test the claim that the random-number generator is generating random integers between 1 and 5 with equal likelihood by performing a chi-square goodness-of-fit test at the $\alpha = 0.01$ level of significance.

16. **Testing the Random-Number Generator** Statistical spreadsheets and graphing calculators with advanced statistical features have random-number generators that create random numbers conforming to a specified distribution.

(a) Use the random-number generator to create a list of 500 trials of a binomial experiment with $n = 5$ and $p = 0.2$.
(b) What proportion of the numbers generated should be 0? 1? 2? 3? 4? 5?
(c) Test the claim that the random-number generator is generating random outcomes of a binomial experiment with $n = 5$ and $p = 0.2$ by performing a chi-square goodness-of-fit test at the $\alpha = 0.01$ level of significance.

In Section 9.4, we tested claims regarding a population proportion using a z-test. However, we can also use the chi-square goodness-of-fit test to test claims with k = 2 possible outcomes. In Problems 17 and 18, we test claims with the use of both methods.

17. Low Birth Weight According to the U.S. Census Bureau, 7.1% of all babies born to nonsmoking mothers are of low birth weight (<5 lb, 8 oz). An obstetrician wanted to know whether mothers between the ages of 35 and 39 years gave birth to a higher percentage of low-birth-weight babies. She randomly selected 120 births for which the mother was 35–39 years old and found that 11 of them were of low birth weight.

(a) If the proportion of low-birth-weight babies for mothers 35–39 years old is 0.071, compute the expected number of low-birth-weight births to mothers 35–39 years old. What is the expected number of non-low-birth-weight births to mothers 35–39 years old? 8.52; 111.48

(b) Test the obstetrician's claim at the $\alpha = 0.05$ level of significance, using the chi-square goodness-of-fit test. Do not reject H_o

(c) Test the claim by using the approach presented in Section 9.4. Do not reject H_o

18. Living Alone? In 1990, 39% of males 15 years of age or older lived alone, according to the Census Bureau. A sociologist claims that this percentage is greater today, conducts a random sample of 400 males 15 years of age or older, and finds that 164 are living alone.

(a) If the proportion of males aged 15 years or older living alone is 0.39, compute the following expected numbers: males 15 years of age or older who live alone; males 15 years of age or older who do not live alone? 156; 244

(b) Test the sociologist's claim at the $\alpha = 0.05$ level of significance, using the chi-square goodness-of-fit test. Do not reject H_o

(c) Test the claim by using the approach presented in Section 9.4. Do not reject H_o

19. Using the results of Problem 3, compute $\sum(O - E)$. Explain why this result is reasonable. 0

11.2   Contingency Tables; Association

Preparing for This Section   Before getting started, review the following:

✓ Side-by-side bar graphs (Section 2.1, pp. 57–58)

✓ Conditional probability (Section 5.4, pp. 296–298)

Objectives   ① Compute the marginal distribution of a variable

② Use the conditional distribution to identify association among categorical data

Note to Instructor
This section is optional and may be omitted without loss of continuity.

As we saw in Section 11.1, data, whether qualitative or quantitative, can be organized into categories. For example, a person might be categorized as a male or as a female. A person might also be categorized as a 20–29-year-old. In fact, many governmental agencies regularly publish quantitative data by first creating categories (classes) of data.

Consider the data (measured in thousands) in Table 7 on page 668, which represent the employment status and level of education of all United States residents 25 years old or older in 1998. By definition, an individual is unemployed if he or she is actively seeking work, but is unable to find work. An individual is considered not to be in the labor force if he or she is not employed and is not actively seeking employment.

Table 7 is referred to as a **contingency table** or a **two-way table**, because it relates two categories of data. The **row variable** is employment status, because each row in the table describes the employment status of a group. The **column variable** is level of education. Each box inside the table is referred to as a **cell**. For example, the cell corresponding to employed individuals who are high school graduates is in the first row, second column. Each cell contains the frequency of the category: There were 11,669 thousand employed individuals who did not finish high school in 1998.

TABLE 7				
	Level of Education			
Employment Status	**Did Not Finish High School**	**High School Graduate**	**Some College**	**Four or More Years of College**
Employed	11,669	36,451	30,339	33,006
Unemployed	1,057	1,784	1,126	625
Not in the Labor Force	16,858	20,040	10,829	8,094

Source: United States Census Bureau, Current Population Survey

The data presented in Table 7 describe two characteristics regarding the population of U.S. residents who are 25 years or older: their employment status and their level of education. Because the data represent the entire population, it does not make sense to perform any type of statistical inference. However, we still might want to investigate whether the two variables are associated. For example, are individuals who have a higher level of education more likely to be employed?

① Marginal Distributions

The first step in analyzing data in a contingency table is to look at the distribution of each variable separately. To determine the distribution of either the column variable or the row variable, we create a *marginal distribution*.

Definition

> A **marginal distribution** of a variable is a frequency or relative frequency distribution of either the row or column variable in the contingency table.

In Your Own Words

The distributions are called marginal distributions because they appear in the right and the bottom margin of the contingency table.

A marginal distribution removes the effect of either the row variable or the column variable in the contingency table.

To create a marginal distribution for a variable, we calculate the row and column totals for each category of the variable. The row totals for each category are found by adding up the cell entries in each column of that row. The row totals represent the distribution of the row variable. The column totals for each category are found by adding up the cell entries in each row of that column. The column totals represent the distribution of the column variable.

▶ **EXAMPLE 1** Determining Frequency Marginal Distributions

Problem: Find the frequency marginal distributions for employment status and level of education from the data in Table 7.

Approach: The row total for the category "employed" is found by adding the number of employed individuals who did not finish high school, the number of employed individuals who finished high school, and so on. We repeat this process for each category of employment status. The column total for the category "did not finish high school" is found by adding the number of employed individuals who did not finish high school, the number of unemployed individuals who did not finish high school, and the number of individuals not in the labor force who did not finish high school. We repeat this process for each level of education.

Solution: In Table 8, the blue entries represent the marginal distribution of the row variable, employment status. For example, there were 11,669 + 36,451 + 30,339 + 33,006 = 111,465 thousand employed individuals in 1998. The red entries represent the marginal distribution of the column variable, level of education.

	TABLE 8				
	Level of Education				
Employment Status	**Did Not Finish High School**	**High School Graduate**	**Some College**	**Four or More Years of College**	**Totals**
Employed	11,669	36,451	30,339	33,006	111,465
Unemployed	1057	1784	1126	625	4592
Not in the Labor Force	16,858	20,040	10,829	8094	55,821
Totals	29,584	58,275	42,294	41,725	171,878

The marginal distribution for employment status removes the effect of level of education; the marginal distribution for level of education removes the effect of employment status. From the marginal distribution of employment status, we can see that there were about twice as many employed Americans as there were Americans not in the labor force (111,465 thousand versus 55,821 thousand) in 1998. From the marginal distribution of level of education, we can see that a majority of Americans were high school graduates (58,275 thousand). We can also learn from the table that there were 171,878 thousand United States residents 25 years old or older. ◄◄

NW *Now Work Problem 1(a).*

We can use the row and column totals obtained in Example 1 to calculate the relative frequency marginal distribution for level of education and employment status.

► **EXAMPLE 2**   **Determining Relative Frequency Marginal Distributions**

Problem: Determine the relative frequency marginal distribution for level of education and employment status from the data in Table 8.

Approach: The relative frequency marginal distribution for the row variable, employment status, is found by dividing the row total for each employment status by the table total, 171,878. The relative frequency marginal distribution for the column variable, level of education, is found by dividing the column total for each level of education by the table total.

Solution: Table 9 on page 670 represents the relative frequency marginal distribution for each variable.

From Table 9, we learn that 17.2% of U.S. residents 25 years old or older did not graduate from high school. We also learn that 64.9% of U.S. residents 25 years old or older were employed in 1998.

TABLE 9					
	Did Not Finish High School	High School Graduate	Some College	Four or More Years of College	Totals
Employed	11,669	36,451	30,339	33,006	111,465/171,878 = 0.649
Unemployed	1057	1784	1126	625	4592/171,878 = 0.027
Not in the Labor Force	16,858	20,040	10,829	8094	55,821/171,878 = 0.325
Totals	29,584/171,878 = 0.172	58,275/171,878 = 0.339	42,294/171,878 = 0.246	41,725/171,878 = 0.243	1*

 *Now Work Problems 1(b), (c) and (d).*

◄◄

② A Measure of Association

As we look at the information contained in Tables 8 and 9, we might ask whether there is a relation between employment status and level of education. In other words, what role does the level of education play in the employment status of an individual? If the level of education does not play any role, we would expect the relative frequencies for employment status at each level of education to be close to the relative frequency marginal distribution for employment status given in blue in Table 9. Thus, we would expect 64.9% of individuals who did not finish high school to be employed, 64.9% of individuals who finished high school to be employed, 64.9% of individuals with some college to be employed and 64.9% of individuals with 4 or more years of college to be employed. If the relative frequencies for the various levels of education are different, we might associate this difference with the level of education.

The marginal distributions in Tables 8 and 9 do allow us to see the distribution of either the row variable, employment status, or the column variable, level of education, but we do not get a sense of association from these tables. When describing any association between two categories of data, we must use relative frequencies instead of frequencies, because frequencies are difficult to compare when there are different numbers of observations for the categories of a variable.

Caution

In order to describe the association between two categorical variables relative frequencies must be used because there are different numbers of observations for the categories.

► EXAMPLE 3   Comparing Two Categories of a Variable

Problem: What proportion of the individuals who did not finish high school are employed? What proportion of the individuals who finished high school are employed? What proportion of the individuals who finished some college are employed? What proportion of the individuals who attended four or more years of college are employed?

Approach: For each question, we calculate the relative frequency of each category. For example, to determine the proportion of employed individuals who did not finish high school, we divide the number of employed people who did not finish high school by the number of people who did not finish high school. We repeat this process for the remaining three questions.

*Row or column totals might not sum exactly to 1, due to rounding.

Solution: In 1998, 29,584 thousand individuals 25 years old or older did not finish high school. (See Table 8.) Of this number, 11,669 thousand were employed. Therefore, 11,669/29,584 = 0.394 represents the proportion of individuals who did not finish high school who were employed. In 1998, 58,275 thousand individuals 25 years old or older were high school graduates. Of this number, 36,451 thousand were employed. Therefore, 36,451/58,275 = 0.625 represents the proportion of individuals who graduated from high school who were employed. In 1998, 42,294 thousand individuals 25 years old or older had some college. Of this number, 30,339 thousand were employed. Therefore, 30,339/42,294 = 0.717 were employed. In 1998, 41,725 thousand individuals 25 years old or older had four or more years of college. Of this number, 33,006 thousand were employed. Therefore, 33,006/41,725 = 0.791 were employed. From these relative frequencies, we can see that, as the level of education increases, the proportion of individuals employed increases. ◀◀

The results in Example 3 are only partial. In general, we create a relative frequency distribution for each employment status of individuals who did not finish high school, a second relative frequency distribution for each employment status of individuals who are high school graduates, and so on. These relative frequency distributions are called *conditional distributions*.

In Your Own Words
Since we are finding the conditional distribution of employment status by level of education, the level of education is the predictor variable and the employment status is the response variable.

Definition

> A **conditional distribution** lists the relative frequency of each category of a variable, given a specific value of the other variable in the contingency table.

An example should help solidify an understanding of the definition.

▶ **EXAMPLE 4** Constructing a Conditional Distribution

Problem: Find the conditional distribution of the variable employment status by level of education for the data in Table 7.

Approach: We first compute the relative frequency for each employment status, given that the individual did not finish high school. We next compute the relative frequency for each employment status, given that the individual is a high school graduate. Then we compute the relative frequency for each employment status, given that the individual had some college. Finally, we compute the relative frequency for each employment status, given that the individual had at least four years of college.

Solution: We start with the individuals who did not finish high school. We use the number of individuals who did not finish high school (29,584 thousand) as the denominator in computing the relative frequencies. For example, the relative frequency of an employed individual among all those who had not finished high school is 11,669/29,584 = 0.394. So, 39.4% of individuals who did not finish high school are employed. We repeat this process for the remaining employment categories (unemployed and not in the labor force).

We then compute the relative frequency for each employment status, given that the individual is a high school graduate. In this case, since we know the individual is a high school graduate, we use the number of individuals who graduated from high school as the denominator in computing relative frequencies. For example, the relative frequency of an employed individual among all those who graduated from high school is 36,451/58,275 = 0.625. Repeat this process for the remaining employment categories.

Finally, compute the relative frequency for each employment status, given that the individual had some college and then given that the individual had four or more years of college. We obtain Table 10.

TABLE 10				
	Level of Education			
Employment Status	**Did Not Finish High School**	**High School Graduate**	**Some College**	**Four or More Years of College**
Employed	11,669/29,584 = 0.394	36,451/58,275 = 0.625	30,339/42,294 = 0.717	33,006/41,725 = 0.791
Unemployed	1057/29,584 = 0.036	1784/58,275 = 0.031	1126/42,294 = 0.027	625/41,725 = 0.015
Not in the Labor Force	16,858/29,584 = 0.570	20,040/58,275 = 0.344	10,829/42,294 = 0.256	8094/41,725 = 0.194
Totals	1	1	1	1

From the conditional distributions by level of education, associations become apparent. As the amount of schooling increases, the proportion employed within each category also increases. As the amount of schooling increases, the proportion unemployed and the proportion not in the labor force decrease.

Information about individuals' level of education provides some insight into their employment status. For example, suppose we were asked to predict the number of employed individuals out of 100. We might predict that about 65 of the 100 were employed, because the employment rate for the entire United States is 64.9%. (See Table 9.) However, if we were given the additional information that the 100 individuals all had completed four or more years of college, we would increase our "guess" to about 79. Do you see why? The additional information about the individuals' level of education allows us to adjust our predictions. ◄◄

NW *Now Work Problem 1(e).*

We could also construct a conditional distribution by employment status. The procedure would be the same, except the distribution would use the rows instead of the columns. In this case, the predictor variable would be the employment status and the response variable would be level of education. For this situation, we could state the proportion of Americans 25 years old or older who did not finish high school (given that they are employed), the proportion of Americans 25 years old or older who have a high school diploma (given that they are employed), and so on.

As is usually the case, a graph can provide a powerful depiction of the data. A bar graph of the conditional distribution is recommended.

▶ **EXAMPLE 5**   **Drawing a Bar Graph of a Conditional Distribution**

Problem: Using the results of Example 4, draw a bar graph that represents the conditional distribution of employment status by level of education.

Approach: We will draw three bars, side by side, for each employment status. The horizontal axis will represent the level of education and the vertical axis will represent the relative frequency.

Solution: Figure 8 contains the bar graph: The blue bars represent the proportion employed for each level of education, the maroon bars represent the proportion unemployed for each level of education, and the yellow bars represent the proportion not in the labor force for each level of education.

Figure 8

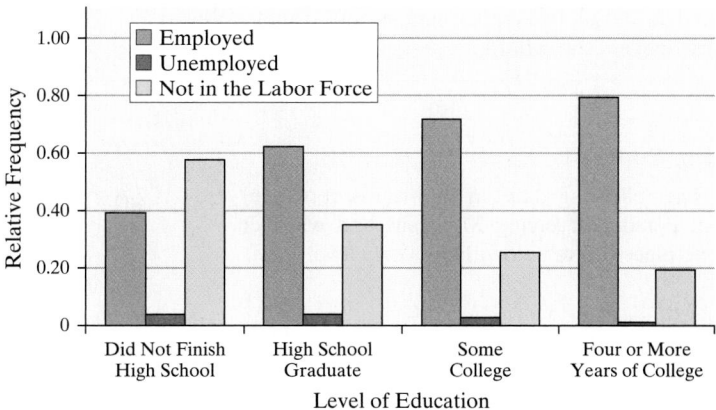

Employment Status by Level of Education

The graph contains the same information as that obtained from Table 10. The proportion employed increases as the level of education increases. We also see that the proportion of individuals unemployed or not in the labor force decreases as the level of education increases. ◄◄

 *Now Work Problems 1(f) and (g).*

The methods presented in this section for identifying the association between two categorical variables are very different from the methods for measuring association between two quantitative variables. The measure of association in this section is based upon whether there are differences in the relative frequencies of the response variable (employment status) for the different categories of the predictor variable (level of education). If differences exist, we might attribute those differences to the predictor variable.

In addition, because the data in Example 4 are observational, we do not make any statements regarding causation. Level of education is not said to be a cause of employment status, because a controlled experiment was not conducted. Again, never make statements about causation when the data are observational.

Finally, we should note that the data that we analyzed were population data. Therefore, we do not perform any inferential statistics on the data. Any differences that exist in the marginal distributions are differences in the populations. For example, we can state that a higher level of education is associated with a higher level of employment with 100% certainty, because the analysis was performed on population data. If the data were sample data, we would not have this level of confidence.

Caution

The data in this section are population data, so there is no need to perform inference. We check for association in sample data in Section 11.3.

11.2 Assess Your Understanding

Concepts and Vocabulary

1. What is meant by a marginal distribution? What is meant by a conditional distribution?
2. Refer to Table 7. Is constructing a conditional distribution by level of education different from constructing a conditional distribution by employment status? If they are different, explain the difference.

3. Explain why we use the term association rather than correlation when describing the relation between two variables in this section.

Exercises

• Applying the Concepts

1. **Medicaid** The following data, in thousands, represent the ages of persons receiving Medicaid and whether their income places them below the poverty level:

Poverty Level	Age			
	<18	18–44	45–64	≥65
Below Poverty Level	8,550	4,356	1,520	958
Above Poverty Level	5,884	3,741	1,756	1,943

Source: Statistical Abstract, 2000

(a) Construct a frequency marginal distribution.
(b) Construct a relative frequency marginal distribution.
(c) What percentage of people receiving Medicaid are below the poverty level? 53.6%
(d) What percentage of people receiving Medicaid are less than 18 years old? 50.3%
(e) Construct a conditional distribution by poverty level.
(f) Draw a bar graph of the conditional distribution.
(g) What, if any, association exists between age and poverty level? Discuss the association.

2. **SAT Verbal Scores** The following data represent the scores received on the 2000 SAT I: Reasoning Test—Verbal, by gender:

SAT Verbal Score	Gender	
	Male	Female
200–299	16,349	18,328
300–399	75,672	90,197
400–499	177,265	213,756
500–599	186,947	216,564
600–699	98,407	108,358
700–800	28,691	29,744

Source: College Board

(a) Construct a frequency marginal distribution.
(b) Construct a relative frequency marginal distribution.
(c) What percentage of the students taking the SAT verbal scores 500–599? 32.0%
(d) What percentage of the students taking the SAT verbal are female? 53.7%
(e) Construct a conditional distribution by gender.
(f) Draw a bar graph of the conditional distribution.
(g) What, if any, association exists between SAT verbal score and gender? Discuss the association.

3. **Driver Fatalities** The following data represent the number of driver fatalities in 1996, by age group, for male and female drivers: (c) 25.5% (d) 26.2%

Age	Gender		Age	Gender	
	Male	Female		Male	Female
16–24	4,736	1,461	55–64	1,321	530
25–34	4,112	1,244	65–74	1,212	626
35–44	3,180	1,089	75–84	1,028	553
45–54	2,028	738	85 or older	329	146

Source: National Highway Traffic Institute

(a) Construct a frequency marginal distribution.
(b) Construct a relative frequency marginal distribution.
(c) What percentage of the drivers killed are 16–24?
(d) What percentage of the drivers killed are female?
(e) Construct a conditional distribution by gender.
(f) Draw a bar graph of the conditional distribution found in part (e).
(g) What, if any, association exists between age and gender? Discuss the association.

4. Marital Status The following data represent the marital status of Americans 25 years old or older and their level of education in 1999:

Marital Status	Level of Education			
	Did Not Graduate High School	High School Graduate	Some College	College Graduate
Never Married	4,012	7,790	6,565	7,685
Married, Spouse Present	15,122	36,076	27,003	29,811
Married, Spouse Absent	1,877	2,006	1,435	1,489
Separated	1,094	1,515	1,214	598
Widowed	5,000	4,757	2,264	1,456
Divorced	2,951	7,047	5,649	3,766

Source: U.S. Census Bureau

(a) Construct a frequency marginal distribution.
(b) Construct a relative frequency marginal distribution.
(c) What percentage of Americans 25 years old or older have never married? 14.6%
(d) What percentage of Americans 25 years old or older have graduated from high school? 33.2%
(e) Construct a conditional distribution by level of education.
(f) Draw a bar graph of the conditional distribution found in part (e).
(g) What, if any, association exists between level of education and marital status? Discuss the association.

5. Abortion The following data represent the number of abortions completed in a year, by age and year:

Age	Year		
	1980	1990	1995
≤19 years old	378,901	320,225	243,387
20–24 years old	460,650	474,620	393,537
≥25 years old	458,055	634,732	573,959

Source: World Almanac, 2000

(a) Construct a frequency marginal distribution.
(b) Construct a relative frequency marginal distribution.
(c) What percentage of the abortions were performed in 1980? 33.0%
(d) What percentage of the women having abortions were 19 years old or younger? 23.9%
(e) Construct a conditional distribution by year.
(f) Draw a bar graph of the conditional distribution.
(g) What, if any, association exists between age and year? Discuss the association.

6. Cause of Death Based upon information provided by the *National Vital Statistics Reports*, Vol. 48, No. 11, July 24, 2000, the following data represent the cause of death for various age groups in 1998:

Age	Cause of Death			
	Accidents and Adverse Effects	Malignant Neoplasms	Diseases of Heart	Cerebrovascular Diseases
1–4 years	1,935	365	214	57
5–14 years	3,254	1,386	326	82
15–24 years	13,349	1,699	1,057	178
25–44 years	27,172	13,077	16,800	3,320
45–64 years	18,286	132,771	100,124	15,362
65 years and older	32,975	384,186	605,673	139,144

(a) Construct a frequency marginal distribution.
(b) Construct a relative frequency marginal distribution.
(c) What percentage of the deaths were due to accidents and adverse effects? 6.4%
(d) What percentage of the deaths were of people 15–24 years old? 1.1%
(e) Construct a conditional distribution by cause of death.
(f) Draw a bar graph of the conditional distribution.
(g) What, if any, association exists between age and cause of death? Discuss the association.

7. **Child Care** The following data, in thousands, represent the type of child care children under six years of age are in, by mother's employment status:

Employment Status	Type of Care			
	In Relative Care	In Nonrelative Care	In Center-based Program	Parental Arrangement
35 Hours or More per Week	2,343	2,272	2,769	852
Less Than 35 Hours per Week	1,210	1,049	1,412	1,009
Looking for Work	262	65	409	948
Not in the Labor Force	585	501	1,838	5,681

Source: Statistical Abstract, 2000

(a) Construct a frequency marginal distribution.
(b) Construct a relative frequency marginal distribution.
(c) What percentage of mothers work 35 hours or more per week? 35.5%
(d) What percentage of children under six years of age are cared for by relatives? 19.0%
(e) Construct a conditional distribution by mother's employment status.
(f) Draw a bar graph of the conditional distribution.
(g) What, if any, association exists between mother's employment status and child care? Discuss the association.

8. **Farm Size** The data to the right represent the size of a farm and the tenure of the operator (a *full owner* owns all the acreage he or she farms; a *part owner* owns some of the land and rents the rest; a *tenant* leases the land he or she farms).

(a) Construct a frequency marginal distribution.
(b) Construct a relative frequency marginal distribution.
(c) What percentage of farms have 50–179 acres? 31.0%
(d) What percentage of farms have a full owner? 60.0%
(e) Construct a conditional distribution by farm size.
(f) Draw a bar graph of the conditional distribution.
(g) What, if any, association exists between farm size and ownership? Discuss the association.

Size	Tenure		
	Full Owner	Part Owner	Tenant
Under 50 Acres	460	57	48
50–179 Acres	409	131	53
180–499 Acres	189	169	45
500–999 Acres	50	103	23
1,000 Acres or More	40	114	22

Source: Statistical Abstract of the United States, 2000

11.3   Chi-Square Test for Independence; Homogeneity of Proportions

Preparing for This Section   Before getting started, review the following:

✓ The language of hypothesis tests (Section 9.1, pp. 518–525)

✓ Independent events (Section 5.3, pp. 288–292)

✓ Mean of a binomial random variable (Section 6.2, pp. 345–346)

✓ Testing a hypothesis about two population proportions (Section 10.3, pp. 619–624)

Objectives   Perform chi-square test for independence

Perform chi-square test for homogeneity of proportions

Note to Instructor
If you covered Section 11.2, be sure to emphasize that the data were population data, so inference was not necessary. When analyzing qualitative sample data for association, we use the chi-square independence test.

In Section 11.2, we discussed the association between two variables in which we had data for an entire population. Under this situation, we could say two variables are associated by examining the relative frequency marginal distributions. If differences existed among the relative frequency marginal distributions, then we could claim association among the variables. However, if we have sample data, we must perform statistical inference to determine whether any differences we have obtained are significant. In this section, we develop methods for performing statistical inference on two categorical variables to determine whether there is any association between the two variables. We call the method the *chi-square independence test*.

 Chi-Square Independence Test

We begin with a definition.

Definition

> The **chi-square independence test** is used to find out whether there is an association between a row variable and column variable in a contingency table constructed from sample data. The null hypothesis is that the variables are not associated; in other words, they are independent. The alternative hypothesis is that the variables are associated, or dependent.

In Your Own Words

In a chi-square independence test, the null hypothesis is always
   H_o: The variables are independent
The alternative hypothesis is always
   H_1: The variables are dependent

The idea behind testing these types of claims is to compare actual counts to the counts we would expect if the null hypothesis were true (if the variables are independent). If a significant difference between the actual counts and expected counts exists, we would take this as evidence against the null hypothesis.

The method for obtaining the expected counts requires that we compute the number of observations expected within each cell under the assumption that the null hypothesis is true. Recall, if two events A and B are independent, then $P(A \text{ and } B) = P(A) \cdot P(B)$. We can use the Multiplication Principle for independent events to obtain the expected proportion of observations within each cell under the assumption of independence. We then multiply this result by n, the sample size, in order to obtain the expected count within each cell.* We present an example in order to introduce the method for obtaining expected counts.

*Recall that the expected value of a binomial random variable for n independent trials of a binomial experiment with probability of success p is given by $E = \mu = np$.

▶ **EXAMPLE 1** **Determining the Expected Counts in a Test for Independence**

Problem: Blood type is classified as A, B, AB, or O. In addition, blood can be classified as Rh^+ or Rh^-. In a survey of 500 randomly selected individuals, a phlebotomist obtained the results shown in Table 11.

		TABLE 11		
		Blood Type		
Rh-Level	**A**	**B**	**AB**	**O**
Rh^+	176	28	22	198
Rh^-	30	12	4	30

Compute the expected counts within each cell, assuming that Rh-level and blood type are independent.

Approach:

Step 1: Compute the row and column totals.

Step 2: Compute the relative marginal frequencies for the row variable and column variable.

Step 3: Use the Multiplication Rule for independent events to compute the proportion of observations within each cell under the assumption of independence.

Step 4: Multiply the proportions by 500, the sample size, to obtain the expected counts within each cell.

Solution:

Step 1: The row totals (blue) and column totals (red) are presented in Table 12.

TABLE 12					
	A	**B**	**AB**	**O**	**Row Totals**
Rh^+	176	28	22	198	424
Rh^-	30	12	4	30	76
Column Totals	206	40	26	228	500

Step 2: The relative frequencies for the row variable (Rh-level) and column variable (blood type) are presented in Table 13.

TABLE 13					
	A	**B**	**AB**	**O**	**Relative Frequency**
Rh^+	176	28	22	198	424/500 = 0.848
Rh^-	30	12	4	30	76/500 = 0.152
Relative Frequency	206/500 = 0.412	40/500 = 0.08	26/500 = 0.052	228/500 = 0.456	1

Step 3: Assuming blood type and Rh-level are independent, we use the Multiplication Rule for independent events to compute the proportion of observations we would expect in each cell. For example, the proportion of individuals who are Rh^+ and of blood type A would be

$$\text{Proportion } Rh^+ \text{ and blood type A} = (\text{Proportion } Rh^+) \cdot (\text{Proportion blood type A})$$

$$= (0.848)(0.412)$$

$$= 0.349376$$

Table 14 contains the expected proportion in each cell, under the assumption of independence.

TABLE 14				
	A	**B**	**AB**	**O**
Rh^+	0.349376	0.06784	0.044096	0.386688
Rh^-	0.062624	0.01216	0.007904	0.069312

Step 4: We multiply the expected proportions in Table 14 by 500, the sample size, to obtain the expected counts under the assumption of independence. The results are presented in Table 15.

TABLE 15				
	A	**B**	**AB**	**O**
Rh^+	500(0.349376) = 174.688	500(0.06784) = 33.92	500(0.044096) = 22.048	193.344
Rh^-	31.312	6.08	3.952	34.656

If blood type and Rh-level are independent, we would expect a random sample of 500 individuals to contain about 175 who are of blood type A and are Rh^+.   ◄◄

The technique used in Example 1 to find the expected counts might seem rather tedious. It certainly would be more pleasant if we could determine a shortcut formula that could be used to obtain the expected counts. Let's consider the expected count for blood type A and Rh^+. This expected count was obtained by multiplying the proportion of individuals who were of blood type A, the proportion of individuals that were Rh^+, and the number of individuals in the sample. That is,

$$\text{Expected Count} = (\text{Proportion } Rh^+)(\text{Proportion blood type A})(\text{Sample size})$$

$$= \frac{424}{500} \cdot \frac{206}{500} \cdot 500$$

$$= \frac{424 \cdot 206}{500} \qquad \text{Cancel the 500s}$$

$$= \frac{(\text{row total for } Rh^+)(\text{column total for blood type A})}{\text{table total}}$$

This leads to the following general result:

Theorem

Expected Frequencies in a Chi-Square Independence Test

To find the expected frequencies in a cell when performing a chi-square independence test, multiply the row total of the row containing the cell by the column total of the column containing the cell and divide this result by the table total. That is,

$$\text{Expected frequency} = \frac{(\text{row total})(\text{column total})}{\text{table total}} \quad \textbf{(1)}$$

For example, to calculate the expected frequency for Rh^+, blood type A, we compute

$$\text{Expected frequency} = \frac{(\text{row total})(\text{column total})}{\text{table total}} = \frac{(424)(206)}{500} = 174.688$$

This result agrees with the result obtained in Table 15.

NW *Now Work Problem 5(a).*

To test a claim, we compare the actual (observed) counts to those expected. If the observed counts are significantly different from the expected counts, we take this as evidence against the null hypothesis. We need a test statistic and sampling distribution in order to test the claim.

Theorem

Test Statistic for the Test of Independence

Let O_i represent the observed number of counts in the ith cell and E_i represent the expected number of counts in the ith cell. Then

$$\chi^2 = \sum \frac{(O_i - E_i)^2}{E_i}$$

approximately follows the chi-square distribution with $(r - 1)(c - 1)$ degrees of freedom, where r is the number of rows and c is the number of columns in the contingency table, provided that (1) all expected frequencies are greater than or equal to 1 and (2) no more than 20% of the expected frequencies are less than 5.

From Example 1, there were $r = 2$ rows and $c = 4$ columns.

We now present a method for testing claims regarding the association between two variables in a contingency table.

The Chi-Square Test for Independence

If a claim is made regarding the association between (or independence of) two variables in a contingency table, we can use the steps that follow to test the claim, provided that

1. the data are randomly selected

2. all expected frequencies are greater than or equal to 1; and

3. no more than 20% of the expected frequencies are less than 5.

Step 1: A claim is made regarding the independence of the data.

H_0: The row variable and column variable are independent.

H_1: The row variable and column variable are dependent.

Figure 9

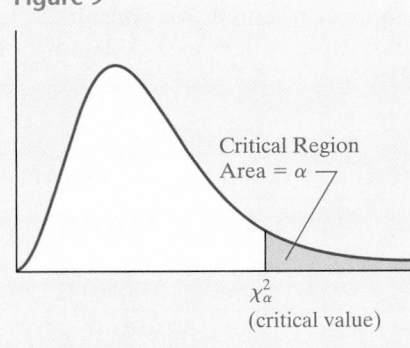

Critical Region
Area = α

χ_α^2
(critical value)

Step 2: Calculate the expected frequencies (counts) for each cell in the contingency table using Formula (1).

Step 3: Verify that the requirements of the test for independence are satisfied.

Step 4: Choose a level of significance, α, based upon the seriousness of making a Type I error. The level of significance is used to determine the critical value. All chi-square independence tests are right-tailed tests, so the critical value is χ_α^2 with $(r-1)(c-1)$ degrees of freedom. The shaded region(s) represents the critical region. See Figure 9.

Step 5: Compute the **test statistic**:

$$\chi^2 = \sum \frac{(O_i - E_i)^2}{E_i}$$

Step 6: Compare the critical value with the test statistic. If $\chi^2 > \chi_\alpha^2$, reject the null hypothesis.

Step 7: State the conclusion.

▶ **EXAMPLE 2**   **Performing a Chi-Square Independence Test**

TABLE 16				
	Blood Type			
Rh-Level	**A**	**B**	**AB**	**O**
Rh$^+$	176	28	22	198
Rh$^-$	30	12	4	30

Problem: Blood is classified as A, B, AB, or O. In addition, blood can be classified as Rh$^+$ or Rh$^-$. In a survey of 500 randomly selected individuals, a phlebotomist obtained the results shown in Table 16.

Test whether blood type and Rh-level are independent at the $\alpha = 0.05$ level of significance.

Approach: We follow Steps 1–7 on pages 680–681.

Solution: The data were obtained through a random sample, so the first requirement needed to perform the chi-square independence test has been satisfied. We will verify requirements 2 and 3 in Step 3.

Step 1: We wish to determine whether blood type and Rh-level are independent. We state the hypotheses as follows:

H_0: Blood type and Rh-level are independent (or not related).
H_1: Blood type and Rh-level are dependent (or somehow related).

Step 2: The expected frequencies were calculated in Example 1. Table 17 presents the observed frequencies, with the expected frequencies in parentheses.

TABLE 17				
Observed (and Expected) Frequencies				
	A	**B**	**AB**	**O**
Rh$^+$	176	28	22	198
	(174.688)	(33.92)	(22.048)	(193.344)
Rh$^-$	30	12	4	30
	(31.312)	(6.08)	(3.952)	(34.656)

Step 3: All the expected frequencies are greater than 1. One of eight, or 12.5%, of the expected frequencies is less than 5. The requirements have been satisfied.

Step 4: There are $r = 2$ rows and $c = 4$ columns, so we find the critical value by using $(2 - 1)(4 - 1) = 3$ degrees of freedom. We consult Table IV and identify the column corresponding to $\alpha = 0.05$ with 3 degrees of freedom. The critical value is $\chi^2_{0.05} = 7.815$.

Step 5: The test statistic is

$$\chi^2 = \frac{(176 - 174.688)^2}{174.688} + \frac{(28 - 33.92)^2}{33.92} + \frac{(22 - 22.048)^2}{22.048} + \frac{(198 - 193.344)^2}{193.344}$$

$$+ \frac{(30 - 31.312)^2}{31.312} + \frac{(12 - 6.08)^2}{6.08} + \frac{(4 - 3.952)^2}{3.952} + \frac{(30 - 34.656)^2}{34.656}$$

$$= 7.601$$

Figure 10

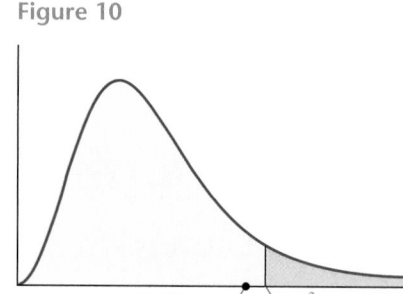

7.601 ⎯⎯ $\chi^2_{0.05} = 7.815$

Step 6: Because the test statistic, 7.601, is less than the critical value, 7.815, we do not reject the null hypothesis. See Figure 10.

Step 7: There is not enough evidence, at the $\alpha = 0.05$ level of significance, to support the belief that Rh-level and blood type are dependent. We conclude that Rh-level and blood type are not related. ◀◀

NW *Now Work Problems 5(b), 5(c), 5(d), and 5(e).*

While we did not reject the null hypothesis that Rh-level and blood type are independent at the $\alpha = 0.05$ level of signficance, the closeness of the test statistic to the critical value could be considered suggestive of some type of relation between Rh-level and blood type.

In order to "see" the relation between Rh-level and blood type, we draw bar graphs of the conditional distributions of Rh-level by blood type. Recall that a conditional distribution lists the relative frequency of each category of a variable, given a specific value of the other variable in a contingency table. For example, we can calculate the relative frequency of Rh^+ and Rh^-, given that an individual is of blood type A. We repeat this for the remaining blood types.

▶ **EXAMPLE 3** **Constructing a Conditional Distribution and Bar Graph**

Problem: Find the conditional distribution of the variable Rh-level by blood type for the data in Table 16. Then draw a bar graph that represents the conditional distribution of Rh-level by blood type.

Approach: First, compute the relative frequency for Rh-level, given that the individual is blood type A. Then compute the relative frequency for Rh-level, given that the individual is blood type B—and so on. We will draw two bars, side by side, for each blood type. The horizontal axis will represent the blood type, and the vertical axis will represent the relative frequency of Rh-level for each blood type.

Solution: We start with the individuals who are blood type A. The relative frequency with which we observe an individual who is Rh^+, given that the individual is blood type A, is 176/206 = 0.854. Therefore, 85.4% of individuals who are blood type A are Rh^+. The relative frequency with which we observe an individual who is Rh^-, given that the individual is blood type A, is 30/206 = 0.146. We now proceed to compute the relative frequency for each Rh-level, given that the individual is blood type B. The relative frequency with which we observe an individual who is Rh$^+$, given that the individual is blood type B, is $28/40 = 0.70$. Repeat this process for individuals who are Rh$^-$. Finally, compute the relative frequency for each Rh$^-$ level, given that the individual is blood type AB and then given that the individual is blood type O. We obtain Table 18.

	A	B	AB	O
TABLE 18				
Rh$^+$	$176/206$ $= 0.854$	$28/40$ $= 0.70$	$22/26$ $= 0.846$	$198/228$ $= 0.868$
Rh$^-$	$30/206 = 0.146$	$12/40 = 0.30$	$4/26 = 0.154$	$30/228 = 0.132$

From the conditional distributions by blood type, the association between blood type and Rh-level should be apparent. The proportion of individuals who are Rh$^+$ is less for those individuals who are of blood type B than with the other blood types; however, the difference is not significant at the $\alpha = 0.05$ level of significance.

Figure 11 contains the bar graph of the conditional distribution; the blue bars represent the proportion of individuals with Rh$^+$ blood for each blood type, and the maroon bars represent the proportion of individuals with Rh$^-$ blood for each blood type.

Figure 11

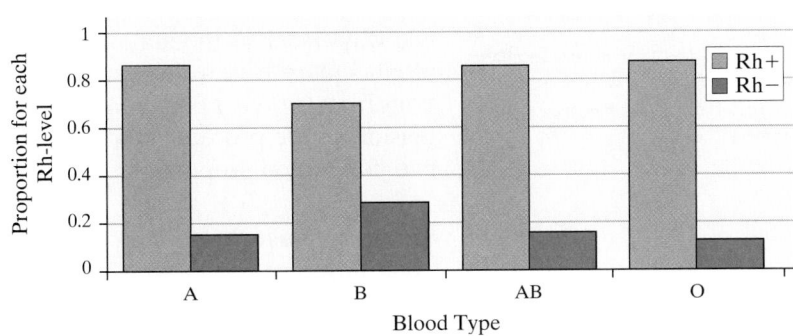

Proportion of Each Rh-level by Blood Type

NW *Now Work Problem 5(f).*

P-Values

Figure 12

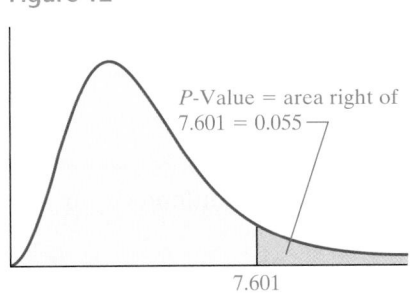

We used the classical approach to test the claim of independence, but we could also use the *P*-value approach. We obtain *P*-values by finding the area under the chi-square distribution to the right of the test statistic with $(r - 1)(c - 1)$ degrees of freedom. This is easily accomplished by using statistical software or a graphing calculator with advanced statistical features. For example, using the χ^2cdf command on a TI-83 Plus graphing calculator, we find the area under the chi-square distribution to the right of 7.601 with 3 degrees of freedom to be 0.055, so the *P*-value is 0.055. See Figure 12. The *P*-value is greater than the level of significance ($\alpha = 0.05$), so we do not reject the null hypothesis at the $\alpha = 0.05$ level of signficance. Although we do not reject the null hypothesis at $\alpha = 0.05$, the low *P*-value does suggest that there is some relation between blood type and Rh-level.

NW *Now Work Problem 5(g).*

Using Technology: Statistical spreadsheets or graphing calculators with advanced statistical features can be used to test claims of independence. Figure 13 shows the results of Example 2 using Minitab.

Figure 13

Chi-Square Test

Expected counts are printed below observed counts

	C1	C2	C3	C4	Total
1	176	28	22	198	424
	174.69	33.92	22.05	193.34	
2	30	12	4	30	76
	31.31	6.08	3.95	34.66	
Total	206	40	26	228	500

Chi-Sq = 0.010 + 1.033 + 0.000 + 0.112 +
  0.055 + 5.764 + 0.001 + 0.626 = 7.601

DF = 3, P-Value = 0.055
1 cells with expected counts less than 5.0

Notice that the *P*-value is given as 0.055, the same result we obtained.

② Chi-Square Test for Homogeneity of Proportions

In Your Own Words

The chi-square test for homogeneity of proportions is used to compare proportions from two or more populations.

The chi-square test for independence is a test regarding a sample from a *single* population. Each individual in this single population is classified in two ways (such as blood type and Rh-level). We now discuss a second type of chi-square test, which can be used to compare the population proportions from *different* populations. The test we are about to introduce is an extension of the procedures introduced in Section 10.3, where we compared two population proportions.

Definition

In a **chi-square test for homogeneity of proportions**, we test the claim that different populations have the same proportion of individuals with some characteristic.

For example, we might look at the proportion of individuals who experience headaches as a side effect for a placebo group (Group 1), for an experimental group that receives 50 mg per day of a medication (Group 2), and for an experimental group that receives 100 mg per day of the medication (Group 3). Under this circumstance, we might claim that the proportion of individuals in each group who experience a headache as a side effect is the same in each population, so that our null hypothesis would be

$$H_0: p_1 = p_2 = p_3$$

versus the alternative,

H_1: At least one of the population proportions is different from the others.

The procedures for performing a test of homogeneity are identical to those for a test of independence.

▶ **EXAMPLE 4**   **A Test for Homogeneity of Proportions**

Problem: Zocor is a drug manufactured by Merck and Co. that is meant to reduce the level of LDL (bad) cholesterol, while increasing the level of HDL (good) cholesterol. In clinical trials of the drug, patients were randomly divided into three groups. Group 1 received Zocor, Group 2 received a placebo, and Group 3 received cholestyramine, a cholesterol-lowering drug currently available. Table 19 contains the number of patients in each group who did and did not experience abdominal pain as a side effect.

TABLE 19			
	Group 1 (Zocor)	Group 2 (Placebo)	Group 3 (Cholestyramine)
Number of People Who Experienced Abdominal Pain	51	5	16
Number of People Who Did Not Experience Abdominal Pain	1532	152	163

Source: Merck and Co.

Is there evidence to indicate that the proportion of subjects in each group who experienced abdominal pain is different at the $\alpha = 0.01$ level of significance?

Approach: We will follow Steps 1–7 on pages 680–681.

Solution: The patients were assigned randomly, so the first requirement needed to perform the chi-square independence test has been satisfied. We will verify requirements 2 and 3 in Step 3.

Step 1: For the sake of the test we assume that the proportion of subjects in each group who experienced abdominal pain is equal. We state the hypotheses as follows:

H_o: $p_1 = p_2 = p_3$
H_1: At least one of the proportions is different from the others.

Here, p_1 is the proportion in Group 1 who experience abdominal pain, and so on.

Step 2: The expected frequency of subjects who experienced abdominal pain in Group 1 is computed by multiplying the row total of individuals who experienced abdominal pain by the column total of number of individuals in Group 1 and dividing this result by the total number of subjects in the study. There were $51 + 5 + 16 = 72$ subjects who experienced abdominal pain and $51 + 1532 = 1583$ subjects in Group 1. There were a total of $51 + 5 + 16 + 1532 + 152 + 163 = 1919$ subjects in the study. The number of subjects expected to experience abdominal pain in Group 1 is

$$E = \frac{72 \cdot 1583}{1919} = 59.393$$

Table 20 on page 686 contains the row and column totals along with the observed frequencies. The expected frequencies are in parentheses.

TABLE 20			
Observed (and Expected) Frequencies			
	Group 1 (Zocor)	**Group 2 (Placebo)**	**Group 3 (Cholestyramine)**	**Row Totals**
Number of People Who Experienced Abdominal Pain	51 (59.393)	5 (5.891)	16 (6.716)	72
Number of People Who Did Not Experience Abdominal Pain	1532 (1523.607)	152 (151.109)	163 (172.284)	1847
Column Totals	1583	157	179	1919

Step 3: All the expected frequencies are greater than 5. The requirements have been satisfied.

Step 4: There are $r = 2$ rows and $c = 3$ columns, so we find the critical value by using $(2 - 1)(3 - 1) = 2$ degrees of freedom. We consult Table IV, and identify the column corresponding to $\alpha = 0.01$ with 2 degrees of freedom. The critical value is $\chi^2_{0.01} = 9.210$.

Step 5: The test statistic is

$$\chi^2 = \frac{(51 - 59.393)^2}{59.393} + \frac{(5 - 5.891)^2}{5.891} + \frac{(16 - 6.716)^2}{6.716} +$$

$$\frac{(1532 - 1523.607)^2}{1523.607} + \frac{(152 - 151.109)^2}{151.109} + \frac{(163 - 172.284)^2}{172.284} = 14.707$$

Step 6: Because the test statistic, 14.707, is greater than the critical value, 9.210, we reject the null hypothesis. See Figure 14.

Step 7: There is sufficient evidence at the $\alpha = 0.01$ level of significance to reject the claim that the proportion of subjects in each group who experience abdominal pain is equal. We conclude that at least one of the three groups experiences abdominal pain at a rate different from the other two groups. ◄◄

Figure 14

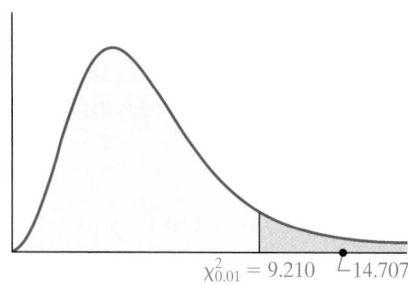

$\chi^2_{0.01} = 9.210$ 14.707

Caution

If we reject the null hypothesis in a chi-square test for homogeneity, we are saying that there is sufficient evidence for us to believe that at least one proportion is different from the others. However, we do not know which proportions differ.

Figure 15 shows the bar graph with the blue bars representing the proportion of individuals who experienced abdominal pain for each group and the maroon bars representing the proportion of individuals who did not experience abdominal pain for each group.

Figure 15

Patients Reporting Abdominal Pain by Treatment

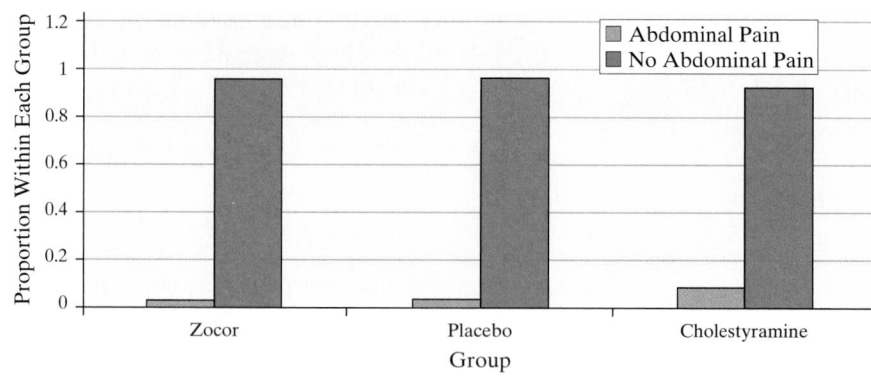

From the graph, it is apparent that a higher proportion of patients taking cholestyramine experience abdominal pain as a side effect.

NW *Now Work Problem 13.*

Recall that the requirements for performing a chi-square test require that all expected frequencies are greater than 1 and that at most 20% of the expected frequencies can be less than 5. If these requirements are not satisfied, the researcher has one of two options: (1) combine two columns (or rows) in order to increase the expected frequencies, or (2) increase the sample size.

11.3 Assess Your Understanding

Concepts and Vocabulary

1. Explain the differences between the chi-square test for independence and the chi-square test for homogeneity. What are the similarities?

2. Why does the test for homogeneity follow the same procedures as the test for independence?

Exercises

- **Basic Skills**

1. The following table contains observed values and expected values in parentheses for two categorical variables, X and Y, where variable X has three categories and variable Y has two categories:

	X_1	X_2	X_3
Y_1	34 (36.26)	43 (44.63)	52 (48.11)
Y_2	18 (15.74)	21 (19.37)	17 (20.89)

(a) Compute the value of the chi-square test statistic. 1.701
(b) Test the claim that X and Y are independent at the $\alpha = 0.05$ level of significance. Do not reject H_o
(c) What is the P-value? 0.427

2. The following table contains observed values and expected values in parentheses for two categorical variables, X and Y, where variable X has three categories and variable Y has two categories: (a) 13.053

	X_1	X_2	X_3
Y_1	87 (75.12)	74 (80.43)	34 (39.46)
Y_2	12 (23.88)	32 (25.57)	18 (12.54)

(a) Compute the value of the chi-square test statistic.
(b) Test the claim that X and Y are independent at the $\alpha = 0.05$ level of significance. Reject H_o
(c) What is the P-value? 0.001

3. The following table contains the number of successes and failures for three categories of a variable:

	Category 1	Category 2	Category 3
Success	76	84	69
Failure	44	41	49

Test the claim that the proportions are equal for each category at the $\alpha = 0.01$ level of significance. What is the P-value? Do not reject H_o; P-value = 0.370

4. The following table contains the number of successes and failures for three categories of a variable:

	Category 1	Category 2	Category 3
Success	204	199	214
Failure	96	121	98

Test the claim that the proportions are equal for each category at the $\alpha = 0.01$ level of significance. What is the P-value? Do not reject H_o; P-value = 0.171

• Applying the Concepts

5. **Family Structure and Sexual Activity** A sociologist wants to discover whether the sexual activity of females between the ages of 15 and 19 years of age and family structure are associated. She randomly selects 380 females between the ages of 15 and 19 years of age and asks each to disclose her family structure at age 14 and whether she has had sexual intercourse. The results are shown in the table below. Data are based on information obtained from the U.S. National Center for Health Statistics.

Sexual Activity	Family Structure			
	Both Biological/Adoptive Parents	Single Parent	Parent and Stepparent	Nonparental Guardian
Had Sexual Intercourse	64	59	44	32
Did Not Have Sexual Intercourse	86	41	36	18

(a) Compute the expected values of each cell, under the assumption of independence.
(b) Verify that the requirements for performing a chi-square test of independence are satisfied.
(c) Compute the chi-square test statistic. 10.357
(d) Test whether family structure and sexual activity of 15–19-year-old females are independent at the $\alpha = 0.05$ level of significance. Reject H_o
(e) Compare the observed frequencies with the expected frequencies. Which cell contributed most to the test statistic? Was the expected frequency greater than or less than the observed frequency? What does this information tell you?
(f) Construct a conditional distribution by family structure and draw a bar graph. Does this evidence support your conclusion in part (d)?
(g) Compute the *P*-value for this test by finding the area under the chi-square distribution to the right of the test statistic. 0.016

6. **Prenatal Care** An obstetrician wants to learn whether the amount of prenatal care and the wantedness of the pregnancy are associated. He randomly selects 939 women that have recently given birth and asks them to disclose whether their pregnancy was intended, unintended, or mistimed. In addition, they were to disclose when they started receiving prenatal care, if ever. The results of the survey are as follows:

Wantedness of Pregnancy	Months Pregnant Before Prenatal Care Began		
	Less Than 3 Months	3–5 Months	More Than 5 Months (or never)
Intended	593	26	33
Unintended	64	8	11
Mistimed	169	19	16

(a) Compute the expected values of each cell, under the assumption of independence.
(b) Verify that the requirements for performing a chi-square test of independence are satisfied.
(c) Compute the chi-square test statistic. 21.357
(d) Test whether prenatal care and the wantedness of pregnancy are independent at the $\alpha = 0.05$ level of significance. Reject H_o
(e) Compare the observed frequencies with the expected frequencies. Which cell contributed most to the test statistic? Was the expected frequency greater than or less than the observed frequency? What does this information tell you?
(f) Construct a conditional distribution by wantedness of the pregnancy and draw a bar graph. Does this evidence support your conclusion in part (d)?

7. **Education versus Area of Country** An urban economist wants to determine whether the location of the United States a resident lives in is associated with level of education. He randomly selects 1804 residents of the United States and asks them to disclose the region of the United States in which they reside and their level of education. He obtains the data in the following table (data are based upon information obtained from the U.S. Census Bureau):

| Area of Country | Level of Education | | | |
	Not a High School Graduate	High School Graduate	Some College	Bachelor's Degree or Higher
Northeast	52	123	70	94
Midwest	123	146	102	96
South	119	204	148	144
West	62	106	111	104

(a) Test whether level of education and region of the United States are independent at the $\alpha = 0.05$ level of significance. *Reject H_o*
(b) Compare the observed frequencies with the expected frequencies. Which cell contributed most to the test statistic? Was the expected frequency greater than or less than the observed frequency? What does this information tell you?
(c) Construct a conditional distribution by level of education and draw a bar graph. Does this evidence support your conclusion in part (a)?

8. **Profile of Smokers** The following data represent the smoking status by level of education for residents of the United States 18 years old or older from a random sample of 1054 residents:

| Number of Years of Education | Smoking Status | | |
	Current	Former	Never
<12 Years	178	88	208
12 Years	137	69	143
13–15 Years	44	25	44
16 or More Years	34	33	51

Source: National Health Interview Survey

(a) Test whether smoking status and level of education are independent at the $\alpha = 0.05$ level of significance. *Do not reject H_o*
(b) Compute the P-value for this test by finding the area under the chi-square distribution to the right of the test statistic. *0.253*
(c) Construct a conditional distribution by number of years of education, and draw a bar graph. Does this evidence support your conclusion in part (a)?

9. **Legalization of Marijuana** On May 14, 2001, the Supreme Court, by a vote of 8–0, struck down state laws that legalized marijuana for medicinal purposes. The Gallup Organization later conducted surveys of randomly selected Americans 18 years old or older and asked whether they support the limited use of marijua-

na when prescribed by physicians to relieve pain and suffering. The results of the survey, by age group, are as follows:

| Opinion | Age | | |
	18–29 Years Old	30–49 Years Old	50 Years or Older
For	172	313	258
Against	52	103	119

(a) Test whether age and opinion regarding the legalization of marijuana are independent at the $\alpha = 0.05$ level of significance. *Reject H_o*
(b) Compute the P-value for this test by finding the area under the chi-square distribution to the right of the test statistic. *0.035*
(c) Construct a conditional distribution by age and draw a bar graph. Does this evidence support your conclusion in part (a)?

10. **Pro Life or Pro Choice** A recent Gallup Organization Poll asked male and female Americans whether they were pro life or pro choice when it comes to abortion issues. The results of the survey are as follows:

| Gender | Pro-Life/Pro-Choice | |
	Pro-Life	Pro-Choice
Men	196	199
Women	239	249

(a) Test whether an individual's opinion regarding abortion is independent of gender at the $\alpha = 0.1$ level of significance. *Do not reject H_o*

(b) Compute the *P*-value for this test by finding the area under the chi-square distribution to the right of the test statistic. *0.849*

(c) Construct a conditional distribution by gender and draw a bar graph. Does this evidence support your conclusion in part (a)?

11. Delinquencies A delinquency offense is an act committed by a juvenile for which an adult could be prosecuted in a criminal court. The following data represent the number of various types of delinquencies by gender in a random sample of 750 delinquencies: *(a) Do not reject H_o*

	Delinquency			
Gender	Person	Property	Drugs	Public Order
Female	24	85	7	28
Male	97	367	39	103

(a) Test whether gender is independent of type of delinquency at the $\alpha = 0.05$ level of significance.

(b) Compute the *P*-value for this test by finding the area under the chi-square distribution to the right of the test statistic. *0.814*

(c) Construct a conditional distribution by type of delinquency and draw a bar graph. Does this evidence support your conclusion in part (a)?

---

12. Visits to the Emergency Room The following data represent the gender and age of 489 randomly selected patients who visited the emergency room with an injury-related emergency:

	Age					
Gender	Under 15	15–24	25–44	45–64	65–74	75 and Older
Male	66	56	92	37	8	11
Female	44	39	66	34	12	24

(a) Test the claim that the age of an individual visiting the emergency room is independent of gender at the $\alpha = 0.1$ level of significance. *Reject H_o*

(b) Compute the *P*-value for this test by finding the area under the chi-square distribution to the right of the test statistic. *0.031*

(c) Construct a conditional distribution by age and draw a bar graph. Does this evidence support your conclusion in part (a)?

13. Smoked Lately? Suppose a researcher wants to investigate whether the proportion of smokers within different age groups is the same. He divides the American population into four age groups: 18–29 years old, 30–49 years old, 50–64 years old, and 65 years or older. Within each age group, he surveys 80 individuals and asks, "Have you smoked at least one cigarette in the past week?" The results of the survey are as follows: *(a) Do not reject*

Smoking Status	Age			
	18–29 Years Old	30–49 Years Old	50–64 Years Old	65 Years or Older
Smoked at least one cigarette in past week	24	21	23	12
Did not smoke at least one cigarette in past week	56	59	57	68

Source: Based on data obtained from Gallup Organization

(a) Is there evidence to indicate that the proportion of individuals within each age group who have smoked at least one cigarette in the past week is different at the $\alpha = 0.05$ level of significance?

(b) Compute the *P*-value for this test by finding the area under the chi-square distribution to the right of the test statistic. *0.112*

(c) Construct a conditional distribution by age and draw a bar graph. Does this evidence support your conclusion in part (a)?

(a) Do not reject

14. **Are You Satisfied?** Suppose an economist wants to gauge the level of satisfaction of Americans. He randomly samples 150 people 18 years old or older from four geographic regions of the United States: East, South, Midwest, and West. He asks the individuals selected, "Are you satisfied or dissatisfied with the way things are going in the United States at this time?" The following are the results of the survey (data are based upon results obtained from the Gallup Organization):

(a) Test whether the proportion of Americans who are satisfied with the way things are going in the United States for each region of the country is equal at the $\alpha = 0.1$ level of significance.

		Region		
Satisfaction	East	South	Midwest	West
Satisfied	77	84	93	83
Dissatisfied	73	66	57	67

(b) Compute the P-value for this test by finding the area under the chi-square distribution to the right of the test statistic. 0.316

(c) Construct a conditional distribution by region of the country and draw a bar graph. Does this evidence support your conclusion in part (a)?

15. **Celebrex** Celebrex is a drug manufactured by Pfizer, Inc., that is indicated to be used to relieve symptoms associated with osteoarthritis and rheumatoid arthritis in adults. It is considered to be one of the nonsteroidal anti-inflammatory drugs. These types of drugs are known to be associated with gastrointestinal toxicity, such as bleeding, ulceration, and perforation of the stomach, small intestine, or large intestine. In clinical trials of the medication, researchers wanted to learn whether the proportion of subjects taking Celebrex who experienced these side effects differed significantly from that in other treatment groups. The following data were collected (Naproxen is a nonsteroidal anti-inflammatory drug that is also used in the treatment of arthritis):

		Treatment			
Side Effect	Placebo	Celebrex (50 mg per day)	Celebrex (100 mg per day)	Celebrex (200 mg per day)	Naproxen (500 mg per day)
Experienced Gastroduodenal Ulcers	5	8	7	13	34
Did Not Experience Gastroduodenal Ulcers	212	225	220	208	176

Source: Pfizer, Inc.

(a) Test whether the proportion of subjects within each treatment group is the same at the $\alpha = 0.01$ level of significance. Reject H_o

(b) Compute the P-value for this test by finding the area under the chi-square distribution to the right of the test statistic. < 0.001

(c) Construct a conditional distribution by treatment and draw a bar graph. Does this evidence support your conclusion in part (a)?

16. **Celebrex** Celebrex is a drug manufactured by Pfizer, Inc., that is indicated to be used to relieve symptoms associated with osteoarthritis and rheumatoid arthritis in adults. It is considered to be a nonsteroidal anti-inflammatory drug. In clinical trials of the medication, some of the subjects reported dizziness as a side effect. The researchers wanted to discover whether the proportion of subjects taking Celebrex who reported dizziness as a side effect differed significantly from that for other treatment groups. The following data were collected:

			Drug		
Side Effect	Celebrex	Placebo	Naproxen	Diclofenac	Ibuprofen
Dizziness	83	32	36	5	8
No Dizziness	4063	1832	1330	382	337

Source: Pfizer, Inc.

(a) Test whether the proportion of subjects within each treatment group who experienced dizziness is the same at the $\alpha = 0.01$ level of significance. *Do not reject*

(b) Compute the *P*-value for this test by finding the area under the chi-square distribution to the right of the test statistic. *0.323*

(c) Construct a conditional distribution by treatment and draw a bar graph. Does this evidence support your conclusion in part (a)?

17. **Dropping a Course** A survey of 50 randomly selected students who dropped a course in the current semester was conducted at a community college. The goal of the survey was to learn why students drop courses. The following data were collected: "Personal" drop reasons include financial, transportation, family issues, health issues, and lack of child care. "Course" drop reasons include reducing one's load, being unprepared for the course, the course was not what was expected, dissatisfaction with teaching, and not getting the desired grade. "Work" drop reasons include an increase in hours, a change in shift, and obtaining full-time employment. "Career" drop reasons include not needing the course and a change of plans. The results of the survey are as follows:

Gender	Drop Reason	Gender	Drop Reason	Gender	Drop Reason	Gender	Drop Reason
Male	Personal	Male	Course	Male	Work	Female	Course
Female	Personal	Male	Course	Female	Course	Male	Work
Male	Work	Male	Work	Male	Work	Male	Course
Male	Personal	Female	Personal	Female	Course	Female	Work
Male	Course	Male	Course	Female	Course	Male	Personal
Male	Course	Female	Work	Female	Course	Male	Work
Female	Course	Male	Work	Male	Work	Female	Course
Female	Course	Male	Work	Male	Personal	Male	Course
Male	Course	Female	Course	Male	Course	Male	Personal
Female	Course	Female	Personal	Female	Course	Female	Course
Male	Personal	Female	Personal	Female	Course	Female	Work
Male	Work	Female	Personal	Male	Course	Male	Work
Male	Work	Male	Work				

(a) Construct a contingency table for the two variables.

(b) Test the claim that gender is independent of drop reason at the $\alpha = 0.1$ level of significance. *Reject H_0*

(c) Compute the *P*-value for this test by finding the area under the chi-square distribution to the right of the test statistic. *0.061*

(d) Construct a conditional distribution by drop reason and draw a bar graph. Does this evidence support your conclusion in part (a)?

18. **Political Affiliation** A political scientist wanted to learn whether there is any association between the education level of a registered voter and his or her political party affiliation. He randomly selected 46 registered voters and obtained the following data:

Education	Political Party	Education	Political Party	Education	Political Party
Grade School	Democrat	College	Republican	High School	Republican
College	Republican	Grade School	Republican	Grade School	Democrat
High School	Democrat	College	Republican	High School	Democrat
High School	Republican	High School	Democrat	College	Democrat
High School	Democrat	College	Democrat	College	Republican
Grade School	Democrat	College	Republican	High School	Republican
College	Republican	College	Democrat	College	Democrat
Grade School	Democrat	High School	Democrat	College	Democrat
High School	Democrat	College	Republican	High School	Democrat
High School	Democrat	College	Republican	College	Republican
Grade School	Democrat	Grade School	Democrat	College	Democrat
College	Republican	High School	Republican	High School	Republican
Grade School	Democrat	High School	Democrat	College	Republican
College	Democrat	High School	Democrat	High School	Republican
College	Democrat	College	Republican	College	Democrat
Grade School	Republican				

(a) Construct a contingency table for the two variables.

(b) Test the claim that level of education is independent of political affiliation at the $\alpha = 0.1$ level of significance. Do not reject H_o

(c) Compute the P-value for this test by finding the area under the chi-square distribution to the right of the test statistic. 0.175

(d) Construct a conditional distribution by level of education and draw a bar graph. Does this evidence support your conclusion in part (a)?

In Problem 19, we demonstrate that the z-test for comparing two population proportions is equivalent to the chi-square test for homogeneity when there are two possible outcomes.

19. **Percentage of Americans Who Smoke on the Decline?** On November 13–15, 2000, the Gallup Organization surveyed 1028 adults and found that 257 of them had smoked at least one cigarette in the past week. In 1990, they also asked 1028 adults the same question and determined that 278 adults had smoked at least one cigarette in the past week. The results are presented in the following table:

Smoking Status	Year	
	1990	2000
Smoked	278	257
Did Not Smoke	750	771

(a) Compute the expected number of adult Americans who have smoked at least one cigarette in the past week and the expected number who have not assuming $P_{1990} = P_{2000}$. 267.5; 760.5

(b) Compute the chi-square test statistic. $\chi^2 = 1.114$

(c) Test the researchers' claim at the $\alpha = 0.05$ level of significance, using the chi-square goodness-of-fit test. Do not reject H_o

(d) Compute the z-test statistic. Now compute z^2. Compare z^2 with the chi-square test statistic. Conclude that $z^2 = \chi^2$. $z = 1.056$; $z^2 = 1.114$

Technology Step-by-Step
Chi-Square Tests

TI-83 Plus

Step 1: Access the MATRX menu. Highlight the EDIT menu, and select 1:[A].

Step 2: Enter the number of rows and columns of the matrix.

Step 3: Enter the cell entries for the matrix, and press 2nd QUIT.

Step 4: Press STAT, highlight the TESTS menu, and select C: χ^2-Test....

Step 5: With the cursor after the **Observed:**, enter matrix [A] by accessing the MATRX menu, highlighting NAMES, and selecting 1:[A].

Step 6: With the cursor after the **Expected:**, enter matrix [B] by accessing the MATRX menu, highlighting NAMES, and selecting 2:[B].

Step 7: Highlight **Calculate** or **Draw**, and press ENTER.

MINITAB

Step 1: Enter the data into the MINITAB spreadsheet.

Step 2: Select the <u>**Stat**</u> menu, highlight <u>**Tables**</u>, and select **Chi-Square Test**....

Step 3: Select the columns that contain the data, and press OK.

Excel

Step 1: Enter the observed frequencies in the spreadsheet.

Step 2: Compute the expected frequencies and enter them in a different location in the spreadsheet.

Step 3: Select *fx* from the tool bar. Select **Statistical** for the function category and highlight CHITEST in the function name.

Step 4: With the cursor in the actual cell, highlight the observed data. With the cursor in the expected cell, highlight the expected frequencies. Click OK. The output provided is the *P*-value.

Note: This test can also be performed by using the PHStat add-in. See the Excel Technology Manual.

CHAPTER 11 REVIEW

Summary

In this chapter, we introduced chi-square methods. The first chi-square method involved tests for goodness of fit. We used the chi-square distribution to test the claim that a random variable followed a certain distribution. This is done by comparing values expected based upon the distribution of the random variable to observed values.

The next section of the chapter introduced methods that allow us to describe any association that might exist between two qualitative variables. This is done through contingency tables. Both marginal and conditional distributions allow us to describe the effect one variable might have on the other variable in the study. We also construct bar graphs to "see" the association between the two variables in the study.

Finally, we introduced chi-square methods that allowed us to perform tests for independence and homogeneity. In a test for independence, the researcher obtains random data for two variables and tests whether the variables are associ-

ated. The null hypothesis in these tests is always that the variables are not associated (i.e., independent). The test statistic compares the values expected if the variables were independent to those observed. If the expected and observed values differ significantly, we reject the null hypothesis and conclude that there is evidence to support the belief that the variables are dependent (i.e., they are associated). We draw bar graphs of the marginal distributions, to help us "see" the association, if any.

The last chi-square test was the test for homogeneity of proportions. This test is similar to the test for independence, except we are testing that the proportion of individuals in the study with a certain characteristic are equal (i.e., $p_1 = p_2 = \ldots = p_k$). To perform this test, we take random samples of a predetermined size from each group under consideration (i.e., a random sample of size n_1 for group 1, a random sample of size n_2 for group 2, and so on).

Formulas

Expected Counts
$$E_i = \mu_i = np_i \quad \text{for} \quad i = 1, 2, \ldots, k$$

Chi-Square Test Statistic
$$\chi^2 = \sum \frac{(O_i - E_i)^2}{E_i} \quad i = 1, 2, \ldots, k$$

Expected Frequencies
$$\text{Expected frequency} = \frac{(\text{row total})(\text{column total})}{\text{table total}}$$

Vocabulary

Goodness-of-fit test (p. 656)
Expected counts (p. 657)
Contingency (or two-way) table (p. 667)

Row variable (p. 667)
Column variable (p. 667)
Cell (p. 667)
Marginal distribution (p. 668)

Conditional distribution (p. 671)
Chi-square independence test (p. 677)
Chi-square test for homogeneity of proportions (p. 684)

Objectives

Section	You should be able to . . .	Review Exercises
11.1	1 Perform a chi-square goodness-of-fit test (p. 656)	1–4
11.2	1 Compute the marginal distribution of a variable (p. 668)	5–8(a) and (b)
	2 Use the conditional distribution to identify association among categorical data (p. 670)	5–8(e)
11.3	1 Perform chi-square test for independence (p. 677)	9–12
	2 Perform chi-square test for homogeneity of proportions (p. 684)	13, 14

Review Exercises

1. **Roulette Wheel** A pit boss suspects that a roulette wheel is out of balance. A roulette wheel has 18 black slots, 18 red slots and 2 green slots. The pit boss spins the wheel 500 times and records the following frequencies:

Outcome	Frequency
Black	233
Red	237
Green	30

Test the claim that the wheel is out of balance at the $\alpha = 0.05$ level of significance. Do not reject H_o

2. **Fair Dice?** A pit boss is concerned that a pair of dice being used in a craps game is not fair. The distribution of the expected sum of two fair dice is as follows:

Sum of Two Die	Probability	Sum of Two Die	Probability
2	1/36	8	5/36
3	2/36	9	4/36
4	3/36	10	3/36
5	4/36	11	2/36
6	5/36	12	1/36
7	6/36		

The pit boss rolls the dice 400 times and records the sum of the dice. The following are the results:

Sum of Two Die	Frequency	Sum of Two Die	Frequency
2	16	8	59
3	23	9	45
4	31	10	34
5	41	11	19
6	62	12	11
7	59		

Test the claim that the dice are fair at the $\alpha = 0.01$ level of significance. Do not reject H_o

3. **Educational Attainment** A researcher wanted to test the claim that the distribution of educational attainment of Americans today is different from the distribution in 1994. The distribution of educational attainment in 1994 is as follows:

Education	Relative Frequency
Not a High School Graduate	0.191
High School Graduate	0.344
Some College	0.174
Associate's Degree	0.070
Bachelor's Degree	0.147
Advanced Degree	0.075

Source: Statistical Abstract of the United States

To test the claim, the researcher randomly selects 500 Americans, learns their levels of education, and obtains the following data:

Education	Frequency
Not a High School Graduate	89
High School Graduate	152
Some College	83
Associate's Degree	39
Bachelor's Degree	93
Advanced Degree	44

At the $\alpha = 0.1$ level of significance, test the claim that the distribution of educational attainment today is different from that of educational attainment in 1994.

Reject H_o

4. **School Violence** A school administrator is concerned that the distribution of school violence has changed and become more violent than it was in 1992. The distribution of school crime for 1992 is as follows:

Crime	Theft	Violent	Serious Violent
Relative Frequency	0.619	0.314	0.067

Source: National Center for Educational Statistics

To test the claim, the researcher randomly selects 800 school crimes, finds out whether they were theft, violent, or serious violent crimes, and obtains the following data:

Crime	Theft	Violent	Serious Violent
Relative Frequency	421	311	68

At the $\alpha = 0.05$ level of significance, test the claim that the distribution of school crime today is different from the 1992 distribution. Reject H_o

5. **Police Officers** The Federal Bureau of Investigation publishes the *Uniform Crime Report*, which contains information regarding various crimes throughout the United States. The following data represent the number of law enforcement officers feloniously killed by type of firearm and by region of the country:

Firearm	Region			
	Northeast	Midwest	South	West
Handgun	58	76	197	82
Rifle	6	28	42	33
Shotgun	4	5	18	5

(a) Construct a frequency marginal distribution.
(b) Construct a relative frequency marginal distribution.
(c) What percentage of law enforcement officers were killed by a handgun? 74.5%
(d) What percentage of law enforcement officers killed were in the Northeast? 12.3%
(e) Construct a conditional distribution by region of the United States.
(f) Draw a bar graph of the conditional distribution.
(g) What, if any, association exists between gun type and region of the United States? Discuss the association.

6. **Educational Attainment versus Age** The following data represent the educational attainment and age of residents of the United States in 1998:

Age	Level of Education			
	Not a High School Graduate	High School Graduate	Some College	Four or More Years of College
25–34 Years	4,683	12,554	11,216	10,822
35–44 Years	5,335	15,117	12,272	11,694
45–54 Years	4,428	10,933	8,957	9,809
55–64 Years	4,562	8,301	4,496	4,941
At Least 65 Years	10,565	11,223	5,537	4,743

Source: U.S. Census Bureau, Current Population Report

(a) Construct a frequency marginal distribution.
(b) Construct a relative frequency marginal distribution.
(c) What percentage of adults 25 years old or older are high school graduates? 33.76%

(d) What percentage of adults 25 years old or older are at least 65 years of age? 18.62%
(e) Construct a conditional distribution by level of education.
(f) Draw a bar graph of the conditional distribution.
(g) What, if any, association exists between level of education and age? Discuss the association.

7. **Child Fatalities** The following data represent the number of fatalities involving children under the age of 13 and a motor vehicle, by type of fatality and gender in 1999:

Type of Fatality	Gender	
	Male	Female
Passenger in Vehicle	677	632
Pedestrian	277	169
Bicycle	109	32

Source: Insurance Institute for Highway Safety

(a) Construct a frequency marginal distribution.
(b) Construct a relative frequency marginal distribution.
(c) What percentage of children under the age of 13 killed by a motor vehicle were male? 56.07%
(d) What percentage of children under the age of 13 were killed in accidents involving motor vehicles while riding a bicycle? 7.44%
(e) Construct a conditional distribution by gender.
(f) Draw a bar graph of the conditional distribution.
(g) What, if any, association exists between type of fatality and gender? Discuss the association.

8. **Firearms** The following data represent the number deaths due to firearms by homicide or legal intervention in the United States in 1998 for individuals less than 45 years of age:

Gender	Age				
	0–4	5–14	15–24	25–34	35–44
Male	36	153	4,070	2,830	1,695
Female	27	101	489	499	466

Source: National Vital Statistics Reports, Vol. 48, No. 11, July 24, 2000

(a) Construct a frequency marginal distribution.
(b) Construct a relative frequency marginal distribution.
(c) What percentage of deaths due to firearms are individuals 5–14 years of age? 2.45%
(d) What percentage of deaths due to firearms are female? 15.26%
(e) Construct a conditional distribution by gender.
(f) Draw a bar graph of the conditional distribution.
(g) What, if any, association exists between age and gender? Discuss the association.

9. **Evolution or Creation?** The Gallup Organization conducted a poll of 1016 randomly selected Americans aged 18 years old or older in February, 2001 and 1017 randomly selected Americans aged 18 years old or older in June, 1993 and asked them the following question:

> Which of the following statements comes closest to your views on the origin and development of human beings? (1) Human beings have developed over millions of years from less advanced forms of life, but God guided this process. (2) Human beings have developed over millions of years from less advanced forms of life, and God had no part in this process. (3) God created human beings pretty much in their present form at one time within the last 10,000 years or so.

The results of the survey are as follows:

Date	Belief			
	Humans Developed, with God Guiding	Humans Developed, But God Had No Part in Process	God Created Humans in Present Form	Other/No Opinion
February, 2001	376	122	457	61
June, 1993	356	112	478	71

(a) Compute the expected values of each cell, under the assumption of independence.
(b) Verify that the requirements for performing a chi-square test of independence are satisfied.
(c) Compute the chi-square test statistic. 2.203

(d) Test the claim that people's opinion regarding human origin is independent of the date the question is asked at the $\alpha = 0.05$ level of significance. *Do not reject H_o*

(e) Compare the observed frequencies with the expected frequencies. Which cell contributed most to the test statistic? Was the expected frequency greater than or less than the observed frequency? What does this information tell you?

(f) Construct a conditional distribution by date and draw a bar graph. Does this evidence support your conclusion in part (d)?

(g) Compute the *P*-value for this test by finding the area under the chi-square distribution to the right of the test statistic. *0.531*

---

10. **Caesarean Sections** An obstetrician wanted to discover whether the method of delivering a baby was independent of race. The following data represent the race of the mother and the method of delivery for 365 randomly selected births, based upon data obtained from the *Statistical Abstract of the United States*:

Race	Delivery Method	
	Vaginal	**Caesarean**
White	242	63
Black	47	13

(a) Compute the expected values of each cell, under the assumption of independence.

(b) Verify that the requirements to perform a chi-square test of independence are satisfied.

(c) Compute the chi-square test statistic. *0.031*

(d) Test the claim that method of delivery is independent of the race of the mother at the $\alpha = 0.05$ level of significance. *Do not reject H_o*

(e) Compare the observed frequencies with the expected frequencies. Which cell contributed most to the test statistic? Was the expected frequency greater than or less than the observed frequency? What does this information tell you?

(f) Construct a conditional distribution by method of delivery and draw a bar graph. Does this evidence support your conclusion in part (d)?

(g) Compute the *P*-value for this test by finding the area under the chi-square distribution to the right of the test statistic. *0.860*

11. **Race versus Region of the United States** A sociologist wanted to determine whether the locations in which individuals live are independent of their races. He randomly selects 2172 U.S. residents and asks them to disclose their race and the location in which they live. He obtains the following data:

Race	Region			
	Northeast	**Midwest**	**South**	**West**
White	421	520	656	400
Black	56	57	158	28
American Indian, Eskimo, Aleut	2	4	6	9
Asian or Pacific Islander	13	8	11	40
Hispanic	38	17	68	101
Other	17	8	24	50

Source: Statistical Abstract of the United States

At the $\alpha = 0.01$ level of significance, test the claim that race is independent of the location in which a resident lives within the United States. *Reject H_o*

12. Marital Status and Gender A sociologist wanted to determine whether marital status and gender were independent. He randomly sampled 201 residents of the United States who were 18 years old or older and asked them to disclose their gender and marital status. The following data were collected:

Marital Status	Gender	
	Male	Female
Never Married	26	22
Married	59	60
Divorced	9	11
Widowed	3	11

At the $\alpha = 0.05$ level of significance, test the claim that gender is independent of marital status. *Do not reject H_o*

13. The Common Cold A doctor wanted to determine whether the proportion of Americans who have had symptoms associated with the common cold is the same for all four regions of the United States. He randomly sampled 120 individuals from each region of the United States and obtained the following data (the data are based upon information obtained from the National Center for Health Statistics):

Symptoms	Region			
	Northeast	Midwest	South	West
Symptoms Within Last Year	26	31	23	35
No Symptoms Within Last Year	94	89	97	85

At the $\alpha = 0.05$ level of significance, test the claim that the proportion of Americans who have had symptoms associated with the common cold is the same for all four regions of the United States. *Do not reject H_o*

14. Hardworking? In a *Newsweek* poll conducted on June 24, 1999, 750 randomly selected adults were asked, "Do you believe Americans today are as willing to work hard at their jobs to get ahead as they were in the past, or are not as willing to work hard to get ahead?". The results of the survey are as follows:

Response	Age		
	18–29 Years Old	30–49 Years Old	50 and Older
As Willing	58	75	70
Not as Willing	192	175	180

Source: pollingreport.com

At the $\alpha = 0.05$ level of significance, test the claim that the proportion of Americans who believe that Americans are willing to work just as hard today is the same for all three age groups. *Do not reject H_o*

Feeling Lucky? Well, Are You?

In fiscal year (FY) 2000–01 (October, 2000–September, 2001), the Florida Lottery generated $2,360,561,022 in total sales. Over that period, the state spent $32,630,000 on advertising to promote its various games. Rand Advertising is interested in gaining access to this lucrative market. You have been assigned the task of preparing a report on the lottery sales structure for three of Florida's on-line (non-scratch-off-ticket) games: Fantasy Five, Mega Money, and Lotto. Your findings will become part of a proposal by Rand to the Florida Lottery.

In Fantasy 5, a player picks five numbers from 1 to 36, at one dollar per play. Drawings are held seven days a week. If there is no jackpot winner for a drawing, the money allocated for the top prize "rolls down" to the next prize tier (4-of-5). In FY 2000–01, Fantasy 5 generated $191,614,355 in sales. The prize structure for this game is as follows:

Prize Structure for Florida's Fantasy 5 On-Line Game

Match	Estimated Prize Amount per Winner	Probability
5 of 5	$100,000	1/376,992
4 of 5	$100	1/2432
3 of 5	$10	1/81
2 of 5	Free Ticket	1/8

The Mega Money game produced $108,841,978 in sales for FY 2000–01. At one dollar per ticket, players pick 4 numbers from 1 to 32 and one MEGABALL number from 1 to 32. Drawings are held on Tuesdays and Fridays. If there is no jackpot winner for a drawing, the money allocated for the top prize rolls over to the next drawing, adding to the total of the next jackpot. The following is the prize structure for Mega Money:

Prize Structure for Florida's Mega Money On-Line Game

Match	Estimated Prize Amount per Winner	Probability
4 of 4 + MEGABALL	$200,000	1/1,150,720
4 of 4	$550	1/37,120
3 of 4 + MEGABALL	$350	1/10,274
3 of 4	$50	1/331
2 of 4 + MEGABALL	$25	1/507
2 of 4	$1	1/16

In terms of sales, Lotto is Florida's most lucrative lottery product, with $845,565,515 in FY 2000–01 sales. Players pick 6 numbers from 1 to 53, at one dollar per play. Drawings are held on Wednesdays and Saturdays. Like Mega Money, if there is no jackpot winner, the top prize is rolled over to the next drawing. Because of the game design, it is much more difficult to win the Lotto jackpot. The difficulty in winning the game leads to numerous jackpot rollovers, creating, at times, jackpots exceeding $50,000,000! The

CASE STUDY

propensity to roll over makes it difficult to determine an estimated prize payout per winner. However, the odds structure is shown to the right.

In order to conduct your study, you have obtained the sales figures for each of the three games by district sales office for the week of September 17–23, 2001. These data are as follows:

Odds Structure for Florida's Lotto On-Line Game

Match	Probability
6 of 6	1/22,957,480
5 of 6	1/81,410
4 of 6	1/1416
3 of 6	1/71

Number of Tickets Sold for Florida Lottery Games by Sales District for the Week of September 17–23, 2001

District	Florida Lottery Game		
	Fantasy 5	Mega Money	Lotto
1	87,030	27,221	270,256
3	186,780	56,822	934,451
4	267,955	94,123	1,004,651
5	232,451	61,019	707,934
6	727,390	262,840	2,746,438
8	462,874	135,321	1,563,491
9	353,532	139,421	1,492,549
10	377,627	140,285	1,433,077
11	470,993	153,591	1,743,370
12	588,154	185,946	1,852,986
13	1,283,042	474,067	2,883,453

Use an $\alpha = 0.05$ significance level to test the claim that the number of tickets sold for each lottery game and sales district are independent. Construct a bar graph that represents the conditional distribution of game by sales district. Does this graphical evidence support your conclusion regarding the relationship between the type of game and the sales district? Explain.

Additionally, you are interested in the daily sales structure for the various districts. The following are the numbers of tickets sold each day for the week of September 17 for the three games in District 1:

Number of Tickets Sold for Florida Lottery Games by Day of the Week (September 17–September 23, 2001) for District 1

Day	Florida Lottery Game		
	Fantasy 5	Mega Money	Lotto
Mon. 9/17	12,794	2082	13,093
Tue. 9/18	11,564	9983	18,200
Wed. 9/19	12,562	1040	60,746
Thu. 9/20	11,408	1677	18,054
Fri. 9/21	15,299	10,439	38,513
Sat. 9/22	15,684	1502	115,686
Sun. 9/23	7728	498	5964

Use an $\alpha = 0.05$ significance level to test the claim that the proportion of Fantasy 5 sales is the same for each day of the week. Perform a similar test for Mega Money and Lotto.

Write a report detailing your assumptions, analyses, findings, and conclusions.

Benefits of College

Are there benefits to attending college? If so, what are they? In this project, we will identify some of the perks that a college education provides. Obtain a random sample of at least 50 people aged 21 years or older, and administer the following survey:

Please answer the following questions:

1. What is the highest level of education you have attained?
   ____ Have not completed high school
   ____ High school graduate
   ____ College graduate

2. What is your employment status?
   ____ Employed
   ____ Unemployed, but actively seeking work
   ____ Unemployed, but not actively seeking work

3. If you are employed, what is your annual income?
   ____ Less than $20,000
   ____ $20,000–$39,999
   ____ $40,000–$60,000
   ____ More than $60,000

4. If you are employed, which statement best describes the level of satisfaction you have with your career? Answer this question only if you are employed.
   ____ Satisfied—I enjoy my job and am happy with my career.
   ____ Somewhat satisfied—Work is work, but I am not unhappy with my career.
   ____ Somewhat dissatisfied—I do not enjoy my work, but I also have no intention of leaving.
   ____ Dissatisfied—Going to work is painful. I would quit tomorrow if I could.

(a) Use the results of the survey to create a contingency table for each of the following categories:
   - Level of education/employment status
   - Level of education/annual income
   - Level of education/job satisfaction
   - Annual income/job satisfaction

(b) Perform a chi-square test for independence on each of the contingency tables from part (a).

(c) Draw bar graphs for each of the contingency tables from part (a).

(d) Write a report that details your findings.

Hungry for a cheap, low-fat alternative to beef, Americans are eating more chicken than ever. Although precise figures are impossible to obtain, the U.S. Centers for Disease Control and Prevention reported that the number of cases of outbreaks of illness caused by chicken rose three-fold between 1988 and 1992. Salmonella bacteria were usually the culprit in those outbreaks.

In a 1998 study for Consumer Reports (March 1998), we purchased 1000 fresh, whole broiler chickens at grocery stores in 36 cities across the United States over a five-week period. Our shoppers packed the birds in coolers and shipped them overnight to the lab. There, tests were conducted to determine the presence of Salmonella and Campylobacter, another chicken-related bug. The results of the study for Salmonella are contained below.

Brand	Salmonella Present	Salmonella Absent	Total
A	8	192	200
B	17	183	200
C	27	173	200
D	14	186	200
E	20	180	200
Total	86	914	1000

Assuming that the chickens represent a random sample from each of the brands included in the study, use the information presented in the table to answer the following:

(a) Calculate the proportion of incidence for each of the brands shown in the table.

(b) Compute a 95% confidence interval for the incidence of Salmonella for Brand C.

(c) Using a chi-square test of homogeneity of proportions, is there evidence that the five brands have the same incidence rate for Salmonella?

(d) Brands A and D are major competitors in the same market. The manufacturer of Brand A claims to have improved its cleanliness and claims that it is substantially cleaner than Brand D. Is there evidence to support this contention?

(e) Write a paragraph for the readers of Consumer Reports magazine that explains your conclusions.

Note to Readers: In many cases, our test protocol and analytical methods are more complicated than described in these examples. The data and discussions have been modified to make the material more appropriate for the audience.

Putting It All Together

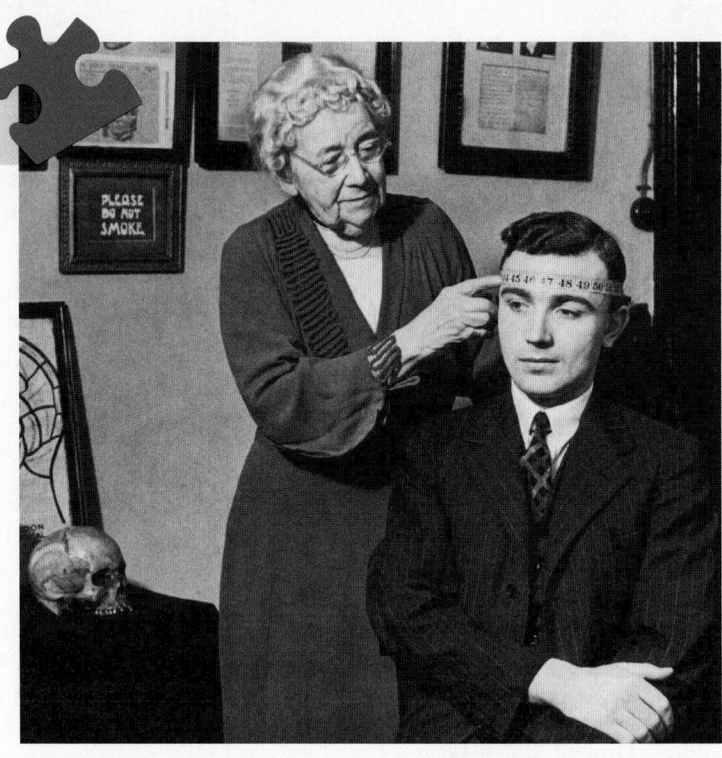

This chapter can be considered in two parts. The first part, Sections 12.1 and 12.2, introduces inferential methods that can be used on the least-squares regression line. This material is a continuation of the discussion presented in Chapter 4. There, we presented methods for describing the relation between two variables—bivariate data. In addition, we performed diagnostic tests such as determining whether a linear model is appropriate, identifying outliers, and identifying influential observations. In Section 12.1, we use the methods of hypothesis testing presented in Chapter 9 to test the claim that a linear relation exists between two quantitative variables. In Section 12.2, we create confidence intervals about a predicted value of the least-squares regression line.

The second part of the chapter, Section 12.3, extends the idea of comparing two means presented in Section 10.2 to comparing three or more means. This is similar to what we did in Section 11.3 when we extended the idea of comparing two population proportions to comparing three or more population proportions (chi-square test for homogeneity of proportions).

Inference on the Least-Squares Regression Model; ANOVA

Outline

 For additional study help, go to www.prenhall.com/sullivanstats

Materials include

- Self-Graded Quizzes

- "Preparing for This Section" Quizzes

- STATLETs

- PowerPoint Downloads

- Step-by-Step Technology Guide

- Graphing Calculator Help

12.1 Inference about the Least-Squares Regression Model

Preparing for This Section — Before getting started, review the following:

✓ Scatter diagrams; correlation (Section 4.1, pp. 192–199)

✓ Least-squares regression (Section 4.2, pp. 210–214)

✓ Diagnostics on the least-squares regression line (Section 4.3, pp. 222–230)

✓ Sample standard deviation (Section 3.2, pp. 137–138)

✓ Testing a hypothesis about μ, σ unknown (Section 9.3, pp. 546–551)

✓ P-values (Section 9.2, pp. 534–538)

✓ Confidence intervals about a mean (Section 8.1, pp. 457–464; Section 8.2, pp. 480–482)

Objectives Understand the requirements of the least-squares regression model

 Compute the standard error of the estimate

Note to Instructor
You might want to continue using the pulse data collected in Chapter 4 for Sections 12.1 and 12.2.

 Verify that residuals are normally distributed

 Test the claim that a linear relation exists between two variables

 Compute a confidence interval about the slope of the least-squares regression model

As a quick review of the topics discussed in Chapter 4, we present the following example.

▶ **EXAMPLE 1** **Least-Squares Regression**

Problem: A family doctor is interested in examining the relationship between a patient's age and total cholesterol. He randomly selects 14 of his female patients and obtains the data presented in Table 1. The data are based upon results obtained from the National Center for Health Statistics.

TABLE 1			
Age	Total Cholesterol	Age	Total Cholesterol
25	180	42	183
25	195	48	204
28	186	51	221
32	180	51	243
32	210	58	208
32	197	62	228
38	239	65	269

Draw a scatter diagram, compute the correlation coefficient, and find the least-squares regression equation and the coefficient of determination.

Approach: We will use a TI-83 Plus graphing calculator to obtain the information requested.

Solution: Figure 1 displays the scatter diagram. Figure 2 displays the output obtained from the calculator. The linear correlation coefficient is 0.718. The least-squares regression equation for this data is $\hat{y} = 151.3537 + 1.3991\,x$, where $\hat{y}$ represents the predicted total cholesterol for a female whose age is x. The coefficient of determination, R^2, is 0.515. So 51.5% of the variation in total cholesterol is explained by the regression line. Figure 3 shows a graph of the least-squares regression equation on the scatter diagram in order to get a "feel" for the fit.

Figure 1

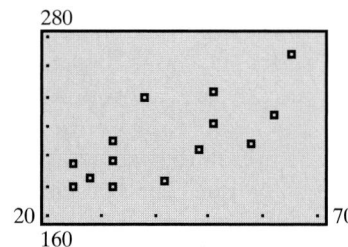

Figure 2

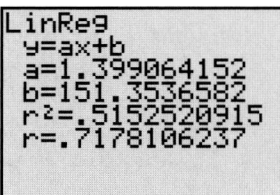

Figure 3

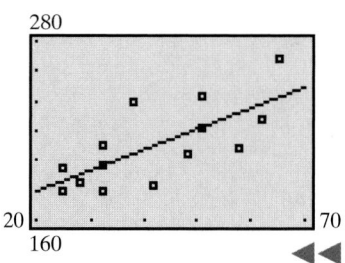

The information obtained in Example 1 is descriptive in nature. Notice that the descriptions are both graphical (as in the scatter diagram) and numerical (as in the correlation coefficient and coefficient of determination).

① The Least-Squares Regression Model

In the least-squares regression equation $\hat{y} = b_0 + b_1 x$, the values for the slope, b_1, and y-intercept, b_0, are statistics, just as the sample mean, $\bar{x}$, and sample standard deviation, s, are statistics. The statistics b_0 and b_1 are estimates for the population y-intercept, β_0, and the population slope, β_1. The true linear relation between the predictor variable, x, and the response variable, y, is given by $y = \beta_0 + \beta_1 x$. Because b_0 and b_1 are statistics, their values vary from sample to sample, so there is a sampling distribution associated with each of them. We use this sampling distribution to conduct inference on b_0 and b_1. For example, we might want to test the claim that β_1 is different from 0. If we have evidence that supports this claim, we conclude that there is a linear relation between the predictor variable, x, and response variable, y.

To test hypotheses about β_0 or β_1, we need to know the sampling distributions of b_0 and b_1. To find these sampling distributions, we must make some assumptions about the population from which the bivariate data (x_i, y_i) were sampled. Just as we did in Section 7.5 when we discussed the sampling distribution of $\bar{x}$, we start by asking what would happen if we took many samples for a given value of the predictor variable, x. For example, in looking back at Table 1, we notice that our sample included three women aged 32 years, so x has the same value, 32, for all three women in our sample, but the corresponding values of y for these three women are different: 180, 210, and 197. Thus, there is a distribution of total cholesterol levels for $x = 32$ years of age. Suppose we looked at *all* women aged 32 years. From these population data, we could find the population mean total cholesterol for 32-year-old women, denoted μ_{32}. We could repeat this process for any other age. In general, different ages will have different population mean total cholesterols. This brings us to our first assumption regarding inference on the least-squares regression model.

In Your Own Words

Because b_0 and b_1 are statistics, they have sampling distributions.

Assumption #1 for Inference on the Least-Squares Regression Model

For any particular value of the predictor variable x (such as 32 in Example 1), the corresponding responses in the population have a mean that depends linearly on x. That is,

$$\mu_x = \beta_0 + \beta_1 x$$

for some numbers β_0 and β_1, where μ_x represents the population mean response when the predictor variable is x.

![quill icon] **In Your Own Words**

When doing inference on the least-squares regression model, we assume (1) that for any predictor variable, x, the mean of the response variable, y, depends on the value of x through a linear equation, and (2) that the response variable, y, is normally distributed with a constant standard deviation, σ. The mean increases/decreases at a constant rate depending on the slope, while the variance remains constant.

We learned how to verify this assumption in Section 4.3. If a plot of the residuals against the predictor variable shows any discernible pattern (such as U-shaped), then the linear model is not appropriate and assumption #1 is violated.

We must also make an assumption regarding the distribution of the response variable for any particular value of the predictor variable.

Assumption #2 for Inference on the Least-Squares Regression Model

The response variables are normally distributed with mean $\mu_x = \beta_0 + \beta_1 x$ and standard deviation σ.

This assumption states that the mean of the response variable changes linearly, but the variance remains constant and the distribution of the response variable is normal. For example, if we obtained a sample of many 32-year-old females and measured their total cholesterol, the distribution would be normal with mean $\mu_{32} = \beta_0 + \beta_1(32)$ and standard deviation σ. If we obtained a sample of many 43-year-old females and measured their total cholesterol, the distribution would be normal with mean $\mu_{43} = \beta_0 + \beta_1(43)$ and standard deviation σ. See Figure 4.

Figure 4

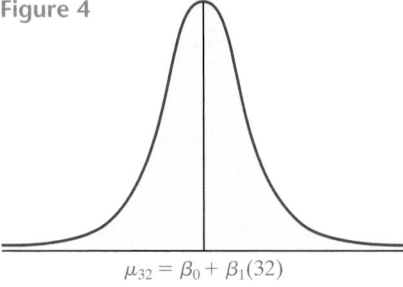

$\mu_{32} = \beta_0 + \beta_1(32)$

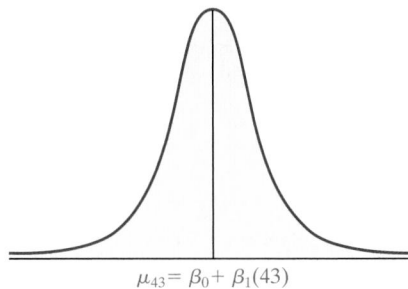

$\mu_{43} = \beta_0 + \beta_1(43)$

![quill icon] **In Your Own Words**

The larger σ is, the more "spread out" the data are around the regression line.

A large value of σ would indicate that the data are widely dispersed about the regression line and a small σ would indicate that the data lie fairly close to the regression line. Figure 5 illustrates the ideas just presented. The regression line represents the mean value of each normal distribution at a specified value of x. The standard deviation of each distribution is σ.

Of course, not all of the observed values of the response variable will lie on the true regression line, $\mu_{x_i} = \beta_0 + \beta_1 x_i$. The difference between the observed and predicted value of the response variable is an error term or residual, ε_i. We now present the least-squares regression model.

Figure 5

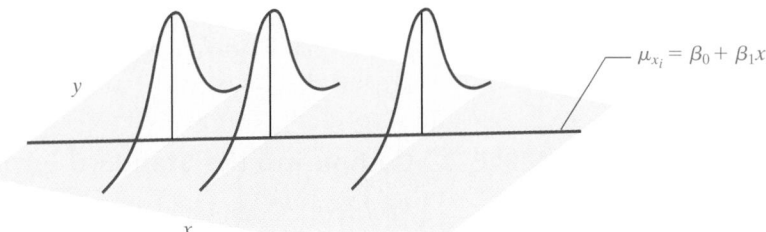

$$\mu_{x_i} = \beta_0 + \beta_1 x_i$$

Definition

The Least-Squares Regression Model

The least-squares regression model is given by

$$y_i = \beta_0 + \beta_1 x_i + \varepsilon_i \tag{1}$$

where

y_i is the value of the response variable for the ith individual,

β_0 and β_1 are the parameters to be estimated based upon sample data,

x_i is the value of the predictor variable for the ith individual,

ε_i is a random error term with mean 0 and variance $\sigma^2_{\varepsilon_i} = \sigma^2$. The error terms are independent, and

$i = 1 \dots n$ where n is the sample size (number of ordered pairs in the data set).

Because the expected value or mean of y_i is $\beta_0 + \beta_1 x_i$ and the expression on the left side of Equation (1) equals the expression on the right side, the expected value or mean of the error term, ε_i, is 0.

NW *Now Work Problem 7(a).*

② The Standard Error

In Section 4.2, we learned how to obtain unbiased estimates for β_0 and β_1. We now present the method for obtaining the unbiased estimate of σ, the standard deviation of the response variable y for any given value of x. The unbiased estimator of σ is called the *standard error of the estimate*.

Remember the formula for the sample standard deviation presented in Section 3.2?

$$s = \sqrt{\frac{\Sigma (x_i - \overline{x})^2}{n - 1}}$$

We compute the deviations about the mean, square them, add up the deviations squared, and divide by $n - 1$. We divide by $n - 1$ because we lost one degree of freedom since one parameter, $\overline{x}$, was estimated. Exactly the same logic is used to compute the standard error of the estimate.

As we mentioned, the predicted values of y, $\hat{y}_i$, represent the mean value of the response variable for any given value of the predictor variable, x_i. So $y_i - \hat{y}_i = \varepsilon_i$ represents the difference between the observed value, y_i, and the mean value, $\hat{y}_i$. This calculation leads to the formula for the standard error of the estimate.

Theorem

The **standard error of the estimate, s_e,** is found using the formula

$$s_e = \sqrt{\frac{\Sigma (y_i - \hat{y}_i)^2}{n - 2}} = \sqrt{\frac{\Sigma \text{residuals}^2}{n - 2}} \tag{2}$$

The standard error of the estimate is usually abbreviated **standard error**. Notice that we divide by $n - 2$ because we have estimated two parameters, β_0 and β_1.

▶ **EXAMPLE 2** **Computing the Standard Error**

Problem: Compute the standard error for the data in Table 1.

Approach: We use the following steps to compute the standard error:

Step 1: Find the least-squares regression line.
Step 2: Obtain predicted values for each of the observations in the data set.
Step 3: Compute the residuals for each of the observations in the data set.
Step 4: Compute $\Sigma \text{residuals}^2$.
Step 5: Compute the standard error, using Formula (2).

Solution:

Step 1: The least squares regression line was found in Example 1.
Step 2: Column 3 of Table 2 represents the predicted values for each of the $n = 14$ observations.
Step 3: Column 4 of Table 2 represents the residuals for each of the 14 observations.

Age, x	Total Cholesterol, y	$\hat{y} = 1.3991 x + 151.3537$	Residuals	Residuals^2
25	180	186.33	−6.33	40.0689
25	195	186.33	8.67	75.1689
28	186	190.53	−4.53	20.5209
32	180	196.12	−16.12	259.8544
32	210	196.12	13.88	192.6544
32	197	196.12	0.88	0.7744
38	239	204.52	34.48	1188.8704
42	183	210.12	−27.12	735.4944
48	204	218.51	−14.51	210.5401
51	221	222.71	−1.71	2.9241
51	243	222.71	20.29	411.6841
58	208	232.50	−24.50	600.25
62	228	238.10	−10.10	102.01
65	269	242.30	26.70	712.89

$$\Sigma \text{residuals}^2 = 4553.708$$

Center of table: **TABLE 2**

Step 4: Column 5 of Table 2 contains the squared residuals. We sum the entries in column 5 to obtain the sum of squared errors. So,

$$\Sigma \text{residuals}^2 = 4553.705$$

Step 5: We use Formula (2) to compute the standard error:

$$s_e = \sqrt{\frac{\Sigma \text{residuals}^2}{n - 2}} = \sqrt{\frac{4553.705}{14 - 2}} = 19.48$$

Caution

Be sure to divide by $n - 2$ when computing the standard error.

◀◀

Using Technology: Statistical spreadsheets, statistical software, and graphing calculators with advanced statistical features have the ability to compute the standard error. Figure 6 displays partial output obtained from Excel. The standard error is highlighted.

Figure 6

Regression Statistics	
Multiple R	0.7178106
R Square	0.5152521
Adjusted R Square	0.4748564
Standard Error	19.480535
Observations	14

 Now Work Problem 7(b).

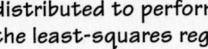 **The Normality of the Residuals**

For the least-squares regression model $y_i = \beta_0 + \beta_1 x_i + \varepsilon_i$, we require that the predictor variable, y_i, be normally distributed. Because $\beta_0 + \beta_1 x_i$ is constant for any x_i, the requirement that y_i is normal implies that the residuals, ε_i must also be normal. In order to perform statistical inference on the regression, it must be the case that the residuals are normally distributed. This requirement is easily verified through a normal probability plot.

> **Caution**
> The residuals must be normally distributed to perform inference on the least-squares regression line.

▶ **EXAMPLE 3**   **Verifying that the Residuals Are Normally Distributed**

Problem: Verify that the residuals obtained in Table 2 from Example 2 are normally distributed.

Approach: We construct a normal probability plot to assess normality. If the normal probability plot is roughly linear, the residuals are said to be normal.

Solution: Figure 7 contains the normal probability plot obtained from Minitab.

Figure 7

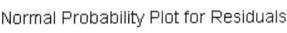

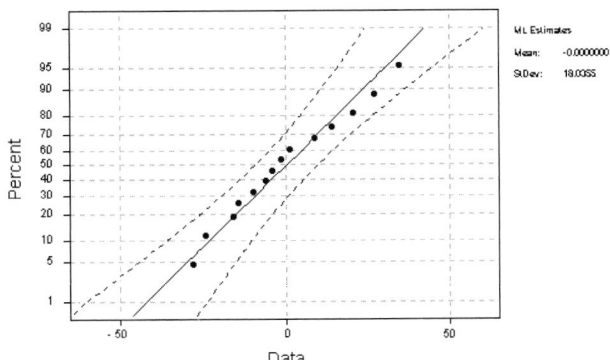

Because all the points lie within the bands created by Minitab, the residuals are normally distributed. We can perform inference on the least-squares regression equation. ◀◀

 Now Work Problem 7(c).

4 Inference on the Slope and y-Intercept

At this point, we know how to estimate the y-intercept and slope of the least-squares regression model. In addition, we can compute the standard error, s_e, which is an estimate of σ, the standard deviation of the response variable about the true least-squares regression model, and we know how to assess the normality of the residuals. We will now use this information to test the hypothesis of no linear relation between the predictor and the response variable.

Here is the question that we would like to answer: Do the sample data provide sufficient evidence to support the claim that a linear relation exists between the two variables? If there is no linear relation between the response and predictor variables, then the slope of the true regression line will be zero. Do you know why? A slope of zero would mean that information about the predictor variable, x, does not change my "guess" as to the value of the response variable, y.

Using the notation of hypothesis testing, we can perform one of three tests:

Two-Tailed	Left-Tailed	Right-Tailed
$H_0: \beta_1 = 0$	$H_0: \beta_1 = 0$	$H_0: \beta_1 = 0$
$H_1: \beta_1 \neq 0$	$H_1: \beta_1 < 0$	$H_1: \beta_1 > 0$

Caution

Before testing $H_0: \beta_1 = 0$, be sure to draw a residual plot to verify that a linear model is appropriate.

In the two-tailed test, we are testing the claim that a linear relation exists between two variables without regard to the sign of the slope. In the left-tailed test, we are testing the claim that the slope of the true regression line is negative. In the right-tailed test, we are testing that the claim the slope of the true regression line is positive.

In order to test any one of these hypotheses, we need to know the sampling distribution of b_1. It turns out that

$$\frac{b_1 - \beta_1}{s_e / \sqrt{\sum (x_i - \overline{x})^2}} = \frac{b_1 - \beta_1}{s_{b_1}}$$

follows Student's t-distribution with $n - 2$ degrees of freedom, where n is the number of observations, b_1 is the unbiased estimator of the hypothesized value of the slope of the true regression line β_1, and s_{b_1} is the sample standard deviation of b_1.

Hypothesis Test Regarding the Slope Coefficient, β_1

Note to Instructor
Remind students that the procedures presented here are similar to those presented for testing hypotheses about μ with σ unknown.

In order to test the claim that two quantitative variables are linearly related, we use the steps that follow, provided that
1. the sample is obtained using random sampling and
2. the residuals are normally distributed with constant error variance.

Step 1: A claim is made regarding the linear relation between a response variable, y, and a predictor variable, x. The claim is used to determine the null and alternative hypotheses. The hypotheses can be structured in one of three ways,

Two-Tailed	Left-Tailed	Right-Tailed
$H_0: \beta_1 = 0$	$H_0: \beta_1 = 0$	$H_0: \beta_1 = 0$
$H_1: \beta_1 \neq 0$	$H_1: \beta_1 < 0$	$H_1: \beta_1 > 0$

Step 2: Choose a level of significance α based upon the seriousness of making a Type I error. The level of significance is used to determine the critical value, using $n - 2$ degrees of freedom. The shaded region(s) represents the critical region.

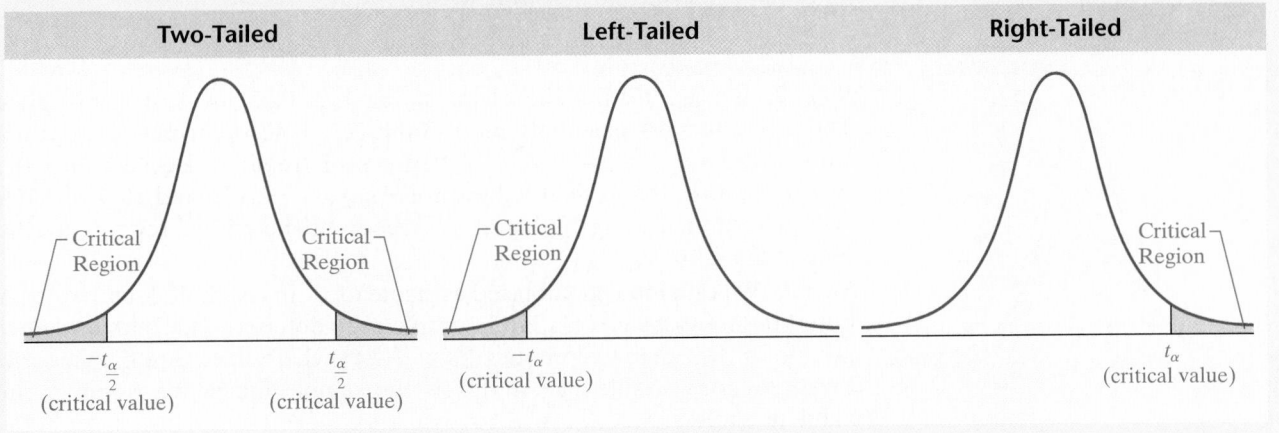

| Two-Tailed | Left-Tailed | Right-Tailed |

Step 3: Compute the **test statistic** $t = \dfrac{b_1 - \beta_1}{s_{b_1}} = \dfrac{b_1}{s_{b_1}},^*$ which follows Student's t-distribution with $n - 2$ degrees of freedom.

Step 4: Compare the critical value with the test statistic.

Two-Tailed	Left-Tailed	Right-Tailed
If $t < -t_{\alpha/2}$ or $t > t_{\alpha/2}$, reject the null hypothesis.	If $t < -t_{\alpha}$, reject the null hypothesis.	If $t > t_{\alpha}$, reject the null hypothesis.

Step 5: State the conclusion.

The procedures just presented are **robust,** which means that minor departures from normality will not adversely affect the results of the test. In fact, for large sample sizes ($n \geq 30$), inferential procedures regarding b_1 can be used even with significant departures from normality.

▶ **EXAMPLE 4** **Testing for a Linear Relation**

Problem: Test the claim that there is a linear relation between age and total cholesterol at the $\alpha = 0.05$ level of significance, using the data given in Table 1 on page 706.

Approach: We verify that the requirements to perform the inference are satisfied. We then follow Steps 1–5.

Solution: Back in Example 1, we were told that the individuals were randomly selected. In Example 3, we confirmed that the residuals were normally distributed by constructing a normal probability plot. We can verify the assumption of constant error variance by plotting the residuals against the values of the predictor variable as shown in Figure 8.

Figure 8

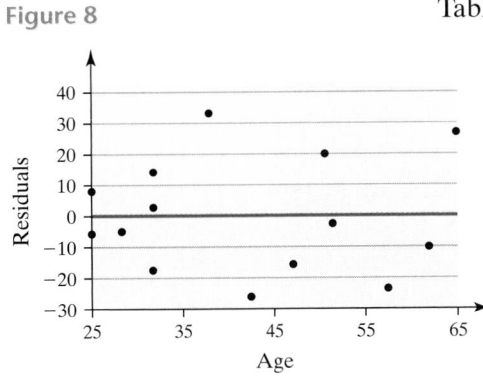

*Remember, when computing the test statistic, we assume the null hypothesis to be true; that is, we assume that $\beta_1 = 0$ in computing the test statistic.

The errors are evenly spread around a horizontal line drawn at 0. The assumption of constant error variance is satisfied. We can now follow Steps 1–5 to test the claim.

Step 1: We are testing the claim that there is no linear relation between age and total cholesterol. Therefore, we are testing

$$H_o: \beta_1 = 0 \qquad \text{versus} \qquad H_1: \beta_1 \neq 0$$

Step 2: We are testing the claim at the $\alpha = 0.05$ level of significance. There are $n = 14$ observations in Table 1, so we determine the critical value with $n - 2 = 14 - 2 = 12$ degrees of freedom. Because this is a two-tailed test, the critical values are $-t_{0.025} = -2.179$ and $t_{0.025} = 2.179$, each determined using 12 degrees of freedom. The critical regions are displayed in Figure 9.

Step 3: We obtained an unbiased estimate of β_1 in Example 1, and we computed the standard error, s_e, in Example 2. To determine the standard deviation of b_1, we need to compute $\sum(x_i - \bar{x})^2$, where the x_i are the values of the predictor variable, age, and $\bar{x}$ is the sample mean. We compute this value in Table 3.

Figure 9

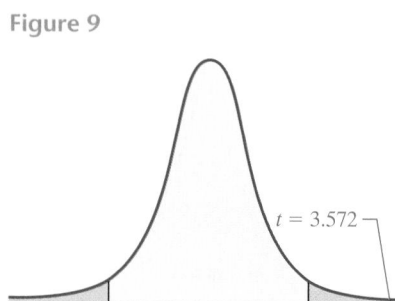

$t = 3.572$
-2.179 2.179 t

TABLE 3			
Age, x	$\bar{x}$	$x_i - \bar{x}$	$(x_i - \bar{x})^2$
25	42.07143	−17.07143	291.4337
25	42.07143	−17.07143	291.4337
28	42.07143	−14.07143	198.0051
32	42.07143	−10.07143	101.4337
32	42.07143	−10.07143	101.4337
32	42.07143	−10.07143	101.4337
38	42.07143	−4.07143	16.5765
42	42.07143	−0.07143	0.0051
48	42.07143	5.92857	35.1479
51	42.07143	8.92857	79.7194
51	42.07143	8.92857	79.7194
58	42.07143	15.92857	253.7193
62	42.07143	19.92857	397.1479
65	42.07143	22.92857	525.7193

$$\sum(x_i - \bar{x})^2 = 2472.9284$$

We have

$$s_{b_1} = \frac{s_e}{\sqrt{\sum(x_i - \bar{x})^2}} = \frac{19.48}{\sqrt{2472.9284}} = 0.3917$$

The test statistic is

$$t = \frac{b_1}{s_{b_1}} = \frac{1.3991}{0.3917} = 3.572$$

In Your Own Words

If we do not reject H_o, then we use the sample mean of y to predict the value of the response for any value of the predictor.

Step 4: Because the test statistic, $t = 3.572$, is greater than the critical value, $t_{0.025} = 2.179$, we reject the null hypothesis. The test statistic is labeled in Figure 9.

Step 5: There is sufficient evidence to support the claim of a linear relation between age and total cholesterol. ◀◀

Using Technology: All of the results in Examples 1–4 can be obtained from statistical software or a graphing calculator with advanced statistical capabilities. Figure 10(a) shows the results obtained from Minitab, Figure 10(b) shows the results obtained from Excel, and Figure 10(c) shows the results obtained from a TI-83 Plus graphing calculator.

Figure 10

Regression Analysis

```
The regression equation is
total cholesterol = 151 + 1.40 age

Predictor         Coef      StDev         T        P
Constant        151.35      17.28      8.76    0.000
Age             1.3991     0.3917      3.57    0.004

S = 19.48      R-Sq = 51.5%      R-Sq(adj) = 47.5%

Analysis of Variance

Source           Df        SS        MS        F        P
Regression        1     4840.5    4840.5    12.76    0.004
Residual Error   12     4553.9     379.5
Total            13     9394.4
```

(a) Minitab Output

SUMMARY OUTPUT

Regression Statisitics	
Multiple R	0.7178106
R Square	0.5152521
Adjusted R Square	0.4748564
Standard Error	19.480535
Observations	14

ANOVA

	df	SS	MS	F
Regression	1	4840.462	4840.462	12.75514
Residual	12	4553.895	379.4912	
Total	13	9394.357		

	Coefficients	Standard Error	t Stat	P-value
Intercept	151.35366	17.28376	8.756987	1.47E-06
Age	1.3990642	0.391737	3.571433	0.003842

(b) Excel Output

```
LinRegTTest
 y=a+bx
 β≠0 and ρ≠0
 t=3.57143321
 p=.0038422614
 df=12
↓a=151.3536582
```

```
LinRegTTest
 y=a+bx
 β≠0 and ρ≠0
↑b=1.399064152
 s=19.48053511
 r²=.5152520915
 r=.7178106237
```

(c) TI-83 Output

In all three sets of output, the *P*-value for the slope is given as 0.004. This means that there is a 0.004 probability of obtaining a slope estimate as extreme as or more extreme than the one obtained if the null hypothesis of no linear relation is true. Because the *P*-value is less than the level of significance, $\alpha = 0.05$, we reject the null hypothesis of no linear relation.

NW *Now Work Problems 7(d) and 7(e).*

⑤ Confidence Intervals for the Slope

We can also obtain confidence intervals for the slope of the least-squares regression line. The procedure is identical to that for obtaining confidence intervals about a mean. As was the case with confidence intervals about a population mean, the confidence interval for the slope of the least-squares regression line is of the form

$$\text{Point Estimate} \pm \text{Margin of Error}$$

Theorem

> **Confidence Intervals for the Slope of the Regression Line**
>
> A $(1 - \alpha) \cdot 100\%$ confidence interval for the slope of the true regression line, β_1, is given by the following formulas:
>
> $$\text{Lower Bound: } b_1 - t_{\alpha/2} \cdot \frac{s_e}{\sqrt{\sum(x_i - \bar{x})^2}}$$
>
> $$\text{Upper Bound: } b_1 + t_{\alpha/2} \cdot \frac{s_e}{\sqrt{\sum(x_i - \bar{x})^2}} \tag{3}$$
>
> Here, $t_{\alpha/2}$ is computed with $n - 2$ degrees of freedom.
>
> **Note:** This interval can be computed only if the data are randomly obtained, the residuals are normally distributed, and there is constant error variance.

▶ **EXAMPLE 5** **Constructing a Confidence Interval about the Slope of the True Regression Line**

Problem: Compute a 95% confidence interval about the slope of the true regression line for the data presented in Table 1.

Approach:

Step 1: Determine the least-squares regression line.
Step 2: Verify the requirements are satisfied.
Step 3: Compute s_e.
Step 4: Determine the critical value $t_{\alpha/2}$ with $n - 2$ degrees of freedom.
Step 5: Compute the bounds on the $(1 - \alpha) \cdot 100\%$ confidence interval for β_1 using Formula (3).
Step 6: Interpret the result by stating, "We are 95% confident that β_1 is somewhere between *lower bound* and *upper bound*."

Solution:

Step 1: The least-squares regression line was determined in Example 1.
Step 2: The requirements were verified in Examples 1, 3, and 4.
Step 3: We computed s_e in Example 2.

Step 4: Because we wish to determine a 95% confidence interval, we have $\alpha = 0.05$. Therefore, we need to find $t_{0.05/2} = t_{0.025}$ with $14 - 2 = 12$ degrees of freedom. Referring to Table III, we find that $t_{0.025} = 2.179$.

Step 5: We find the lower and upper bounds:

$$\text{Lower Bound: } b_1 - t_{\alpha/2} \cdot \frac{s_e}{\sqrt{\sum (x_i - \bar{x})^2}} = 1.3991 - 2.179 \cdot \frac{19.48}{\sqrt{2472.9284}} = 1.3991 - 0.8536 = 0.5455$$

$$\text{Upper Bound: } b_1 + t_{\alpha/2} \cdot \frac{s_e}{\sqrt{\sum (x_i - \bar{x})^2}} = 1.3991 + 2.179 \cdot \frac{19.48}{\sqrt{2472.9284}} = 1.3991 + 0.8536 = 2.2527$$

Step 6: We are 95% confident that the mean increase in cholesterol for each additional year of life is somewhere between 0.5455 and 2.2527. ◄◄

Caution

It is best that the predictor variables be "spread out" when doing regression analysis.

In looking carefully at the formula for the standard deviation of b_1, we should notice that the larger the value of $\sum (x_i - \bar{x})^2$, the smaller the value of s_{b_1}. This result implies that whenever we are finding a least-squares regression line, we should attempt to make the values of the predictor variable, x, as spread out as possible, so that b_1, our estimate of β_1, is as precise as possible.

 Now Work Problem 7(f).

Inference on the Linear Correlation Coefficient

Perhaps you are wondering why we have not presented hypothesis tests regarding the linear correlation coefficient. There are two basic reasons: (1) The hypothesis test on the slope and a hypothesis test on the linear correlation coefficient will yield the same conclusion, and (2) inferential methods on the linear correlation coefficient, ρ, require that the Y's at any given X are normally distributed and that the X's at any given Y are normally distributed. That is, testing a hypothesis such as $H_0\colon \rho = 0$ versus $H_1\colon \rho \neq 0$ requires that the two variables follow a **bivariate normal distribution** or be **jointly normally distributed**. Verifying this assumption is a difficult task. Although a normal probability plot of the x_i's and a separate normal probability plot of the y_i's generally means that the joint distribution is normal, it is not guaranteed. For these two reasons, we will be content in verifying the linearity of the data by performing inference on the slope coefficient only.

12.1 Assess Your Understanding

Concepts and Vocabulary

1. State the requirements in order to perform inference on the least-squares regression model. How are these requirements verified?
2. Why is it important to perform graphical as well as analytical analysis when analyzing relations between two quantitative variables?
3. What do the y-coordinates on the least-squares regression line represent?

4. Why is it desirable to have the predictor variables "spread out" in order to test a claim regarding β_1 or construct confidence intervals about β_1?
5. If $H_0\colon \beta_1 = 0$ is not rejected, what is the best "guess" for the value of the response variable for any value of the predictor variable?

Exercises

- ## Skill Building

In Problems 1–6, use the results of Problems 3–8, respectively, from Section 4.2 to answer the following questions:

(a) What are the unbiased estimates of β_0 and β_1?
(b) Compute the standard error, the point estimate for σ.
(c) Assuming the residuals are normally distributed, determine s_{b_1}.

(d) Assuming the residuals are normally distributed, test $H_0: \beta_1 = 0$ vs $H_1: \beta_1 \neq 0$ at the $\alpha = 0.05$ level of significance.

1.

x	3	4	5	7	8
y	4	6	7	12	14

2.

x	3	5	7	9	11
y	0	2	3	6	9

3.

x	-2	-1	0	1	2
y	-4	0	1	4	5

4.

x	-2	-1	0	1	2
y	7	6	3	2	0

5.

x	20	30	40	50	60
y	100	95	91	83	70

6.

x	5	10	15	20	25
y	2	4	7	11	18

- ## Applying the Concepts

7. Height versus Head Circumference A pediatrician wants to determine the relation that may exist between a child's height and head circumference. She randomly selects 11 children from her practice, measures their height and head circumference, and obtains the following data: (a) $b_0 = 12.4932$; $b_1 = 0.1827$

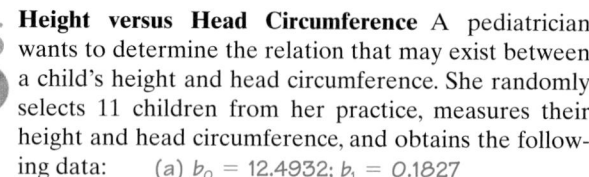

Height (inches)	Head Circumference (inches)
27.75	17.5
24.5	17.1
25.5	17.1
26	17.3
25	16.9
27.75	17.6
26.5	17.3
27	17.5
26.75	17.3
26.75	17.5
27.5	17.5

Source: Denise Slucki, Student at Joliet Junior College

Use the results from Problem 9 in Section 4.2 to answer the following questions:

(a) What are the unbiased estimates of β_0 and β_1?
(b) Compute the standard error, s_e. 0.0954
(c) Determine whether the residuals are normally distributed.
(d) If the residuals are normally distributed, determine s_{b_1}. 0.02756
(e) If the residuals are normally distributed, test the claim that a linear relation exists between height and head circumference at the $\alpha = 0.01$ level of significance. Reject H_o
(f) If the residuals are normally distributed, construct a 95% confidence interval about the slope of the true least-squares regression line. (0.1204, 0.2450)

(g) A child comes in for a physical, and the nurse determines his height to be 26.5 inches. However, the child is being rather uncooperative, so the nurse is unable to measure the head circumference of the child. What would be a good "guess" as to this child's head circumference? Why is this a good guess? 17.3 inches

8. Concrete As concrete cures, it gains strength. The following data represent the 7-day and 28-day strength (in pounds per square inch) of a certain type of concrete:

7-day Strength, x	28-day Strength, y	7-day Strength, x	28-day Strength, y
2300	4070	2480	4120
3390	5220	3380	5020
2430	4640	2660	4890
2890	4620	2620	4190
3330	4850	3340	4630

(a) Treating the 7-day strength as the predictor variable, x, determine the unbiased estimates of β_0 and β_1.
(b) Compute the standard error, s_e. 271.0
(c) Determine whether the residuals are normally distributed.
(d) If the residuals are normally distributed, determine s_{b_1}. 0.2055
(e) If the residuals are normally distributed, test the claim that a linear relation exists between 7-day strength and 28-day strength at the $\alpha = 0.05$ level of significance. Reject H_o
(f) If the residuals are normally distributed, construct a 95% confidence interval about the slope of the true least-squares regression line. (0.2025, 1.1503)
(g) What is the mean 28-day strength of this concrete if the 7-day strength is 3000 psi? 4705

(8a) $b_0 = 2675.6$, $b_1 = 0.6764$

9. **Bone Length** Research performed at NASA and led by Dr. Emily R. Morey-Holton measured the lengths of the right humerus and right tibia in 11 rats that were sent into space on Spacelab Life Sciences 2. The following data were collected: (a) $b_0 = 1.114; b_1 = 1.3902$

Right Humerus (mm)	Right Tibia (mm)	Right Humerus (mm)	Right Tibia (mm)
24.8	36.05	25.9	37.38
24.59	35.57	26.11	37.96
24.59	35.57	26.63	37.46
24.29	34.58	26.31	37.75
23.81	34.2	26.84	38.5
24.87	34.73		

Source: NASA Life Sciences Data Archive

Use the results from Problem 13 in Section 4.2 to answer the following questions:

(a) What are the unbiased estimates of β_0 and β_1?
(b) Compute the standard error, the point estimate for σ. 0.4944
(c) Determine whether the residuals are normally distributed.
(d) If the residuals are normally distributed, determine s_{b_1}. 0.1501
(e) If the residuals are normally distributed, test the claim that a linear relation exists between the predictor variable, x, and response variable, y, at the $\alpha = 0.01$ level of significance. Reject H_o
(f) If the residuals are normally distributed, construct a 99% confidence interval about the slope of the true least-squares regression line. (0.902, 1.878)
(g) What is the mean length of the right tibia on a rat whose right humerus is 25.93 mm? 37.16

10. **Tar and Nicotine** Every year the Federal Trade Commission (FTC) must report tar and nicotine levels in cigarettes to the Congress. The FTC obtains the tar and nicotine levels in over 1200 brands of cigarettes. A random sample from those reported to Congress is given in the following table: (a) $b_0 = 0.2088; b_1 = 0.0575$

Brand	Tar (mg)	Nicotine (mg)
Barclay 100	5	0.4
Benson and Hedges King	16	1.1
Camel Regular	24	1.7
Chesterfield King	24	1.4
Doral	8	0.5
Kent Golden Lights	9	0.8
Kool Menthol	9	0.8
Lucky Strike	24	1.5
Marlboro Gold	15	1.2
Newport Menthol	18	1.3
Salem Menthol	17	1.3
Virginia Slims Ultra Light	5	0.5
Winston Light	10	0.8

Source: Federal Trade Commission

Use the results from Problem 12 in Section 4.2 to answer the following questions:

(a) What are the unbiased estimates of β_0 and β_1?
(b) Compute the standard error, the point estimate for σ. 0.1121
(c) Determine whether the residuals are normally distributed.
(d) If the residuals are normally distributed, determine s_{b_1}. 0.0046
(e) If the residuals are normally distributed, test the claim that a linear relation exists between the predictor variable, x, and response variable, y, at the $\alpha = 0.1$ level of significance. Reject H_o
(f) If the residuals are normally distributed, construct a 90% confidence interval about the slope of the true least-squares regression line. (0.0492, 0.0658)
(g) What is the mean amount of nicotine in a cigarette that has 12 mg of tar? 0.899

11. Cisco Systems versus the S&P 500 The following data represent the rate of return of Cisco Systems stock for 13 months, compared with the rate of return of the Standard and Poors Index of 500 stocks.

Month	Rate of Return of S&P 500	Rate of Return in Cisco Systems	Month	Rate of Return of S&P 500	Rate of Return in Cisco Systems
Sep-99	−2.9	1.1	Apr-00	−3.1	−10.3
Oct-99	6.3	7.9	May-00	−2.2	−17.9
Nov-99	1.9	2.1	Jun-00	2.4	11.6
Dec-99	5.8	20.1	Jul-00	−1.6	2.9
Jan-00	−5.1	2.2	Aug-00	6.1	4.9
Feb-00	−2.0	20.7	Sep-00	−5.3	−19.5
Mar-00	9.7	17.0			

Source: Yahoo! Finance

(a) Treating the rate of return of the S&P 500 as the predictor variable, x, determine the unbiased estimates of β_0 and β_1. $b_0 = 2.034$; $b_1 = 1.6363$
(b) Compute the standard error, the point estimate for σ. 10.66
(c) Determine whether the residuals are normally distributed.
(d) If the residuals are normally distributed, determine s_{b_1}. 0.6265
(e) Reject H_o
(e) If the residuals are normally distributed, test the claim that a linear relation exists between the predictor variable, x, and response variable, y, at the $\alpha = 0.1$ level of significance.
(f) If the residuals are normally distributed, construct a 99% confidence interval about the slope of the true least-squares regression line. $(−0.31, 3.58)$
(g) What is the mean rate of return for Cisco Systems stock if the rate of return of the S&P 500 is 4.2 percent? 8.91

12. Fat-free Mass versus Energy Expenditure In an effort to measure the dependence of energy expenditure on body build, researchers used underwater weighing techniques to determine the fat-free body mass in seven men. In addition, they measured the total 24-hour energy expenditure during inactivity. The results are as follows:

Fat-free Mass (kg)	Energy Expenditure (Kcal)
49.3	1,894
59.3	2,050
68.3	2,353
48.1	1,838
57.6	1,948
78.1	2,528
76.1	2,568

Source: Webb, P. (1981) Energy expenditure and fat-free mass in men and women. *American Journal of Clinical Nutrition*, **34**, 1816–1826

Use the results from Problem 16 in Section 4.2 to answer the following questions: (a) $b_0 = 607.7$, $b_1 = 25.012$

(a) What are the unbiased estimates of β_0 and β_1?
(b) Compute the standard error, the point estimate for σ. 64.85
(c) Determine whether the residuals are normally distributed.
(d) If the residuals are normally distributed, determine s_{b_1}. 2.189
(e) If the residuals are normally distributed, test the claim that a linear relation exists between the predictor variable, x, and response variable, y, at the $\alpha = 0.01$ level of significance. Reject H_o
(f) If the residuals are normally distributed, construct a 99% confidence interval about the slope of the true least-squares regression line. $(16.186, 33.838)$
(g) What is the mean energy expenditure of a man if his fat-free mass is 57.3 kg? 2040.9

13. Calories versus Sugar The following data represent the number of calories per serving and the number of grams of sugar per serving for a random sample of high-fiber cereals: (h) No, $\bar{y} = 17.1$

Calories, x	Sugar, y	Calories, x	Sugar, y
200	18	210	23
210	23	210	16
170	17	210	17
190	20	190	12
200	18	190	11
180	19	200	11

Source: Consumer Reports, October, 1999

(a) Draw a scatter diagram of the data, treating calories as the predictor variable. What type of relation, if any, appears to exist between calories and sugar?

(b) Determine the least-squares regression equation from the sample data. $\hat{y} = 0.93 + 0.0821x$

(c) Compute the standard error, s_e. 4.151

(d) Determine whether the residuals are normally distributed.

(e) Determine s_{b_1}. 0.0961

(f) If the residuals are normally distributed, test the claim that a linear relation exists between calories and sugar content at the $\alpha = 0.01$ level of significance. Do not reject H_o

(g) If the residuals are normally distributed, construct a 95% confidence interval about the slope of the true least-squares regression line. $(-0.13, 0.30)$

(h) Suppose a high-fiber cereal is randomly selected. Would you recommend using the least-squares regression line obtained in part (b) to predict the sugar content of the cereal? Why? What would be a good guess as to the sugar content of the cereal?

14. Age versus HDL Cholesterol A doctor wanted to determine whether there is a relation between a male's age and his HDL (so-called good) cholesterol. He randomly selected 17 of his patients and determined their HDL cholesterol. He obtained the following data:

(d) Yes

Age	HDL Cholesterol	Age	HDL Cholesterol
38	57	38	44
42	54	66	62
46	34	30	53
32	56	51	36
55	35	27	45
52	40	52	38
61	42	49	55
61	38	39	28
26	47		

Source: Data based upon information obtained from the National Center for Health Statistics

(a) Draw a scatter diagram of the data, treating age as the predictor variable. What type of relation, if any, appears to exist between age and HDL cholesterol?

(b) Determine the least-squares regression equation from the sample data. HDL $= 50.784 - 0.1298$ Age

(c) Plot the residuals against the predictor variable, age. Does a linear model seem appropriate, on the basis of the residual plot? (*Hint:* See Section 4.3.)

(d) Are there any outliers or influential observations?

(e) Compute the standard error, s_e. 9.953

(f) Determine whether the residuals are normally distributed.

(g) If the residuals are normally distributed, determine s_{b_1}. 0.2021

(h) If the residuals are normally distributed, test the claim that a linear relation exists between time between age and HDL cholesterol levels at the $\alpha = 0.01$ level of significance. Do not reject H_o

(i) If the residuals are normally distributed, construct a 95% confidence interval about the slope of the true least-squares regression line. $(-0.56, 0.30)$

(j) Suppose a 42-year-old male patient visits the doctor's office. Would you recommend using the least-squares regression line obtained in part (b) to predict the HDL cholesterol of this patient? Why? What would be a good guess as to the HDL cholesterol of this patient? No, $\bar{y} = 44.94$

15. The U.S. Population The following data, obtained from the U.S. Census Bureau, represent the population of the United States: (a) $\hat{y} = -3,771,542,830 + 2,018,994x$

Year, x	Population, y	Year, x	Population, y
1900	76,212,168	1960	179,323,175
1910	92,228,496	1970	203,302,031
1920	106,021,537	1980	226,542,203
1930	123,202,624	1990	248,709,873
1940	132,164,569	2000	281,421,906
1950	151,325,798		

Source: United States Census Bureau

An ecologist is interested in finding an equation that describes the population of the United States over time.

(a) Determine the least-squares regression equation, treating year as the predictor variable.

(b) A normal probability plot of the residuals indicates that the residuals are approximately normally distributed. Test the claim that there is a linear relation between year and population. Reject H_o

(c) Draw a scatter diagram, treating year as the predictor variable.

(d) Plot the residuals against the predictor variable, year.

(e) Does a linear model seem appropriate, based upon the scatter diagram and residual plot? (*Hint:* See Section 4.3.) No

(f) What is the moral?

16. **Kepler's Law of Planetary Motion** The time it takes for a planet to complete its orbit around the sun is called the planet's *sidereal year*. Johann Kepler studied the relation between the sidereal year of a planet and its distance from the sun in 1618. The following data show the distances that the planets are from the sun and their sidereal years: (b) Reject H_o

Planet	Distance from Sun, x (millions of miles)	Sidereal Year, y
Mercury	36	0.24
Venus	67	0.62
Earth	93	1.00
Mars	142	1.88
Jupiter	483	11.9
Saturn	887	29.5
Uranus	1,785	84.0
Neptune	2,797	165.0
Pluto	3,675	248.0

(a) Determine the least-squares regression equation, treating distance from the sun as the predictor variable. $\hat{y} = -12.497 + 0.0657x$

(b) A normal probability plot of the residuals indicates that the residuals are approximately normally distributed. Test the claim that there is a linear relation between distance from the sun and sidereal year.

(c) Draw a scatter diagram, treating distance from the sun as the predictor variable.

(d) Plot the residuals against the predictor variable, distance from the sun.

(e) Does a linear model seem appropriate, based upon the scatter diagram and residual plot? (*Hint*: See Section 4.3.)

(f) What is the moral?

17. **Influential Observations** The following data represent the heights and weights of a random sample of professional baseball players:

Player	Height (inches)	Weight (pounds)	Player	Height (inches)	Weight (pounds)
Albert Belle	74	225	Barry Bonds	74	210
Alex Rodriguez	75	210	Mike Bordick	71	175
Derek Jeter	75	195	Ron Gant	72	196
Greg Maddux	72	185	Pete Harnisch	72	228
Randy Johnson	82	230	Randy Velarde	72	200
David Justice	75	200	Ray Lankford	71	200
Al Leiter	75	220	Jason Isringhausen	75	210

Source: Yahoo! Sports

(a) Draw a scatter diagram of the data, treating height as the predictor variable and weight as the response variable.

(b) Determine the least-squares regression line. Test the claim that there is a linear relation between height and weight at the $\alpha = 0.05$ level of significance.

(c) Remove the values listed for Randy Johnson. Test the claim that there is a linear relation between height and weight. What effect does Randy Johnson have on the hypothesis test? Do you think that Randy Johnson is influential?

18. Output obtained from Minitab to the right.

(a) The least-squares regression equation is $\hat{y} = 12.396 + 1.3962x$. What is the predicted value of y at $x = 10$? 26.36

(b) What is the mean of y at $x = 10$? 26.36

(c) The standard error, s_e, is 2.167. What is the standard deviation of y at $x = 10$? 2.167

(d) If the assumptions required for inference on the least-squares regression model are satisfied, what is the distribution of y at $x = 10$? Normal; $\mu \approx 26.36$, $\sigma \approx 2.167$

```
The regression equation is
Y = 12.4 + 1.40 x

Predictor        Coef      StDev        T        P
Constant       12.396      1.381     8.97    0.000
x              1.3962     0.1245    11.21    0.000

S = 2.167           R-Sq = 91.3%        R-Sq(adj) = 90.6%
```

(17b) Weight $= -36.8 + 3.284$ height; Reject H_o

(17c) Weight $= -85.3 + 3.948$ height; Do not reject H_o

Technology Step-by-Step
Testing the Least-Squares Regression Model

TI-83 Plus   **Step 1:** Enter the predictor variable in L1 and the response variable in L2.

Step 2: Press STAT, highlight TESTS and select `E:LinRegTTest...`

Step 3: Be sure that Xlist is L1 and Ylist is L2. Make sure that Freq: is set to 1. Select the direction of the alternative hypothesis. Place the cursor on Calculate and press ENTER.

MINITAB   **Step 1:** With the predictor variable in C1 and the response variable in C2, select the **Stat** menu and highlight **Regression**. Highlight **Regression . . .**

Step 2: Select the predictor and response variables and click OK.

Excel   **Step 1:** Make sure the Data Analysis Tool Pak is activated by selecting the **Tools** menu and highlighting **Add-Ins . . .** Check the box for the Analysis ToolPak and click OK.

Step 2: Enter the predictor variable in column A and the response variable in column B.

Step 3: Select the **Tools** menu and highlight **DataAnalysis . . .**

Step 4: Select the **Regression** option.

Step 5: With the cursor in the Y-range cell, highlight the column that contains the response variable. With the cursor in the X-range cell, highlight the column that contains the predictor variable. Click OK.

12.2   Confidence and Prediction Intervals

Preparing for This Section   Before getting started, review the following:

✓ Confidence intervals (Section 8.1, pp. 457–464; Section 8.2, pp. 480–482)

Objectives   ① Construct confidence intervals about a predicted value
② Construct prediction intervals about a predicted value

Note to Instructor
Given the tedious calculations in this section, it is recommended that hand solutions be de-emphasized. Let software do the work, so that students can concentrate on the results.

① We know how to obtain the least-squares regression equation of best fit from data. We also know how to use the least-squares regression equation to obtain a predicted value. For example, the least-squares regression equation for the cholesterol data introduced in Example 1 from Section 12.1 was

$$\hat{y} = 151.3537 + 1.3991\, x$$

where $\hat{y}$ represents the predicted total cholesterol for a female whose age is x. The predicted value of total cholesterol for a given age x actually has two interpretations:

1. It represents the mean total cholesterol for all females whose age is x.
2. It represents the predicted total cholesterol for a randomly selected female whose age is x.

So if we let $x = 42$ in the least-squares regression equation $\hat{y} = 151.3537 + 1.3991\,x$, we would obtain $\hat{y} = 151.3537 + 1.3991(42) = 210.1$. We can interpret this result in one of two ways:

1. The mean total cholesterol for all females 42 years old is 210.1.
2. Our best guess as to the total cholesterol for a randomly selected 42-year-old female is 210.1.

Of course, there is a margin of error in making predictions, so we construct intervals about any predicted value in order to describe the accuracy of the prediction. The type of interval constructed is going to depend upon whether we are predicting a mean total cholesterol for all 42-year-old females or the total cholesterol for an individual 42-year-old female. In other words, the margin of error is going to be different for predicting the mean total cholesterol for all females who are 42 years old versus the total cholesterol for one individual. Which prediction (the mean or the individual) do you think will be more accurate? It seems logical that the distribution of means should have less variability (and therefore a lower margin of error) than the distribution of individuals. After all, in the distribution of means, high total cholesterols can be offset by low total cholesterols.

Definition

Confidence intervals are intervals constructed about the predicted value of y, at a given level of x, that are used to measure the accuracy of the mean response of all the individuals in the population.

Prediction intervals are intervals constructed about the predicted value of y that are used to measure the accuracy of a single individual's predicted value.

In Your Own Words

Confidence intervals are intervals for the mean of the population. Prediction intervals are intervals for an individual from the population.

If we use the least-squares regression equation to predict the mean total cholesterol for all 42-year-old females, we construct a confidence interval. If we use the least-squares regression equation to predict the total cholesterol for a single 42-year-old female, we construct a prediction interval.

Confidence Intervals

The structure of a confidence interval is the same as it was in Section 8.1. The interval is of the form

$$\text{Point Estimate} \pm \text{Margin of Error}$$

The following formula can be used to construct a confidence interval about $\hat{y}$:

Theorem

Confidence Interval about the Mean Response of y, $\hat{y}$

A $(1 - \alpha) \cdot 100\%$ confidence interval for $\hat{y}$, the mean response of y, is given by

$$\text{Lower Bound: } \hat{y} - t_{\alpha/2} \cdot s_e \sqrt{\frac{1}{n} + \frac{(x^* - \overline{x})^2}{\sum(x_i - \overline{x})^2}}$$

$$\text{Upper Bound: } \hat{y} + t_{\alpha/2} \cdot s_e \sqrt{\frac{1}{n} + \frac{(x^* - \overline{x})^2}{\sum(x_i - \overline{x})^2}} \tag{1}$$

where x^* is the given value of the predictor variable, n is the number of observations, and $t_{\alpha/2}$ is the critical value with $n - 2$ degrees of freedom.

▶ **EXAMPLE 1** **Constructing a Confidence Interval about the Mean Predicted Value**

Problem: Construct a 95% confidence interval about the predicted mean total cholesterol of all 42-year-old females, using the data in Table 1 on page 706.

Approach: We need to determine the predicted mean total cholesterol at $x^* = 42$, s_e, $\sum(x_i - \bar{x})^2$, $\bar{x}$ and find the critical t value to use Formula (1).

Solution: The least-squares regression equation is $\hat{y} = 151.3537 + 1.3991\, x$. To find the predicted mean total cholesterol of all 42-year-olds, let $x = x^* = 42$ in the regression equation and obtain $\hat{y} = 151.3537 + 1.3991\,(42) = 210.1$. From Example 2 in Section 12.1, we found that $s_e = 19.48$, and from Example 4 in Section 12.1, we found that $\sum(x_i - \bar{x})^2 = 2472.9284$ and $\bar{x} = 42.07143$. We find $t_{\alpha/2} = t_{0.025}$ with $n - 2 = 14 - 2 = 12$ degrees of freedom to be 2.179. The 95% confidence interval about the predicted mean total cholesterol for 42-year-old females is therefore

$$\text{Lower Bound: } \hat{y} - t_{\alpha/2} \cdot s_e \cdot \sqrt{\frac{1}{n} + \frac{(x^* - \bar{x})^2}{\sum(x_i - \bar{x})^2}} = 210.1 - 2.179 \cdot 19.48 \cdot \sqrt{\frac{1}{14} + \frac{(42 - 42.07143)^2}{2472.9284}} = 198.8$$

$$\text{Upper Bound: } \hat{y} + t_{\alpha/2} \cdot s_e \cdot \sqrt{\frac{1}{n} + \frac{(x^* - \bar{x})^2}{\sum(x_i - \bar{x})^2}} = 210.1 + 2.179 \cdot 19.48 \cdot \sqrt{\frac{1}{14} + \frac{(42 - 42.07143)^2}{2472.9284}} = 221.4$$

We are 95% confident that the mean total cholesterol of all 42-year-old females is somewhere between 198.8 and 221.4. ◀◀

NW *Now Work Problems 1(a) and 1(b).*

② **Prediction Intervals**

The procedure for obtaining a prediction interval is identical to that for finding a confidence interval. The only difference is the standard error. There is more variability associated with individuals than with means. Therefore, the computation of the interval must account for this increased variability. Again, the form of the interval is

In Your Own Words

Prediction intervals are wider than confidence intervals because it is tougher to "guess" the value of an individual than the mean of a population.

$$\text{Point Estimate} \pm \text{Margin of Error}$$

The following formula can be used to construct a prediction interval about $\hat{y}$:

Theorem

Prediction Interval about $\hat{y}$

A $(1 - \alpha) \cdot 100\%$ prediction interval for $\hat{y}$, the individual response of y, is given by

$$\text{Lower Bound: } \hat{y} - t_{\alpha/2} \cdot s_e \sqrt{1 + \frac{1}{n} + \frac{(x^* - \bar{x})^2}{\sum(x_i - \bar{x})^2}}$$

$$\text{Upper Bound: } \hat{y} + t_{\alpha/2} \cdot s_e \sqrt{1 + \frac{1}{n} + \frac{(x^* - \bar{x})^2}{\sum(x_i - \bar{x})^2}} \qquad \textbf{(2)}$$

where x^* is the given value of the predictor variable, n is the number of observations, and $t_{\alpha/2}$ is the critical value with $n - 2$ degrees of freedom.

► **EXAMPLE 2** **Constructing a Prediction Interval about a Predicted Value**

Problem: Construct a 95% prediction interval about the predicted total cholesterol of a 42-year-old female.

Approach: We need to determine the predicted total cholesterol at $x^* = 42$, s_e, $\sum(x_i - \overline{x})^2$, $\overline{x}$ and find the critical t value using the data in Table 1 on page 706.

Solution: The least-squares regression equation is $\hat{y} = 151.3537 + 1.3991 x$. To find the predicted total cholesterol of a 42-year-old, let $x = x^* = 42$ in the regression equation and obtain $\hat{y} = 151.3537 + 1.3991(42) = 210.1$. From Example 2 in Section 12.1, we found that $s_e = 19.48$; from Example 4 in Section 12.1, we found that $\sum(x_i - \overline{x})^2 = 2472.9284$ and $\overline{x} = 42.07143$. We find $t_{\alpha/2} = t_{0.025}$ with $n - 2 = 14 - 2 = 12$ degrees of freedom to be 2.179.

The 95% confidence interval about the predicted total cholesterol for a 42-year-old female is

$$\text{Lower Bound: } \hat{y} - t_{\alpha/2} \cdot s_e \sqrt{1 + \frac{1}{n} + \frac{(x^* - \overline{x})^2}{\sum(x_i - \overline{x})^2}} =$$

$$210.1 - 2.179 \cdot 19.48 \cdot \sqrt{1 + \frac{1}{14} + \frac{(42 - 42.07143)^2}{2472.9284}} = 166.2$$

$$\text{Upper Bound: } \hat{y} + t_{\alpha/2} \cdot s_e \sqrt{1 + \frac{1}{n} + \frac{(x^* - \overline{x})^2}{\sum(x_i - \overline{x})^2}} =$$

$$210.1 + 2.179 \cdot 19.48 \cdot \sqrt{1 + \frac{1}{14} + \frac{(42 - 42.07143)^2}{2472.9284}} = 254.0$$

We are 95% confident that the total cholesterol of a randomly selected 42-year-old female is somewhere between 166.2 and 254.0. ◄◄

NW *Now Work Problems 1(c) and 1(d).*

Notice that the interval about the individual (prediction interval) is wider than the interval about the mean (confidence interval). The reason for this should be clear: There is more variability associated with individuals than with groups of individuals. That is, it is more difficult to predict a single 42-year-old female's total cholesterol than it is to predict the mean total cholesterol of all 42-year-old females.

Using Technology: Statistical software packages will provide confidence and prediction intervals as part of their output if the user requests them. Figure 11 shows the results of Examples 1 and 2, using Minitab.

Figure 11

```
Predicted Values

        Fit      StDev Fit           95.0% CI              95.0% PI
      210.11          5.21    ( 198.77, 221.46)      ( 166.18, 254.05)
```

12.2 Assess Your Understanding

Concepts and Vocabulary

1. Explain the difference between a confidence interval and prediction interval.
2. Suppose a normal probability plot of residuals indicates that the requirement of normally distributed residuals is violated. Explain the circumstances under which confidence and prediction intervals could still be constructed.

Exercises

- **Skill Building**

In Problems 1–4, use the results of Problems 3–6 in Section 4.2 and Problems 1–4 in Section 12.1.

1. Using the sample data from Problem 1 in Section 12.1,
   (a) Predict the mean value of y if $x = 7$. 11.84
   (b) Construct a 95% confidence interval about the mean value of y if $x = 7$. (10.87, 12.80)
   (c) Predict the value of y if $x = 7$. 11.84
   (d) Construct a 95% prediction interval about the value of y if $x = 7$. (9.94, 13.74)
   (e) Explain the difference between the prediction in part (a) and part (c).

2. Using the sample data from Problem 2 in Section 12.1,
   (a) Predict the mean value of y if $x = 8$. 5.1
   (b) Construct a 95% confidence interval about the mean value of y if $x = 8$. (4.0, 6.2)
   (c) Predict the value of y if $x = 8$. 5.1
   (d) Construct a 95% prediction interval about the value of y if $x = 8$. (2.5, 7.7)
   (e) Explain the difference between the prediction in part (a) and part (c).

3. Using the sample data from Problem 3 in Section 12.1,
   (a) Predict the mean value of y if $x = 1.4$. 4.28
   (b) Construct a 95% confidence interval about the mean value of y if $x = 1.4$. (2.49, 6.07)
   (c) Predict the value of y if $x = 1.4$. 4.28
   (d) Construct a 95% prediction interval about the value of y if $x = 1.4$. (0.92, 7.64)

4. Using the sample data from Problem 4 in Section 12.1,
   (a) Predict the mean value of y if $x = 1.8$. 0.36
   (b) Construct a 90% confidence interval about the mean value of y if $x = 1.8$. $(-0.52, 1.24)$
   (c) Predict the value of y if $x = 1.8$. 0.36
   (d) Construct a 90% prediction interval about the value of y if $x = 1.8$. $(-1.14, 1.86)$

- **Applying the Concepts**

5. **Height versus Head Circumference** Use the results of Problem 7 from Section 12.1 to answer the following questions: (*d*) (16.97, 17.43)
   (a) Predict the mean head circumference of children who are 25.75 inches tall. 17.20
   (b) Construct a 95% confidence interval about the mean head circumference of children who are 25.75 inches tall. (17.12, 17.28)
   (c) Predict the head circumference of a randomly selected child who is 25.75 inches tall. 17.20
   (d) Construct a 95% prediction interval about the head circumference of a child who is 25.75 inches tall.
   (e) Explain the difference between the prediction in part (a) and the prediction in part (c).

6. **Concrete** Use the results of Problem 8 from Section 12.1 to answer the following questions:
   (a) Predict the mean 28-day strength of concrete whose 7-day strength is 2550 psi. 4400.4
   (b) Construct a 95% confidence interval about the mean 28-day strength of concrete whose 7-day strength is 2550 psi. (4147.8, 4653.1)

   (c) Predict the 28-day strength of a cylinder of concrete whose 7-day strength is 2550 psi. 4400.4
   (d) Construct a 95% prediction interval about the 28-day strength of concrete whose 7-day strength is 2550 psi. (3726.3, 5074.6)
   (e) Explain the difference between the prediction in part (a) and the prediction in part (c).

7. **Bone Length** Use the results of Problem 9 in Section 12.1 to answer the following questions:
   (a) Predict the mean length of the right tibia of all rats whose right humerus is 25.83 mm. 37.02
   (b) Construct a 95% confidence interval about the mean length found in part (a). (36.65, 37.40)
   (c) Predict the length of the right tibia of a randomly selected rat whose right humerus is 25.83 mm. 37.02
   (d) Construct a 95% prediction interval about the length found in part (c). (35.84, 38.20)
   (e) Explain why the predicted lengths found in parts (a) and (c) are the same, yet the intervals are different.

8. **Tar and Nicotine** Use the results of Problem 10 in Section 12.1 to answer the following questions:

    (a) Predict the mean nicotine content of all cigarettes whose tar content is 12 mg. *0.899*

    (b) Construct a 95% confidence interval about the tar content found in part (a). *(0.827, 0.971)*

    (c) Predict the nicotine content of a randomly selected cigarette whose tar content is 12 mg. *0.899*

    (d) Construct a 95% prediction interval about the nicotine content found in part (c). *(0.642, 1.156)*

    (e) Explain why the predicted nicotine contents found in parts (a) and (c) are the same, yet the intervals are different.

9. **Cisco Systems versus the S&P 500** Use the results of Problem 11 in Section 12.1 to answer the following questions:

    (a) What is the mean rate of return for Cisco Systems stock if the rate of return of the S&P 500 is 4.2 percent? *8.91*

    (b) Construct a 90% confidence interval about the mean rate of return found in part (a). *(2.34, 15.47)*

    (c) Predict the rate of return on Cisco Systems stock if the rate of return on the S&P 500 for a randomly selected month is 4.2 percent. *8.91*

    (d) Construct a 90% prediction interval about the rate of return found in part (c). *(−11.34, 29.15)*

    (e) Explain why the predicted rates of return found in parts (a) and (c) are the same, yet the intervals are different.

10. **Fat-free Mass versus Energy Expenditure** Use the results of Problem 12 in Section 12.1 to answer the following questions: *(b) (1932.3, 2149.5) (c) 2040.9*

    (a) What is the mean energy expenditure for individuals whose fat-free mass is 57.3 kg? *2040.9*

    (b) Construct a 99% confidence interval about the mean energy expenditure found in part (a).

    (c) Predict the energy expenditure of a randomly selected individual whose fat-free mass is 57.3 kg.

    (d) Construct a 99% prediction interval about the energy expenditure found in part (c). *(1757.8, 2324.0)*

    (e) Explain why the predicted energy expenditures found in parts (a) and (c) are the same, yet the intervals are different.

11. **Calories versus Sugar** Use the results of Problem 13 from Section 12.1 to answer the following:

    (a) Explain why it does not make sense to construct confidence or prediction intervals based upon the least-squares regression equation.

    (b) Construct a 95% confidence interval for the mean sugar content of high-fiber cereals. *(14.5, 19.7)*

12. **Age versus HDL Cholesterol** Use the results of Problem 14 from Section 12.1 to answer the following:

    (a) Explain why it does not make sense to construct confidence or prediction intervals based upon the least-squares regression equation.

    (b) Construct a 95% confidence interval for the mean HDL cholesterol of males. *(39.9, 50.0)*

Technology Step-by-Step
Confidence and Prediction Intervals

TI-83 Plus The TI-83 Plus does not compute confidence or prediction intervals.

MINITAB **Step 1:** With the predictor variable in C1 and the response variable in C2, select the **Stat** menu, highlight **Regression**. Highlight **Regression . . . .**

Step 2: Select the predictor and response variables.

Step 3: Click the Options . . . button.

Step 4: In the cell marked "Prediction intervals for new observations:", enter the value of x^*. Select a confidence level. Click OK twice.

Excel **Step 1:** Load the PhStat Add-in.

Step 2: Enter the values of the predictor variable in column A and the corresponding values of the response variable in column B.

Step 3: Select the **PHStat** menu. Highlight **Regression**. Highlight **Simple Linear Regression**.

Step 4: With the cursor in the Y variable cell range, highlight the data in column B. With the cursor in the X variable cell range, highlight the data in column A. Select Confidence & Prediction Interval for X and enter the value of x^*. Choose a level of confidence. Click OK.

12.3 One-way Analysis of Variance

Preparing for This Section Before getting started, review the following:

- ✓ Completely randomized design (Section 1.5, pp. 37–38)
- ✓ Nature of hypothesis testing (Section 9.1, pp. 518–525)
- ✓ Comparing two population means (Section 10.2, pp. 607–614)
- ✓ Normal probability plots (Section 7.4, pp. 415–420)
- ✓ *F*-distribution (Section 10.4, pp. 631–635)
- ✓ Confidence intervals about μ, σ unknown (Section 8.2, pp. 480–482)
- ✓ Boxplots (Section 3.5, pp. 169–171)

Objectives ① Verify the requirements to perform a one-way ANOVA
② Conduct a one-way ANOVA hypothesis test

Note to Instructor
It is recommended that hand computations be de-emphasized in this section. Concentrate on the concepts, and let technology do the number crunching.

In Section 10.2, we compared two population means. Just as we extended the concept of comparing two population proportions (Section 10.3) to comparing three or more population proportions ("Tests for Homogeneity of Proportions," Section 11.3), we now extend the concept of comparing two population means to comparing three or more population means. The procedure for doing this is called *Analysis of Variance* or *ANOVA* for short.

Definition   **Analysis of Variance (ANOVA)** is an inferential method that is used to test the equality of three or more population means.

In Your Own Words

In ANOVA, the null hypothesis is always that the means of the different populations are equal. The alternative hypothesis is always that the mean of at least one population is different from the others.

For example, a family doctor might claim that the mean HDL (so-called good) levels of cholesterol of males in the age groups 20–29 years old, 40–49 years old, and 60–69 years old are different. To test this claim, we assume that the mean HDL cholesterol of each age group is the same. If we call the 20–29-year-olds Population 1, 40–49-year-olds Population 2, and 60–69-year-olds Population 3, then our null hypothesis would be

$$H_0: \mu_1 = \mu_2 = \mu_3$$

versus the alternative hypothesis,

H_1: At least one of the population means is different from the others

As another example, a medical researcher might want to compare the effect different levels of an experimental drug have on hair growth. The researcher might randomly divide a group of subjects into three different treatment groups. Group 1 might receive a placebo once a day, Group 2 might receive 50 mg of the experimental drug once a day, and Group 3 might receive 100 mg of the experimental drug once a day. The researcher would then compare the mean numbers of new hair follicles for each of the three treatment groups. The three different treatment groups correspond to three different populations.

It is tempting to test the null hypothesis $H_0: \mu_1 = \mu_2 = \mu_3$ by comparing the population means two at a time using the techniques introduced in Section 10.2. If we proceeded this way, we would need to test three different hypotheses:

$$H_0: \mu_1 = \mu_2 \quad \text{and} \quad H_0: \mu_1 = \mu_3 \quad \text{and} \quad H_0: \mu_2 = \mu_3$$

Caution

Do not test H_o: $\mu_1 = \mu_2 = \mu_3$ by conducting three separate hypothesis tests, because the probability of making a Type I error will be much higher than α.

Caution

It is vital that individuals be randomly assigned to treatments.

Each of these hypotheses would have a probability of Type I error (rejecting the null when the null is true) of α. If we used an $\alpha = 0.05$ level of significance, then each hypothesis would have a 95% probability of rejecting the null hypothesis when the alternative hypothesis is true. The probability that all three hypotheses will correctly reject the null is $0.95^3 = 0.86$ (because each hypothesis is tested independently of the others). There is a $1 - 0.95^3 = 1 - 0.86 = 0.14$, or 14%, probability that at least one of the hypotheses will lead to an incorrect rejection of H_o. Obviously, a 14% probability of a Type I error is much higher than the desired 5% probability. As the number of populations that are to be compared increases, the probability of making a Type I error using multiple t-tests for a given value of α also increases.

To address this problem, Sir Ronald A. Fisher (1890–1962) introduced the method of analysis of variance. Although it seems strange to name a procedure that is used to compare *means* analysis of *variance*, the justification for the name will become clear as we see the procedure.

The procedure used in this section is called one-way analysis of variance because there is only one factor that distinguishes the various populations in the study. For example, in comparing the mean HDL cholesterol levels of males, the only factor that distinguishes the three groups is age. In comparing the effectiveness of the hair growth drug, the only factor that distinguishes the three groups is the amount of the experimental drug received (none, 50 mg, or 100 mg).

In performing one-way analysis of variance, care must be taken so that the subjects are similar in all characteristics except the treatment. Fisher stated that this is easiest to accomplish through randomization, which neutralizes the effect of the uncontrolled variables. In the hair growth example, the subjects should be similar in terms of eating habits, age, and so on simply by randomly assigning the subjects to the three groups.

In order to perform a one-way ANOVA test, certain requirements must be satisfied:

> **Requirements of a One-Way ANOVA Test**
>
> 1. There are k simple random samples from k populations.
> 2. The k samples are independent of each other; that is, the subjects in one group cannot be related in any way to subjects in a second group.
> 3. The populations are normally distributed.
> 4. The populations have the same variance; that is, each treatment group has population variance σ^2.

For example, in the HDL cholesterol example, there are $k = 3$ populations. If the requirements are satisfied, the ANOVA procedure tests the hypothesis

$$H_o: \mu_1 = \mu_2 = \mu_3$$

versus

H_1: At least one of the population means differs from the others

The methods of one-way ANOVA are **robust**, so that departures from the requirement of normality will not significantly affect the results of the procedure. In addition, the requirement of equal population variances does not need to be strictly adhered to, especially if the sample size for each

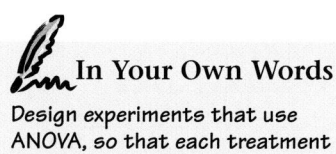

In Your Own Words

Design experiments that use ANOVA, so that each treatment group is the same size.

treatment group is the same. Therefore, it is worthwhile to design an experiment in which the samples from the populations are roughly equal in size. We can verify the requirement of normality by constructing normal probability plots. The requirement of equal population variances is more difficult to verify. However, a general rule of thumb is as follows:

Verifying the Requirement of Equal Population Variances

The one-way ANOVA procedures may be used, provided that the largest sample standard deviation is no more than two times larger than the smallest sample standard deviation.

▶ EXAMPLE 1   **Testing the Requirements of a One-Way ANOVA**

Problem: A family doctor claims that the mean HDL cholesterol levels of males in the age groups 20–29 years old, 40–49 years old, and 60–69 years old are equal. He obtains a simple random sample of 12 individuals from each age group and determines their HDL cholesterol levels. The results are presented in Table 4.

TABLE 4			
Subject Number	20–29 Years Old	40–49 Years Old	60–69 Years Old
1	54	61	44
2	43	41	65
3	38	44	62
4	30	47	53
5	61	33	51
6	53	29	49
7	35	59	49
8	34	35	42
9	39	34	35
10	46	74	44
11	50	50	37
12	35	65	38

Verify that the requirements to perform a one-way ANOVA are satisfied.

Approach: We must verify the requirements listed on page 730.

Solution:

1. As was stated in the problem, the data were collected using simple random sampling.
2. None of the subjects selected are related in any way, so the samples are independent.
3. Figure 12(a) on page 732 contains a normal probability plot for the 20–29-year-olds, Figure 12(b) contains a normal probability plot for the 40–49-year-olds, and Figure 12(c) contains a normal probability plot for the 60–69-year-olds.

    All of the normal probability plots are roughly linear. We conclude that the sample data come from populations that are normally distributed.

Figure 12

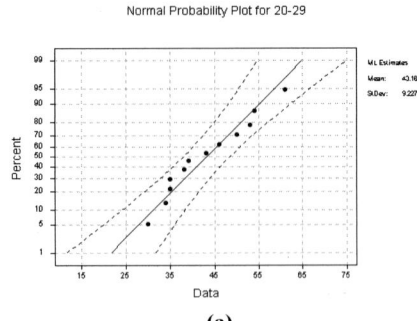

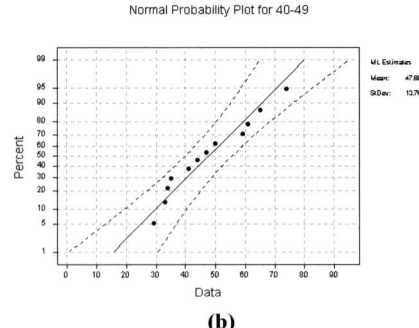

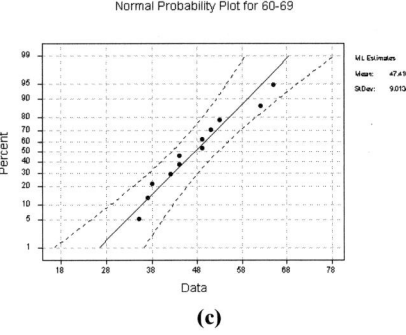

(a)   (b)   (c)

4. The sample standard deviations for each population are computed using Minitab and presented in Figure 13.

Figure 13

Descriptive Statistics

Variable	N	Mean	Median	TrMean	StDev	SEMean
20-29	12	43.17	41.00	42.70	9.64	2.78
40-49	12	47.67	45.50	46.90	14.38	4.15
60-69	12	47.42	46.50	46.90	9.41	2.72

Variable	Minimum	Maximum	Q1	Q3
20-29	30.00	61.00	35.00	52.25
40-49	29.00	74.00	34.25	60.50
60-69	35.00	65.00	39.00	52.50

The largest standard deviation of 14.38 is from the 40–49-year-olds, and the smallest standard deviation of 9.41 is from the 60–69-year-olds. Because the largest standard deviation is not more than two times larger than the smallest standard deviation ($2 \cdot 9.41 = 18.82 > 14.38$), the requirement of equal population variances is satisfied.

Because all four requirements are satisfied, we can perform a one-way ANOVA. ◀◀

 Now Work Problems 1(a) and 1(b).

Because the computations in performing any analysis of variance test are tedious, virtually all researchers use statistical software to conduct the test. When using software, it is easiest to use the *P*-value approach. The nice thing about *P*-values is that the decision rule is always the same, regardless of the type of hypothesis being tested.

Decision Rule in the One-Way ANOVA Test

If the *P*-value is less than or equal to the level of significance, α, reject the null hypothesis. If the *P*-value is greater than the level of significance, α, do not reject the null hypothesis.

▶ **EXAMPLE 2**   **Using Technology to Perform One-Way ANOVA Tests**

Problem: Test the claim made by the doctor in Example 1 at the $\alpha = 0.05$ level of significance.

Approach: We will use Minitab, Excel, and a TI-83 Plus graphing calculator to test the hypothesis. If the *P*-value is less than the level of significance, we reject the null hypothesis.

Solution: The claim is that the mean HDL cholesterol is not the same for each population. Let the 20–29-year-olds be Population 1, the 40–49-year-olds be Population 2, and the 60–69-year-olds be Population 3. The null hypothesis is

$$H_o: \mu_1 = \mu_2 = \mu_3$$

versus the alternative hypothesis,

H_1: At least one of the population means is different from the others

Figure 14(a) shows the output from Minitab, Figure 14(b) shows the output from Excel, and Figure 14(c) shows the output from a TI-83 Plus graphing calculator.

Figure 14

One-way Analysis of Variance

```
Analysis of Variance
Source      DF        SS        MS        F        P
Factor       2       154        77     0.59    0.558
Error       33      4271       129
Total       35      4425
                                 Individual 95% CIs For Mean
                                 Based on Pooled StDev
Level        N      Mean     StDev  --------+---------+---------+--------
20-29       12     43.17      9.64  (------------*-------------)
40-49       12     47.67     14.38              (------------*-------------)
60-69       12     47.42      9.41              (------------*-------------)
                                     --------+---------+---------+--------
Pooled St Dev =    11.38                    40.0      45.0      50.0
```

(a) Minitab Output

Anova: Single Factor

SUMMARY

Groups	Count	Sum	Average	Variance
20–29	12	518	43.16667	92.87879
40–49	12	572	47.66667	206.7879
60–69	12	569	47.41667	88.62879

ANOVA

Source of Variation	SS	df	MS	F	P-value	F crit
Between Groups	153.5	2	76.75	0.592976	0.558461	3.284924
Within Groups	4271.25	33	129.4318			
Total	4424.75	35				

(b) Excel Output

P-value ───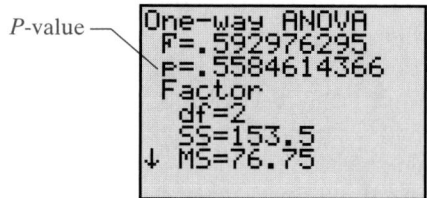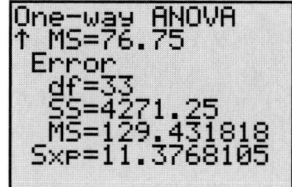

(c) TI-83 Output

The *P*-value equals 0.558, which is greater than the level of significance, 0.05, so we do not reject the null hypothesis. There is not sufficient evidence to support the claim that the mean HDL cholesterol among the three populations is different. ◀◀

Whenever performing analysis of variance, it's always a good idea to present visual evidence that supports the conclusions of the test. Side-by-side boxplots are a great way to help "see" the results of the ANOVA procedure. Figure 15 shows the side-by-side boxplots of the data presented in Table 4.

Figure 15

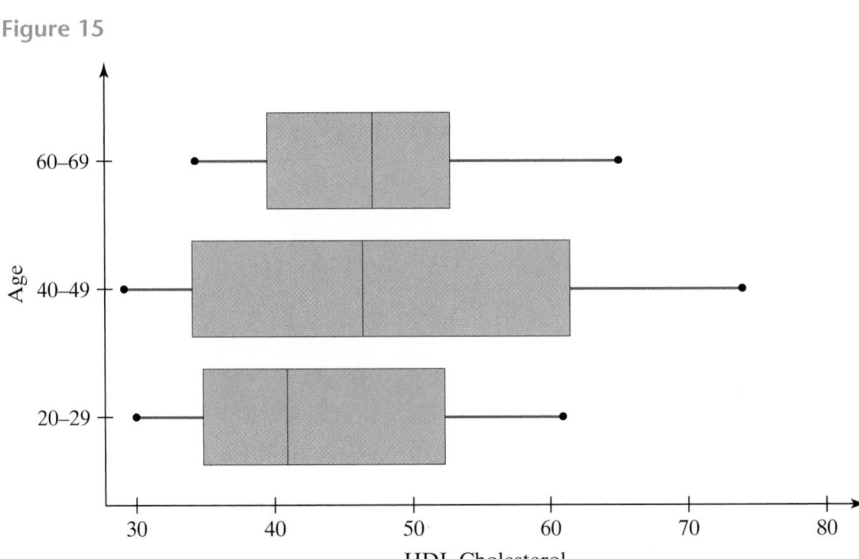

NW *Now Work Problems 1(c) and 1(d).*

The boxplots support the ANOVA results from Example 2.

A Conceptual Understanding of One-Way ANOVA

We will use the data in Table 4 to illustrate the idea behind the ANOVA procedure. Remember, in testing any hypothesis, the null hypothesis is assumed to be true. Therefore, in testing the claim made in Example 1, we assume that $\mu_1 = \mu_2 = \mu_3 = \mu$. That is, we assume that each of the three samples come from the same normal population, whose mean is μ and whose variance is σ^2. (Remember, the variance must be the same for each population.) If the null hypothesis is true, then the sample variance computed from the entire set of data should be close to the "average" of the sample variances from each individual population. In other words, combine the three groups (20–29-year-olds, 40–49-year-olds, and 60–69-year-olds) into one big data set. Compute the sample variance of this data set. We call this the **between-samples estimate of σ^2 (also called the variation due to treatment)**. If the null hypothesis is true, then this is a good estimator of σ^2, the variance of each population.

As a second approach to estimating σ^2, compute the sample variance for each population (20–29-year-olds, 40–49-year-olds, and 60–69-year-olds), and then find a weighted average of the three sample variances. We call this the **within-samples estimate of σ^2 (also called the variation due to error)**. The within-samples estimate of σ^2 will be an unbiased estimator of σ^2 whether the null hypothesis is true or not.

If the null hypothesis is true, then the between-samples estimate of σ^2 should be close to the within-samples estimate of σ^2. If the between-samples estimate is substantially larger than the within-samples estimate of σ^2, then we have evidence against the null hypothesis. The only way the between-samples estimate of σ^2 is a good estimate of σ^2 is if the null hypothesis is true. Think long and hard about this statement. Remember, the between-samples estimate of σ^2 was computed by combining all three data sets into one (because we assumed that $\mu_1 = \mu_2 = \mu_3$, so that they came from the same population). If one of the means from the three populations does not equal the others, then the between-samples estimate of σ^2 will overestimate the true value of σ^2.

We compute the F test statistic by forming a ratio of the between-samples estimate and the within-samples estimate of σ^2.

Theorem

Note to Instructor
If you did not cover Section 10.4, then it might be helpful to introduce the F-distribution by covering pages 631–635.

Test Statistic for One-Way ANOVA

$$F = \frac{\text{Between estimate of } \sigma^2}{\text{Within estimate of } \sigma^2}$$

We now present the steps to be used in the computation of the F test statistic.

Computing the F Test Statistic

Step 1: Compute the sample mean of the combined data set by adding up all the observations and dividing by the number of observations. Call this value $\bar{x}$.

Step 2: Find the sample mean for each population (or treatment). Let $\bar{x}_1$ represent the sample mean of Population 1, $\bar{x}_2$ represent the sample mean of Population 2, and so on.

Step 3: Find the sample variance for each population (or treatment). Let s_1^2 represent the sample variance for Population 1, s_2^2 represent the sample variance for Population 2, and so on.

Step 4: The between-samples estimate, denoted MSB,* of σ^2 is given by

$$\text{MSB} = \frac{n_1(\bar{x}_1 - \bar{x})^2 + n_2(\bar{x}_2 - \bar{x})^2 + \ldots + n_k(\bar{x}_k - \bar{x})^2}{k - 1}$$

n_1 is the sample size of Population 1,
n_2 is the sample size of Population 2, and so on,
and k is the number of populations (or treatment levels).

Step 5: The within-samples estimate, denoted MSW,** of σ^2 is given by

$$\text{MSW} = \frac{(n_1 - 1)s_1^2 + (n_2 - 1)s_2^2 + \ldots + (n_k - 1)s_k^2}{n - k}$$

Step 6: Compute the F test statistic:

$$F = \frac{\text{Between estimate of } \sigma^2}{\text{Within estimate of } \sigma^2} = \frac{\text{MSB}}{\text{MSW}}$$

*The between-samples estimate of the population variance is also referred to as the mean square due to treatment, denoted MST.

**The within-samples estimate of the population variance is also referred to as the mean square error, denoted MSE.

▶ **EXAMPLE 3** **Computing the *F* Test Statistic**

Problem: Compute the *F* test statistic for the data presented in Example 1.

Approach: We follow Steps 1–6 just presented.

Solution:

Step 1: Compute the mean of the entire data set:

$$\bar{x} = \frac{54 + 43 + 38 + \cdots + 37 + 38}{36} = 46.0833$$

Step 2: Find the sample mean of each population. Call the 20–29-year-olds Population 1, the 40–49-year-olds Population 2, and the 60–69-year-olds Population 3. Then

$$\bar{x}_1 = \frac{54 + 43 + \cdots + 50 + 35}{12} = 43.1667$$

$$\bar{x}_2 = \frac{61 + 41 + \cdots + 50 + 65}{12} = 47.6667$$

$$\bar{x}_3 = \frac{44 + 65 + \cdots + 37 + 38}{12} = 47.4167$$

Step 3: Find the sample variance for each population.

$$s_1^2 = \frac{(54 - 43.1667)^2 + (43 - 43.1667)^2 + \cdots + (35 - 43.1667)^2}{12 - 1} = 92.87878788$$

$$s_2^2 = \frac{(61 - 47.6667)^2 + (41 - 47.6667)^2 + \cdots + (65 - 47.6667)^2}{12 - 1} = 206.7878788$$

$$s_3^2 = \frac{(44 - 47.4167)^2 + (65 - 47.4167)^2 + \cdots + (38 - 47.4167)^2}{12 - 1} = 88.62878788$$

Step 4: Compute MSB:

$$\text{MSB} = \frac{12(43.1667 - 46.0833)^2 + 12(47.6667 - 46.0833)^2 + 12(47.4167 - 46.0833)^2}{3 - 1} = \frac{153.5}{2} = 76.75$$

Step 5: Compute MSW:

$$\text{MSW} = \frac{(12 - 1)92.87878788 + (12 - 1)206.7878788 + (12 - 1)88.62878788}{36 - 3} = \frac{4271.25}{33} = 129.4318$$

Step 6: Compute the *F* test statistic.

$$F = \frac{\text{Between estimate of } \sigma^2}{\text{Within estimate of } \sigma^2} = \frac{\text{MSB}}{\text{MSW}} = \frac{76.75}{129.4318} = 0.59$$

This is the same result provided by the statistical software and graphing calculator in Example 2. ◀◀

NW *Now Work Problem 1(e).*

Looking back at the formula for the between-samples estimate of σ^2, we notice that if the null hypothesis is true, then the overall mean, $\bar{x}$, should be close to the means computed from each population, $\bar{x}_1, \bar{x}_2$, and so on.

The value of MSB will consequently be relatively small, and the F test statistic will in turn be small. However, if at least one of the population means is substantially different from the overall mean, $\overline{x}$, then MSB will be relatively large, making the F test statistic large. A large F test statistic is evidence against the null hypothesis of equal population means.

The results of the computations that lead to the F test statistic are presented in an **ANOVA table**, the form of which is shown in Figure 16.

Figure 16

Source of Variation	Sum of Squares	Degrees of Freedom	Mean Squares	F-Test Statistic
Between	153.5	$k - 1 = 3 - 1 = 2$	76.75	0.59
Within	4271.25	$n - k = 36 - 3 = 33$	129.4318	
Total	4424.75	$n - 1 = 36 - 1 = 35$		

Notice that the "sum of squares between" is the numerator of the computation for the between-samples estimate of σ^2. The "sum of squares within" is the numerator of the computation for the within-samples estimate of σ^2. Each entry in the mean square column is the sum of squares divided by the corresponding degrees of freedom. In addition,

Sum of squares total = Sum of squares between + Sum of squares within

This result is a consequence of the requirement of independence.

If we were conducting this ANOVA test by hand, we would compare the F test statistic with a critical F value. The critical F value is the F value whose area in the right tail is α with $k - 1$ degrees of freedom in the numerator and $n - k$ degrees of freedom in the denominator. The critical F value for the claim made in Example 1 at the $\alpha = 0.05$ level of significance is $F_{2,33} = 3.28$. Because the F test statistic, 0.59, is not greater than the critical F, do not reject the null hypothesis. See Figure 17.

Suppose the null hypothesis of equal population means is rejected. This conclusion tells us that at least one of the population means is different from the others, but we don't know which one. We can determine which population mean is different by constructing confidence intervals about each sample mean. The confidence interval that does not overlap with the others is said to have a significantly different population mean. The intervals are constructed in the usual fashion:

Point estimate $\pm$ Margin of error

We use within-samples estimate of σ^2 (often called the **pooled estimate of** $\boldsymbol{\sigma^2}$) as the estimate of the sample variance. The pooled estimate, denoted s_p^2, is a better estimate than any of the estimates within a population, because ANOVA assumes that each population has a common variance, σ^2. Therefore, the pooled estimate represents an average of the sample variances from each population. The pooled estimate of σ for the data presented in Example 1 is $s_p = \sqrt{129.4318182} = 11.3768$.

Figure 17

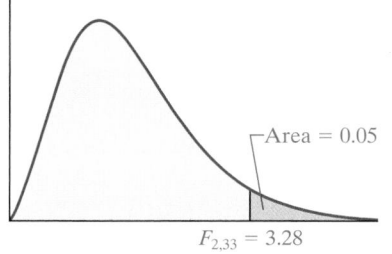

Area = 0.05

$F_{2,33} = 3.28$

In Your Own Words

If we reject the null hypothesis when doing ANOVA, then we are rejecting the assumption that the population means are all equal. However, we don't know which means differ. We use confidence intervals to make this determination.

Theorem

Confidence Interval about any Population Mean, μ_i

For any population i, the confidence interval for μ_i is given by

Lower Bound: $\overline{x}_i - t_{\alpha/2} \cdot \dfrac{s_p}{\sqrt{n_i}}$ Upper Bound: $\overline{x}_i + t_{\alpha/2} \cdot \dfrac{s_p}{\sqrt{n_i}}$

where $t_{\alpha/2}$ is the critical t value with $n - k$ degrees of freedom.

For example, a 95% confidence interval about μ_1, the population mean HDL cholesterol level for 20–29-year-olds, is

$$\text{Lower Bound: } \bar{x}_i - t_{\alpha/2} \cdot \frac{s_p}{\sqrt{n_i}} = 43.1667 - 2.035 \cdot \frac{11.3768}{\sqrt{12}} = 36.48$$

$$\text{Upper Bound: } \bar{x}_i + t_{\alpha/2} \cdot \frac{s_p}{\sqrt{n_i}} = 43.1667 + 2.035 \cdot \frac{11.3768}{\sqrt{12}} = 49.85$$

We are 95% confident that the mean HDL cholesterol for 20–29-year-old males is somewhere between 36.48 and 49.85.

NW *Now Work Problems 1(f) and 1(g).*

Notice that Minitab provides the pooled estimate for σ, along with confidence intervals for each population. See Figure 14(a).

12.3 Assess Your Understanding

Concepts and Vocabulary

1. What is the between-samples estimate of σ^2? What is the within-samples estimate of σ^2?

2. Why does a large value of $F = \dfrac{\text{Between estimate of } \sigma^2}{\text{Within estimate of } \sigma^2}$ provide evidence against the null hypothesis $H_0: \mu_1 = \mu_2 = \ldots = \mu_k$?

3. What are the requirements to perform a one-way ANOVA? Is the test robust?

Exercises

• Skill Building

1. Corn Production The data to the right represent the number of **NW** corn plants in randomly sampled rows (a 17-foot-by-5-inch strip) for various types of plot. An agricultural researcher wants to know whether the mean number of plants for each plot type are equal.

(a) Write the null and alternative hypotheses.
(b) State the requirements that must be satisfied to use the one-way ANOVA procedure.
(c) Use the following Minitab output to test the researcher's claim at the $\alpha = 0.05$ level of significance. Reject H_0

Plot Type	Number of Plants
Sludge Plot	25 27 33 30 28 27
Spring Disk	32 30 33 35 34 34
No Till	30 26 29 32 25 29
Spring Chisele	30 32 26 28 31 29
Great Lakes Bt	28 32 27 30 29 27

Source: Andrew Dieter and Brad Schmidgall, Joliet Junior College

One-way Analysis of Variance

```
Analysis of Variance
Source      DF        SS        MS       F       P
Factor       4     90.20     22.55    4.30   0.009
Error       25    131.00      5.24
Total       29    221.20

                           Individual 95% CIs For Mean
                           Based on Pooled StDev
Level        N      Mean    StDev  -----+---------+---------+---------+-
Sludge P     6    28.333    2.805  (------*-------)
Spring D     6    33.000    1.789                     (-------*-------)
No Till      6    28.500    2.588  (-------*-------)
Spring C     6    29.333    2.160     (------*-------)
Great La     6    28.833    1.941  (------*-------)
                                   -----+---------+---------+---------+-
Pooled StDev =     2.289           27.5      30.0      32.5      35.0
```

(d) On the right are side-by-side boxplots of each type of plot. Do these boxplots support the analytic results?

(e) Verify that the F test statistic is 4.30.

(f) Based upon the confidence intervals provided by Minitab, which type of plot results in a significantly different mean number of plants?

(g) Which plot type would you recommend? Why?
Spring Disk

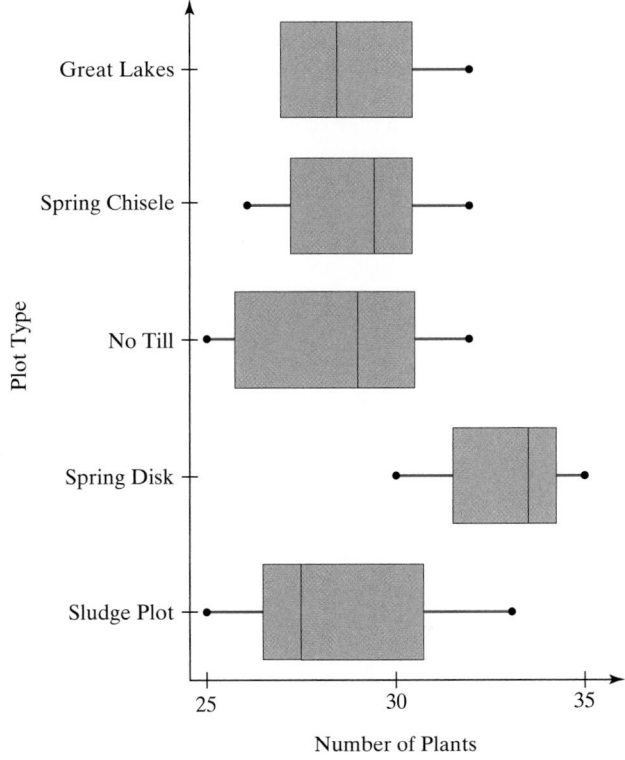

2. **Soybean Yield** The data to the right represent the number of pods on a random sample of soybean plants for various plot types. An agricultural researcher wants to test the claim that the mean number of pods for each plot type is equal.

(a) Write the null and alternative hypotheses.

(b) State the requirements that must be satisfied to use the one-way ANOVA procedure.

(c) Use the following Minitab output to test the researcher's claim at the $\alpha = 0.05$ level of significance: *Reject H_o*

Plot Type	Pods
Liberty	32 31 36 35 41 34 39 37 38
Fall Plowed	29 31 33 22 19 30 36 30
No Till	34 30 31 27 40 33 37 42 39
Chisel Plowed	34 37 24 23 32 33 27 34 30
Round-up Ready	27 34 36 32 35 29 35

Source: Andrew Dieter and Brad Schmidgall, Joliet Junior College

One-way Analysis of Variance

```
Analysis of Variance
Source      DF        SS        MS        F        P
Factor       4      300.4      75.1     3.64    0.013
Error       37      763.9      20.6
Total       41     1064.3
                                 Individual 95% CIs For Mean
                                 Based on Pooled StDev
Level        N      Mean      StDev  ------+---------+---------+--------
Liberty      9     35.889     3.257                     (-------*------)
Fall Plo     8     28.750     5.600   (-------*-------)
No Till      9     34.778     5.044                 (-------*-------)
Chisele      9     30.444     4.825        (-------*-------)
Round-up     7     32.571     3.409            (-------*--------)
                                       ------+---------+---------+--------
Pooled StDev =    4.544                28.0      32.0      36.0
```

(d) On the right are side-by-side boxplots of each type of plot. Do these boxplots support the analytic results?
(e) Verify that the F test statistic is 3.64.
(f) Based upon the confidence intervals provided by Minitab, which type of plot results in a significantly different mean number of plants?
(g) Which type of plot would you recommend? Why?
Liberty or No Till

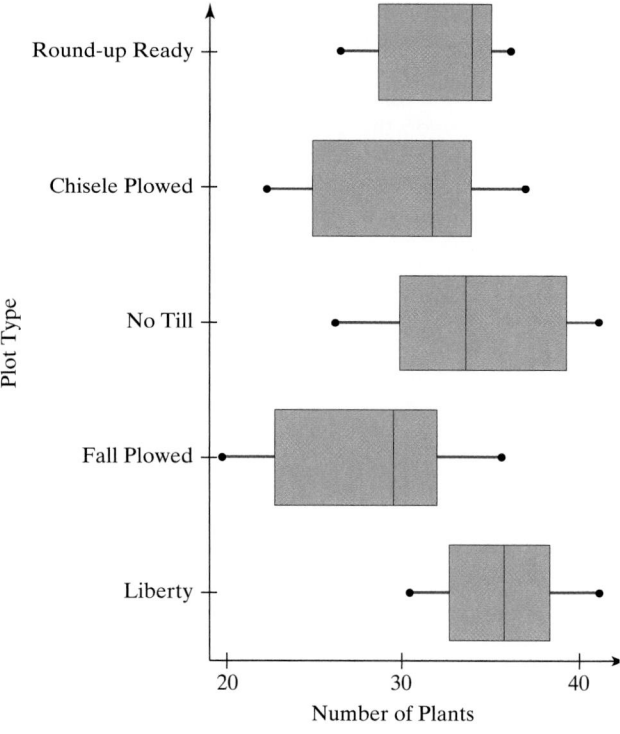

3. **Births by Day of Week** An obstetrician knew that there were more live births during the week than on weekends. She wanted to determine whether the mean number of births was the same for each of the five days of the week. She randomly selected eight dates for each of the five days of the week and obtained the data on the right.

(a) Write the null and alternative hypotheses.
(b) State the requirements that must be satisfied to use the one-way ANOVA procedure.
(c) Use the following Minitab output to test the researcher's claim at the $\alpha = 0.01$ level of significance:

Monday	Tuesday	Wednesday	Thursday	Friday
10,456	11,621	11,084	11,171	11,545
10,023	11,944	11,570	11,745	12,321
10,691	11,045	11,346	12,023	11,749
10,283	12,927	11,875	12,433	12,192
10,265	12,577	12,193	12,132	12,422
11,189	11,753	11,593	11,903	11,627
11,198	12,509	11,216	11,233	11,624
11,465	13,521	11,818	12,543	12,543

Source: National Center for Health Statistics

One-way ANOVA

```
Analysis of Variance
Source      DF        SS       MS       F       P
Factor       4  11507633  2876908    9.80   0.000
Error       35  10270781   293451
Total       39  21778414

                               Individual 95% CIs For Mean
                               Based on Pooled StDev
Level        N      Mean    StDev  ---+---------+---------+---------+---
Monday       8     10696      528  (-----*----)
Tuesday      8     12237      796                      (-----*----)
Wednesday    8     11587      369             (-----*-----)
Thursday     8     11898      502                (-----*----)
Friday       8     12003      408                  (----*-----)
                                   ---+---------+---------+---------+---
Pooled StDev =       542            10500     11200     11900     12600
```

(d) On the right are side-by-side boxplots of each type of plot. Do these boxplots support the analytic results?

(e) Verify that the F test statistic is 9.80.

(f) Based upon the confidence intervals provided by Minitab, which day of the week exhibits a significantly different mean number of births? Monday

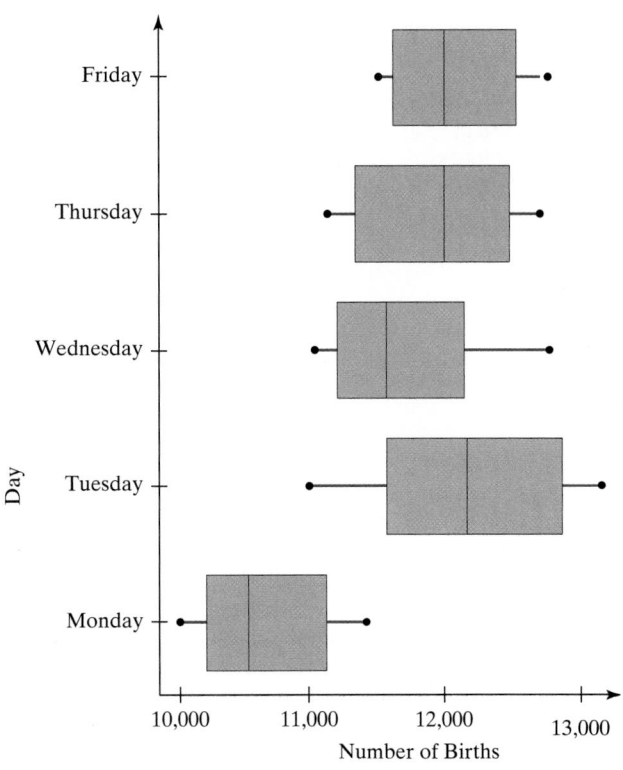

4. **Births by Season** An obstetrician wanted to know whether the mean number of births differed for the periods January–March, April–June, July–September, and October–December. She randomly selected 10 days within each time frame and obtained the results shown in the following table:

January–March	April–June	July–September	October–December
10,456	10,799	11,465	11,261
11,574	11,743	12,475	11,406
12,321	11,657	12,454	11,627
11,661	11,608	12,193	8,706
8,521	10,982	11,244	12,022
11,621	9,184	12,081	11,930
11,321	12,357	11,387	11,054
7,706	12,251	9,055	11,431
10,872	11,916	12,319	12,618
10,837	11,212	12,927	10,824

Source: National Center for Health Statistics

(a) Write the null and alternative hypotheses.

(b) State the requirements that must be satisfied to use the one-way ANOVA procedure.

(c) Use the following Minitab output to test the researcher's claim at the $\alpha = 0.01$ level of significance:

One-way ANOVA

```
Analysis of Variance
Source      DF        SS        MS        F       P
Factor       3   5879690   1959897    1.48   0.235
Error       36  47548216   1320784
Total       39  53427906
                                 Individual 95% CIs For Mean
                                 Based on Pooled StDev
Level        N     Mean    StDev --------+---------+---------+--------
Jan - Mar   10    10689    1467  (----------*---------)
Apr - Jun   10    11371     919            (----------*----------)
Jul - Sep   10    11760    1094                 (----------*----------)
Oct - Dec   10    11288    1044            (---------*----------)
                                 --------+---------+---------+--------
Pooled StDev =    1149            10500     11200     11900
```

(d) On the right are side-by-side boxplots of each type of plot. Do these boxplots support the analytic results?
(e) Verify that the F test statistic is 1.48.
(f) Based upon the confidence intervals provided by Minitab, does any period exhibit a significantly different number of births? No

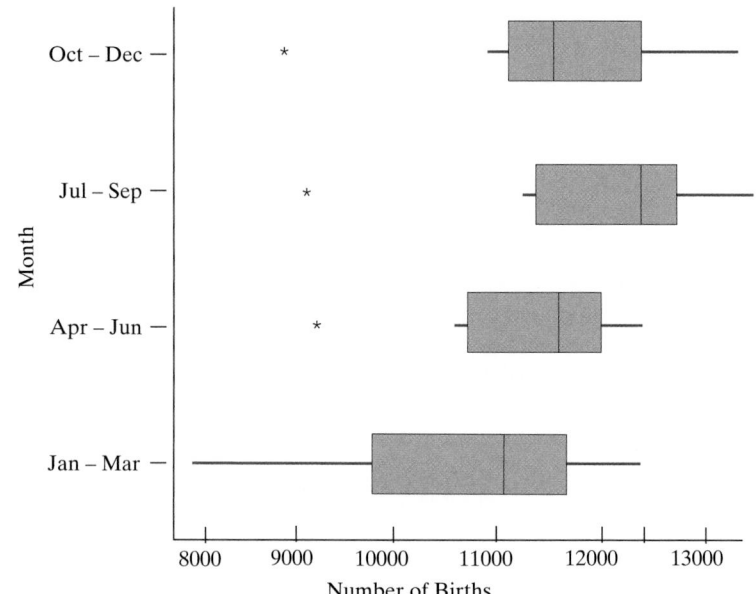

• Applying the Concepts

5. Reaction Time In an on-line psychology experiment sponsored by the University of Mississippi, researchers asked study participants to respond to various stimuli. Participants were randomly assigned to one of three groups. Subjects in Group 1 were in the simple group. They were required to respond as quickly as possible after a stimulus was presented. Subjects in Group 2 were in the go/no-go group. These subjects were required to respond to a particular stimulus while disregarding other stimuli. Finally, subjects in Group 3 were in the choice group. They needed to respond differently, depending on the stimuli presented. Depending upon the type of whistle sound, the subject must press a certain button. The reaction time (in seconds) for each stimulus is presented in the table to the right.

Simple	Go/No Go	Choice
0.43	0.588	0.561
0.498	0.375	0.498
0.480	0.409	0.519
0.376	0.613	0.538
0.402	0.481	0.464
0.329	0.355	0.725

Source: PsychExperiments; The University of Mississippi; http://www.olemiss.edu/psychexps/

The researcher wants to test the claim that the mean reaction times for each stimulus are equal.

(a) State the null and alternative hypotheses.
(b) Verify that the requirements to use the one-way ANOVA procedure are satisfied. Normal probability plots indicate that the sample data come from a normal population.
(c) Test the claim that the mean reaction time to the three stimuli are the same at the $\alpha = 0.05$ level of significance. Do not reject H_o
(d) Draw boxplots of the three stimuli to support the analytic results obtained in part (c).
(e) Construct 95% confidence intervals about each population mean using the pooled estimate of the standard deviation. Do the intervals support the conclusion obtained in part (c)?

6. **Math Scores** Researchers wanted to compare math test scores of students at the end of secondary school from various countries. Eight randomly selected students from Canada, Denmark, and the United States were administered the same exam, with their results presented in the table to the right. The researcher wants to test the claim that the mean test scores from each country are equal.

Canada		Denmark		United States	
578	548	568	563	506	458
548	530	530	535	518	456
521	502	571	561	485	513
555	492	569	513	480	491

Source: Based on data obtained from the International Association for the Evaluation of Educational Achievement

(a) State the null and alternative hypotheses.
(b) Verify that the requirements to use the one-way ANOVA procedure are satisfied. Normal probability plots indicate that the sample data come from a normal population.
(c) Test the claim that the mean test scores for each country are the same at the $\alpha = 0.05$ level of significance. Reject H_o
(d) Draw boxplots of the test scores for each country to support the analytic results obtained in part (c).
(e) Construct 95% confidence intervals about each population mean, using the pooled estimate of the standard deviation. Do the intervals support the conclusion obtained in part (c)?

7. **Crash Data** The Insurance Institute for Highway Safety conducts experiments in which cars are crashed into a fixed barrier at 40 mph. In the Institute's 40-mph offset test, 40 percent of the total width of each vehicle strikes a barrier on the driver's side. The barrier's deformable face is made of aluminum honeycomb, which makes the forces in the test similar to those involved in a frontal offset crash between two vehicles of the same weight, each going just less than 40 mph. Suppose you are in the market to by a new family car. You want to know whether the mean chest compression resulting from this offset crash is the same for large family cars, passenger vans, and midsize utility vehicles. The following data were collected from the Institute's study:

Large Family Cars	Chest Compression (mm)	Passenger Vans	Chest Compression (mm)	Midsize Utility Vehicles	Chest Compression (mm)
Chevrolet Lumina	34	Toyota Sienna	37	Mercedes M Class	42
Ford Taurus	28	Honda Odyssey	29	Toyota 4Runner	28
Buick LeSabre	28	Ford Windstar	27	Mitsubishi Montero	39
Chevrolet Impala	26	Mazda MPV	30	Nissan Xterra	40
Chrysler LHS	22	Chevrolet Astro	34	Ford Explorer	29
Pontiac Grand Prix	34	Nissan Quest	39	Jeep Grand Cherokee	28
Dodge Intrepid	24	Pontiac Trans Sport	23	Nissan Pathfinder	36

Source: Insurance Institute for Highway Safety

The researcher wants to test the claim that the mean chest compression for each class of vehicle are equal.

(a) State the null and alternative hypotheses.
(b) Verify that the requirements to use the one-way ANOVA procedure are satisfied. Normal probability plots indicate that the sample data come from a normal population.
(c) Test the claim that the mean chest compression for each vehicle type is the same at the $\alpha = 0.01$ level of significance. Do not reject H_o
(d) Draw boxplots of the three types of vehicle to support the analytic results obtained in part (c).

(a) $H_o: \mu_L = \mu_P = \mu_M$ vs.
H_1: at least one mean is not equal

(5a) $H_o: \mu_S = \mu_G = \mu_C$ vs. H_1: at least one mean is not equal   (6a) $H_o: \mu_C = \mu_D = \mu_U$ vs. H_1: at least one of the means is not equal

8. **Crash Data** The Insurance Institute for Highway Safety conducts experiments in which cars are crashed into a fixed barrier at 40 mph. In the Institute's 40-mph offset test, 40 percent of the total width of each vehicle strikes a barrier on the driver's side. The barrier's deformable face is made of aluminum honeycomb, which makes the forces in the test similar to those involved in a frontal offset crash between two vehicles of the same weight, each going just less than 40 mph. Suppose you are in the market to buy a new family car. You want to know if the mean head injury resulting from this offset crash is the same for large family cars, passenger vans and midsize utility vehicles. The following data were collected from the Institute's study:

Large Family Cars	Head Injury (hic)	Passenger Vans	Head Injury (hic)	Midsize Utility Vehicles	Head Injury (hic)
Chevrolet Lumina	337	Toyota Sienna	205	Mercedes M Class	308
Ford Taurus	170	Honda Odyssey	166	Toyota 4Runner	463
Buick LeSabre	409	Ford Windstar	183	Mitsubishi Montero	397
Chevrolet Impala	204	Mazda MPV	693	Nissan Xterra	617
Chrysler LHS	332	Chevrolet Astro	152	Ford Explorer	242
Pontiac Grand Prix	627	Nissan Quest	442	Jeep Grand Cherokee	351
Dodge Intrepid	303	Pontiac Trans Sport	311	Nissan Pathfinder	607

Source: Insurance Institute for Highway Safety

The researcher wants to test the claim that the means for head injury for each class of vehicle are equal.

(a) State the null and alternative hypotheses.
(b) Verify that the requirements to use the one-way ANOVA procedure are satisfied. Normal probability plots indicate that the sample data come from a normal population.
(c) Test the claim that the mean head injury for each vehicle type is the same at the $\alpha = 0.01$ level of significance. Do not reject H_o
(d) Draw boxplots of the three vehicle types to support the analytic results obtained in part (c).

(a) H_o: $\mu_L = \mu_P = \mu_M$ vs. H_1: at least one of the means is not equal

9. **Concrete Strength** An engineer wants to know whether the mean strengths of three different concrete mix designs differ significantly. He randomly selects 9 cylinders that measure 6 inches in diameter and 12 inches in height in which mixture 67-0-301 is poured, 9 cylinders of mixture 67-0-400, and 9 cylinders of mixture 67-0-353. After 28 days, he measures the strength (in pounds per square inch) of the cylinders. The results are presented in the following table:

Mixture 67-0-301		Mixture 67-0-400		Mixture 67-0-353	
3960	4090	4070	4120	4150	3820
4040	3830	4330	4640	3820	3750
3780	3940	4620	4190	4010	3990
3890	4080	3730	3850	4150	4320
3990		4890		4190	

(a) State the null and alternative hypotheses.
(b) Explain why we cannot use one-way ANOVA to test these hypotheses.

10. **Analyzing Journal Article Results** Researchers (Brian G. Feagan, et al., "Erythropoietin with Iron Supplementation To Prevent Allogeneic Blood Transfusion in Total Hip Joint Arthroplasty" *Annals of Internal Medicine, 5 Dec 2000, Vol. 133, No. 11*) wanted to determine whether epoetin alfa was effective in increasing the hemoglobin concentration in patients undergoing hip arthroplasty. The researchers screened patients for eligibility by performing a complete medical history and physical of the patients. Once eligible patients were identified, the researchers used a computer-generated schedule to assign the patients to the high-dose epoetin group, low-dose epoetin group, or placebo group. The study was double blind. Based upon an analysis of variance, it was determined that there were significant differences in the increase in hemoglobin concentration in the three groups with a *P*-value less than 0.001. The mean increase in hemoglobin in the high-dose epoetin group was 19.5 g/L, the mean increase in hemoglobin in the low-dose epoetin group was 17.2 g/L, and mean increase in hemoglobin in the placebo group was 1.2 g/L.

(a) Why do you think it was necessary to screen patients for eligibility?

(b) Why was a computer-generated schedule used to assign patients to the various treatment groups?

(c) What does it mean for a study to be double blind? Why do you think the researchers desired a double-blind study?

(d) Interpret the reported *P*-value.

Technology Step-by-Step
ANOVA

TI-83 Plus   *Step 1:* Enter the raw data into L1,L2,L3, and so on, for each population or treatment.

Step 2: Press STAT, highlight TESTS, and select F:ANOVA(.

Step 3: Enter the list names for each population or treatment after ANOVA(. For example, if there are three treatments in L1, L2, and L3, enter

$$ANOVA(L1,L2,L3)$$

Press ENTER.

MINITAB   *Step 1:* Enter the raw data into C1, C2, C3, and so on, for each population or treatment.

Step 2: Select **Stat**, then highlight **ANOVA**, and select **One-way (Unstacked)**.

Step 3: Enter the column names in the cell marked "Responses." Click OK.

Excel   *Step 1:* Enter the raw data in columns A, B, C, and so on, for each population or treatment.

Step 2: Be sure the Data Analysis Tool Pak is activated. This is done by selecting the **Tools** menu and highlighting **Add-Ins . . .** Check the box for the Analysis ToolPak and select OK.

Step 3: With the cursor in the "Input Range:" cell, highlight the data. Click OK.

CHAPTER 12 REVIEW

Summary

The first two sections of this chapter dealt with inferential techniques that can be used on the least-squares regression model $y_i = \beta_0 + \beta_1 x_i + \varepsilon_i$. In this model, we use sample data in order to obtain estimates of an intercept and slope. These estimates are unbiased estimators of the unknown population parameters. The residuals are required to be normally distributed, with mean 0 and constant variance σ^2. The residuals are independent as well. We verify these assumptions through residual plots and a normal probability plot of the residuals. Provided that these requirements are satisfied, we can test hypotheses regarding the slope to determine whether the relation between the predictor and response variable is linear. In addition, we can construct confidence and prediction intervals about a predicted value. We construct confidence intervals about a mean response and prediction intervals about an individual response.

We wrapped up the chapter with a discussion of Analysis of Variance (ANOVA). We use ANOVA in order to compare three or more means for equality. In order to perform an ANOVA test, the data must be obtained using a simple random sample. The samples must be independent. In addition, the populations must be normally distributed and the largest sample standard deviation can be no more than two times the smallest sample standard deviation. The ANOVA procedures are robust, so that minor departures from the assumptions do not seriously affect the results. The ANOVA procedures are based upon Fisher's *F* distribution.

Formulas

Standard error of the estimate

$$s_e = \sqrt{\frac{\Sigma(y_i - \hat{y}_i)^2}{n - 2}} = \sqrt{\frac{\Sigma\text{residuals}^2}{n - 2}}$$

Standard deviation of b_1

$$s_{b_1} = \frac{s_e}{\sqrt{\Sigma(x_i - \overline{x})^2}}$$

Confidence Intervals for the Slope of the Regression Line

A $(1 - \alpha) \cdot 100\%$ confidence interval for the slope of the true regression line, β_1, is given by the following formulas:

Lower Bound: $b_1 - t_{\alpha/2} \cdot \dfrac{s_e}{\sqrt{\Sigma(x_i - \overline{x})^2}} = b_1 - t_{\alpha/2} \cdot s_{b_1}$ Upper Bound: $b_1 + t_{\alpha/2} \cdot \dfrac{s_e}{\sqrt{\Sigma(x_i - \overline{x})^2}} = b_1 + t_{\alpha/2} \cdot s_{b_1}$

Here, $t_{\alpha/2}$ is computed with $n - 2$ degrees of freedom.

Confidence Interval about the Mean Response of y, $\hat{y}$

A $(1 - \alpha) \cdot 100\%$ confidence interval for the mean response of y, $\hat{y}$, is given by the following formulas:

Lower Bound: $\hat{y} - t_{\alpha/2} \cdot s_e \sqrt{\dfrac{1}{n} + \dfrac{(x^* - \overline{x})^2}{\Sigma(x_i - \overline{x})^2}}$ Upper Bound: $\hat{y} + t_{\alpha/2} \cdot s_e \sqrt{\dfrac{1}{n} + \dfrac{(x^* - \overline{x})^2}{\Sigma(x_i - \overline{x})^2}}$

Here, x^* is the given value of the predictor variable and $t_{\alpha/2}$ is the critical value with $n - 2$ degrees of freedom.

Prediction Interval about $\hat{y}$

A $(1 - \alpha) \cdot 100\%$ prediction interval for the individual response of y, $\hat{y}$, is given by

Lower Bound: $\hat{y} - t_{\alpha/2} \cdot s_e \sqrt{1 + \dfrac{1}{n} + \dfrac{(x^* - \overline{x})^2}{\Sigma(x_i - \overline{x})^2}}$ Upper Bound: $\hat{y} + t_{\alpha/2} \cdot s_e \sqrt{1 + \dfrac{1}{n} + \dfrac{(x^* - \overline{x})^2}{\Sigma(x_i - \overline{x})^2}}$

where x^* is the given value of the predictor variable and $t_{\alpha/2}$ is the critical value with $n - 2$ degrees of freedom.

Test Statistic for One-Way ANOVA

$$F = \frac{\text{Between estimate of } \sigma^2}{\text{Within estimate of } \sigma^2} = \frac{\text{MSB}}{\text{MSW}}, \quad \text{where}$$

$$\text{MSB} = \frac{n_1(\overline{x}_1 - \overline{x})^2 + n_2(\overline{x}_2 - \overline{x})^2 + \dots + n_k(\overline{x}_k - \overline{x})^2}{k - 1}$$

and

$$\text{MSW} = \frac{(n_1 - 1)s_1^2 + (n_2 - 1)s_2^2 + \dots + (n_k - 1)s_k^2}{n - k}$$

Confidence Interval about any Population Mean, μ_i

For any population i, the confidence interval for μ_i is given by

Lower Bound: $\overline{x}_i - t_{\alpha/2} \cdot \dfrac{s_p}{\sqrt{n_i}}$ Upper Bound: $\overline{x}_i + t_{\alpha/2} \cdot \dfrac{s_p}{\sqrt{n_i}}$

where $t_{\alpha/2}$ is the critical t value with $n - k$ degrees of freedom and $s_p = \sqrt{\text{MSW}}$.

Vocabulary

Least-squares regression model (p. 709)
Standard error of the estimate (p. 709)
Robust (pp. 713, 730)
Bivariate normal distribution (p. 717)
Confidence interval (p. 724)

Prediction interval (p. 724)
One-way analysis of variance, or
  ANOVA (p. 729)
Between-samples estimate of σ^2
  (p. 734)

Within-samples estimate of σ^2 (p. 734)
Pooled estimate of σ^2 (p. 737)

Objectives

Section	You should be able to ...	Review Exercises
12.1	1 Understand the requirements of the least-squares regression model (p. 707)	10
	2 Compute the standard error of the estimate (p. 709)	1(b), 2(b), 3(b), 4(b), 5(b)
	3 Verify that residuals are normally distributed (p. 711)	1(c), 2(c), 3(c), 4(c), 5(c)
	4 Test the claim that a linear relation exists between two variables (p. 712)	1(e), 2(e), 3(e), 4(e), 5(e)
	5 Compute a confidence interval about the slope of the least-squares regression model (p. 716)	1(f), 2(f), 3(f), 4(f), 5(f)
12.2	1 Construct confidence intervals about a predicted value (p. 723)	1(g), 2(g), 3(g), 4(g)
	2 Construct prediction intervals about a predicted value (p. 725)	1(i), 2(i), 3(i), 4(i)
12.3	1 Verify the requirements to perform a one-way ANOVA (p. 730)	7(b), 8(b), 9(b)
	2 Conduct a one-way ANOVA hypothesis test (p. 732)	7(c), 8(c), 9(c)

Exercises

1. **Engine Displacement versus Fuel Economy** The following data represent the size of a car's engine (in liters) versus its miles per gallon in the city for a random sample of 2001 domestic automobiles:

Car	Engine Displacement (in liters), x	City Miles per Gallon, y	Car	Engine Displacement (in liters), x	City Miles per Gallon, y
Buick Century	3.1	20	Ford Crown Victoria	4.6	17
Buick LeSabre	3.8	19	Ford Focus	2.0	28
Cadillac DeVille	4.6	16	Ford Mustang	3.8	20
Chevrolet Camaro	3.8	19	Oldsmobile Aurora	3.5	19
Chevrolet Cavalier	2.2	24	Pontiac Grand Am	2.4	22
Chevrolet Malibu	3.1	23	Pontiac Sunfire	2.2	23
Chrysler LHS	3.5	18	Saturn Coupe	1.9	28
Dodge Intrepid	2.7	19			

Source: Road and Track Magazine

Using the results from Problems 1, 5, and 15 from the chapter review of Chapter 4, answer the following questions:
   (a) What are the unbiased estimates of β_0 and β_1? What is the mean number of miles per gallon of all cars that have a 3.8-liter engine? $b_0 = 32.12; b_1 = -3.5339; 18.7$
   (b) Compute the standard error, the point estimate for σ. 1.848
   (c) Determine whether the residuals are normally distributed.
   (d) If the residuals are normally distributed, determine s_{b_1}. 0.5528
   (e) If the residuals are normally distributed, test the claim that a linear relation exists between the predictor variable, x, and the response variable, y, at the $\alpha = 0.05$ level of significance. *(e) Reject H_0*
   (f) If the residuals are normally distributed, construct a 95% confidence interval about the slope of the true least-squares regression line. $(-4.7279, -2.3399)$
   (g) Construct a 90% confidence interval about the mean miles per gallon found in part (a). *(g) (17.6, 19.8)*
   (h) Predict the miles per gallon of a car with a 3.8-liter engine. 18.7
   (i) Construct a 90% prediction interval about the miles per gallon found in part (h). (15.3, 22.1)
   (j) Explain why the predicted miles per gallon found in parts (a) and (h) are the same, yet the intervals are different.

2. Temperature versus Cricket Chirps Crickets make a chirping noise by sliding their wings rapidly over each other. Perhaps you have noticed that the number of chirps seems to increase with the temperature. The following table lists the temperature (in Fahrenheit) and the number of chirps per second for the striped ground cricket: (a) $b_0 = -0.309$, $b_1 = 0.2119$; 16.69

Temperature	Chirps per Second	Temperature	Chirps per Second
88.6	20.0	71.6	16.0
93.3	19.8	84.3	18.4
80.6	17.1	75.2	15.5
69.7	14.7	82.0	17.1
69.4	15.4	83.3	16.2
79.6	15.0	82.6	17.2
80.6	16.0	83.5	17.0
76.3	14.4		

Source: The Songs of Insects, Pierce, George W., Cambridge, Mass.: Harvard University Press, 1949, pp. 12–21

Using the results from Problems 2, 6, and 16 from the chapter review of Chapter 4, answer the following questions:

(a) What are the unbiased estimates of β_0 and β_1? What is the mean number of chirps when the temperature is 80.2°F?

(b) Compute the standard error, the point estimate for σ. 0.9715

(c) Determine whether the residuals are normally distributed.

(d) If the residuals are normally distributed, determine s_{b_1}. 0.0387

(e) If the residuals are normally distributed, test the claim that a linear relation exists between the predictor variable, x, and response variable, y, at the $\alpha = 0.05$ level of significance. Reject H_o

(f) If the residuals are normally distributed, construct a 95% confidence interval about the slope of the true least-squares regression line. (0.1283, 0.2955)

(g) Construct a 90% confidence interval about the mean number of chirps found in part (a). (16.24, 17.13).

(h) Predict the number of chirps on a day when the temperature is 80.2°F. 16.69

(i) Construct a 90% prediction interval about the number of chirps found in part (h). (14.91, 18.46)

(j) Explain why the predicted number of chirps found in parts (a) and (h) are the same, yet the intervals are different.

3. Apartments The data above and to the right represent the square footage and rents for apartments in the western suburbs of Chicago.

(3a) $b_0 = -132.6$; $b_1 = 1.1702$; $920.60   (3h) $920.60

Square Footage, x	Rent per Month, y
1161	1265
1000	1050
1034	915
910	1003
934	920
860	890
1056	1035
1000	1190
784	730
962	1005
897	940

Source: apartments.com

(a) What are the unbiased estimates of β_0 and β_1? What is the mean rent of a 900-square-foot apartment in the western suburbs of Chicago?

(b) Compute the standard error, the point estimate for σ. 85.95

(c) Determine whether the residuals are normally distributed.

(d) If the residuals are normally distributed, determine s_{b_1}. 0.2636

(e) If the residuals are normally distributed, test the claim that a linear relation exists between the predictor variable, x, and response variable, y, at the $\alpha = 0.05$ level of significance. Reject H_o

(f) If the residuals are normally distributed, construct a 95% confidence interval about the slope of the true least-squares regression line. (0.5739, 1.7665)

(g) Construct a 90% confidence interval about the mean rent found in part (a). ($864, $977.10)

(h) Predict the rent of a 900-square-foot apartment.

(i) Construct a 90% prediction interval about the rent found in part (h). ($753.20, $1088)

(j) Explain why the predicted rents found in parts (a) and (h) are the same, yet the intervals are different.

4. Boys' Heights The following data, based upon results obtained from the National Center for Health Statistics, represent the height (in inches) of boys between the ages of 2 and 10 years:

Age	Boy Height	Age	Boy Height	Age	Boy Height
2	36.1	5	45.6	8	48.3
2	34.2	5	44.8	8	50.9
2	31.1	5	44.6	9	52.2
3	36.3	6	49.8	9	51.3
3	39.5	7	43.2	10	55.6
4	41.5	7	47.9	10	59.5
4	38.6	8	51.4		

(a) Treating age as the predictor variable, determine the unbiased estimates of β_0 and β_1. What is the mean height of a seven-year-old boy?

(b) Compute the standard error, the point estimate for σ. 2.450

(c) Determine whether the residuals are normally distributed.

(d) If the residuals are normally distributed, determine s_{b_1}. 0.2067

(e) If the residuals are normally distributed, test the claim that a linear relation exists between the predictor variable, age, and response variable, height, at the $\alpha = 0.05$ level of significance. Reject H_o

(f) If the residuals are normally distributed, construct a 95% confidence interval about the slope of the true least-squares regression line. (2.2008, 3.0694)

(g) Construct a 90% confidence interval about the mean height found in part (a). (47.1, 49.2)

(h) Predict the height of a seven-year-old boy. 48.2

(i) Construct a 90% prediction interval about the height found in part (h). (43.8, 52.5)

(j) Explain why the predicted heights found in parts (a) and (h) are the same, yet the intervals are different.

5. Grip Strength A researcher believes that as age increases, the grip strength (in pounds per square inch) of an individual's dominant hand decreases. From a random sample of 17 females, he obtains the following data:

Age	Grip Strength	Age	Grip Strength
15	65	34	45
16	60	37	58
28	58	41	70
61	60	43	73
53	46	49	45
43	66	53	60
16	56	61	56
25	75	68	30
28	46		

Source: Kevin McCarthy, Student at Joliet Junior College

(a) Treating age as the predictor variable, determine the unbiased estimates of β_0 and β_1.

(b) Compute the standard error, the point estimate for σ.

(c) Determine whether the residuals are normally distributed.

(d) If the residuals are normally distributed, determine s_{b_1}.

(e) If the residuals are normally distributed, test the claim that a linear relation exists between the predictor variable, age, and response variable, grip strength, at the $\alpha = 0.05$ level of significance.

(f) Based on your answers to (d) and (e), what would be a good guess as to the grip strength of a randomly selected 42-year-old female?

6. Depreciation The following data represent the price of a random sample of used Chevy Camaros by age:

Age (in years)	Price (in dollars)	Age (in years)	Price (in dollars)
2	15,900	1	20,365
5	10,988	2	16,463
2	16,980	6	10,824
5	9,995	1	19,995
4	11,995	1	18,650
5	10,995	4	10,488

Source: www.onlineauto.com

(a) Determine the least-squares regression equation, treating age as the predictor variable.

(b) A normal probability plot of the residuals indicates that the residuals are approximately normally distributed. Test the claim that there is a linear relation between age and price at the $\alpha = 0.05$ level of significance. Reject H_o

(c) Plot the residuals against the predictor variable, time.

(d) Does a linear model seem appropriate, based upon the scatter diagram and residual plot? (*Hint:* See Section 4.3.) What is the moral?

(4a) $b_0 = 29.705$; $b_1 = 2.6351$; 48.2 inches   (5a) $b_0 = 67.388$; $b_1 = -0.2632$ (5b) 11.19   (5d) 0.1680
(5e) Do not reject H_o (5f) 57   (6a) Price $= 20,976.2 - 2054.6$ Age   (6d) No

7. **Soil Testing** A researcher took water samples in a forest with a stream running through it. The samples were collected over the course of a year. Each sample was analyzed for the concentration of dissolved organic carbon (mg/l) in it, with the results presented in the following table:

Organic				Mineral					Surface				
22.74	14.9	17.9	11.4	8.5	5.5	3.02	7.31	4.85	10.83	11.94	15.76	15.03	15.77
29.8	14.86	18.3	5.3	3.91	4.71	7.45	16.92	11.97	8.74	12.4	10.96	14.53	6.4
27.1	15.91	5.2	15.72	9.29	7.66	11.33	4.6	7.85	9.2	10.3	19.78	12.04	14.19
16.51	15.35	11.9	20.46	21	11.72	7.11	8.5	9.11	8.12	10.48	20.56	16.82	13.89
6.51	9.72	14	16.87	10.89	11.8	17.99	4.8	8.79	7.6	12.88	17.93	10.7	8.69
8.81	19.8	7.4	15.42	10.3	8.05	21.4	4.9	9.6	6.3	19.01	14.28	16	10.46
5.29	14.86	17.5	22.49	11.56	10.72	8.37	9.1	12.57	6.68	19.19	13.11	20.7	16.23
20.46	8.09	10.3		7	21.82	7.92	7.9	12.89	7.34	13.14	12.27	13.7	15.43
				3.99	22.62	17.9	11.72	9.81	9.52	12.51	16.47	16.12	
				3.79	10.74								

Source: Lisa Emili, PhD Candidate, Department of Geography and Wetlands Research Centre, University of Waterloo

Each sample was then categorized according to the type of water that was collected. Water was collected from streams (surface water), groundwater was collected from organic soil, and groundwater was collected from mineral soil. The researcher wanted to test the claim that the mean concentration of dissolved organic carbon was the same for each collection area.

(a) State the null and alternative hypotheses.

(b) State the requirements that must be satisfied in order to use the one-way ANOVA procedure.

(c) Use the following Minitab output to test the researcher's claim at the $\alpha = 0.01$ level of significance:

One-way Analysis of Variance

```
Analysis of Variance
Source      DF        SS        MS        F        P
Factor       2     471.4     235.7     9.43    0.000
Error      119    2973.8      25.0
Total      121    3445.1
                                   Individual 95% CIs For Mean
                                   Based on Pooled StDev
Level        N      Mean     StDev  ------+---------+---------+---------+
Organic     31    14.867     6.246                       (------*-------)
Mineral     47    10.027     4.979  (-----*-----)
Surface     44    13.045     3.927                (-----*-----)
                                   ------+---------+---------+---------+
Pooled StDev =     4.999              10.0      12.5      15.0      17.5
```

(d) On the right are side-by-side boxplots of each type of plot. Do the boxplots support the analytic results?

(e) Based upon the confidence intervals provided by Minitab, does the collection area result in a significantly different mean concentration?

(f) Verify that the F test statistic is 9.43.

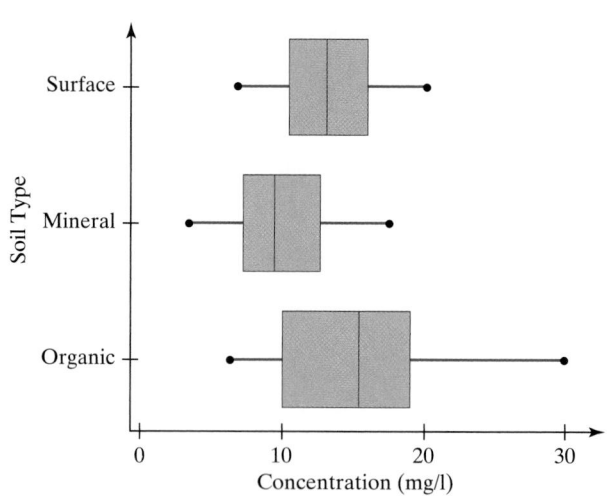

8. **Crash Data** The Insurance Institute for Highway Safety conducts experiments in which cars are crashed into a fixed barrier at 40 mph. In the Institute's 40-mph offset test, 40 percent of the total width of each vehicle strikes a barrier on the driver's side. The barrier's deformable face is made of aluminum honeycomb, which makes the forces in the test similar to those involved in a frontal offset crash between two vehicles of the same weight, each going just less than 40 mph. Suppose you are in the market to buy a new family car. You want to know if the mean femur force (kN) on the left leg resulting from this offset crash is the same for large family cars, passenger vans and midsize utility vehicles. The following data were collected from the Institute's study:

Large Family Cars	Femur Force (kN)	Passenger Vans	Femur Force (kN)	Midsize Utility Vehicles	Femur Force (kN)
Chevrolet Lumina	5.8	Toyota Sienna	1.8	Mercedes M Class	3.5
Ford Taurus	2.1	Honda Odyssey	3.0	Toyota 4Runner	1.2
Buick LeSabre	2.8	Ford Windstar	2.1	Mitsubishi Montero	3.6
Chevrolet Impala	4.7	Mazda MPV	6.8	Nissan Xterra	1.2
Chrysler LHS	6.2	Chevrolet Astro	8.2	Ford Explorer	3.7
Pontiac Grand Prix	2.4	Nissan Quest	2.9	Jeep Grand Cherokee	6.7
Dodge Intrepid	4.7	Pontiac Trans Sport	6.7	Nissan Pathfinder	1.8

Source: Insurance Institute for Highway Safety

The researcher wants to test the claim that the mean femur forces for the three classes of vehicle are equal.

(a) $H_o: \mu_L = \mu_V = \mu_U$ vs $H_1:$ at least one of the means is different

(a) State the null and alternative hypotheses.
(b) Verify that the requirements to use the one-way ANOVA procedure are satisfied. Normal probability plots indicate that the sample data come from a population that is normal.
(c) Test the claim that the mean femur force for each vehicle type is the same at the $\alpha = 0.05$ level of significance. Do not reject H_o
(d) Draw boxplots of the three types of vehicle to support the analytic results obtained in part (c).

9. **Thermocouples** A thermocouple is a temperature sensor. One use of a thermocouple is to measure the temperature inside a furnace. A company has three thermocouples, but one is suspected of being broken. The company wraps the three thermocouples together, places them in an oven, and records the temperature. The process is repeated 20 times and produces the following data:

Thermocouple 1				Thermocouple 2				Thermocouple 3			
326.06	326.05	326.20	326.11	323.59	323.60	323.55	323.66	326.03	326.02	325.97	326.08
326.09	326.03	326.00	326.00	323.63	323.62	323.76	323.57	326.06	326.01	326.20	325.98
326.07	326.08	325.97	326.20	323.62	323.64	323.55	323.75	326.03	326.01	325.95	326.16
326.08	326.00	326.20	326.13	323.64	323.58	323.74	323.70	326.06	325.99	326.18	326.12
326.05	326.16	326.07	326.12	323.64	323.70	323.66	323.68	326.02	326.13	326.04	326.08

Source: Christenson, Ronald and Blackwood, Larry, "Tests for Precision and Accuracy of Multiple Measuring Devices" *Technometrics*, Nov. 93, Vol 35, Issue 4, pp. 411–421

The researchers want to test the claim that one of the thermocouples has a mean temperature that is different from the others at the $\alpha = 0.05$ level of significance.

(a) $H_o: \mu_1 = \mu_2 = \mu_3$ vs $H_1:$ at least one of the means is different

(a) State the null and alternative hypotheses.
(b) Verify that the requirements to use the one-way ANOVA procedure are satisfied. Normal probability plots indicate that the sample data come from a population that is normal.
(c) Test the claim that the mean temperature is the same for each thermocouple the $\alpha = 0.05$ level of significance. Reject H_o
(d) Draw boxplots of the three thermocouples to support the analytic results obtained in part (c).

10. What is the least-squares regression model? What are the requirements of the data in order to perform inference on a least-squares regression line?

Craniometry: Hat Size and Intelligence

In the mid-19th century, Paul Broca, a professor of clinical surgery, effectively argued that the degree of a person's intelligence was directly related to the size of the brain. Broca concluded that

> In general, the brain is larger in mature adults than in the elderly, in men than in women, in eminent men than in men of mediocre talent. . . . Other things equal, there is a remarkable relationship between the development of intelligence and the volume of the brain. [Quoted in Stephen Jay Gould, *The Mismeasure of Man* (New York: W.W. Norton & Company, 1981), p. 83.]

During the 20th century, arguments regarding brain size diminished as scientists turned to intelligence tests—a more direct method to measure and compare mental capacities, they claimed. Yet, the older argument still manages to creep into modern discussions of intelligence. In a book published in 1978 that was designed to acquaint educators with modern brain research, H. T. Epstein declared,

> First we shall ask if there is any indication of a linkage of any kind between brain and intelligence. It is generally stated that there is no such linkage. . . . But the one set of data I have found seems to show clearly that there is a substantial connection. Hooton studied the head circumferences of white Bostonians as part of his massive study of criminals. The following table shows that the ordering of people according to head size yields an entirely plausible ordering according to vocational status. It is not at all clear how the impression has been spread that there is no such correlation. [Quoted in Stephen Jay Gould, *The Mismeasure of Man* (New York: W.W. Norton & Company, 1981), p. 109.]

Epstein's table is reproduced here:

Mean and Standard Deviation (in mm) of Head Circumference for People of Vocational Status

Vocational Status	n	Mean	S.D.
Professional	25	569.9	1.9
Semiprofessional	61	566.5	1.5
Clerical	107	566.2	1.1
Trades	194	565.7	0.8
Public Service	25	564.1	2.5
Skilled Trades	351	562.9	0.6
Personal Services	262	562.7	0.7
Laborers	647	560.7	0.3

Source: Stephen Jay Gould, *The Mismeasure of Man* (New York: W.W. Norton & Company, 1981), p. 109.

At first glance, this table seems to support the assertion that those with more prestigious vocations have a larger head circumference. However, we can examine the alleged relationship more closely through a one-way analysis of variance. Specifically, we test the claim that all of the head-circumference population means are equal. We use an $\alpha = 0.05$ significance level and obtain the following ANOVA table, derived from Epstein's statistics:

ANOVA Table for Epstein's Data on Head Circumference by Vocational Status

Source of Variation	Sum of Squares	Degrees of Freedom	Mean Squares	F-Test Statistic
Between	7865.359	7	1123.6284	1998.6275
Within	935.450	1664	0.5622	
Total	8800.809	1671		

From these results, does it appear that at least one of the head-circumference means is different from the others? Explain.

Examine Epstein's table closely. Does it appear that the ANOVA procedure's requirement of equal variances is satisfied? Explain.

Subsequently, it was revealed that there was an error in Epstein's table. The column labeled S.D. (standard deviation) should have been labeled *standard error*. For each of the vocational categories, calculate the correct standard deviation by multiplying the tabled value by the square root of its sample size, n.

If the ANOVA table was recalculated with the correct standard deviations, predict the effect on the F-test statistic. Would you be more or less likely to reject the null hypothesis? Explain.

Using the equation for MSW, calculate a revised within-sum-of-squares, within-mean-squares, and F-test statistic. Retest the claim that all of the head-circumference population means are equal. Use an $\alpha = 0.05$ significance level. From the corrected values for the standard deviation, does it appear that the ANOVA procedure's requirement of equal variances is satisfied? Did any of your conclusions change in light of the new information? Explain.

If the null hypothesis of equal population means was rejected, calculate the confidence interval for the mean of each vocational-status category. Which of these categories appear to have significantly different means?

Further research revealed that results for three vocational status groups were not presented in Epstein's table. Inexplicably deleted were factory workers (rank 7 out of 11 in status), transportation employees (rank 8), and "extractive" trades (farming and mining, rank 11). The mean head-circumference sizes for these three groups were 564.7 mm, 564.9 mm, and 564.7 mm, respectively. Also, it was discovered that Epstein's table did not list each group in the order of Hooton's prestige ranking, but, rather, listed the groups in order of mean head circumference; this manipulation suggested a perfect correlation where one does not exist. [Source: Stephen Jay Gould, *The Mismeasure of Man* (New York: W.W. Norton & Company, 1981), p. 110.]

Using all of this new information and your previous analyses, write a brief report summarizing your findings and conclusions.

You are still in the market to buy a car. As we all know, cars lose value over time. Therefore, another item to consider when purchasing a car is its depreciation rate. The lower the depreciation rate, the less value the car loses each year. Using the same three cars that you used in the Chapter 3 and Chapter 4 "decisions," answer the questions that follow in order to determine the depreciation rate. Remember that, in Chapter 4 we found the exponential equation of best fit $y = ab^x$, where y is the price of the car and x is the age of the car. To do this, we linearized the data by computing the logarithm of the asking price, y, so that the least-squares regression equation was $\log y = \log a + (\log b) x$. We can rewrite this as $Y = A + Bx$, where $Y = \log y$, $A = \log a$ and $B = \log b$.

For each car that you are considering, answer the following:

1. What is the standard error, the point estimate for σ of the equation $Y = A + Bx$?

2. Are the residuals normally distributed?

3. If the residuals are normally distributed, test the claim that a linear relation exists between the predictor variable, x, and the response variable, Y, at the $\alpha = 0.05$ level of significance.

4. What is the mean price of a 10-year-old car? Construct a 90% confidence interval about the mean price of a 10-year-old car.

5. Predict the price of a 7-year-old car.

6. Construct a 90% prediction interval about the price of a 7-year-old car.

7. Write a report that describes which car you would buy, given the information collected. Be sure to justify your conclusions.

Antioxidant compounds are thought to be beneficial to human health. In a recent study for Consumer Reports (November 1999), fifteen brands of tea were tested for total antioxidant content. The antioxidant content was measured as Oxygen Radical Absorbance Capacity (ORAC) per 8-oz serving at an outside laboratory. Among the fifteen brands, four were bagged black, three were bagged green, two were instant, and six were ready-to-drink teas.

The data for the six ready-to-drink teas are given in the table below. To avoid potential sources of bias, measurements were taken from three different lots of each brand and the tests were conducted in a randomly chosen order. A control was also run repeatedly throughout the test period to determine if there was a time effect, but the data are not included here.

Brand	ORAC	Brand	ORAC
1	427.4	4	484.3
1	481.1	4	617.3
1	428.3	4	624.9
2	667.7	5	664.1
2	737.6	5	623.1
2	630.9	5	647.5
3	715.2	6	606.0
3	724.1	6	793.9
3	686.9	6	668.7

Minitab (release 13.1) was used to perform a one-way analysis of variance of the data. The results are shown below:

Using the Minitab output, answer the following questions:

(a) What are the null and alternative hypotheses?

(b) Do there appear to be any outliers or other unusual observations? What must be true regarding the distribution of the response variable, ORAC, in order to perform a one-way analysis of variance?

(c) Is there a statistical difference among brands? What is the significance level of the test?

(d) Which brands, if any, appear to have similar amounts of ORAC?

(e) Compute and interpret the confidence interval for brand 6.

(f) Write a paragraph for the readers of Consumer Reports magazine that explains your findings. Which brand of tea would you recommend? Why?

Note to Readers: In many cases, our test protocol and analytical methods are more complicated than described in these examples. The data and discussions have been modified to make the material more appropriate for the audience.

Analysis of Variance for ORAC

```
Source       DF         SS       MS       F       P
BRAND         5     147257    29451    8.80   0.001
Error        12      40180     3348
Total        17     187437
                                  Individual 95% CIs For Mean
                                  Based on Pooled StDev
Level       N       Mean    StDev  ---------+---------+---------+-------
1           3     445.60    30.75  (-----*-----)
2           3     678.73    54.20                  (-----*-----)
3           3     708.73    19.42                    (-----*-----)
4           3     575.50    79.07          (-----*-----)
5           3     644.90    20.62                (-----*-----)
6           3     689.53    95.67                   (-----*-----)
                                  ---------+---------+---------+-------
Pooled StDev =    57.87             480       600       720
```

Putting It All Together

In Chapters 8–10 and 12, we introduced inferential methods for testing claims regarding a population parameter. These methods required that certain conditions be satisfied before proceeding with the test. We have not yet addressed how to handle the situations in which these requirements were not satisfied. For example, suppose that we wish to test a claim regarding a population mean in which we have a small sample size, but the population is not normal?

To deal with this type of circumstance, we could increase the sample size and utilize the Central Limit Theorem, but we could also use nonparametric statistics. Nonparametric methods use techniques to test claims that are "distribution free." In other words, we do not need the requirement that a sample come from a population that is, for example, normal. Because of this, the tests can be used more often than so-called "parametric tests", such as the single-sample t-test.

Nonparametric Statistics

Outline

 For additional study help, go to
www.prenhall.com/sullivanstats

Materials include

- Self-Graded Quizzes
- "Preparing for This Section" Quizzes
- STATLETs
- PowerPoint Downloads
- Step-by-Step Technology Guide
- Graphing Calculator Help

13.1   An Overview of Nonparametric Statistics

Objective   Understand the difference between parametric statistical procedures and nonparametric statistical procedures

   Up to this point, the inferential statistics that we performed were based upon *parametric statistical procedures*. To use these procedures, we needed to make assumptions regarding the underlying distribution of the random variable. For example, in order to test a hypothesis regarding a population mean, μ, we needed the population to be normally distributed (if $n < 30$).

Definition   **Parametric statistical procedures** are inferential procedures that rely on testing claims regarding parameters such as the population mean, μ, the population standard deviation, σ, or the population proportion, p. In some circumstances, the use of parametric procedures requires that certain assumptions regarding the distribution of the population, such as normality, be satisfied.

The inferential procedures presented in Chapters 8, 9, 10, and 12 were all parametric statistical procedures–but what if the assumptions that need to be satisfied in order to conduct parametric statistical procedures are not satisfied? Then we utilize *nonparametric statistical procedures*.

Definition   **Nonparametric statistical procedures** are inferential procedures that are not based upon parameters and that require fewer assumptions to be satisfied in order to perform the tests. They do not require that the population follow a specific type of distribution (such as the normal distribution) and, therefore, are often referred to as **distribution-free procedures**.

Caution

Do not use nonparametric procedures if parametric procedures can be used.

So parametric procedures are based upon the underlying probability distribution of the population and its parameters, while nonparametric procedures are not based upon an underlying probability distribution. Why would we ever use parametric procedures when nonparametric procedures exist? Well, there are advantages and disadvantages to utilizing nonparametric statistical procedures.

Advantages of Nonparametric Statistical Procedures

- Most of the tests require very few assumptions, so it is unlikely that these tests will be used improperly.
- For some nonparametric procedures, the computation is fairly easy.
- The procedures can be used for count data or rank data, so nonparametric methods can be used on data such as rankings of a movie as excellent, good, fair, or poor.

Disadvantages of Nonparametric Statistical Procedures

- Because there are fewer requirements that must be satisfied to conduct these tests, researchers sometimes use these procedures when parametric procedures can be used.

- The results of the test are typically less powerful. Recall that the **power of a test** refers to the probability of making a Type II error. A Type II error occurs when a researcher does not reject the null hypothesis when the alternative hypothesis is true.
- Nonparametric procedures are less efficient than parametric procedures. This means that a larger sample size is required when conducting a nonparametric procedure in order to have the same probability of a Type I error as the equivalent parametric procedure.

As is typically the case, the more assumptions that are made (and satisfied), the stronger the results. If the assumptions required to perform parametric statistical procedures are satisfied, these tests should be used because the results will be more powerful and efficient. Nonparametric statistical procedures should be used only if the assumptions are not satisfied.

Let's explore this idea of **efficiency** a little more. If a nonparametric statistical test has an efficiency of 0.85, then a sample size of 100 would be required in the nonparametric test in order to achieve the same results a sample of 85 would produce in the equivalent parametric test. The "cost" of fewer assumptions is that additional individuals must be sampled. Table 1 shows some of the nonparametric tests that we will study in this chapter, their efficiencies, and the corresponding parametric test.

*✍ **In Your Own Words***

The lower the efficiency, the larger the sample size must be for a nonparametric test to keep the probability of a Type I error the same as it would be for its equivalent parametric test.

TABLE 1		
Nonparametric Test	**Parametric Test**	**Efficiency**
Sign Test	Single-sample z-test or t-test	0.955 (for small samples that come from a normal population)
		0.75 (for samples of size 13 or larger if data are normal)
Mann–Whitney Test	Inference about the Difference of Two Means—Independent Samples	0.955 (if data are normal)
Wilcoxon Matched-Pairs Test	Inference about the Difference of Two Means—Dependent Samples	0.955 (if the differences are normal)
Kruskal–Wallis Test	One-Way ANOVA	0.955 (if the data are normal)
		0.864 (if the distributions are identical except for medians)
Spearman Rank-Correlation Coefficient	Linear Correlation	0.912 (if the data are bivariate normal)

13.1 Assess Your Understanding

Concepts and Vocabulary

1. Describe the difference between parametric statistical procedures and nonparametric statistical procedures.
2. Explain the idea of efficiency.
3. Explain the concept of the power of a test.
4. List the advantages of using nonparametric statistical procedures.
5. List the disadvantages of using nonparametric statistical procedures.
6. Why is it appropriate to call nonparametric statistical procedures "distribution-free procedures"?

13.2 Runs Test for Randomness

Preparing for This Section   Before getting started, review the following:

✓ Mutually exclusive (Section 5.2, pp. 276–278)

✓ The logic of hypothesis testing (Section 9.1, pp. 518–525)

Objectives Perform a runs test for randomness

 In many situations, we would like to know whether a set of data is random. By this we mean that we would like to know whether or not a series of observations appears to follow a particular pattern, even if the data were obtained in a systematic fashion. For example, we might record the gender of the next 20 people who leave a store. Certainly, our method for obtaining the individuals is not random, but we would like to test for whether the observations occurred randomly—as if we pulled them from a hat.

If a researcher is not certain that data have been obtained randomly, a *runs test for randomness* can be conducted.

Definition   A **runs test for randomness** is used to test claims that data have been obtained or occur randomly. A **run** is a sequence of similar events, items, or symbols that is followed by an event, item, or symbol that is mutually exclusive from the first event, item, or symbol. The number of events, items, or symbols in a run is called its **length**.

Caution

Runs tests are used to test whether it is reasonable to conclude data occur randomly, not whether the data are collected randomly. For example, we might wonder whether defective parts come off an assembly line randomly or systematically. If broken parts occur in a systematic (such as every 4th part) fashion, we might be led to believe we have a broken machine. We don't collect the data randomly; instead, we select 100 consecutive parts. We want to know whether the defective parts in the 100 selected occur randomly.

As an example, suppose we record the gender of the 15 students enrolled in an introductory statistics course as they enter the classroom. The males are denoted by a blue M and the females are denoted by a red F.

$$M\ M\ F\ M\ M\ F\ M\ M\ F\ F\ M\ M\ M\ M\ F$$

The first two males constitute a run of length 2 because they are the same gender. The third individual is run of length 1. The longest run is length 4. Do you see it? The number of runs is 8.

The goal of this section is to discover whether a sequence of observations is random. The randomness of a sequence would be called into question if there are too few or too many runs. For example, the sequence

$$M\ M\ M\ M\ M\ M\ M\ M\ F\ F\ F\ F\ F\ F\ F$$

is nonrandom, because it contains too few runs (only 2 runs). The sequence

$$M\ F\ M\ F\ M\ F\ M\ F\ M\ F\ M\ F\ M\ F\ M$$

is also nonrandom, because it contains too many runs (15 runs).

The following notation is to be used in testing claims regarding randomness:

Notation Used in Conducting a Runs Test for Randomness

Let n represent the sample size of which there are two mutually exclusive types

Let n_1 represent the number of observations of the first type

Let n_2 represent the number of observations of the second type

Let r represent the number of runs

▶ **EXAMPLE 1**   **Utilizing the Notation in a Runs Test for Randomness**

Problem: Suppose we record the gender of the 15 students enrolled in an introductory statistics course as they enter the classroom. The males are denoted by a blue M and the females are denoted by a red F.

M M F M M F M M F F M M M M F

Identify the values of n, n_1, n_2, and r.

Approach: We let n represent the number of students sampled. Let n_1 represent the number of male students and n_2 represent the number of females students. Finally, let r represent the number of runs.

The Solution: We have $n = 15$ students in the sample, $n_1 = 10$ males, $n_2 = 5$ females and $r = 8$ runs.   ◀◀

NW *Now Work Problem 1(a).*

In order to conduct a runs test for randomness, we need a test statistic and a critical value.

Theorem

Test Statistic for a Runs Test for Randomness

Small-Sample Case: If $n_1 \leq 20$ and $n_2 \leq 20$, the test statistic in the runs test for randomness is r, the number of runs.

Large-Sample Case: If $n_1 > 20$ or $n_2 > 20$, the test statistic in the runs test for randomness is

$$z = \frac{r - \mu_r}{\sigma_r}$$

where

$$\mu_r = \frac{2n_1 n_2}{n} + 1 \quad \text{and} \quad \sigma_r = \sqrt{\frac{2n_1 n_2 (2n_1 n_2 - n)}{n^2 (n - 1)}}$$

Theorem

Critical Values for a Runs Test for Randomness

Small-Sample Case: To find the critical value at the $\alpha = 0.05$ level of significance for a runs test, we use Table VI if $n_1 \leq 20$ and $n_2 \leq 20$.

Large-Sample Case: If $n_1 > 20$ or $n_2 > 20$, the critical value is found from Table II, the standard normal table.

▶ **EXAMPLE 2**   **Obtaining Critical Values from Table VI**

Problem: Find the upper and lower critical values at the $\alpha = 0.05$ level of significance from Table VI if $n_1 = 10$ and $n_2 = 5$.

Approach: Determine the intersection of the row corresponding to $n_1 = 10$ and the column corresponding to $n_2 = 5$ to identify the lower and upper critical values.

Solution: The lower critical value is 3 and the upper critical value is 12. Figure 1 on page 762 shows a partial display of Table VI.

NW *Now Work Problem 1(b).*

Figure 1

Critical Values for the Number of Runs

Value of n_2

Value of n_1		2	3	4	5	6	7	8	9	10	11	12	13	14
	2	1 6	1 6	1 6	1 6	1 6	1 6	1 6	1 6	1 6	1 6	2 6	2 6	2 6
	3	1 6	1 8	1 8	1 8	2 8	2 8	2 8	2 8	2 8	2 8	2 8	2 8	2 8
	4	1 6	1 8	1 9	2 9	2 9	2 10	3 10	3 10	3 10	3 10	3 10	3 10	3 10
	5	1 6	1 8	2 9	2 10	3 10	3 11	3 11	3 12	3 12	4 12	4 12	4 12	4 12
	6	1 6	2 8	2 9	3 10	3 11	3 12	3 12	4 13	4 13	4 13	4 13	5 14	5 14
	7	1 6	2 8	2 10	3 11	3 12	3 13	4 13	4 14	5 14	5 14	5 14	5 15	5 15
	8	1 6	2 8	3 10	3 11	3 12	4 13	4 14	5 14	5 15	5 15	6 16	6 16	6 16
	9	1 6	2 8	3 10	3 12	4 13	4 14	5 14	5 15	5 16	6 16	6 16	6 17	7 17
	10	1 6	2 8	3 10	3 12	4 13	5 14	5 15	5 16	6 16	6 17	7 17	7 18	7 18
	11	1 6	2 8	3 10	4 12	4 13	5 14	5 15	6 16	6 17	7 17	7 18	7 19	8 19
	12	2 6	2 8	3 10	4 12	4 13	5 14	6 16	6 16	7 17	7 18	7 19	8 19	8 20

◄◄

We now present the steps required to conduct a runs test for randomness.

Runs Test for Randomness

If a claim is made regarding the randomness of data, we can use the following steps to test the claim, provided that
1. the sample is a sequence of observations recorded in the order of their occurrence and
2. the observations can be categorized into two mutually exclusive categories.

Step 1: A claim is made regarding the randomness of data. The claim is used to determine the null and alternative hypotheses, which are structured as follows:

H_0: The sequence of data is random.
H_1: The sequence of data is not random.

Step 2: Determine a level of significance, α, based upon the seriousness of making a Type I error. The level of significance is used to determine the *critical value*.
Note: For the small-sample case, we must use the level of significance $\alpha = 0.05$.

In Your Own Words

In the runs test, we always assume that the sample data occur (or are collected) randomly.

Step 3: Use the number of runs, r, to compute the **test statistic**.

Small-Sample Case	Large-Sample Case
r	$z = \dfrac{r - \mu_r}{\sigma_r}$

Step 4: Compare the critical value to the test statistic.

Small-Sample Case	Large-Sample Case
If $r \leq$ lower critical value or $r \geq$ upper critical value, reject the null hypothesis	If $z < -z_{\alpha/2}$ or $z > z_{\alpha/2}$, reject the null hypothesis

Step 5: State the conclusion.

▶ **EXAMPLE 3**   **Testing for Randomness (Small-Sample Case)**

Problem: Suppose we record the gender of the 15 students enrolled in an introductory statistics course as they enter the classroom. The males are denoted by a blue M and the females are denoted by a red F:

M M F M M F M M F F M M M M F

Test the claim that the individuals enter the room in a nonrandom way as it pertains to gender at the $\alpha = 0.05$ level of significance.

Approach: After verifying the requirements that the data were collected in the order they occurred and that there are two mutually exclusive categories of data, we follow Steps 1–5 presented on pages 762–763.

Solution: The sample is a sequence of observations (the first person that walked in was male, second person male, and so on) recorded in the order of occurrence. The observations are in two mutually exclusive categories: male or female. The requirements are satisfied.

Step 1: We are testing the claim the data were collected randomly. Thus,

H_0: The sequence of data is random.
H_1: The sequence of data is not random.

Step 2: The level of significance is $\alpha = 0.05$. The lower critical value is 3, and the upper critical value is 12 (Example 2).
Step 3: The test statistic is $r = 8$ (Example 1).
Step 4: Because the test statistic, $r = 8$, is not less than or equal to the lower critical value, 3, and is not greater than or equal to the upper critical value, 12, we do not reject the null hypothesis.
Step 5: There is not sufficient evidence to support the claim that the students enter the room in a nonrandom way as it pertains to gender. We have reason to believe that students enter the classroom, as it pertain to gender, in a random fashion.   ◀◀

Using Technology: Some statistical software has the ability to perform a runs test. Figure 2 on page 764 shows the output obtained from Minitab. Notice that the observed number of runs is 8 (this is our test statistic) and the P-value is 0.8392. Because the P-value is greater than the level of significance, α, we do not reject the null hypothesis. There is reason to believe that students enter the classroom in a random way as it pertains to gender.

Figure 2

```
Runs Test
  gender

  K = 0.5000

     The observed number of runs = 8
     The expected number of runs = 7.6667
     5 Observations above K   10 below

 * N Small -- The following approximation may be invalid
              The test is significant at   0.8392
              Cannot reject at alpha = 0.05
```

NW *Now Work Problem 1(c).*

▶ **EXAMPLE 4** **Testing for Randomness (Large-Sample Case)**

Problem: The data in Table 2 represent the rates of return of the Standard and Poor's Index of 500 Stocks from January 1998 through May 2001. Is there sufficient evidence to support the claim that positive monthly rates of return are random at the $\alpha = 0.05$ level of significance?

TABLE 2							
Date	**Return**	**Date**	**Return**	**Date**	**Return**	**Date**	**Return**
Jan-98	1.02%	Jan-99	4.10%	Jan-00	−5.09%	Jan-01	3.46%
Feb-98	7.04%	Feb-99	−3.23%	Feb-00	−2.01%	Feb-01	−9.23%
Mar-98	4.99%	Mar-99	3.88%	Mar-00	9.67%	Mar-01	−6.42%
Apr-98	0.91%	Apr-99	3.79%	Apr-00	−3.08%	Apr-01	7.68%
May-98	−1.88%	May-99	−2.50%	May-00	−2.19%	May-01	0.51%
Jun-98	3.94%	Jun-99	5.44%	Jun-00	2.39%		
Jul-98	−1.16%	Jul-99	−3.20%	Jul-00	−1.63%		
Aug-98	−14.58%	Aug-99	−0.63%	Aug-00	6.07%		
Sep-98	6.24%	Sep-99	−2.86%	Sep-00	−5.35%		
Oct-98	8.03%	Oct-99	6.25%	Oct-00	−0.49%		
Nov-98	5.91%	Nov-99	1.92%	Nov-00	−8.01%		
Dec-98	5.64%	Dec-99	5.77%	Dec-00	0.41%		

Source: Yahoo! Finance

Historical Note

The idea behind this problem is based upon the book A Random Walk Down Wall Street by Burton Malkiel, 1996, W.W. Norton & Co.

Approach: Let P represent a positive monthly rate of return and let N represent a negative or zero monthly rate of return. We list the sequence of Ps and Ns in chronological order and determine n (the sample size), n_1 (the number of Ps), n_2 (the number of Ns), and r (the number of runs). We then verify that the requirements are satisfied and follow Steps 1–5 on pages 762–763.

Solution: The rates of return are represented by the following sequence:

P P P P N P N N P P P P P N P P N P N P N N N P P P N N P N N N P N P N N N P P N N P P

There are $n = 41$ months of observations, with $n_1 = 23$ positive months and $n_2 = 18$ negative months. There are $r = 21$ runs. Because (1) the sample is a sequence of observations recorded in the order of their occurrence and (2) the observations can be categorized into two mutually exclusive categories (P and N), the requirements are satisfied. We now follow Steps 1–5 in order to test the claim.

Step 1: The null and alternative hypotheses are as follows:

H_0: The sequence of data is random.
H_1: The sequence of data is not random.

Step 2: The level of significance is $\alpha = 0.05$.
Step 3: Because $n_1 > 20$, we proceed as for a large-sample case. First, we calculate μ_r and σ_r:

$$\mu_r = \frac{2n_1n_2}{n} + 1 = \frac{2(23)(18)}{41} + 1 = 21.195$$

$$\sigma_r = \sqrt{\frac{2n_1n_2(2n_1n_2 - n)}{n^2(n-1)}} = \sqrt{\frac{2(23)(18)[2(23)(18) - 41]}{41^2(41-1)}} = 3.113$$

Now we can compute the test statistic:

$$z = \frac{r - \mu_r}{\sigma_r} = \frac{21 - 21.195}{3.113} = -0.06$$

Step 4: The critical values at the $\alpha = 0.05$ level of significance are $-z_{0.025} = -1.96$ and $z_{0.025} = 1.96$. The test statistic, -0.06, does not lie within the critical region, so we do not reject the null hypothesis.
Step 5: There is not sufficient evidence to reject the claim that monthly rates of return are random. There is evidence to support the belief that monthly rates of return occur in random fashion. ◄◄

NW *Now Work Problem 11.*

13.2 Assess Your Understanding

Concepts and Vocabulary

1. What is meant by random?
2. In your own words, explain what a run is.

3. We have evidence against the null hypothesis that the data are random if there are *either* too few *or* too many runs. Explain the logic behind this criterion.

Exercises

• Skill Building

In Problems 1–4, a sequence is given. (a) Identify the values of n, n_1, n_2, and r. (b) Calculate the critical value at the $\alpha = 0.05$ level of significance. (c) Test the claim that the sequence is not random.

1. M M M F F F M M F M F F F F Do not reject H_0

2. M M M F F F F M M F F F F F F Do not reject H_0

3. Y Y N Y Y Y Y Y N N N N N N N N Y Y Reject H_0

4. Y Y Y N N Y N N Y Y Y N N N Y Y Y N Y Y N N
   Do not reject H_0

• Applying the Concepts

5. **Baseball** Keith Foulke is a relief pitcher for the Chicago White Sox. He features two pitches—a fastball (F) and a change-up (C). The other night, Foulke threw 18

pitches in an inning. The following sequence represents the pitches he threw, in order.

F F F C C F F C F C C F F F F F C C

Is there sufficient evidence at the $\alpha = 0.05$ level of significance to support the claim that Keith Foulke's pitch selection is random? *Do not reject H_o*

6. **Football** A certain NFL coach likes to select the first 15 offensive plays before the game begins. The coach can select either a running play (R) or a pass play (P). The following sequence represents the first 15 plays, in order:

R P P P R P R R P R R R P R R

Is there sufficient evidence at the $\alpha = 0.05$ level of significance to support the claim that the coach's play selection is random? *Do not reject H_o*

7. **On-time Flights** The following data represent the arrival status of Southwest Flight 093 from Chicago's Midway Airport to Lambert–St. Louis International Airport for 14 consecutive flights [data are obtained from the U.S. Department of Transportation]:

O O L O O L O L L L O O O L

Status is indicated as on time (O) or late (L). A late arrival is defined as a gate arrival that is more than 10 minutes after the scheduled arrival. Is there sufficient evidence to support the claim that the arrival status of the flight is random, at the $\alpha = 0.05$ level of significance? *Do not reject H_o*

8. **On-time Flights** The following data represent the arrival status of American Airlines Flight 417 from Dallas–Fort Worth Airport to Albuquerque International Airport for 15 consecutive flights [data are obtained from the U.S. Department of Transportation]:

O O L O L L O L O O O L O L O

Status is indicated as on time (O) or late (L). A late arrival is defined as a gate arrival that is more than 10 minutes after the scheduled arrival. Is there sufficient evidence to support the claim that the arrival status of the flight is not random, at the $\alpha = 0.05$ level of significance? *Do not reject H_o*

9. **Quality Control** The quality-control manager of a bottling company wants to discover whether a filling machine over- or underfills 16-ounce bottles randomly. The following data represent the filling status of 20 consecutive bottles:

A A A A A A A R R R A A A A A A A A R R

A bottle is rejected (R) if it is either overfilled or underfilled. A bottle is accepted (A) if it is filled according to specification. Is there sufficient evidence to support the claim that the filling machine is random in the way that it over- or underfills, at the $\alpha = 0.05$ level of significance? *Reject H_o*

10. **Quality Control** The quality-control manager of a bottling company wants to discover whether a filling machine over- or underfills 64-ounce bottles randomly. The following data represent the filling status of 18 consecutive bottles:

A A A A A R R R A A A A A A A A A A

A bottle is rejected (R) if it is either overfilled or underfilled. A bottle is accepted (A) if it is filled according to specification. Is there sufficient evidence to support the claim that the filling machine is random in the way that it over- and underfills, at the $\alpha = 0.05$ level of significance? *Reject H_o*

11. **Random Walk Down Wall Street?** Does a stock price fluctuate randomly from day to day? In
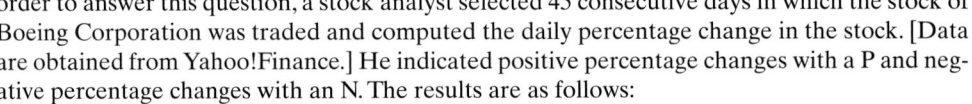
order to answer this question, a stock analyst selected 45 consecutive days in which the stock of Boeing Corporation was traded and computed the daily percentage change in the stock. [Data are obtained from Yahoo!Finance.] He indicated positive percentage changes with a P and negative percentage changes with an N. The results are as follows:

Date	Return	Date	Return	Date	Return	Date	Return	Date	Return
04-Apr-01	P	18-Apr-01	N	01-May-01	P	14-May-01	N	25-May-01	P
05-Apr-01	N	19-Apr-01	P	02-May-01	N	15-May-01	P	29-May-01	N
06-Apr-01	P	20-Apr-01	N	03-May-01	P	16-May-01	P	30-May-01	N
09-Apr-01	P	23-Apr-01	P	04-May-01	P	17-May-01	N	31-May-01	P
10-Apr-01	N	24-Apr-01	N	07-May-01	N	18-May-01	P	01-Jun-01	P
11-Apr-01	P	25-Apr-01	P	08-May-01	N	21-May-01	N	04-Jun-01	P
12-Apr-01	N	26-Apr-01	P	09-May-01	P	22-May-01	N	05-Jun-01	P
16-Apr-01	P	27-Apr-01	P	10-May-01	P	23-May-01	N	06-Jun-01	N
17-Apr-01	P	30-Apr-01	P	11-May-01	P	24-May-01	N	07-Jun-01	N

Is there sufficient evidence to support the claim that the stock price fluctuates randomly from day to day, at the $\alpha = 0.05$ level of significance? *Do not reject H_o*

12. **Random Walk Down Wall Street?** Does the stock market fluctuate randomly from quarter to quarter? [A quarter refers to a quarter of the year. For example, January–March is the first quarter, April–June is the second quarter, and so on.] In order to answer this question, a stock analyst selected 41 consecutive quarters and computed the percentage change in the stock market. [Data were obtained from the Vanguard Group.] He indicated positive percentage changes with a P and negative percentage changes with an N. The following are results:

Quarter	Return	Quarter	Return	Quarter	Return
1st quarter, 1991	P	3rd quarter, 1994	P	1st quarter, 1998	P
2nd quarter, 1991	N	4th quarter, 1994	P	2nd quarter, 1998	P
3rd quarter, 1991	P	1st quarter, 1995	P	3rd quarter, 1998	N
4th quarter, 1991	P	2nd quarter, 1995	P	4th quarter, 1998	P
1st quarter, 1992	N	3rd quarter, 1995	P	1st quarter, 1999	P
2nd quarter, 1992	P	4th quarter, 1995	P	2nd quarter, 1999	P
3rd quarter, 1992	P	1st quarter, 1996	P	3rd quarter, 1999	N
4th quarter, 1992	P	2nd quarter, 1996	P	4th quarter, 1999	P
1st quarter, 1993	P	3rd quarter, 1996	P	1st quarter, 2000	P
2nd quarter, 1993	N	4th quarter, 1996	P	2nd quarter, 2000	N
3rd quarter, 1993	P	1st quarter, 1997	P	3rd quarter, 2000	N
4th quarter, 1993	P	2nd quarter, 1997	P	4th quarter, 2000	N
1st quarter, 1994	N	3rd quarter, 1997	P	1st quarter, 2001	N
2nd quarter, 1994	P	4th quarter, 1997	P		

Is there sufficient evidence to support the claim that the stock market fluctuates randomly from quarter to quarter, at the $\alpha = 0.05$ level of significance? *Do not reject* H_o

13. **Random Residuals** In a least-squares regression model, the residuals are assumed to be random. The following data represent the life expectancy of a male born in the given year (e.g., a male born in 1988 is expected to live 71.4 years):

Year, x	Life Expectancy, y	Year, x	Life Expectancy, y
1988	71.4	1994	72.3
1989	71.7	1995	72.5
1990	71.8	1996	73.0
1991	72.0	1997	73.6
1992	72.3	1998	73.9
1993	72.2		

Source: Statistical Abstract of the United States

The least-squares regression equation treating year as the independent variable is $\hat{y} = -375.09 + 0.225x$. The residuals are, in order,

$$0.095455 \quad 0.170909 \quad 0.046364 \quad 0.021818 \quad 0.097273 \quad -0.227273$$
$$-0.351818 \quad -0.376364 \quad -0.100909 \quad 0.274545 \quad 0.350000$$

(a) Denote residuals above 0 with an "A" and those below 0 with a "B" to form a sequence.
(b) Test the claim that the residuals are random, at the $\alpha = 0.05$ level of significance.

Do not reject H_o

14. **Random Residuals** In a least-squares regression model, the residuals are assumed to be random. The following data represent the life expectancy of a female born in the given year (e.g., a female born in 1988 is expected to live 78.3 years):   (b) Do not reject H_o

Year, x	Life Expectancy, y	Year, x	Life Expectancy, y
1988	78.3	1994	79.0
1989	78.5	1995	78.9
1990	78.8	1996	79.0
1991	78.9	1997	79.4
1992	79.1	1998	79.4
1993	78.8		

The least-squares regression equation treating the year as the independent variable is $\hat{y} = -95.02 + 0.087x$. The residuals are, in order,

$$-0.181818 \quad -0.069091 \quad 0.143636 \quad 0.156364 \quad 0.269091 \quad -0.118182$$
$$-0.005455 \quad -0.192727 \quad -0.180000 \quad 0.132727 \quad 0.045455$$

(a) Denote residuals above 0 with an "A" and those below 0 with a "B" to form a sequence.
(b) Test the claim that the residuals are random, at the $\alpha = 0.05$ level of significance.

15. **Random-Number Generators** Using statistical software or a graphing calculator with advanced statistical features, randomly generate a sequence of 20 integer values, each either 0 or 1. Test the claim that the integers form a sequence that is random at the $\alpha = 0.05$ level of significance.

Technology Step-by-Step
Conducting a Runs Test

TI-83 Plus   The TI-83 Plus does not have this feature

MINITAB   **Step 1:** Enter raw data in column C1. Enter 0 for one category and 1 for the other category.
Step 2: Select the **Stat** menu, highlight **Nonparametrics**, then highlight **Runs Test . . . .**
Step 3: Enter C1 in the cell marked "Variables." If the data are binomial with $p = 0.5$, select "Above and Below," and enter 0.5. If the data are numerical, select "Above and Below," and enter the appropriate value. Click OK.

Excel   Excel is not programmed to conduct the runs test.

13.3 Inferences about Measures of Central Tendency

Preparing for This Section   Before getting started, review the following:

✓ Median (Section 3.1, pp. 116–117)

✓ Binomial probability distribution (Section 6.2, pp. 339–345)

✓ The logic of hypothesis testing (Section 9.1, pp. 518–525)

✓ Testing claims regarding a population mean, σ known (Section 9.2, pp. 527–538)

✓ Testing claims regarding a population mean, σ unknown (Section 9.3, pp. 546–551)

Objectives ① Conduct a one-sample sign test

Note to Instructor
Ask students to think about why we use the median as the measure of central tendency in nonparametric tests. A good answer would be that the median is resistant.

In Sections 9.2 and 9.3, we introduced parametric techniques that are used to test claims regarding a population mean, μ. In order to test these claims, we required that either the population be normal (if $n < 30$) or the sample size be large ($n \geq 30$). If these requirements are not satisfied, we can use nonparametric procedures to test claims regarding the central tendency of the population. These nonparametric procedures make inferences regarding the median, rather than the mean. In this section, we will discuss the *one-sample sign test*.

Remember, in hypothesis testing, the null hypothesis must always contain a statement of equality and the null hypothesis is assumed true. In the context of testing a claim regarding the median, there are three ways to structure the hypothesis test:

Two-Tailed	Left-Tailed	Right-Tailed
$H_0: M = M_o$	$H_0: M = M_o$	$H_0: M = M_o$
$H_1: M \neq M_o$	$H_1: M < M_o$	$H_1: M > M_o$

Note: M_o is the assumed value of the median.

① The One-Sample Sign Test

The sign test is one of the oldest nonparametric procedures. It is sometimes attributed to John Arbuthnot, who reported its use in 1710.

Definition

The **one-sample sign test** converts data to plus and minus signs in order to test a claim regarding the median.

In Your Own Words

The one-sample sign test is the nonparametric equivalent of tests regarding a population mean.

For example, suppose we have the following set of data:

$$3, 3, 5, 6, 6, 7, 8, 9, 9, 9, 10, 12$$

We might want to test the hypotheses

$$H_0: M = 7$$
$$H_1: M \neq 7$$

To use the sign test, convert all observations less than 7 to minus $(-)$ signs and all observations greater than 7 to plus $(+)$ signs. We have five minus signs and six plus signs in this set of data. If an observation in the data set equals the value of the median, we assign 0 to the observation. The sample size, n, is the number of minus and plus signs, so $n = 11$. In other words, ignore data values equal to the value of the median stated in the null hypothesis.

Remember, the median divides the bottom 50% of a set of data from the top 50%. Therefore, if the null hypothesis were true, then we would expect about half the data to result in minus signs and half to result in plus signs. If there are significantly different numbers of minus and plus signs, we have evidence against the null hypothesis.

In order to conduct a one-sample sign test for the median, we need a test statistic and a critical value.

Theorem

Test Statistic for a One-Sample Sign Test

The test statistic will depend upon the structure of the hypothesis test and upon the sample size.

Small-Sample Case ($n \leq 25$)

Two-Tailed	Left-Tailed	Right-Tailed
$H_0: M = M_0$	$H_0: M = M_0$	$H_0: M = M_0$
$H_1: M \neq M_0$	$H_1: M < M_0$	$H_1: M > M_0$
The test statistic, k, will be the smaller of the number of minus signs or plus signs.	The test statistic, k, will be the number of plus signs.	The test statistic, k, will be the number of minus signs.

Large-Sample Case ($n > 25$)

The test statistic, z, is

$$z = \frac{(k + 0.5) - \dfrac{n}{2}}{\dfrac{\sqrt{n}}{2}}$$

where n is the number of minus and plus signs and k is obtained as described in the small-sample case.

In the previous data set, we had five minus signs and six plus signs, so the test statistic would be $k = 5$, and $n = 11$.

Theorem

Critical Values for a One-Sample Sign Test

Small-Sample Case: To find the critical value for a one-sample sign test, we use Table VII if $n \leq 25$.

Large-Sample Case: If $n > 25$, the critical value is found from Table II, the standard normal table. The critical value is always located in the left tail of the standard normal distribution. For a two-tailed test, the critical value is $-z_{\alpha/2}$. For a left-tailed or right-tailed test, the critical value is $-z_\alpha$.

Let's take a closer look at the test statistic for the left-tailed test. For the left-tailed test, the alternative hypothesis is $H_1: M < M_0$. So, if the true median is less than M_0, there should not be many observations that are above the hypothesized median, M_0. If there are not many observations above the hypothesized median, then there will be few plus signs, so the value of k will be small. If k is *sufficiently* small, we reject the null hypothesis. A similar argument could be made for the right-tailed and the two-tailed tests. (See Problems 3 and 4 in "Concepts and Vocabulary.")

We now present the steps required to conduct a one-sample sign test.

One-Sample Sign Test

If a claim is made regarding the median of a population, we use the following steps to test the claim, provided that the sample is a random sample:

Step 1: A claim is made regarding the median. The claim is used to construct the null and alternative hypotheses. The hypotheses are structured as follows:

Historical Note

John Arbuthnot was born in April, 1667 in Inverbervie, Kincardine, Scotland. He earned a degree in medicine in 1696 from the University of St. Andrews. Around 1700, he went to London to tutor mathematics. In 1704, he was elected a Fellow of the Royal Society. After curing Prince George when he was ill, he was appointed the physician of Queen Anne in 1705. In 1710, he published "An Argument of Divine Providence Taken from the Constant Regularity Observed in the Birth of Both Sexes." It was in this article that he developed the sign test. In addition, this is thought to be the first paper that applied probability to social statistics. He is also famous for his wit. One of his famous quotes is "All political parties die at last of swallowing their own lies." Arbuthnot died on February 27, 1735.

Two-Tailed	Left-Tailed	Right-Tailed
$H_0: M = M_0$	$H_0: M = M_0$	$H_0: M = M_0$
$H_1: M \neq M_0$	$H_1: M < M_0$	$H_1: M > M_0$

Note: M_0 is the assumed value of the median.

Step 2: Count the number of observations below M_0, and assign them minus $(-)$ signs. Count the number of observations above M_0, and assign them plus $(+)$ signs.

Step 3: Select a level of significance α based upon the seriousness of making a Type I error. The level of significance is used to determine the critical value. The critical value for small samples $(n \leq 25)$ is found from Table VII. The critical value for large samples $(n > 25)$ is found from Table II.

Step 4: Compute the test statistic, k. Note that k is the smaller of the number of minus signs and plus signs in the two-tailed test, that k is the number of plus signs in the left-tailed test, and that k is the number of minus signs in the right-tailed test. In addition, n is the total number of plus and minus signs.

Small-Sample Case	Large-Sample Case
k	$z = \dfrac{(k + 0.5) - \dfrac{n}{2}}{\dfrac{\sqrt{n}}{2}}$

Step 5: Compare the critical value to the test statistic.

Small-Sample Case	Large-Sample Case
If $k \leq$ critical value, reject the null hypothesis.	**Two-tailed**: If $z < -z_{\alpha/2}$, reject the null hypothesis. **Left-tailed or right-tailed**: If $z < -z_\alpha$, reject the null hypothesis.

Step 6: State the conclusion.

► **EXAMPLE 1**   Conducting a One-Sample Sign Test (Small-Sample Case)

Problem: A recent article in the school newspaper reported that the typical credit-card debt of a student is $500. Professor Michael McCraith claims that the median credit-card debt of students at Joliet Junior College is different from $500. To test this claim, he obtains a random sample of 20 students enrolled at the college and asks them to disclose their credit-card debt. The results of the survey are presented in Table 3. Test Professor McCraith's claim at the $\alpha = 0.05$ level of significance.

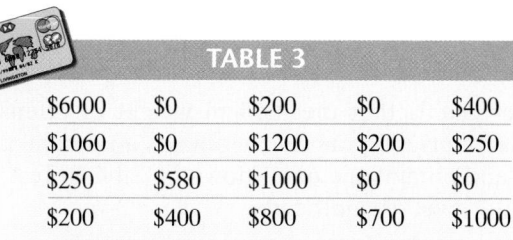

TABLE 3				
$6000	$0	$200	$0	$400
$1060	$0	$1200	$200	$250
$250	$580	$1000	$0	$0
$200	$400	$800	$700	$1000

Source: Professor Michael McCraith, Joliet Junior College

Approach: A normal probability plot indicates that the sample data do not come from a population that is normal and that the sample size is small. Therefore, we must use nonparametric techniques. We will use the sign test to test the claim.

Note to Instructor
Ask students whether the results of
this hypothesis test would change if
the student whose debt is $6000 had
been recorded as $60,000. Students
should conclude that this test is
robust to outliers.

Solution: The data were obtained via a random sample, so we can perform the test.

Step 1: The claim is that the median debt is different from $500. This claim can be written $M \neq 500$, and we have

$$H_o: M = 500 \qquad \text{versus} \qquad H_1: M \neq 500$$

This is a two-tailed test.

Step 2: There are 12 observations less than $500 and 8 observations greater than $500. Therefore, we have 12 minus signs and 8 plus signs, so $n = 20$.

Step 3: Because Professor McCraith is performing a two-tailed test and $n \leq 25$, we find the critical value for the two-tailed test at the $\alpha = 0.05$ level of significance with $n = 20$ (from Table VII) to be 5. See Figure 3.

Figure 3

	Critical Values for the Sign Test			
	α			
n	0.005 (one tail) 0.01 (two tails)	0.01 (one tail) 0.02 (two tails)	0.025 (one tail) 0.05 (two tails)	0.05 (one tail) 0.10 (two tails)
1	*	*	*	*
2	*	*	*	*
3	*	*	*	*
17	2	3	4	4
18	3	3	4	5
19	3	4	4	5
20	3	4	5	5
21	4	4	5	6
22	4	5	5	6

* Indicates that it is not possible to get a value in the critical region.

Step 4: The test statistic is the smaller of the number of plus signs and minus signs. The test statistic is $k = 8$, the number of plus signs.

Step 5: Because the test statistic, $k = 8$, is greater than the critical value, 5, we do not reject the null hypothesis.

Step 6: There is not sufficient evidence to support Professor McCraith's claim that the median credit-card debt of students at Joliet Junior College is different from $500. ◄◄

NW *Now Work Problem 11.*

► EXAMPLE 2   Conducting a One-Sample Sign Test (Large-Sample Case)

Problem: A sports reporter claims that the median weight of offensive linemen in the NFL is greater than 300 pounds. He obtains a random sample of 30 offensive linemen and obtains the data shown in Table 4. Test the reporter's claim at the $\alpha = 0.1$ level of significance.

Approach: Because the claim is in regard to a median, we use the sign test. We verify that the data were obtained via a random sample and then follow Steps 1–6.

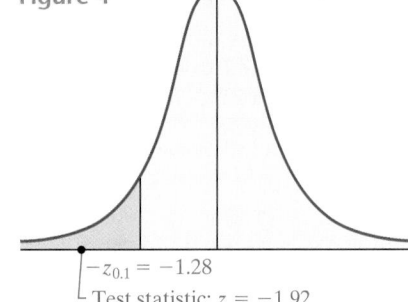

TABLE 4		
285	310	300
300	320	308
310	293	329
293	326	310
297	301	315
332	305	340
242	310	312
329	320	300
311	286	309
292	287	305

Source: espn.com

Figure 4

$-z_{0.1} = -1.28$
Test statistic: $z = -1.92$

Solution: The data were obtained through a random sample.

Step 1: The claim is that the median weight of NFL offensive linemen is greater than 300 pounds. We have

$$H_o: M = 300 \qquad \text{versus} \qquad H_1: M > 300$$

This is a right-tailed test.

Step 2: There are 8 observations below 300, 19 observations above 300, and 3 observations equal to 300. Because this is a right-tailed test, k is the number of minus signs, so $k = 8$. There are 8 minus signs and 19 plus signs, so $n = 27$.

Step 3: Because this is a right-tailed test and $n > 25$, we calculate the critical value for the right-tailed test at the $\alpha = 0.1$ level of significance as $-z_{0.1} = -1.28$.

Step 4: The test statistic is

$$z = \frac{(k + 0.5) - \dfrac{n}{2}}{\dfrac{\sqrt{n}}{2}} = \frac{(8 + 0.5) - \dfrac{27}{2}}{\dfrac{\sqrt{27}}{2}} = -1.92$$

Step 5: The test statistic is less than the critical value, so we reject the null hypothesis. See Figure 4.

Step 6: There is sufficient evidence at the $\alpha = 0.1$ level of significance to support the claim that the median weight of offensive linemen in the NFL is greater than 300 pounds.   ◄◄

NW *Now Work Problem 3.*

13.3 Assess Your Understanding

Concepts and Vocabulary

1. In the large-sample case, we compute $z = \dfrac{(k + 0.5) - \dfrac{n}{2}}{\dfrac{\sqrt{n}}{2}}$. This should remind us of the Z-score $\left(Z = \dfrac{x - \mu}{\sigma} \right)$, so that $\mu = \dfrac{n}{2}$. Why is this reasonable?

2. In the large-sample case, we compare $z = \dfrac{(k + 0.5) - \dfrac{n}{2}}{\dfrac{\sqrt{n}}{2}}$ to $-z_\alpha$, regardless of whether we are conducting a left-tailed or right-tailed test. Provide a justification for this.

3. Write a paragraph that describes the logic of the test statistic in a right-tailed sign test.

4. Write a paragraph that describes the logic of the test statistic in a two-tailed sign test.

Exercises

• Skill Building

In Problems 1–6, use the sign test to test the given claim at the $\alpha = 0.05$ level of significance.

1. Claim: the median is less than 8. An analysis of the data reveals that there are 13 minus signs and eight plus signs. Do not reject H_o

2. Claim: the median is more than 50. An analysis of the data reveals that there are seven minus signs and 12 plus signs. Do not reject H_o

3. Claim: the median is different from 100. An analysis of the data reveals that there are 21 minus signs and 28 plus signs. Do not reject H_o

4. Claim: the median is different from 68. An analysis of the data reveals that there are 45 plus signs and 27 minus signs. Reject H_o

5. Claim: the median is more than 12. The following data were obtained via a random sample: Reject H_o

18	16	15	13	9
15	13	11	15	18
10	14	20	14	12

6. Claim: the median is less than 15. The following data were obtained via a random sample: Do not reject H_o

18	6	2	12	6
36	33	14	18	13
18	21	34	9	12

• Applying the Concepts

7. **Acid Rain** In 1990, the median pH level of the rain in Pierce County, Washington, was 4.90. A biologist claims that the acidity of rain has increased since then. (This would mean that the pH level of the rain has decreased.) She obtains a random sample of 19 rain dates in 2000 and obtains the following data: Do not reject H_o

5.08	4.66	4.70	4.87
4.78	5.00	4.50	4.73
4.79	4.65	4.91	5.07
5.03	4.78	4.77	4.60
4.73	5.05	4.70	

Source: National Atmospheric Deposition Program

Test the claim that the median pH level has decreased from 4.90 at the $\alpha = 0.05$ level of significance.

8. **Age of the Bride** A sociologist claims that the median age at which women marry in Cook County is less than the median age throughout the United States (26.7, obtained from data from the Monthly Vital Statistics Report published by the Centers for Disease Control). Based on a random sample of 20 marriage certificates from the county, she obtains the ages shown in the following table:

31	27	24	30
27	32	24	23
25	23	28	22
21	30	25	24
24	22	26	27

Test the sociologist's claim at the $\alpha = 0.05$ level of significance. Do not reject H_o

9. **Income** An economist claims that the median income of lawyers who recently graduated from law school is more than $62,000. He queries a random sample of 12 lawyers and obtains the following data:

67,000	70,000	60,000	67,000
63,000	91,000	86,000	62,000
66,000	67,000	60,000	62,500

Source: *The Business Journal*, May 10, 1997

Test the economist's claim at the $\alpha = 0.05$ level of significance. (*Note*: A normal probability plot indicates that the data are not normal.) Reject H_o

10. **Housing Prices** A recent newspaper article stated that the median price of a home in Lemont, IL is $225,000. A realtor felt that the actual median price was higher, so she queried a random sample of 16 homes that had recently sold and obtained the following data:

137,500	246,000	312,500	188,000
154,000	130,000	155,000	295,000
150,000	250,000	200,000	400,000
627,900	226,500	323,000	382,500

Source: chicagotribune.com

Test the realtor's claim that the median price of a home in Lemont is more than $225,000 at the $\alpha = 0.05$ level of significance. (*Note*: A normal probability plot indicates the data are not normal.) Do not reject H_o

11. Baseball Salaries The following data represent the salaries of 14 randomly selected baseball players in the 2000 season (data are in thousands of dollars, so 2350 means $2,350,000):

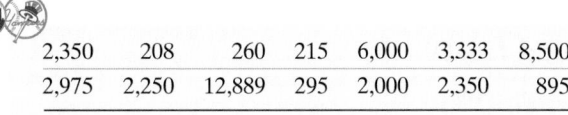

2,350	208	260	215	6,000	3,333	8,500
2,975	2,250	12,889	295	2,000	2,350	895

Source: espn.com

Test the claim that the median salary is more than $1000 thousand ($1 million) at the $\alpha = 0.05$ level of significance. (*Note:* A normal probability plot indicates the data are not normal.) Do not reject H_o

12. Miles on a Cavalier A random sample of 18 three-year-old Chevrolet Cavaliers was obtained in the Miami, Florida area, and the number of miles on each car was recorded as follows:

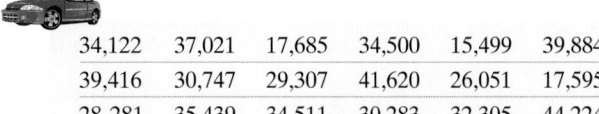

34,122	37,021	17,685	34,500	15,499	39,884
39,416	30,747	29,307	41,620	26,051	17,595
28,281	35,439	34,511	30,283	32,305	44,224

Source: cars.com

Test the claim that the median miles on three-year-old Cavaliers is less than 36,300 miles at the $\alpha = 0.05$ level of significance. (*Note:* A normal probability plot indicates that the data are not normal.) Reject H_o

---

Problems 13–16 discuss the P-value approach to testing claims regarding the median by using the sign test.

We can use the *P*-value approach when determining whether to reject the null hypothesis regarding a median via the sign test. Recall that the *P*-value is the probability of observing a test statistic as extreme or more extreme than what was actually observed, under the assumption the null hypothesis is true. In the sign test, we assume that the median is M_0, so 50% of the data should be less than M_0 and 50% of the data greater than M_0; hence, we *expect* half the data to result in minus signs and half the data to result in plus signs. We can think of the data as a bunch of plus and minus signs that follow a binomial probability distribution, with $p = \frac{1}{2}$ if the null hypothesis is true. So, the *P*-value is computed from the binomial probability formula, with $X = k$ and n equal to the number of plus and minus signs:

$$P\text{-value} = P(X \leq k) = {}_nC_k\, 0.5^k\, (1 - 0.5)^{n-k} + {}_nC_{k-1}\, 0.5^{k-1}(1 - 0.5)^{n-(k-1)} + \cdots + {}_nC_0\, (1 - 0.5)^n$$

For Example 1 in this section, the *P*-value is

$$P\text{-value} = P(X \leq 8) = {}_{20}C_8\, 0.5^8\, (1 - 0.5)^{20-8} + {}_{20}C_7\, 0.5^7(1 - 0.5)^{15} + \cdots + {}_{20}C_0\, (1 - 0.5)^{20} = 0.2517$$

Because the *P*-value is greater than the level of significance, $\alpha = 0.05$, we do not reject the null hypothesis. These binomial probabilities are easiest to compute with statistical software or a graphing calculator having advanced statistical features.

13. Determine the *P*-value of the hypothesis test performed in Problem 7. 0.0835

14. Determine the *P*-value of the hypothesis test performed in Problem 8. 0.2517

15. Determine the *P*-value of the hypothesis test performed in Problem 9. 0.0327

16. Determine the *P*-value of the hypothesis test performed in Problem 10. 0.4018

Technology Step-by-Step
One-Sample Sign Test

TI-83 Plus	The TI-83 Plus does not have this feature.
MINITAB	**Step 1:** Enter raw data in column C1.
	Step 2: Select the **Stat** menu, highlight **Nonparametrics**, then highlight **1-Sample Sign . . . .**
	Step 3: Enter C1 in the cell marked "Variables." Select "Test Median," and enter the assumed value of the median, M_0. Determine the direction of the alternative. Click OK.
Excel	Excel is not programmed to conduct the one-sample sign test.

13.4 Inferences about the Difference between Two Measures of Central Tendency: Dependent Samples

Preparing for This Section Before getting started, review the following:

✓ Median (Section 3.1, pp. 116–117)

✓ Boxplots (Section 3.5, pp. 169–173)

✓ Dependent versus independent sampling (Section 10.1, pp. 594–595)

✓ Inference about two means: dependent samples (Section 10.1, pp. 595-600)

Objectives   Test a claim about the difference between the medians of dependent samples

In this section, we compare two population medians using dependent sampling. Recall that dependent sampling occurs when the observations in each sample are somehow related, such as the measuring of a person's pulse before and after a workout regimen to discover the effect the workout has on pulse. We introduced inferential techniques on dependent samples in Section 10.1, where we first computed the differences between the matched observations. The inference was then performed on these differences by comparing the sample mean difference to the claimed difference (usually, the claimed difference is 0). If the sample size was small ($n < 30$), we needed the differences to be normally distributed. In this section, we introduce a nonparametric procedure that can be used to compare population medians even if this assumption is not satisfied. Again, we first compute differences in the matched observations.

 ### Wilcoxon Matched-Pairs Signed-Ranks Test

In 1945, F. Wilcoxon wrote an article entitled "Individual Comparisons by Ranking Methods" that was published in *Biometrics*. In this article, Wilcoxon introduced the *Wilcoxon Matched-Pairs Signed-Ranks Test*.

Definition The **Wilcoxon Matched-Pairs Signed-Ranks Test** is a nonparametric procedure that is used to test the equality of two population medians by dependent sampling.

The idea behind the Wilcoxon Matched-Pairs Signed-Ranks Test is to first compute the differences in the matched observations and then rank the differences from smallest to largest. Suppose we have the matched-pairs data shown to the right.

X	Y
5	8
3	4
7	6
9	9
8	6

We compute the differences as follows:

X	Y	D = Y − X
5	8	8 − 5 = 3
3	4	4 − 3 = 1
7	6	6 − 7 = −1
9	9	9 − 9 = 0
8	6	6 − 8 = −2

Any difference that equals 0 is eliminated from analysis. We eliminate the fourth matched-pair from the analysis, and our sample size is then reduced to $n = 4$. Now, we rank the absolute value of the differences from smallest to largest. For positive differences, the rank will be positive; for negative differences, the rank will be negative. In the case of ties, assign the mean value of the ranks that would have been assigned. For example, notice that the absolute value difference 1 occurs twice. To find the ranks, we recognize that the 1's occupy the first and second ranking positions, so the mean rank is $(1 + 2)/2 = 1.5$.

X	Y	D = Y − X	|D|	Rank
5	8	8 − 5 = 3	|3| = 3	+4
3	4	4 − 3 = 1	|1| = 1	+1.5
7	6	6 − 7 = −1	|−1| = 1	−1.5
8	6	6 − 8 = −2	|−2| = 2	−3

In Your Own Words

Just as in Section 10.1, the direction of the alternative hypothesis will depend upon how the differences are computed.

Once the ranks have been identified, we sum the ranks of the *positive differences* and denote this sum as T_+. Then we sum the ranks of the *negative differences* and denote this sum as T_-. For example, $T_+ = 4 + 1.5 = +5.5$, and $T_- = -1.5 + (-3) = -4.5$. The value of T_+ or T_- will be the test statistic, depending on the structure of the alternative hypothesis.

Suppose we were conducting a two-tailed test and the true median difference is 0 (that is, if the null hypothesis is true), then we would expect T_+ to be close to T_-. If the median for population X is greater than the median for population Y (the left-tailed test), what would we expect for the values of T_+ and T_-? Remember, we compute the differences by computing "sample population Y" − "sample population X", so if the median for population X is greater than the median for population Y, then we would expect a majority of the differences to be negative. This would lead to large values of T_- and small values of T_+. If T_+ is sufficiently small, we would reject the null hypothesis. A similar argument could be made for the right-tailed test. The test statistic is based upon this rationale.

Theorem

Test Statistic for the Wilcoxon Matched-Pairs Signed-Ranks Test

The test statistic will depend upon the size of the sample and upon the alternative hypothesis. Let n represent the number of non-zero differences.

Small-Sample Case ($n \leq 30$)

Two-Tailed	Left-Tailed	Right-Tailed
$H_0: M_D = 0$	$H_0: M_D = 0$	$H_0: M_D = 0$
$H_1: M_D \neq 0$	$H_1: M_D < 0$	$H_1: M_D > 0$
Test Statistic: T is the smaller of T_+ or T_-	**Test Statistic**: $T = T_+$	**Test Statistic**: $T = \|T_-\|$

Large-Sample Case ($n > 30$)

Following the Central Limit Theorem, the test statistic is given by

$$z = \frac{T - \dfrac{n(n + 1)}{4}}{\sqrt{\dfrac{n(n + 1)(2n + 1)}{24}}}$$

where T is the test statistic from the small-sample case.

For a left-tailed test, we would reject H_o if T_+ is too small. Do you see why? If T_+ is small, then the sum of the ranks for the positive differences is small. This happens if the values in the sample from population 1 (the x-values) are greater than the corresponding values in the sample from population 2 (the y-values), which would imply that $M_D < 0$. For a right-tailed test, we would reject H_o if T_- is too small. Do you know why?

Now that we know the procedure for obtaining the test statistic, we need to obtain a critical value.

Theorem

Critical Value for Wilcoxon Matched-Pairs Signed-Ranks Test

Small-Sample Case ($n \leq 30$)

Using α as the level of significance, the critical value(s) is obtained from Table VIII in Appendix A.

Two-Tailed	Left-Tailed	Right-Tailed
$T_{\alpha/2}$	T_α	T_α

Large-Sample Case ($n > 30$)

Using α as the level of significance, the critical value(s) is obtained from Table II in Appendix A. The critical value is always in the left tail of the standard normal distribution.

Two-Tailed	Left-Tailed	Right-Tailed
$-z_{\alpha/2}$	$-z_\alpha$	$-z_\alpha$

We now present the steps required to conduct a Wilcoxon Matched-Pairs Signed-Ranks Test.

Wilcoxon Matched-Pairs Signed-Ranks Test

If a claim is made regarding the medians of two populations, we can use the following steps to test the claim, provided that
1. the samples are dependent random samples and
2. the distribution of the differences is symmetric.
Although tests for verifying the symmetry of data exist, we shall not present them in this text. All of the data given satisfy the second requirement.

Step 1: A claim is made regarding the median difference between two populations. The claim is used to construct the null and alternative hypotheses, which are structured as follows:

Two-Tailed	Left-Tailed	Right-Tailed
$H_o: M_D = 0$	$H_o: M_D = 0$	$H_o: M_D = 0$
$H_1: M_D \neq 0$	$H_1: M_D < 0$	$H_1: M_D > 0$

Note: M_D is the median of the differences of matched pairs.

Step 2: Compute the differences in the matched-pairs observations. Rank the absolute value of all sample differences from smallest to largest after discarding those differences that equal 0. Handle ties by finding the mean of the ranks for tied values. Assign negative values to

the ranks where the differences are negative and positive values to the ranks where the differences are positive. Find the sum of the positive ranks, T_+, and the sum of the negative ranks, T_-.

Step 3: Draw a boxplot of the differences to compare the sample data from the two populations. This helps to visualize the difference in the medians.

Step 4: Choose a level of significance α based upon the seriousness of making a Type I error. The level of significance is used to determine the critical value. The critical value is found from Table VIII for small samples ($n \leq 30$). The critical value is found from Table II for large samples ($n > 30$).

Step 5: Compute the test statistic.

Small-Sample Case ($n \leq 30$)

Two-Tailed	Left-Tailed	Right-Tailed
$H_0: M_D = 0$	$H_0: M_D = 0$	$H_0: M_D = 0$
$H_1: M_D \neq 0$	$H_1: M_D < 0$	$H_1: M_D > 0$
Test Statistic: T is the smaller of T_+ and T_-.	**Test Statistic:** $T = T_+$	**Test Statistic:** $T = |T_-|$

Large-Sample Case ($n > 30$)

$$z = \frac{T - \dfrac{n(n + 1)}{4}}{\sqrt{\dfrac{n(n + 1)(2n + 1)}{24}}}$$

where T is the test statistic from the small-sample case.

Step 6: Compare the critical value with the test statistic.

Small-Sample Case	Large-Sample Case
Two-tailed: If $T < T_{\alpha/2}$, reject H_0.	**Two-tailed**: If $z < -z_{\alpha/2}$, reject H_0.
Left-tailed: If $T < T_\alpha$, reject H_0.	**Left-tailed**: If $z < -z_\alpha$, reject H_0.
Right-tailed: If $T < T_\alpha$, reject H_0.	**Right-tailed**: If $z < -z_\alpha$, reject H_0.

Step 7: State the conclusion.

▶ **EXAMPLE 1** **Illustrating the Wilcoxon Matched-Pairs Signed-Ranks Test (Small-Sample Case)**

Problem: A stock analyst read a report stating that the median daily volume of JDS Uniphase was the same as that of Nortel Networks. The analyst felt that the median daily volume of JDS Uniphase was greater than that of Nortel Networks. To test his claim, the analyst randomly selected 14 trading days, recorded the volume for each stock, and obtained the data presented in Table 5 on page 780. Test the analyst's claim at the $\alpha = 0.05$ level of significance. Note that the data are presented in millions of shares and that normal probability plots indicate that the volume for neither stock is normally distributed.

Approach: First, we recognize that this is a matched-pairs sample from the fact that the variable is measured on the same day for both stocks. Because

	TABLE 5				
Day	Nortel Networks Volume	JDS Uniphase Volume	Day	Nortel Networks Volume	JDS Uniphase Volume
1	11.5	26.0	8	17.1	16.9
2	14.1	26.2	9	27.3	50.2
3	19.3	24.6	10	13.8	33.1
4	35.0	30.8	11	43.2	99.9
5	15.9	37.5	12	11.2	26.1
6	21.7	36.0	13	34.2	43.8
7	11.7	25.9	14	26.7	63.8

Source: Yahoo! Finance

the data are not normal, we test the claim by using the Wilcoxon Matched-Pairs Signed-Ranks Test. We verify the requirements needed to perform the Wilcoxon Matched-Pairs Signed-Ranks Test and then follow Steps 1–7 on pages 778–779.

Solution: The data were obtained randomly. We assume throughout this section that the requirement of symmetry is satisfied.

Step 1: The claim is that the median volume of JDS Uniphase is greater than the median volume of Nortel Networks. We subtract the volume of Nortel Networks from the volume of JDS Uniphase for each day. If the analyst's claim is true, then the median difference should be positive, so that $M_D > 0$. We have

$$H_o: M_D = 0 \qquad \text{versus} \qquad H_1: M_D > 0$$

This is a right-tailed test.

Step 2: First, we compute the differences in the matched-pairs observations (column 4 of Table 6). Second, we calculate the absolute values of the dif-

		TABLE 6			
Day	Nortel Networks, X	JDS Uniphase, Y	$D = Y - X$	$|D|$	Signed Ranks
1	11.5	26.0	14.5	14.5	+8
2	14.1	26.2	12.1	12.1	+5
3	19.3	24.6	5.3	5.3	+3
4	35.0	30.8	−4.2	4.2	−2
5	15.9	37.5	21.6	21.6	+11
6	21.7	36.0	14.3	14.3	+7
7	11.7	25.9	14.2	14.2	+6
8	17.1	16.9	−0.2	0.2	−1
9	27.3	50.2	22.9	22.9	+12
10	13.8	33.1	19.3	19.3	+10
11	43.2	99.9	56.7	56.7	+14
12	11.2	26.1	14.9	14.9	+9
13	34.2	43.8	9.6	9.6	+4
14	26.7	63.8	37.1	37.1	+13

ferences (column 5 of the table). Next, we rank the absolute value of the sample differences from smallest to largest. Assign negative values to the ranks where the differences are negative and positive values to the ranks where the differences are positive (column 6 of the table). Because we are conducting a right-tailed test, we determine T_- by adding the negative signed ranks.

$$T_- = -2 + (-1) = -3$$

Step 3: Figure 5 shows a boxplot of the differences.

Figure 5

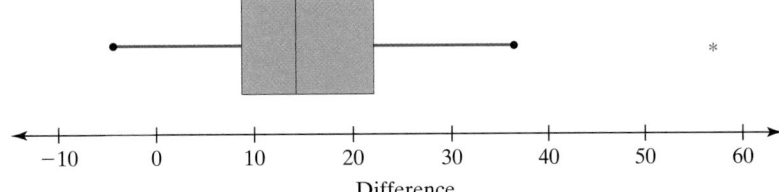

Difference

The boxplot indicates that the sample-median difference is about 14. The sample median difference is greater than 0. We need to discover whether the difference exists because the median volume of JDS Uniphase is greater than volume of Nortel Networks or can be attributed to sampling error.

Step 4: We are testing the hypothesis at the $\alpha = 0.05$ level of significance. Because we are performing a right-tailed test and the sample size is less than 30, we find the critical value with $n = 14$ at the $\alpha = 0.05$ level of significance by using Table VIII and obtain $T_{0.05} = 25$. See Figure 6.

Figure 6

	Critical Values for the Wilcoxon Signed-Rank Test Level of Significance, α			
n	0.005	0.01	0.025	0.05
5	*	*	*	0
6	*	*	0	2
7	*	0	2	3
8	0	1	3	5
9	1	3	5	8
10	3	5	8	10
11	5	7	10	13
12	7	9	13	17
13	9	12	17	21
14	12	15	21	25
15	15	19	25	30

* Indicates that it is not possible to get a value in the critical region.

Step 5: Compute the test statistic. The sample size is small, and we are conducting a right-tailed test, so the test statistic is $T = |T_-| = |-3| = 3$

Step 6: Compare the critical value to the test statistic. The test statistic is less than the critical value ($3 < 25$), so we reject the null hypothesis.

Step 7: There is sufficient evidence at the $\alpha = 0.05$ level of significance to support the claim that the median volume in JDS Uniphase is greater than the median volume in Nortel Networks. ◄◄

NW *Now Work Problem 9.*

Using Technology: The statistical software package Minitab has the ability to perform the Wilcoxon Matched-Pairs Signed-Ranks Test. Figure 7 shows the output obtained from Minitab for the hypothesis presented in Example 1. In order to perform this test, we first compute the differences and then allow Minitab to perform the test.

Figure 7

Wilcoxon Signed-Rank Test

Test of median = 0.000000 versus median > 0.000000

	N	N for Test	Wilcoxon Statistic	P	Estimated Median
differen	14	14	105.0	0.001	17.90

Minitab uses a method different from the one introduced in this section to compute the test statistic. The results are equivalent, however. We can use the *P*-value provided by Minitab to test the hypothesis: The *P*-value, 0.001, is less than the level of significance, $\alpha = 0.05$, so we reject the null hypothesis.

 Now Work Problem 17.

13.4 Assess Your Understanding

Concepts and Vocabulary

1. Suppose a researcher claims the median from population 1 is less than the median from population 2 in matched-pairs data. How would you define M_D? How would you compute the differences?

2. State the requirements of the Wilcoxon Signed-Ranks Test.

Exercises

• **Skill Building**

In Problems 1–8, use the Wilcoxon Matched-Pairs Signed-Ranks Test to test the given hypotheses at the $\alpha = 0.05$ level of significance. The dependent samples were obtained randomly.

1. Hypotheses: $H_0: M_D = 0$ versus $H_1: M_D > 0$ with $n = 12$ and $T_- = 16$. Reject H_o

2. Hypotheses: $H_0: M_D = 0$ versus $H_1: M_D > 0$ with $n = 20$ and $T_- = 65$. Do not reject H_o

3. Hypotheses: $H_0: M_D = 0$ versus $H_1: M_D < 0$ with $n = 15$ and $T_+ = 33$. Do not reject H_o

4. Hypotheses: $H_0: M_D = 0$ versus $H_1: M_D < 0$ with $n = 25$ and $T_+ = 95$. Reject H_o

5. Hypotheses: $H_0: M_D = 0$ versus $H_1: M_D \neq 0$ with $n = 18$, $T_- = 121$, and $T_+ = 50$. Do not reject H_o

6. Hypotheses: $H_0: M_D = 0$ versus $H_1: M_D \neq 0$ with $n = 14$, $T_- = 45$, and $T_+ = 60$. Do not reject H_o

7. Hypotheses: $H_0: M_D = 0$ versus $H_1: M_D > 0$ with $n = 40$ and $T_- = 300$. Do not reject H_o

8. Hypotheses: $H_0: M_D = 0$ versus $H_1: M_D < 0$ with $n = 35$ and $T_+ = 210$. Reject H_o

• **Applying the Concepts**

9. **The Effects of Exercise** In order to learn the effectiveness of an exercise regimen, a physical therapist randomly selects 10 women to participate in a study. She measures their waistlines before a rigorous exercise program and 8 weeks after the program begins. She obtains the following data:

Waistline Before (inches)	23.5	18.5	21.5	24	25	19.75	35	36.5	52	30
Waistline After (inches)	19.75	19.25	21.75	22.5	25	19.5	34.25	35	51.5	31

Test the claim that the median waistline before the exercise program is more than the median waistline after the exercise program at the $\alpha = 0.05$ level of significance. *Do not reject H_o*

10. **The Effects of Exercise** A physical therapist wishes to learn whether an exercise program increases flexibility. She measures the flexibility (in inches) of 12 randomly selected subjects both before and after an intensive eight-week training program and obtains the following data:

Before	18.5	21.5	16.5	21	20	15	19.75	15.75	18	22	15	20.5
After	19.25	21.75	16.5	20.25	22.25	16	19.5	17	19.25	19.5	16.5	20

Test the claim that the median flexibility before the exercise program is less than the median flexibility after the exercise program at the $\alpha = 0.05$ level of significance. *Do not reject H_o*

11. **Reaction Time** In an experiment conducted on-line at the University of Mississippi, participants are asked to react to a stimulus. In one particular experiment, the participant must press a key upon seeing a blue screen. The time to press the key (in seconds) is measured. The same person is then asked to press a key upon seeing a red screen, again with the time to react measured. The results for six study participants are as follows:

Do not reject H_o

Participant Number	Reaction Time to Blue	Reaction Time to Red
1	0.582	0.408
2	0.481	0.407
3	0.841	0.542
4	0.267	0.402
5	0.685	0.456
6	0.45	0.533

Source: PsychExperiments at the University of Mississippi

Test the claim that the median reaction time to the blue stimulus is different from the median reaction time to the red stimulus at the $\alpha = 0.05$ level of significance.

12. **Rat Hemoglobin** Hemoglobin helps the red blood cells transport oxygen and remove carbon dioxide. Researchers at NASA wanted to discover the effects of space flight on a rat's hemoglobin. The following data represent the hemoglobin (in grams per deciliter) at lift-off minus three days (H-L3) and immediately upon the return (H-R0) for 12 randomly selected rats sent to space on the Spacelab Sciences 1 flight: *Reject H_o*

Rat #	H-L3	H-R0	Rat #	H-L3	H-R0
1	15.2	15.8	7	14.3	16.4
2	16.1	16.5	8	14.5	16.5
3	15.3	16.7	9	15.2	16.0
4	16.4	15.7	10	16.1	16.8
5	15.7	16.9	11	15.1	17.6
6	14.7	13.1	12	15.8	16.9

Source: NASA Life Sciences Data Archive

Test the claim that the median hemoglobin level at lift-off minus 3 days is less than the median hemoglobin level upon return at the $\alpha = 0.05$ level of significance.

13. **Secchi Disk** A Secchi disk is an eight-inch-diameter weighted disk that is painted black and white and attached to a rope. The disk is lowered into water, and the depth (in inches) at which it is no longer visible is recorded. The measurement is an indication of water clarity. A environmental biologist is interested in discovering whether the water clarity of the lake at Joliet Junior College is improving. She takes measurements at

the same location on the same dates during the course of a year and repeats the measurements on the same dates 5 years later. She obtains the following results:

Observation	Date	Initial Depth	Depth 5 Years Later
1	5/11	38	52
2	6/7	58	60
3	6/24	65	72
4	7/8	74	72
5	7/27	56	54
6	8/31	36	48
7	9/30	56	58
8	10/12	52	60

Source: Virginia Piekarski, Joliet Junior College

Do not reject H_o

Test the claim that the median clarity of the lake is improving at the $\alpha = 0.05$ level of significance.

14. **The Effect of Aspirin on Blood Clotting** Blood clotting is due to a sequence of chemical reactions. The protein thrombin initiates blood clotting by working with another protein, prothrombin. It is common to measure a individual's blood clotting time as *prothrombin time*—the time between the start of the thrombin–prothrombin reaction and the formation of the clot. Researchers wanted to study the effect of aspirin on prothrombin time. They randomly selected 12 subjects and measured the prothrombin time (in seconds) without taking aspirin and three hours after taking two aspirin tablets. They obtained the following data:

Subject	Before Aspirin	After Aspirin	Subject	Before Aspirin	After Aspirin
1	12.3	12.0	7	11.3	10.3
2	12.0	12.3	8	11.8	11.3
3	12.0	12.5	9	11.5	11.5
4	13.0	12.0	10	11.0	11.5
5	13.0	13.0	11	11.0	11.0
6	12.5	12.5	12	11.3	11.5

Source: Yochem, Donald; and Roach, Darrell. "Aspirin: Effect of Thrombus Formation Time and Prothrombin Time of Human Subjects." *Angiology*, 22 (1971), pg. 70–76.

Test the claim that aspirin affects the median time it takes for a clot to form at the $\alpha = 0.05$ level of significance. *Do not reject H_o*

15. **Car Rentals** The following data represent the daily rental rate for a compact car charged by two car-rental companies, Thrifty and Hertz, in 10 locations:

City	Thrifty	Hertz
Chicago	21.81	18.99
Los Angeles	29.89	48.99
Houston	17.90	19.99
Orlando	27.98	35.99
Boston	24.61	25.60
Seattle	21.96	22.99
Pittsburgh	20.90	19.99
Phoenix	47.75	36.99
New Orleans	33.81	26.99
Minneapolis	33.49	20.99

Source: Yahoo! Travel

Test the claim that Thrifty charges less than Hertz at the $\alpha = 0.05$ level of significance. *Do not reject H_o*

16. **Does Octane Affect Miles per Gallon?** A researcher wants to know whether the octane level of gasoline affects the miles per gallon of a car. She randomly selects 10 cars and puts 5 gallons of 87 octane gasoline in the tank. On a closed track, each car is driven at 50 miles per hour until it runs out of gas. The experiment is repeated, with each car getting 5 gallons of 92 octane gasoline. The miles per gallon for each car are then computed. The results are as follows:

87 Octane	92 Octane	87 Octane	92 Octane
18.0	18.5	23.4	22.8
23.2	23.1	23.1	23.5
31.5	31.9	19.0	19.5
24.9	26.7	26.8	26.2
24.1	25.1	31.8	30.7

Test the claim that the median miles per gallon for 92 octane is greater than the median miles per gallon for 87 octane at the $\alpha = 0.05$ level of significance. *Do not reject H_o*

17. Rats' Red Blood Cell Counts Researchers at NASA wanted to learn the effects of spaceflight on a rat's red blood cell count (RBC). The following data represent the red blood cell count at lift-off minus 3 days (RBC-L3) and immediately upon the return (RBC-R0) of 27 rats sent to space on the Spacelab Sciences 1 flight:

Rat #	RBC–L3	RBC–R0	Rat #	RBC–L3	RBC–R0	Rat #	RBC–L3	RBC–R0	Rat #	RBC–L3	RBC–R0
112	7.53	8.16	136	7.95	9.55	79	7.79	8.52	156	7.27	9.11
145	7.79	9.15	127	8.44	9.38	47	8.24	8.59	128	8.23	9.81
15	7.84	9.09	153	6.70	9.66	109	7.69	7.29	99	14.50	9.86
142	6.86	8.42	97	6.95	8.83	13	7.23	8.93	90	7.73	9.90
45	7.93	8.96	94	6.73	8.46	74	7.83	8.64	82	7.31	7.64
150	7.48	9.25	124	7.21	9.04	126	8.09	9.65	55	7.84	9.54
162	7.94	7.40	117	6.95	9.48	157	8.27	8.76			

Source: NASA Life Sciences Data Archive

They used Minitab to test the claim that the median red blood cell count three days prior to lift-off was different from the median red blood cell count upon return. The results are as follows:

Wilcoxon Signed-Rank Test

```
Test of median = 0.000000 versus median not = 0.000000

                       N for   Wilcoxon              Estimated
               N       Test    Statistic        P       Median
differen      27        27         343.0    0.000        1.255
```

(a) State the null and alternative hypotheses. $H_o: M_D = 0$ vs $H_i: M_D \neq 0$
(b) Does it appear that the flight to space affected the red blood cell count of the rats at the $\alpha = 0.05$ level of significance? Support your answer. Yes

18. Reaction-Time Experiment Researchers at the University of Mississippi wanted to learn the reaction times of students to different stimuli. In the data that follow, the reaction time for subjects was measured after they received a simple stimulus and a go/no-go stimulus. The simple stimulus presented an auditory cue, and the time from when the cue was given to when the student reacted was measured. The go/no-go stimulus required the student to respond to a particular stimulus and not respond to other stimuli. Again, the reaction time was measured. The following data were obtained:

Subject Number	Simple	Go/No Go	Subject Number	Simple	Go/No Go
1	0.22	0.375	16	0.498	0.565
2	0.43	1.759	17	0.262	0.402
3	0.338	0.652	18	0.62	0.643
4	0.266	0.467	19	0.3	0.351
5	0.381	0.651	20	0.424	0.38
6	0.738	0.442	21	0.478	0.434
7	0.885	1.246	22	0.305	0.452
8	0.683	0.224	23	0.281	0.745
9	0.25	0.654	24	0.291	0.29
10	0.255	0.442	25	0.453	0.79
11	0.198	0.347	26	0.376	0.792
12	0.352	0.698	27	0.328	0.613
13	0.285	0.803	28	0.952	1.179
14	0.259	0.488	29	0.355	0.636
15	0.2	0.281	30	0.368	0.391

Source: PsychExperiments at The University of Mississippi

The researchers used Minitab to test the claim that the simple stimulus had a lower reaction time than the go/no-go stimulus. The results of the analysis are as follows:

Wilcoxon Signed-Rank Test

```
Test of median = 0.000000 versus median   >    0.000000

                 N for   Wilcoxon                     Estimated
           N     Test    Statistic           P           Median
differen   30     30        408.0         0.000         1.1920
```

(a) State the null and alternative hypotheses. $H_o: M_D = 0$ vs $H_1: M_D > 0$
(b) Is the median reaction time for the go/no-go stimulus higher than the median reaction time for the simple stimulus at the $\alpha = 0.05$ level of significance? Why? Yes

Technology Step-by-Step
Wilcoxon Signed-Rank Test of Matched-Pairs Data

TI-83 Plus   The TI-83 Plus does not have this feature.

MINITAB   **Step 1:** Enter the differenced data in column C1.

Step 2: Select the **Stat** menu, highlight **Nonparametrics**, then highlight **1-Sample Wilcoxon . . . .**

Step 3: Enter C1 in the cell marked "Variables." Click "Test Median," and enter "0" in the cell. Click OK.

Excel   Excel is not programmed to conduct this test.

13.5   Inferences about the Difference between Two Measures of Central Tendency: Independent Samples

Preparing for This Section   Before getting started, review the following:

✓ Median (Section 3.1, pp. 116–117)

✓ Boxplots (Section 3.5, pp. 169–173)

✓ Independent versus dependent sampling (Section 10.1, pp. 594–595)

✓ Inference about two means: independent samples (Section 10.2, pp. 607–614)

Objectives   Test a claim about the difference between the medians of two independent samples

In Section 10.2, we learned how to test for the equality of two population means with independent sampling. With independent sampling, the individuals in the sample from population 1 are not related to the individuals in the sample from population 2. The methods used to test for the difference between two population means required that each of the populations be normally distributed when the sample size was small ($n_1 < 30, n_2 < 30$). In this section, we introduce nonparametric procedures that can test claims regarding the equality of two measures of central tendency even if this requirement is not satisfied.

Mann–Whitney Test

In 1947, H.B. Mann and D.R. Whitney introduced a nonparametric technique that can be used to test the equality of two population medians in the case of independent sampling.

Definition

> The **Mann–Whitney Test** is a nonparametric procedure that is used to test the equality of two population medians from independent samples.

The idea behind the Mann–Whitney Test is to combine the two samples and rank *all* the observations from smallest to largest. We handle ties by finding the mean of the ranks for tied values. For example, if the data for the sample corresponding to population X are

$$2, 3, 5, 8$$

and the data for the sample corresponding to population Y are

$$1, 3, 4$$

then we combine and rank the data as follows:

Combined Data	Rank
1	1
2	2
3	3.5
3	3.5
4	5
5	6
8	7

D. Ransom Whitney

⧗ Historical Note

Henry B. Mann and his graduate student D. Ransom Whitney were comparing wage data from 1940 with wage data from 1944. Their goal was to show that the distribution of wages in 1940 was less than the distribution of wages in 1944. To conduct this analysis, they devised the Mann–Whitney test; they published the technique used to analyze the data in 1947, in an article entitled "On a Test of Whether One of Two Random Variables Is Stochastically Larger than the Other" in the *Annals of Mathematical Statistics*.

Notice that we observed a 3 twice. To find the rank of 3, we recognize that the 3s occupy the third and fourth ranking positions. So the mean rank is $(3 + 4)/2 = 3.5$.

Once the ranks have been identified, we sum the ranks of the sample observations from population X *only*. The sum of the ranks from the sample observations from population X would be $2 + 3.5 + 6 + 7 = 18.5$. If the two populations have the same median (that is, if the null hypothesis is true), then we would expect the sum of the ranks for the sample observations from population X to be close to the sum of the ranks for the sample observations from population Y. If the median for population X is less than the median for population Y (left-tailed test), we would expect the sum of the ranks for the sample observations from population X to be less than the sum of the ranks for the sample observations from population Y.

Suppose we were conducting a right-tailed test and the alternative hypothesis were true. What would we expect the sum of the ranks for the sample observations for population X to be in relation to the sum of the ranks for the sample observations for population Y? We should expect the sum of the ranks for the sample observations from population X to be greater than the sum of the ranks for the sample observations from population Y. The test statistic is based upon this rationale.

Theorem

Test Statistic for the Mann–Whitney Test

The test statistic will depend upon the size of the samples from each population. Let n_1 represent the sample size for population X and n_2 represent the sample size for population Y.

Small-Sample Case ($n_1 \le 20$ and $n_2 \le 20$)

If S is the sum of the ranks corresponding to the sample from population X, then the test statistic, T, is given by

$$T = S - \frac{n_1(n_1 + 1)}{2}$$

Note: The value of S is always obtained by summing the ranks of the sample data that correspond to M_x, the median of population X, in the hypothesis.

Large-Sample Case ($n_1 > 20$ or $n_2 > 20$)

From the Central Limit Theorem, the test statistic is given by

$$z = \frac{T - \dfrac{n_1 n_2}{2}}{\sqrt{\dfrac{n_1 n_2 (n_1 + n_2 + 1)}{12}}}$$

where T is the test statistic from the small-sample case.

For a two-tailed test, we would reject $H_0: M_X = M_Y$ if T is too large or too small. To test $H_1: M_X < M_Y$ (a left-tailed test), we would reject $H_0: M_X = M_Y$ if T is too small. Do you see why? If T is small, then the sum of the ranks for population X is small. This happens if the sample observations from population X are less than the sample observations from population Y, which would imply that $M_x < M_y$. For a right-tailed test, we would reject H_0 if T is too large. Do you know why?

Now that we know the procedure for obtaining the test statistic, we need to obtain a critical value.

Theorem

Critical Value for Mann–Whitney Test

Small-Sample Case ($n_1 \le 20$ and $n_2 \le 20$)

Using α as the level of significance, the critical value(s) is(are) obtained from Table IX in Appendix A.

Two-Tailed	**Left-Tailed**	**Right-Tailed**
$w_{\alpha/2}$	w_α	$w_{1-\alpha} = n_1 n_2 - w_\alpha$
$w_{1-\alpha/2} = n_1 n_2 - w_{\alpha/2}$		

Large-Sample Case ($n_1 > 20$ or $n_2 > 20$)

Using α as the level of significance, the critical value(s) is(are) obtained from Table II in Appendix A.

Two-Tailed	**Left-Tailed**	**Right-Tailed**
$z_{\alpha/2}$ and $-z_{\alpha/2}$	$-z_\alpha$	z_α

We now present the steps required to conduct a Mann–Whitney Test.

Mann–Whitney Test

If a claim is made regarding the medians of a population, we can use the following steps to test the claim, provided that
1. the samples are independent random samples and
2. the distributions of the two populations are the same, except possibly for the median.

Throughout this section, we will assume that the condition that the distributions for the two populations be the same is satisfied.

Step 1: Draw a side-by-side boxplot to compare the sample data from the two populations. This helps to visualize the difference in the medians.

Step 2: A claim is made regarding the medians of the two populations. The claim is used to determine the null and alternative hypotheses. The hypotheses are structured as follows:

Two-Tailed	Left-Tailed	Right-Tailed
$H_0: M_x = M_y$	$H_0: M_x = M_y$	$H_0: M_x = M_y$
$H_1: M_x \neq M_y$	$H_1: M_x < M_y$	$H_1: M_x > M_y$

Note: M_x is the median of population X, and M_y is the median of population Y.

Step 3: Rank all sample observations from smallest to largest. Handle ties by finding the mean of the ranks for tied values. Find the sum of the ranks for the sample from population X.

Step 4: Choose a level of significance α to match the seriousness of making a Type I error. The level of significance is used to determine the critical value. The critical value is found from Table IX for small samples ($n_1 \leq 20$ and $n_2 \leq 20$) and from Table II for large samples ($n_1 > 20$ or $n_2 > 20$).

Step 5: Compute the test statistic. Note that S is the sum of the ranks obtained from the sample observations from population X. In addition, n_1 is the size of the sample from population X, and n_2 is the size of the sample from population Y.

Small-Sample Case	Large-Sample Case
$T = S - \dfrac{n_1(n_1 + 1)}{2}$	$z = \dfrac{T - \dfrac{n_1 n_2}{2}}{\sqrt{\dfrac{n_1 n_2 (n_1 + n_2 + 1)}{12}}}$

Step 6: Compare the critical value with the test statistic.

Small-Sample Case	Large-Sample Case
Two-tailed: If $T < w_{\alpha/2}$ or $T > w_{1-\alpha/2}$, reject H_0. *Note*: $w_{1-\alpha/2} = n_1 n_2 - w_{\alpha/2}$	**Two-tailed**: If $z < -z_{\alpha/2}$ or $z > z_{\alpha/2}$, reject H_0.
Left-tailed: If $T < w_\alpha$, reject H_0.	**Left-tailed**: If $z < -z_\alpha$, reject H_0.
Right-tailed: If $T > w_{1-\alpha}$, reject H_0. *Note*: $w_{1-\alpha} = n_1 n_2 - w_\alpha$	**Right-tailed**: If $z > z_\alpha$, reject H_0.

Step 7: State the conclusion.

▶ **EXAMPLE 1** **Illustrating the Mann–Whitney Test (Small-Sample Case)**

Problem: When a person is exposed to an infection, the person typically develops antibodies. The extent to which the antibodies respond can be measured by looking at a person's titer, which is a measure of the number of antibodies present. The higher the titer, the more antibodies are present. The data in Table 7 represent the titers of 11 ill people and 11 healthy people exposed to the tularemia virus in Vermont.

TABLE 7							
Ill				**Healthy**			
640	160	1280	320	10	320	160	160
80	640	640	160	320	320	10	320
1280	640	160		320	80	640	

Source: Adapted from "An Introduction to Mathematical Statistics and Its Applications" by R. Larsen and M. Marx. Prentice-Hall, 2001

Test the claim that the level of titer in the ill group is greater than the level of titer in the healthy group, at the $\alpha = 0.1$ level of significance.

Approach: Normal probability plots indicate that the sample data do not come from a population that is normal. Therefore, we will use the Mann–Whitney Test. Throughout the section, we assume the distribution of the populations is the same. We then proceed to follow Steps 1–7 listed on page 789.

Solution: The titer levels were obtained from independent, random samples.

Step 1: Figure 8 shows the boxplots of the two samples. The median for the ill group equals Q_3, which equals 640. The median for the healthy group equals Q_3, which equals 320.

Figure 8

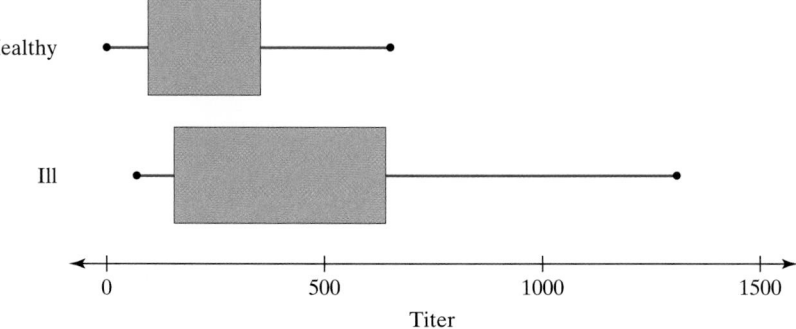

The sample median for the ill individuals is more than the sample median for the healthy individuals. We need to estimate whether this difference is due to differences in the population medians or to sampling error.

Step 2: The claim is that the median titer for the ill group is greater than the median titer for the healthy group. This claim can be written $M_{ILL} > M_{HEALTHY}$. We have

$$H_0: M_{ILL} = M_{HEALTHY} \qquad \text{versus} \qquad H_1: M_{ILL} > M_{HEALTHY}$$

This is a right-tailed test.

TABLE 8			
Titer	Rank	Titer	Rank
10	1.5	320	12.5
10	1.5	320	12.5
80	3.5	320	12.5
80	3.5	320	12.5
160	7	640	18
160	7	640	18
160	7	640	18
160	7	640	18
160	7	640	18
320	12.5	1280	21.5
320	12.5	1280	21.5

Step 3: We combine the two sample data sets into one data set and arrange the data in ascending order. Be sure to keep track of the population from which the sample was drawn. Then assign ranks to each observation. See Table 8. We now add up the ranks corresponding to ill individuals (because this group corresponds to the median on the left in the hypothesis) and obtain

$$S = 18 + 3.5 + 21.5 + 7 + 18 + 18 + 21.5 + 18 + 7 + 12.5 + 7 = 152$$

Step 4: Because we are performing a right-tailed test and both sample sizes are less than 20, we determine the right critical value with $n_1 = 11$ and $n_2 = 11$ at the $\alpha = 0.10$ level of significance from Table IX and obtain $w_{0.9} = n_1 n_2 - w_{0.10} = (11)(11) - 41 = 80$. See Figure 9.

Step 5: The test statistic is

$$T = S - \frac{n_1(n_1 + 1)}{2} = 152 - \frac{11(11 + 1)}{2} = 86$$

Step 6: Because the test statistic ($T = 86$) is greater than the critical value, 80, we reject the null hypothesis.

Figure 9

n_1	p	$n_2 = 2$	3	4	5	6	7	8	9	10	11	12	13	14	15
							Critical Values of the Mann–Whitney Test Statistic								
	0.001	0	0	1	2	4	6	7	9	11	13	15	18	20	22
	0.005	0	1	3	5	7	10	12	14	17	19	22	25	27	30
10	0.01	0	2	4	7	9	12	14	17	20	23	25	28	31	34
	0.025	1	4	6	9	12	15	18	21	24	27	30	34	37	40
	0.05	2	5	8	12	15	18	21	25	28	32	35	38	42	45
	0.10	4	7	11	14	18	22	25	29	33	37	40	44	48	52
	0.001	0	0	1	3	5	7	9	11	13	16	18	21	23	25
	0.005	0	1	3	6	8	11	14	17	19	22	25	28	31	34
11	0.01	0	2	5	8	10	13	16	19	23	26	29	32	35	38
	0.025	1	4	7	10	14	17	20	24	27	31	34	38	41	45
	0.05	2	6	9	13	17	20	24	28	32	35	39	43	47	51
	0.10	4	8	12	16	20	24	28	32	37	41	45	49	53	58
	0.001	0	0	1	3	5	8	10	13	15	18	21	24	26	29
	0.005	0	2	4	7	10	13	16	19	22	25	28	32	35	38
12	0.01	0	3	6	9	12	15	18	22	25	29	32	36	39	43
	0.025	2	5	8	12	15	19	23	27	30	34	38	42	46	50
	0.05	3	6	10	14	18	22	27	31	35	39	43	48	52	56
	0.10	5	9	13	18	22	27	31	36	40	45	50	54	59	64
	0.001	0	0	2	4	6	9	12	15	18	21	24	27	30	33
	0.005	0	2	4	8	11	14	18	21	25	28	32	35	39	43
13	0.01	1	3	6	10	13	17	21	24	28	32	36	40	44	48
	0.025	2	5	9	13	17	21	25	29	34	38	42	46	51	55
	0.05	3	7	11	16	20	25	29	34	38	43	48	52	57	62
	0.10	5	10	14	19	24	29	34	39	44	49	54	59	64	69
	0.001	0	0	2	4	7	10	13	16	20	23	26	30	33	37
	0.005	0	2	5	8	12	16	19	23	27	31	35	39	43	47
14	0.01	1	3	7	11	14	18	23	27	31	35	39	44	48	52
	0.025	2	6	10	14	18	23	27	32	37	41	46	51	56	60
	0.05	4	8	12	17	22	27	32	37	42	47	52	57	62	67
	0.10	5	11	16	21	26	32	37	42	48	53	59	64	70	75
	0.001	0	0	2	5	8	11	15	18	22	25	29	33	37	41
	0.005	0	3	6	9	13	17	21	25	30	34	38	43	47	52
15	0.01	1	4	8	12	16	20	25	29	34	38	43	48	52	57
	0.025	2	6	11	15	20	25	30	35	40	45	50	55	60	65

Step 7: There is sufficient evidence to support the claim that the median titer of the ill individuals is greater than the median titer of the healthy individuals at the $\alpha = 0.1$ level of significance. ◄◄

NW *Now Work Problem 9.*

We now present an example of the Mann–Whitney Test with large samples.

► EXAMPLE 2   **Illustrating the Mann–Whitney Test (Large-Sample Case)**

Problem: An environmentalist wanted to test the claim that the pH level of rainwater in Colorado County, Texas, is less than the pH level of rainwater in Hill County, Montana. A lower pH level means that the acidity of the rain is higher. She randomly selects 22 weeks in which it rained at least once during the week between January 1999 and January 2000 in the Texas location and measures the pH level of the rainwater. She obtains an independent random sample of 20 weeks in which it rained at least once during the week between January 1999 and January 2000 for the Montana location. Test the environmentalist's claim at the $\alpha = 0.05$ level of significance, using the data in Table 9.

TABLE 9							
Texas				**Montana**			
4.53	5.10	5.23	4.52	5.11	5.75	5.28	5.15
4.05	6.44	4.95	4.40	5.26	5.29	5.46	4.82
5.55	4.86	5.20	4.38	5.41	5.74	5.44	5.96
4.94	5.35	5.56	4.55	5.13	4.98	4.89	5.85
5.13	4.49	4.25		5.91	5.31	5.88	4.75
4.79	4.49	5.29					

Source: National Atmospheric Deposition Program

The Approach: We verify that the assumption of independent, random samples is satisfied and then proceed to follow Steps 1–7 on page 789.

The Solution: The samples are independent, random samples.

Step 1: To visualize the difference in the medians, we construct a side-by-side boxplot of the two data sets. See Figure 10. We need to determine whether this difference is due to differences in the population medians or to sampling error.

Figure 10

Montana

Texas

4.0   4.5   5.0   5.5   6.0   6.5

pH

Step 2: The claim is that the median pH level in Texas is less than the median pH level in Montana. This claim can be written $M_{\text{Texas}} < M_{\text{Montana}}$. We have

$$H_o: M_{\text{Texas}} = M_{\text{Montana}} \qquad \text{versus} \qquad H_1: M_{\text{Texas}} < M_{\text{Montana}}.$$

This is a left-tailed test.

Step 3: We combine the two sample data sets into one data set and arrange the data in ascending order. Be sure to keep track of the population from which the sample was drawn. Then assign ranks to each observation. See Table 10.

TABLE 10					
State	**pH-level**	**Rank**	**State**	**pH-level**	**Rank**
Texas	4.05	1	Montana	5.15	22
Texas	4.25	2	Texas	5.20	23
Texas	4.38	3	Texas	5.23	24
Texas	4.40	4	Montana	5.26	25
Texas	4.49	5.5	Montana	5.28	26
Texas	4.49	5.5	Texas	5.29	27.5
Texas	4.52	7	Montana	5.29	27.5
Texas	4.53	8	Montana	5.31	29
Texas	4.55	9	Texas	5.35	30
Montana	4.75	10	Montana	5.41	31
Texas	4.79	11	Montana	5.44	32
Montana	4.82	12	Montana	5.46	33
Texas	4.86	13	Texas	5.55	34
Montana	4.89	14	Texas	5.56	35
Texas	4.94	15	Montana	5.74	36
Texas	4.95	16	Montana	5.75	37
Montana	4.98	17	Montana	5.85	38
Texas	5.10	18	Montana	5.88	39
Montana	5.11	19	Montana	5.91	40
Texas	5.13	20.5	Montana	5.96	41
Montana	5.13	20.5	Texas	6.44	42

We now add up the ranks corresponding to the Texas data (because this group corresponds to the median on the left in the hypothesis) and obtain

$$S = 1 + 2 + 3 + \ldots + 34 + 35 + 42 = 354$$

Step 4: Because we are performing a left-tailed test and the sample size for Texas is greater than 20, we locate the critical value in Table II, for the $\alpha = 0.05$ level of significance, and obtain $-z_{0.05} = -1.645$. Figure 11 shows the standard normal curve with the critical region shaded.

Step 5: We first need to find the value of T:

$$T = S - \frac{n_1(n_1 + 1)}{2} = 354 - \frac{22(22 + 1)}{2} = 101$$

Figure 11

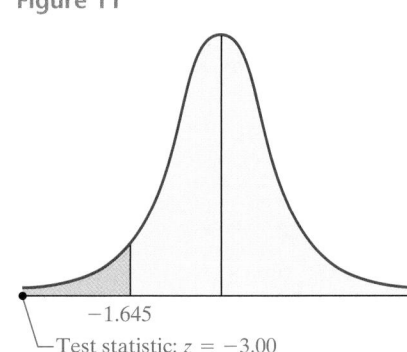

-1.645

Test statistic: $z = -3.00$

The test statistic is

$$z = \dfrac{T - \dfrac{n_1 n_2}{2}}{\sqrt{\dfrac{n_1 n_2 (n_1 + n_2 + 1)}{12}}} = \dfrac{101 - \dfrac{22(20)}{2}}{\sqrt{\dfrac{22(20)(22 + 20 + 1)}{12}}} = -3.00$$

Step 6: Because the test statistic, $z = -3.00$, is less than the critical value, $-z_{0.05} = -1.645$, we reject the null hypothesis. Figure 11 shows the test statistic along with the critical value.

Step 7: There is sufficient evidence to support the claim that the median pH level in Colorado County, Texas is less than the median pH level of rainwater in Hill County, Montana. ◄◄

NW *Now Work Problem 13.*

Using Technology: The statistical software package Minitab has the ability to perform the Mann–Whitney Test. Figure 12 shows the output obtained for the hypothesis presented in Example 2.

Figure 12

Mann–Whitney Confidence Interval and Test

```
texas          N = 22        Median =     4.9000
montana        N = 20        Median =     5.3000
Point estimate for ETA1-ETA2 is     -0.5000
95.2 Percent CI for ETA1-ETA2 is (−0.7799,−0.1900)
W = 354.0
Test of ETA1 = ETA2 vs ETA1 < ETA2 is significant at 0.0014
The test is significant at 0.0014 (adjusted for ties)
```

Notice that Minitab presents a W test statistic. The W given by Minitab is the sum of the ranks from sample 1. That is, it is the S that we computed. Notice that Minitab provides the P-value of the test as 0.0014. Because the P-value is less than the level of significance, we reject the null hypothesis.

13.5 Assess Your Understanding

Concepts and Vocabulary

1. Explain the rationale behind the test statistic for the Mann–Whitney Test.

2. Explain the rationale behind the decision rule for the Mann–Whitney Test.

Exercises

• Skill Building

In Problems 1–8, use the Mann–Whitney Test to test the given hypotheses at the $\alpha = 0.05$ level of significance. The independent samples were obtained randomly.

1. Hypotheses: $H_0: M_x = M_y$ versus $H_1: M_x \neq M_y$ with $n_1 = 12, n_2 = 15$ and $S = 170$. Do not reject H_o

2. Hypotheses: $H_0: M_x = M_y$ versus $H_1: M_x \neq M_y$ with $n_1 = 10, n_2 = 8$ and $S = 100$. Do not reject H_o

3. Hypotheses: $H_0: M_x = M_y$ versus $H_1: M_x < M_y$ with $n_1 = 18, n_2 = 16$ and $S = 210$. Reject H_o

4. Hypotheses: $H_0: M_x = M_y$ versus $H_1: M_x < M_y$ with $n_1 = 13, n_2 = 17$ and $S = 180$. Do not reject H_o

5. Hypotheses: $H_0: M_x = M_y$ versus $H_1: M_x > M_y$ with $n_1 = 15, n_2 = 15$ and $S = 250$. Do not reject H_o

6. Hypotheses: $H_0: M_x = M_y$ versus $H_1: M_x > M_y$ with $n_1 = 12, n_2 = 15$ and $S = 220$. Reject H_o

7. Hypotheses: $H_0: M_x = M_y$ versus $H_1: M_x \neq M_y$ with $n_1 = 22, n_2 = 25$ and $S = 590$. Do not reject H_o

8. Hypotheses: $H_0: M_x = M_y$ versus $H_1: M_x > M_y$ with $n_1 = 34, n_2 = 30$ and $S = 1310$. Reject H_o

• Applying the Concepts

9. **Housing Prices** In 2001, the Boeing Company decided to move its corporate headquarters out of Seattle, Washington. Two of the cities it was considering for the new corporate headquarters were Denver, Colorado, and Chicago, Illinois. Suppose one of the factors in the decision was the cost of housing. The following data represent a random sample of properties recently sold in each of the two cities:

Denver					
99,000	429,700	227,000	180,000	189,900	202,900
161,900	122,900	865,000	245,000	267,500	305,700
209,900	170,000	135,900	137,000	154,200	

Source: Denver Post web site

Chicago					
198,000	172,000	680,000	107,000	74,500	285,000
183,000	150,000	116,500	592,000	283,500	120,000
38,500	53,500				

Source: Chicago Tribune web site

Test the claim that the median price of a home in Denver is different from the median price of a home in Chicago at the $\alpha = 0.05$ level of significance. *Note*: Neither city's normal probability plot indicates that its data are normally distributed. Do not reject H_o

10. **Weights of Linemen** A researcher claimed that the median weight of an NFL offensive tackle was higher than the median weight of an NFL defensive tackle. He randomly selected 10 offensive tackles and 8 defensive tackles and obtained the following data:

Offensive Linemen				
323	295	305	380	309
320	328	313	318	305

Defensive Linemen			
289	250	305	310
295	278	300	339

Source: nfl.com

Test the researcher's claim at the $\alpha = 0.05$ level of significance. *Note*: A normal probability plot indicates that the weight of offensive linemen is not normally distributed. Reject H_o

11. **Bacteria in Carpeting** Researchers wanted to discover whether the median amount of bacteria in carpeted rooms was greater than the median amount of bacteria in uncarpeted rooms. To determine the amount of bacteria in a room, researchers pumped the air from the room over a Petri dish at the rate of 1 cubic foot per minute for 8 carpeted rooms and 8 uncarpeted rooms. Colonies of bacteria were allowed to form in the 16 Petri dishes. The results are presented in the following table:

Carpeted Rooms (Bacteria/cubic foot)		Uncarpeted Rooms (Bacteria/cubic foot)	
11.8	10.8	12.1	12.0
8.2	10.1	8.3	11.1
7.1	14.6	3.8	10.1
13.0	14.0	7.2	13.7

Source: Walter, William G., and Stober, Angie, "Microbial Air Sampling in a Carpeted Hospital." *Journal of Environmental Health*, **30** (1968), p. 405.

Test the claim that the median amount of bacteria in carpeted rooms was greater than the median amount of bacteria in uncarpeted rooms at the $\alpha = 0.05$ level of significance. Do not reject H_o

12. **Rats in Space** Researchers at NASA wanted to judge the effects of spaceflight on a rat's tibia. The following data represent the length (in millimeters) of the right tibia upon return from the Spacelab Life Sciences 2 flight for a flight (experimental) group and ground (control) group of six rats each:

Experimental Group	Control Group
36.05	34.93
35.57	34.68
35.57	34.20
34.58	34.41
34.20	34.42
34.73	34.93

Source: NASA Life Sciences Data Archive

Test the claim that the median tibia length in the experimental group was greater than the median tibia length in the control group at the $\alpha = 0.1$ level of significance. Do not reject H_o

13. **Calcium in Rainwater** An environmentalist wants to test the claim that the median amount of calcium (mg/L) in rainwater in Lincoln County, Nebraska, is different from the median amount of calcium (mg/L) in the rainwater in Clarendon County, South Carolina. She randomly selects 22 weeks in which it rained at least once during the week between January 1999 and January 2000 in the Nebraska location and determines the calcium level of the rainwater. She obtains an independent random sample of 20 weeks in which it rained at least once during the week between January 1999 and January 2000 for the South Carolina location and determines the calcium level of the rainwater. Her data are shown in the following table:

Lincoln County				Clarendon County			
Calcium Level (mg/L)				Calcium Level (mg/L)			
0.11	0.41	0.19	0.33	0.06	0.12	0.14	0.10
0.09	0.33	0.67	0.20	0.09	0.29	0.14	0.21
0.21	0.20	0.75	0.42	0.14	0.10	0.12	0.16
0.09	0.22	0.19	0.25	0.16	0.41	0.08	0.13
0.07	0.34	0.30	0.47	0.03	0.08	0.09	0.12
0.30	0.46						

Source: National Atmospheric Deposition Program

Test the environmentalist's claim at the $\alpha = 0.05$ level of significance. *Reject H_o*

14. **Potassium in Rainwater** An environmentalist wants to test the claim that the median amount of potassium (mg/L) in rainwater in Lincoln County, Nebraska, is different from the median amount of potassium (mg/L) in the rainwater in Clarendon County, South Carolina. She randomly selects 22 weeks in which it rained at least once during the week between January 1999 and January 2000 in the Nebraska location and determines the potassium level of the rainwater. She obtains an independent random sample of 20 weeks in which it rained at least once during the week between January 1999 and January 2000 for the South Carolina location and determines the potassium level of the rainwater. Her data are shown in the following table:

Lincoln County				Clarendon County			
Potassium Level (mg/L)				Potassium Level (mg/L)			
0.013	0.062	0.078	0.064	0.016	0.059	0.037	0.019
0.014	0.044	0.096	0.028	0.023	0.033	0.031	0.019
0.016	0.018	0.101	0.065	0.057	0.064	0.058	0.022
0.085	0.100	0.035	0.030	0.118	0.025	0.035	0.051
0.011	0.116	0.043	0.054	0.024	0.069	0.027	0.053
0.005	0.080						

Source: National Atmospheric Deposition Program

Test the environmentalist's claim at the $\alpha = 0.05$ level of significance. *Do not reject H_o*

15. **Mann–Whitney Using Qualitative Data** The Mann–Whitney Test can be performed on qualitative data if data can be ranked. For example, a letter grade received in a class is qualitative data that can be ranked—an "A" ranks higher than a "B." Suppose a department chair wants to discover whether the grades of students in two different teachers' statistics courses are different. The chair randomly selects 15 students from Professor A's class and 15 students from Professor B's class and obtains the data on the right.

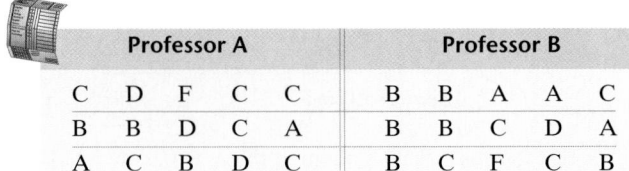

Professor A					Professor B				
C	D	F	C	C	B	B	A	A	C
B	B	D	C	A	B	B	C	D	A
A	C	B	D	C	B	C	F	C	B

Do the following to test the claim that the grades administered in each class are equivalent:

(a) Rank the grades in ascending order (*A*s first, then *B*s, and so on.)

(b) Perform a two-tailed test on the hypotheses

H_0: the grades administered in each class are equivalent

and

H_1: the grades administered in each class are different

by following Steps 2–7 (boxplots cannot be drawn) on page 789. *Do not reject H_0*

---

16. **Mann–Whitney Using Qualitative Data** The Mann–Whitney Test can be performed on qualitative data if data can be ranked. For example, a restaurant critic ranks restaurants as "excellent," "good," "fair," or "poor." Suppose we want to judge whether two restaurant critics have the same distribution of opinions. The opinions of Critic A regarding 15 randomly selected restaurants are presented together with the opinions of Critic B regarding 15 randomly selected restaurants (the samples are independent):

Critic A				
Excellent	Good	Fair	Fair	Poor
Excellent	Good	Good	Fair	Fair
Fair	Good	Excellent	Poor	Fair

Critic B				
Fair	Fair	Good	Good	Fair
Fair	Poor	Fair	Good	Good
Excellent	Fair	Good	Fair	Poor

Do the following to test the claim that the opinions of each critic are equivalent:

(a) Rank the opinions in ascending order (excellent first, then good, and so on).

(b) Perform a two-tailed test on the hypotheses *Do not reject H_0*

H_0: the opinions given are equivalent

and

H_1: the opinions given are different

by following Steps 2–7 (boxplots cannot be drawn) on page 789.

Technology Step-by-Step
Mann–Whitney Test

TI-83 Plus   The TI-83 Plus does not have this feature.

MINITAB   **Step 1:** Enter the first-sample data in column C1. Enter the second-sample data in column C2.

Step 2: Select the **Stat** menu, highlight **Nonparametrics**, then highlight **Mann-Whitney . . . .**

Step 3: Enter C1 in the cell marked "First Sample." Enter C2 in the cell marked "Second Sample." Select the appropriate alternative. Click OK.

Excel   Excel is not programmed to conduct this test.

13.6 Spearman's Rank-Correlation Test

Preparing for This Section   Before getting started, review the following:

✓ Linear correlation coefficient (Section 4.1, pp. 194–199)

✓ Tests for a linear relation (Section 12.1, pp. 712–716)

Objectives   Perform Spearman's rank-correlation test

In Section 4.1, we introduced Pearson's linear correlation coefficient. Recall that the correlation coefficient measures the strength of linear relation between two quantitative variables that are collected as ordered pairs (i.e., $(x_1, y_1), (x_2, y_2), \ldots, (x_n, y_n)$). In Section 12.1, we learned that, in order to test a claim regarding Pearson's correlation coefficient, the data had to be bivariate normal. This requirement is difficult to verify. We therefore tested the linear relation between the two variables by determining whether the slope coefficient, β_1, was significantly different from 0. But this test required that the residuals be normally distributed. In this section, we introduce the nonparametric *Spearman's Rank-Correlation Test*, which can be used to test the claim that two variables are associated.

 Spearman's Rank-Correlation Test

Definition   The **rank-correlation test** is a nonparametric procedure that is used to test claims regarding the association between two variables.

When performing the rank-correlation test, we are testing the claim that there is association between the two variables. There are three ways to structure the hypothesis test. Assume the data are represented as ordered pairs (X, Y).

Two-Tailed	Left-Tailed	Right-Tailed
H_0: X and Y are not associated	H_0: X and Y are not associated	H_0: X and Y are not associated
H_1: X and Y are associated	H_1: X and Y are positively associated	H_1: X and Y are negatively associated

X	Y	Rank of X-values	Rank of Y-values
5	8	2	4
3	4	1	1
7	6	3	2.5
9	9	5	5
8	6	4	2.5

The idea behind the rank correlation test is to rank the X-values and then separately rank the Y-values, from smallest to largest. We handle ties by finding the mean of the ranks for tied values. For example, if the bivariate data are (5, 8), (3, 4), (7, 6), (9, 9), and (8, 6), then we form a table of X-values and their corresponding Y-values. Rank the X-values and then rank the Y-values. The smallest X-value is 3, so we assign it the rank 1; the second smallest X-value is 5, so we assign it the rank 2; and so on. The smallest Y-value is 4, so we assign it the rank 1. The next smallest Y-value is 6, but it occurs twice, so we assign the value 6 the rank $(2 + 3)/2 = 2.5$; and so on.

Once the ranks have been identified, we compute the differences between them by subtracting the rank value of Y from the rank value of X. The idea is that, if there is a positive association between X and Y, then the small values of X will be paired with small values of Y, so that their ranks are both small, resulting in a small difference. Large values of X will be paired with large values of Y, so that their ranks are both large. Again, the difference between the ranks will be close to zero for each ordered pair. The test statistic is based upon this rationale.

Theorem

Test Statistic for Spearman's Rank-Correlation Test

The test statistic will depend upon the size of the sample, n, and on the sum of the squared differences.

$$r_s = 1 - \frac{6\sum d_i^2}{n(n^2 - 1)}$$

where d_i = the difference in the ranks of the two observations in the ith ordered pair.

The test statistic, r_s, is also called **Spearman's rank-correlation coefficient**. Now that we know the procedure for obtaining the test statistic, we need to obtain a critical value.

Theorem

Critical Value for Spearman's Rank-Correlation Test

Using α as the level of significance, the critical value(s) is (are) obtained from Table X in Appendix A. For a two-tailed test, be sure to divide the level of significance, α, by 2.

We now present the steps required to conduct a Spearman's Rank-Correlation Test.

Spearman's Rank-Correlation Test

If a claim is made regarding the association between two variables X and Y, we can use the following steps to test the claim, provided that
1. the data are a random sample of n ordered pairs and
2. each pair of observations is two measurements taken on the same individual.

Notice there is no requirement about the form of the distribution of the data.

Step 1: A claim is made regarding the association between two variables, X and Y. The claim is used to construct the null and alternative hypotheses, which are structured as follows:

Two-Tailed	One-Tailed	One-Tailed
H_0: X and Y are not associated	H_0: X and Y are not associated	H_0: X and Y are not associated
H_1: X and Y are associated	H_1: X and Y are positively associated	H_1: X and Y are negatively associated

Step 2: Rank the X-values, and rank the Y-values. Compute the differences between ranks and then square those differences. Compute the sum of the squared differences.

Step 3: Choose a level of significance, α, based upon the seriousness of making a Type I error. The level of significance is used to determine the critical value. The critical value is found in Table X.

Step 4: Compute the test statistic.

$$r_s = 1 - \frac{6\sum d_i^2}{n(n^2 - 1)}$$

where n is the sample size and d_i is the difference in the ranks of the two observations in the ith ordered pair.

Step 5: Compare the critical value with the test statistic.

Hypothesis	Decision Rule
H_o: X and Y are not associated H_1: X and Y are associated	Reject H_o if r_s is greater than the critical value in Table X. Reject H_o if r_s is less than the negative of the critical value in Table X.
H_o: X and Y are not associated H_1: X and Y are positively associated	Reject H_o if r_s is greater than the critical value in Table X.
H_o: X and Y are not associated H_1: X and Y are negatively associated	Reject H_o if r_s is less than the negative of the critical value in Table X.

Step 6: State the conclusion.

▶ **EXAMPLE 1** **Illustrating Spearman's Rank-Correlation Test**

Problem: A researcher would like to know whether per capita GDP is associated with life expectancy. The data in Table 11 represent the per capita gross domestic product (in thousands of U.S. dollars) for randomly selected countries in Western Europe and the life expectancy of residents of those countries. Test the claim that per capita GDP and life expectancy are associated at the $\alpha = 0.05$ level of significance.

			TABLE 11			
Country	Per Capita GDP (000s)	Life Expectancy	Country	Per Capita GDP (000s)	Life Expectancy
Austria	21.4	77.48	Ireland	18.6	76.39
Belgium	23.2	77.53	Italy	21.5	78.51
Finland	20.0	77.32	Netherlands	22.0	78.15
France	22.7	78.63	Switzerland	23.8	78.99
Germany	20.8	77.17	United Kingdom	21.2	77.37

Source: Time Almanac, 2000

Approach: We need to verify the requirements and proceed to follow Steps 1–6.

Solution: The data were obtained randomly, and each pair of observations is taken on the same individual (the country). We now follow Steps 1–6.

Step 1: The claim is that per capita GDP and life expectancy are associated. Let X represent per capita GDP and Y represent life expectancy; then the null and alternative hypothesis are as follows:

H_o: X and Y are not associated
H_1: X and Y are associated

Step 2: Rank the X-values and rank the Y-values (columns 4 and 5 of Table 12). Compute the differences in ranks (column 6) and then square the differences (column 7). Compute the sum of the squared differences.

		TABLE 12				
Country	Per Capita GDP (000s), X	Life Expectancy, Y	Rank of X	Rank of Y	$d = Y - X$	d^2
Austria	21.4	77.48	5	5	0	0
Belgium	23.2	77.53	9	6	−3	9
Finland	20.0	77.32	2	3	1	1
France	22.7	78.63	8	9	1	1
Germany	20.8	77.17	3	2	−1	1
Ireland	18.6	76.39	1	1	0	0
Italy	21.5	78.51	6	8	2	4
Netherlands	22.0	78.15	7	7	0	0
Switzerland	23.8	78.99	10	10	0	0
United Kingdom	21.2	77.37	4	4	0	0

Adding up the entries in column 7, we find that

$$\Sigma d_i^2 = 9 + 1 + 1 + 1 + 4 = 16$$

Step 3: The level of significance is given as $\alpha = 0.05$. We enter Table X and look for the row that corresponds to $n = 10$ (the 10 countries) and the column with $\alpha = 0.05$ for a two-tailed test. The critical value is 0.648. See Figure 13.

Figure 13

			Critical Values of Spearman's Rank Correlation Coefficient						
$\alpha(2)$:	0.50	0.20	0.10	0.05	0.02	0.01	0.005	0.002	0.001
$\alpha(1)$:	0.25	0.10	0.05	0.025	0.01	0.005	0.0025	0.001	0.0005
n									
4	0.600	1.000	1.000						
5	0.500	0.800	0.900	1.000	1.000				
6	0.371	0.657	0.829	0.886	0.943	1.000	1.000		
7	0.321	0.571	0.714	0.786	0.893	0.929	0.964	1.000	1.000
8	0.310	0.524	0.643	0.738	0.833	0.881	0.905	0.952	0.976
9	0.267	0.483	0.600	0.700	0.783	0.833	0.867	0.917	0.933
10	0.248	0.455	0.564	0.648	0.745	0.794	0.830	0.879	0.903
11	0.236	0.427	0.536	0.618	0.709	0.755	0.800	0.845	0.873
12	0.217	0.406	0.503	0.587	0.678	0.727	0.769	0.818	0.846
13	0.209	0.385	0.484	0.560	0.648	0.703	0.747	0.791	0.824
14	0.200	0.367	0.464	0.538	0.626	0.679	0.723	0.771	0.802
15	0.189	0.354	0.446	0.521	0.604	0.654	0.700	0.750	0.779
16	0.182	0.341	0.429	0.503	0.582	0.635	0.679	0.729	0.762

Step 4: Compute the test statistic:

$$r_s = 1 - \frac{6\Sigma d_i^2}{n(n^2 - 1)} = 1 - \frac{6(16)}{10(10^2 - 1)} = 1 - 0.097 = 0.903$$

Step 5: Compare the critical value with the test statistic. Because the test statistic, $r_s = 0.903$, is greater than the critical value, 0.648, we reject the null hypothesis.

Step 6: There is sufficient evidence to support the claim that per capita GDP and life expectancy are associated. ◄◄

Historical Note

Charles Spearman was born in London in 1863. After earning a degree at Leamington College, he joined the army in 1883. After a very good career, he resigned with the rank of captain in 1897 to pursue additional studies. He earned his Ph.D. in experimental psychology in 1906 from the University of Leipzig. He is most famous for his "two-factor theory of intelligence." This theory basically states that the ability to perform an intellectual task is based on an individual's general intelligence, "g," and specific intelligence, "s," for the task. The rank-correlation coefficient is named in honor of Spearman, who first published the idea in 1904 in an article entitled "The Proof and Measurement of Association between Two Things" in the American Journal of Psychiatry. Spearman died in 1945 in London.

Using Technology: Although Minitab, Excel, and the TI-83 Plus graphing calculator do not have the ability to compute Spearman's rank correlation directly, it can be done indirectly by listing the ranks of the X- and Y-values and then finding the linear correlation of the ranks. Figure 14 shows Spearman's rank correlation, obtained from Minitab.

Figure 14

Correlations (Pearson)

Correlation of C3 and C4 = 0.903, P-Value = 0.000

NW *Now Work Problem 5.*

Looking at Table X, we notice that critical values do not exist for $n > 100$. In this case, we can utilize the *large-sample approximation*.

Theorem **Large-Sample ($n > 100$) Approximation**

If $n > 100$, the test statistic for Spearman's Rank-Correlation Test is

$$z = r_s \sqrt{n - 1}$$

Compare this test statistic with the critical value obtained from the standard normal table, Table II in Appendix A. For a two-tailed test, the critical values are $\pm z_{\alpha/2}$. When testing for positive association, the critical value is z_α. When testing for negative association, the critical value is $-z_\alpha$.

13.6 Assess Your Understanding

Concepts and Vocabulary

1. The Pearson correlation coefficient requires that the data be quantitative. Does the Spearman rank correlation require that data be quantitative? Explain.

2. Provide an intuitive explanation of how the Spearman rank correlation measures association.

Exercises

• **Skill Building**

In Problems 1–4, (a) draw a scatter diagram, (b) compute r_s, and (c) test the claim that X and Y are associated at the $\alpha = 0.05$ level of significance.

1.

X	2	4	8	8	9
Y	1.4	1.8	2.1	2.3	2.6

2.

X	0	2	3	5	6	6
Y	5.8	5.7	5.2	2.8	1.9	2.2

3.

X	0	1.2	1.8	2.3	3.5	4.1
Y	2	6.4	7	7.3	4.5	2.4

4.

X	0	0.5	1.4	1.4	3.9	4.6
Y	0.8	2.3	1.9	2.5	5.0	6.8

• **Applying the Concepts**

5. **Income versus Education** It is common to think that the more education an individual receives, the higher the person's income is likely to be. Does this idea translate to states? The following data represent the percentage of the population that has at least a bachelor's degree and the per capita personal income for a random sample of states:

State	Percentage of Population with at Least a Bachelor's Degree	Per Capita Personal Income (Dollars)
Arkansas	18.4	22,257
California	27.5	32,275
Iowa	25.5	26,723
Louisiana	22.5	23,334
Maine	24.1	25,623
Nebraska	24.6	27,829
Ohio	24.6	28,400
Oregon	27.2	28,350
Texas	23.9	27,871

Source: Statistical Abstract of the United States, 2001

(a) $r_s = 0.778$; Reject H_o

(a) Test the claim that states with a higher percentage of the population with at least a bachelor's degree have a higher per capita personal income at the $\alpha = 0.05$ level of significance.
(b) Draw a scatter diagram to support your conclusion.

6. **Crime Rate versus Population** Is a state with a higher population likely to have a higher crime rate? The following data represent the population and crime rate (crimes per 100,000 population) for a random sample of states:

State	Population (in thousands)	Crime Rate per 100,000 Population
Alabama	4,447	490
Colorado	4,301	341
Illinois	12,419	733
Kansas	2,688	383
Minnesota	4,919	274
North Carolina	8,049	542
South Dakota	4,012	167
Virginia	7,079	315

Source: Statistical Abstract of the United States, 2001

(a) Test the claim that states with a higher population have a higher crime rate at the $\alpha = 0.05$ level of significance. $r_s = 0.524$; Do not reject H_o
(b) Draw a scatter diagram to support your conclusion.
(c) Illinois' population is an outlier. Recall that a single observation can have a dramatic effect on the value of the linear correlation coefficient and slope of the least-squares regression line. Test the hypotheses

$H_o: \beta_1 = 0$ vs $H_1: \beta_1 \neq 0$ at the $\alpha = 0.05$ level of significance. Now remove Illinois and redo the test. What do you notice? Is Spearman's rank correlation resistant?

7. **Per Capita Personal Income versus Birth Rate** A sociologist claims that as the per capita personal income of a state increases, the birthrate decreases. She randomly selects nine states and obtains the following data:

State	Per Capita Personal Income ($)	Birth Rate
Delaware	28,493	13.9
Maryland	28,674	13.0
District of Columbia	35,704	15.7
Virginia	26,109	13.2
West Virginia	18,724	11.3
North Carolina	23,168	14.2
South Carolina	20,508	13.6
Georgia	23,822	15.8
Florida	24,799	13.1

Source: Time Almanac, 2000

(a) Test the sociologist's claim at the $\alpha = 0.05$ level of significance. $r_s = 0.200$; Do not reject H_o
(b) Draw a scatter diagram to support your conclusion.

8. **Does Defense Win?** "Defense wins championships" is a common phrase used in the National Football League. Is defense associated with winning? The following data represent the final standing of a team based on their winning percentage and the total number of yards allowed during the 2001–2002 season for a random sample of teams: (a) $r_s = 0.179$; Do not reject H_o

Team	Rank	Total Yards
Baltimore Ravens	4	4,446
Cleveland Browns	6	5,297
Denver Broncos	5	4,774
Jacksonville Jaguars	7	5,070
New England Patriots	2	5,352
Oakland Raiders	3	5,071
Pittsburgh Steelers	1	4,137

(a) Test the claim that defense wins championships by determining whether a higher rank is associated with a lower number of total yards given up at the $\alpha = 0.05$ level of significance.
(b) Draw a scatter diagram to support your conclusion.

9. **Top Cities** Every year, *Money* magazine publishes its list of top places to live. The following data represent a list of top places to live for a recent year, along with the average housing price and average commute time:

City	Housing Cost (dollars)	Commute Time (minutes)
Portland, OR	165,700	20.7
Providence, RI	128,900	19.5
Chicago, IL	170,200	28
Raleigh-Durham, NC	164,600	20
Salt Lake City, UT	138,700	19.5
Sarasota, FL	126,100	18.4

Source: Money magazine

(a) Test the claim that there is a positive association between housing cost and commute time at the $\alpha = 0.05$ level of significance. $r_s = 0.986$; Reject H_o
(b) Draw a scatter diagram to support your conclusion.

10. **CEO Compensation** A stock analyst would like to know whether the annual compensation of chief executive officers is related to the stock's annual rate of re-

turn. The following data represent the annual compensation (salary plus stock options in thousands of dollars) and annual rate of return for the company's stock for some publicly traded companies:

State	CEO Compensation (thousands of dollars)	Annual Stock Return
Baxter International	20,337.7	23.1%
McDonald's Corporation	15,250.4	−20.9%
Allstate Corporation	12,743.2	−20.9%
Sears Roebuck and Co.	11,054.3	40.1%
Motorola Inc.	9,443.7	−25.0%
Fortune Brands Inc.	6,673.5	35.5%
Boeing Co.	4,037.0	−40.0%
Tootsie Roll Industries Inc.	3,472.8	−12.0%
First Midwest Bancorp Inc.	1,877.0	30.1%

Source: Yahoo! Finance

(a) Test the claim that there is a relation between compensation and stock returns at the $\alpha = 0.05$ level of significance. $r_s = 0.026$; Do not reject H_o
(b) Draw a scatter diagram to support your conclusion.

11. Compute r_s for the following data:

X	Y
2	5
3	8
4	11
5	14
6	17

What type of relation exists between X and Y? Draw a scatter diagram to confirm your results. $r_s = 1$

12. Compute r_s for the following data:

X	Y
2	23
3	19
4	15
5	11
6	7

What type of relation exists between X and Y? Draw a scatter diagram to confirm your results. $r_s = -1$

13.7   Kruskal–Wallis Test of One-Way Analysis of Variance

Preparing for This Section   Before getting started, review the following:

✓ Median (Section 3.1, pp. 116–117)

✓ Boxplots (Section 3.5 pp. 169–173)

✓ One-way analysis of variance (Section 12.3 pp. 729–738)

Objectives   ① Test a claim using the Kruskal–Wallis test

In Section 12.3, we introduced one-way analysis of variance (ANOVA). This was used to test the null hypothesis that the means of different populations are equal. In order to perform the one-way ANOVA test, we required that the populations have equal population variances and that each of the populations be normally distributed. If either of these requirements was not satisfied, we could not perform the test.

 Kruskal–Wallis One-Way Analysis of Variance

Definition

The **Kruskal–Wallis Test** is a nonparametric test that is used to test the claim that k independent samples come from populations with the same distribution.

Recall that the null hypothesis in one-way ANOVA was stated as

$$H_o: \mu_1 = \mu_2 = \ldots = \mu_k$$

versus the alternative hypothesis

H_1: at least one of the means is not equal to the others.

The null hypothesis in the Kruskal–Wallis test is stated as

H_o: the distributions of the populations are identical

versus

H_1: the distributions of the populations are not identical

The idea behind the Kruskal–Wallis test is to combine the samples from the different populations together and rank *all* the observations from smallest to largest. We handle ties by finding the mean of the ranks for tied values. For example, if the data for samples from three populations is

Historical Note

In 1952, W. H. Kruskal and W. A. Wallis (shown above) published "Use of Ranks in One-Criterion Variance Analysis" in the *Journal of the American Statistical Association.* This article presented a nonparametric version of one-way ANOVA.

Sample 1	Sample 2	Sample 3
5.1	7.6	7.2
6.5	5.2	8.7
7.2	4.7	6.2

then we combine and rank the data as

Combined Data	Rank
4.7	1
5.1	2
5.2	3
6.2	4
6.5	5
7.2	6.5
7.2	6.5
7.6	8
8.7	9

Notice that we observed 7.2 twice. To find the rank of 7.2, we recognize that the two occurrences occupy the sixth and seventh ranking position. So the mean rank is $(6 + 7)/2 = 6.5$.

Once the ranks have been identified, we sum the ranks of the observations from each sample. The sum of the ranks from sample 1 would be $2 + 5 + 6.5 = 13.5$. If the populations have the same distribution (i.e., if the null hypothesis is true), then we would expect the sums of the ranks for all the samples to be close to each other. The test statistic is based upon this rationale.

Theorem

Test Statistic for the Kruskal–Wallis Test

The test statistic for the Kruskal–Wallis test is

$$H = \frac{12}{N(N + 1)} \sum \frac{1}{n_i} \left[R_i - \frac{n_i(N + 1)}{2} \right]^2 \qquad (1)$$

A computational formula for the test statistic is

$$H = \frac{12}{N(N + 1)} \left[\frac{R_1^2}{n_1} + \frac{R_2^2}{n_2} + \dots + \frac{R_k^2}{n_k} \right] - 3(N + 1) \qquad (2)$$

where

R_1^2 is the sum of the ranks squared for the first sample,
R_2^2 is the sum of the ranks squared for the second sample, and so on;
n_1 is the number of observations in the first sample,
n_2 is the number of observations in the second sample, and so on;
N is the total number of observations $(N = n_1 + n_2 + \dots + n_k)$; and
k is the number of populations being compared.

The Kruskal–Wallis test is always a right-tailed test, so we reject the null hypothesis if H is too large. We shall use Formula (1) to justify the rejection of the null hypothesis if H is too large. In Formula (1), the expression $\frac{n_i(N + 1)}{2}$ is the expected sum of ranks for the ith population if the null hypothesis is true. To compute H, we square the deviation between the actual sum of ranks, R_i, and the expected sum of ranks. If the sum of the squared deviations is large, we have evidence against the null hypothesis.

Now that we know the procedure for obtaining the test statistic, we need to obtain a critical value.

Theorem

Critical Value for Kruskal–Wallis Test

Small-Sample Case

When there are three populations being compared and when the sample size from each of the populations is 5 or less, the critical value is obtained from Table XI in Appendix A.

Large-Sample Case

When there are four or more populations being compared or the sample size from one of the populations is more than 5, the critical value is χ_α^2 with $k - 1$ degrees of freedom, where k is the number of populations and α is the level of significance.

We now present the steps required to conduct a Kruskal–Wallis test.

Kruskal–Wallis Test

If a claim is made regarding the distribution of three or more populations, we can use the following steps to test the claim, provided that the following requirements are satisfied:

1. The samples are independent random samples.

2. The data can be ranked.

Step 1: Draw side-by-side boxplots to compare the sample data from the populations. This helps to visualize the differences, if any, between the medians.

Step 2: A claim is made regarding the distribution of three or more populations. The claim is used to construct the null and alternative hypotheses, which are structured as follows:

H_o: the distributions of the populations are the same
H_1: the distributions of the populations are not the same

Step 3: Rank all sample observations from smallest to largest. Handle ties by finding the mean of the ranks for tied values. Find the sum of the ranks for each sample.

Step 4: Choose a level of significance, α, to match the seriousness of making a Type I error. The level of significance is used to determine the *critical value*. The critical value is found from Table XI for small samples. The critical value is χ_α^2 with $k - 1$ degrees of freedom (found in Table IV) for large samples.

Step 5: Compute the **test statistic**:

$$H = \frac{12}{N(N + 1)}\left[\frac{R_1^2}{n_1} + \frac{R_2^2}{n_2} + \ldots + \frac{R_k^2}{n_k}\right] - 3(N + 1)$$

Step 6: Compare the critical value to the test statistic. We reject the null hypothesis if the test statistic is greater than the critical value.

Step 7: State the conclusion.

▶ **EXAMPLE 1** **Illustrating the Kruskal–Wallis Test**

Problem: A family doctor claims that the distributions of HDL cholesterol in males for the age groups 20–29 years old, 40–49 years old, and 60–69 years old are different. He obtains a simple random sample of 12 individuals from each age group and determines their HDL cholesterol. The results are presented in Table 13. Test the doctor's claim at the $\alpha = 0.05$ level of significance.

TABLE 13

Subject Number	20–29 years old	40–49 years old	60–69 years old
1	54 (29)	61 (31.5)	44 (18)
2	43 (16)	41 (14)	65 (34.5)
3	38 (11.5)	44 (18)	62 (33)
4	30 (2)	47 (21)	53 (27.5)
5	61 (31.5)	33 (3)	51 (26)
6	53 (27.5)	29 (1)	49 (22.5)
7	35 (7.5)	59 (30)	49 (22.5)
8	34 (4.5)	35 (7.5)	42 (15)
9	39 (13)	34 (4.5)	35 (7.5)
10	46 (20)	74 (36)	44 (18)
11	50 (24.5)	50 (24.5)	37 (10)
12	35 (7.5)	65 (34.5)	38 (11.5)

Approach: We verify that the requirements needed to perform the Kruskal–Wallis test are satisfied. We then proceed to follow Steps 1–7.

Solution: The samples obtained are independent random samples.

Step 1: Figure 15 shows side-by-side boxplots of the sample data. We notice that the sample median for the 20–29 year olds is less than the sample medians of the other two groups. We need to learn whether this difference is significant or is attributable to sampling error.

Figure 15

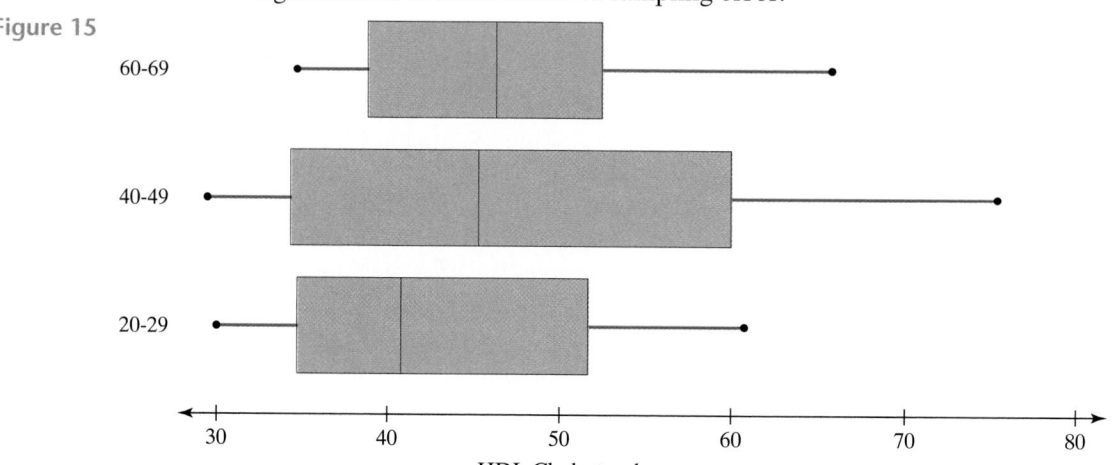

HDL Cholesterol

Step 2: The doctor's claim is that the distributions of HDL cholesterol in males for the age groups 20–29 years old, 40–49 years old, and 60–69 years old are not the same. The null and alternative hypotheses are as follows:

H_0: the distributions of HDL cholesterol for the three age groups are the same;

H_1: the distributions of HDL cholesterol for the three age groups are not the same.

Step 3: The ranks of the data are presented in parentheses in Table 13. The smallest data value is 29, and we assign this observation the rank 1. We sum the ranks in the first sample (20–29 year olds) to obtain R_1, so $R_1 = 29 + 16 + \ldots + 7.5 = 194.5$. Similar computations are performed to obtain $R_2 = 225.5$ and $R_3 = 246$. The results are summarized as follows:

	20–29 Year Olds	40–49 Year Olds	60–69 Year Olds
Sample size	$n_1 = 12$	$n_2 = 12$	$n_3 = 12$
Sum of ranks	$R_1 = 194.5$	$R_2 = 225.5$	$R_3 = 246$

Step 4: Because the samples for each population are greater than five, we find the critical value from the chi-square distribution with $k - 1 = 3 - 1 = 2$ degrees of freedom, with $\alpha = 0.05$. Thus, the critical value is $\chi^2_{0.05} = 5.991$.

Step 5: Note that $N = n_1 + n_2 + n_3 = 36$. The test statistic is computed as follows:

$$H = \frac{12}{N(N+1)}\left[\frac{R_1^2}{n_1} + \frac{R_2^2}{n_2} + \frac{R_3^2}{n_3}\right] - 3(N+1)$$

$$= \frac{12}{36(36+1)}\left[\frac{194.5^2}{12} + \frac{225.5^2}{12} + \frac{246^2}{12}\right] - 3(36+1) = 1.009$$

Step 6: Because the test statistic, 1.009, is not greater than the critical value, 5.991, we do not reject the null hypothesis.

Step 7: There is not sufficient evidence to support the claim that the distributions of HDL cholesterol for the three age groups are different. ◄◄

 *Now Work Problem 3.*

The computations for determining the test statistic, H, in the Kruskal–Wallis test can be tedious. Typically, these calculations are left to statistical software.

Using Technology: We can test the claim made in Example 1, using Minitab. The results are shown in Figure 16.

Figure 16

Kruskal-Wallis Test
```
Kruskal-Wallis Test on C5

C4            N     Median    Ave Rank         Z
1            12      41.00        16.2     -0.92
2            12      45.50        18.8      0.12
3            12      46.50        20.5      0.81
Overall      36                   18.5

H = 1.01    DF = 2    P = 0.604
H = 1.01    DF = 2    P = 0.603  (adjusted for ties)
```

Minitab reports the *P*-value of the test to be 0.604. We do not reject the null hypothesis because the *P*-value is greater than the level of significance, α.

Notice that Minitab reports a test statistic that is adjusted for ties. When the combined set of sample data has a large number of ties, the test statistic may be adjusted. Notice that the ties in the data from Example 1 did not seriously affect the test statistic. If the conclusion based upon the test statistic adjusted for ties differs from the conclusion based upon the standard H test statistic, the researcher should use the conclusion based upon the H test statistic adjusted for ties.

13.7 Assess Your Understanding

Concepts and Vocabulary

1. Discuss the logic behind the computation of the H test statistic.

2. Compare the logic behind the one-way ANOVA procedures with that behind the Kruskal–Wallis procedure.

Exercises

• Skill Building

In Problems 1 and 2, (a) determine the test statistic, H, (b) determine the critical value at the $\alpha = 0.05$ level of significance, and (c) test the claim that the distributions of the populations are different.

1.

X	Y	Z
13	16	12
9	18	14
17	11	9
12	13	15

2.

X	Y	Z
7	9	4
4	4	5
3	8	10
	3	7

• Applying the Concepts

3. **Births by Day of Week** An obstetrician knew that  there were more live births during the week than on weekends. She wanted to discover whether the distribution for number of births was the same for each of the five days of the week. She randomly selected 8 dates for each of the five days of the week and obtained the data to the right.

Monday	Tuesday	Wednesday	Thursday	Friday
10,456	11,621	11,084	11,171	11,545
10,023	11,944	11,570	11,745	12,321
10,691	11,045	11,346	12,023	11,749
10,283	12,927	11,875	12,433	12,192
10,265	12,577	12,193	12,132	12,422
11,189	11,753	11,593	11,903	11,627
11,198	12,509	11,216	11,233	11,624
11,465	13,521	11,818	12,543	12,543

Source: National Center for Health Statistics

(a) State the null and alternative hypotheses.
(b) The sums of the ranks in each category are as follows:

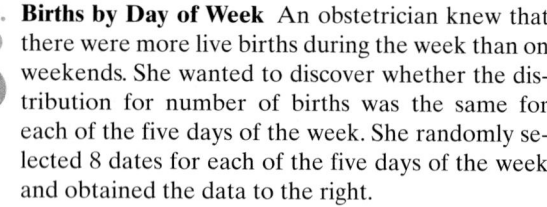

	Monday	Tuesday	Wednesday	Thursday	Friday
Sample size	8	8	8	8	8
Sum of ranks	48	226	144	194.5	207.5

Use this information to compute the test statistic. $H = 18.77$
(c) What is the critical value if we test the claim at the $\alpha = 0.05$ level of significance? 9.488
(d) State your conclusion. Reject H_o
(e) Draw side-by-side boxplots to support your conclusion.

4. Births by Season An obstetrician claimed that the distribution of births was the same for the periods January–March, April–June, July–September, and October–December. She randomly selected 10 days within each time frame and obtained the results shown in the following table:

January–March	April–June	July–September	October–December
10,456	10,799	11,465	11,261
11,574	11,743	12,475	11,406
12,321	11,657	12,454	11,627
11,661	11,608	12,193	8,706
8,521	10,982	11,244	12,022
11,621	9,184	12,081	11,930
11,321	12,357	11,387	11,054
7,706	12,251	9,055	11,431
10,872	11,916	12,319	12,618
10,837	11,212	12,927	10,824

Source: National Center for Health Statistics

(a) State the null and alternative hypotheses.
(b) The sums of the ranks in each category are as follows:

	January–March	April–June	July–September	October–December
Sample size	10	10	10	10
Sum of ranks	149	207	267	197

Use this information to compute the test statistic. $H = 5.16$
(c) What is the critical value if we test the claim at the $\alpha = 0.05$ level of significance? 7.815
(d) State your conclusion. Do not reject H_o
(e) Draw side-by-side boxplots to support your conclusion.

---

5. Corn Production The following data represent the number of corn plants in randomly sampled rows (a 17-foot by 5-inch strip) for various types of plot:

Plot Type	Number of Plants
Sludge Plot	25 27 33 30 28 27
Spring Disk	32 30 33 35 34 34
No Till	30 26 29 32 25 29
Spring Chisele	30 32 26 28 31 29
Great Lakes Bt.	28 32 27 30 29 27

Source: Andrew Dieter and Brad Schmidgall, Joliet Junior College

Test the claim of an agricultural researcher that the distribution for each type of plot is the same at the $\alpha = 0.05$ level of significance. Reject H_o

6. Soybean Yield The following data represent the number of pods on a random sample of soybean plants for various types of plot:

Plot Type	Pods
Liberty	32 31 36 35 41 34 39 37 38
Fall Plowed	29 31 33 22 19 30 36 30
No Till	34 30 31 27 40 33 37 42 39
Chisele Plowed	34 37 24 23 32 33 27 34 30
Round-up Ready	27 34 36 32 35 29 35

Source: Andrew Dieter and Brad Schmidgall, Joliet Junior College

Test the claim of an agricultural researcher that the distribution for each type of plot is the same at the $\alpha = 0.05$ level of significance. Reject H_o

7. **Reaction Time** In an on-line psychology experiment sponsored by the University of Mississippi, researchers asked study participants to respond to various stimuli. Participants were randomly assigned to one of three groups. Subjects in Group 1 were in the simple group. They were required to respond as quickly as possible after a stimulus was presented. Subjects in Group 2 were in the go/no-go group. These subjects were required to respond to a particular stimulus while disregarding other stimuli. Finally, subjects in Group 3 were in the choice group. They needed to respond differently to different stimuli. Depending upon the type of whistle sound, the subject had to press a certain button. The reaction time (in seconds) for each stimulus is presented in the following table:

Simple	Go/No Go	Choice
0.43	0.588	0.561
0.498	0.375	0.498
0.480	0.409	0.519
0.376	0.613	0.538
0.402	0.481	0.464
0.329	0.355	0.725

Source: PsychExperiments; The University of Mississippi; http://www.olemiss.edu/psychexps/

Test the claim that the distribution for each stimulus is the same at the $\alpha = 0.01$ level of significance. Do not reject H_o

8. **Math Scores** Researchers wanted to compare math test scores of students at the end of secondary school from various countries. Eight randomly selected students from Canada, Denmark, and the United States were administered the same exam; the results are presented in the following table:

Canada		Denmark		United States	
578	548	568	563	506	458
548	530	530	535	518	456
521	502	571	561	485	513
555	492	569	513	480	491

Source: Based on data obtained from the International Association for the Evaluation of Educational Achievement

Test the claim that the distribution of exam scores is the same for each country at the $\alpha = 0.01$ level of significance. Reject H_o

9. **Crash Data** The Insurance Institute for Highway Safety conducts experiments in which cars are crashed into a fixed barrier at 40 mph. In the Institute's 40-mph offset test, 40 percent of the total width of each vehicle strikes a barrier on the driver side. The barrier's deformable face is made of aluminum honeycomb, which makes the forces in the test similar to those involved in a frontal offset crash between two vehicles of the same weight, each going just less than 40 mph. Suppose you are in the market to buy a new family car. You want to know whether the distribution of chest compression resulting from this crash is the same for each vehicle category at the $\alpha = 0.01$ level of significance. The following data were collected from the Institute's study: Do not reject H_o

Large Family Cars	Chest Compression (mm)	Passenger Vans	Chest Compression (mm)	Midsize Utility Vehicles	Chest Compression (mm)
Chevrolet Lumina	34	Toyota Sienna	37	Mercedes M Class	42
Ford Taurus	28	Honda Odyssey	29	Toyota 4Runner	28
Buick LeSabre	28	Ford Windstar	27	Mitsubishi Montero	39
Chevrolet Impala	26	Mazda MPV	30	Nissan Xterra	40
Chrysler LHS	22	Chevrolet Astro	34	Ford Explorer	29
Pontiac Grand Prix	34	Nissan Quest	39	Jeep Grand Cherokee	28
Dodge Intrepid	24	Pontiac Trans Sport	23	Nissan Pathfinder	36

Source: Insurance Institute for Highway Safety

10. **Crash Data** The Insurance Institute for Highway Safety conducts experiments in which cars are crashed into a fixed barrier at 40 mph. In the Institute's 40-mph offset test, 40 percent of the total width of each vehicle strikes a barrier on the driver side. The barrier's deformable face is made of aluminum honeycomb, which makes the forces in the test similar to those involved in a frontal offset crash between two vehicles of the same weight, each going just less than 40 mph. Suppose you are in the market to buy a new family car. You want to know whether the distribution of head injury resulting from this offset crash is the same for large family cars, passenger vans, and midsize utility vehicles at the $\alpha = 0.01$ level of significance. The following data were collected from the Institute's study: *Do not reject H_o*

Large Family Cars	Head Injury (hic)	Passenger Vans	Head Injury (hic)	Midsize Utility Vehicles	Head Injury (hic)
Chevrolet Lumina	337	Toyota Sienna	205	Mercedes M Class	308
Ford Taurus	170	Honda Odyssey	166	Toyota 4Runner	463
Buick LeSabre	409	Ford Windstar	183	Mitsubishi Montero	397
Chevrolet Impala	204	Mazda MPV	693	Nissan Xterra	617
Chrysler LHS	332	Chevrolet Astro	152	Ford Explorer	242
Pontiac Grand Prix	627	Nissan Quest	442	Jeep Grand Cherokee	351
Dodge Intrepid	303	Pontiac Trans Sport	311	Nissan Pathfinder	607

Source: Insurance Institute for Highway Safety

CHAPTER 13 REVIEW

Summary

In this chapter, we studied nonparametric procedures. These procedures paralleled parametric procedures introduced throughout the text. Nonparametric procedures allow researchers to test claims regarding measures of central tendency without requiring that certain assumptions, such as normality, be satisfied. If the populations from which samples are drawn are normal, then nonparametric tests are less efficient than the corresponding parametric procedures.

We summarize the procedures presented in this chapter in the following table, along with the corresponding parametric procedures:

Nonparametric Test	Parametric Test	Purpose
Runs Test	No equivalent procedure	To test for randomness
Sign Test (Section 13.3)	z test or t test (Sections 9.2 and 9.3)	To test a claim regarding a measure of central tendency
Wilcoxon Matched–Pairs Signed-Ranks Test (Section 13.4)	Test for the difference of means of dependent samples (Section 10.1)	To test a claim regarding the difference between two measures of central tendency when the sampling is dependent
Mann–Whitney Test (Section 13.5)	Test for the difference of means of independent samples (Section 10.1)	To test a claim regarding the difference between two measures of central tendency when the sampling is independent
Spearman Rank-Correlation Coefficient (Section 13.6)	Test for linear relation (Section 12.1)	To test whether two variables are associated
Kruskal–Wallis Test (Section 13.7)	One-way Analysis of Variance (Section 12.3)	To test whether three or more populations come from the same distribution

Formulas

- **Test Statistic for a Runs Test for Randomness**
    Let n represent the sample size, containing two mutually exclusive types
    Let n_1 represent the number of observations of the first type
    Let n_2 represent the number of observations of the second type
    Let r represent the number of runs

Small-Sample Case: If $n_1 \leq 20$ and $n_2 \leq 20$, the test statistic in the runs test for randomness is r, the number of runs.

Large-Sample Case: If $n_1 > 20$ or $n_2 > 20$, the test statistic in the runs test for randomness is

$$z = \frac{r - \mu_r}{\sigma_r}$$

where

$$\mu_r = \frac{2n_1n_2}{n} + 1 \quad \text{and} \quad \sigma_r = \sqrt{\frac{2n_1n_2(2n_1n_2 - n)}{n^2(n - 1)}}$$

- **Test Statistic for a One-Sample Sign Test**
The test statistic will depend upon the structure of the hypothesis test and the sample size.

Small-Sample Case ($n \leq 25$)

Two-tailed $H_0: M = M_o$ $H_1: M \neq M_o$	Left-tailed $H_0: M = M_o$ $H_1: M < M_o$	Right-tailed $H_0: M = M_o$ $H_1: M > M_o$
The test statistic, k, will be the smaller of the number of minus signs or plus signs	The test statistic, k, will be the number of plus signs	The test statistic, k, will be the number of minus signs

Large-Sample Case ($n > 25$)
The test statistic is

$$z = \frac{(k + 0.5) - \dfrac{n}{2}}{\dfrac{\sqrt{n}}{2}}$$

where n is the number of minus and plus signs and k is obtained as described in the small-sample case.

- **Test Statistic for the Wilcoxon Matched-Pairs Signed-Ranks Test**
The test statistic will depend upon the size of the sample and the alternative hypothesis. Let n represent the sample size.

Small-Sample Case ($n \leq 30$)

Two-Tailed	Left-Tailed	Right-Tailed
$H_0: M_D = 0$ $H_1: M_D \neq 0$	$H_0: M_D = 0$ $H_1: M_D < 0$	$H_0: M_D = 0$ $H_1: M_D > 0$
Test Statistic: T is the smaller of T_+ or T_-	**Test Statistic:** $T = T_+$	**Test Statistic:** $T = |T_-|$

Large-Sample Case ($n > 30$)
From the Central Limit Theorem, the test statistic is given by

$$z = \frac{T - \dfrac{n(n + 1)}{4}}{\sqrt{\dfrac{n(n + 1)(2n + 1)}{24}}}$$

where T is the test statistic from the small-sample case.

- **Test Statistic for the Mann–Whitney Test**

The test statistic will depend upon the size of the samples from each population. Let n_1 represent the sample size for population X and n_2 represent the sample size for population Y.

Small-Sample Case ($n_1 \leq 20$ and $n_2 \leq 20$):

If S is the sum of the ranks corresponding to the sample from population X, then the test statistic, T, is given by

$$T = S - \frac{n_1(n_1 + 1)}{2}$$

Note: The value of S is always obtained by summing the ranks of the sample data that correspond to M_x in the hypothesis.

Large-Sample Case ($n_1 > 20$ or $n_2 > 20$):

From the Central Limit Theorem, the test statistic is given by

$$z = \frac{T - \frac{n_1 n_2}{2}}{\sqrt{\frac{n_1 n_2 (n_1 + n_2 + 1)}{12}}}$$

- **Test Statistic for Spearman's Rank-Correlation Test**

The test statistic will depend upon the size of the sample, n, and on the sum of the squared differences and is given by

$$r_s = 1 - \frac{6 \sum d_i^2}{n(n^2 - 1)}$$

where d_i = the difference in the ranks of the two observations in the ith ordered pair.

- **Test Statistic for the Kruskal–Wallis Test**

The test statistic for the Kruskal-Wallis Test is

$$H = \frac{12}{N(N + 1)} \sum \frac{1}{n_i} \left[R_i - \frac{n_i(N + 1)}{2} \right]^2$$

A computational formula for the test statistic is

$$H = \frac{12}{N(N + 1)} \left[\frac{R_1^2}{n_1} + \frac{R_2^2}{n_2} + \ldots + \frac{R_k^2}{n_k} \right] - 3(N + 1)$$

where

R_1^2 is the sum of the ranks squared for the first sample, R_2^2 is the sum of the ranks squared for the second sample, and so on;

n_1 is the number of observations in the first sample, n_2 is the number of observations in the second sample, and so on;

N is the total number of observations ($N = n_1 + n_2 + \ldots + n_k$); and

k is the number of populations being compared.

Vocabulary

Parametric statistical procedures (p. 758)
Nonparametric (or distribution-free) statistical procedures (p. 758)
Power of a test (p. 759)

Efficiency (p. 759)
Runs test for randomness (p. 760)
Run (p. 760)
Length (p. 760)
One-sample sign test (p. 769)

Wilcoxon Matched-Pairs Signed-Ranks test (p. 776)
Mann–Whitney test (p. 787)
Rank-correlation test (p. 798)
Kruskal–Wallis test (p. 805)

Objectives

Review Exercises

1. **The Stanley Cup** The division from which the winner of the Stanley Cup came for the years 1980–2002 is given in the following table, where the Western Division is represented by a W the Eastern Division is represented by an E:

E E E E E W W E W W W W E E E E E W W W W E W

Is there sufficient evidence to support the claim that the winning division occurs randomly at the $\alpha = 0.05$ level of significance? *Do not reject H_o*

2. **The NBA** The division from which the winner of the National Basketball Association's champion came for the years 1980–2002 is given in the following table, where the Western Division is represented by a W and the Eastern Division is represented by an E:

W W W W E E E W W E E E E W W E W E E W E

Is there sufficient evidence to support the claim that the winning division occurs randomly at the $\alpha = 0.05$ level of significance? *Do not reject H_o*

3. **On the Phone** An introductory statistics instructor claimed that the median number of hours students talk on the phone per week is more than 15. He randomly sampled 20 students, asked them to disclose the number of hours they talked on the phone each week, and obtained the following data:

30	30	60	70	30
5	60	100	60	20
20	5	60	1	20
10	20	2	10	5

Source: Michael McCraith, Joliet Junior College

Test the instructor's claim at the $\alpha = 0.05$ level of significance. *Do not reject H_o*

4. **Study Hard** The same introductory statistics instructor from Problem 3 claimed that the median number of hours students study each week is less than 15. He randomly sampled 20 students, asked them to disclose the number of hours they study each week, and obtained the following data:

8	17	8	10	5
12	8	8	12	5
22	10	20	20	2
10	4	8	5	15

Source: Michael McCraith, Joliet Junior College

Test the instructor's claim at the $\alpha = 0.05$ level of significance. *Reject H_o*

5. **Air-Traffic Control Errors** An air-traffic control error is said to occur when planes come too close to one another. The following data represent the number of air-traffic control errors for various regions around the United States for fiscal years 1996 and 2000:

Center	Errors, 2000	Errors, 1996	Center	Errors, 2000	Errors, 1996
Washington	102	24	Cleveland	74	32
New York ARTCC	71	44	Chicago ARTCC	70	26
Indianapolis	54	39	Atlanta	40	36
Memphis	38	21	Dallas–Ft. Worth	34	23
Los Angeles	33	19	Denver	33	11
Jacksonville, FL	30	27	Kansas City, MO	28	20
New York TRACON	27	33	Albuquerque	25	21
Miami	21	15	Boston	21	13
Northern California	18	30	Houston	18	7
Oakland	17	20	Minneapolis	15	13
Chicago TRACON	14	13	Salt Lake City	12	8
Oakland Bay	8	6	Miami	8	2
Washington Dulles	7	2			

Source: Associated Press

Test the claim that the median number of errors in 2000 is greater than the median number of errors in 1996 at the $\alpha = 0.05$ level of significance. *Reject H_o*

6. **Pulse** A physical therapist wants to investigate whether a new exercise program reduces the pulse rate of subjects. She randomly selects 10 women to participate in the study. Each subject is asked to step up and down on a 6-inch step for three minutes. Her pulse (in beats per minute) is then recorded. After a 10-week training program, the pulse is again measured, with the same technique. The results are presented in the following table: *Do not reject H_o*

Before	136	120	129	143	115	113	89	122	102	122
After	128	111	129	148	110	112	98	103	103	103

Test the claim that the exercise program is effective at the $\alpha = 0.05$ level of significance.

7. **Measuring Reaction Time** Researchers at the University of Mississippi claimed that the median reaction time (in seconds) of males differed from the median reaction time of females to a "choice" stimulus. The researchers randomly selected 16 females and 12 males to participate in the study. The "choice" stimulus required the student to respond differently to different stimuli. The data come courtesy of PsychExperiments at the University of Mississippi. The results are as follows:

Female Students

0.474	0.436	0.398	0.633	0.831	0.887	0.711
0.743	0.48	0.561	0.596	0.725	0.905	0.338
0.538	0.531					

Male Students

0.541	1.05	0.577	0.849	0.464	0.626
0.659	0.88	0.752	0.544	0.675	0.393

Test the researcher's claim at the $\alpha = 0.01$ level of significance. *Do not reject H_o*

8. **Acid Rain** A researcher wants to know whether the median pH of rain near Houston, Texas, was significantly greater than the median pH of rain near Chicago, Illinois. He randomly selects 12 rain dates in Texas and obtains the following data:

Texas

4.69	5.10	5.22	4.46	4.93	4.65
5.22	4.76	4.25	5.14	4.11	4.71

Source: National Atmospheric Deposition Program

Independently, he randomly selects 14 rain dates in Illinois and obtains the following data:

Illinois

4.40	4.69	4.22	4.64	4.54	4.35	4.69
4.40	4.75	4.63	4.45	4.49	4.36	4.52

Source: National Atmospheric Deposition Program

Test the claim that the median pH of rain in Houston is greater than the median pH of rain near Chicago at the $\alpha = 0.05$ level of significance. *Reject H_o*

9. **Engine Displacement versus Fuel Economy** The following data represent the size of a car's engine (in liters) versus its miles per gallon in the city for various 2001 domestic automobiles:

Car	Engine Displacement (in liters), x	City Miles per Gallon, y
Buick Century	3.1	20
Buick LeSabre	3.8	19
Cadillac DeVille	4.6	16
Chevrolet Camaro	3.8	19
Chevrolet Cavalier	2.2	24
Chevrolet Malibu	3.1	23
Chrysler LHS	3.5	18
Dodge Intrepid	2.7	19
Ford Crown Victoria	4.6	17
Ford Focus	2.0	28
Ford Mustang	3.8	20
Oldsmobile Aurora	3.5	19
Pontiac Grand Am	2.4	22
Pontiac Sunfire	2.2	23
Saturn Coupe	1.9	28

Source: Road & Track magazine

Test the claim that the engine displacement and fuel economy are negatively associated at the $\alpha = 0.05$ level of significance. *$r_s = -0.872$; Reject H_o*

10. **Temperature versus Cricket Chirps** Crickets make a chirping noise by sliding their wings rapidly over each other. Perhaps you have noticed that the number of chirps seems to increase with the temperature. The data to the right list the temperature (in Fahrenheit) and the number of chirps per second for the striped ground cricket. Test the claim that the temperature and number of chirps per second are associated at the $\alpha = 0.05$ level of significance. $r_s = 0.850$; Reject H_o

Temperature	Chirps per Second	Temperature	Chirps per Second
88.6	20.0	71.6	16.0
93.3	19.8	84.3	18.4
80.6	17.1	75.2	15.5
69.7	14.7	82.0	17.1
69.4	15.4	83.3	16.2
79.6	15.0	82.6	17.2
80.6	16.0	83.5	17.0
76.3	14.4		

Source: *The Songs of Insects*, Pierce, George W., Cambridge, Mass.: Harvard University Press, 1949, pp. 12–21

11. **Water Samples** A researcher took water samples in a forest with a stream running through it. These samples were collected over the course of a year. Each sample was analyzed for the concentration of dissolved organic carbon (mg/l) in that sample, with the results presented in the following table:

Organic				Mineral					Surface				
22.74	14.9	17.9	11.4	8.5	5.5	3.02	7.31	4.85	10.83	11.94	15.76	15.03	15.77
29.8	14.86	18.3	5.3	3.91	4.71	7.45	16.92	11.97	8.74	12.4	10.96	14.53	6.4
27.1	15.91	5.2	15.72	9.29	7.66	11.33	4.6	7.85	9.2	10.3	19.78	12.04	14.19
16.51	15.35	11.9	20.46	21	11.72	7.11	8.5	9.11	8.12	10.48	20.56	16.82	13.89
6.51	9.72	14	16.87	10.89	11.8	17.99	4.8	8.79	7.6	12.88	17.93	10.7	8.69
8.81	19.8	7.4	15.42	10.3	8.05	21.4	4.9	9.6	6.3	19.01	14.28	16	10.46
5.29	14.86	17.5	22.49	11.56	10.72	8.37	9.1	12.57	6.68	19.19	13.11	20.7	16.23
20.46	8.09	10.3		7	21.82	7.92	7.9	12.89	7.34	13.14	12.27	13.7	15.43
				3.99	22.62	17.9	11.72	9.81	9.52	12.51	16.47	16.12	
				3.79	10.74								

Source: Lisa Emili, PhD Candidate, Department of Geography and Wetlands Research Centre, University of Waterloo

Each sample was then categorized according to the water type that was collected. Water was collected from streams (surface water), groundwater was collected from organic soil, and groundwater was collected from mineral soil. The researcher wanted to test the claim that the distribution of concentration of dissolved organic carbon was the same for each collection area.
(a) State the null and alternative hypotheses.
(b) The sums of the ranks in each category are as follows:

	Organic	Mineral	Surface
Sample size	31	47	44
Sum of ranks	2355.5	2119.5	3028

Use this information to compute the test statistic. $H = 17.20$
(c) What is the critical value if we test the claim at the $\alpha = 0.05$ level of significance? 5.991
(d) State your conclusion. Reject H_o
(e) Draw side-by-side boxplots to support your conclusion.

12. **Crash Data** The Insurance Institute for Highway Safety conducts experiments in which cars are crashed into a fixed barrier at 40 mph. In the Institute's 40-mph offset test, 40 percent of the total width of each vehicle strikes a barrier on the driver side. The barrier's deformable face is made of aluminum honeycomb, which makes the forces in the test similar to those involved in a frontal offset crash between two vehicles of the same weight, each going just less than 40 mph. Suppose you are in the market to buy a new family car. Test the claim that the distribution of femur force (kN) on the left leg resulting from this offset crash is the same for large family cars, passenger vans, and midsize utility vehicles, at the $\alpha = 0.05$ level of significance. The following data were collected from the Institute's study: *Do not reject H_o*

Large Family Cars	Femur Force (kN)	Passenger Vans	Femur Force (kN)	Midsize Utility Vehicles	Femur Force (kN)
Chevrolet Lumina	5.8	Toyota Sienna	1.8	Mercedes M Class	3.5
Ford Taurus	2.1	Honda Odyssey	3.0	Toyota 4Runner	1.2
Buick LeSabre	2.8	Ford Windstar	2.1	Mitsubishi Montero	3.6
Chevrolet Impala	4.7	Mazda MPV	6.3	Nissan Xterra	1.2
Chrysler LHS	6.2	Chevrolet Astro	8.2	Ford Explorer	3.7
Pontiac Grand Prix	2.4	Nissan Quest	2.9	Jeep Grand Cherokee	6.7
Dodge Intrepid	4.7	Pontiac Trans Sport	6.7	Nissan Pathfinder	1.8

Source: Insurance Institute for Highway Safety

13. In general, how do parametric tests differ from nonparametric tests? For each of the nonparametric tests listed in this chapter, identify the corresponding parametric test and explain the difference between the two.

Prior to the Civil War, Confederate State constitutions paid little, if any, attention to public education. Nonetheless, blacks were legally prohibited formal schooling, and black literacy was not sanctioned in these states. This situation would soon change. For example, the Pre-Civil War general educational clauses of Alabama's constitution were replaced by new ones with very specific language in 1868. The new legislation provided for sufficient funds for a state-wide public school system, while actively discouraging donations from private sources. The new constitution promised equal educational opportunity regardless of race or economic status but did not mandate racial segregation of public schools. This decision was left in the hands of the state board of education.

In spite of the state's promise, equal educational opportunity for blacks was not a reality. Nevertheless, blacks made significant educational gains during the next two decades. Unfortunately, storm clouds were brewing as white Democrats began to regain power in the state.

The white-authored Alabama state constitution of 1875 severely restricted public funding for education, though it did provide for financing based on a per child basis. Segregated schools became the law of the state. In spite of the legally enforced segregation, black education continued to flourish, while the conditions for whites eroded.

In 1891, Alabama House Bill 504 passed both legislative houses. The constitutionally guaranteed per capita education funding mechanism was preserved, though effectively circumvented, when this bill turned over state education revenues directly to white county officials, who dispersed the money as they saw fit.

As an educational historian, you are interested in evaluating the impact of House Bill 504. Your research has uncovered the average length of the school year and the average monthly teacher salary by race for various counties in Alabama in 1887 (prior to the passage of the bill) and 1915 (after its passage). The data are presented in the tables on page 821.

Average Length of Public School Year in Days, by Race of Students, in Selected Alabama Counties in 1887 and 1915

County	1887		1915		County	1887		1915	
	Black	White	Black	White		Black	White	Black	White
Autauga	89	61	93	140	Lowndes	83	60	91	142
Barbour	85	71	91	148	Macon	70	60	101	158
Bullock	106	70	86	163	Marengo	95	70	93	126
Butler	82	65	84	122	Monroe	59	63	65	120
Chambers	131	120	91	156	Montgomery	100	97	121	174
Choctaw	65	65	56	120	Perry	96	72	109	152
Clarke	82	72	72	110	Pickens	60	60	80	108
Dallas	75	60	108	172	Russell	83	71	80	152
Greene	106	74	94	158	Sumter	79	79	86	152
Hale	80	64	102	115	Wilcox	78	60	81	151
Lee	95	71	89	156					

Average Monthly Pay (in dollars) of Teachers, by Race of Students, in Selected Alabama Counties in 1887 and 1915

County	1887		1915		County	1887		1915	
	Black	White	Black	White		Black	White	Black	White
Autauga	22.08	26.50	24.78	47.93	Lowndes	29.47	26.44	27.84	74.58
Barbour	29.30	23.33	27.54	55.72	Macon	20.00	20.00	28.87	56.65
Bullock	27.50	20.00	25.57	60.48	Marengo	34.50	25.18	22.48	68.66
Butler	26.04	25.56	25.54	55.30	Monroe	19.93	21.77	30.52	49.27
Chambers	31.57	38.00	30.87	49.76	Montgomery	22.00	30.00	31.52	78.96
Choctaw	25.93	22.95	22.12	52.58	Perry	32.39	20.57	26.08	53.65
Clarke	22.33	24.75	30.65	64.23	Pickens	14.00	16.00	20.75	50.22
Dallas	34.33	17.00	22.93	71.73	Russell	31.00	36.95	29.26	70.71
Greene	29.22	19.30	24.29	55.89	Sumter	27.75	27.07	26.46	66.68
Hale	36.86	19.53	25.68	63.55	Wilcox	25.60	16.30	19.88	62.63
Lee	20.75	18.00	32.93	62.28					

Source: Steven E. Tozer, Paul C. Violas, and Guy Senese. *School and Society: Historical and Contemporary Perspectives*, 3d ed. Boston: McGraw-Hill, 1998; pp. 158–159.

Use the Wilcoxon Matched-Pairs Signed-Ranks test procedure with an $\alpha = 0.05$ significance level to answer the following questions:

1. In 1887, was the median school-year length different for black and white children? How about in 1915?
2. In 1887, was the median salary different for black and white teachers? How about in 1915?

Are there any other analyses that you would like to conduct, using these data? Explain. Conduct these analyses, if any.

Write a report detailing your assumptions, analyses, findings, and conclusions regarding the impact of Alabama House Bill 504 on the education provided to black and white children.

Suppose that you have just graduated from college and must choose in what part of the country you would like to live. To do this, you must judge which characteristics of a neighborhood are most important to you, such as spending on education, access to health care, typical commute times, and so on. To determine the best place to live, go to http://money.cnn.com/best/bplive/. (This is *Money* magazine's "Best Places to Live" site.) Select the detailed search option. Fill in the survey questions presented, on the basis of your personal desires for a community. Choose two regions of the country. (You might want to select one region at a time, to avoid confusion.) Use the Mann–Whitney test to learn whether there are differences in certain characteristics of one area of the country versus the other you have chosen. For example, is the average spending per pupil different for cities in the South versus those in the Midwest? Identify any type of association in variables for the most desirable cities. For example, is a higher home price associated with higher spending per pupil? Use the results of this type of analysis to help you make a decision about which city you would like to live in.

DECISIONS

After the mini-scooter craze hit the United States, scooters could be found virtually everywhere. Prices ranged from as much as several hundred dollars to as little as $30.00. Given such disparities in prices, Consumer Reports decided to test whether the more expensive scooters were worth the difference in cost. Although safety and durability were issues, the biggest determinant of the quality of a scooter is how much fun it is to ride. And who better to test how much fun it is to ride a scooter than kids?

As part of the study, Consumer Reports staffers "lent" us their children to race eight of the most popular scooters around the Consumer's Union parking lot. To avoid potential scoring problems, we asked the children to rank their preferences. As an added incentive, we told our testers that they would get to keep the one they liked best!

The table below contains the ranked scores for ten of our staffers' kids.

Child	Scooter 1	Scooter 2	Scooter 3	Scooter 4	Scooter 5	Scooter 6	Scooter 7	Scooter 8
1	7	2	5	3	4	1	6	8
2	3	1	4	5	6	2	8	7
3	8	3	4	2	5	1	6	7
4	6	1	4	2	5	3	7	8
5	7	3	2	4	5	1	6	8
6	6	2	5	3	4	1	8	7
7	6	3	5	2	4	1	7	8
8	7	2	4	3	5	1	6	8
9	6	2	3	4	5	1	7	8
10	6	2	4	3	5	1	7	8

We used Minitab (release 13.1) to perform a Kruskal–Wallis test on the preference scores. The results are shown below:

Kruskal-Wallis Test: Score versus Scooter

```
Kruskal-Wallis Test on Score

Scooter      N    Median   Ave Rank      Z
Scooter1    10    6.000      57.5      2.47
Scooter2    10    2.000      16.5     -3.49
Scooter3    10    4.000      35.5     -0.73
Scooter4    10    3.000      26.5     -2.04
Scooter5    10    5.000      43.5      0.44
Scooter6    10    1.000       8.5     -4.66
Scooter7    10    7.000      63.5      3.35
Scooter8    10    8.000      72.5      4.66
Overall     80               40.5

H = 68.00   DF = 7   P = 0.000
H = 69.07   DF = 7   P = 0.000   (adjusted for ties)
```

Using the Minitab output, answer the following questions:

(a) What are the null and alternative hypotheses?

(b) What is the value of the test statistic?

(c) What is the *P*-value of the test?

(d) Write a paragraph for the readers of Consumer Reports that details your findings.

Note to Readers: In many cases, our test protocol and analytical methods are more complicated than described in these examples. The data and discussions have been modified to make the material more appropriate for the audience.

APPENDIX A   TABLES

TABLE I

Random Numbers

Row Number	Column Number									
	01–05	06–10	11–15	16–20	21–25	26–30	31–35	36–40	41–45	46–50
01	89392	23212	74483	36590	25956	36544	68518	40805	09980	00467
02	61458	17639	96252	95649	73727	33912	72896	66218	52341	97141
03	11452	74197	81962	48443	90360	26480	73231	37740	26628	44690
04	27575	04429	31308	02241	01698	19191	18948	78871	36030	23980
05	36829	59109	88976	46845	28329	47460	88944	08264	00843	84592
06	81902	93458	42161	26099	09419	89073	82849	09160	61845	40906
07	59761	55212	33360	68751	86737	79743	85262	31887	37879	17525
08	46827	25906	64708	20307	78423	15910	86548	08763	47050	18513
09	24040	66449	32353	83668	13874	86741	81312	54185	78824	00718
10	98144	96372	50277	15571	82261	66628	31457	00377	63423	55141
11	14228	17930	30118	00438	49666	65189	62869	31304	17117	71489
12	55366	51057	90065	14791	62426	02957	85518	28822	30588	32798
13	96101	30646	35526	90389	73634	79304	96635	6626	94683	16696
14	38152	55474	30153	26525	83647	31988	82182	98377	33802	80471
15	85007	18416	24661	95581	45868	15662	28906	36392	07617	50248
16	85544	15890	80011	18160	33468	84106	40603	01315	74664	20553
17	10446	20699	98370	17684	16932	80449	92654	02084	19985	59321
18	67237	45509	17638	65115	29757	80705	82686	48565	72612	61760
19	23026	89817	05403	82209	30573	47501	00135	33955	50250	72592
20	67411	58542	18678	46491	13219	84084	27783	34508	55158	78742

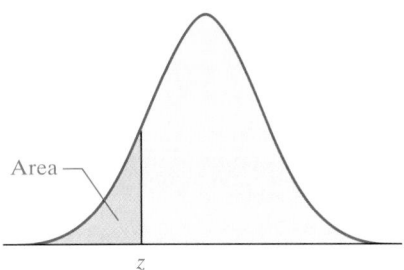

					TABLE II					
				Standard Normal Distribution						
z	.00	.01	.02	.03	.04	.05	.06	.07	.08	.09
−3.4	0.0003	0.0003	0.0003	0.0003	0.0003	0.0003	0.0003	0.0003	0.0003	0.0002
−3.3	0.0005	0.0005	0.0005	0.0004	0.0004	0.0004	0.0004	0.0004	0.0004	0.0003
−3.2	0.0007	0.0007	0.0006	0.0006	0.0006	0.0006	0.0006	0.0005	0.0005	0.0005
−3.1	0.0010	0.0009	0.0009	0.0009	0.0008	0.0008	0.0008	0.0008	0.0007	0.0007
−3.0	0.0013	0.0013	0.0013	0.0012	0.0012	0.0011	0.0011	0.0011	0.0010	0.0010
−2.9	0.0019	0.0018	0.0018	0.0017	0.0016	0.0016	0.0015	0.0015	0.0014	0.0014
−2.8	0.0026	0.0025	0.0024	0.0023	0.0023	0.0022	0.0021	0.0021	0.0020	0.0019
−2.7	0.0035	0.0034	0.0033	0.0032	0.0031	0.0030	0.0029	0.0028	0.0027	0.0026
−2.6	0.0047	0.0045	0.0044	0.0043	0.0041	0.0040	0.0039	0.0038	0.0037	0.0036
−2.5	0.0062	0.0060	0.0059	0.0057	0.0055	0.0054	0.0052	0.0051	0.0049	0.0048
−2.4	0.0082	0.0080	0.0078	0.0075	0.0073	0.0071	0.0069	0.0068	0.0066	0.0064
−2.3	0.0107	0.0104	0.0102	0.0099	0.0096	0.0094	0.0091	0.0089	0.0087	0.0084
−2.2	0.0139	0.0136	0.0132	0.0129	0.0125	0.0122	0.0119	0.0116	0.0113	0.0110
−2.1	0.0179	0.0174	0.0170	0.0166	0.0162	0.0158	0.0154	0.0150	0.0146	0.0143
−2.0	0.0228	0.0222	0.0217	0.0212	0.0207	0.0202	0.0197	0.0192	0.0188	0.0183
−1.9	0.0287	0.0281	0.0274	0.0268	0.0262	0.0256	0.0250	0.0244	0.0239	0.0233
−1.8	0.0359	0.0351	0.0344	0.0336	0.0329	0.0322	0.0314	0.0307	0.0301	0.0294
−1.7	0.0446	0.0436	0.0427	0.0418	0.0409	0.0401	0.0392	0.0384	0.0375	0.0367
−1.6	0.0548	0.0537	0.0526	0.0516	0.0505	0.0495	0.0485	0.0475	0.0465	0.0455
−1.5	0.0668	0.0655	0.0643	0.0630	0.0618	0.0606	0.0594	0.0582	0.0571	0.0559
−1.4	0.0808	0.0793	0.0778	0.0764	0.0749	0.0735	0.0721	0.0708	0.0694	0.0681
−1.3	0.0968	0.0951	0.0934	0.0918	0.0901	0.0885	0.0869	0.0853	0.0838	0.0823
−1.2	0.1151	0.1131	0.1112	0.1093	0.1075	0.1056	0.1038	0.1020	0.1003	0.0985
−1.1	0.1357	0.1335	0.1314	0.1292	0.1271	0.1251	0.1230	0.1210	0.1190	0.1170
−1.0	0.1587	0.1562	0.1539	0.1515	0.1492	0.1469	0.1446	0.1423	0.1401	0.1379
−0.9	0.1841	0.1814	0.1788	0.1762	0.1736	0.1711	0.1685	0.1660	0.1635	0.1611
−0.8	0.2119	0.2090	0.2061	0.2033	0.2005	0.1977	0.1949	0.1922	0.1894	0.1867
−0.7	0.2420	0.2389	0.2358	0.2327	0.2296	0.2266	0.2236	0.2206	0.2177	0.2148
−0.6	0.2743	0.2709	0.2676	0.2643	0.2611	0.2578	0.2546	0.2514	0.2483	0.2451
−0.5	0.3085	0.3050	0.3015	0.2981	0.2946	0.2912	0.2877	0.2843	0.2810	0.2776
−0.4	0.3446	0.3409	0.3372	0.3336	0.3300	0.3264	0.3228	0.3192	0.3156	0.3121
−0.3	0.3821	0.3783	0.3745	0.3707	0.3669	0.3632	0.3594	0.3557	0.3520	0.3483
−0.2	0.4027	0.4168	0.4129	0.4090	0.4052	0.4013	0.3974	0.3936	0.3897	0.3859
−0.1	0.4602	0.4562	0.4522	0.4483	0.4443	0.4404	0.4364	0.4325	0.4286	0.4247
−0.0	0.5000	0.4960	0.4920	0.4880	0.4840	0.4801	0.4761	0.4721	0.4681	0.4641

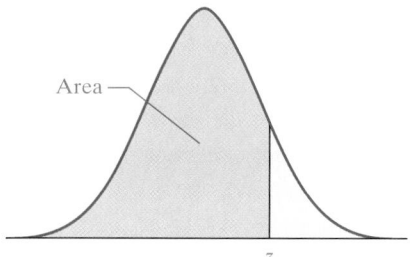

Area

z

				TABLE II (continued)					

Standard Normal Distribution

z	.00	.01	.02	.03	.04	.05	.06	.07	.08	.09
0.0	0.5000	0.5040	0.5080	0.5120	0.5160	0.5199	0.5239	0.5279	0.5319	0.5359
0.1	0.5398	0.5438	0.5478	0.5517	0.5557	0.5596	0.5636	0.5675	0.5714	0.5753
0.2	0.5793	0.5832	0.5871	0.5910	0.5948	0.5987	0.6026	0.6064	0.6103	0.6141
0.3	0.6179	0.6217	0.6255	0.6293	0.6331	0.6368	0.6406	0.6443	0.6480	0.6517
0.4	0.6554	0.6591	0.6628	0.6664	0.6700	0.6736	0.6772	0.6808	0.6844	0.6879
0.5	0.6915	0.6950	0.6985	0.7019	0.7054	0.7088	0.7123	0.7157	0.7190	0.7224
0.6	0.7257	0.7291	0.7324	0.7357	0.7389	0.7422	0.7454	0.7486	0.7517	0.7549
0.7	0.7580	0.7611	0.7642	0.7673	0.7704	0.7734	0.7764	0.7794	0.7823	0.7852
0.8	0.7881	0.7910	0.7939	0.7967	0.7995	0.8023	0.8051	0.8078	0.8106	0.8133
0.9	0.8159	0.8186	0.8212	0.8238	0.8264	0.8289	0.8315	0.8340	0.8365	0.8389
1.0	0.8413	0.8438	0.8461	0.8485	0.8508	0.8531	0.8554	0.8577	0.8599	0.8621
1.1	0.8643	0.8665	0.8686	0.8708	0.8729	0.8749	0.8770	0.8790	0.8810	0.8830
1.2	0.8849	0.8869	0.8888	0.8907	0.8925	0.8944	0.8962	0.8980	0.8997	0.9015
1.3	0.9032	0.9049	0.9066	0.9082	0.9099	0.9115	0.9131	0.9147	0.9162	0.9177
1.4	0.9192	0.9207	0.9222	0.9236	0.9251	0.9265	0.9279	0.9292	0.9306	0.9319
1.5	0.9332	0.9345	0.9357	0.9370	0.9382	0.9394	0.9406	0.9418	0.9429	0.9441
1.6	0.9452	0.9463	0.9474	0.9484	0.9495	0.9505	0.9515	0.9525	0.9535	0.9545
1.7	0.9554	0.9564	0.9573	0.9582	0.9591	0.9599	0.9608	0.9616	0.9625	0.9633
1.8	0.9641	0.9649	0.9656	0.9664	0.9671	0.9678	0.9686	0.9693	0.9699	0.9706
1.9	0.9713	0.9719	0.9726	0.9732	0.9738	0.9744	0.9750	0.9756	0.9761	0.9767
2.0	0.9772	0.9778	0.9783	0.9788	0.9793	0.9798	0.9803	0.9808	0.9812	0.9817
2.1	0.9821	0.9826	0.9830	0.9834	0.9838	0.9842	0.9846	0.9850	0.9854	0.9857
2.2	0.9861	0.9864	0.9868	0.9871	0.9875	0.9878	0.9881	0.9884	0.9887	0.9890
2.3	0.9893	0.9896	0.9898	0.9901	0.9904	0.9906	0.9909	0.9911	0.9913	0.9916
2.4	0.9918	0.9920	0.9922	0.9925	0.9927	0.9929	0.9931	0.9932	0.9934	0.9936
2.5	0.9938	0.9940	0.9941	0.9943	0.9945	0.9946	0.9948	0.9949	0.9951	0.9952
2.6	0.9953	0.9955	0.9956	0.9957	0.9959	0.9960	0.9961	0.9962	0.9963	0.9964
2.7	0.9965	0.9966	0.9967	0.9968	0.9969	0.9970	0.9971	0.9972	0.9973	0.9974
2.8	0.9974	0.9975	0.9976	0.9977	0.9977	0.9978	0.9979	0.9979	0.9980	0.9981
2.9	0.9981	0.9982	0.9982	0.9983	0.9984	0.9984	0.9985	0.9985	0.9986	0.9986
3.0	0.9987	0.9987	0.9987	0.9988	0.9988	0.9989	0.9989	0.9989	0.9990	0.9990
3.1	0.9990	0.9991	0.9991	0.9991	0.9992	0.9992	0.9992	0.9992	0.9993	0.9993
3.2	0.9993	0.9993	0.9994	0.9994	0.9994	0.9994	0.9994	0.9995	0.9995	0.9995
3.3	0.9995	0.9995	0.9995	0.9996	0.9996	0.9996	0.9996	0.9996	0.9996	0.9997
3.4	0.9997	0.9997	0.9997	0.9997	0.9997	0.9997	0.9997	0.9997	0.9997	0.9998

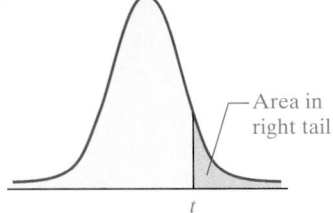
Area in
right tail

t

TABLE III

t-Distribution
Area in Right Tail

df	0.25	0.20	0.15	0.10	0.05	0.025	0.02	0.01	0.005	0.0025	0.001	0.0005
1	1.000	1.376	1.963	3.078	6.314	12.706	15.894	31.821	63.657	127.321	318.289	636.558
2	0.816	1.061	1.386	1.886	2.920	4.303	4.849	6.965	9.925	14.089	22.328	31.600
3	0.765	0.978	1.250	1.638	2.353	3.182	3.482	4.541	5.841	7.453	10.214	12.924
4	0.741	0.941	1.190	1.533	2.132	2.776	2.999	3.747	4.604	5.598	7.173	8.610
5	0.727	0.920	1.156	1.476	2.015	2.571	2.757	3.365	4.032	4.773	5.893	6.869
6	0.718	0.906	1.134	1.440	1.943	2.447	2.612	3.143	3.707	4.317	5.208	5.959
7	0.711	0.896	1.119	1.415	1.895	2.365	2.517	2.998	3.499	4.029	4.785	5.408
8	0.706	0.889	1.108	1.397	1.860	2.306	2.449	2.896	3.355	3.833	4.501	5.041
9	0.703	0.883	1.100	1.383	1.833	2.262	2.398	2.821	3.250	3.690	4.297	4.781
10	0.700	0.879	1.093	1.372	1.812	2.228	2.359	2.764	3.169	3.581	4.144	4.587
11	0.697	0.876	1.088	1.363	1.796	2.201	2.328	2.718	3.106	3.497	4.025	4.437
12	0.695	0.873	1.083	1.356	1.782	2.179	2.303	2.681	3.055	3.428	3.930	4.318
13	0.694	0.870	1.079	1.350	1.771	2.160	2.282	2.650	3.012	3.372	3.852	4.221
14	0.692	0.868	1.076	1.345	1.761	2.145	2.264	2.624	2.977	3.326	3.787	4.140
15	0.691	0.866	1.074	1.341	1.753	2.131	2.249	2.602	2.947	3.286	3.733	4.073
16	0.690	0.865	1.071	1.337	1.746	2.120	2.235	2.583	2.921	3.252	3.686	4.015
17	0.689	0.863	1.069	1.333	1.740	2.110	2.224	2.567	2.898	3.222	3.646	3.965
18	0.688	0.862	1.067	1.330	1.734	2.101	2.214	2.552	2.878	3.197	3.611	3.922
19	0.688	0.861	1.066	1.328	1.729	2.093	2.205	2.539	2.861	3.174	3.579	3.883
20	0.687	0.860	1.064	1.325	1.725	2.086	2.197	2.528	2.845	3.153	3.552	3.850
21	0.686	0.859	1.063	1.323	1.721	2.080	2.189	2.518	2.831	3.135	3.527	3.819
22	0.686	0.858	1.061	1.321	1.717	2.074	2.183	2.508	2.819	3.119	3.505	3.792
23	0.685	0.858	1.060	1.319	1.714	2.069	2.177	2.500	2.807	3.104	3.485	3.768
24	0.685	0.857	1.059	1.318	1.711	2.064	2.172	2.492	2.797	3.091	3.467	3.745
25	0.684	0.856	1.058	1.316	1.708	2.060	2.167	2.485	2.787	3.078	3.450	3.725
26	0.684	0.856	1.058	1.315	1.706	2.056	2.162	2.479	2.779	3.067	3.435	3.707
27	0.684	0.855	1.057	1.314	1.703	2.052	2.158	2.473	2.771	3.057	3.421	3.690
28	0.683	0.855	1.056	1.313	1.701	2.048	2.154	2.467	2.763	3.047	3.408	3.674
29	0.683	0.854	1.055	1.311	1.699	2.045	2.150	2.462	2.756	3.038	3.396	3.659
30	0.683	0.854	1.055	1.310	1.697	2.042	2.147	2.457	2.750	3.030	3.385	3.646
31	0.682	0.853	1.054	1.309	1.696	2.040	2.144	2.453	2.744	3.022	3.375	3.633
32	0.682	0.853	1.054	1.309	1.694	2.037	2.141	2.449	2.738	3.015	3.365	3.622
33	0.682	0.853	1.053	1.308	1.692	2.035	2.138	2.445	2.733	3.008	3.356	3.611
34	0.682	0.852	1.052	1.307	1.691	2.032	2.136	2.441	2.728	3.002	3.348	3.601
35	0.682	0.852	1.052	1.306	1.690	2.030	2.133	2.438	2.724	2.996	3.340	3.591
36	0.681	0.852	1.052	1.306	1.688	2.028	2.131	2.435	2.719	2.990	3.333	3.582
37	0.681	0.851	1.051	1.305	1.687	2.026	2.129	2.431	2.715	2.985	3.326	3.574
38	0.681	0.851	1.051	1.304	1.686	2.024	2.127	2.429	2.712	2.980	3.319	3.566
39	0.681	0.851	1.050	1.304	1.685	2.023	2.125	2.426	2.708	2.976	3.313	3.558
40	0.681	0.851	1.050	1.303	1.684	2.021	2.123	2.423	2.704	2.971	3.307	3.551
50	0.679	0.849	1.047	1.299	1.676	2.009	2.109	2.403	2.678	2.937	3.261	3.496
60	0.679	0.848	1.045	1.296	1.671	2.000	2.099	2.390	2.660	2.915	3.232	3.460
70	0.678	0.847	1.044	1.294	1.667	1.994	2.093	2.381	2.648	2.899	3.211	3.435
80	0.678	0.846	1.043	1.292	1.664	1.990	2.088	2.374	2.639	2.887	3.195	3.416
90	0.677	0.846	1.042	1.291	1.662	1.987	2.084	2.368	2.632	2.878	3.183	3.402
100	0.677	0.845	1.042	1.290	1.660	1.984	2.081	2.364	2.626	2.871	3.174	3.390
1000	0.675	0.842	1.037	1.282	1.646	1.962	2.056	2.330	2.581	2.813	3.098	3.300
z	0.674	0.841	1.036	1.282	1.645	1.960	2.054	2.326	2.576	2.807	3.091	3.291

TABLE IV

Chi-Square (χ^2) Distribution
Area to the Right of Critical Value

Degrees of Freedom	0.995	0.99	0.975	0.95	0.90	0.10	0.05	0.025	0.01	0.005
1	—	—	0.001	0.004	0.016	2.706	3.841	5.024	6.635	7.879
2	0.010	0.020	0.051	0.103	0.211	4.605	5.991	7.378	9.210	10.597
3	0.072	0.115	0.216	0.352	0.584	6.251	7.815	9.348	11.345	12.838
4	0.207	0.297	0.484	0.711	1.064	7.779	9.488	11.143	13.277	14.860
5	0.412	0.554	0.831	1.145	1.610	9.236	11.071	12.833	15.086	16.750
6	0.676	0.872	1.237	1.635	2.204	10.645	12.592	14.449	16.812	18.548
7	0.989	1.239	1.690	2.167	2.833	12.017	14.067	16.013	18.475	20.278
8	1.344	1.646	2.180	2.733	3.490	13.362	15.507	17.535	20.090	21.955
9	1.735	2.088	2.700	3.325	4.168	14.684	16.919	19.023	21.666	23.589
10	2.156	2.558	3.247	3.940	4.865	15.987	18.307	20.483	23.209	25.188
11	2.603	3.053	3.816	4.575	5.578	17.275	19.675	21.920	24.725	26.757
12	3.074	3.571	4.404	5.226	6.304	18.549	21.026	23.337	26.217	28.299
13	3.565	4.107	5.009	5.892	7.042	19.812	22.362	24.736	27.688	29.819
14	4.075	4.660	5.629	6.571	7.790	21.064	23.685	26.119	29.141	31.319
15	4.601	5.229	6.262	7.261	8.547	22.307	24.996	27.488	30.578	32.801
16	5.142	5.812	6.908	7.962	9.312	23.542	26.296	28.845	32.000	34.267
17	5.697	6.408	7.564	8.672	10.085	24.769	27.587	30.191	33.409	35.718
18	6.265	7.015	8.231	9.390	10.865	25.989	28.869	31.526	34.805	37.156
19	6.844	7.633	8.907	10.117	11.651	27.204	30.144	32.852	36.191	38.582
20	7.434	8.260	9.591	10.851	12.443	28.412	31.410	34.170	37.566	39.997
21	8.034	8.897	10.283	11.591	13.240	29.615	32.671	35.479	38.932	41.401
22	8.643	9.542	10.982	12.338	14.042	30.813	33.924	36.781	40.289	42.796
23	9.260	10.196	11.689	13.091	14.848	32.007	35.172	38.076	41.638	44.181
24	9.886	10.856	12.401	13.848	15.659	33.196	36.415	39.364	42.980	45.559
25	10.520	11.524	13.120	14.611	16.473	34.382	37.652	40.646	44.314	46.928
26	11.160	12.198	13.844	15.379	17.292	35.563	38.885	41.923	45.642	48.290
27	11.808	12.879	14.573	16.151	18.114	36.741	40.113	43.194	46.963	49.645
28	12.461	13.565	15.308	16.928	18.939	37.916	41.337	44.461	48.278	50.993
29	13.121	14.257	16.047	17.708	19.768	39.087	42.557	45.722	49.588	52.336
30	13.787	14.954	16.791	18.493	20.599	40.256	43.773	46.979	50.892	53.672
40	20.707	22.164	24.433	26.509	29.051	51.805	55.758	59.342	63.691	66.766
50	27.991	29.707	32.357	34.764	37.689	63.167	67.505	71.420	76.154	79.490
60	35.534	37.485	40.482	43.188	46.459	74.397	79.082	83.298	88.379	91.952
70	43.275	45.442	48.758	51.739	55.329	85.527	90.531	95.023	100.425	104.215
80	51.172	53.540	57.153	60.391	64.278	96.578	101.879	106.629	112.329	116.321
90	59.196	61.754	65.647	69.126	73.291	107.565	113.145	118.136	124.116	128.299
100	67.328	70.065	74.222	77.929	82.358	118.498	124.342	129.561	135.807	140.169

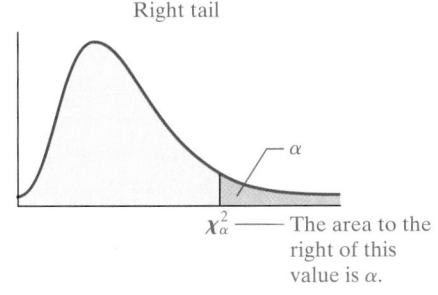

Right tail. χ_α^2 — The area to the right of this value is α.

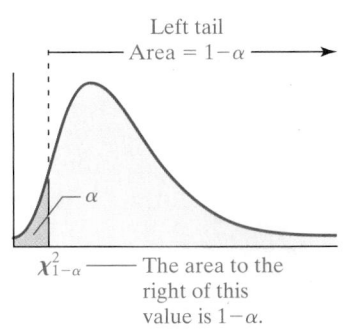

Left tail. Area = $1-\alpha$. $\chi_{1-\alpha}^2$ — The area to the right of this value is $1-\alpha$.

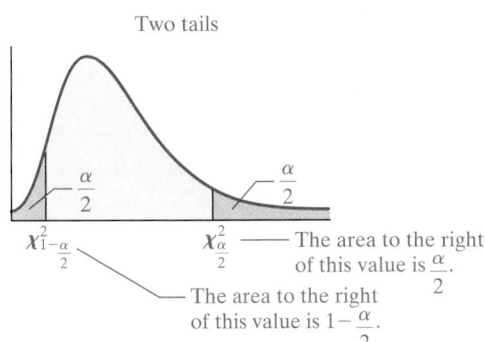

Two tails. $\chi_{1-\frac{\alpha}{2}}^2$, $\chi_{\frac{\alpha}{2}}^2$ — The area to the right of this value is $\frac{\alpha}{2}$. The area to the right of this value is $1-\frac{\alpha}{2}$.

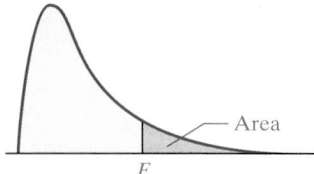

TABLE V

F-Distribution Critical Values
Degrees of Freedom in the Numerator

	Area in Right Tail	1	2	3	4	5	6	7	8
1	0.100	39.86	49.59	53.59	55.83	57.24	58.20	58.91	59.44
	0.050	161.45	199.50	215.71	224.58	230.16	233.99	236.77	238.88
	0.025	647.79	799.50	864.16	899.58	921.85	937.11	948.22	956.66
	0.010	4052.20	4999.50	5403.40	5624.60	5763.60	5859.00	5928.40	5981.10
	0.001	405284.00	500000.00	540379.00	562500.00	576405.00	585937.00	592873.00	598144.00
2	0.100	8.53	9.00	9.16	9.24	9.29	9.33	9.35	9.37
	0.050	18.51	19.00	19.16	19.25	19.30	19.33	19.35	19.37
	0.025	38.51	39.00	39.17	39.25	39.30	39.33	39.36	39.37
	0.010	98.50	99.00	99.17	99.25	99.30	99.33	99.36	99.37
	0.001	998.50	999.00	999.17	999.25	999.30	999.33	999.36	999.37
3	0.100	5.54	5.46	5.39	5.34	5.31	5.28	5.27	5.25
	0.050	10.13	9.55	9.28	9.12	9.01	8.94	8.89	8.85
	0.025	17.44	16.04	15.44	15.10	14.88	14.73	14.62	14.54
	0.010	34.12	30.82	29.46	28.71	28.24	27.91	27.67	27.49
	0.001	167.03	148.50	141.11	137.10	134.58	132.85	131.58	130.62
4	0.100	4.54	4.32	4.19	4.11	4.05	4.01	3.98	3.95
	0.050	7.71	6.94	6.59	6.39	6.26	6.16	6.09	6.04
	0.025	12.22	10.65	9.98	9.60	9.36	9.20	9.07	8.98
	0.010	21.20	18.00	16.69	15.98	15.52	15.21	14.98	14.80
	0.001	74.14	61.25	56.18	53.44	51.71	50.53	49.66	49.00
5	0.100	4.06	3.78	3.62	3.52	3.45	3.40	3.37	3.34
	0.050	6.61	5.79	5.41	5.19	5.05	4.95	4.88	4.82
	0.025	10.01	8.43	7.76	7.39	7.15	6.98	6.85	6.76
	0.010	16.26	13.27	12.06	11.39	10.97	10.67	10.46	10.29
	0.001	47.18	37.12	33.20	31.09	29.75	28.83	28.16	27.65
6	0.100	3.78	3.46	3.29	3.18	3.11	3.05	3.01	2.98
	0.050	5.99	5.14	4.76	4.53	4.39	4.28	4.21	4.15
	0.025	8.81	7.26	6.60	6.23	5.99	5.82	5.70	5.60
	0.010	13.75	10.92	9.78	9.15	8.75	8.47	8.26	8.10
	0.001	35.51	27.00	23.70	21.92	20.80	20.03	19.46	19.03
7	0.100	3.59	3.26	3.07	2.96	2.88	2.83	2.78	2.75
	0.050	5.59	4.74	4.35	4.12	3.97	3.87	3.79	3.73
	0.025	8.07	6.54	5.89	5.52	5.29	5.12	4.99	4.90
	0.010	12.25	9.55	8.45	7.85	7.46	7.19	6.99	6.84
	0.001	29.25	21.69	18.77	17.20	16.21	15.52	15.02	14.63
8	0.100	3.46	3.11	2.92	2.81	2.73	2.67	2.62	2.59
	0.050	5.32	4.46	4.07	3.84	3.69	3.58	3.50	3.44
	0.025	7.57	6.06	5.42	5.05	4.82	4.65	4.53	4.43
	0.010	11.26	8.65	7.59	7.01	6.63	6.37	6.18	6.03
	0.001	25.41	18.49	15.83	14.39	13.48	12.86	12.40	12.05

Degrees of Freedom in the Denominator

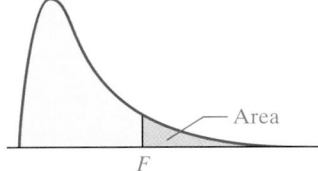

TABLE V (*continued*)

F-Distribution Critical Values
Degrees of Freedom in the Numerator

	Area in Right Tail	9	10	15	20	30	60	120	1000
1	0.100	59.86	60.19	61.22	61.74	62.26	62.79	63.06	63.30
	0.050	240.54	241.88	245.95	248.01	250.10	252.20	253.25	254.19
	0.025	963.28	968.63	984.87	993.10	1001.4	1009.8	1014.0	1017.7
	0.010	6022.5	6055.8	6157.3	6208.7	6260.6	6313.0	6339.4	6362.7
	0.001	602284.0	605621.0	615764.0	620908.0	626099.0	631337.0	633972.0	636301.0
2	0.100	9.38	9.39	9.42	9.44	9.16	9.47	9.48	9.49
	0.050	19.38	19.40	19.43	19.45	19.46	19.48	19.49	19.49
	0.025	39.39	39.40	39.43	39.45	39.46	39.48	39.49	39.50
	0.010	99.39	99.40	99.43	99.45	99.47	99.48	99.49	99.50
	0.001	999.39	999.40	999.43	999.45	999.47	999.48	999.49	999.50
3	0.100	5.24	5.23	5.20	5.18	5.17	5.15	5.14	5.13
	0.050	8.81	8.79	8.70	8.66	8.62	8.57	8.55	8.53
	0.025	14.47	14.42	14.25	14.17	14.08	13.99	13.95	13.91
	0.010	27.35	27.23	26.87	26.69	26.50	26.32	26.22	26.14
	0.001	129.86	129.25	127.37	126.42	125.45	124.47	123.97	123.53
4	0.100	3.94	3.92	3.87	3.84	3.82	3.79	3.78	3.76
	0.050	6.00	5.96	5.86	5.80	5.75	5.69	5.66	5.63
	0.025	8.90	8.84	8.66	8.56	8.46	8.36	8.31	8.26
	0.010	14.66	14.55	14.20	14.02	13.84	13.65	13.56	13.47
	0.001	48.47	48.05	46.76	46.10	45.43	44.75	44.40	44.09
5	0.100	3.32	3.30	3.24	3.21	3.17	3.14	3.12	3.11
	0.050	4.77	4.74	4.62	4.56	4.50	4.43	4.40	4.37
	0.025	6.68	6.62	6.43	6.33	6.23	6.12	6.07	6.02
	0.010	10.16	10.05	9.72	9.55	9.38	9.20	9.11	9.03
	0.001	27.24	26.92	25.91	25.39	24.87	24.33	24.06	23.82
6	0.100	2.96	2.94	2.87	2.84	2.80	2.76	2.74	2.72
	0.050	4.10	4.06	3.94	3.87	3.81	3.74	3.70	3.67
	0.025	5.52	5.46	5.27	5.17	5.07	4.96	4.90	4.86
	0.010	7.98	7.87	7.56	7.40	7.23	7.06	6.97	6.89
	0.001	18.69	18.41	17.56	17.12	16.67	16.21	15.98	15.77
7	0.100	2.72	2.70	2.63	2.59	2.56	2.51	2.49	2.47
	0.050	3.68	3.64	3.51	3.44	3.38	3.30	3.27	3.23
	0.025	4.82	4.76	4.57	4.47	4.36	4.25	4.20	4.15
	0.010	6.72	6.62	6.31	6.16	5.99	5.82	5.74	5.66
	0.001	14.33	14.08	13.32	12.93	12.53	12.12	11.91	11.72
8	0.100	2.56	2.54	2.46	2.42	2.38	2.34	2.32	2.30
	0.050	3.39	3.35	3.22	3.15	3.08	3.01	2.97	2.93
	0.025	4.36	4.30	4.10	4.00	3.89	3.78	3.73	3.68
	0.010	5.91	5.81	5.52	5.36	5.20	5.03	4.95	4.87
	0.001	11.77	11.54	10.84	10.48	10.11	9.73	9.53	9.36

Degrees of Freedom in the Denominator

TABLE V (continued)

F-Distribution Critical Values
Degrees of Freedom in the Numerator

	Area in Right Tail	1	2	3	4	5	6	7	8	9	10
9	0.100	3.36	3.01	2.81	2.69	2.61	2.55	2.51	2.47	2.44	2.42
	0.050	5.12	4.26	3.86	3.63	3.48	3.37	3.29	3.23	3.18	3.14
	0.025	7.21	5.71	5.08	4.72	4.48	4.32	4.20	4.10	4.03	3.96
	0.010	10.56	8.02	6.99	6.42	6.06	5.80	5.61	5.47	5.35	5.26
	0.001	22.86	16.39	13.90	12.56	11.71	11.13	10.70	10.37	10.11	9.89
10	0.100	3.29	2.92	2.73	2.61	2.52	2.46	2.41	2.38	2.35	2.32
	0.050	4.96	4.10	3.71	3.48	3.33	3.22	3.14	3.07	3.02	2.98
	0.025	6.94	5.46	4.83	4.47	4.24	4.07	3.95	3.85	3.78	3.72
	0.010	10.04	7.56	6.55	5.99	5.64	5.39	5.20	5.06	4.94	4.85
	0.001	21.04	14.91	12.55	11.28	10.48	9.93	9.52	9.20	8.96	8.75
12	0.100	3.18	2.81	2.61	2.48	2.39	2.33	2.28	2.24	2.21	2.19
	0.050	4.75	3.89	3.49	3.26	3.11	3.00	2.91	2.85	2.80	2.75
	0.025	6.55	5.10	4.47	4.12	3.89	3.73	3.61	3.51	3.44	3.37
	0.010	9.33	6.93	5.95	5.41	5.06	4.82	4.64	4.50	4.39	4.30
	0.001	18.64	12.97	10.80	9.63	8.89	8.38	8.00	7.71	7.48	7.29
15	0.100	3.07	2.70	2.49	2.36	2.27	2.21	2.16	2.12	2.09	2.06
	0.050	4.54	3.68	3.29	3.06	2.90	2.79	2.71	2.64	2.59	2.54
	0.025	6.20	4.77	4.15	3.80	3.58	3.41	3.29	3.20	3.12	3.06
	0.010	8.68	6.36	5.42	4.89	4.56	4.32	4.14	4.00	3.89	3.80
	0.001	16.59	11.34	9.34	8.25	7.57	7.09	6.74	6.47	6.26	6.08
20	0.100	2.97	2.59	2.38	2.25	2.16	2.09	2.04	2.00	1.96	1.94
	0.050	4.35	3.49	3.10	2.87	2.71	2.60	2.51	2.45	2.39	2.35
	0.025	5.87	4.46	3.86	3.51	3.29	3.13	3.01	2.91	2.84	2.77
	0.010	8.10	5.85	4.94	4.43	4.10	3.87	3.70	3.56	3.46	3.37
	0.001	14.82	9.95	8.10	7.10	6.46	6.02	5.69	5.44	5.24	5.08
25	0.100	2.92	2.53	2.32	2.18	2.09	2.02	1.97	1.93	1.89	1.87
	0.050	4.24	3.39	2.99	2.76	2.60	2.49	2.40	2.34	2.28	2.24
	0.025	5.69	4.29	3.69	3.35	3.13	2.97	2.85	2.75	2.68	2.61
	0.010	7.77	5.57	4.68	4.18	3.85	3.63	3.46	3.32	3.22	3.13
	0.001	13.88	9.22	7.45	6.49	5.89	5.46	5.15	4.91	4.71	4.56
50	0.100	2.81	2.41	2.20	2.06	1.97	1.90	1.84	1.80	1.76	1.73
	0.050	4.03	3.18	2.79	2.56	2.40	2.29	2.20	2.13	2.07	2.03
	0.025	5.34	3.97	3.39	3.05	2.83	2.67	2.55	2.46	2.38	2.32
	0.010	7.17	5.06	4.20	3.72	3.41	3.19	3.02	2.89	2.78	2.70
	0.001	12.22	7.96	6.34	5.46	4.90	4.51	4.22	4.00	3.82	3.67
100	0.100	2.76	2.36	2.14	2.00	1.91	1.83	1.78	1.73	1.69	1.66
	0.050	3.94	3.09	2.70	2.46	2.31	2.19	2.10	2.03	1.97	1.93
	0.025	5.18	3.83	3.25	2.92	2.70	2.54	2.42	2.32	2.24	2.18
	0.010	6.90	4.82	3.98	3.51	3.21	2.99	2.82	2.69	2.59	2.50
	0.001	11.50	7.41	5.86	5.02	4.48	4.11	3.83	3.61	3.44	3.30
200	0.100	2.73	2.33	2.11	1.97	1.88	1.80	1.75	1.70	1.66	1.63
	0.050	3.89	3.04	2.65	2.42	2.26	2.14	2.06	1.98	1.93	1.88
	0.025	5.10	3.76	3.18	2.85	2.63	2.47	2.35	2.26	2.18	2.11
	0.010	6.76	4.71	3.88	3.41	3.11	2.89	2.73	2.60	2.50	2.41
	0.001	11.15	7.15	5.63	4.81	4.29	3.92	3.65	3.43	3.26	3.12
1000	0.100	2.71	2.31	2.09	1.95	1.85	1.78	1.72	1.68	1.64	1.61
	0.050	3.85	3.00	2.61	2.38	2.22	2.11	2.02	1.95	1.89	1.84
	0.025	5.04	3.70	3.13	2.80	2.58	2.42	2.30	2.20	2.13	2.06
	0.010	6.66	4.63	3.80	3.34	3.04	2.82	2.66	2.53	2.43	2.34
	0.001	10.89	6.96	5.46	4.65	4.14	3.78	3.51	3.30	3.13	2.99

Degrees of Freedom in the Denominator

TABLE V (continued)

F-Distribution Critical Values

Degrees of Freedom in the Numerator

Denom. df	Area in Right Tail	12	15	20	25	30	40	50	60	120	1000
9	0.100	2.38	2.34	2.30	2.27	2.25	2.23	2.22	2.21	2.18	2.16
	0.050	3.07	3.01	2.94	2.89	2.86	2.83	2.80	2.79	2.75	2.71
	0.025	3.87	3.77	3.67	3.60	3.56	3.51	3.47	3.45	3.39	3.34
	0.010	5.11	4.96	4.81	4.71	4.65	4.57	4.52	4.48	4.40	4.32
	0.001	9.57	9.24	8.90	8.69	8.55	8.37	8.26	8.19	8.00	7.84
10	0.100	2.28	2.24	2.20	2.17	2.16	2.13	2.12	2.11	2.08	2.06
	0.050	2.91	2.85	2.77	2.73	2.70	2.66	2.64	2.62	2.58	2.54
	0.025	3.62	3.52	3.42	3.35	3.31	3.26	3.22	3.20	3.14	3.09
	0.010	4.71	4.56	4.41	4.31	4.25	4.17	4.12	4.08	4.00	3.92
	0.001	8.45	8.13	7.80	7.60	7.47	7.30	7.19	7.12	6.94	6.78
12	0.100	2.15	2.10	2.06	2.03	2.01	1.99	1.97	1.96	1.93	1.91
	0.050	2.69	2.62	2.54	2.50	2.47	2.43	2.40	2.38	2.34	2.30
	0.025	3.28	3.18	3.07	3.01	2.96	2.91	2.87	2.85	2.79	2.73
	0.010	4.16	4.01	3.86	3.76	3.70	3.62	3.57	3.54	3.45	3.37
	0.001	7.00	6.71	6.40	6.22	6.09	5.93	5.83	5.76	5.59	5.44
15	0.100	2.02	1.97	1.92	1.89	1.87	1.85	1.83	1.82	1.79	1.76
	0.050	2.48	2.40	2.33	2.28	2.25	2.20	2.18	2.16	2.11	2.07
	0.025	2.96	2.86	2.76	2.69	2.64	2.59	2.55	2.52	2.46	2.40
	0.010	3.67	3.52	3.37	3.28	3.21	3.13	3.08	3.05	2.96	2.88
	0.001	5.81	5.54	5.25	5.07	4.95	4.80	4.70	4.64	4.47	4.33
20	0.100	1.89	1.84	1.79	1.76	1.74	1.71	1.69	1.68	1.64	1.61
	0.050	2.28	2.20	2.12	2.07	2.04	1.99	1.97	1.95	1.90	1.85
	0.025	2.68	2.57	2.46	2.40	2.35	2.29	2.25	2.22	2.16	2.09
	0.010	3.23	3.09	2.94	2.84	2.78	2.69	2.64	2.61	2.52	2.43
	0.001	4.82	4.56	4.29	4.12	4.00	3.86	3.77	3.70	3.54	3.40
25	0.100	1.82	1.77	1.72	1.68	1.66	1.63	1.61	1.59	1.56	1.52
	0.050	2.16	2.09	2.01	1.96	1.92	1.87	1.84	1.82	1.77	1.72
	0.025	2.51	2.41	2.30	2.23	2.18	2.12	2.08	2.05	1.98	1.91
	0.010	2.99	2.85	2.70	2.60	2.54	2.45	2.40	2.36	2.27	2.18
	0.001	4.31	4.06	3.79	3.63	3.52	3.37	3.28	3.22	3.06	2.91
50	0.100	1.68	1.63	1.57	1.53	1.50	1.46	1.44	1.42	1.38	1.33
	0.050	1.95	1.87	1.78	1.73	1.69	1.63	1.60	1.58	1.51	1.45
	0.025	2.22	2.11	1.99	1.92	1.87	1.80	1.75	1.72	1.64	1.56
	0.010	2.56	2.42	2.27	2.17	2.10	2.01	1.95	1.91	1.80	1.70
	0.001	3.44	3.20	2.95	2.79	2.68	2.53	2.44	2.38	2.21	2.05
100	0.100	1.61	1.56	1.49	1.45	1.42	1.38	1.35	1.34	1.28	1.22
	0.050	1.85	1.77	1.68	1.62	1.57	1.52	1.48	1.45	1.38	1.30
	0.025	2.08	1.97	1.85	1.77	1.71	1.64	1.59	1.56	1.46	1.36
	0.010	2.37	2.22	2.07	1.97	1.89	1.80	1.74	1.69	1.57	1.45
	0.001	3.07	2.84	2.59	2.43	2.32	2.17	2.08	2.01	1.83	1.64
200	0.100	1.58	1.52	1.46	1.41	1.38	1.34	1.31	1.29	1.23	1.16
	0.050	1.80	1.72	1.62	1.56	1.52	1.46	1.41	1.39	1.30	1.21
	0.025	2.01	1.90	1.78	1.70	1.64	1.56	1.51	1.47	1.37	1.25
	0.010	2.27	2.13	1.97	1.87	1.79	1.69	1.63	1.58	1.45	1.30
	0.001	2.90	2.67	2.42	2.26	2.15	2.00	1.90	1.83	1.64	1.43
1000	0.100	1.55	1.49	1.43	1.38	1.35	1.30	1.27	1.25	1.18	1.08
	0.050	1.76	1.68	1.58	1.52	1.47	1.41	1.36	1.33	1.24	1.11
	0.025	1.96	1.85	1.72	1.64	1.58	1.50	1.45	1.41	1.29	1.13
	0.010	2.20	2.06	1.90	1.79	1.72	1.61	1.54	1.50	1.35	1.16
	0.001	2.77	2.54	2.30	2.14	2.02	1.87	1.77	1.69	1.49	1.22

Degrees of Freedom in the Denominator

TABLE VI

Critical Values for the Number of Runs

Value of n_2

Value of n_1	2	3	4	5	6	7	8	9	10	11	12	13	14	15	16	17	18	19	20
2	1	1	1	1	1	1	1	1	1	1	2	2	2	2	2	2	2	2	2
	6	6	6	6	6	6	6	6	6	6	6	6	6	6	6	6	6	6	6
3	1	1	1	1	2	2	2	2	2	2	2	2	2	3	3	3	3	3	3
	6	8	8	8	8	8	8	8	8	8	8	8	8	8	8	8	8	8	8
4	1	1	1	2	2	2	3	3	3	3	3	3	3	3	4	4	4	4	4
	6	8	9	9	9	10	10	10	10	10	10	10	10	10	10	10	10	10	10
5	1	1	2	2	3	3	3	3	3	4	4	4	4	4	4	4	5	5	5
	6	8	9	10	10	11	11	12	12	12	12	12	12	12	12	12	12	12	12
6	1	2	2	3	3	3	3	4	4	4	4	5	5	5	5	5	5	6	6
	6	8	9	10	11	12	12	13	13	13	13	14	14	14	14	14	14	14	14
7	1	2	2	3	3	3	4	4	5	5	5	5	5	6	6	6	6	6	6
	6	8	10	11	12	13	13	14	14	14	14	15	15	15	16	16	16	16	16
8	1	2	3	3	3	4	4	5	5	5	6	6	6	6	6	7	7	7	7
	6	8	10	11	12	13	14	14	15	15	16	16	16	16	17	17	17	17	17
9	1	2	3	3	4	4	5	5	5	6	6	6	7	7	7	7	8	8	8
	6	8	10	12	13	14	14	15	16	16	16	17	17	18	18	18	18	18	18
10	1	2	3	3	4	5	5	5	6	6	7	7	7	7	8	8	8	8	9
	6	8	10	12	13	14	15	16	16	17	17	18	18	18	19	19	19	20	20
11	1	2	3	4	4	5	5	6	6	7	7	7	8	8	8	9	9	9	9
	6	8	10	12	13	14	15	16	17	17	18	19	19	19	20	20	20	21	21
12	2	2	3	4	4	5	6	6	7	7	7	8	8	8	9	9	9	10	10
	6	8	10	12	13	14	16	16	17	18	19	19	20	20	21	21	21	22	22
13	2	2	3	4	5	5	6	6	7	7	8	8	9	9	9	10	10	10	10
	6	8	10	12	14	15	16	17	18	19	19	20	20	21	21	22	22	23	23
14	2	2	3	4	5	5	6	7	7	8	8	9	9	9	10	10	10	11	11
	6	8	10	12	14	15	16	17	18	19	20	20	21	22	22	23	23	23	24
15	2	3	3	4	5	6	6	7	7	8	8	9	9	10	10	11	11	11	12
	6	8	10	12	14	15	16	18	18	19	20	21	22	22	23	23	24	24	25
16	2	3	4	4	5	6	6	7	8	8	9	9	10	10	11	11	11	12	12
	6	8	10	12	14	16	17	18	19	20	21	21	22	23	23	24	25	25	25
17	2	3	4	4	5	6	7	7	8	9	9	10	10	11	11	11	12	12	13
	6	8	10	12	14	16	17	18	19	20	21	22	23	23	24	25	25	26	26
18	2	3	4	5	5	6	7	8	8	9	9	10	10	11	11	12	12	13	13
	6	8	10	12	14	16	17	18	19	20	21	22	23	24	25	25	26	26	27
19	2	3	4	5	6	6	7	8	8	9	10	10	11	11	12	12	13	13	13
	6	8	10	12	14	16	17	18	20	21	22	23	23	24	25	26	26	27	27
20	2	3	4	5	6	6	7	8	9	9	10	10	11	12	12	13	13	13	14
	6	8	10	12	14	16	17	18	20	21	22	23	24	25	25	26	27	27	28

From "Tables for testing randomness of groupings in a sequence of alternatives," *The Annals of Mathematical Statistics,* Vol. 14, No. 1. Reprinted with permission of the Institute of Mathematical Statistics.

TABLE VII

Critical Values for the Sign Test
α

n	0.005 (one tail) 0.01 (two tails)	0.01 (one tail) 0.02 (two tails)	0.025 (one tail) 0.05 (two tails)	0.05 (one tail) 0.10 (two tails)
1	*	*	*	*
2	*	*	*	*
3	*	*	*	*
4	*	*	*	*
5	*	*	*	0
6	*	*	0	0
7	*	0	0	0
8	0	0	0	1
9	0	0	1	1
10	0	0	1	1
11	0	1	1	2
12	1	1	2	2
13	1	1	2	3
14	1	2	2	3
15	2	2	3	3
16	2	2	3	4
17	2	3	4	4
18	3	3	4	5
19	3	4	4	5
20	3	4	5	5
21	4	4	5	6
22	4	5	5	6
23	4	5	6	7
24	5	5	6	7
25	5	6	7	7
26	6	6	7	8
27	6	7	7	8
28	6	7	8	9
29	7	7	8	9
30	7	8	9	10

* Indicates that it is not possible to get a value in the critical region.
Source: Jerrold H. Zar, *Biostatistical Analysis,* 4e, 1999, p. Appl 33.

TABLE VIII

Critical Values for the Wilcoxon Signed-Rank Test

n	α			
	0.005	**0.01**	**0.025**	**0.05**
5	*	*	*	0
6	*	*	0	2
7	*	0	2	3
8	0	1	3	5
9	1	3	5	8
10	3	5	8	10
11	5	7	10	13
12	7	9	13	17
13	9	12	17	21
14	12	15	21	25
15	15	19	25	30
16	19	23	29	35
17	23	27	34	41
18	27	32	40	47
19	32	37	46	53
20	37	43	52	60
21	42	49	58	67
22	48	55	65	75
23	54	62	73	83
24	61	69	81	91
25	68	76	89	100
26	75	84	98	110
27	83	92	107	119
28	91	101	116	130
29	100	110	126	140
30	109	120	137	151

* Indicates that it is not possible to get a value in the critical region.
Source: Jerrold H. Zar, *Biostatistical Analysis,* 4th Edition, 1999.
Prentice Hall.

TABLE IX

Critical Values of the Mann–Whitney Test Statistic

n_1	α	$n_2=2$	3	4	5	6	7	8	9	10	11	12	13	14	15	16	17	18	19	20
2	0.001	0	0	0	0	0	0	0	0	0	0	0	0	0	0	0	0	0	0	0
	0.005	0	0	0	0	0	0	0	0	0	0	0	0	0	0	0	0	0	1	1
	0.01	0	0	0	0	0	0	0	0	0	0	0	1	1	1	1	1	1	2	2
	0.025	0	0	0	0	0	0	1	1	1	1	2	2	2	2	2	3	3	3	3
	0.05	0	0	0	1	1	1	2	2	2	2	3	3	4	4	4	4	5	5	5
	0.10	0	1	1	2	2	2	3	3	4	4	5	5	5	6	6	7	7	8	8
3	0.001	0	0	0	0	0	0	0	0	0	0	0	0	0	0	0	1	1	1	1
	0.005	0	0	0	0	0	0	0	1	1	1	2	2	2	3	3	3	3	4	4
	0.01	0	0	0	0	0	1	1	2	2	2	3	3	3	4	4	5	5	5	6
	0.025	0	0	0	1	2	2	3	3	4	4	5	5	6	6	7	7	8	8	9
	0.05	0	1	1	2	3	3	4	5	5	6	6	7	8	8	9	10	10	11	12
	0.10	1	2	2	3	4	5	6	6	7	8	9	10	11	11	12	13	14	15	16
4	0.001	0	0	0	0	0	0	0	0	1	1	1	2	2	2	3	3	4	4	4
	0.005	0	0	0	0	1	1	2	2	3	3	4	4	5	6	6	7	7	8	9
	0.01	0	0	0	1	2	2	3	4	4	5	6	6	7	9	8	9	10	10	11
	0.025	0	0	1	2	3	4	5	5	6	7	8	9	10	11	12	12	13	14	15
	0.05	0	1	2	3	4	5	6	7	8	9	10	11	12	13	15	16	17	18	19
	0.10	1	2	4	5	6	7	8	10	11	12	13	14	16	17	18	19	21	22	23
5	0.001	0	0	0	0	0	0	1	2	2	3	3	4	4	5	6	6	7	8	8
	0.005	0	0	0	1	2	2	3	4	5	6	7	8	8	9	10	11	12	13	14
	0.01	0	0	1	2	3	4	5	6	7	8	9	10	11	12	13	14	15	16	17
	0.025	0	1	2	3	4	6	7	8	9	10	12	13	14	15	16	18	19	20	21
	0.05	1	2	3	5	6	7	9	10	12	13	14	16	17	19	20	21	23	24	26
	0.10	2	3	5	6	8	9	11	13	14	16	18	19	21	23	24	26	28	29	31
6	0.001	0	0	0	0	0	0	2	3	4	5	5	6	7	8	9	10	11	12	13
	0.005	0	0	1	2	3	4	5	6	7	8	10	11	12	13	14	16	17	18	19
	0.01	0	0	2	3	4	5	7	8	9	10	12	13	14	16	17	19	20	21	23
	0.025	0	2	3	4	6	7	9	11	12	14	15	17	18	20	22	23	25	28	28
	0.05	1	3	4	6	8	9	11	13	15	17	18	20	22	24	26	27	29	31	33
	0.10	2	4	6	8	10	12	14	16	18	20	22	24	26	28	30	32	35	37	39
7	0.001	0	0	0	0	1	2	3	4	6	7	8	9	10	11	12	14	15	16	17
	0.005	0	0	1	2	4	5	7	8	10	11	13	14	16	17	19	20	22	23	25
	0.01	0	1	2	4	5	7	8	10	12	13	15	17	18	20	22	24	25	27	29
	0.025	0	2	4	6	7	9	11	13	15	17	19	21	23	25	27	29	31	33	35
	0.05	1	3	5	7	9	12	14	16	18	20	22	25	27	29	31	34	36	38	40
	0.10	2	5	7	9	12	14	17	19	22	24	27	29	32	34	37	39	42	44	47
8	0.001	0	0	0	1	2	3	5	6	7	9	10	12	13	15	16	18	19	21	22
	0.005	0	0	2	3	5	7	8	10	12	14	16	18	19	21	23	25	27	29	31
	0.01	0	1	3	5	7	8	10	12	14	16	18	21	23	25	27	29	31	33	35
	0.025	1	3	5	7	9	11	14	16	18	20	23	25	27	30	32	35	37	39	42
	0.05	2	4	6	9	11	14	16	19	21	24	27	29	32	34	37	40	42	45	48
	0.10	3	6	8	11	14	17	20	23	25	28	31	34	37	40	43	46	49	52	55
9	0.001	0	0	0	2	3	4	6	8	9	11	13	15	16	18	20	22	24	26	27
	0.005	0	1	2	4	6	8	10	12	14	17	19	21	23	25	28	30	32	34	37
	0.01	0	2	4	6	8	10	12	15	17	19	22	24	27	29	32	34	37	39	41
	0.025	1	3	5	8	11	13	16	18	21	24	27	29	32	35	38	40	43	46	49
	0.05	2	5	7	10	13	16	19	22	25	28	31	34	37	40	43	46	49	52	55
	0.10	3	6	10	13	16	19	23	26	29	32	36	39	42	46	49	53	56	59	63

TABLE IX (continued)

Critical Values of the Mann–Whitney Test Statistic

n_1	α	$n_2=2$	3	4	5	6	7	8	9	10	11	12	13	14	15	16	17	18	19	20
10	0.001	0	0	1	2	4	6	7	9	11	13	15	18	20	22	24	26	28	30	33
	0.005	0	1	3	5	7	10	12	14	17	19	22	25	27	30	32	35	38	40	43
	0.01	0	2	4	7	9	12	14	17	20	23	25	28	31	34	37	39	42	45	48
	0.025	1	4	6	9	12	15	18	21	24	27	30	34	37	40	43	46	49	53	56
	0.05	2	5	8	12	15	18	21	25	28	32	35	38	42	45	49	52	56	59	63
	0.10	4	7	11	14	18	22	25	29	33	37	40	44	48	52	55	59	63	67	71
11	0.001	0	0	1	3	5	7	9	11	13	16	18	21	23	25	28	30	33	35	38
	0.005	0	1	3	6	8	11	14	17	19	22	25	28	31	34	37	40	43	46	49
	0.01	0	2	5	8	10	13	16	19	23	26	29	32	35	38	42	45	48	51	54
	0.025	1	4	7	10	14	17	20	24	27	31	34	38	41	45	48	52	56	59	63
	0.05	2	6	9	13	17	20	24	28	32	35	39	43	47	51	55	58	62	66	70
	0.10	4	8	12	16	20	24	28	32	37	41	45	49	53	58	62	66	70	74	79
12	0.001	0	0	1	3	5	8	10	13	15	18	21	24	26	29	32	35	38	41	43
	0.005	0	2	4	7	10	13	16	19	22	25	28	32	35	38	42	45	48	52	55
	0.01	0	3	6	9	12	15	18	22	25	29	32	36	39	43	47	50	54	57	61
	0.025	2	5	8	12	15	19	23	27	30	34	38	42	46	50	54	58	62	66	70
	0.05	3	6	10	14	18	22	27	31	35	39	43	48	52	56	61	65	69	73	78
	0.10	5	9	13	18	22	27	31	36	40	45	50	54	59	64	68	73	78	82	87
13	0.001	0	0	2	4	6	9	12	15	18	21	24	27	30	33	36	39	43	46	49
	0.005	0	2	4	8	11	14	18	21	25	28	32	35	39	43	46	50	54	58	61
	0.01	1	3	6	10	13	17	21	24	28	32	36	40	44	48	52	56	60	64	68
	0.025	2	5	9	13	17	21	25	29	34	38	42	46	51	55	60	64	68	73	77
	0.05	3	7	11	16	20	25	29	34	38	43	48	52	57	62	66	71	76	81	85
	0.10	5	10	14	19	24	29	34	39	44	49	54	59	64	69	75	80	85	90	95
14	0.001	0	0	2	4	7	10	13	16	20	23	26	30	33	37	40	44	47	51	55
	0.005	0	2	5	8	12	16	19	23	27	31	35	39	43	47	51	55	59	64	68
	0.01	1	3	7	11	14	18	23	27	31	35	39	44	48	52	57	61	66	70	74
	0.025	2	6	10	14	18	23	27	32	37	41	46	51	56	60	65	70	75	79	84
	0.05	4	8	12	17	22	27	32	37	42	47	52	57	62	67	72	78	83	88	93
	0.10	5	11	16	21	26	32	37	42	48	53	59	64	70	75	81	86	92	98	103
15	0.001	0	0	2	5	8	11	15	18	22	25	29	33	37	41	44	48	52	56	60
	0.005	0	3	6	9	13	17	21	25	30	34	38	43	47	52	56	61	65	70	74
	0.01	1	4	8	12	16	20	25	29	34	38	43	48	52	57	62	67	71	76	81
	0.025	2	6	11	15	20	25	30	35	40	45	50	55	60	65	71	76	81	86	91
	0.05	4	8	13	19	24	29	34	40	45	51	56	62	67	73	78	84	89	95	101
	0.10	6	11	17	23	28	34	40	46	52	58	64	69	75	81	87	93	99	105	111
16	0.001	0	0	3	6	9	12	16	20	24	28	32	36	40	44	49	53	57	61	66
	0.005	0	3	6	10	14	19	23	28	32	37	42	46	51	56	61	66	71	75	80
	0.01	1	4	8	13	17	22	27	32	37	42	47	52	57	62	67	72	77	83	88
	0.025	2	7	12	16	22	27	32	38	43	48	54	60	65	71	76	82	87	93	99
	0.05	4	9	15	20	26	31	37	43	49	55	61	66	72	78	84	90	96	102	108
	0.10	6	12	18	24	30	37	43	49	55	62	68	75	81	87	94	100	107	113	120
17	0.001	0	1	3	6	10	14	18	22	26	30	35	39	44	48	53	58	62	67	71
	0.005	0	3	7	11	16	20	25	30	35	40	45	50	55	61	66	71	76	82	87
	0.01	1	5	9	14	19	24	29	34	39	45	50	56	61	67	72	78	83	89	94
	0.025	3	7	12	18	23	29	35	40	46	52	58	64	70	76	82	88	94	100	106
	0.05	4	10	16	21	27	34	40	46	52	58	65	71	78	84	90	97	103	110	118
	0.10	7	13	19	26	32	39	46	53	59	66	73	80	86	93	100	107	114	121	128
18	0.001	0	1	4	7	11	15	19	24	28	33	38	43	47	52	57	62	67	72	77
	0.005	0	3	7	12	17	22	27	32	38	43	48	54	59	65	71	76	82	88	93
	0.01	1	5	10	15	20	25	31	37	42	48	54	60	66	71	77	83	89	95	101
	0.025	3	8	13	19	25	31	37	43	49	56	62	68	75	81	87	94	100	107	113
	0.05	5	10	17	23	29	36	42	49	56	62	69	76	83	89	96	103	110	117	124
	0.10	7	14	21	28	35	42	49	56	63	70	78	85	92	99	107	114	121	129	136

TABLE IX (continued)

Critical Values of the Mann–Whitney Test Statistic

n_1	α	$n_2=2$	3	4	5	6	7	8	9	10	11	12	13	14	15	16	17	18	19	20
	0.001	0	1	4	8	12	16	21	26	30	35	41	46	51	56	61	67	72	78	83
	0.005	1	4	8	13	18	23	29	34	40	46	52	58	64	70	75	82	88	94	100
19	0.01	2	5	10	16	21	27	33	39	45	51	57	64	70	76	83	89	95	102	108
	0.025	3	8	14	20	26	33	39	46	53	59	66	73	79	86	93	100	107	114	120
	0.05	5	11	18	24	31	38	45	52	59	66	73	81	88	95	102	110	117	124	131
	0.10	8	15	22	29	37	44	52	59	67	74	82	90	98	105	113	121	129	136	144
	0.001	0	1	4	8	13	17	22	27	33	38	43	49	55	60	66	71	77	83	89
	0.005	1	4	9	14	19	25	31	37	43	49	55	61	68	74	80	87	93	100	106
20	0.01	2	6	11	17	23	29	35	41	48	54	61	68	74	81	88	94	101	108	115
	0.025	3	9	15	21	28	35	42	49	56	63	70	77	84	91	99	106	113	120	128
	0.05	5	12	19	26	33	40	48	55	63	70	78	85	93	101	108	116	124	131	139
	0.10	8	16	23	31	39	47	55	63	71	79	87	95	103	111	120	128	136	144	152

Source: Adapted from L. R. Verdooren, "Extended Tables of Critical Values for Wilcoxon's Test Statistic," *Biometrika*, 60 (1963), 177–186; used by permission of the Biometrika Trustees. The adaptation is due to W. J. Conover, *Practical Nonparametric Statistics*, New York: Wiley, 1971, 384–388.

					TABLE X				
	Critical Values of Spearman's Rank Correlation Coefficient								
α(2):	0.50	0.20	0.10	0.05	0.02	0.01	0.005	0.002	0.001
α(1):	0.25	0.10	0.05	0.025	0.01	0.005	0.0025	0.001	0.0005
n									
4	0.600	1.000	1.000						
5	0.500	0.800	0.900	1.000	1.000				
6	0.371	0.657	0.829	0.886	0.943	1.000	1.000		
7	0.321	0.571	0.714	0.786	0.893	0.929	0.964	1.000	1.000
8	0.310	0.524	0.643	0.738	0.833	0.881	0.905	0.952	0.976
9	0.267	0.483	0.600	0.700	0.783	0.833	0.867	0.917	0.933
10	0.248	0.455	0.564	0.648	0.745	0.794	0.830	0.879	0.903
11	0.236	0.427	0.536	0.618	0.709	0.755	0.800	0.845	0.873
12	0.217	0.406	0.503	0.587	0.678	0.727	0.769	0.818	0.846
13	0.209	0.385	0.484	0.560	0.648	0.703	0.747	0.791	0.824
14	0.200	0.367	0.464	0.538	0.626	0.679	0.723	0.771	0.802
15	0.189	0.354	0.446	0.521	0.604	0.654	0.700	0.750	0.779
16	0.182	0.341	0.429	0.503	0.582	0.635	0.679	0.729	0.762
17	0.176	0.328	0.414	0.485	0.566	0.615	0.662	0.713	0.748
18	0.170	0.317	0.401	0.472	0.550	0.600	0.643	0.695	0.728
19	0.165	0.309	0.391	0.460	0.535	0.584	0.628	0.677	0.712
20	0.161	0.299	0.380	0.447	0.520	0.570	0.612	0.662	0.696
21	0.156	0.292	0.370	0.435	0.508	0.556	0.599	0.648	0.681
22	0.152	0.284	0.361	0.425	0.496	0.544	0.586	0.634	0.667
23	0.148	0.278	0.353	0.415	0.486	0.532	0.573	0.622	0.654
24	0.144	0.271	0.344	0.406	0.476	0.521	0.562	0.610	0.642
25	0.142	0.265	0.337	0.398	0.466	0.511	0.551	0.598	0.630
26	0.138	0.259	0.331	0.390	0.457	0.501	0.541	0.587	0.619
27	0.136	0.255	0.324	0.382	0.448	0.491	0.531	0.577	0.608
28	0.133	0.250	0.317	0.375	0.440	0.483	0.522	0.567	0.598
29	0.130	0.245	0.312	0.368	0.433	0.475	0.513	0.558	0.589
30	0.128	0.240	0.306	0.362	0.425	0.467	0.504	0.549	0.580
31	0.126	0.236	0.301	0.356	0.418	0.459	0.496	0.541	0.571
32	0.124	0.232	0.296	0.350	0.412	0.452	0.489	0.533	0.563
33	0.121	0.229	0.291	0.345	0.405	0.446	0.482	0.525	0.554
34	0.120	0.225	0.287	0.340	0.399	0.439	0.475	0.517	0.547
35	0.118	0.222	0.283	0.335	0.394	0.433	0.488	0.510	0.539
36	0.116	0.219	0.279	0.330	0.388	0.427	0.462	0.504	0.533
37	0.114	0.216	0.275	0.325	0.383	0.421	0.456	0.497	0.526
38	0.113	0.212	0.271	0.321	0.378	0.415	0.450	0.491	0.519
39	0.111	0.210	0.267	0.317	0.373	0.410	0.444	0.485	0.513
40	0.110	0.207	0.264	0.313	0.368	0.405	0.439	0.479	0.507
41	0.108	0.204	0.261	0.309	0.384	0.400	0.433	0.473	0.501
42	0.107	0.202	0.257	0.305	0.359	0.395	0.428	0.468	0.495
43	0.105	0.199	0.254	0.301	0.355	0.391	0.423	0.463	0.490
44	0.104	0.197	0.251	0.298	0.351	0.386	0.419	0.458	0.484
45	0.103	0.194	0.248	0.294	0.347	0.382	0.414	0.453	0.479
46	0.102	0.192	0.246	0.291	0.343	0.378	0.410	0.448	0.474
47	0.101	0.190	0.243	0.288	0.340	0.374	0.406	0.443	0.469
48	0.100	0.188	0.240	0.285	0.336	0.370	0.401	0.439	0.465
49	0.098	0.186	0.238	0.282	0.333	0.366	0.397	0.434	0.460
50	0.097	0.184	0.235	0.279	0.329	0.363	0.393	0.430	0.456

TABLE X (*continued*)								
Critical Values of Spearman's Rank Correlation Coefficient								

$\alpha(2)$:	0.50	0.20	0.10	0.05	0.02	0.01	0.005	0.002	0.001
$\alpha(1)$:	0.25	0.10	0.05	0.025	0.01	0.005	0.0025	0.001	0.0005
n									
51	0.096	0.182	0.233	0.276	0.326	0.359	0.390	0.426	0.451
52	0.095	0.180	0.231	0.274	0.323	0.356	0.386	0.422	0.447
53	0.095	0.179	0.228	0.271	0.320	0.352	0.382	0.418	0.443
54	0.094	0.177	0.226	0.268	0.317	0.349	0.379	0.414	0.439
55	0.093	0.175	0.224	0.266	0.314	0.346	0.375	0.411	0.435
56	0.092	0.174	0.222	0.264	0.311	0.343	0.372	0407	0.432
57	0.091	0.172	0.220	0.261	0.308	0.340	0.369	0.404	0.428
58	0.090	0.171	0.218	0.259	0.306	0.337	0.366	0.400	0.424
59	0.089	0.169	0.216	0.257	0.303	0.334	0.363	0.397	0.421
60	0.089	0.168	0.214	0.255	0.300	0.331	0.360	0.394	0.418
61	0.088	0.166	0.213	0.252	0.298	0.329	0.357	0.391	0.414
62	0.087	0.165	0.211	0.250	0.296	0.326	0.354	0.388	0.411
63	0.086	0.163	0.209	0.248	0.293	0.323	0.351	0.385	0.408
64	0.086	0.162	0.207	0.246	0.291	0.321	0.348	0.382	0.405
65	0.085	0.161	0.206	0.244	0.289	0.318	0.346	0.379	0.402
66	0.084	0.160	0.204	0.243	0.287	0.316	0.343	0.376	0.399
67	0.084	0.158	0.203	0.241	0.284	0.314	0.341	0.373	0.396
68	0.083	0.157	0.201	0.239	0.282	0.311	0.338	0.370	0.393
69	0.082	0.156	0.200	0.237	0.280	0.309	0.336	0.368	0.390
70	0.082	0.155	0.198	0.235	0.278	0.307	0.333	0.365	0.388
71	0.081	0.154	0.197	0.234	0.276	0.305	0.331	0.363	0.385
72	0.081	0.153	0.195	0.232	0.274	0.303	0.329	0.360	0.382
73	0.080	0.152	0.194	0.230	0.272	0.301	0.327	0.358	0.380
74	0.080	0.151	0.193	0.229	0.271	0.299	0.324	0.355	0.377
75	0.079	0.150	0.191	0.227	0.269	0.297	0.322	0.353	0.375
76	0.078	0.149	0.190	0.226	0.267	0.295	0.320	0.351	0.372
77	0.078	0.148	0.189	0.224	0.265	0.293	0.318	0.349	0.370
78	0.077	0.147	0.188	0.223	0.264	0.291	0.316	0.346	0.368
79	0.077	0.146	0.186	0.221	0.262	0.289	0.314	0.344	0.365
80	0.076	0.145	0.185	0.220	0.260	0.287	0.312	0.342	0.363
81	0.076	0.144	0.184	0.219	0.259	0.285	0.310	0.340	0.361
82	0.075	0.143	0.183	0.217	0.257	0.284	0.308	0.338	0.359
83	0.075	0.142	0.182	0.216	0.255	0.282	0.306	0.336	0.357
84	0.074	0.141	0.181	0.215	0.254	0.280	0.305	0.334	0.355
85	0.074	0.140	0.180	0.213	0.252	0.279	0.303	0.332	0.353
86	0.074	0.139	0.179	0.212	0.251	0.277	0.301	0.330	0.351
87	0.073	0.139	0.177	0.211	0.250	0.276	0.299	0.328	0.349
88	0.073	0.138	0.176	0.210	0.248	0.274	0.298	0.327	0.347
89	0.072	0.137	0.175	0.209	0.247	0.272	0.296	0.325	0.345
90	0.072	0.136	0.174	0.207	0.245	0.271	0.294	0.323	0.343
91	0.072	0.135	0.173	0.206	0.244	0.269	0.293	0.321	0.341
92	0.071	0.135	0.173	0.205	0.243	0.268	0.291	0.319	0.339
93	0.071	0.134	0.172	0.204	0.241	0.267	0.290	0.318	0.338
94	0.070	0.133	0.171	0.203	0.240	0.265	0.288	0.316	0.336
95	0.070	0.133	0.170	0.202	0.239	0.264	0.287	0.314	0.334
96	0.070	0.132	0.169	0.201	0.238	0.262	0.285	0.313	0.332
97	0.069	0.131	0.168	0.200	0.236	0.261	0.284	0.311	0.331
98	0.069	0.130	0.167	0.199	0.235	0.260	0.282	0.310	0.329
99	0.068	0.130	0.166	0.198	0.234	0.258	0.281	0.308	0.327
100	0.068	0.129	0.165	0.197	0.233	0.257	0.279	0.307	0.326

Source: Jerrold H. Zar, *Biostatistical Analysis*, 4e, © 1999. Reprinted by permission of Prentice Hall, Inc., Upper Saddle River, New Jersey.

TABLE XI

Critical Values of the Kruskal–Wallis Test Statistic

Sample Sizes					Sample Sizes				
n_1	n_2	n_3	Critical Value	α	n_1	n_2	n_3	Critical Value	α
2	1	1	2.7000	0.500				4.7000	0.101
2	2	1	3.6000	0.200	4	4	1	6.6667	0.010
2	2	2	4.5714	0.067				6.1667	0.022
			3.7143	0.200				4.9667	0.048
3	1	1	3.2000	0.300				4.8667	0.054
3	2	1	4.2857	0.100				4.1667	0.082
			3.8571	0.133				4.0667	0.102
3	2	2	5.3572	0.029	4	4	2	7.0364	0.006
			4.7143	0.048				6.8727	0.011
			4.5000	0.067				5.4545	0.046
			4.4643	0.105				5.2364	0.052
3	3	1	5.1429	0.043				4.5545	0.098
			4.5714	0.100				4.4455	0.103
			4.0000	0.129	4	4	3	7.1439	0.010
3	3	2	6.2500	0.011				7.1364	0.011
			5.3611	0.032				5.5985	0.049
			5.1389	0.061				5.5758	0.051
			4.5556	0.100				4.5455	0.099
			4.2500	0.121				4.4773	0.102
3	3	3	7.2000	0.004	4	4	4	7.6538	0.008
			6.4889	0.011				7.5385	0.011
			5.6889	0.029				5.6923	0.049
			5.6000	0.050				5.6538	0.054
			5.0667	0.086				4.6539	0.097
			4.6222	0.100				4.5001	0.104
4	1	1	3.5714	0.200	5	1	1	3.8571	0.143
4	2	1	4.8214	0.057	5	2	1	5.2500	0.036
			4.5000	0.076				5.0000	0.048
			4.0179	0.114				4.4500	0.071
4	2	2	6.0000	0.014				4.2000	0.095
			5.3333	0.033				4.0500	0.119
			5.1250	0.052	5	2	2	6.5333	0.008
			4.4583	0.100				6.1333	0.013
			4.1667	0.105				5.1600	0.034
4	3	1	5.8333	0.021				5.0400	0.056
			5.2083	0.050				4.3733	0.090
			5.0000	0.057				4.2933	0.122
			4.0556	0.093	5	3	1	6.4000	0.012
			3.8889	0.129				4.9600	0.048
4	3	2	6.4444	0.008				4.8711	0.052
			6.3000	0.011				4.0178	0.095
			5.4444	0.046				3.8400	0.123
			5.4000	0.051	5	3	2	6.9091	0.009
			4.5111	0.098				6.8218	0.010
			4.4444	0.102				5.2509	0.049
4	3	3	6.7455	0.010				5.1055	0.052
			6.7091	0.013				4.6509	0.091
			5.7909	0.046				4.4945	0.101
			5.7273	0.050	5	3	3	7.0788	0.009
			4.7091	0.092				6.9818	0.011

TABLE XI (*continued*)

Critical Values of the Kruskal–Wallis Test Statistic

Sample Sizes					Sample Sizes				
n_1	n_2	n_3	Critical Value	α	n_1	n_2	n_3	Critical Value	α
5	3	3	5.6485	0.049	5	5	1	6.8364	0.011
			5.5152	0.051				5.1273	0.046
			4.5333	0.097				4.9091	0.053
			4.4121	0.109				4.1091	0.086
5	4	1	6.9545	0.008				4.0364	0.105
			6.8400	0.011	5	5	2	7.3385	0.010
			4.9855	0.044				7.2692	0.010
			4.8600	0.056				5.3385	0.047
			3.9873	0.098				5.2462	0.051
			3.9600	0.102				4.6231	0.097
5	4	2	7.2045	0.009				4.5077	0.100
			7.1182	0.010	5	5	3	7.5780	0.010
			5.2727	0.049				7.5429	0.010
			5.2682	0.050				5.7055	0.046
			4.5409	0.098				5.6264	0.051
			4.5182	0.101				4.5451	0.100
5	4	3	7.4449	0.010				4.5363	0.102
			7.3949	0.011	5	5	4	7.8229	0.010
			5.6564	0.049				7.7914	0.010
			5.6308	0.050				5.6657	0.049
			4.5487	0.099				5.6429	0.050
			4.5231	0.103				4.5229	0.099
5	4	4	7.7604	0.009				4.5200	0.101
			7.7440	0.011	5	5	5	8.0000	0.009
			5.6571	0.049				7.9600	0.010
			5.6176	0.050				5.7800	0.049
			4.6187	0.100				5.6600	0.051
			4.5527	0.102				4.5600	0.100
5	5	1	7.3091	0.009				4.5000	0.102

Source: W. H. Kruskal and W. A. Wallis, "Use of Ranks in One-Criterion Analysis of Variance," *J. Amer. Statist. Assoc.*, **47** (1952), 583–621, Addendum, *Ibid.*, **48** (1953), 907–911.

APPENDIX B   LINES

Objectives

1 Calculate and interpret the slope of a line
2 Graph lines, given a point and the slope
3 Use the point–slope form of a line; identify horizontal lines
4 Find the equation of a line, given two points
5 Write the equation of a line in slope–intercept form
6 Identify the slope and y-intercept of a line from its equation

In this section we review a certain type of equation that contains two variables, called a *linear equation*, and its graph, a *line*.

1 **Slope of a Line**

Figure 1

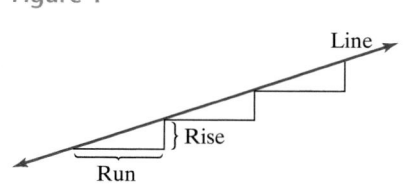

Consider the staircase illustrated in Figure 1. Each step contains exactly the same horizontal run and the same vertical rise. The ratio of the rise to the run, called the *slope*, is a numerical measure of the steepness of the staircase. For example, if the run is increased and the rise remains the same, the staircase becomes less steep. If the run is kept the same, but the rise is increased, the staircase becomes more steep. This important characteristic of a line is best defined using rectangular coordinates.

Definition | Let $P = (x_1, y_1)$ and $Q = (x_2, y_2)$ be two distinct points. If $x_1 \neq x_2$, the **slope** m of the nonvertical line L containing P and Q is defined by the formula

$$m = \frac{y_2 - y_1}{x_2 - x_1}, \quad x_1 \neq x_2 \tag{1}$$

If $x_1 = x_2$, L is a vertical line and the slope m of L is undefined (since this results in division by 0).

Figure 2(a) provides an illustration of the slope of a nonvertical line; Figure 2(b) illustrates a vertical line.

Figure 2

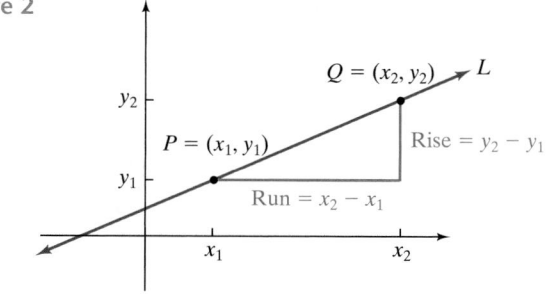

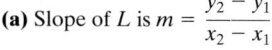

(a) Slope of L is $m = \dfrac{y_2 - y_1}{x_2 - x_1}$

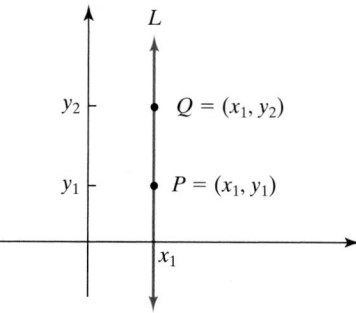

(b) Slope is undefined; L is vertical

As Figure 2(a) illustrates, the slope m of a nonvertical line may be viewed as

$$m = \frac{y_2 - y_1}{x_2 - x_1} = \frac{\text{Rise}}{\text{Run}}$$

We can also express the slope m of a nonvertical line as

$$m = \frac{y_2 - y_1}{x_2 - x_1} = \frac{\text{Change in } y}{\text{Change in } x} = \frac{\Delta y}{\Delta x}$$

That is, the slope m of a nonvertical line L measures the amount that y changes as x changes from x_1 to x_2.

Two comments about computing the slope of a nonvertical line may prove helpful:

1. Any two distinct points on the line can be used to compute the slope of the line.
2. The slope of a line may be computed from $P = (x_1, y_1)$ to $Q = (x_2, y_2)$ or from Q to P, because

$$\frac{y_2 - y_1}{x_2 - x_1} = \frac{y_1 - y_2}{x_1 - x_2}$$

▶ **EXAMPLE 1**   **Finding and Interpreting the Slope of a Line Containing Two Points**

Problem: Find the slope m of the line containing the points $(1, 2)$ and $(5, -3)$.

Solution:

$$m = \frac{-3 - 2}{5 - 1} = \frac{-5}{4} = -\frac{5}{4} \quad \text{or} \quad m = \frac{2 - (-3)}{1 - 5} = \frac{5}{-4} = \frac{-5}{4} = -\frac{5}{4}$$

For every 4-unit change in x, y will change by -5 units. That is, if x increases by 4 units, then y will decrease by 5 units.   ◀◀

NW *Now Work Problems 1 and 7.*

②   The next example illustrates how the slope of a line can be used to graph the line.

▶ **EXAMPLE 2**   **Graphing a Line, Given a Point and a Slope**

Problem: Draw a graph of the line that contains the point $(3, 2)$ and has a slope of

(a) $\dfrac{3}{4}$ **(b)** $-\dfrac{4}{5}$

Solution:

(a) Slope $= \dfrac{\text{Rise}}{\text{Run}}$. The fact that the slope is $\dfrac{3}{4}$ means that for every horizontal movement (run) of 4 units to the right, there will be a vertical movement (rise) of 3 units. If we start at the given point $(3, 2)$ and move 4 units to the right and 3 units up, we reach the point $(7, 5)$. By drawing

Figure 3

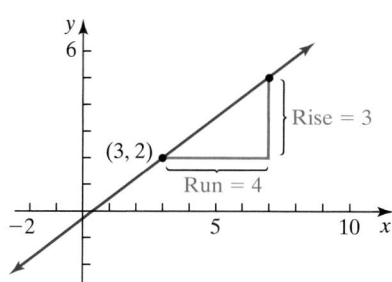

the line through this point and the point $(3, 2)$, we create the graph. See Figure 3.

(b) The fact that the slope is

$$-\frac{4}{5} = \frac{-4}{5} = \frac{\text{Rise}}{\text{Run}}$$

means that for every horizontal movement of 5 units to the right, there will be a corresponding vertical movement of -4 units (a downward movement). If we start at the given point $(3, 2)$ and move 5 units to the right and then 4 units down, we arrive at the point $(8, -2)$. By drawing the line through these points, we create the graph. See Figure 4.

Figure 4

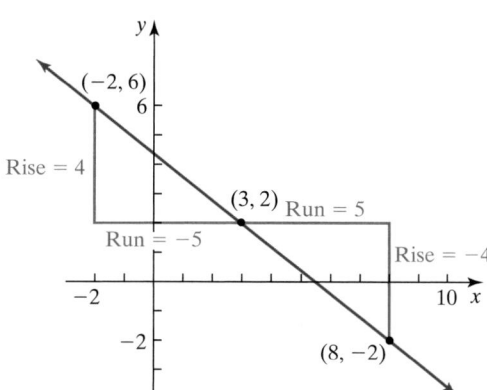

Alternately, we can set

$$-\frac{4}{5} = \frac{4}{-5} = \frac{\text{Rise}}{\text{Run}}$$

so that for every horizontal movement of -5 units (a movement to the left) there will be a corresponding vertical movement of 4 units (upward). This approach brings us to the point $(-2, 6)$, which is also on the graph shown in Figure 4. ◀◀

NW *Now Work Problem 13.*

③ Equations of Lines

Figure 5

Now that we have discussed the slope of a line, we are ready to derive equations of lines. As we shall see, there are several forms of the equation of a line. Let's start with an example.

Let L be a nonvertical line with slope m and containing the point (x_1, y_1). See Figure 5. For any other point (x, y) on L, we have

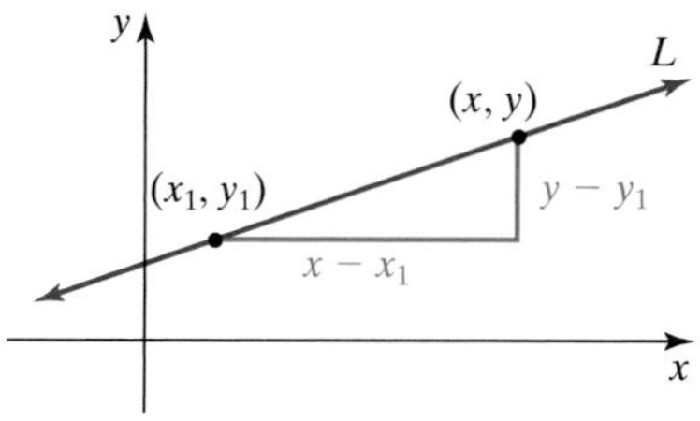

$$m = \frac{y - y_1}{x - x_1} \quad \text{or} \quad y - y_1 = m(x - x_1)$$

Theorem

Point-Slope Form of an Equation of a Line

An equation of a nonvertical line of slope m that contains the point (x_1, y_1) is

$$y - y_1 = m(x - x_1) \tag{2}$$

Figure 6

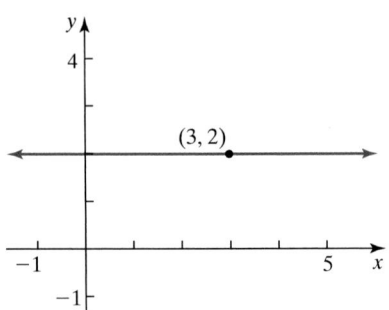

▶ **EXAMPLE 3**   **Using the Point-Slope Form of a Line**

Problem: Find an equation of the line with slope 4 and containing the point $(1, 2)$.

Solution: The equation of the line can be found by using the point–slope form with $m = 4$, $x_1 = 1$, and $y_1 = 2$:

$$y - y_1 = m(x - x_1)$$
$$y - 2 = 4(x - 1) \qquad m = 4, x_1 = 1, y_1 = 2$$
$$y = 4x - 2$$

See Figure 6.   ◀◀

▶ **EXAMPLE 4**   **Finding the Equation of a Horizontal Line**

Problem: Find an equation of the horizontal line containing the point $(3, 2)$.

Solution: Because all the y-values are equal, the slope of a horizontal line is 0. To get an equation, we use the point-slope form with $m = 0$, $x_1 = 3$, and $y_1 = 2$.

Figure 7

$$y - y_1 = m(x - x_1)$$
$$y - 2 = 0 \cdot (x - 3) \qquad m = 0, x_1 = 3, \text{and } y_1 = 2$$
$$y - 2 = 0$$
$$y = 2$$

See Figure 7 for the graph.   ◀◀

As suggested by Example 4, we have the following result:

Theorem   **Equation of a Horizontal Line**

A horizontal line is given by an equation of the form

$$y = b$$

where b is the y-intercept.

 ▶ **EXAMPLE 5**   **Finding an Equation of a Line, Given Two Points**

Problem: Find an equation of the line L containing the points $(2, 3)$ and $(-4, 5)$. Graph the line L.

Solution: We first compute the slope of the line:

$$m = \frac{5 - 3}{-4 - 2} = \frac{2}{-6} = -\frac{1}{3}$$

Figure 8

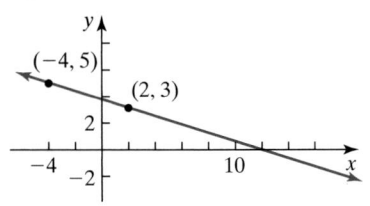

We use the point $(2, 3)$ and the slope $m = -\dfrac{1}{3}$ to get the point–slope form of the equation of the line:

$$y - 3 = -\frac{1}{3}(x - 2)$$

See Figure 8 for the graph.   ◀◀

In the solution to Example 5, we could have used the other point $(-4, 5)$, instead of the point $(2, 3)$. Although the equation that results looks different, it is equivalent to the equation that we obtained in the example. (Try it for yourself.)

NW *Now Work Problem 27.*

⑤ Another useful equation of a line is obtained when the slope m and y-intercept b are known. In this event, we know both the slope m of the line and a point $(0, b)$ on the line; thus, we may use the point–slope form, equation (2), to obtain the following equation:

$$y - b = m(x - 0) \text{ or } y = mx + b$$

Theorem | **Slope-Intercept Form of an Equation of a Line**
An equation of a line L with slope m and y-intercept b is

$$y = mx + b \qquad (3)$$

⑥ When the equation of a line is written in slope–intercept form, it is easy to find the slope m and y-intercept b of the line. For example, suppose that the equation of a line is

$$y = -2x + 3$$

Compare it with $y = mx + b$.

$$y = -2x + 3$$
$$y = \quad mx + b$$

NW *Now Work Problem 31.* The slope of this line is -2 and its y-intercept is 3.

▶ **EXAMPLE 6** **Finding the Slope and y-Intercept**

Problem: Find the slope m and y-intercept b of the equation $2x + 4y = 8$. Graph the equation.

Solution: To obtain the slope and y-intercept, we transform the equation into its slope-intercept form by solving for y:

$$2x + 4y = 8$$
$$4y = -2x + 8$$
$$y = -\frac{1}{2}x + 2 \qquad y = mx + b$$

The coefficient of x, $-\frac{1}{2}$, is the slope, and the y-intercept is 2.

We can graph the line by observing that the y-intercept is 2 and the slope is $-\frac{1}{2}$. Starting at the point $(0, 2)$, go to the right 2 units and then down 1 unit to the point $(2, 1)$. See Figure 9. ◀◀

Figure 9

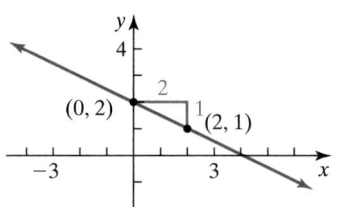

NW *Now Work Problem 37.*

Appendix B Assess Your Understanding

Appendix Exercises

In Problems 1–4, (a) find the slope of the line and (b) interpret the slope.

1.
NW

2.

3.

4.
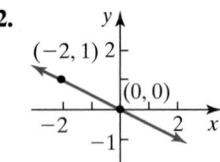
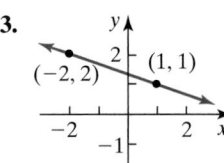
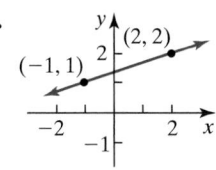

In Problems 5–12, plot each pair of points and determine the slope of the line containing them. Graph the line.

5. $(2, 3); (4, 0)$

6. $(4, 2); (3, 4)$

7. $(-2, 3); (2, 1)$
NW

8. $(-1, 1); (2, 3)$

9. $(-3, -1); (2, -1)$

10. $(4, 2); (-5, 2)$

11. $(-1, 2); (-1, -2)$

12. $(2, 0); (2, 2)$

In Problems 13–20, graph the line containing the point P and having slope m.

13. $P = (1, 2); m = 3$
NW

14. $P = (2, 1); m = 4$

15. $P = (2, 4); m = -\dfrac{3}{4}$

16. $P = (1, 3); m = -\dfrac{2}{5}$

17. $P = (-1, 3); m = 0$

18. $P = (2, -4); m = 0$

19. $P = (0, 3);$ slope undefined

20. $P = (-2, 0);$ slope undefined

In Problems 21–26, the slope and a point on a line are given. Use this information to locate three additional points on the line. Answers may vary. [Hint: It is not necessary to find the equation of the line. See Example 2.]

21. Slope 4; point $(1, 2)$

22. Slope 2; point $(-2, 3)$

23. Slope $-\dfrac{3}{2}$; point $(2, -4)$

24. Slope $\dfrac{4}{3}$; point $(-3, 2)$

25. Slope -2; point $(-2, -3)$

26. Slope -1; point $(4, 1)$

In Problems 27–30, find an equation of the line L.

27.
NW

28.

29.

30.
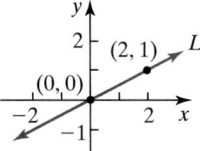
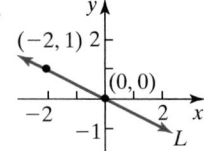
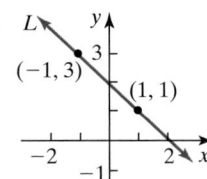
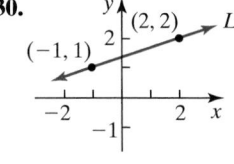

In Problems 31–50, find the slope and y-intercept of each line. Graph the line.

31. $y = 2x + 3$
NW

32. $y = -3x + 4$

33. $\dfrac{1}{2}y = x - 1$

34. $\dfrac{1}{3}x + y = 2$

35. $y = \dfrac{1}{2}x + 2$

36. $y = 2x + \dfrac{1}{2}$

37. $x + 2y = 4$
NW

38. $-x + 3y = 6$

39. $2x - 3y = 6$

40. $3x + 2y = 6$

41. $x + y = 1$

42. $x - y = 2$

43. $x = -4$

44. $y = -1$

45. $y = 5$

46. $x = 2$

47. $y - x = 0$

48. $x + y = 0$

49. $2y - 3x = 0$

50. $3x + 2y = 0$

ANSWERS

CHAPTER 1   Data Collection

1.1 Exercises (page 9)

1. Qualitative   2. Quantitative   3. Quantitative
4. Qualitative   5. Quantitative   6. Quantitative
7. Quantitative   8. Quantitative   9. Qualitative
10. Quantitative   11. Discrete   12. Continuous
13. Continuous   14. Discrete   15. Continuous
16. Discrete   17. Discrete   18. Continuous
19. Continuous   20. Continuous

21. Population: all United States residents 18 years or older; Sample: the 1019 residents
22. Population: Coca-Cola bottles filled on October 15; Sample: the 50 Coca-Cola bottles selected
23. Population: The entire soybean crop; Sample: the 100 plants selected
24. Population: all United States households; Sample: the 50,000 households surveyed
25. (a) To determine the genetic and nongenetic factors of structural brain abnormalities on schizophrenia.
  (b) The 58 pairs of twins in the study.
  (c) Whole-brain volumes were 2.2% smaller in the schizophrenic patients.
  (d) An increased genetic risk to develop schizophrenia is related to reduced brain growth early in life.
26. (a) To determine whether blood-pressure level is associated with dietary micronutrients in adolescents at risk for hypertension.
  (b) The adolescents aged 14 to 16 years who had high blood pressure.
  (c) For boys: high-folate group had blood pressure of 72 mm Hg versus 67 mm Hg for low-folate group. For girls: high-folate group had blood pressure of 76 mm Hg versus 73 mm Hg for low-folate group.
  (d) For adolescents who are at risk for high blood pressure, a diet rich in folic acid could help to prevent hypertension.
27. (a) To determine whether music cognition and cognitions pertaining to abstract operations such as mathematical or spatial reasoning were related.
  (b) Thirty-six college students.
  (c) The mean test score following the Mozart piece was 119, while the mean test score following silence was 110.
  (d) Subjects perform better on abstract/spatial reasoning tests after listening to Mozart.
28. (a) To determine whether Propecia treats male pattern hair loss on the vertex and anterior midscalp area in men.
  (b) Over 1800 men aged 18 to 41 with mild to moderate amounts of ongoing hair loss.
  (c) Hair counts in the men who took Propecia maintained or increased, while hair counts in men who did not take Propecia declined.
  (d) Propecia is effective in maintaining or increasing the amount of hair on the vertex and anterior midscalp area.
29. (a) To determine the proportion of households in the United States that have been a victim of a crime in the past 12 months.
  (b) The 1012 adults aged 18 years or older.
  (c) Twenty-four percent of the respondents stated that they, or someone in the household, experienced some type of crime.
  (d) Twenty-four percent of all households in the United States have been victimized by crime in the past 12 months.

30. (a) To determine the proportion of adults who have a great deal of concern regarding global warming.
  (b) The 1004 adults aged 18 years or older.
  (c) Forty percent of the respondents stated that they have a great deal of concern regarding global warming.
  (d) Forty percent of all adults aged 18 years or older have a great deal of concern regarding global warming.
31. Individuals: Neta Van Duyne, Dave Ebert, Kristin Bols, Michael Wirth, Jinita Desai; Variables: Gender, age, number of siblings; Data for "gender": F, M, F, M, F; Data for "age": 19, 19, 19, 19, 20; Data for "number of siblings": 1, 1, 2, 1, 1. The variable "gender" is qualitative; the variable "age" is continuous; the variable "number of siblings" is discrete.
32. Individuals: M/Z3 Coupe, M/Z3 Roadster, 3 Series, 5 Series, 7 Series, Z8; Variables: Body Style, Weight, Number of Seats; Data for "Body style": Coupe, Convertible, Coupe, Sedan, Sedan, Convertible; Data for "Weight": 2945, 2690, 2780, 3450, 4255, 3600; Data for "Number of Seats": 2, 2, 5, 5, 5, 2. The variable "body style" is qualitative; the variable "weight" is continuous; the variable "number of seats" is discrete.
33. Individuals: Alabama, Illinois, Montana, New York, Texas; Variables: Age for driver's license, blood-alcohol concentration limit, mandatory belt-use law seating positions, maximum allowable speed, 1999. Data for "age for driver's license": 16, 18, 18, 17, 18; data for "blood-alcohol concentration limit": 0.08, 0.08, 0.10, 0.10, 0.10; data for "mandatory belt-use law seating positions": Front, Front, All, Front, Front; Data for "Maximum allowable speed limit, 1999": 70, 65, 75, 65, 70. The variable "age for driver's license" is continuous; the variable "blood-alcohol concentration limit" is continuous; the variable "mandatory belt-use law seating positions" is qualitative; the variable "maximum allowable speed limit, 1999" is continuous.
34. Individuals: Tamika Whitmore, Jackie Stiles, Kim Knuth, Kristina Behnfeldt, Jamie Cassidy; Variables: College, Number of games, Points scored. Data for "college": Memphis, SW Missouri State, Toledo, Marshall, Maine. Data for "number of games": 32, 32, 31, 26, 31. Data for "Points scored": 843, 823, 788, 621, 738. The variable "college" is discrete; the variable "number of games" is discrete; the variable "points scored" is discrete.

1.2 Exercises (page 19)

1. Observational study   2. Experiment
3. Experiment   4. Observational study
5. Observational study   6. Experiment
7. Observational study   8. Observational study
9. Experiment   10. Experiment
11. Observational study   12. Observational study

13. (a)

Graham, Murkowski	Graham, Kyl	Graham, Baucus
Graham, Conrad	Murkowski, Kyl	Murkowski, Baucus
Murkowski, Conrad	Kyl, Baucus	Kyl, Conrad
Baucus, Conrad		

  (b) There is a 1 in 10 chance that the two individuals selected are Bob Graham and Max Baucus.

14. (a)

Secy of State, Secy of Treasury	Secy of State, Secy of War	Secy of State, Attorney General
Secy of State, Postmaster General	Secy of State, Secy of Navy	Secy of Treasury, Secy of War
Secy of Treasury, Attorney General	Secy of Treasury, Postmaster General	Secy of Treasury, Secy of Navy
Secy of War, Attorney General	Secy of War, Postmaster General	Secy of War, Secy of Navy
Attorney General, Postmaster General	Attorney General, Secy of Navy	Postmaster General, Secy of Navy

(b) There is a 1 in 15 chance that the two individuals selected are Secretary of State and Attorney General.

15. (a) Answers will vary   **(b)** Answers will vary
16. (a) Answers will vary   **(b)** Answers will vary
17. (a) First, find a list of all currently enrolled students. This list will serve as the frame. Number the students on the list from 1 through 19,935. Using a random-number generator, set a seed (or select a starting point if using Table I). Generate 25 different numbers randomly. The students corresponding to these numbers will be the 25 students in the sample.
(b) Answers will vary.
18. (a) First, find a list of all current residents of the village. This list will serve as the frame. Number the residents on the list from 1 through 5832. Using a random-number generator, set a seed (or select a starting point if using Table I). Generate 20 different numbers randomly. The residents corresponding to these numbers will be the 20 residents in the sample.
(b) Answers will vary.

1.3 Exercises (page 29)

1. Systematic   **2.** Cluster   **3.** Cluster
4. Stratified   **5.** Simple random   **6.** Convenience
7. Cluster   **8.** Stratified   **9.** Convenience
10. Systematic
11. Answers will vary. A good choice might be stratified sampling with the strata being commuters and noncommuters.
12. Answers will vary. One option would be cluster sampling. Each cluster would be a class. Randomly select clusters and then survey all the students in the selected classes.
13. Answers will vary. One option would be cluster sampling. The clusters could be the city blocks. Randomly select clusters and then survey all the households in the selected city blocks.
14. Answers will vary. Probably the most logical choice is systematic sampling.
15. Answers will vary. Simple random sampling will work fine here, especially because a list of 6600 individuals who meet the needs of our study already exists (the frame).
16. Answers will vary. Simple random sampling will work because a list of all households in the population exists. Just number the households $1 - N$ and use a random number generator to obtain the households in the survey.
17. (a) 90
(b) Randomly select a number between 1 and 90. Suppose that we randomly select 15; then the individuals in the survey will be 15, 105, 195, 285, ..., 4425.
18. (a) 7269
(b) Randomly select a number between 1 and 7269. Suppose that we randomly select 2000; then the individuals in the survey will be 2000, 9269, 16,538, ..., 939,701.

1.4 Exercises (page 34)

1. (a) Flawed sampling method because only the first 50 students who enter the building have a chance of being surveyed.
(b) Could use systematic sampling, but a better choice would be cluster or simple random sampling because the vice president should have access to a complete frame.
2. (a) Flawed sampling method because only homes in the SW corner have a chance to be interviewed.
(b) Cluster sampling should be used here. The clusters would be households with similar incomes.
3. (a) Flawed survey due to the wording of the question.
(b) The survey should begin by stating the current penalty for selling a gun illegally. The question might be rewritten as "Do you approve or disapprove harsher penalties for individuals that sell guns illegally?" The words "approve" and "disapprove" should be rotated from individual to individual.
4. (a) Flawed survey due to the wording of the question.
(b) The question should be reworded so that it doesn't imply the opinion of the editors. One possibility might be "Do you believe that a marriage can be maintained after an extramarital relation?"
5. (a) Flawed survey because the response rate is low.
(b) The survey can be improved through face-to-face or telephone interviews.
6. (a) Flawed survey because of nonresponse.
(b) Petland could provide some sort of incentive, such as a coupon, for filling out the survey.
7. (a) Flawed survey because the students are not likely to respond truthfully with their teachers administering the survey.
(b) The survey should be administered by an impartial party so that the students are more likely to respond truthfully.
8. (a) Flawed survey because the wording of the question is ambiguous.
(b) The question might be rewritten as "How many hours per week do you study?"
9. The ordering of the questions is likely to affect the survey results. Perhaps question B should be asked first. Another possibility is to rotate the questions randomly.
10. The choices need to be rotated so that any response bias due to the ordering of the questions is minimized.

1.5 Exercises (page 41)

1. (a) Achievement test score   **(b)** Method of teaching; 2
(c) Grade level, teacher, school district
(d) Students are from the same district
(e) Completely randomized design   **(f)** the 500 students

(g)
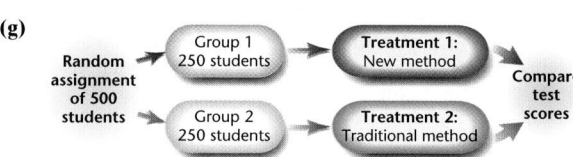

2. (a) Percentage of experimental units with a cold
(b) The drug; 2   **(c)** Gender, age, location
(d) The experimental units are from the same city
(e) Completely randomized design   **(f)** The 300 males

(g)
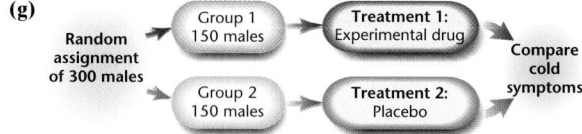

3. (a) Sales of the product **(b)** Advertising dollars; 3
(c) Region of the country **(d)** Randomized block design
(e)

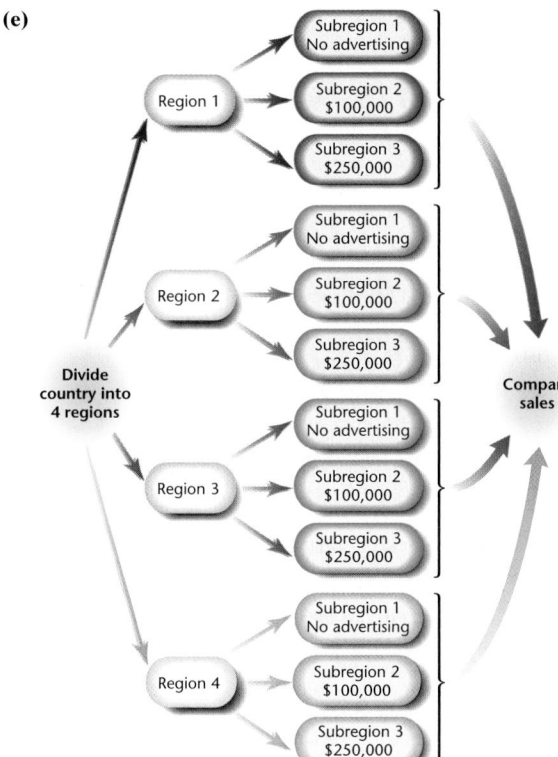

4. (a) Yield **(b)** Tilling method; 4
(c) Fertilizer, acidity of the soil, tilling method, amount of water
(d) Randomized block design
(e)

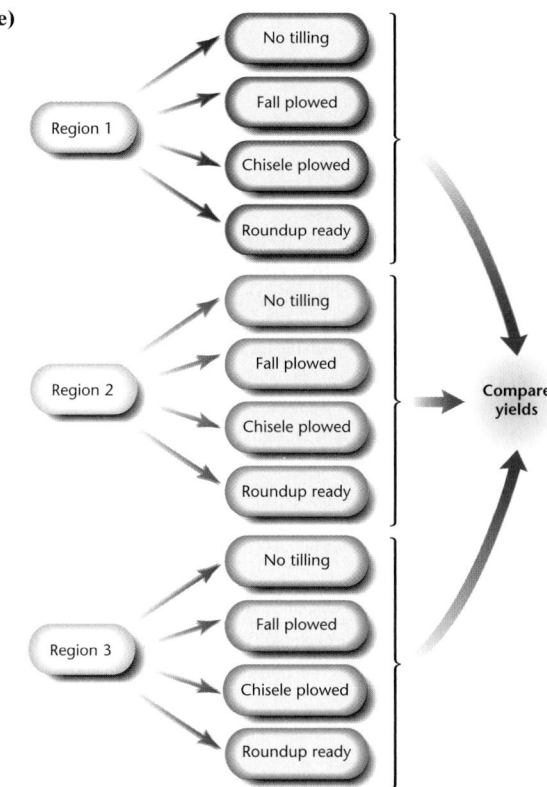

5. (a) Proportion of cancer cases **(b)** Servings of tomatoes; 3
(c) Servings of tomatoes, age, amount of exercise, eating habits
(d) Completely randomized design
(e) The 600 males in the study
(f)

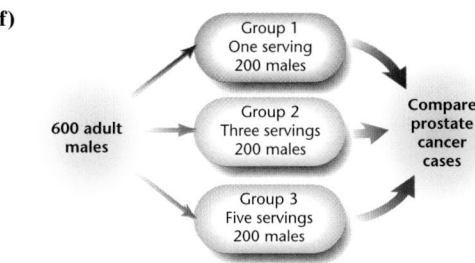

6. (a) Number of truancies **(b)** Method of intervention; 3
(c) School district
(d) Age, gender, guardianship (both parents, single parent, and so on)
(e) Completely randomized design **(f)** The 300 students
(g)

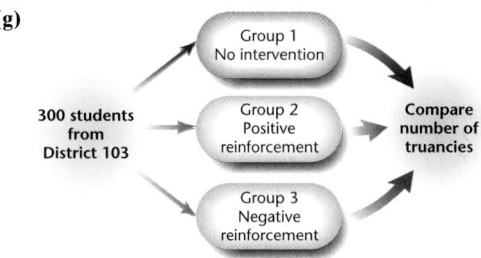

7. (a) Difference in weight before spaceflight and after spaceflight
(b) Spaceflight **(c)** Matched pairs
(d)

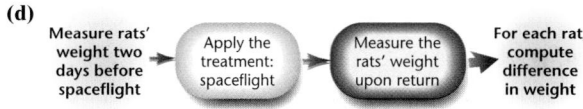

8. (a) The test score **(b)** Music **(c)** Matched pairs
(d)

9. (a) Hair counts **(b)** The drug; 2
(c) Completely randomized design
(d)

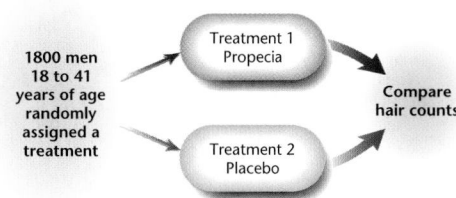

10. Answers will vary. Factors to consider are geographic location of the house, direction the house faces, application method (brush, roller, spray). A matched-pairs design would probably work best, where each experimental unit is a house. Each side of the house should get both the Benjamin Moore and Sherwin Williams paint with varying levels of coats (1 coat, 2 coats, and so on).

11. Answers will vary. A matched-pairs design would work best. Measure the lung capacity of each experimental unit before the workout regimen and after. The researcher may want to have various levels of exercise (i.e. no exercise, 20 minutes a day, and so on) to see the effect of the more arduous exercise. Be sure to keep other factors, such as diet, constant for all groups.

12. Answers will vary.

13. **(a)** Completely randomized.   **(b)** Answers will vary.

Chapter Review Exercises (page 44)

1. The science of collecting, organizing, summarizing, and analyzing data in order to draw conclusions.

2. A group of individuals that a researcher wishes to study.

3. A subset of the population.

4. Often called *ex post facto* studies because the value of the response variable has already been determined. In observational studies, there is no attempt to influence the value of the response variable.

5. Applies a treatment to the individuals in the study in order to isolate the effect of the treatment on the response variable.

6. (1) Identify the research objective. (2) Collect data needed to answer the research questions. (3) Organize and summarize the data. (4) Draw conclusions from the data.

7. There are two main types of errors: nonsampling errors and sampling errors. Nonsampling errors are errors that result from the survey process, such as an incomplete frame, poorly worded questions, inaccurate responses, and so on. Sampling errors are errors that result from using a sample to estimate characteristics of a population. They result because samples contain incomplete information regarding a population.

8. Control, manipulation, randomization, and replication.

9. Qualitative   10. Qualitative

11. Quantitative, continuous   12. Quantitative, discrete

13. Quantitative, discrete   14. Quantitative, discrete

15. Observational study   16. Experiment

17. Observational study   18. Observational study

19. Systematic   20. Cluster

21. Stratified   22. Simple random

23. Answers will vary   24. Answers will vary

25. Answers will vary   26. Answers will vary

27. **(a)** Hamilton Rating Scale score   **(b)** Group; 2
    (c) Age, medical history; none are controlled
    (d) Completely randomized   **(e)** The 120 women

(f)

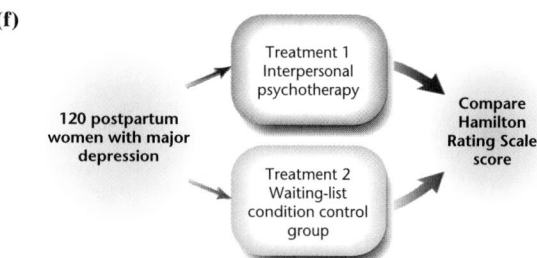

28. **(a)** Young–Mania Rating Scale score   **(b)** Drug; 2
    (c) Completely randomized design   **(d)** The 115 patients

(e) Neither the patient nor the doctor administering the drug knows which treatment the patient is receiving.

(f)

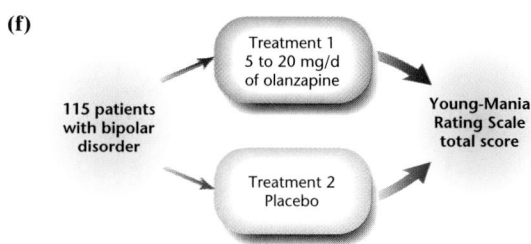

29. **(a)** Lymphocyte count   **(b)** Spaceflight
    (c) Matched pairs   **(d)** The four flight members

(e)

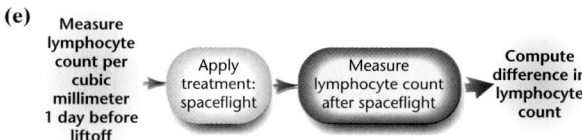

30. In a completely randomized design, the experimental units are randomly assigned to one of the treatments. The value of the response variable is compared for each treatment. In a randomized block design, the experimental units are first divided according to some common characteristic (such as gender). Then each of the experimental units within each block is randomly assigned to one of the treatments. The value of the response variable is compared for each treatment. By blocking, we prevent the effect of the variable from confounding with the treatment.

31. In a completely randomized design, the experimental units are randomly assigned to one of the treatments. The value of the response variable is compared for each treatment. In a matched-pairs design, experimental units are "matched up" on the basis of some common characteristic (such as husband/wife or twins). The difference in the "matched-up" experimental units is analyzed.

CHAPTER 2   Organizing and Summarizing Data

2.1 Exercises (page 60)

1. **(a)** 34–52   **(b)** 18–33   **(c)** 27%
2. **(a)** Large; 52%   **(b)** X-Large; 9%   **(c)** 23%
3. **(a)** United States   **(b)** ≈ 18 million
4. **(a)** 21,922   **(b)** 19.1%
   (c) The graph could be misleading because it doesn't account for the population size of each ethnicity.
5. **(a)** 447,927   **(b)** 48.3%; 48.1%   **(c)** No
6. **(a)** ≈ 28%   **(b)** ≈ 16,945,320
7. **(a)** 16%   **(b)** Natural gas   **(c)** LPG
8. **(a)** 23%   **(b)** 29%   **(c)** 1 to 4 rooms
9. **(a)**

Source of Income	Relative Frequency
Individual Income Tax and Tax Withholdings	0.4932
Corporate Income Taxes	0.1147
Social Insurance and Retirement Receipts	0.3378
Excise, Estate, and Gift Taxes; Customs; and Miscellaneous Receipts	0.0543

(b) 49.32%

9. (c)

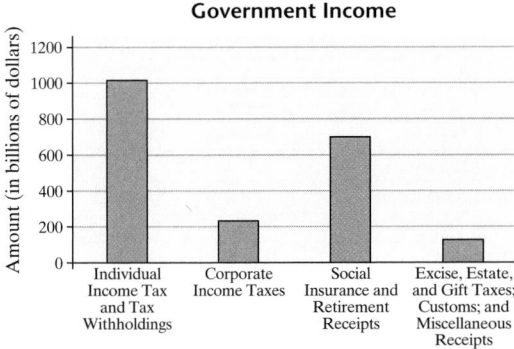

Government Income

(d)

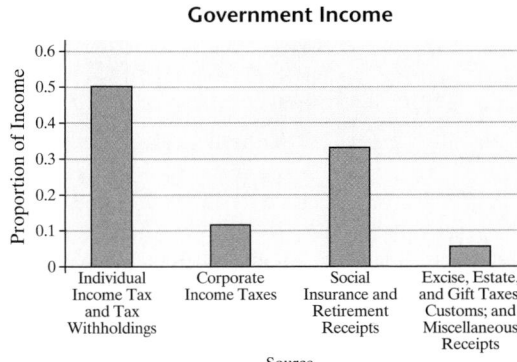

Government Income

(e)

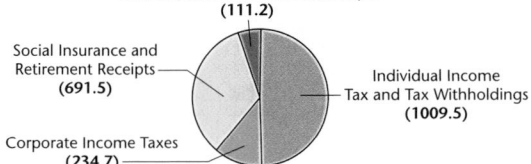

Government Income

10. (a)

Expenditure	Relative Frequency
National Defense and Foreign Affairs	0.1988
Human Resources	0.5602
Physical Resources	0.0605
Net Interest on the Debt	0.1152
Other Functions	0.0653

(b) 11.52%

(c)

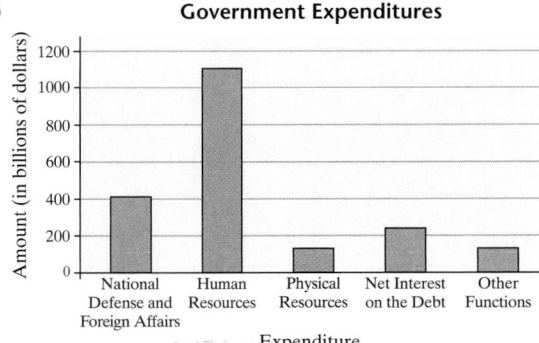

Government Expenditures

(d)

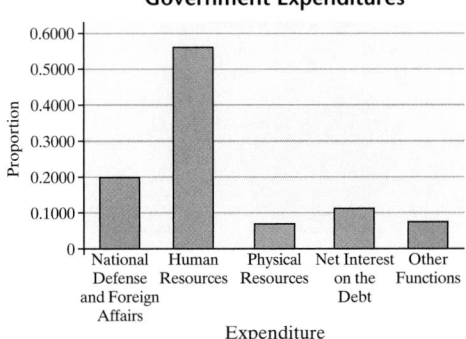

Government Expenditures

(e)

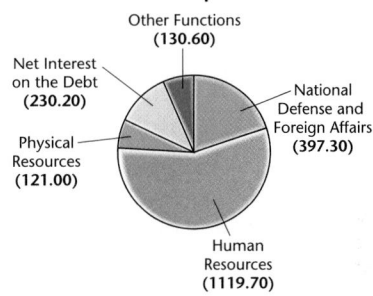

Government Expenditures

11. (a)

Response	Relative Frequency
Never	0.0262
Rarely	0.0678
Sometimes	0.1156
Most of the time	0.2632
Always	0.5272

(b) 52.72%   **(c)** 9.4%

(d)

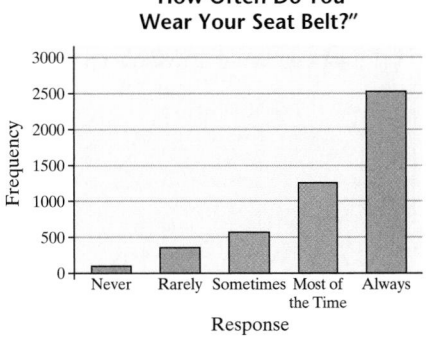

"How Often Do You Wear Your Seat Belt?"

(e)

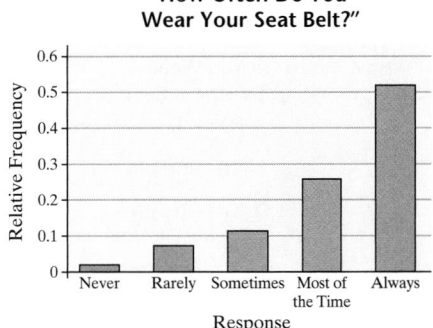

"How Often Do You Wear Your Seat Belt?"

11. (f)

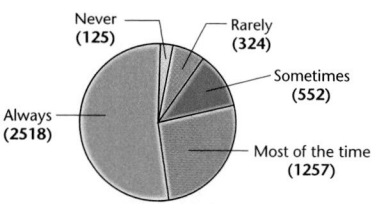

"How Often Do You Wear Your Seat Belt?"

Never (125)
Rarely (324)
Sometimes (552)
Always (2518)
Most of the time (1257)

12. (a)

Response	Frequency
I do not drive a car	0.0522
Never	0.0247
Rarely	0.0522
Sometimes	0.0723
Most of the time	0.1501
Always	0.6484

(b) 64.84%　　**(c)** 7.69%

(d)

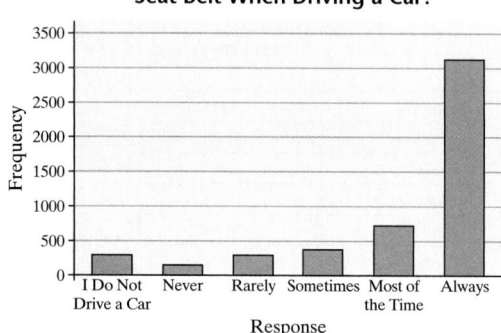

"How Often Do You Wear a Seat Belt When Driving a Car?"

(e)

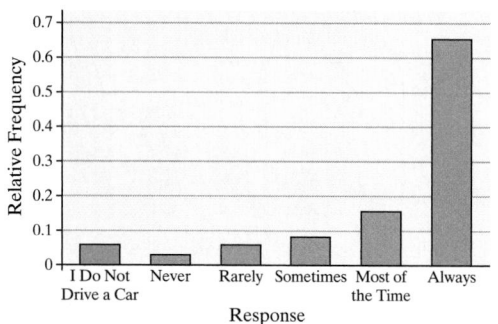

"How Often Do You Wear a Seat Belt When Driving a Car?"

(f)

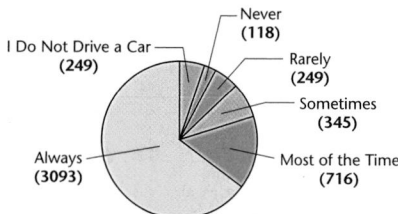

"How Often Do You Wear a Seat Belt When Driving a Car?"

Never (118)
I Do Not Drive a Car (249)
Rarely (249)
Sometimes (345)
Always (3093)
Most of the Time (716)

13. (a)

Region	Relative Frequency
Europe	0.1566
Asia	0.2746
Africa	0.0276
Oceania	0.0059
Latin America	0.5079
North America	0.0274

(b) 2.76%

(c)

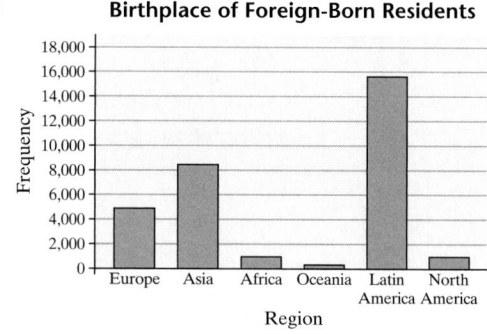

Birthplace of Foreign-Born Residents

(d)

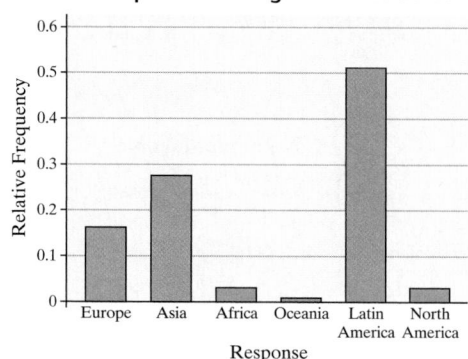

Birthplace of Foreign-Born Residents

(e) Birthplace of Foreign-Born Residents

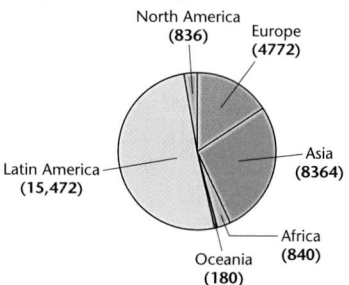

North America (836)
Europe (4772)
Asia (8364)
Africa (840)
Oceania (180)
Latin America (15,472)

14. (a)

Type of Crime	Relative Frequency
Street or highway	0.5778
Commercial house	0.1609
Gas station	0.0264
Convenience store	0.0686
Residence	0.1425
Bank	0.0237

(b) 2.64%

14. (c)

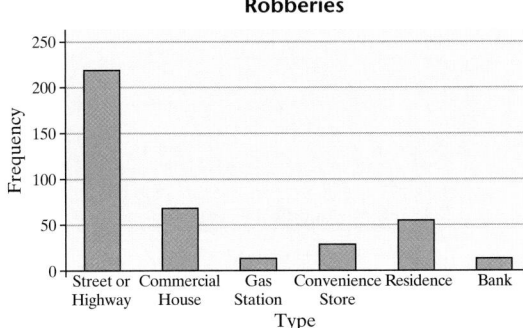

Robberies

(d)

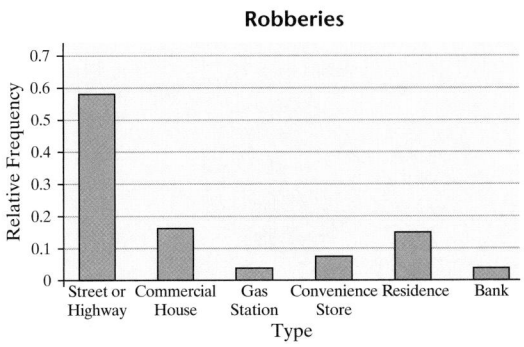

Robberies

(e)

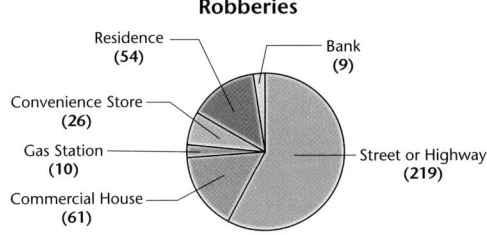

Robberies

Residence (54)
Bank (9)
Convenience Store (26)
Gas Station (10)
Street or Highway (219)
Commercial House (61)

15. (a), (b)

Educational Attainment	Relative Frequency Males	Relative Frequency Females
Not a high school graduate	0.166	0.166
High school graduate	0.318	0.348
Some college, but no degree	0.171	0.175
Associate's degree	0.070	0.080
Bachelor's degree	0.179	0.162
Advanced degree	0.096	0.070

(c)

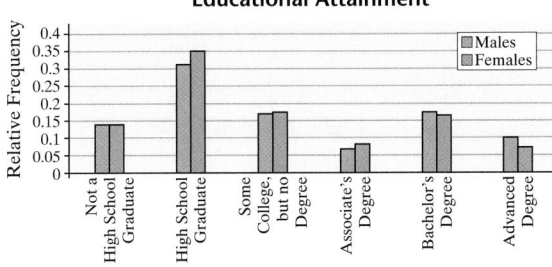

Educational Attainment

16. (a)

Educational Attainment	1997	2000
No College	0.2697	0.2725
Some College	0.3538	0.3476
Graduated College	0.3765	0.3799

(b)

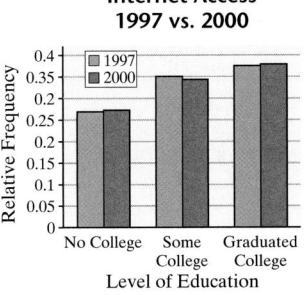

Internet Access 1997 vs. 2000

17. (a)

Country	Number of Launches, 1995	Number of Launches, 1998
Soviet Union/Commonwealth of Independent States	0.4267	0.3117
United States	0.3600	0.4416
Japan	0.0267	0.0260
European Space Agency	0.1467	0.1429
China	0.0267	0.0779
Israel	0.0133	0.0000

(b)

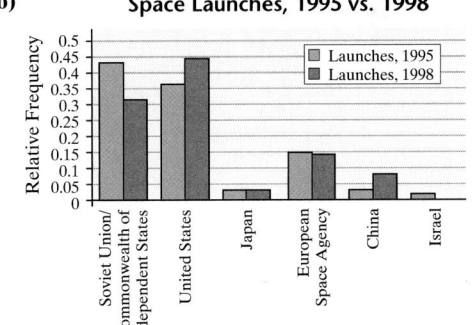

Space Launches, 1995 vs. 1998

18. (a)

Transplant	1990	1998
Heart	0.1363	0.1058
Liver	0.1740	0.2024
Kidney	0.6388	0.5926
Heart-lung	0.0034	0.0021
Lung	0.0131	0.0389
Pancreas/Islet cell	0.0341	0.0551
Intestine	0.0003	0.0031

(b) 13.63%; 10.58%

(c)

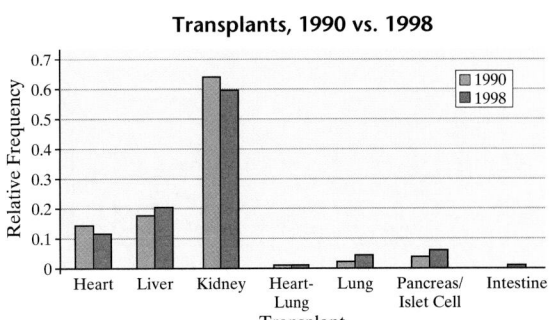

Transplants, 1990 vs. 1998

19. (a), (b)

Candidate	Frequency	Relative Frequency
Gore	25	0.625
Bush	14	0.350
Nader	1	0.025

(c)

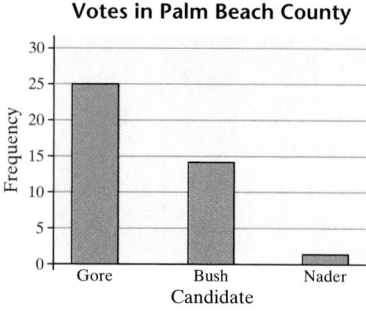

(d)

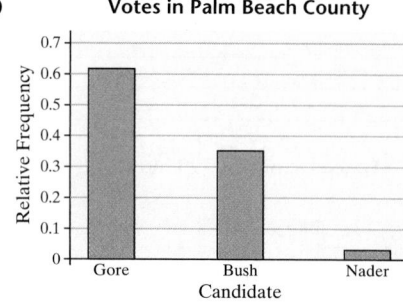

(e)

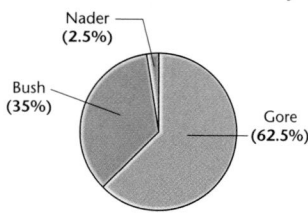

20. (a), (b)

Diagnosis	Frequency	Relative Frequency
Assault	1	0.05
Cancer	1	0.05
Congestive Heart Failure	1	0.05
Fall	2	0.10
Gun Shot Wound	8	0.40
Motor Vehicle Accident	7	0.35

(c) Gun shot wound   **(d)** 35%

(e)

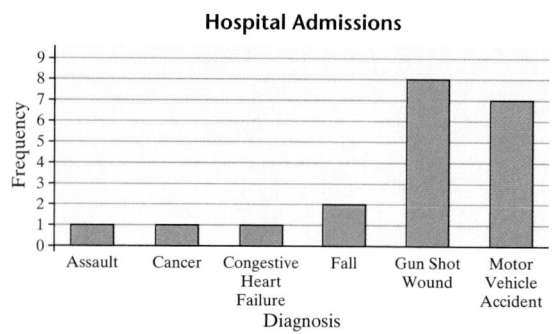

(f)

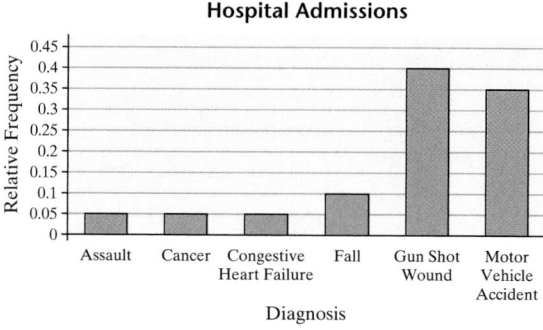

(g)

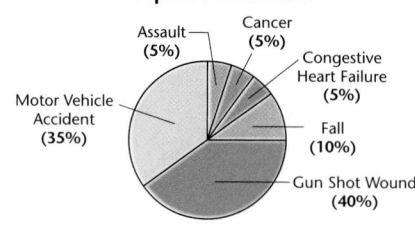

21. (a), (b)

Position	Frequency	Relative Frequency
First Base	7	0.1944
Third Base	2	0.0556
Catcher	2	0.0556
Center Field	5	0.1389
Pitcher	12	0.3333
Right Field	6	0.1667
Shortstop	2	0.0556

(c) Pitcher   **(d)** Second Base, Left Field

(e)

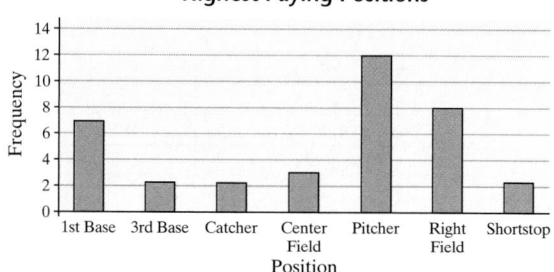

(f)

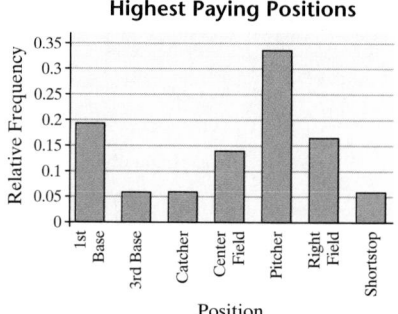

21. (g)   **Highest Paying Positions**

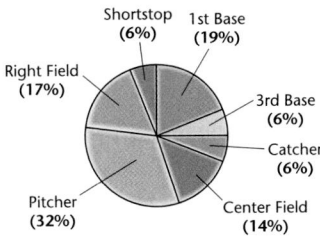

22. (a), (b)

Blood Type	Frequency	Relative Frequency
A	18	0.36
AB	4	0.08
B	6	0.12
O	22	0.44

(c) O   **(d)** AB   **(e)** 44%; inferential
(f) Answers will vary

(g)   **Blood Types**

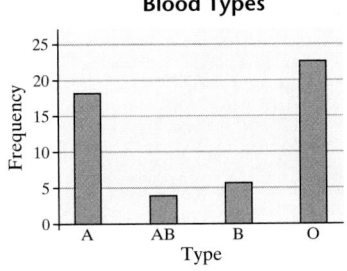

(h)   **Blood Types**

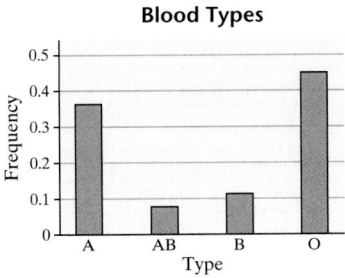

(i)   **Blood Types**

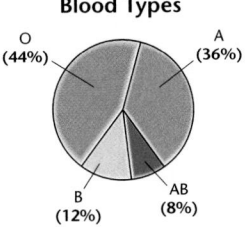

2.2 Exercises (page 77)

1. (a) 8   **(b)** 2   **(c)** 15
   (d) 15%   **(e)** Bell shaped
2. (a) 4   **(b)** 9   **(c)** 17.3%   **(d)** Skewed right
3. (a) 200   **(b)** 10   **(c)** 60–69, 2; 70–79, 3; 80–89, 13; 90–99,
   42; 100–109, 58; 110–119, 40; 120–129, 31; 130–139, 8;
   140–149, 2; 150–159, 1   **(d)** 100–109   **(e)** 150–159
   (f) 0.155   **(g)** Bell shaped
4. (a) 5   **(b)** 15–19, 20–24, 25–29, 30–34, 35–39, 40–44, 45–49,
   50–54, 55–59, 60–64, 65–69, 70–74, 75–79, 80–84   **(c)** 35–39
   (d) 80–84   **(e)** Skewed right

5. (a)

Number of Children Under 5	Relative Frequency
0	0.32
1	0.36
2	0.24
3	0.06
4	0.02

(b) 24%   **(c)** 60%

6. (a)

Number of Free Throws until a Miss	Relative Frequency
1	0.32
2	0.22
3	0.18
4	0.14
5	0.04
6	0.06
7	0
8	0.02
9	0
10	0.02

(b) 14%   **(c)** 2%   **(d)** 14%

7. 10, 11, 14, 21, 24, 24, 27, 29, 33, 35, 35, 35, 37, 37, 38, 40, 40, 41, 42,
   46, 46, 48, 49, 49, 53, 53, 55, 58, 61, 62
8. 40, 44, 47, 52, 52, 53, 59, 59, 63, 64, 65, 68, 68, 69, 70, 71, 71, 73, 76,
   76, 82, 83, 88
9. (a) 4   **(b)** Lower class limits: 25, 35, 45, 55; Upper class limits:
   34, 44, 54, 64   **(c)** 10
10. (a) 8   **(b)** Lower class limits: 0, 1.0, 2.0, 3.0, 4.0, 5.0, 6.0, 7.0;
   Upper class limits: 0.9, 1.9, 2.9, 3.9, 4.9, 5.9, 6.9, 7.9   **(c)** 1
11. (a) 6   **(b)** Lower class limits: 50, 60, 70, 80, 90, 100; Upper
   class limits: 59, 69, 79, 89, 99, 109   **(c)** 10
12. (a) 6   **(b)** Lower class limits: 15, 20, 25, 30, 35, 40; Upper class
   limits: 19, 24, 29, 34, 39, 44   **(c)** 5

13. (a)

Age	Relative Frequency
25–34	0.2522
35–44	0.3184
45–54	0.2616
55–64	0.1678

(b) Number Covered by Health Insurance

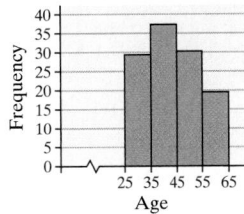

(c) Number Covered by Health Insurance

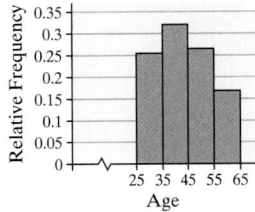

25.2%; 57.1%

14. (a)

Magnitude	Relative Frequency	Magnitude	Relative Frequency
0–0.9	0.116372	4.0–4.9	0.338204
1.0–1.9	0.036631	5.0–5.9	0.040528
2.0–2.9	0.187588	6.0–6.9	0.005504
3.0–3.9	0.274685	7.0–7.9	0.000487

(b)

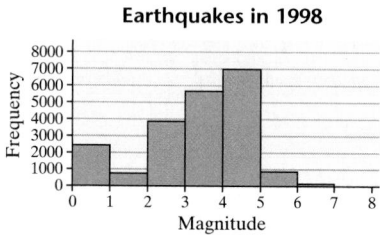

(c)

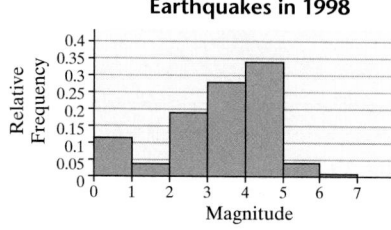

33.8%; 95.4%

15. (a)

Temperature	Relative Frequency
50–59	0.0003
60–69	0.0776
70–79	0.3828
80–89	0.4098
90–99	0.1268
100–109	0.0028

(b)

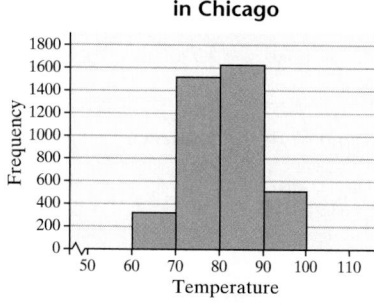

(c)

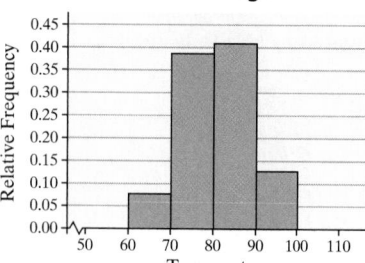

38.28%; 46.07%

16. (a)

Age	Relative Frequency	Age	Relative Frequency
15–19	0.0084	30–34	0.3739
20–24	0.0525	35–39	0.2317
25–29	0.2112	40–44	0.1222

(b)

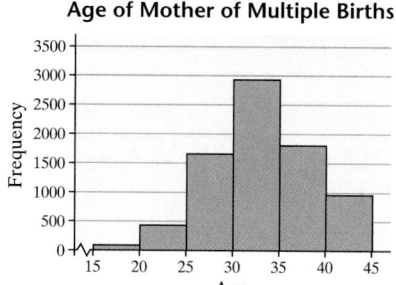

(c)

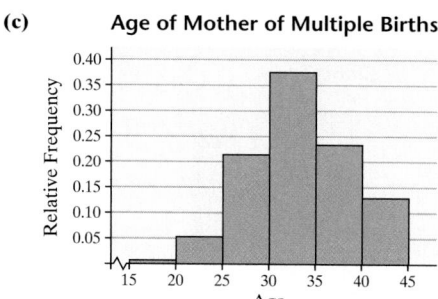

12.22%; 6.09%

17. (a), (b)

Number of Customers	Frequency	Relative Frequency	Number of Customers	Frequency	Relative Frequency
3	2	0.050	9	4	0.1
4	3	0.075	10	4	0.1
5	3	0.075	11	4	0.1
6	5	0.125	12	0	0
7	4	0.1	13	2	0.05
8	8	0.2	14	1	0.025

(c) 27.5%   **(d)** 20%

(e)

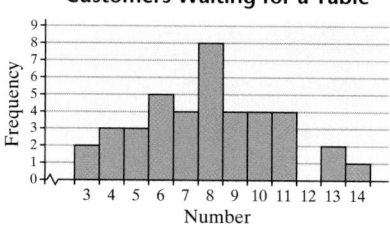

(f)

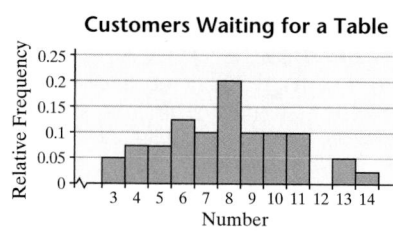

(g) Symmetric

18. (a), (b)

Number of Potholes	Frequency	Relative Frequency	Number of Potholes	Frequency	Relative Frequency
1	6	0.12	6	1	0.02
2	15	0.30	7	5	0.10
3	9	0.18	8	0	0
4	6	0.12	9	1	0.02
5	6	0.12	10	1	0.02

(c) 14%   **(d)** 42%

(e)

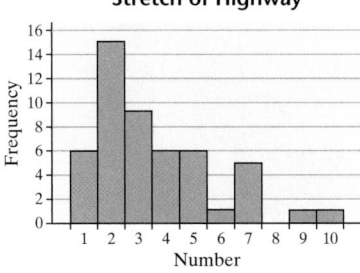

Potholes per 1-Mile Stretch of Highway

(f)

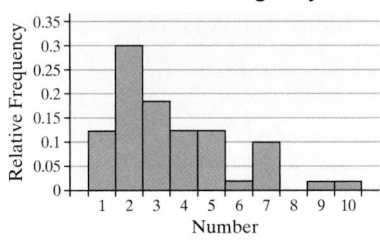

Potholes per 1-Mile Stretch of Highway

(g) Skewed right

19. (a), (b)

Class	Tally	Frequency	Relative Frequency
160–169.99	I	1	$\frac{1}{25} = 0.04$
170–179.99	I	1	$\frac{1}{25} = 0.04$
180–189.99	IIII	4	$\frac{4}{25} = 0.16$
190–199.99	I	1	$\frac{1}{25} = 0.04$
200–209.99	ҢҢ IIII	9	0.36
210–219.99	ҢҢ I	6	0.24
220–229.99	I	1	0.04
230–239.99	I	1	0.04
240–249.99	I	1	0.04
		$\Sigma f_i = 25$	

(c)

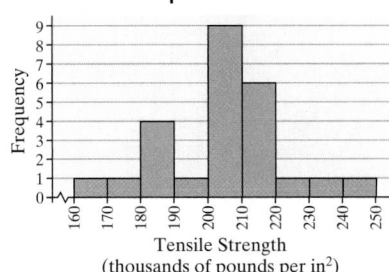

Tensile Strength of Composite Material
Tensile Strength (thousands of pounds per in^2)

(d)

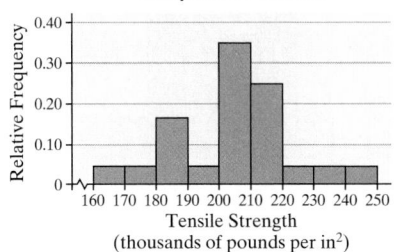

Tensile Strength of Composite Material

(e) Symmetric

19. (f)

Class	Frequency	Relative Frequency
160–174.99	2	0.08
175–189.99	4	0.16
190–204.99	5	0.20
205–219.99	11	0.44
220–234.99	2	0.08
235–249.99	1	0.04

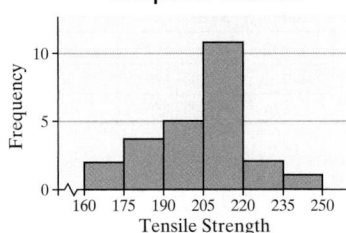

Tensile Strength of Composite Material

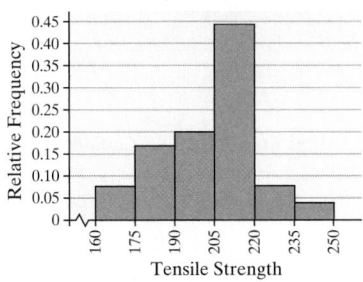

Tensile Strength of Composite Material

Symmetric

20. (a),(b)

Class	Tally	Frequency	Relative Frequency
15,000–18,999	III	3	$\frac{3}{36} = 0.083$
19,000–22,999		0	0
23,000–26,999	III	3	0.083
27,000–30,999	ҢҢ III	8	0.222
31,000–34,999	ҢҢ I	6	0.167
35,000–38,999	ҢҢ II	7	0.194
39,000–42,999	ҢҢ II	7	0.194
43,000–46,999	II	2	0.056
		$\Sigma f_i = 36$	

20. (c)

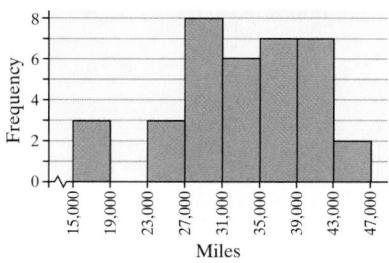

Miles on 3-Year-Old Cavaliers

(d)

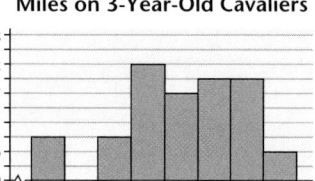

Miles on 3-Year-Old Cavaliers

(e) Symmetric

20. (f)

Class	Frequency	Relative Frequency	Class	Frequency	Relative Frequency
15,000–20,999	3	0.0833	33,000–38,999	10	0.2778
21,000–26,999	3	0.0833	39,000–44,999	9	0.25
27,000–32,999	11	0.3056	45,000–50,999	0	0

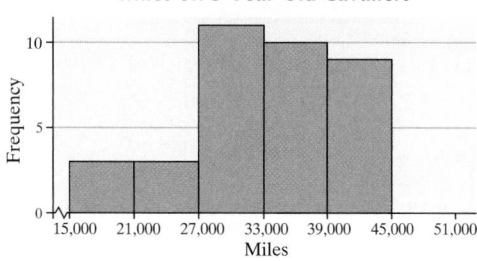

Miles on 3-Year-Old Cavaliers

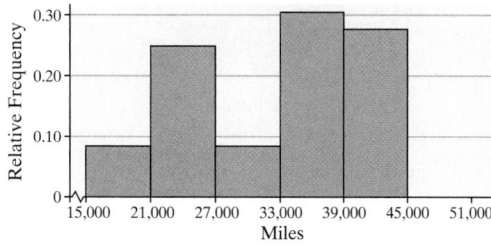

Miles on 3-Year-Old Cavaliers

21. (a), (b)

Class	Tally	Frequency	Relative Frequency
20–29	I	1	$\frac{1}{40} = 0.025$
30–39	IIII I	6	$\frac{6}{40} = 0.15$
40–49	IIII IIII	10	$\frac{10}{40} = 0.25$
50–59	IIII IIII IIII	14	0.35
60–69	IIII I	6	0.15
70–79	III	$\dfrac{3}{\sum f_i = 40}$	0.075

(c)

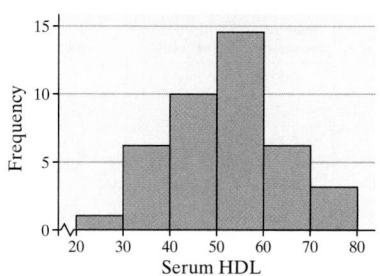

Serum HDL of 20–29 Year Olds

(d)

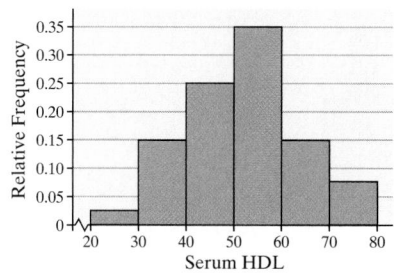

Serum HDL of 20–29 Year Olds

(e) Bell shaped

(f)

Class	Frequency	Relative Frequency
20–24	0	0
25–29	1	0.025
30–34	2	0.05
35–39	4	0.1
40–44	2	0.05
45–49	8	0.2
50–54	9	0.225
55–59	5	0.125
60–64	4	0.1
65–69	2	0.05
70–74	3	0.075
75–79	0	0

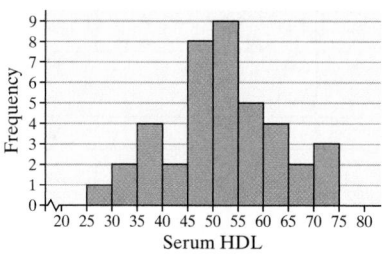

Serum HDL of 20–29 Year Olds

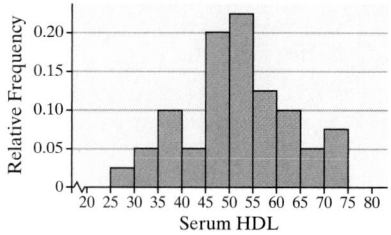

Serum HDL of 20–29 Year Olds

Bell shaped

22. (a),(b)

Class	Tally	Frequency	Relative Frequency
3–6.99	|||| ||	7	$\frac{7}{35} = 0.2$
7–10.99	|||| |||| ||||	14	$\frac{14}{35} = 0.4$
11–14.99	|||| |||	8	0.229
15–18.99	|||	3	0.086
19–22.99		0	0
23–26.99	||	2	0.057
27–30.99			1 $\sum f_i = 35$	0.029

(c)

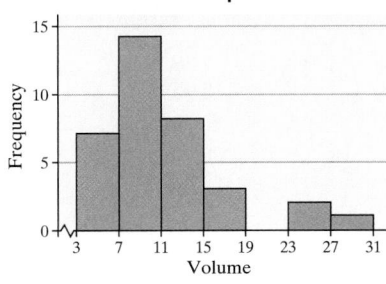

Volume of Philip Morris Stock

(d)

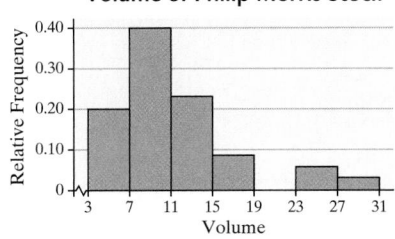

Volume of Philip Morris Stock

(e) Skewed right

(f)

Class	Frequency	Relative Frequency
3–8.99	15	0.4286
9–14.99	14	0.4
15–20.99	3	0.0857
21–26.99	2	0.0571
27–32.99	1	0.0286

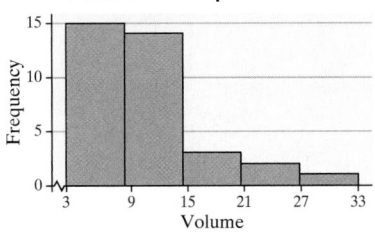

Volume of Philip Morris Stock

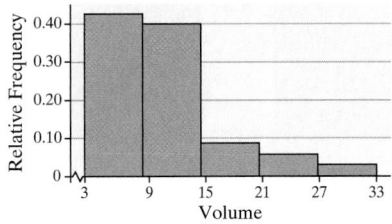

Volume of Philip Morris Stock

Skewed right

23. (a), (b)

Class	Frequency	Relative Frequency	Class	Frequency	Relative Frequency
0.76–0.77	1	0.02	0.86–0.87	11	0.22
0.78–0.79	2	0.04	0.88–0.89	10	0.20
0.8–0.81	0	0	0.90–0.91	9	0.18
0.82–0.83	4	0.08	0.92–0.93	5	0.1
0.84–0.85	6	0.12	0.94–0.95	2	0.04

(c)

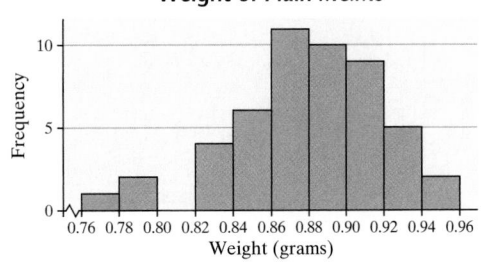

Weight of Plain M&Ms

(d)

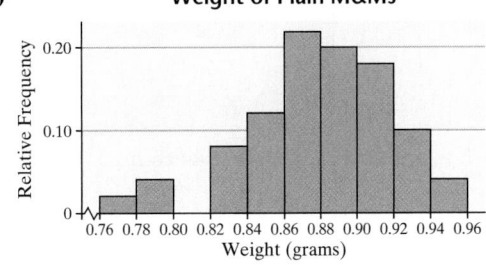

Weight of Plain M&Ms

(e) Symmetric

(f)

Class	Frequency	Relative Frequency
0.76–0.79	3	0.06
0.80–0.83	4	0.08
0.84–0.87	17	0.34
0.88–0.91	19	0.38
0.92–0.95	7	0.14

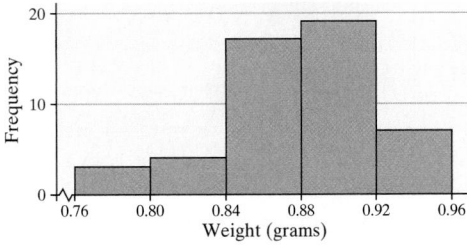

Weight of Plain M&Ms

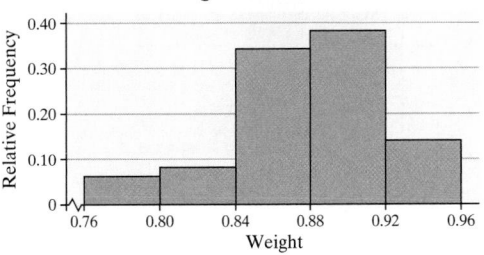

Weight of Plain M&Ms

Symmetric

24. (a), (b)

Class	Frequency	Relative Frequency
90–94	4	0.0909
95–99	3	0.0682
100–104	17	0.3864
105–109	11	0.25
110–114	7	0.1591
115–119	1	0.0227
120–124	1	0.0227

(c)

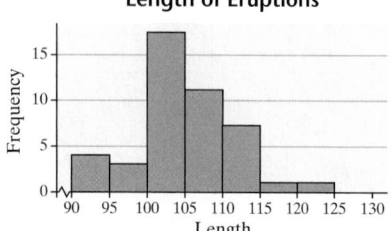

(d)

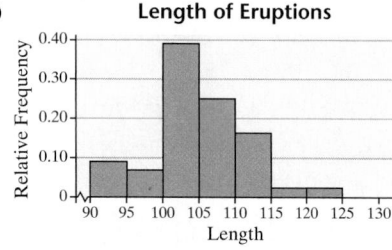

(e) Fairly symmetric

(f)

Class	Frequency	Relative Frequency
90–99	7	0.1591
100–109	28	0.6364
110–119	8	0.1818
120–129	1	0.0227

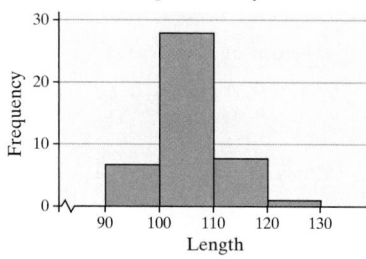

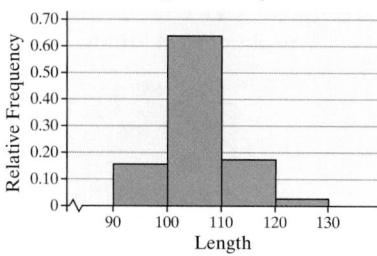

Symmetric

25.
```
4 | 23
4 | 667899
5 | 0011112244444
5 | 555566677778
6 | 0111244
6 | 589
```

26.
```
0 | 567
1 | 22233
1 | 5578889
2 | 14
2 | 5668
3 | 4
3 | 5899
4 | 01133
4 | 569
5 | 23
5 | 566
6 | 1334
6 | 58
```

27.
```
0 | 2
0 | 88
1 | 12
1 | 567
2 | 033
2 | 8
3 | 114
3 | 78
```

28.
```
2 | 0344
2 | 555666667788888888999
3 | 000000022223344
3 | 55788
4 | 00
```

29. (a)

Age	Relative Frequency (Males)	Relative Frequency (Females)
0–9	0.1491	0.1362
10–19	0.1513	0.1372
20–29	0.1370	0.1293
30–39	0.1575	0.1527
40–49	0.1541	0.1512
50–59	0.1064	0.1086
60–69	0.0698	0.0765
70–79	0.0519	0.0659
80–89	0.02	0.0343
90–99	0.0029	0.0080

(b) Males; females

(c)

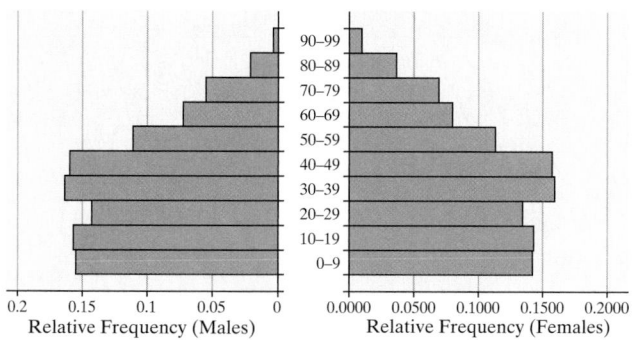

30. (a)

Age of Mother	Relative Frequency (1980)	Relative Frequency (1997)
10–14	0.0030	0.0029
15–19	0.1441	0.1297
20–24	0.3129	0.2719
25–29	0.3069	0.2802
30–34	0.1683	0.2094
35–39	0.0538	0.0883
40–44	0.0106	0.0169
45–49	0.0005	0.0007

(b) 30.69%; 28.02%

(c)

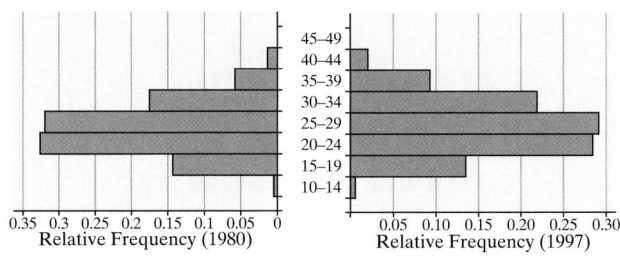

2.3 Exercises (page 89)

1. (a) 5   **(b)** 20   **(c)** 24   **(d)** 40–44   **(e)** 20–24
2. (a) 5   **(b)** 5   **(c)** 9   **(d)** 35–39   **(e)** 5–9
3. (a) 2   **(b)** 11.9   **(c)** 40%   **(d)** 60%   **(e)** 13.9
4. (a) 60   **(b)** 279   **(c)** 50; 105

5. (a), (b)

Age	Cumulative Frequency	Cumulative Relative Frequency
25–34	29.3	0.2522
35–44	66.3	0.5706
45–54	96.7	0.8322
55–64	116.2	1

(c) Number of People Covered by Health Insurance, 1998

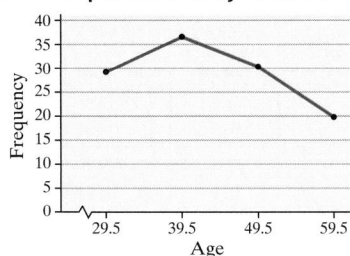

(d) Number of People Covered by Health Insurance, 1998

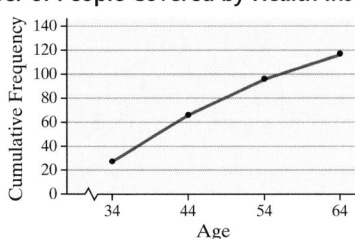

(e) Number of People Covered by Health Insurance, 1998

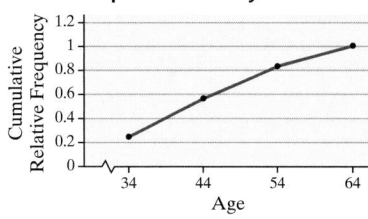

6. (a), (b)

Magnitude	Cumulative Frequency	Cumulative Relative Frequency	Magnitude	Cumulative Frequency	Cumulative Relative Frequency
0–0.9	2389	0.1164	4.0–4.9	19,574	0.9535
1.0–1.9	3141	0.1530	5.0–5.9	20,406	0.9940
2.0–2.9	6992	0.3406	6.0–6.9	20,519	0.9995
3.0–3.9	12,631	0.6153	7.0–7.9	20,529	1.0000

(c)   Magnitude of Earthquakes, 1998

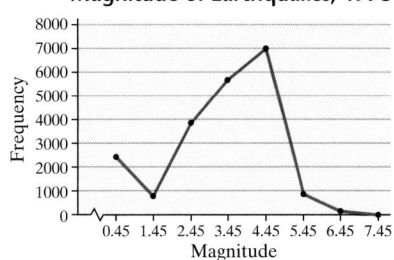

(d)   Magnitude of Earthquakes, 1998

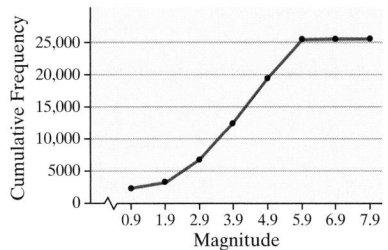

(e)   Magnitude of Earthquakes, 1998

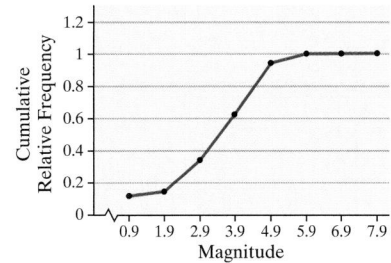

7. (a), (b)

Temperature	Cumulative Frequency	Cumulative Relative Frequency
50–59	1	0.0003
60–69	309	0.0779
70–79	1828	0.4607
80–89	3454	0.8705
90–99	3957	0.9973
100–109	3968	1

(c)

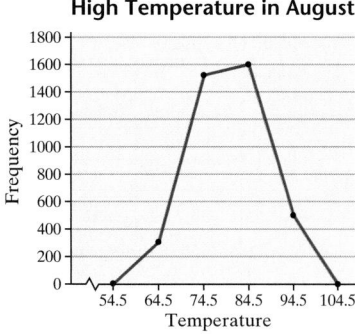

High Temperature in August

(d)

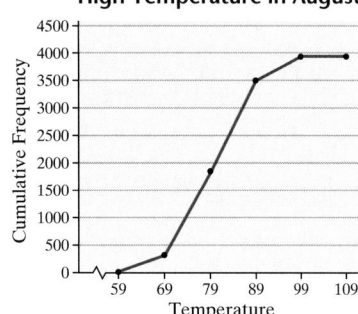

High Temperature in August

(e)

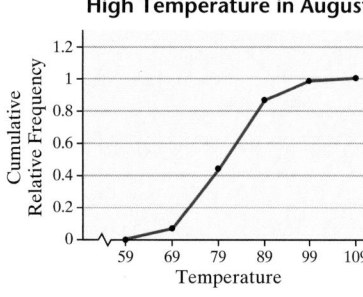

High Temperature in August

8. (a), (b)

Age	Cumulative Frequency	Cumulative Relative Frequency
15–19	66	0.0084
20–24	477	0.0610
25–29	2130	0.2722
30–34	5056	0.6461
35–39	6869	0.8778
40–44	7825	1

(c)

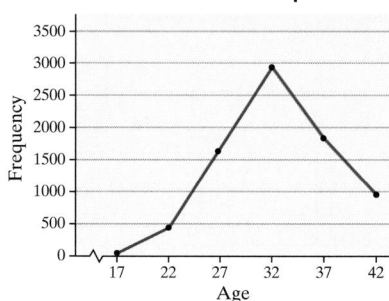

Number of Live Multiple Births

(d)

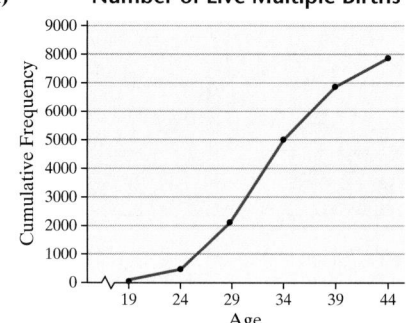

Number of Live Multiple Births

(e)

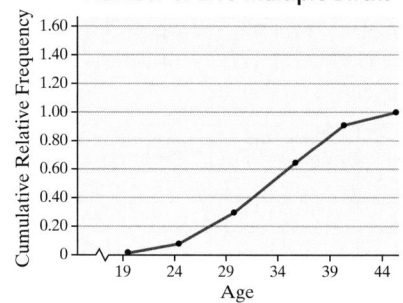

Number of Live Multiple Births

9. (a), (b)

Class	Cumulative Frequency	Cumulative Relative Frequency	Class	Cumulative Frequency	Cumulative Relative Frequency
160–169.99	1	0.04	210–219.99	22	0.88
170–179.99	2	0.08	220–229.99	23	0.92
180–189.99	6	0.24	230–239.99	24	0.96
190–199.99	7	0.28	240–249.99	25	1.00
200–200.99	16	0.64			

(c)

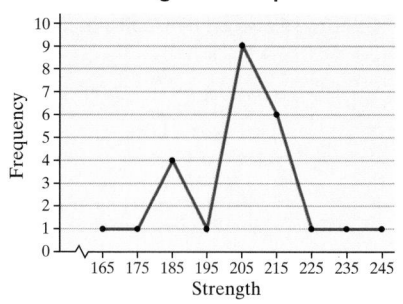

Tensile Strength of Composite Material

9. (d)

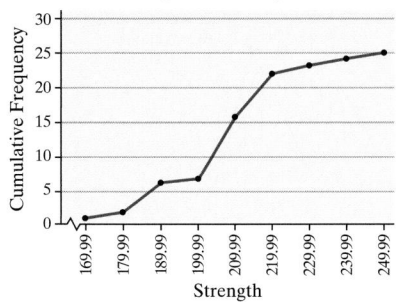

Tensile Strength of Composite Material

(e)

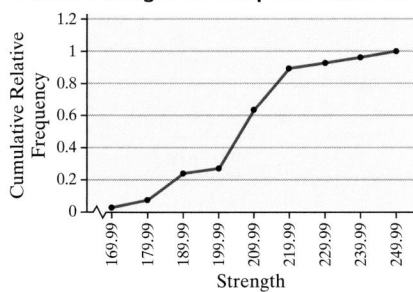

Tensile Strength of Composite Material

10. (a), (b)

Class	Cumulative Frequency	Cumulative Relative Frequency
15,000–18,999	3	0.083
19,000–22,999	3	0.083
23,000–26,999	6	0.167
27,000–30,999	14	0.389
31,000–34,999	20	0.556
35,000–38,999	27	0.750
39,000–42,999	34	0.944
43,000–46,999	36	1

(c)

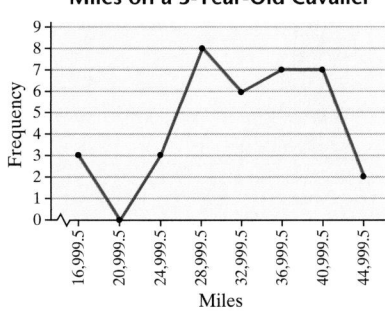

Miles on a 3-Year-Old Cavalier

(d)

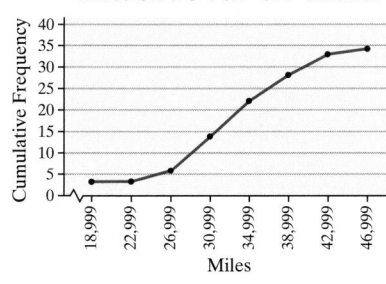

Miles on a 3-Year-Old Cavalier

(e)

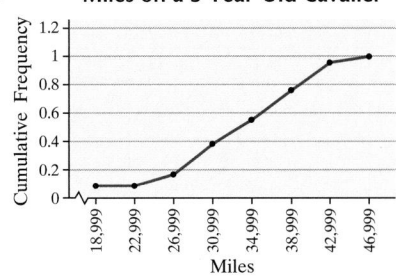

Miles on a 3-Year-Old Cavalier

11.

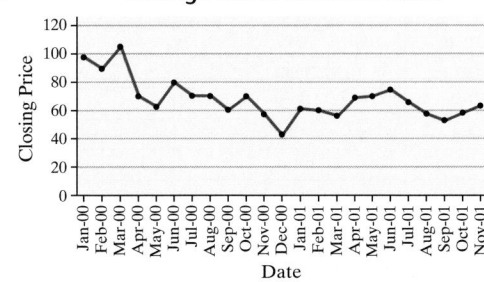

Closing Price of Microsoft Stock

12.

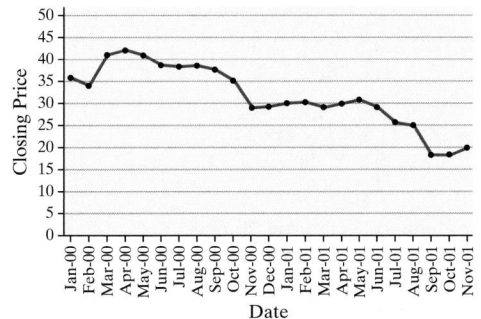

Closing Price of Walt Disney Stock

13.

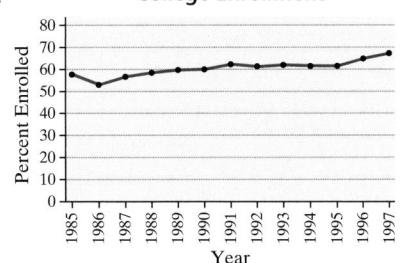

College Enrollment

14.

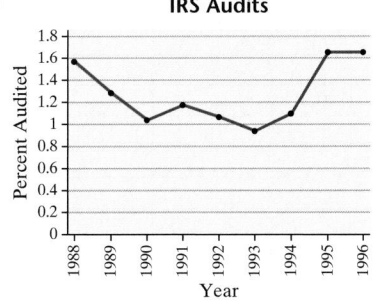

IRS Audits

15. (a)

Class	Frequency (Financial)	Frequency (Energy)
0–4.99	9	3
5–9.99	12	20
10–14.99	9	9
15–19.99	5	0
20–24.99	2	2
25–29.99	2	0
30–34.99	1	1

(b)

Class	Relative Frequency (Financial)	Relative Frequency (Energy)
0–4.99	0.225	0.0857
5–9.99	0.3	0.5714
10–14.99	0.225	0.2571
15–19.99	0.125	0.0000
20–24.99	0.05	0.0571
25–29.99	0.05	0.0000
30–34.99	0.025	0.0286

(c)

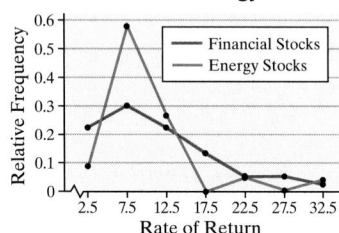

Financial vs Energy Stocks

(d)

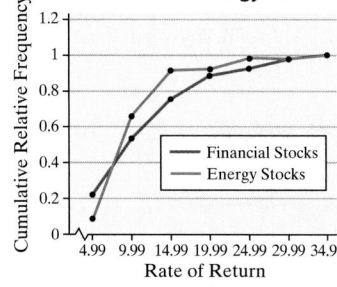

Financial vs Energy Stocks

16. (a) Since the sample sizes are the same, we can use frequencies to compare the two leagues.

(b)

Class	Frequency (American League)	Frequency (National League)
2.40–2.79	0	1
2.80–3.19	3	5
3.20–3.59	7	8
3.60–3.99	6	3
4.00–4.39	10	7
4.40–4.79	5	10
4.80–5.19	4	3
5.20–5.59	1	0
5.60–5.99	1	0

(c)

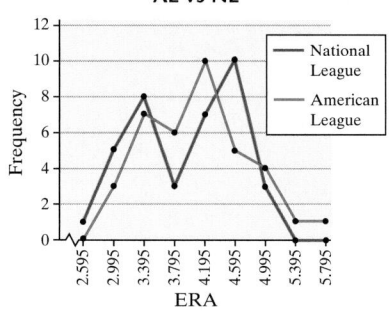

AL vs NL

(d)

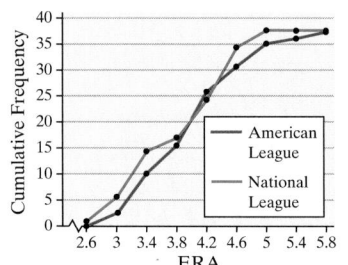

AL vs NL

2.4 Exercises (page 95)

1. The ketchup "stain" should be more than twice as long as the mustard or mayonnaise "stain."

2. In the pie chart on the right, the area corresponding to "same number of jobs" is not 68.8% of the area of the circle.

3. The graphic has a large portion "cut out" from the center on the vertical axis, yet the graphs are drawn continuously.

4. **(a)** Vertical axis starts at 0.1

(b)

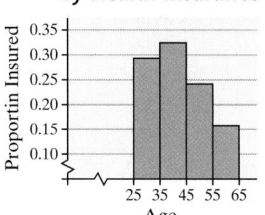

Proportion Covered by Health Insurance

5. **(a)** Vertical axis starts at 1000

(b)

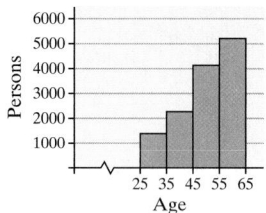

Number of Persons with Work Disability

6. (a) Vertical axis starts at 15000.

(b)

Average Cost for Making a Movie

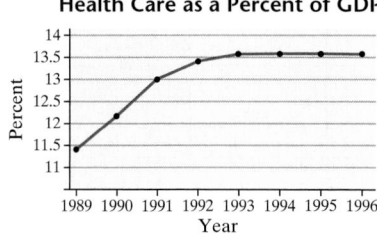

7. (a) Vertical axis starts at 1500
(b) Health-care expenditures are increasing more rapidly than they really are.

8. 1300 times

9. (a) The bar for housing should be a little more than twice the length of the bar for transportation, but it is not.
(b) Adjust the graphs so that the lengths of the bars are proportional.

10. (a)

Health Care as a Percent of GDP

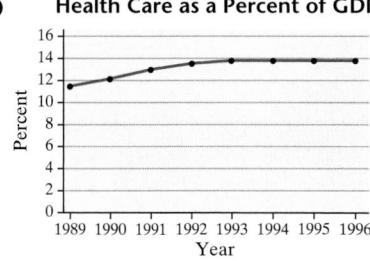

(b)

Health Care as a Percent of GDP

(c)

Health Care as a Percent of GDP

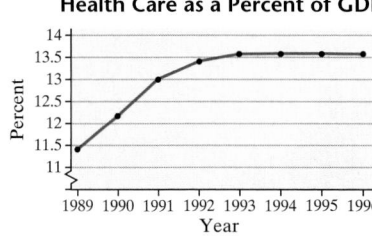

11. (a)

Waste Generated per Person

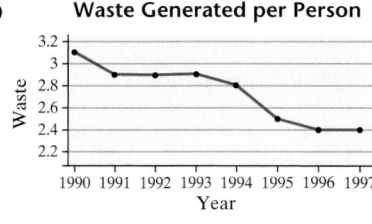

(b)

Waste Generated per Person

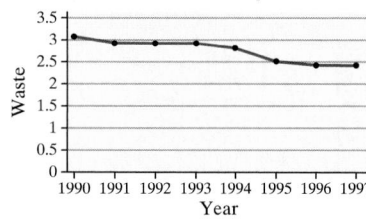

(c)

Waste Generated per Person

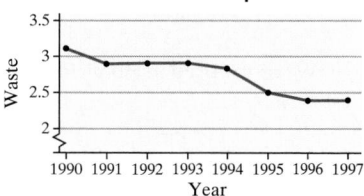

12. (a) Because the second graphic must be two times as large as the first graphic, the height and width of the second graphic must increase by a factor of $\sqrt{2}$. So if the first graphic is 1 inch by 1 inch, the second graphic should be $\sqrt{2}$ inches by $\sqrt{2}$ inches.
(b) Any graphic that is misleading will not have the dimensions mentioned in part (a). Typically, the second graphic would have a width and length that both increase by a factor of two, which makes the area four times as large.

13. (a) Because the second graphic must have an area that is three times as large as the first graphic, the height and width of the second graphic must increase by a factor of $\sqrt{3}$. So if the first graphic is 1 inch by 1 inch, the second graphic should be $\sqrt{3}$ inches by $\sqrt{3}$ inches.
(b) Any graphic that is misleading will not have the dimensions mentioned in part (a). Typically, the second graph would have a width and length that both increase by a factor of three, which makes the area nine times as large.

Chapter Review Exercises (page 99)

1. (a) 22 quadrillion btus
(b) 4 quadrillion btus
(c) 95 quadrillion btus

2. (a) 96
(b) 3
(c) 0–2.9, 1; 3–5.9, 16; 6–8.9, 36; 9–11.9, 31; 12–14.9, 7; 15–17.9, 3; 18–20.9, 1; 21–23.9, 1
(d) 6–8.9
(e) 0.167
(f) Skewed right

3. (a)

Cause of Death	Relative Frequency
Gun Shot	0.649
Cutting/Stabbing	0.133
Blunt Object	0.053
Personal Weapons (hand, fist, etc.)	0.067
Strangulation	0.022
Other	0.076

(b) 5.3%

3. (c)

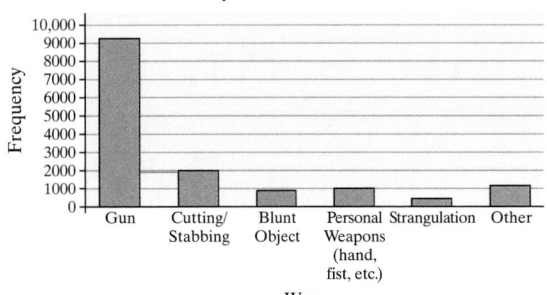

Weapons Used in Homicides

(d)

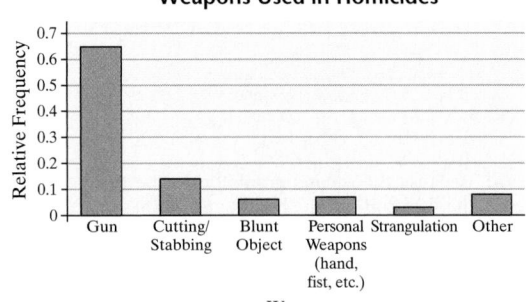

Weapons Used in Homicides

(e)

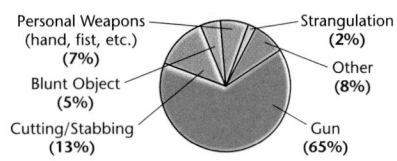

Weapons Used in Homicides

4. (a)

Gas	Relative Frequency
Carbon Dioxide	0.8204
Methane	0.0990
Nitrous Oxide	0.0601
Hydrofluorocarbons, perfluorocarbons, and sulfur hexafluoride	0.0205

(b) 82.04%

(c)

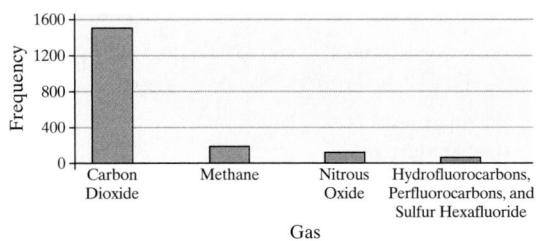

U.S. Greenhouse Gas Emissions

(d)

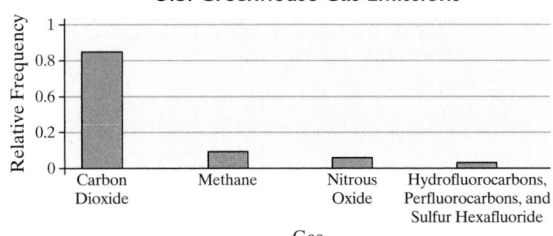

U.S. Greenhouse Gas Emissions

(e)

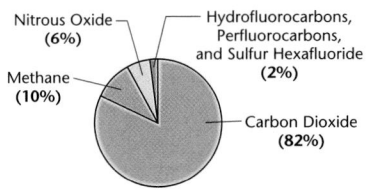

U.S. Greenhouse Gas Emissions

5. (a), (b), (c)

Age	Frequency	Relative Frequency	Cumulative Frequency	Cumulative Relative Frequency
20–24	8067	0.1770	8,067	0.1770
25–29	6195	0.1359	14,262	0.3129
30–34	6274	0.1376	20,536	0.4505
35–39	5130	0.1125	25,666	0.5630
40–44	4631	0.1016	30,297	0.6646
45–49	3636	0.0798	33,933	0.7444
50–54	3021	0.0663	36,954	0.8106
55–59	2332	0.0512	39,286	0.8618
60–64	1606	0.0352	40,892	0.8970
65–69	1341	0.0294	42,233	0.9264
70–74	1273	0.0279	43,506	0.9544
75–79	1179	0.0259	44,685	0.9802
80–84	902	0.0198	45,587	1.0000

(d)

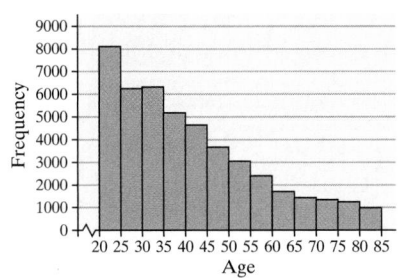

Male Vehicle Fatalities

(e)

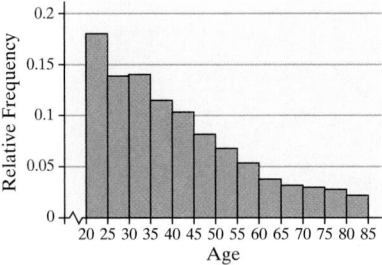

Male Vehicle Fatalities

(f)

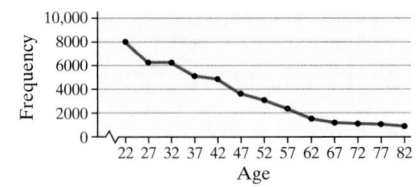

Male Vehicle Fatalities

5. (g)

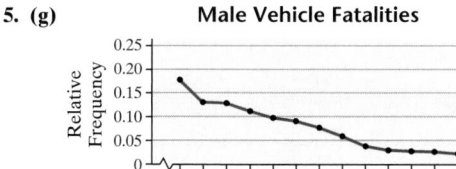

Male Vehicle Fatalities

(h)

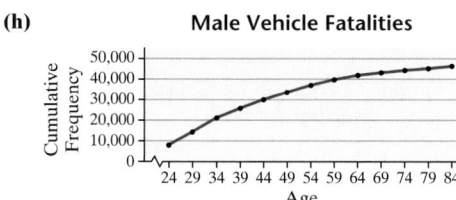

Male Vehicle Fatalities

(i)

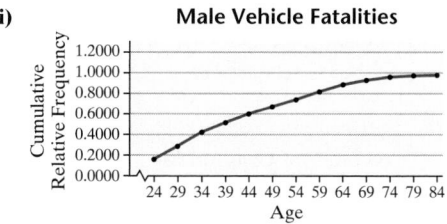

Male Vehicle Fatalities

(j) 17.7%   **(k)** 31.29%

6. (a), (b), (c)

Age	Frequency	Relative Frequency	Cumulative Frequency	Cumulative Relative Frequency
20–24	3190	0.1456	3,190	0.1456
25–29	2446	0.1116	5,636	0.2572
30–34	2366	0.1080	8,002	0.3652
35–39	2396	0.1094	10,398	0.4746
40–44	2204	0.1006	12,602	0.5752
45–49	1813	0.0828	14,415	0.6579
50–54	1480	0.0676	15,895	0.7255
55–59	1236	0.0564	17,131	0.7819
60–64	956	0.0436	18,087	0.8256
65–69	1015	0.0463	19,102	0.8719
70–74	1050	0.0479	20,152	0.9198
75–79	978	0.0446	21,130	0.9644
80–84	779	0.0356	21,909	1.0000

(d)

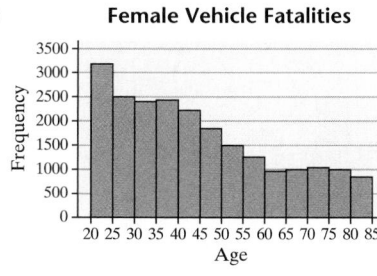

Female Vehicle Fatalities

Skewed right

(e)

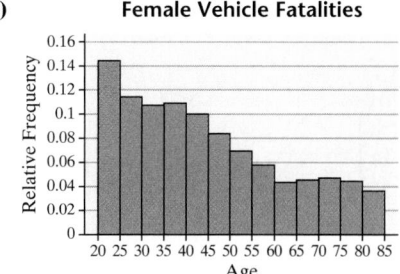

Female Vehicle Fatalities

(f)

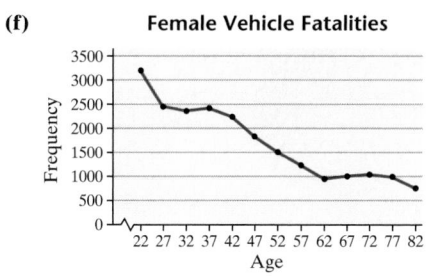

Female Vehicle Fatalities

(g)

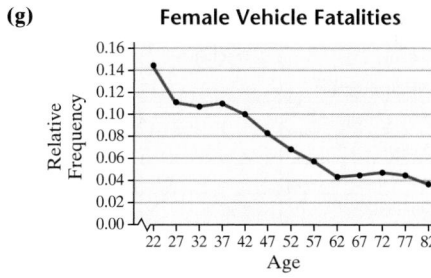

Female Vehicle Fatalities

(h)

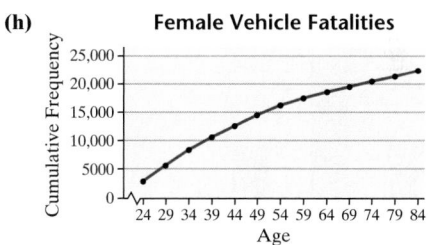

Female Vehicle Fatalities

(i)

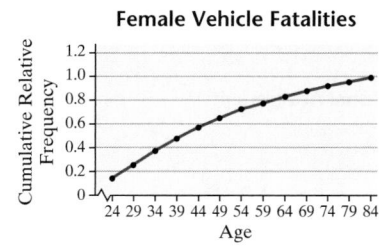

Female Vehicle Fatalities

(j) 14.56%   **(k)** 25.72%

7. (a), (b)

Affiliation	Frequency	Relative Frequency
Democrat	46	0.46
Independent	16	0.16
Republican	38	0.38

7. (c)

Political Affiliation

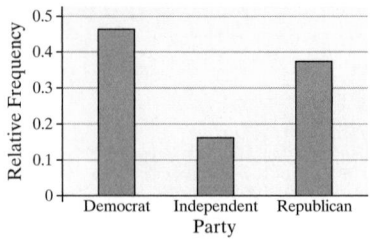

(d)

Political Affiliation

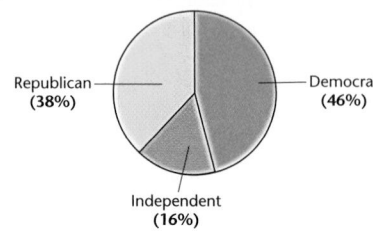

Republican (38%)

Democrat (46%)

Independent (16%)

(e) Democrat

8. (a), (b)

Educational Attainment	Frequency	Relative Frequency
No high school degree	9	0.18
High school graduate	16	0.32
Some college	9	0.18
Associate's degree	4	0.08
Bachelor's degree	8	0.16
Advanced degree	4	0.08

(c)

Educational Attainment of Commuters

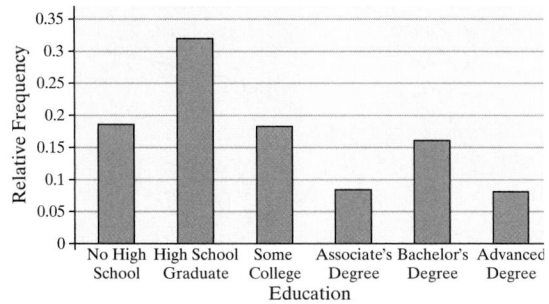

(d)   **Educational Attainment**

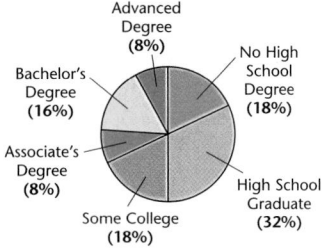

Advanced Degree (8%)

Bachelor's Degree (16%)

Associate's Degree (8%)

Some College (18%)

No High School Degree (18%)

High School Graduate (32%)

(e) High school graduate

9. (a), (b), (c), (d)

Number of Children	Frequency	Relative Frequency	Cumulative Frequency	Cumulative Relative Frequency
0	7	0.1167	7	0.1167
1	7	0.1167	14	0.2333
2	18	0.3000	32	0.5333
3	20	0.3333	52	0.8667
4	7	0.1167	59	0.9833
5	1	0.0167	60	1.0000

(e)

Number of Children for Couples Married 7 Years

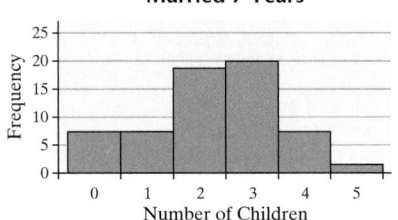

Symmetric

(f)

Number of Children for Couples Married 7 Years

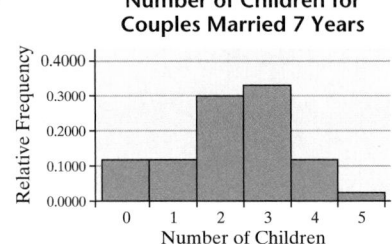

(g) 30%   **(h)** 76.7%

10. (a), (b), (c), (d)

Number of Customers	Frequency	Relative Frequency	Cumulative Frequency	Cumulative Relative Frequency
1	5	0.10	5	0.10
2	7	0.14	12	0.24
3	12	0.24	24	0.48
4	6	0.12	30	0.60
5	8	0.16	38	0.76
6	5	0.10	43	0.86
7	2	0.04	45	0.90
8	4	0.08	49	0.98
9	1	0.02	50	1.00

(e)

Number of People Waiting in Line at McDonald's

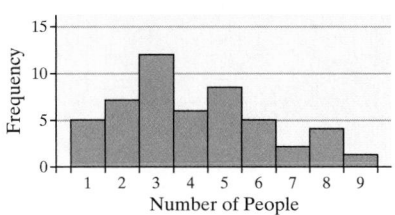

Slightly skewed right

10. (f)

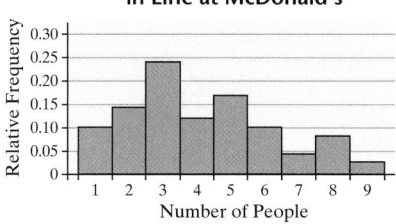

Number of People Waiting
in Line at McDonald's

(g) 24%   **(h)** 76%

11. (a), (b), (c), (d)

Class	Frequency	Relative Frequency	Cumulative Frequency	Cumulative Relative Frequency
2000–2499	1	0.0196	1	0.0196
2500–2999	4	0.0784	5	0.0980
3000–3499	4	0.0784	9	0.1765
3500–3999	9	0.1765	18	0.3529
4000–4499	9	0.1765	27	0.5294
4500–4999	7	0.1373	34	0.6667
5000–5499	8	0.1569	42	0.8235
5500–5999	4	0.0784	46	0.9020
6000–6499	1	0.0196	47	0.9216
6500–6999	3	0.0588	50	0.9804
7000–7499	0	0.0000	50	0.9804
7500–7999	0	0.0000	50	0.9804
8000–8499	0	0.0000	50	0.9804
8500–8999	1	0.0196	51	1.0000

(e)   Crime Rates per 100,000 Population

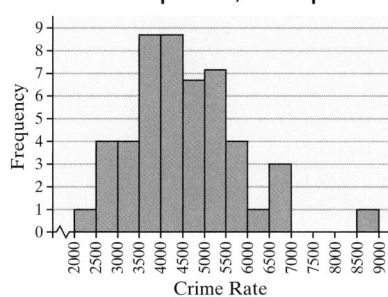

Fairly symmetric

(f)   Crime Rates per 100,000 Population

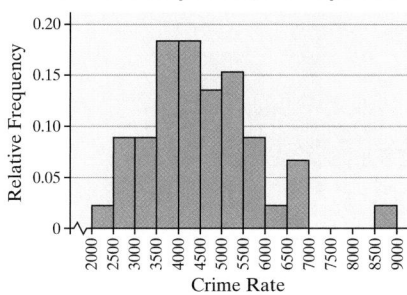

(g)

Class	Frequency	Relative Frequency	Cumulative Frequency	Cumulative Relative Frequency
2000–2999	5	0.0980	5	0.0980
3000–3999	13	0.2549	18	0.3529
4000–4999	16	0.3137	34	0.6667
5000–5999	12	0.2353	46	0.9020
6000–6999	4	0.0784	50	0.9804
7000–7999	0	0.0000	50	0.9804
8000–8999	1	0.0196	51	1.0000

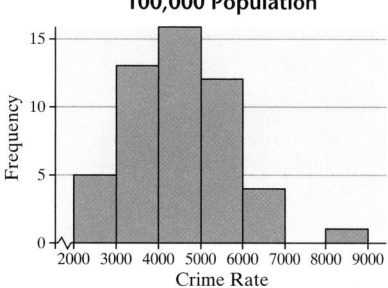

Crime Rates per
100,000 Population

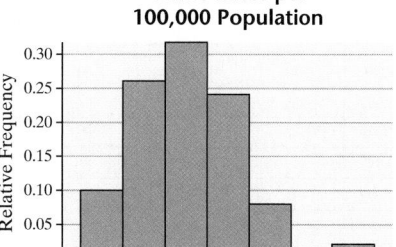

Crime Rates per
100,000 Population

12. (a), (b), (c), (d)

Class	Frequency	Relative Frequency	Cumulative Frequency	Cumulative Relative Frequency
18,000–18,999	2	0.039216	2	0.039216
19,000–19,999	5	0.098039	7	0.137255
20,000–20,999	6	0.117647	13	0.254902
21,000–21,999	2	0.039216	15	0.294118
22,000–22,999	11	0.215686	26	0.509804
23,000–23,999	5	0.098039	31	0.607843
24,000–24,999	4	0.078431	35	0.686275
25,000–25,999	4	0.078431	39	0.764706
26,000–26,999	7	0.137255	46	0.901961
27,000–27,999	0	0	46	0.901961
28,000–28,999	1	0.019608	47	0.921569
29,000–29,999	1	0.019608	48	0.941176
30,000–30,999	1	0.019608	49	0.960784
31,000–31,999	2	0.039216	51	1

12. (e)

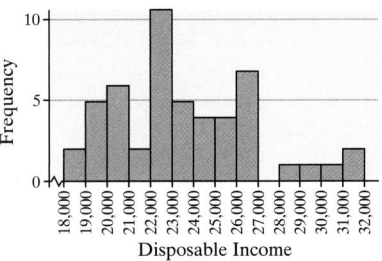

Disposable Income, 1999

(f)

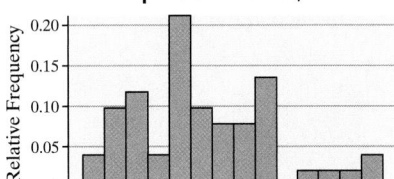

Disposable Income, 1999

(g)

Class	Frequency	Relative Frequency	Cumulative Frequency	Cumulative Relative Frequency
18,000–19,999	7	0.137255	7	0.137255
20,000–21,999	8	0.156863	15	0.294118
22,000–23,999	16	0.313725	31	0.607843
24,000–25,999	8	0.156863	39	0.764706
26,000–27,999	7	0.137255	46	0.901961
28,000–29,999	2	0.039216	48	0.941176
30,000–31,999	3	0.058824	51	1

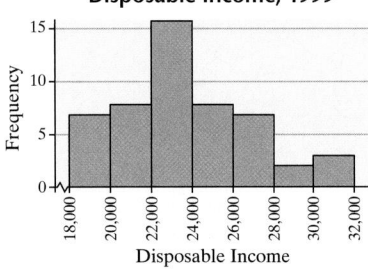

Disposable Income, 1999

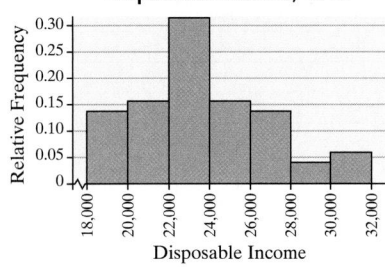

Disposable Income, 1999

13. (a), (b)

Class	Frequency	Relative Frequency	Class	Relative Frequency	Frequency
3000–3999	5	0.1613	8000–8999	5	0.1613
4000–4999	4	0.1290	9000–9999	0	0.0000
5000–5999	8	0.2581	10,000–10,999	1	0.0323
6000–6999	3	0.0968	11,000–11,999	0	0.0000
7000–7999	3	0.0968	12,000–12,999	2	0.0645

(c)

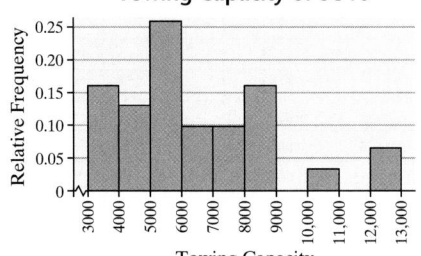

Towing Capacity of SUVs

Skewed right

(d)

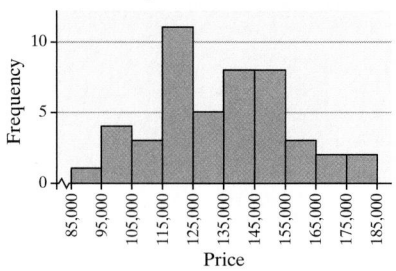

Towing Capacity of SUVs

14. (a), (b)

Class	Frequency	Relative Frequency
85,000–94,999	1	0.0213
95,000–104,999	4	0.0851
105,000–114,999	3	0.0638
115,000–124,999	11	0.2340
125,000–134,999	5	0.1064
135,000–144,999	8	0.1702
145,000–154,999	8	0.1702
155,000–164,999	3	0.0638
165,000–174,999	2	0.0426
175,000–184,999	2	0.0426

(c)

Closing Price of Home Sales

(d)

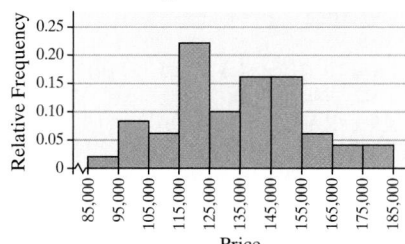

Closing Price of Home Sales

15.
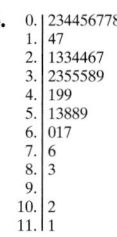

Skewed right

16.
```
0. | 234456778
1. | 47
2. | 1334467
3. | 2355589
4. | 199
5. | 13889
6. | 017
7. | 6
8. | 3
9. |
10. | 2
11. | 1
```
Skewed right

17. (a)

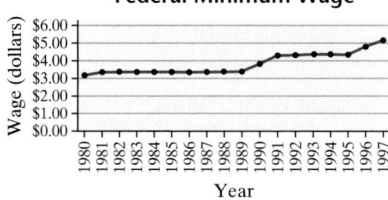

Federal Minimum Wage

(b) Slightly upward

18. (a)

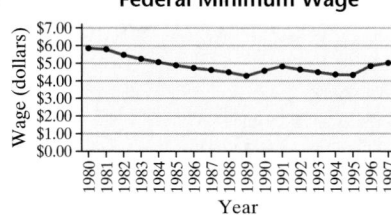

Federal Minimum Wage

(b) Slightly downward

19. There is no vertical scale.

20. Very difficult to read three-dimensional graphs. Is the height of the stair the scale, or is it the width of the stair?

21. (a) A misleading graph would be a graph that is 75% wider and 75% taller.
(b) A graph that does not mislead would be one that has total area or total volume that is 75% larger.

CHAPTER 3 Numerically Summarizing Data

3.1 Exercises (page 123)

1. Mean: $381.75; Median: $414.50; No Mode
2. Mean: $41.41; Median: $40.76; No Mode
3. Mean: 3668.9 psi; Median: 3830 psi; No Mode
4. Mean: 266 minutes; Median: 266 minutes; Mode: 260 minutes

5. Sludge Plot: Mean = 28.3; Median = 27.5; Mode = 27
Spring Disk: Mean = 33; Median = 33.5; Mode = 34
No Till: Mean = 28.5; Median = 29; Mode = 29
Spring Chisele: Mean = 29.3; Median = 29.5; No Mode
Great Lakes Bt: Mean = 28.8; Median = 28.5; Mode = 27
6. Liberty: Mean = 35.9; Median = 36; No Mode
Fall Plowed: Mean = 26.3; Median = 30; Mode = 30
No Till: Mean = 34.8; Median = 34; No Mode
Chisele Plowed: Mean = 30.4; Median = 32; Mode = 34
Roundup Ready: Mean = 34.1; Median = 34; Mode = 35
7. Monday: Mean = 10,511.3; Median = 10,491.5; No Mode
Saturday: Mean = 8476.3; Median = 8449.5; No Mode
8. March: Mean = 11,360; Median = 11,570; No Mode
September: Mean = 12,153.4; Median = 12,372; No Mode
9. Control: Mean = 323.2 g; Median = 320g; No Mode
Flight: Mean = 333.8 g; Median = 326 g; No Mode
10. Blue: Mean = 0.551 sec; Median = 0.5315sec; No Mode
Red: Mean = 0.458 sec; Median = 0.432 sec; No Mode
11. (a) 72.2 **(b)** Answers will vary
(c) Answers will vary
12. (a) 26.4 minutes **(b)** Answers will vary
(c) Answers will vary
13. (a) Mean = 7.9 customers; Median = 8 customers
(b) Symmetric
14. (a) Mean = 3.5 potholes; Median = 3 potholes
(b) Skewed right
15. (a) Mean = 203.9 psi; Median = 206.51 psi **(b)** Symmetric
16. (a) Mean = 33,242.7 miles; Median = 34,311 miles
(b) Symmetric
17. (a) Mean = 51.1; Median = 51 **(b)** Symmetric
18. (a) Mean = 11.191 million shares; Median = 10.14 million shares **(b)** Skewed right
19. (a) Mean = 0.874 g; Median = 0.88 g **(b)** Symmetric
20. (a) Mean = 104.1 sec; Median = 104 sec **(b)** Symmetric
21. Latin America **22.** Street or highway **23.** Gore
24. Gun shot wound **25.** Pitcher **26.** O
27. Mean = 229.1 psi; Median = 207.88 psi
28. Mean = 36,020.4 miles; Median = 34,505.5 miles
29. (a) Mean > Median **(b)** Mean = Median
(c) Mean < Median
30. (a) IV **(b)** III **(c)** II **(d)** I
31. Median, because it is resistant **32.** Less **33.** 204
34. (a) 75.2 **(b)** 71 **(c)** The median **(d)** 79.2
(e) Added 4 to the mean
35. (a) Median **(b)** Mode **(c)** Mean
(d) Median **(e)** Median
36. 0.875 g; it is resistant only if there is only one extreme (large or small) data value
37. 0.85 g; No
38. (a) 6.4% **(b)** 3.5%
39. (a) 49.5 mph **(b)** 4.1 Kb/sec **(c)** $1.43 per pound

3.2 Exercises (page 142)

1. Range = $226; s^2 = 9962.9; s = $99.8
2. Range = $13.92; s^2 = 22.584; s = $4.75
3. Range = 1150 psi; s^2 = 210,236.1; s = 458.5 psi
4. Range = 25 minutes; s^2 = 71; s = 8.4 minutes

5. Sludge Plot: Range = 8; s = 2.8
Spring Disk: Range = 5; s = 1.8
No Till: Range = 7; s = 2.6
Spring Chisele: Range = 6; s = 2.2
Great Lakes Bt: Range = 5; s = 1.9

6. Liberty: Range = 10; s = 3.3
Fall Plowed: Range = 29; s = 8.9
No Till: Range = 15; s = 5.0
Chisele Plowed: Range = 14; s = 4.8
Roundup Ready: Range = 29; s = 9.0

7. Monday: Range = 511.0 births; s = 170.8 births
Saturday: Range = 294.0 births; s = 126.0 births

8. March: Range = 1661 births; s = 571.4 births
September: Range = 1584 births; s = 575.4 births

9. Control: Range = 40 g; s = 15.1 g
Flight: Range = 73 g; s = 28.5 g

10. Blue: Range = 0.574 sec; s = 0.1994 sec
Red: Range = 0.14 sec; s = 0.0647 sec

11. **(a)** σ^2 = 58.8; σ = 7.7   **(b)** Answers will vary
(c) Answers will vary

12. **(a)** σ^2 = 164.9; σ = 12.8 min   **(b)** Answers will vary
(c) Answers will vary

13. Range = 11 min; s^2 = 7.4 min²; s = 2.7 min

14. Range = 9 potholes; s^2 = 4.7 potholes²; s = 2.2 potholes

15. Range = 82.32 psi; s^2 = 335.638 psi²; s = 18.320 psi

16. Range = 28,949 miles; s^2 = 54,141,591.0 miles²;
s = 7358.1 miles

17. Range = 45; s^2 = 118.0; s = 10.9

18. Range = 23.56 million shares; s^2 = 33.4 million shares²;
s = 5.8 million shares

19. Range = 0.18 g; s^2 = 0.002 g²; s = 0.040 g

20. Range = 30 sec; s^2 = 39.1 sec²; s = 6.2 sec

21. **(a)** Financial: Mean = 11.12%; Median = 9.33%;
Energy: Mean = 9.71%; Median = 9.09%
(b) Financial: s = 8.06%; Energy: s = 5.852%; Financial is riskier

22. **(a)** AL: Mean = 4.124; Median = 4.09; NL: Mean = 3.928;
Median = 4.05
(b) AL: s = 0.676; NL: 0.638; AL

23. **(a)** Michael: Mean = 81.1; Kevin: Mean = 81.2
(b) Michael: Median = 81; Kevin: Median = 82
(c) Michael: Mode = 83; Kevin: Mode = 73
(d) Michael: Range = 13; Kevin: Range = 17
(e) Michael: s = 3.2; Kevin: s = 5.9
(f) Michael; s is lower

24. **(a)** 115: Mean = 497.4; 231: Mean = 497.4
(b) 115: Median = 523; 231: Median = 514
(c) 115: No Mode; 231: No Mode
(d) 115: Range = 217; 231: Range = 150
(e) 115: s = 62.9; 231: s = 41.3
(f) District 231

25. **(a)** 99.7%   **(b)** 95%   **(c)** 88.9%   **(d)** 75%

26. **(a)** 99.7%   **(b)** 95%   **(c)** 88.9%   **(d)** 75%

27. **(a)** Okay to use   **(b)** 99.7%   **(c)** 95%
(d) 88.9%   **(e)** 75%   **(f)** 95%

28. **(a)** Okay to use   **(b)** 99.7%   **(c)** 95%
(d) 88.9%   **(e)** 75%   **(f)** 94%

29. Range = 655.53 psi; s = 123.57 psi; Range and s increased;
Data is more dispersed; No.

30. Range = 102,186 miles; s = 15,589 miles; Range and s increased; Data is more dispersed; No.

31. **(a)** s = 11.6   **(b)** s = 11.6   **(c)** No effect
(d) s = 23.3   **(e)** s doubled

32. (b)   **33.** **(a)** III   **(b)** I   **(c)** IV   **(d)** II

34. s = 0; there is no dispersion, so s = 0

35. **(a)** After   **(b)** High

36. MAD = $72.875

37. **(a)** 3   **(b)** 0   **(c)** −2.5   **(d)** −0.4
(e) −0.4   **(f)** 0.03   **(g)** 0.5

38. **(a)** Return: 14.9%; Risk: 14.7%   **(b)** 30%
(c) Answers will vary
(d) Between −12.8% and 44.4%; Between −27.1% and 58.7%

3.3 Exercises (page 155)

1. μ = 42.5 years; σ = 10.4 years   **2.** μ = 2.8; σ = 1.3
3. **(a)** μ = 80.4°F; σ = 8.2°F

(b)

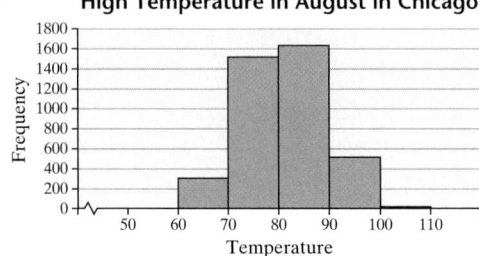

High Temperature in August in Chicago

(c) 64 and 96.8 degrees Fahrenheit
4. **(a)** μ = 32.1 years; σ = 5.2 years

(b)

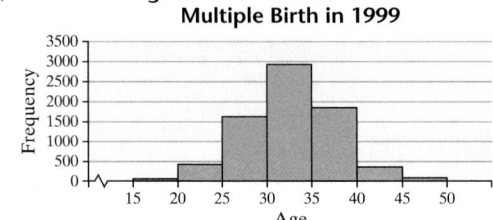

Age of Women Who Had a Live Multiple Birth in 1999

(c) 21.7 and 42.5 years
5. Mean = 204.6 psi; s = 17.9 psi
6. Mean = 33,110.6 miles; s = 7436.5 miles
7. Mean = 51.3; s = 12.1
8. Mean = 11.281 million shares; s = 5.844 million shares
9. 3.27   **10.** 87.15%   **11.** $2.97 per pound
12. $3.38 per pound
13. **(a)** μ = 34.6 years; σ = 21.7 years
(b) μ = 37.2 years; σ = 23.0 years
(c) Female   **(d)** Female
14. **(a)** μ = 25.5 years; σ = 5.7 years
(b) μ = 26.5 years; σ = 6.2 years
(c) 1997   **(d)** 1997
15. 42.2 years   **16.** 3.06   **17.** 81.0°F
18. 32.6 years   **19.** 35–44 years   **20.** 3.0–3.9
21. 80–89°F   **22.** 30–34 years

3.4 Exercises (page 164)

1. SAT   **2.** SAT   **3.** 40-week baby
4. 40-week baby   **5.** Woman   **6.** Woman
7. **(a)** $609,483.50   **(b)** $2,462,846   **(c)** $410,357
(d) 15th percentile   **(e)** 78th percentile
8. **(a)** $523,740.50   **(b)** $2,024,623   **(c)** $393,059
(d) 27th percentile   **(e)** 84th percentile

9. (a) −1.70; The rainfall in 1971 is 1.70 standard deviations below the mean
(b) $Q_1 = 2.625; Q_2 = 3.985; Q_3 = 5.36$
(c) $IQR = 2.735$
(d) Lower Fence: −1.478; Upper Fence: 9.463; No outliers

10. (a) −1.21; The hemoglobin of Blackie is 1.21 standard deviations below the mean.
(b) $Q_1 = 9.15; Q_2 = 9.95; Q_3 = 11.1$
(c) $IQR = 1.95$
(d) Lower Fence: 6.225; Upper Fence: 14.025; Yes, 5.7 is an outlier

11. (a) −3.70; The red blood cell count of Sampson is 3.70 standard deviations below the mean.
(b) $Q_1 = 6.05; Q_2 = 6.45; Q_3 = 6.95$
(c) $IQR = 0.97$
(d) Lower Fence: 4.7; Upper Fence = 8.3; Yes, 0.2 is an outlier

12. (a) 1.57; The pH level of 5.08 is 1.57 standard deviations above the mean.
(b) $Q_1 = 4.70; Q_2 = 4.78; Q_3 = 5$
(c) $IQR = 0.3$
(d) Lower Fence: 4.25; Upper Fence: 5.45; No outliers

13. (a) 0.61; The concentration of 20.46 is 0.61 standard deviations above the mean.
(b) $Q_1 = 10.01; Q_2 = 15.42; Q_3 = 20.13$
(c) $IQR = 10.12$
(d) Lower Fence: −5.17; Upper Fence: 35.31; No outliers

14. (a) 1.60; The concentration of 17.99 is 1.60 standard deviations above the mean.
(b) $Q_1 = 7.11; Q_2 = 9.1; Q_3 = 11.72$
(c) $IQR = 4.61$
(d) Lower Fence: 0.195; Upper Fence: 18.635; Yes, 21.82, 22.62, and 21.4 are outliers

15. (a) Financial: 34.22% is an outlier; Energy: 23.72%, 21.67%, and 30.39% are outliers.

(b)

Financial Stocks Rate of Return

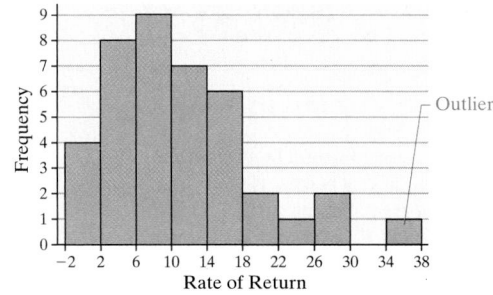

Energy Stocks Rate of Return

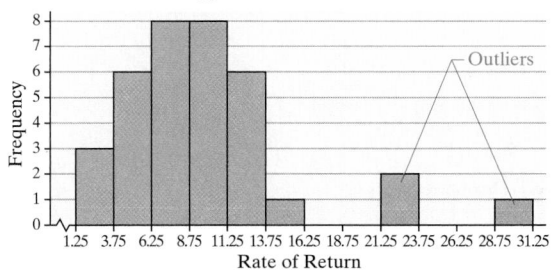

16. (a) AL: 5.82 is an outlier; NL: No outliers

American League Earned Run Averages

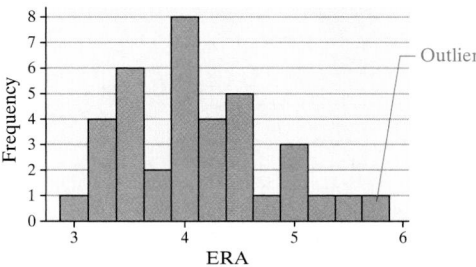

17. (a) Lower Fence: −$551; Upper Fence: $1097. The only outlier is $12,777.
(b) Student probably thought survey asked for annual income.

18. (a) Lower Fence: −28.5; Upper Fence: 103.5. The outliers will be all dollar amounts greater than $103.50.
(b) Either the question was misunderstood or this is a data entry error.

19. $\mu = 0, \sigma = 1$ **20.** $\mu = 0, \sigma = 1$

3.5 Exercises (page 173)

1. Skewed right   **2.** Symmetric
3. Five-number summary: 42   51   55   58   69

Age of Presidents at Inauguration

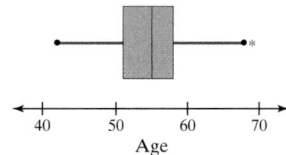

Graph is symmetric.
4. Five-number Summary: 5   17.5   35   50.5   68

Divorce Rate of Countries

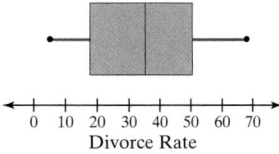

Graph is symmetric.
5. Five-number Summary: 2   11.5   20   31   38

Grams of Fat in McDonald's Breakfast Meals

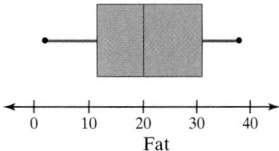

Graph is symmetric.

6. Five-number Summary: 20 26 29 32 40

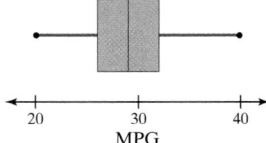

Miles per Gallon for Domestic 2001 Cars

Graph is symmetric.

7. (a) 160.44 188.32 206.51 212.75 242.76

(b) Tensile Strength of a Composite Material

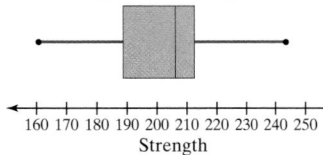

(c) Skewed slightly left

8. (a) 15,499 29,298 34,311 39,205.5 44,448

(b) Number of Miles on 3-Year-Old Cavaliers

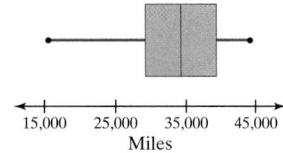

(c) Skewed slightly left

9. (a) 28 45 51 57.5 73

(b) Serum HDL of 20–29 Year Olds

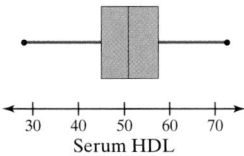

(c) Symmetric; Bell shaped

10. (a) 3.98 7.24 10.14 13.84 27.54

(b) Volume of Philip Morris Stock

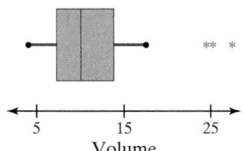

(c) Skewed right

11. (a) 0.76 0.85 0.88 0.90 0.94

(b) Weights of Plain M&Ms (in grams)

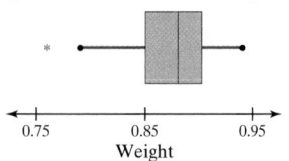

(c) Skewed slightly left

12. (a) 90 101 104 108.5 120

(b) Length of Eruptions at Old Faithful (in minutes)

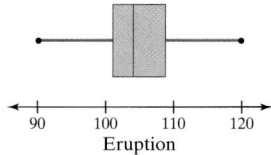

(c) Symmetric

13. Van: 18 23.5 41 47 81
SUV: 39 45 90.5 151 231

Death Rates of Vans vs. SUVs

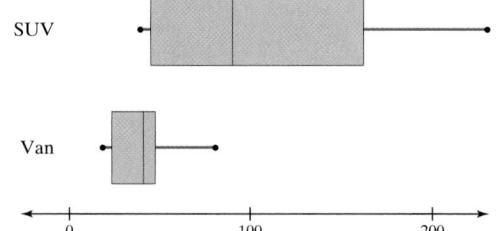

Vans appear to be safer.

14. Group Size 24: 500 550 600 675 800
Group Size 35: 525 540 565 640 675

Cold Cranking Amps

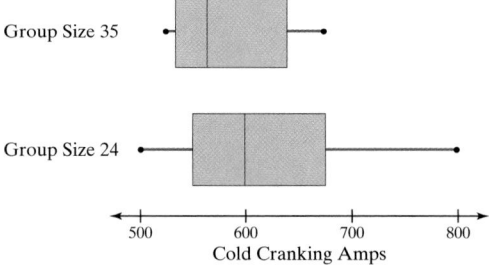

A group size of 24 would be preferable.

15. Thermocouple 1: 325.97 326.04 326.08 326.13 326.20
Thermocouple 2: 323.55 323.60 323.64 323.70 323.76
Thermocouple 3: 325.95 326.01 326.04 326.11 326.20

Thermocouple Temperatures

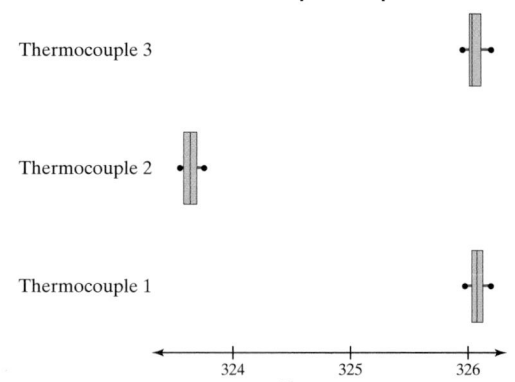

16. West: 2.07   3.49   5.65   11.98   19.77
  East: 0.00   5.53   10.75   14.01   23.96

Homicide Rates in 1999

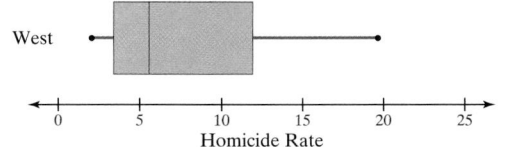

Chapter Review Exercises (page 179)

1. (a) Mean = 792.51 m/s; Median = 792.40 m/s
  (b) Range = 4.8 m/s; s^2 = 2.03; s = 1.42 m/s
2. (a) Mean = 126.8 beats/min; Median = 128.5 beats/min
  (b) Range = 83 beats/min; s^2 = 589.07; s = 24.3 beats/min
3. (a) Mean = \$13,068.1; Median = \$12,995
  (b) Range = \$5595; s = \$2034.2
  (c) Mean = \$18,068.1; Median = \$12,995; Range = \$50,595;
    s = \$16,361.3. The median is resistant.
4. (a) Mean = \$138,068.3; Median = \$136,924
  (b) Range = \$70,541, s = \$17,286.3
5. (a) μ = 58.3 years; Median = 58.5 years; Bimodal: 56 and
    62 years
  (b) Range = 25 years; σ = 6.9 years
  (c) Answers will vary
6. (a) μ = 171.8 feet; Median = 131.5 feet; No mode
  (b) Range = 264 feet; σ = 99.8 feet
  (c) Answers will vary
7. (a) Mean = 2.2 children; Median = 2.5 children
  (b) Range = 4 children; s = 1.3 children
8. (a) Mean = 4.5 cars; Median = 4.5 cars
  (b) Range = 8 cars; s = 2.3 cars
9. (a) 84%   **(b)** 75%   **(c)** 441; 759
  (d) 95%   **(e)** 0.15%
10. (a) 55.6%   **(b)** 88.9%   **(c)** 3282; 5322
  (d) 95%   **(e)** 2.5%
11. (a) μ = 40.3 years   **(b)** σ = 16.0 years
12. (a) μ = 42.6 years   **(b)** σ = 17.1 years
  (c) Answers will vary
13. 3.33   **14.** 2.17
15. (a) μ_M = \$2,973,911; μ_Y = \$4,278,218.4
  (b) M_M = \$2,200,000; M_Y = \$3,500,000
  (c) Mets: Skewed right; Yankees: Skewed right
  (d) σ_M = \$3,005,819.2; σ_Y = \$3,581,882.8
  (e) Mets: \$200,000   \$366,250   \$2,200,000   \$4,375,000
    \$12,121,428
    Yankees: \$200,00   \$1,000,000   \$3,500,000   \$6,750,000
    \$12,357,143
  (f)

Salaries of Mets vs. Yankees

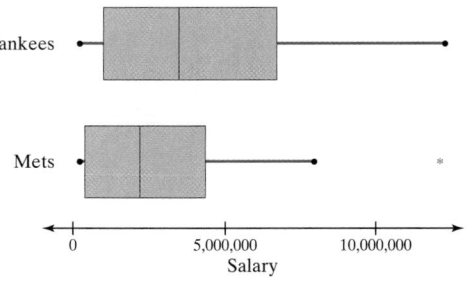

(g) Both are skewed right.
(h) The Mets have one player whose salary, \$12,121,428, is an
    outlier: Mike Piazza
16. (a) $\bar{x}_{1996}$ = 20.2; $\bar{x}_{2000}$ = 32.7
  (b) M_{1996} = 20; M_{2000} = 27
  (c) 1996: Symmetric; 2000: Skewed right
  (d) s_{1996} = 11.42; s_{2000} = 24.11
  (e) 1996: 2   12   20   28.5   44   2000: 7   16   27   39   102

Air Traffic Control Errors 1996 vs. 2000

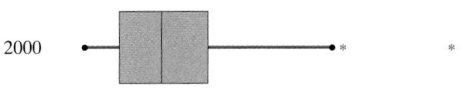

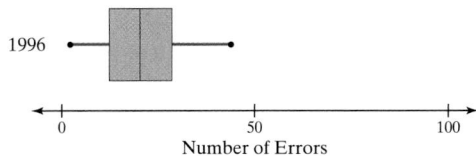

17. Male   **18.** Male
19. (a) 7.9   **(b)** 120.06   **(c)** 148.66
  (d) 17th percentile   **(e)** 82nd percentile
  (f) Q_1 = 9.61; M = 24.7; Q_3 = 64.9

(g)   **Infant Mortality Rate**

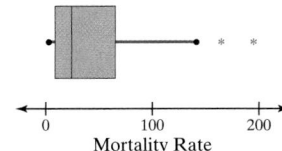

There are two outliers.
20. (a) 4500   **(b)** 3600
  (c) Yes, 8900   **(d)** 2200

CHAPTER 4   Describing the Relation between Two Variables

4.1 Exercises (page 199)

1. Nonlinear   **2.** Linear, negative
3. Linear, positive   **4.** Nonlinear
5. (a) III   **(b)** IV   **(c)** II   **(d)** I
6. (a) IV   **(b)** III   **(c)** I   **(d)** II

7. (a)

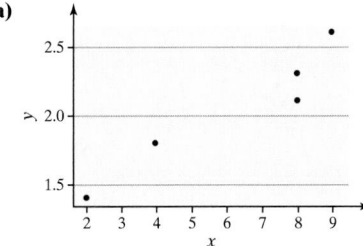

(b) r = 0.9572   **(c)** Positive association

8. (a)

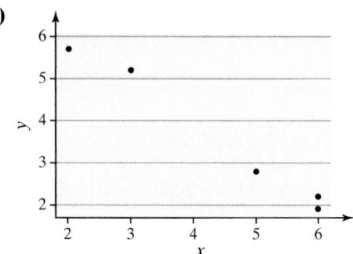

(b) $r = -0.9922$ **(c)** Negative association

9. (a)

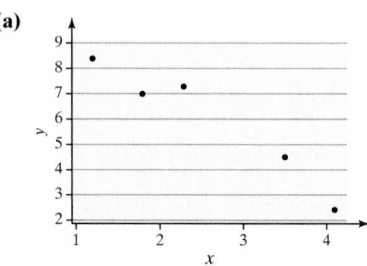

(b) $r = -0.9703$ **(c)** Negative association

10. (a)

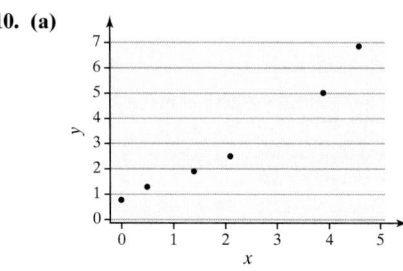

(b) $r = 0.9806$ **(c)** Positive association

11. (a) Predictor: Height; Response: Head Circumference

(b)

(c) $r = 0.911$ **(d)** Positive association

12. (a) Predictor: Carats; Response: Price

(b)

(c) $r = 0.9917$ **(d)** Positive association
(e) $r = 0.9707$; The linear correlation decreased

13. (a) Predictor: Gestation Period; Response: Life Expectancy

(b)

(c) $r = 0.7257$
(d) Positive association
(e) $r = 0.592$; Correlation decreased. The gestation period of the goat is much higher than the mean gestation period. Therefore, the deviation about the mean is large, which means that the goat contributes a lot to the correlation.

14. (a) Predictor: Tar; Response: Nicotine

(b)

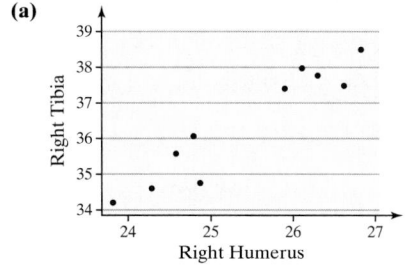

(c) $r = 0.9666$ **(d)** Positive association

15. (a)

(b) $r = 0.9513$ **(c)** Positive association
(d) None

16. (a) Predictor: Weight; Response: Miles per Gallon

(b)

(c) $r = -0.9163$ **(d)** Negative association

17. (a)

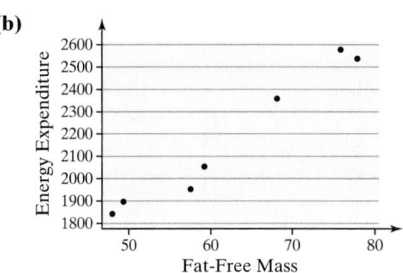

(b) $r = 0.8290$ **(c)** Positive association

18. (a) Predictor: Fat-Free Mass; Response: Energy Expenditure

(b)

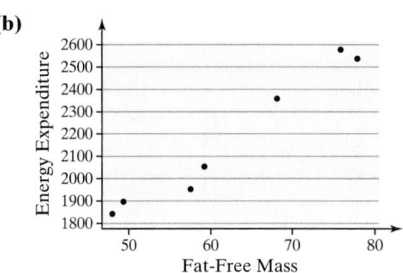

(c) $r = 0.9814$ **(d)** Positive association

19. (a)

(b) -0.164 **(c)** No relation

20. (a)

(b) No, the relation between distance and intensity is not linear.

21. (a)

(b) $r = 0.548$. It would appear that there is a positive association between MRI count and IQ.

(c)

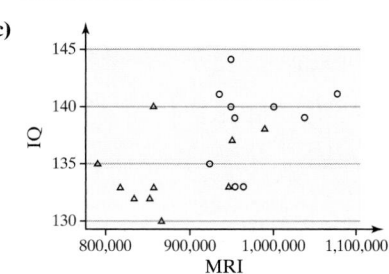

The females have lower MRI counts (presumably because females are typically shorter than males). Looking at each gender's plot, we see that the relation that appeared to exist between brain size and IQ disappears.

(d) Linear correlation, females: 0.359; Linear correlation, males: 0.236. There does not appear to be any relation between MRI count (brain size) and IQ. The moral of the story is that relations which appear to exist can occur simply because one forgets to study the data carefully.

22. (a)

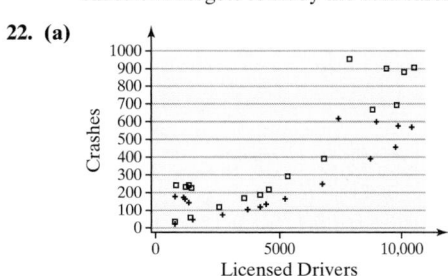

(b) Yes, the plus plotting symbols (females) do not rise as fast as the square plotting symbols (males). This implies that as the number of licensed drivers increases, the number of crashes for females does not rise as much as that for males.

(c) 0.899   **(d)** 0.863

(e) Males, because of the higher linear correlation coefficient.

23. (a)

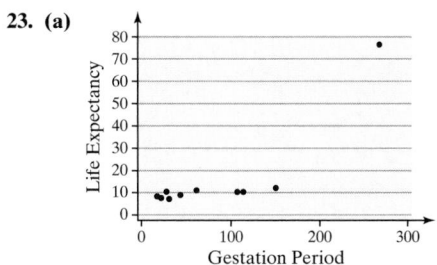

(b) 0.847

(c) The point corresponding to humans is far away from the other points in the scatter diagram. Because the deviation about the mean for humans is very large, this point has a large influence on the value of the linear correlation coefficient.

24. (a)

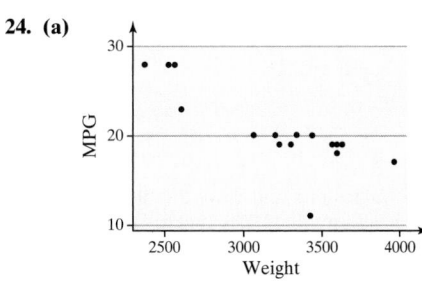

24. (b) -0.819
(c) The MPG of the Viper is well below the average MPG for cars that weigh around 3400 pounds. This increases the standard deviation for y substantially, which decreases the linear correlation coefficient.

25. (a)

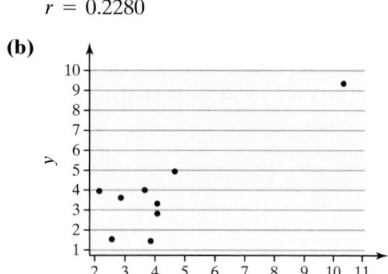

$r = 0.2280$

(b)

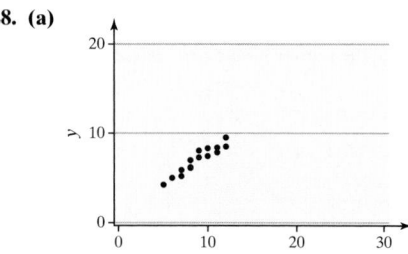

$r = 0.8598$

26. Although there is no linear relation between age and median income, the two variables are certainly related.

27. (a) Positive   **(b)** Negative   **(c)** Negative
(d) Negative   **(e)** No correlation

28. (a)

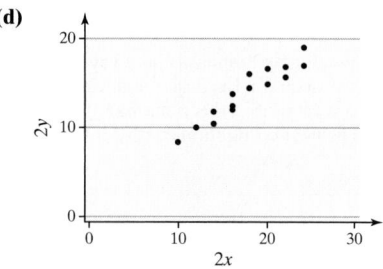

(b) 0.9518

(d)

(e) 0.9518
(f) By doubling the values of x and y, we double the standard deviations and deviations about the mean. Therefore, the z scores for each point are unchanged.

29. (a) $r = 0.82$ for all four data sets.
(b)

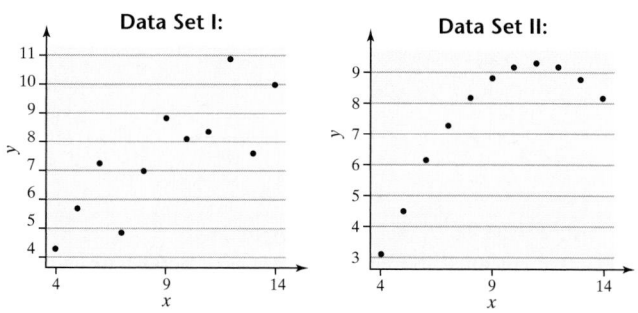

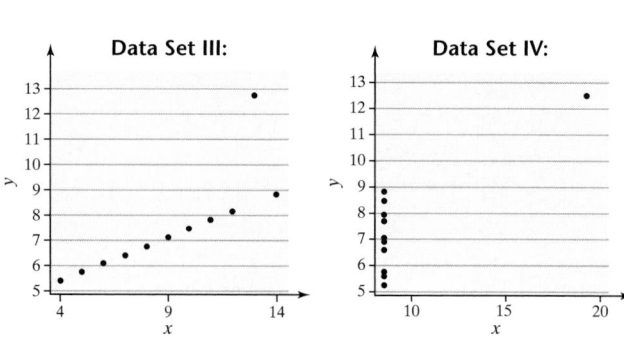

30. Weight of parents; health consciousness of parents
31. $r = 1$ **32.** $r = -1$
33. Lurking variables may have a high correlation with the response variable and predictor variable.

4.2 Exercises (page 216)

1. (a)

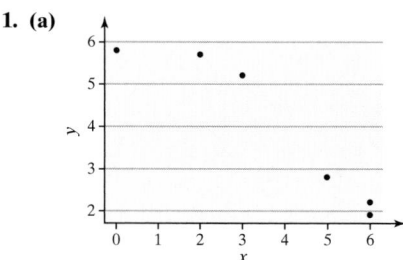

(b) $\hat{y} = -0.7136x + 6.55$

(c)

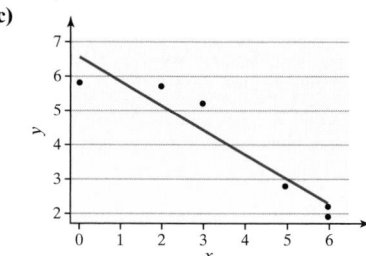

2. (a)

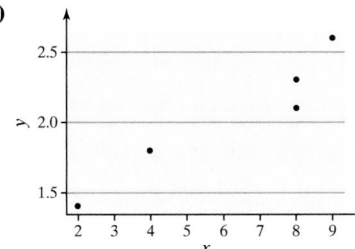

(b) $\hat{y} = 0.1457x + 1.1370$

(c)

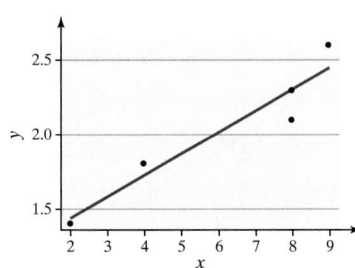

3. (a)

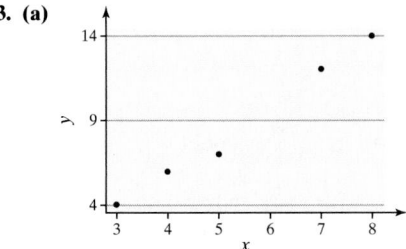

(b) Using points $(3, 4)$ and $(8, 14)$: $\hat{y} = 2x - 2$

(c)

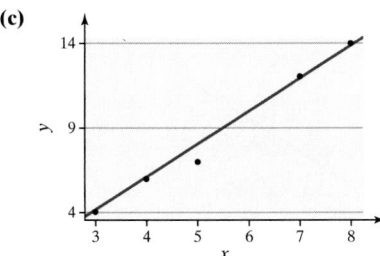

(d) $\hat{y} = 2.0233x - 2.3236$

(e)

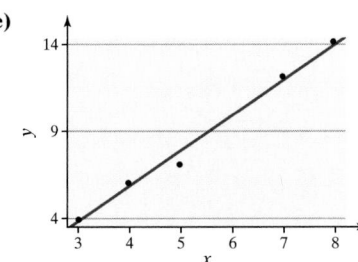

(f) 1   **(g)** 0.7907

4. (a)

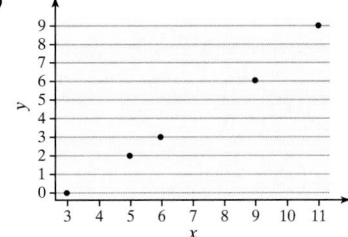

(b) Using points $(3, 0)$ and $(11, 9)$: $\hat{y} = \dfrac{9}{8}x - \dfrac{27}{8}$

(c)

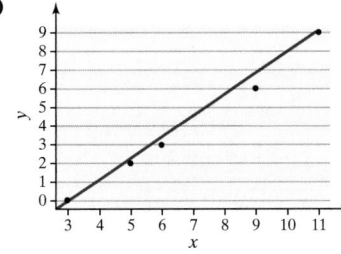

(d) $\hat{y} = 1.1x - 3.7$

(e)

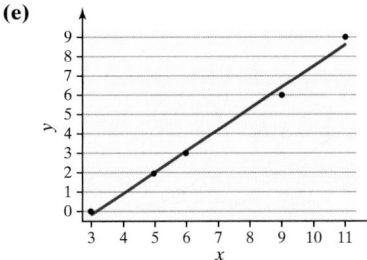

(f) 2.875   **(g)** 1.6

5. (a)

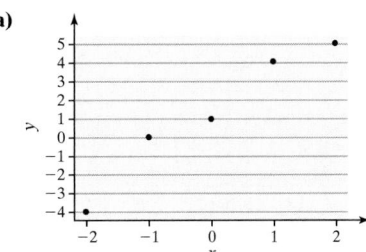

(b) Using points $(-2, -4)$ and $(1, 4)$: $\hat{y} = \dfrac{8}{3}x + \dfrac{4}{3}$

(c)

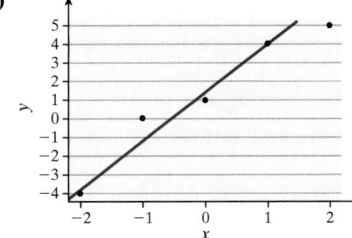

(d) $\hat{y} = 2.2x + 1.2$

5. (e)

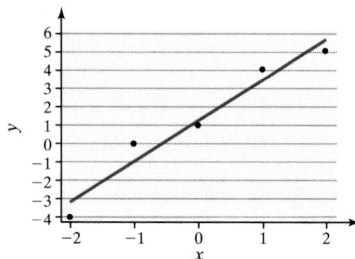

(f) 4.6667   **(g)** 2.4

6. (a)

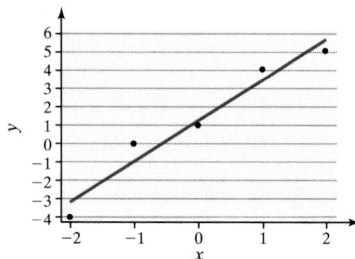

(b) Using points $(-2, 7)$ and $(2, 0)$: $\hat{y} = \dfrac{7}{4}x + \dfrac{7}{2}$

(c)

(d) $\hat{y} = -1.8x + 3.6$

(e)

(f) 0.875   **(g)** 0.8

7. (a)

(b) Using points $(30, 95)$ and $(60, 70)$: $\hat{y} = -\dfrac{5}{6}x + 120$

(c)

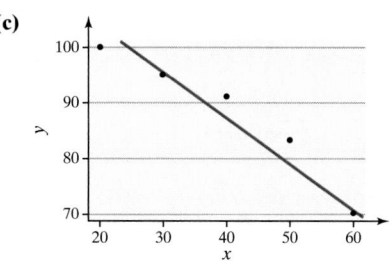

(d) $\hat{y} = -0.72x + 116.6$

(e)

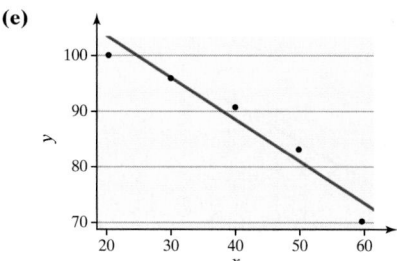

(f) 51.6667   **(g)** 32.4

8. (a)

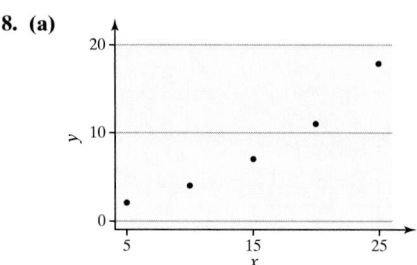

(b) Using points $(10, 4)$ and $(25, 18)$: $\hat{y} = \dfrac{14}{15}x - \dfrac{16}{3}$

(c)

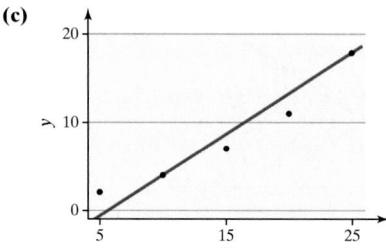

(d) $\hat{y} = 0.78x - 3.3$

(e)

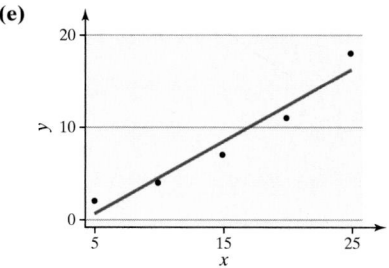

(f) 15.3333   **(g)** 9.1

9. (a) Head = 0.1827(Height) + 12.4932
  (b) If height increases by 1 inch, head circumference increases by about 0.1827 inch. It is not appropriate to interpret the intercept.
  (c) 17.1 inches   **(d)** −0.2 inch; below

  (e)

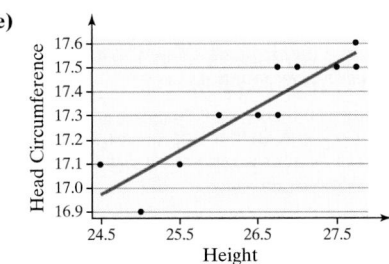

  (f) For children that are 26.75 inches tall, head circumference varies.
  (g) No, outside the scope of the model.
10. (a) Price = 12092.16(Carats) − 4969.01
  (b) If the number of carats increases by 1, the price increases by about $12,092.16. If the number of carats increases by 0.1, the price increases by about $1209.22. It does not make sense to interpret the intercept.
  (c) $6034.86   **(d)** $391.14; above

  (e)

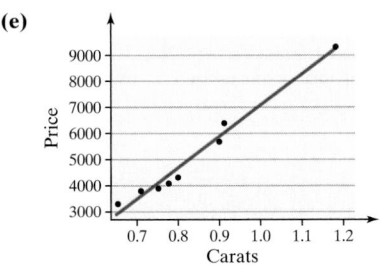

  (f) $5309.33
  (g) There are measures of the cut of a diamond other than its shape. The cut of a diamond is often categorized as ideal, excellent, or very good.
  (h) No, outside the scope of the model.
11. (a) Life Expectancy = 0.0261(Gestation) + 7.8738
  (b) If the gestation period increases by 1 day, the life expectancy increases by 0.0261 year. It is not appropriate to interpret the intercept, because a gestation period of 0 days does not make sense.
  (c) 10.4 years   **(d)** 8.3 years
  (e) 9.6 years   **(f)** −6.6 years
12. (a) Nicotine = 0.0575(Tar) + 0.2088
  (b) If tar increases by 1 mg, nicotine increases by 0.0575 mg. It is not appropriate to interpret the intercept.
  (c) 0.1 mg; above

  (d)

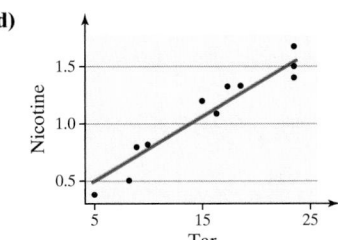

  (e) 1.4 mg

13. (a) Tibia = 1.3902(Humerus) + 1.1140
  (b) If the humerus increases by 1 mm, the length of the tibia increases by about 1.3902 mm. It does not make sense to interpret the intercept.
  (c) 0.55 mm; above

  (d)

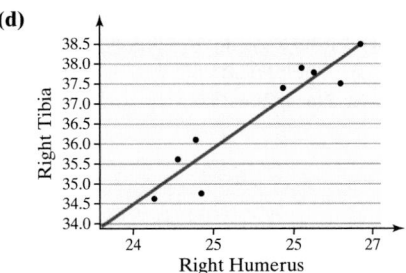

  (e) 36.30 mm
14. (a) MPG = −0.0073(Weight) + 44.2657
  (b) If the weight of a car increases by 1 pound, the gas mileage decreases by about 0.0073. It does not make sense to interpret the intercept.
  (c) 18; above

  (d)

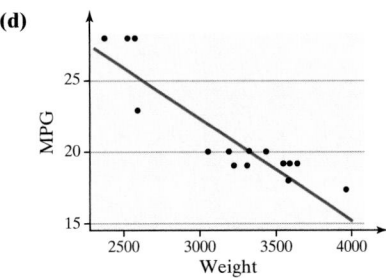

  (e) No, we did not sample from a population that included hybrid cars.
15. (a) GE = 1.6028(S&P 500) + 2.5331
  (b) If the S&P 500 increases by 1 percent, then GE stock will increase by about 1.6 percent. The intercept implies that if the rate of return of the S&P 500 is 0%, then the rate of return on GE stock should be 2.5%.
  (c) 16.8%
16. (a) Energy = 25.0116(Mass) + 607.7034
  (b) If mass increases by 1 kg, then energy expenditure will increase by about 25.0116 Kcal. It does not make sense to interpret the intercept.
  (c) 1918 Kcal.
17. (a) IQ = 0.00002863(MRI) + 109.894
  (b) The slope is close to zero.
18. (a) Males: Crash = 0.0802(Drivers) + 8.14;
      Females: Crash = 0.0505(Drivers) + 15.16
  (b) Males: If the number of drivers increases by 1, then the number of crashes increases by about 0.08. Females: If the number of drivers increases by 1, then the number of crashes increases by 0.05.
  (c) Males: 706 thousand; Females: 455 thousand

4.3 Exercises (page 230)

1. Constant error variance   **2.** None   **3.** Outlier
4. Patterned residuals
5. (a) III   **(b)** II   **(c)** IV   **(d)** I

6. (a) $R^2 = 10.24\%$; 10.24% of the variance in the predictor variable is explained by the least-squares regression line.
(b) $R^2 = 1.69\%$; 1.69% of the variance in the predictor variable is explained by the least-squares regression line.
(c) $R^2 = 16\%$; 16% of the variance in the predictor variable is explained by the least-squares regression line.
(d) $R^2 = 86.49\%$; 86.49% of the variance in the predictor variable is explained by the least-squares regression line.

7. Influential   **8.** Not influential
9. Influential   **10.** Not influential

11. (a)

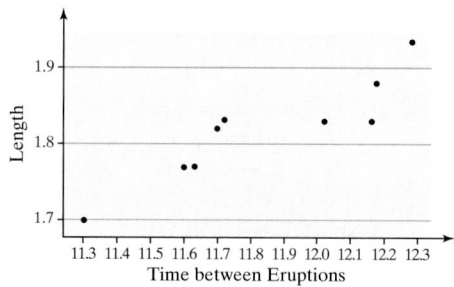

$\hat{y} = 0.1854x - 0.3779$

(b)

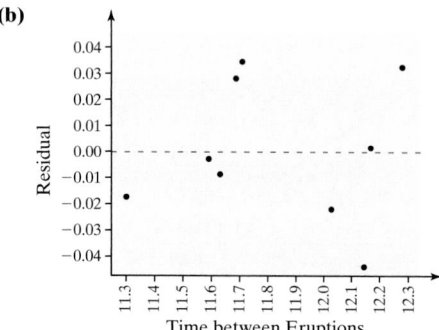

Length of eruption and time between eruptions appear to be linearly related, because the residual plot does not show any violations of the model.
(c) 83.0% of the variation in length of eruption is explained by the least-squares regression equation.

12. (a)

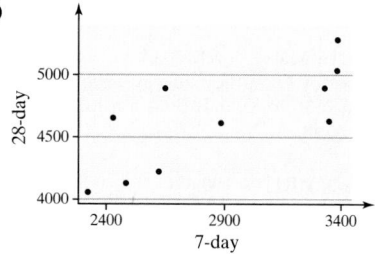

$\hat{y} = 0.6764x + 2675.6$

(b)

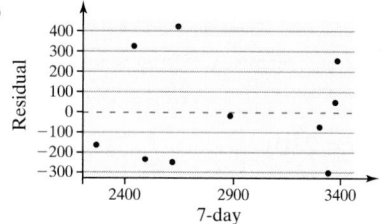

Yes, the residuals appear to be randomly distributed, with no obvious departures from the requirements of the model.

(c) 57.5% of the variation in 28-day strength is explained by the least-squares regression equation.

13. (a) No, the data do not appear to follow a linear pattern.
(b) 6.8% of the variation in sugar content is explained by the least-squares regression equation. Yes.
(c) Yes, it is influential, because the slope of the least-squares regression equation changed substantially.
(d) 42.1% of the variability in sugar content is explained by the least-squares regression equation.

14. (a) Yes, the data follow a linear pattern.
(b) 99.0% of the variation in per capita consumption is explained by the least-squares regression equation.
(c) There is a possible outlier.

15. (a) $R^2 = 83.0\%$

(b)

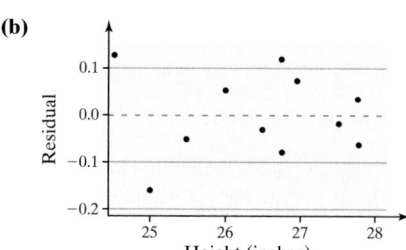

(c) 83.0% of the variation in head circumference is explained by the least-squares regression equation. The linear model appears to be appropriate, based on the residual plot.

16. (a) $R^2 = 98.3\%$

(b)

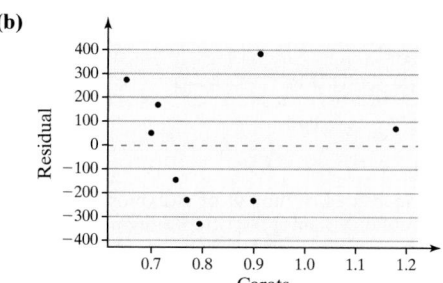

(c) 98.3% of the variation in price is explained by the least-squares regression equation. The 1.18-carat diamond may be influential, although the slope doesn't change that much if we exclude it from the analysis. It may be a good idea to obtain more diamonds that weigh from 1.1 to 1.3 carats.

17. (a) $R^2 = 52.7\%$

(b)

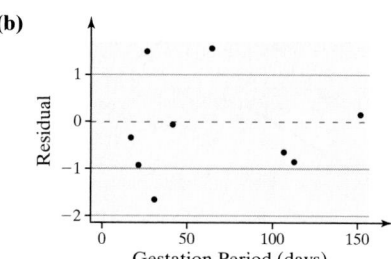

(c) 52.7% of the variation in life expectancy is explained by the least-squares regression line. The least-squares regression model appears to be appropriate.

18. (a) $R^2 = 93.4\%$

(b)

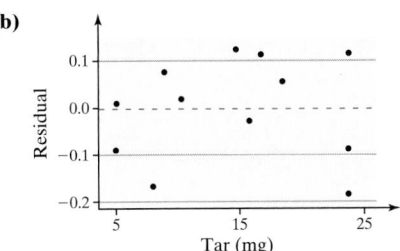

(c) 93.4% of the variation in nicotine content is explained by the least-squares regression line. The least-squares regression model appears to be appropriate.

19. (a) $R^2 = 90.5\%$

(b)

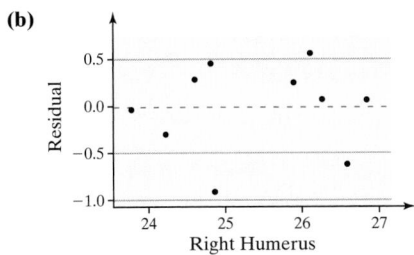

(c) 90.5% of the variation in the length of the right humerus is explained by the least-squares regression line. The least-squares regression model appears to be appropriate.

20. (a) $R^2 = 84.0\%$

(b)

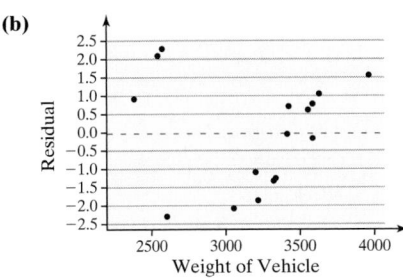

(c) 84.0% of the variation in gas mileage is explained by the least-squares regression line. The least-squares regression model appears to be appropriate.

21. (a) $R^2 = 68.7\%$

(b)

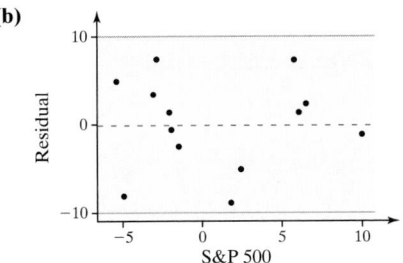

(c) 68.7% of the variation in the rate of return in GE stock is explained by the least-squares regression line. The least-squares regression model appears to be appropriate.

22. (a) $R^2 = 96.3\%$

(b)

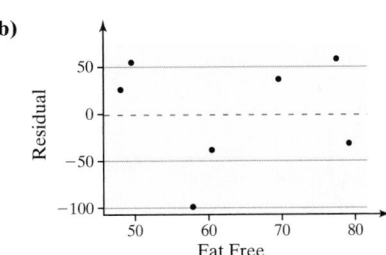

(c) 96.3% of the variation in energy expenditure is explained by the least-squares regression line. The least-squares regression model appears to be appropriate.

23. (a)

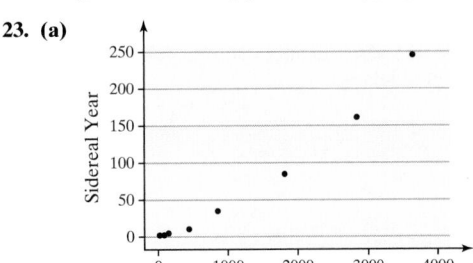

(b) $\hat{y} = 0.0657x - 12.4967$

(c)

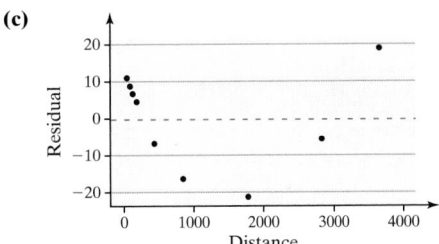

(d) No, the residuals follow a U-shaped pattern.

24. (a)

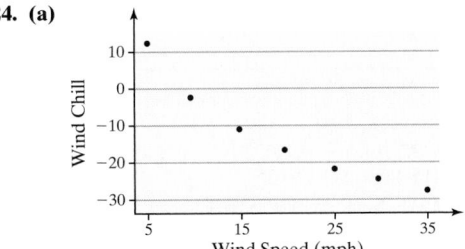

(b) Chill $= -1.2286(\text{Speed}) + 11.2857$

(c)

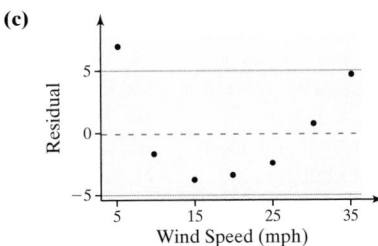

(d) No, the residuals follow a U-shaped pattern.

25. (a) $R^2 = 71.7\%$ **(b)** Yes; Yes **(c)** Yes; No
26. (a) $R^2 = 67.0\%$ **(b)** No; Yes

27. (a)

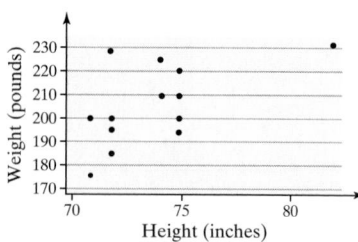

(b) Weight $= 3.28$(Height) $- 36.77$; $r = 0.572$
(c) Weight $= 3.948$(Height) $- 85.3$; $r = 0.429$; the slope of the least-squares regression line increases substantially, while the linear correlation decreases.
(d) Yes, because the slope changes substantially with the removal of Randy Johnson.

28. (a)

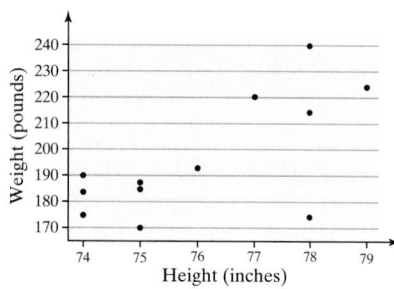

(b) Weight $= 8.113$(Height) $- 420.2$; $r = 0.685$
(c) Weight $= 10.536$(Height) $- 600.6$; $r = 0.872$
(d) Yes, and she is an outlier.

29. (a), (d)

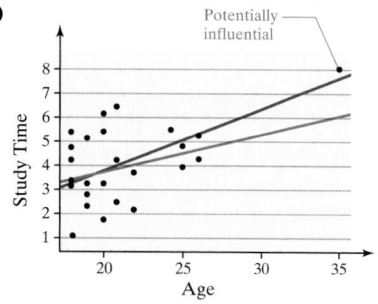

(b) Hours $= 0.232$(Age) $- 0.920$
(c) Hours $= 0.1549$(Age) $+ 0.635$
(e) The 35-year-old student is influential

30. Yes **31.** Yes

4.4 Exercises (page 244)

1. $2 = \log_4 16$ **2.** $5 = \log_2 32$ **3.** $5 = \log_x 18$
4. $3 = \log_c 21$ **5.** $x = \log_7 15$ **6.** $x = \log_{12} 43$
7. $3 = \log_5 y$ **8.** $1.5 = \log_6 y$ **9.** $3^4 = 81$
10. $4^3 = 64$ **11.** $a^3 = 14$ **12.** $b^4 = 19$
13. $4^3 = c$ **14.** $5^4 = b$ **15.** $2^k = 5$
16. $6^w = 24$ **17.** $\log_3 u + \log_3 v$ **18.** $\log_2 a + \log_2 b$
19. $4\log_5 x$ **20.** $3\log_7 y$ **21.** $\log_a u + 2\log_a v$
22. $3\log_a x + \log_a y$ **23.** $4\log x + 3\log y$ **24.** $6\log x + 2\log y$
25. 1.531 **26.** 1.255 **27.** 1.121
28. 1.533 **29.** 39.811 **30.** 199.526
31. 2.291 **32.** 5.495

33. (a)

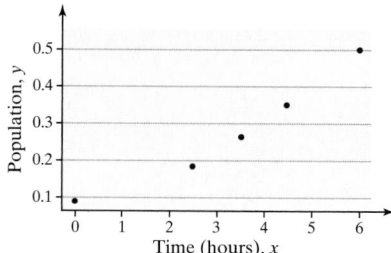

(b)

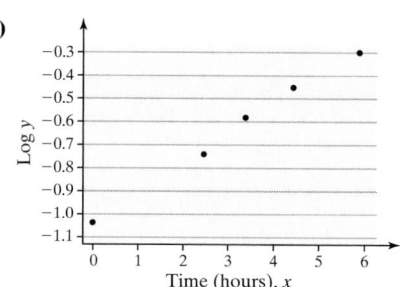

(c) $Y = 0.1226x - 1.0443$ **(d)** $y = 0.0903(1.3384)^x$ **(e)** 0.69

34. (a)

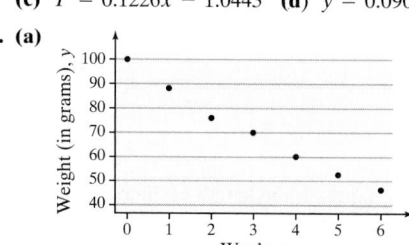

(b)

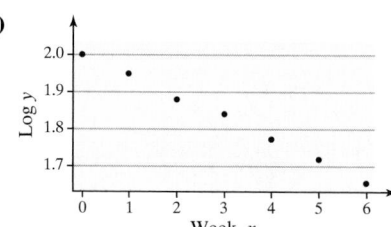

(c) $Y = -0.0571x + 2.0014$ **(d)** $y = 100.32(0.877)^x$
(e) 27.0 grams

35. (a)

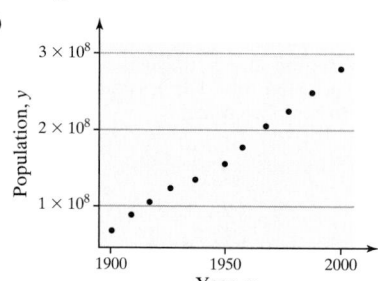

(b)

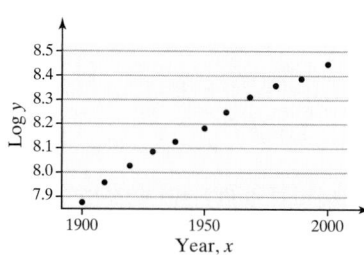

35. (c) $Y = 0.0056x - 2.6593$ **(d)** $y = 0.0022(1.013)^x$
(e) 339,805,699

36. (a)

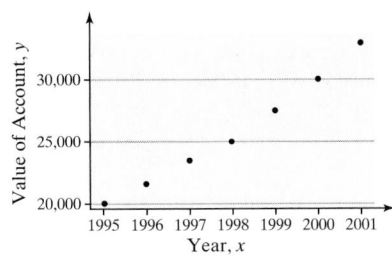

(b)

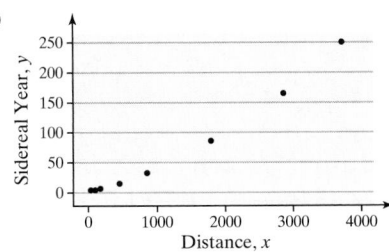

(c) $Y = 0.0357x + 4.2971$ **(d)** $y = 19820(1.086)^x$
(e) \$235,504   **(f)** 8.6%

37. (a)

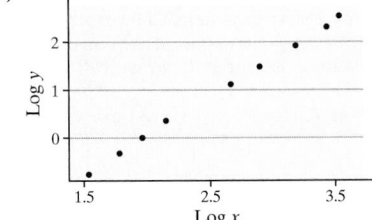

(b)

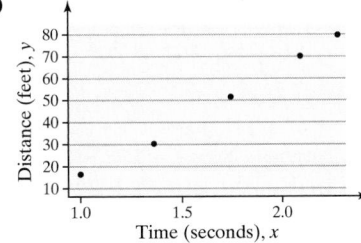

(c) $Y = 1.4994X - 2.9506$ **(d)** $y = 0.0011x^{1.4994}$

38. (a)

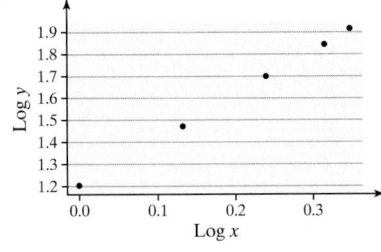

(b)

(c) $Y = 2.0018X + 1.2034$ **(d)** $y = 15.973x^{2.0018}$
(e) 54.7 feet   **(f)** 31.95 ft/sec^2

39. (a)

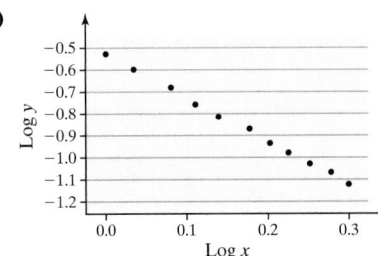

(b)

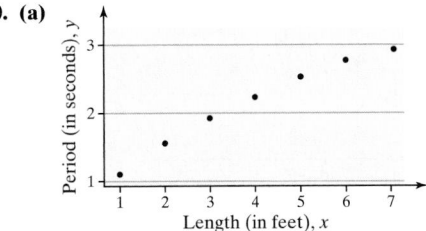

(c) $Y = -2.012X - 0.5236$ **(d)** $y = 0.2995x^{-2.012}$
(e) 0.05605

40. (a)

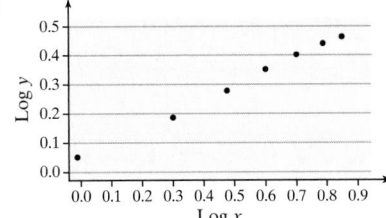

(b)

(c) $Y = 0.5098X + 0.0394$
(d) $y = 1.095x^{0.5098}$
(e) 1.67 seconds

Chapter Review Exercises (page 249)

1. (a)

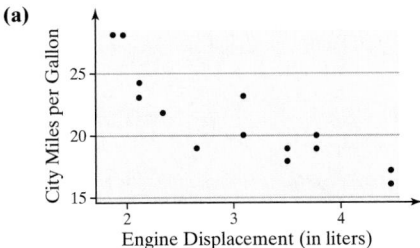

(b) $r = -0.871$
(c) Negative association

2. (a)

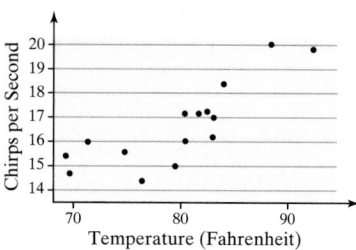

(b) $r = 0.835$ **(c)** Positive association

3. (a)

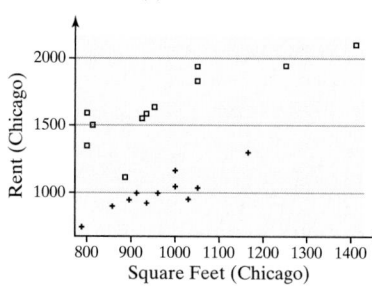

(b) Chicago: $r = 0.835$; Suburbs: $r = 0.829$
(c) Positive association   **(d)** Absolutely!

4. (a)

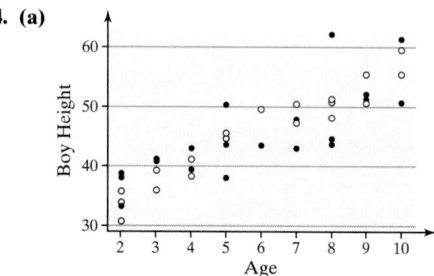

(b) Boys: $r = 0.949$; Girls: $r = 0.802$
(c) Positive association   **(d)** Not really.

5. (a) MPG $= -3.5339(\text{Engine}) + 32.1201$

(b)

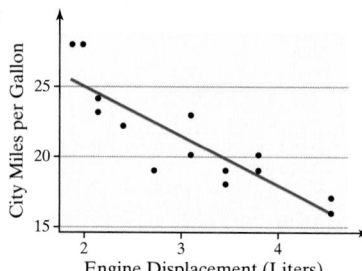

(c) If engine size increases by 1 liter, then gas mileage decreases by about 3.5 miles per gallon. It does not make sense to interpret the intercept.
(d) 18.7 mpg   **(e)** 1.3   **(f)** Above

6. (a) Chirps $= 0.2119(\text{Temp}) - 0.309$

(b)

(c) If the temperature increases $1°$ F, then the number of chirps per second will increase by about 0.2119. Since there are no observations for $0°$ F, it does not make sense to interpret the intercept.
(d) 17.3 chirps per second   **(e)** -1.1 **(f)** Below

7. (a) Rent $= 1.1702(\text{Area}) - 132.6$

(b)

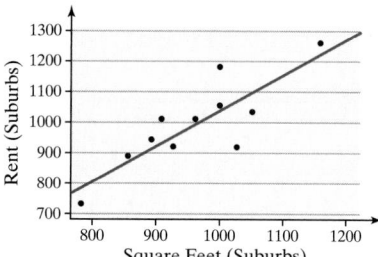

(c) If the area increases by 1 square foot then rent will increase by about \$1.17. It does not make sense to interpret the intercept.
(d) \$960   **(e)** $-\$40$ **(f)** Below

8. (a) Height $= 2.6351(\text{Age}) + 29.705$

(b)

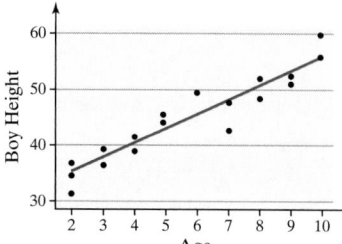

(c) If age increases by 1 year, then height increases by about 2.6 inches. Although an age of 0 makes sense (birth), we do not have any observations near $x = 0$, so we will not interpret the intercept.
(d) 45.5 inches   **(e)** 4.3 inches   **(f)** Above

9. (a)

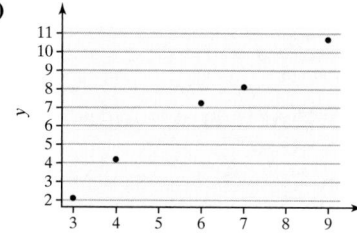

(b) Using points $(3, 2.1)$ and $(7, 8.1)$: $\hat{y} = 1.5x - 2.4$

(c)

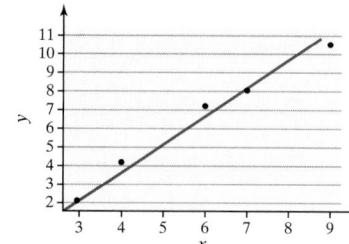

(d) $\hat{y} = 1.3877x - 1.6088$

9. (e)

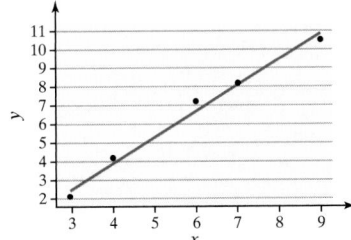

(f) 0.97
(g) 0.585

10. (a)

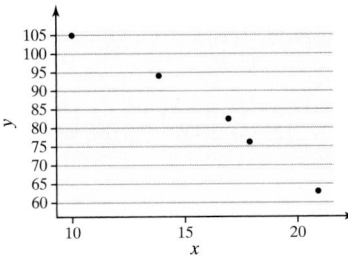

(b) Using points: $(10, 105)$ and $(18, 76)$: $\hat{y} = -\dfrac{29}{8}x + \dfrac{565}{4}$

(c)

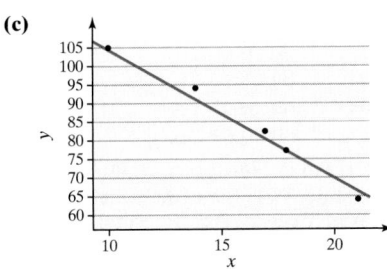

(d) $\hat{y} = -3.8429x + 145.4857$

(e)

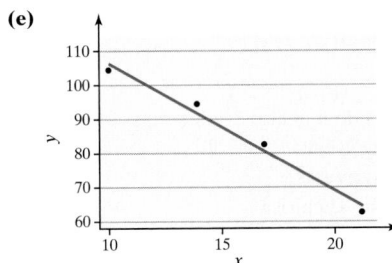

(f) 22.406
(g) 16.271

11. Linear model is appropriate.
12. Linear model is not appropriate; residuals are patterned.
13. Linear model is not appropriate; nonconstant error variance.
14. Linear model is not appropriate; residuals are patterned.
15. (a) $R^2 = 75.9\%$; 75.9% of the variance in miles per gallon is explained by the least-squares regression equation.

(b)

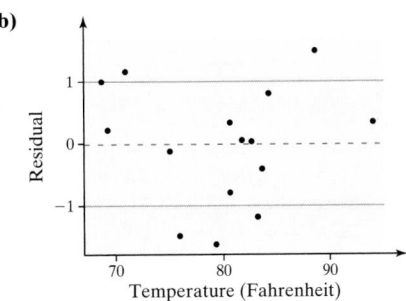

(c) There may be a violation of the requirement of constant error variance, since the residuals appear to be more spread out for smaller engine sizes.
(d) No
(e) With Viper: MPG $= 29.2 - 2.56$(Engine); The Viper is influential
16. (a) $R^2 = 69.7\%$; 69.7% of the variation in chirps per second is explained by the least-squares regression equation.

(b)

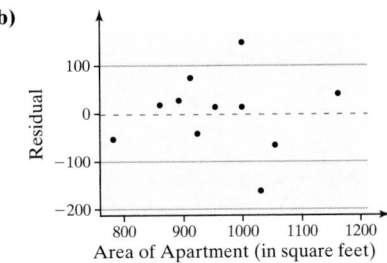

(c) Yes
(d) No
17. (a) $R^2 = 68.7\%$; 68.7% of the variation in rent is explained by the least-squares regression equation.

(b)

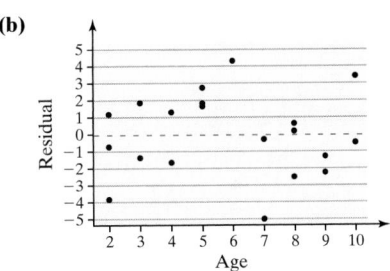

(c) Yes   **(d)** No
18. (a) $R^2 = 90.1\%$; 90.1% of the variation in height is explained by age.

(b)

(c) Yes   **(d)** No

19. (a) Rent = 1.2787Footage + 384.0
(b) Yes, the 1415-square-foot apartment is influential. The 891-square-foot apartment is an outlier.

20. (a)

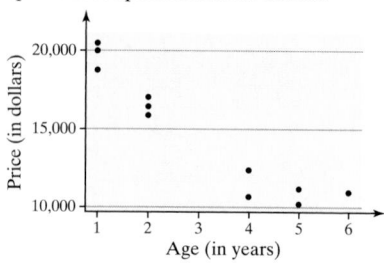

(b) Price = −2054.6(Age) + 20,976.2

(c)

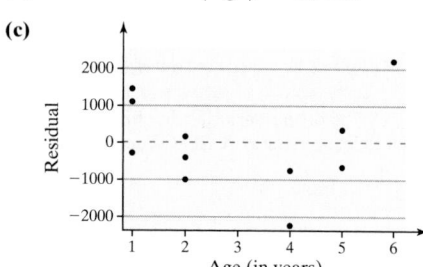

(d) No, the residuals follow a U-shaped pattern.
21. $3 = \log_5 125$ **22.** $5 = \log_4 1024$ **23.** $6 = \log_a 22$
24. $2 = \log_b 7$ **25.** $4^8 = x$ **26.** $6^2 = b$
27. $a^5 = 11$ **28.** $b^4 = 9$ **29.** $2\log u + \log v$
30. $4\log a + \log b$ **31.** $6\log x$ **32.** $8\log y$

33. (a)

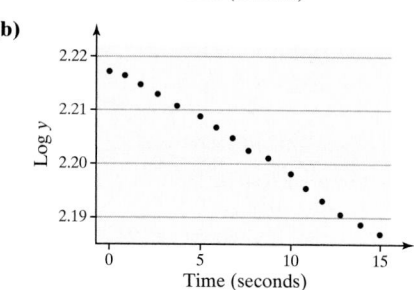

(b)

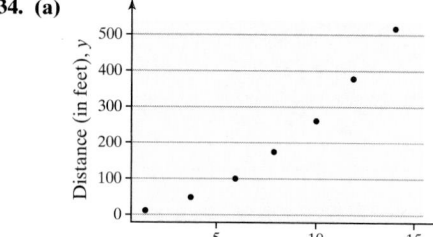

(c) $Y = -0.0022x + 2.2194$ **(d)** $y = 165.73(0.9951)^x$
(e) 152.96° F

34. (a)

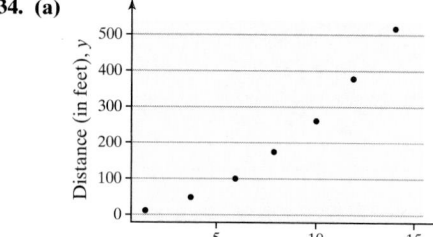

(b)

(c) $Y = 2X + 0.4263$ **(d)** $y = 2.669x^2$ **(e)** 5.34 ft/sec²

CHAPTER 5   Probability

5.1 Exercises (page 270)

1. 0, 0.01, 0.35, 1   **2.** 1/2, 3/4, 2/3, 0   **3.** 3/10   **4.** 2/5
5. 1/2   **6.** 1/2   **7.** 1/8   **8.** 1/8
9. 1/4   **10.** 3/8
11. (a) 0.4   **(b)** 0.25   **12. (a)** 0.4375   **(b)** 0.25
13. (a) {0, 00, 1, 2, ..., 36}   **(b)** 1/38   **(c)** 9/19
14. (a) 52 cards   **(b)** 1/52   **(c)** 1/4   **(d)** 1/13
15. (a) 12/365   **(b)** 7/365   **(c)** 31/365
    (d) 1/365   **(e)** No
    (f) Not unless we know that each birth date is equally likely.
16. (a) {SS, Ss, sS, ss}   **(b)** 1/4   **(c)** 1/2
17. (a) 0.026   **(b)** A little unusual, since the probability is low.
    (c) 0.116
18. (a) 0.026   **(b)** A little unusual, since the probability is low.
    (c) 0.076
19. (a) 0.277   **(b)** 0.007   **(c)** Yes
20. (a) 0.198   **(b)** 0.008   **(c)** Yes
21. (a) 0.007   **(b)** 0.085   **(c)** 0.002; Yes
22. (a) 0.374   **(b)** 0.122   **(c)** 0.008; Yes
23. 0.114; No   **24.** 0.011; Yes   **25.** 0.243   **26.** 0.265
27. (a) {State, Treasury; State, War; State, AG; State, PG; State, Navy; Treasury, War; Treasury, AG; Treasury, PG; Treasury, Navy; War, AG; War, PG; War, Navy; AG, PG; AG, Navy; PG, Navy}
    (b) 1/15   **(c)** 1/3
28. (a) {Wash, Adams; Adams, Wash; Wash, Clinton; Clinton, Wash; Wash, Jeff; Jeff, Wash; Wash, Burr; Burr, Wash; Adams, Clinton; Clinton, Adams; Adams, Jeff; Jeff, Adams; Adams, Burr; Burr, Adams; Clinton, Jeff; Jeff, Clinton; Clinton, Burr; Burr, Clinton; Jeff, Burr; Burr, Jeff}
    (b) 1/20   **(c)** 1/5
29. (a) 26/62 = 0.419   **(b)** 0
    (c) No, he just didn't do it in his 62 home runs.
32. No, not equally likely events
33. No, not equally likely events
34. (a) Classical   **(b)** Empirical
    (c) Subjective   **(d)** Empirical
35. Probably, since we observe "one" with a very high frequency.
37. 0.5   **38.** 0.17

5.2 Exercises (page 281)

1. {5, 6, 7}; No   **2.** {9}; No
3. {5, 6, 7, 8, 9, 10, 11, 12}; 8/12 = 2/3
4. {2, 3, 4, 5, 6, 7}; 1/2   **5.** { }; Yes   **6.** { }; Yes
7. {1, 8, 9, 10, 11, 12}; 1/2   **8.** {1, 2, 3, 4, 10, 11, 12}; 7/12
9. 0.55   **10.** 0.1   **11.** 0.7   **12.** 0   **13.** 0.75
14. 0.55   **15.** 0.3   **16.** 0.5   **17.** 17/20   **18.** 11/20
19. 11/20   **20.** 17/20   **21.** 0.75   **22.** 0.5

23. (a) 1/2   (b) 3/4   (c) 4/13
24. (a) 2/13   (b) 3/13   (c) 4/13
25. (a) 364/365   (b) 353/365   (c) 358/365   (d) 334/365
26. (a) 10/19   (b) 18/19   **27.** (a) 0.094   (b) 0.473
28. (a) 0.081   (b) 0.316
29. (a) 0.43   (b) 0.937   (c) 0.847
30. (a) 0.207   (b) 0.215   (c) 0.992
31. (a) 0.007   (b) 0.993   (c) 0.998   (d) 0.998
32. (a) 0.606   (b) 0.394   (c) 0.878   (d) 0.992
33. 0.886   **34.** 0.989
35. (a) 0.536   (b) 0.503   (c) 0.298   (d) 0.741
36. (a) 0.537   (b) 0.104   (c) 0.054   (d) 0.586
37. (a) 0.738   (b) 0.144   (c) 0.116   (d) 0.766
38. (a) 0.146   (b) 0.332   (c) 0.044   (d) 0.435

5.3 Exercises (page 293)

1. (a) Dependent   (b) Independent   (c) Dependent
2. (a) Dependent   (b) Dependent   (c) Independent
3. No   **4.** Yes   **5.** (a) 1/4   (b) 1/4   (c) Yes
6. (a) 1/13   (b) 1/13   (c) Yes   **7.** 0.4   **8.** 2/7
9. (a) 1/221   (b) 1/169   **10.** (a) 1/17   (b) 1/16
11. 1/20   **12.** 1/20
13. (a) 5/39; No   (b) 14/39
     (c) 20/39   (d) $(5/13)^2$; $(8/13)^2$; 0.473
14. (a) 1/22   (b) 6/11; No   (c) 9/22
15. (a) 0.152   (b) 0.138   (c) 0.138   (d) 0.276
16. (a) 0.319   (b) 0.134   (c) 0.134   (d) 0.269
17. 0.051   **18.** 0.031
19. (a) 0.994   (b) 0.986   (c) 0.014; Not that unusual
20. (a) 0.997   (b) 0.993   (c) 0.007; Yes
21. (a) 0.9801   (b) 0.9415   (c) 0.0585; No
22. (a) 0.04   (b) 3   **23.** (a) 0.883   (b) 0.117
24. 0.507   **25.** (a) 0.000495   (b) 0.002
26. 0.00000154   **27.** (a) 0.028   (b) Not that unusual
28. (a) 0.000015
     (b) Eventually, but it is expected to take a while
29. (a) 0.0000245   (b) 0.000025
30. (a) 0.0000000237   (b) 0.0000000237
31. (a) 13   (b) 41; 8   (c) 8/41   (d) 0.034
32. (a) 1/5   (b) 0

5.4 Exercises (page 299)

1. 0.75   **2.** 0.525   **3.** 0.568   **4.** 0.411   **5.** Yes   **6.** No
7. (a) 0.592   (b) 0.556
8. (a) 0.016   (b) 0.509
9. (a) 0.157   (b) 0.801   (c) Male; higher probability
10. (a) 0.299   (b) 0.132
11. 0.568   **12.** 0.102   **13.** 0.637   **14.** 0.230   **15.** No
16. No   **17.** No   **18.** No   **19.** 0.228

5.5 Exercises (page 311)

1. 120   **2.** 5040   **3.** 3,628,800   **4.** 479,001,600
5. 1   **6.** 1   **7.** 30   **8.** 42
9. 24   **10.** 5040   **11.** 1   **12.** 1
13. 336   **14.** 3024   **15.** 56   **16.** 36
17. 45   **18.** 220   **19.** 52   **20.** 1
21. 17,296   **22.** 27,405

23. {ab, ba, ac, ca, ad, da, ae, ea, bc, cb, bd, db, be, eb, cd, dc, ce, ec, de, ed}; 20
24. {ab, ba, ac, ca, ad, da, bc, cb, bd, db, cd, dc}; 12
25. {ab, ac, ad, ae, bc, bd, be, cd, ce, de}; 10
26. {ab, ac, ad, bc, bd, cd}; 6
27. 24   **28.** 15   **29.** 12!   **30.** 15!   **31.** 8!
32. 10!   **33.** 18,278   **34.** 12,338,352
35. (a) 10,000   (b) 0.0001   **36.** (a) 10^9 (b) $1/10^9$
37. 26^8 **38.** $26(36^7)$ **39.** (a) 50^3 (b) $1/50^3$
40. 2,600,000   **41.** 59,280   **42.** 90   **43.** 116,280
44. $_{50}P_4$ **45.** 303,600   **46.** 293,930   **47.** 2,118,760
48. $_{100}C_7$ **49.** 15   **50.** 56   **51.** 50,400
52. 90,720   **53.** 6930   **54.** 2520   **55.** 1/142,506
56. $\dfrac{1}{36 \cdot (_{50}C_5)}$ **57.** (a) 56/8568   (b) 252/8568   (c) 3360/8568
58. (a) 0.0127   (b) 0.0028   (c) 0.2442   **59.** 0.1283
60. 0.3517   **61.** (a) 0.3916   (b) 0.1119   (c) 0.007
62. (a) 0.1227   (b) 0.4909   (c) 0.0045
63. (a) 2,598,960   (b) 52   (c) 1056   (d) 0.0211
64. 0.4226   **65.** 0.4912   **66.** 0.7291

Chapter Review Exercises (page 316)

1. (a) 0, 0.75, 0.41   (b) 2/5, 1/3, 6/7
2. 1/5   **3.** 2/5   **4.** 3/5   **5.** 4/5   **6.** 0.89
7. 0.48   **8.** 0.09   **9.** No   **10.** 0.2655   **11.** 0.5
12. (a) 5040   (b) 1   (c) 126
     (d) 120   (e) 72   (f) 11,880
13. (a) 1/19   (b) 10/19   (c) 19/38   (d) 0; impossible
14. (a) 2/9   (b) 1/9
15. (a) 129/192   (b) 21/64   (c) 0.45   (d) 0.893
16. 0.11; 0.89
17. (a) 0.0598   (b) 0.001; Yes   (c) 0.0618   (d) 0.999
18. (a) 0.1518   (b) 0.1638   (c) 0.0320   (d) 0.2836
     (e) 0.2108   (f) 0.0556   (g) 0.9444   (h) No
19. (a) 0.0727   (b) 0.3793   (c) 0.0302   (d) 0.4217
     (e) 0; Yes   (f) 0.4158   (g) No
20. (a) 0.5371   (b) 0.1095   (c) 0.0513   (d) 0.5953
21. (a) 0.950625   (b) 0.8811   (c) 0.1189
22. (a) 0.1849   (b) 0.0027   (c) 0.9973
23. 0.8   **24.** 0.00018   **25.** 6,760,000   **26.** 5040
27. 6!   **28.** 12,600   **29.** $_{55}C_8$
30. $_{29}C_5$ **31.** 1/324,632   **32.** 1/575,757
33. (a) 0.0455   (b) 0.3182   (c) 0.1591

CHAPTER 6   Discrete Probability Distributions

6.1 Exercises (page 335)

1. (a) Discrete; $x = 0, 1, 2, \ldots, 20$ (b) Continuous, $t > 0$
     (c) Discrete, $x = 0, 1, 2, \ldots$ (d) Continuous, $s \geq 0$
2. (a) Continuous, $t > 0$ (b) Continuous, $w > 0$
     (c) Discrete, $x = 0, 1, 2, \ldots$
     (d) Discrete, $x = 0, 1, 2, \ldots, 20$
3. Yes   **4.** Yes
5. No, $P(X = 50) < 0$
6. No, $P(X = 40) < 0$
7. No, $\sum P(X = x) \neq 1$
8. No, $\sum P(X = x) \neq 1$
9. $P(X = 4) = 0.3$
10. $P(X = 2) = 0.15$

11. (a) All probabilities are between 0 and 1, inclusive, and the sum of the probabilities is 1.

(b)

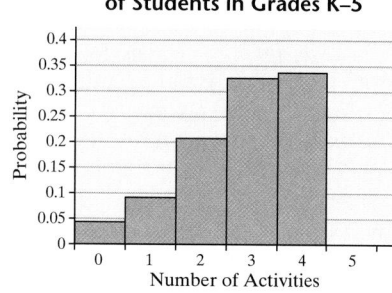

Involvement of Mothers of Students in Grades K–5

(c) $\mu_X = 2.8$ **(d)** $\sigma_X^2 = 1.2$ **(e)** $\sigma_X = 1.1$
(f) 0.325 **(g)** 0.663

12. (a) All probabilities are between 0 and 1, inclusive, and the sum of the probabilities is 1.

(b)

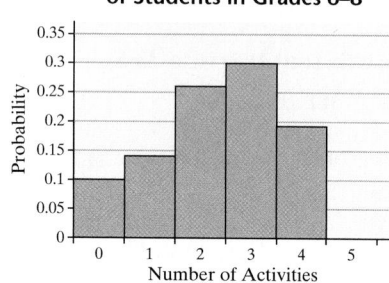

Involvement of Mothers of Students in Grades 6–8

(c) $\mu_X = 2.3$ **(d)** $\sigma_X^2 = 1.5$ **(e)** $\sigma_X = 1.2$
(f) 0.302 **(g)** 0.493

13. (a) All probabilities are between 0 and 1, inclusive, and the sum of the probabilities is 1.

(b)

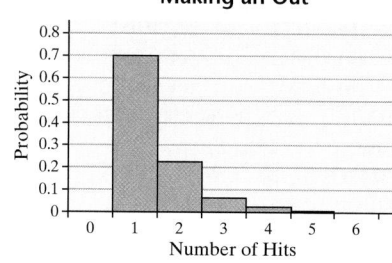

Number of Hits Until Making an Out

(c) $\mu_X = 1.4$ **(d)** $\sigma_X^2 = 0.6$ **(e)** $\sigma_X = 0.8$
(f) 0.0189 **(g)** 0.027

14. (a) All probabilities are between 0 and 1, inclusive, and the sum of the probabilities is 1.

(b)

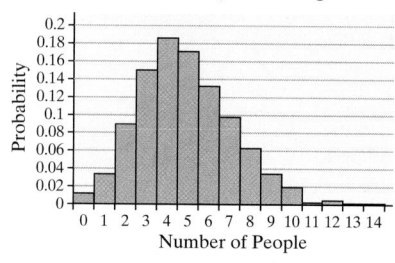

Number of People Waiting in Line

(c) $\mu_X = 4.9$ **(d)** $\sigma_X^2 = 5.0$ **(e)** $\sigma_X = 2.2$
(f) 0.063 **(g)** 0.029; A little unusual

15. (a)

x (age)	P(X = x)
5	0.1930
6	0.1956
7	0.2005
8	0.2032
9	0.2077

(b)

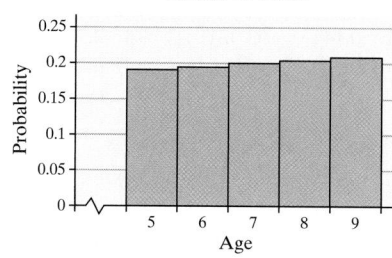

Distribution of 5–9-Year-Old Males in 2000

(c) $\mu_X = 7.0$ **(d)** $\sigma_X = 1.4$

16. (a)

x (age)	P(X = x)
5	0.1929
6	0.1956
7	0.2003
8	0.2036
9	0.2076

(b)

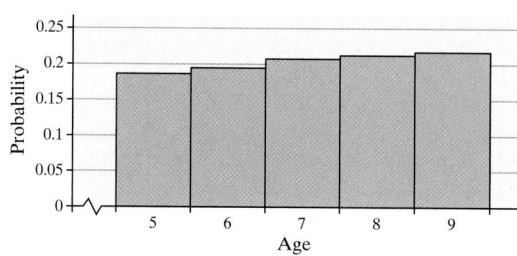

Distribution of 5–9-Year-Old Females in 2000

(c) $\mu_X = 7.0$ **(d)** $\sigma_X = 1.4$

17. (a)

x (grade level)	P(X = x)	x (grade level)	P(X = x)
1	0.1321	5	0.1216
2	0.1297	6	0.1228
3	0.1265	7	0.1238
4	0.1233	8	0.1201

(b)

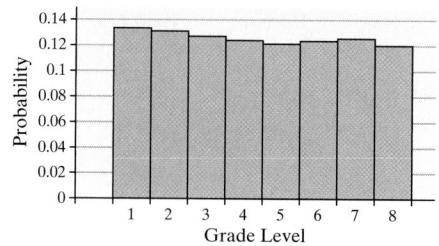

Distribution of Grade Levels in 1997

(c) $\mu_X = 4.4$ **(d)** $\sigma_X = 2.3$

18. (a)

x (grade level)	P(X = x)
9	0.2974
10	0.2630
11	0.2314
12	0.2082

(b)

**Distribution of Grade
Levels in 1997**

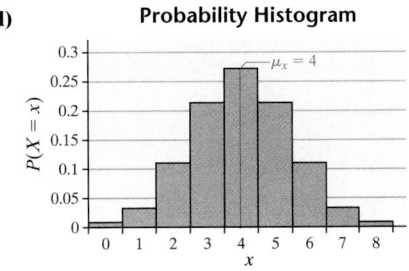

(c) $\mu_X = 10.4$ **(d)** $\sigma_X = 1.1$

19. (a) 0.124   **(b)** 0.148   **(c)** 0.112
20. (a) 0.204   **(b)** 0.306   **(c)** 0.06
21. $80   **22.** $65   **23.** −$0.26; About $260   **24.** −$0.42

6.2 Exercises (page 352)

1. Not binomial, because the random variable is continuous.
2. Not binomial, because the random variable is continuous.
3. Binomial   4. Binomial
5. Not binomial, because the events are not independent.
6. Binomial
7. Not binomial, because the number of trials is not fixed.
8. Not binomial, because the number of trials is not fixed.
9. Binomial
10. Not binomial, because the events are not independent.
11. 0.2150   12. 0.2184   13. 0.0532   14. 0.0607

15. (a)

x	P(X = x)	x	P(X = x)
0	0.117649	4	0.059535
1	0.302526	5	0.010206
2	0.324135	6	0.000729
3	0.18522		

(b) $\mu_X = 1.8; \sigma_X = 1.12$ **(c)** $\mu_X = 1.8; \sigma_X = 1.12$

(d) **Probability Histogram**

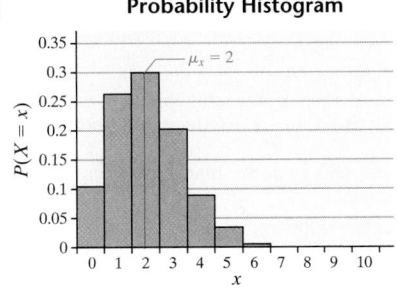

16. (a)

x	P(X = x)	x	P(X = x)
0	0.003906	5	0.21875
1	0.03125	6	0.109375
2	0.109375	7	0.03125
3	0.21875	8	0.003906
4	0.273438		

(b) $\mu_X = 4; \sigma_X = 1.41$ **(c)** $\mu_X = 4; \sigma_X = 1.41$

(d) **Probability Histogram**

17. (a)

x	P(X = x)	x	P(X = x)
0	0.0000038	5	0.1168
1	0.0001	6	0.2336
2	0.0012	7	0.3003
3	0.0087	8	0.2253
4	0.0389	9	0.0751

(b) $\mu_X = 6.75; \sigma_X = 1.3$ **(c)** $\mu_X = 6.75; \sigma_X = 1.3$

(d) **Probability Histogram**

18. (a)

x	P(X = x)	x	P(X = x)
0	0.1073742	6	0.0055050
1	0.2684355	7	0.0007864
2	0.3019899	8	0.0000737
3	0.2013266	9	0.0000041
4	0.0880804	10	0.0000001
5	0.0264241		

(b) $\mu_X = 2; \sigma_X = 1.26$ **(c)** $\mu_X = 2; \sigma_X = 1.26$

(d) **Probability Histogram**

19. (a)

x	P(X = x)	x	P(X = x)
0	0.0010	6	0.2051
1	0.0098	7	0.1172
2	0.0439	8	0.0439
3	0.1172	9	0.0098
4	0.2051	10	0.0010
5	0.2461		

19. (b) $\mu_X = 5; \sigma_X = 1.58$ **(c)** $\mu_X = 5; \sigma_X = 1.58$

(d)

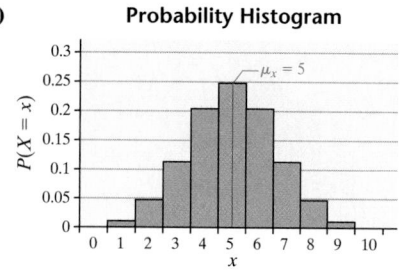

Probability Histogram

20. (a)

x	P(X = x)	x	P(X = x)
0	0.0000005	5	0.0660603
1	0.0000184	6	0.1761608
2	0.0002949	7	0.3019899
3	0.0027525	8	0.3019899
4	0.0165151	9	0.1342177

(b) $\mu_X = 7.2; \sigma_X = 1.2$ **(c)** $\mu_X = 7.2; \sigma_X = 1.2$

(d)

Probability Histogram

21. (a) 0.2501   **(b)** 0.6482   **(c)** 0.3518   **(d)** 0.5409
22. (a) 0.3020   **(b)** 0.6778   **(c)** 0.3222   **(d)** 0.7718
23. (a) 0.1280   **(b)** 0.9684   **(c)** 0.0316   **(d)** 0.5197
24. (a) 0.0476   **(b)** 0.0617   **(c)** 0.9383   **(d)** 0.5025
25. (a) 0.0188   **(b)** 0.9971   **(c)** 0.0029   **(d)** 0.4542
26. (a) 0.1863   **(b)** 0.5165   **(c)** 0.4835   **(d)** 0.3981
27. (a) 0.1596   **(b)** 0.2616   **(c)** 0.0233   **(d)** 0.6389
28. (a) 0.1850   **(b)** 0.9365   **(c)** 0.0111   **(d)** 0.2471
29. (a) $\mu_X = 80; \sigma_X = 4$
   (b) In a random sample of 100 flights, we would expect 80 to be on time.
   (c) Yes, because 90 is more than two standard deviations above the mean.

30. (a) $\mu_X = 160; \sigma_X = 5.66$
   (b) In a random sample of 200 adult smokers, we would expect 160 to report that they started smoking before turning 18 years old.
   (c) Yes, because 180 is more than two standard deviations above the mean.

31. (a) $\mu_X = 188; \sigma_X = 3.36$
   (b) In a random sample of 200 computer users, we would expect 188 to use Microsoft Windows as their operating system.
   (c) Yes, because 195 is more than two standard deviations above the mean.

32. (a) $\mu_X = 65; \sigma_X = 4.77$
   (b) In a random sample of 100 murders, we would expect 65 to have been committed with a firearm.
   (c) No, because 70 is within two standard deviations of the mean.

33. (a) $\mu_X = 12; \sigma_X = 3.43$
   (b) In a random sample of 600 users of Depakote, we would expect 12 to have experienced weight gain as a side effect.
   (c) No, because 16 is within two standard deviations of the mean.

34. (a) $\mu_X = 73.6; \sigma_X = 7.75$
   (b) In a random sample of 400 users of Singulair, we would expect about 74 to have experienced headaches as a side effect.
   (c) No, because 86 is within two standard deviations of the mean.
35. (a) 0.85   **(b)** 0.0128
   (c) It is likely that a higher percentage of community college male students that are 18–24 years of age live at home than the general 18–24-year-old male population.
36. (a) 0.8   **(b)** 0.0035
   (c) It is likely that a higher percentage of community college female students that are 18–24 years of age live at home than the general 18–24-year-old female population.
37. (a) 0.53   **(b)** 0.2630
   (c) No, the probability does not indicate that the results of the survey are unusual.
38. (a) 0.05   **(b)** 0.1821
   (c) No, the probability does not indicate that the results of the survey are unusual.
39. (a) 0.3   **(b)** 0.0339
   (c) Yes; because the probability indicates an unusual outcome, we are inclined to believe that the proportion of students graduating from college in five years or less is decreasing.
40. (a) 0.5   **(b)** 0.0305
   (c) Yes; because the probability indicates an unusual outcome, we are inclined to believe that the proportion of licensed drivers who are 16 years of age or older and students who want a 0.08% BAC drunk driving limit is less than 0.72.
43. (a) 40   **(b)** 70
44. (a) 0.1154

(b)

x	P(X = x)	x	P(X = x)
1	0.5360	6	0.0115
2	0.2487	7	0.0053
3	0.1154	8	0.0025
4	0.0535	9	0.0012
5	0.0248	10	0.0005

   (c) $\mu_X = 1.86$ **(d)** $\mu_X = 1.866; 1.866$
45. (a) 0.2065   **(b)** 0.5314   **(c)** 0.2023; 0.5259
46. (a) 0.0526   **(b)** 0.0199   **(c)** 0.0137   **(d)** 57

6.3 Exercises (page 366)

1. $\lambda = 10, t = 5$ **2.** $\lambda = 5, t = 10$
3. $\lambda = 0.07, t = 20$ **4.** $\lambda = 3.4, t = 10$
5. (a) 0.1462   **(b)** 0.6160   **(c)** 0.3840   **(d)** 0.4001
6. (a) 0.0710   **(b)** 0.8305   **(c)** 0.1695   **(d)** 0.3808
7. (a) 0.0050   **(b)** 0.9942   **(c)** 0.0058
   (d) 0.0057   **(e)** $0.7, \sqrt{0.7}$
8. (a) 0.1839   **(b)** 0.7358   **(c)** 0.2642
   (d) 0.6131   **(e)** 1, 1
9. (a) 0.1490   **(b)** 0.4497   **(c)** 0.5503
10. (a) 0.1009   **(b)** 0.1785   **(c)** 0.8215
11. (a) 0.2510   **(b)** 0.5578   **(c)** 0.4422
   (d) 0.7769; there is a good chance that a 1-gram sample of peanut butter will contain at least one insect fragment.
12. (a) 0.847   **(b)** 0.1180   **(c)** 0.8820
13. (a) 0.9512   **(b)** 0.0488
14. (a) 0.2019   **(b)** 0.7981   **(c)** fly

15. (a), (b)

x	$P(X = x)$	Expected	x	$P(X = x)$	Expected
0	0.0025	0.50	9	0.0688	13.77
1	0.0149	2.97	10	0.0413	8.26
2	0.0446	8.92	11	0.0225	4.51
3	0.0892	17.85	12	0.0113	2.25
4	0.1339	26.77	13	0.0052	1.04
5	0.1606	32.12	14	0.0022	0.45
6	0.1606	32.12	15	0.0009	0.18
7	0.1377	27.54	16	0.0003	0.07
8	0.1033	20.65			

(c) The observed frequencies are lower for fewer cars (x small) and higher for more cars (x large), so the advertising campaign appears to be effective.

16. (a), (b)

x	$P(X = x)$	Expected
0	0.6703	134.06
1	0.2681	53.63
2	0.0536	10.73
3	0.0072	1.43

(c) The expected values are fairly close to the observed values, so the boards appear to be grade-A quality.

17. (a)

Number of Deaths, x	Relative Frequency
0	0.55
1	0.33
2	0.11
3	0.02
4	0.01

(b) $\mu_X = 0.61$

(c)

Number of Deaths, x	$P(X = x)$
0	0.5434
1	0.3314
2	0.1011
3	0.0206
4	0.0031

(d) The probabilities are very close to the relative frequencies, so the random variable X appears to follow a Poisson distribution.

18. (a) $n \geq 100$ and $np \leq 10$ **(b)** 0.0189
   (c) 0.0103   **(d)** 0.0183; 0.0098
19. (a) $n \geq 100$ and $np \leq 10$ **(b)** 0.0506
   (c) 0.0429   **(d)** 0.0487; 0.0395
20. (a) 28   **21. (a)** 119   **22.** approximately 0.3 minute

Chapter Review Exercises (page 371)

1. (a) Continuous, $s \geq 0$
   (b) Discrete, $x = 0, 1, \ldots, 91$ (assuming 91 days of winter)
   (c) Discrete, $x = 0, 1, 2, \ldots, n$ where n is the number of tee shots hit
2. (a) Continuous, $m > 0$ **(b)** Discrete, $x = 0, 1, 2, \ldots$
   (c) Discrete, $x = 0, 1, 2, \ldots$
3. No, $\sum P(X = x) \neq 1$ **4.** Yes

5. (a)

x	$P(X = x)$
4	0.3226
5	0.2419
6	0.2742
7	0.1613

(b) Number of Games Necessary to Win the Stanley Cup

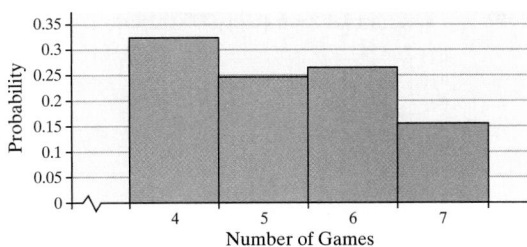

(c) $\mu_X = 5.3$ **(d)** $\sigma_X = 1.1$

6. (a)

x	$P(X = x)$
0	0.0046
1	0.0520
2	0.2221
3	0.4214
4	0.2999

(b)   **Victims of Property Crime**

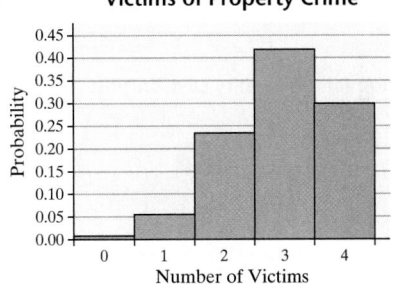

(c) $\mu_X = 2.96$ **(d)** $\sigma_X = 0.88$
7. $2   **8.** $-$0.26; $26
9. Binomial experiment
10. Not a binomial experiment, because the number of trials is not fixed.
11. (a) 0.4344   **(b)** 0.1478   **(c)** 0.1879
   (d) 0.3777   **(e)** 20; 4.3
   (f) No, because 12 is within two standard deviations of 20.
   (g) Yes, because the probability of observing four or more successes if $p = 0.08$ is 0.0058.
   (h) 0.0993
12. (a) 0.1520   **(b)** 0.0211   **(c)** 0.9789
   (d) 0.0042   **(e)** 112; 7.02
   (f) No, because 102 is within two standard deviations of 112.
   (g) No, because the probability of observing 11 or more successes if $p = 0.56$ is 0.1367.
13. (a) 0.0022   **(b)** 0.9441   **(c)** 0.4417
   (d) 0.1250   **(e)** 37; 5.85
   (f) Yes, because 50 is more than two standard deviations from the mean, 37.
   (g) No, because the probability of observing one or fewer successes if $p = 0.074$ is 0.3384.
14. (a) 0.1607   **(b)** 0.0097   **(c)** 0.9680
   (d) 0.0506   **(e)** 350; 15.08
   (f) No, because 330 is within two standard deviations of the mean, 350.
   (g) Yes, because the probability of observing two or fewer successes if $p = 0.35$ is 0.0021.

15. (a)

x	$P(X = x)$	x	$P(X = x)$
0	0.3277	3	0.0512
1	0.4096	4	0.0064
2	0.2048	5	0.0003

15. (b) $\mu_X = 1; \sigma_X = 0.9$ **(c)** $\mu_X = 1; \sigma_X = 0.9$

(d)   **Binomial Probability Distribution**

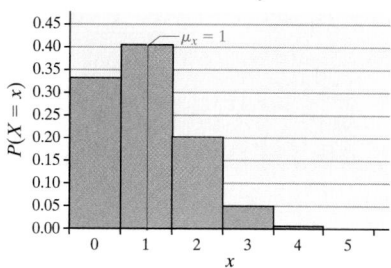

16. (a)

x	$P(X = x)$	x	$P(X = x)$
0	0.00002	5	0.20764
1	0.00037	6	0.31146
2	0.00385	7	0.26697
3	0.02307	8	0.10011
4	0.08652		

(b) $\mu_X = 6; \sigma_X = 1.2$ **(c)** $\mu_X = 6; \sigma_X = 1.2$

(d)   **Binomial Probability Distribution**

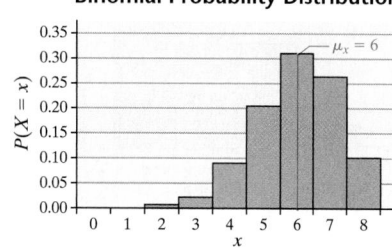

17. (a) 0.0072   **(b)** 0.9921   **(c)** 0.0079
(d) 0.0079   **(e)** 0.4; $\sqrt{0.4}$

18. (a) 0.2510   **(b)** 0.5578   **(c)** 0.4422
(d) 0.7112   **(e)** 1.5; $\sqrt{1.5}$

19. (a) 0.1404   **(b)** 0.1247   **(c)** 0.8753   **(d)** 5; $\sqrt{5}$

20. (a) 0.1951   **(b)** 0.4142   **(c)** 0.5858

21. (a)

x	$P(X = x)$
0	0.53125
1	0.28125
2	0.12500
3	0.03125
4	0.03125

(b) 0.75

(c)

x	$P(X = x)$
0	0.47237
1	0.35427
2	0.13285
3	0.03321
4	0.00623

(d) The probabilities computed from the Poisson distribution are fairly close to the actual values. It seems reasonable to use the Poisson distribution to model the number of earthquakes per year.

CHAPTER 7   The Normal Probability Distribution

7.1 Exercises (page 388)

1. 1/6   **2.** 1/3   **3.** 1/3   **4.** 1/6

5. (a)

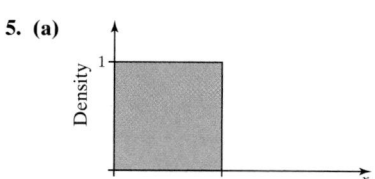

(b) 0.2   **(c)** 0.35   **(d)** 0.05   **(e)** Answers will vary

6. (a)

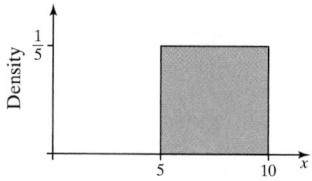

(b) 2/5   **(c)** 3/5   **(d)** 1/5

7. Normal   **8.** Not normal
9. Not normal   **10.** Normal
11. $\mu = 2, \sigma = 3$ **12.** $\mu = 5, \sigma = 2$
13. $\mu = 100, \sigma = 15$ **14.** $\mu = 530, \sigma = 100$

15. (a), (b)

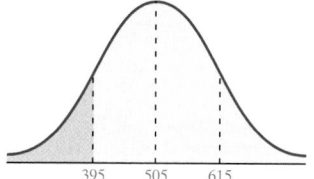

(c) (i) The proportion of SAT Verbal scores less than 395 is 0.1587. **(ii)** The probability that a randomly selected student scored less than 395 on the SAT Verbal is 0.1587.

16. (a), (b)

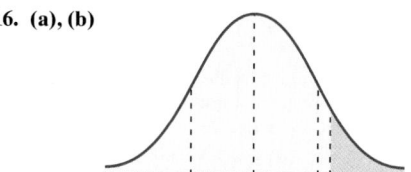

(c) (i) The proportion of ACT English scores that are more than 27 is 0.1186. **(ii)** The probability that a randomly selected student scored more than 27 on the ACT English test is 0.1186.

17. (a),(b)

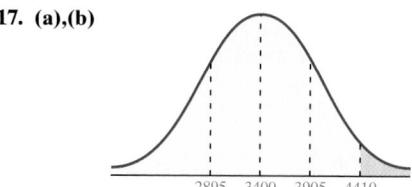

(c) (i) The proportion of full-term babies that weigh more than 4410 grams is 0.0228. **(ii)** The probability that a randomly selected full-term baby weighs more than 4410 grams is 0.0228.

18. (a), (b)

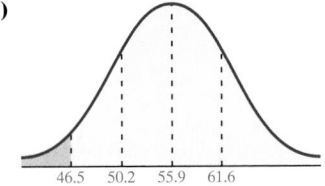

46.5 50.2 55.9 61.6

(c) (i) The proportion of 10-year-old males who are less than 46.5 inches tall is 0.0496. (ii) The probability that a randomly selected 10-year-old male is less than 46.5 inches tall is 0.0496.

19. (a) (i) The proportion of human pregnancies that last more than 280 days is 0.1908. (ii) The probability that a randomly selected human pregnancy lasts more than 280 days is 0.1908.
   (b) (i) The proportion of human pregnancies that last between 230 and 260 days is 0.3416. (ii) The probability that a randomly selected human pregnancy lasts between 230 and 260 days is 0.3416.

20. (a) (i) The proportion of times that Elena will get more than 26 miles per gallon is 0.3309. (ii) The probability that a randomly selected fill-up will yield at least 26 miles per gallon is 0.3309.
   (b) (i) The proportion of times that Elena will get between 18 and 21 miles per gallon is 0.1107. (ii) The probability that a randomly selected fill-up will yield between 18 and 21 miles per gallon is 0.1107.

21. (a) -0.67 **(b)** 0.67   **(c)** 0.495
22. (a) -1.17 **(b)** 0.83   **(c)** 0.6760
23. (a)–(c) Answers will vary   **24. (a)–(c)** Answers will vary

7.2 Exercises *(page 403)

1. (a) 0.0071   **(b)** 0.3336   **(c)** 0.9115   **(d)** 0.9998
2. (a) 0.0002   **(b)** 0.0233   **(c)** 0.8212   **(d)** 0.9981
3. (a) 0.9987   **(b)** 0.9441   **(c)** 0.0375   **(d)** 0.0009
4. (a) 0.9998   **(b)** 0.7088   **(c)** 0.0129   **(d)** 0.0003
5. (a) 0.9586   **(b)** 0.2088   **(c)** 0.8479
6. (a) 0.9892   **(b)** 0.4525   **(c)** 0.9749
7. (a) 0.0455   **(b)** 0.0646   **(c)** 0.5202
8. (a) 0.0033   **(b)** 0.0476   **(c)** 0.2988
9. (a) 0.8877   **(b)** 0.9802   **(c)** 0.0198
10. (a) 0.4942   **(b)** 0.95   **(c)** 0.05
11. -1.28 **12.** -0.84 **13.** 2.05   **14.** 1.04
15. 0.67   **16.** 0.39   **17.** -1.23 **18.** -0.67
19. $-1.28; 1.28$ **20.** $-1.04; 1.04$ **21.** $-2.575; 2.575$
22. $-1.88; 1.88$ **23.** 1.645   **24.** 0.39
25. 2.33   **26.** 2.05   **27.** 0.84
28. 1.04   **29.** 0.9732   **30.** 0.2709
31. 0.9986   **32.** 0.1788   **33.** 0.8753
34. 0.05   **35.** 0.0329   **36.** 0.8212
37. 0.7642   **38.** 0.0036   **39.** 0.0875
40. 0.3788   **42.** 0.0901   **43.** 0.0054
44. 0.4332   **45.** 0.1906
46. (a) 2.50   **(b)** 0.15   **(c)** 1.53

7.3 Exercises *(page 411)

1. 0.9839   **2.** 0.0161   **3.** 0.2375   **4.** 0.8735   **5.** 0.9074
6. 0.1906   **7.** 0.2354   **8.** 0.3666   **9.** 0.7192   **10.** 0.1845
11. (a) 0.1481   **(b)** 0.0896   **(c)** 0.2504
   (d) 0.2752   **(e)** 0.2879

(f) A little unusual, because the probability that a randomly selected 20–29-year-old female would have a serum HDL less than 30 is 0.0430.

12. (a) 0.6554   **(b)** 0.6554   **(c)** 0.7522
   (d) Yes, because the proportion of Earthquakes with a magnitude of 8.25 or higher is 0.000021.
13. (a) 0.4763   **(b)** 0.6170   **(c)** 0.5709
   (d) A little unusual, because the proportion of monthly returns greater than 9.7 percent is only 0.0165.
14. (a) 0.1949   **(b)** 0.2946   **(c)** 0.1508
   (d) 95th percentile   **(e)** 23rd percentile
15. (a) 7.16%   **(b)** 0.24%   **(c)** 91.09%   **(d)** 0.9109
   (e) A little unusual, because the proportion of 20–29-year-old females who are more than 5 feet, 10 inches, is 0.0176.
16. (a) 2.28%   **(b)** 0.7340   **(c)** 0.6284
17. (a) 14.56%   **(b)** 27.06%   **(c)** 33.41%
   (d) 0.1587   **(e)** 0.3220
18. (a) 40.13%   **(b)** 15.87%   **(c)** 75.71%
   (d) 0.1908   **(e)** 0.0947   **(f)** 0.0043
19. (a) 10.56%   **(b)** 0.62%   **(c)** 25.98%
   (d) 0.1056   **(e)** 0.3413
20. (a) 42.86%   **(b)** 20.61%
   (c) Not that unusual, since the proportion of years in which there are 51 or more shark attacks is 0.0274.
21. (a) 44   **(b)** Exact   **(c)** 35.8; 70.2
22. (a) 6.1   **(b)** 5.5; 6.9
23. (a) 4.28%   **(b)** $-7.48\%; 8.98\%$ **24. (a)** 25   **(b)** 29
25. (a) 63.4 inches   **(b)** 69.9 inches   **(c)** 58.6–69.6 inches
26. (a) 133   **(b)** 89–111   **27. (a)** 170   **(b)** 146–176
28. (a) 299 days   **(b)** 233–299 days
29. (a) 70° F   **(b)** 94° F   **(c)** 70° F–90° F
30. (a) 52 attacks   **(b)** 19–45 attacks

31. (a)

Score	Theoretical Proportion	Score	Theoretical Proportion
200–249	0.0068	500–549	0.1709
250–299	0.0188	550–599	0.1491
300–349	0.0430	600–649	0.1072
350–399	0.0811	650–699	0.0636
400–449	0.1260	700–749	0.0311
450–499	0.1616	750–800	0.0127

32. (a)

Score	Theoretical Proportion	Score	Theoretical Proportion
200–249	0.0075	500–549	0.1721
250–299	0.0209	550–599	0.1440
300–349	0.0476	600–649	0.0988
350–399	0.0885	650–699	0.0555
400–449	0.1349	700–749	0.0255
450–499	0.1683	750–800	0.0097

33. (a)

Temperature	Relative Frequency	Temperature	Relative Frequency
5.0–9.9	0.0005	40.0–44.9	0.2000
10.0–14.9	0.0053	45.0–49.9	0.1499
15.0–19.9	0.0080	50.0–54.9	0.1243
20.0–24.9	0.0213	55.0–59.9	0.0853
25.0–29.9	0.0507	60.0–64.9	0.0539
30.0–34.9	0.1157	65.0–69.9	0.0112
35.0–39.9	0.1733	70.0–74.9	0.0005

*These answers were found via technology. "By hand" answers can be found on the website of this text.

(b)

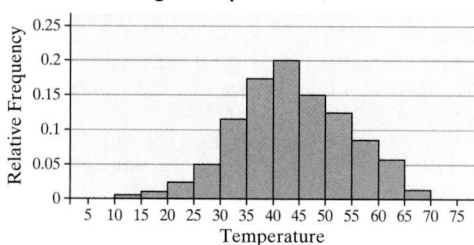

Chicago Temperatures, Nov. 16–30

(c) $\mu = 43.5°$ F, $\sigma = 10.5°$ F

(d)

Temperature	Theoretical Proportion
5.0–9.9	0.0006
10.0–14.9	0.0025
15.0–19.9	0.0090
20.0–24.9	0.0256
25.0–29.9	0.0586
30.0–34.9	0.1071
35.0–39.9	0.1567
40.0–44.9	0.1836
45.0–49.9	0.1721
50.0–54.9	0.1291
55.0–59.9	0.0776
60.0–64.9	0.0373
65.0–69.9	0.0143
70.0–74.9	0.0044

7.4 Exercises (page 421)

1. Not normal **2.** Not normal **3.** Normal
4. Not normal **5.** Normal **6.** Normal
7. Normal

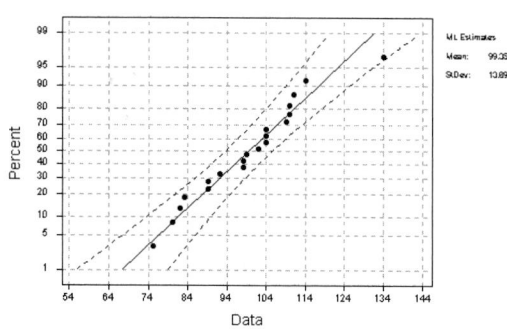

Normal Probability Plot for Score

8. Normal

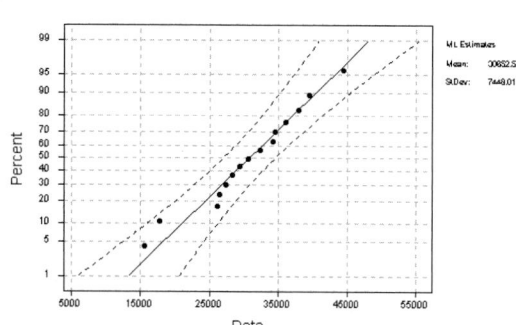

Normal Probability Plot for Miles

9. Not normal

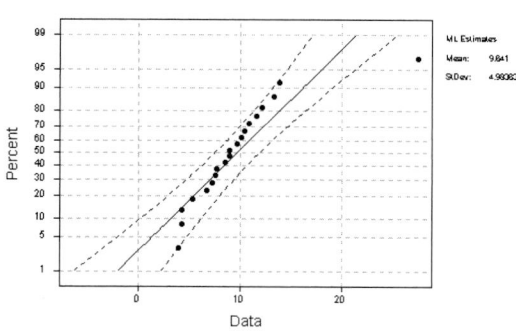

Normal Probability Plot for Volume

10. Not normal

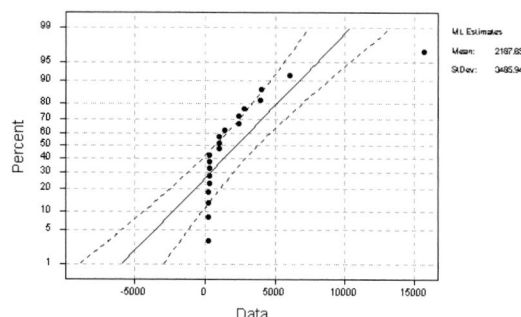

Normal Probability Plot for Salaries

7.5 Exercises *(page 434)

1. $\mu_{\bar{x}} = 50$; $\sigma_{\bar{x}} = \dfrac{6}{\sqrt{40}}$ **2.** $\mu_{\bar{x}} = 30$; $\sigma_{\bar{x}} = \dfrac{4}{\sqrt{34}}$

3. $\mu_{\bar{x}} = 100$; $\sigma_{\bar{x}} = \dfrac{12}{\sqrt{20}}$ **4.** $\mu_{\bar{x}} = 120$; $\sigma_{\bar{x}} = \dfrac{16}{\sqrt{10}}$

5. (a) Approximately normal; $\mu_{\bar{x}} = 50$; $\sigma_{\bar{x}} = \dfrac{6}{\sqrt{40}}$

(b) 0.1459 **(c)** 0.0175 **(d)** 0.8928

6. (a) Approximately normal, $\mu_{\bar{x}} = 30$; $\sigma_{\bar{x}} = \dfrac{4}{\sqrt{34}}$

(b) 0.3853 **(c)** 0.8091 **(d)** 0.9165

7. (a) Population must be normal. $\bar{x}$ is normal with $\mu_{\bar{x}} = 105$, $\sigma_{\bar{x}} = \dfrac{16}{\sqrt{10}}$.

(b) 0.6390 **(c)** 0.1300

8. (a) Population must be normal. $\bar{x}$ is normal with $\mu_{\bar{x}} = 105$, $\sigma_{\bar{x}} = \dfrac{16}{\sqrt{20}}$.

(b) 0.6926 **(c)** 0.0556

(d) For part (b), the probability in #8 is higher because 103.2 is fewer standard errors from μ.

9. (a) 0.3007 **(b)** 0.0215 **(c)** 0.0097

(d) The larger the sample size, the lower is the probability. This is due to the Law of Large Numbers. As the sample size increases, the standard error decreases. Therefore, as the sample size increases, 60 is more standard errors from μ, making 60 a less likely occurrence.

*These answers were found via technology. "By hand" answers can be found on the website of this text.

10. (a) 0.2946   **(b)** 0.0439   **(c)** 0.0079
  (d) Since $P(\overline{x} < 18) = 0.0079$ if $\mu = 20.7$, we can conclude one of two things: (i) We just happened to randomly select 20 test takers who did not do well on the test, or (ii) The population mean is less than 20.7. Since μ is known to be 20.7, we are inclined to believe explanation (i).

11. (a) 0.3538   **(b)** 0.0468   **(c)** 0.0040
  (d) Since the probability of obtaining a sample mean of 260 or less from a sample of $n = 50$ pregnancies is 0.004, we can conclude one of two things: (i) We just happened to select 50 pregnancies that had short gestation periods, or (ii) the population mean is less than 266. Explanation (ii) would be reasonable if our sample came from a specific population—say, "at-risk" women whose labor may have been induced for medical reasons and who therefore had a gestation period less than 266 days. Since we do not have any indication that explanation (ii) is reasonable, we are inclined to believe explanation (i).

12. (a) 0.4013   **(b)** 0.0855   **(c)** 0.0385
13. (a) Because the sample size, n, is large.
  (b) $\mu_{\overline{x}} = 3, \sigma_{\overline{x}} = \dfrac{\sqrt{3}}{\sqrt{50}}$
  (c) The probability of obtaining a sample mean of 3.6 insect fragments or more is 0.0072. Since this result is unusual if the population mean is 3, we are inclined to believe that the population mean is more than 3.
14. (a) Because the sample size, n, is large.
  (b) $\mu_{\overline{x}} = 20, \sigma_{\overline{x}} = \dfrac{\sqrt{20}}{\sqrt{40}}$
  (c) The probability of obtaining a sample mean of of 22.1 cars per hour or more is 0.0015. Since this result is unusual if the population mean is 20, we are inclined to believe that the population mean is more than 20.
15. The probability of obtaining a sample mean of 68.3° F or higher from a population whose mean is 67.6° F is 0.1193. This is not an unusual result.
16. The probability of obtaining a sample mean of 5.7 years or less from a population whose mean is 8.5 years is 0.0014. This result is unusual. We are inclined to believe that the population mean is less than 8.5 years.
17. (a) The probability of obtaining a sample mean of $32,030 from a population whose mean is $45,127 is 0.0043. This result is unusual. We conclude that the population mean for households in Cook County, IL is likely less than $45,127.
  (b) No; since the median is less than the mean, the distribution is skewed to the right.
18. 0.0912
19. (a) $\mu = 107$
  (b) 98, 106; 98, 104; 98, 120; 98, 100; 98, 114; 106, 104; 106, 120; 106, 100; 106, 114; 104, 120; 104, 100; 104, 114; 120, 100; 120, 114; 100, 114

(c)

$\overline{x}$	Probability
99	1/15
101	1/15
102	2/15
103	1/15
105	1/15
106	1/15
107	1/15
109	2/15
110	2/15
112	1/15
113	1/15
117	1/15

(d) $\mu_{\overline{x}} = 107$ **(e)** $P\left(102 \le \overline{x} \le 112\right) = \dfrac{11}{15}$

(f)

$\overline{x}$	Probability	$\overline{x}$	Probability
100.7	1/20	107.3	1/20
101.3	1/20	108	3/20
102.7	1/20	108.7	1/20
103.3	1/20	110	1/20
104	1/20	110.7	1/20
105.3	1/20	111.3	1/20
106	3/20	112.7	1/20
106.7	1/20	113.3	1/20

$\mu_{\overline{x}} = 107; P\left(102 \le \overline{x} \le 112\right) = \dfrac{4}{5}$; With the larger sample size, the probability of obtaining a sample mean within five IQ points of the population mean has increased.

20. (a) $\mu = 35$
  (b) 24, 28; 24, 35; 24, 36; 24, 58; 24, 29; 28, 35; 28, 36; 28, 58; 28, 29; 35, 36; 35, 58; 35, 29; 36, 58; 36, 29; 58, 29

(c)

$\overline{x}$	Probability	$\overline{x}$	Probability
26	1/15	32.5	1/15
26.5	1/15	35.5	1/15
28.5	1/15	41	1/15
29.5	1/15	43	1/15
30	1/15	43.5	1/15
31.5	1/15	46.5	1/15
32	2/15	47	1/15

(d) $\mu_{\overline{x}} = 35$ **(e)** $P\left(30 \le \overline{x} \le 40\right) = \dfrac{6}{15}$

(f)

$\overline{x}$	Probability	$\overline{x}$	Probability
27	1/20	36.7	1/20
29	1/20	37	1/20
29.3	2/20	38.3	1/20
29.7	1/20	39	1/20
30.7	1/20	39.3	1/20
31	1/20	40.3	1/20
31.7	1/20	40.7	2/20
33	1/20	41	1/20
33.3	1/20	43	1/20

$\mu_{\overline{x}} = 35; P\left(30 \le \overline{x} \le 40\right) = \dfrac{10}{20} = \dfrac{1}{2}$; With the larger sample size, the probability of obtaining a sample mean within five years of the population mean has increased.

21. (a)–(c) Answers will vary.   **(d)** $\mu_{\overline{x}} = 100; \sigma_{\overline{x}} = \dfrac{16}{\sqrt{20}}$
  (e) Answers will vary.   **(f)** 0.0127
  (g) Answers will vary.
22. (a)–(c) Answers will vary.   **(d)** $\mu_{\overline{x}} = 266; \sigma_{\overline{x}} = \dfrac{16}{\sqrt{15}}$
  (e) Answers will vary.   **(f)** 0.1665
  (g) Answers will vary.
23. Answers will vary.   **24.** Answers will vary.

7.6 Exercises *(page 442)

1. Area under the normal curve to the right of $X = 39.5$
2. Area under the normal curve to the left of $X = 20.5$
3. Area under the normal curve between $X = 7.5$ and $X = 8.5$

*These answers were found via technology. "By hand" answers can be found on the website of this text.

4. Area under the normal curve between $X = 11.5$ and $X = 12.5$

5. Area under the normal curve between $X = 17.5$ and $X = 24.5$

6. Area under the normal curve between $X = 29.5$ and $X = 40.5$

7. Area under the normal curve to the right of $X = 20.5$

8. Area under the normal curve to the left of $X = 39.5$

9. 0.0616; 0.0603   **10.** 0.0221; 0.0216

11. 0.0677; 0.0645   **12.** 0.0970; 0.0932

13. (a) 0.0584   **(b)** 0.1478   **(c)** 0.0261   **(d)** 0.4146

14. (a) 0.0995   **(b)** 0.5497   **(c)** 0.0043   **(d)** 0.9913

15. (a) 0.0071   **(b)** 0.9872   **(c)** 0.2283   **(d)** 0.0128

16. (a) 0.0070   **(b)** 0.3660   **(c)** 0.1154   **(d)** 0.3660

17. (a) 0.0078   **(b)** 0.9934   **(c)** 0.0028   **(d)** 0.0144

18. (a) 0.0299   **(b)** 0.9296   **(c)** 0.3513   **(d)** 0.8943

19. (a) 0.0484   **(b)** 0.0018   **(c)** 0.8655   **(d)** 0.0018

20. (a) 0.0084   **(b)** 0.6225   **(c)** 0.3775   **(d)** 0.6125

21. (a) 0.0088
  (b) Either the proportion of males between 18 and 24 years of age is higher than 59%, or the sample just happened to result in a lot of 18–24-year-olds who live at home.

22. (a) 0.0004
  (b) Either the proportion of females between 18 and 24 years of age is higher than 48%, or the sample just happened to result in a lot of 18–24-year-olds who live at home.

23. (a) 0.0090
  (b) Yes, assuming that our sampling was done appropriately, we are inclined to believe that the proportion of respondents who would prefer a boy is higher than 42%.

24. (a) 0.1191   **(b)** No

25. (a) 0.0763   **(b)** No

26. (a) 0.0167
  (b) Yes, assuming that the sampling was done appropriately, we are inclined to believe that the proportion of licensed drivers who favor a BAC of 0.08% is less than 0.72.

Chapter Review Exercises (page 445)

1. (a) 60   **(b)** 10
  (c) (i) The proportion of random variables to the right of $X = 75$ is 0.0668. (ii) The probability that a randomly selected random variable is greater than $X = 75$ is 0.0668.
  (d) (i) The proportion of random variables between $X = 50$ and $X = 75$ is 0.7745. (ii) The probability that a randomly selected random variable is between $X = 50$ and $X = 75$ is 0.7745.

2. (a) 7   **(b)** 2
  (c) (i) The proportion of random variables to the left of $X = 10$ is 0.9332. (ii) The probability that a randomly selected random variable is less than $X = 10$ is 0.9332.
  (d) (i) The proportion of random variables between $X = 5$ and $X = 8$ is 0.5328. (ii) The probability that a randomly selected random variable is between $X = 5$ and $X = 8$ is 0.5328.

3. (a) -0.5 **(b)** 0.25   **(c)** 0.2912

4. (a) -0.25 **(b)** 1.25   **(c)** 0.4931

5. 0.1492   **6.** 0.0207   **7.** 0.4816   **8.** 0.0268   **9.** 0.8830

10. 0.0537   **11.** 0.8756   **12.** 0.3713   **13.** 0.99   **14.** 0.04

15. -1.75; 1.75   **16.** -1.55; 1.55   **17.** 0.84   **18.** 1.75

19. 0.2023   **20.** 0.0808   **21.** 0.6247   **22.** 0.2427

23. (a) 0.1279   **(b)** 0.0115   **(c)** 0.8606   **(d)** 60,964 miles

  (e) Normal; $\mu_{\bar{x}} = 70{,}000$; $\sigma_{\bar{x}} = \dfrac{4400}{\sqrt{10}}$ **(f)** 0.0362

  (g) Normal; $\mu_{\bar{x}} = 70{,}000$; $\sigma_{\bar{x}} = \dfrac{4400}{\sqrt{25}}$ **(h)** 0.0022

24. (a) 0.8413   **(b)** 0.7475   **(c)** 0.5808
  (d) 344 minutes   **(e)** 285–363 minutes

  (f) Normal; $\mu_{\bar{x}} = 324$; $\sigma_{\bar{x}} = \dfrac{24}{\sqrt{15}}$ **(g)** 0.1665

  (h) Normal; $\mu_{\bar{x}} = 324$; $\sigma_{\bar{x}} = \dfrac{24}{\sqrt{30}}$ **(i)** 0.0855

25. (a) 0.4105   **(b)** 0.4680   **(c)** 0.2180   **(d)** 120
  (e) Yes, 144   **(f)** 0.3881   **(g)** 0.3265

26. (a) 0.0478   **(b)** 0.2525   **(c)** 0.2487   **(d)** 0.0004
  (e) 125   **(f)** 71–129   **(g)** Yes

27. (a) $np(1 - p) = 14.72 \geq 10$ **(b)** 0.1002   **(c)** 0.1204
  (d) 0.6521   **(e)** 0.9866   **(f)** 0.6454

28. (a) $np(1 - p) = 61.6 \geq 10$ **(b)** 0.0082   **(c)** 0.0045
  (d) 0.5254   **(e)** 0.0065

29. Not normal   **30.** Normal

31. Not normal

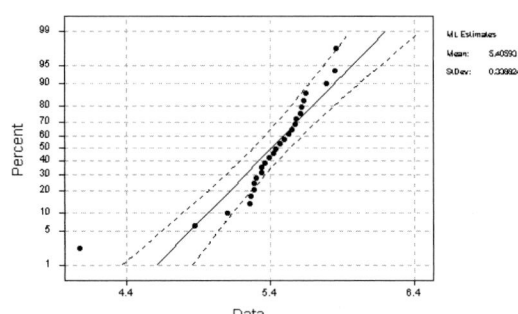

Normal Probability Plot for Density

32. Normal

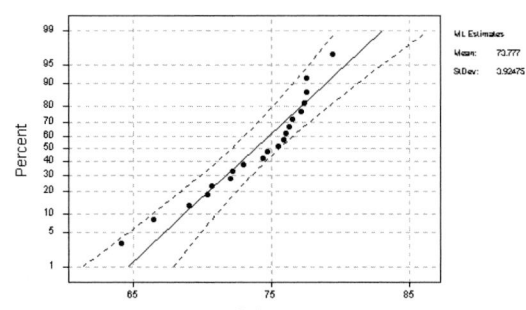

Normal Probability Plot for Life Exp

33. (a)

Birth Weight	Relative Frequency
0–499 grams	0.00002
500–999 grams	0.00037
1000–1499 grams	0.00343
1500–1999 grams	0.03078
2000–2499 grams	0.17073
2500–2999 grams	0.36342
3000–3499 grams	0.29324
3500–3999 grams	0.10936
4000–4499 grams	0.02388
4500–4999 grams	0.00415
5000–5499 grams	0.00062

(b)

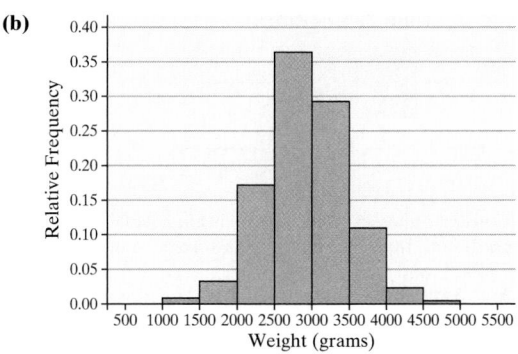

(c) $\mu = 2929.1$; $\sigma = 554.5$

(d)

Birth Weight	Theoretical Proportion	Birth Weight	Theoretical Proportion
0–499 grams	0.000006	3000–3499 grams	0.2971
500–999 grams	0.00024	3500–3999 grams	0.1248
1000–1499 grams	0.0047	4000–4499 grams	0.0244
1500–1999 grams	0.0418	4500–4999 grams	0.0022
2000–2499 grams	0.1721	5000–5499 grams	0.000092
2500–2999 grams	0.3306		

34. (a)

Birth Weight	Relative Frequency	Birth Weight	Relative Frequency
0–499 grams	0.00000	3000–3499 grams	0.36539
500–999 grams	0.00008	3500–3999 grams	0.34828
1000–1499 grams	0.00076	4000–4499 grams	0.12048
1500–1999 grams	0.00275	4500–4999 grams	0.02267
2000–2499 grams	0.01824	5000–5499 grams	0.00256
2500–2999 grams	0.11880		

(b)

Birthweight of Postterm Babies

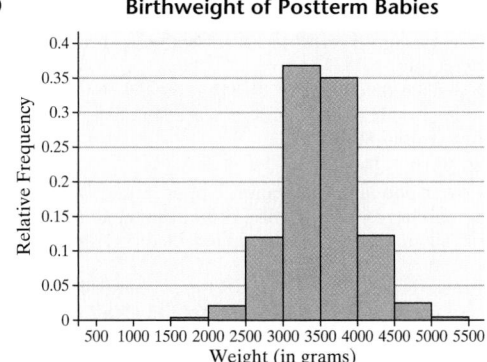

(c) $\mu = 3499.7$; $\sigma = 513.6$

(d)

Birth Weight	Theoretical Proportion	Birth Weight	Theoretical Proportion
0–499 grams	0.00000	3000–3499 grams	0.3342
500–999 grams	0.00000	3500–3999 grams	0.3343
1000–1499 grams	0.00005	4000–4499 grams	0.1392
1500–1999 grams	0.0017	4500–4999 grams	0.0240
2000–2499 grams	0.0239	5000–5499 grams	0.0017
2500–2999 grams	0.1390		

35. (a) Normal; $\mu_{\bar{x}} = 120$; $\sigma_{\bar{x}} = \dfrac{17}{\sqrt{100}}$ **(b)** 0.0016

36. (a) Normal; $\mu_{\bar{x}} = 39.40$; $\sigma_{\bar{x}} = \dfrac{17.4}{\sqrt{50}}$ **(b)** 0.0369

37. (a)

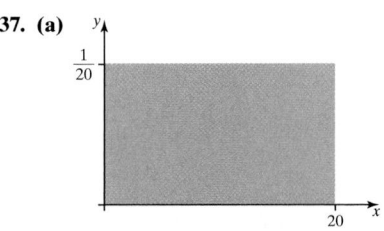

(b) 0.25   **(c)** 0.4   **38.** See page 384

CHAPTER 8   Confidence Intervals about a Single Parameter

8.1 Exercises (page 466)

1. No   **2.** No   **3.** No   **4.** No   **5.** Yes
6. Yes   **7.** 2.33   **8.** 1.88   **9.** 1.44   **10.** 1.28
11. (a) Lower bound: 32.44; Upper bound: 35.96
  (b) Lower bound: 32.73; Upper bound: 35.67; the margin of error decreases.
  (c) Lower bound: 31.89; Upper bound: 36.51; the margin of error increases.
  (d) Only if the population is normal
12. (a) Lower bound: 58.27; Upper bound: 60.13
  (b) Lower bound: 58.36; Upper bound: 60.04; the margin of error decreases.
  (c) Lower bound: 57.88; Upper bound: 60.52; the margin of error increases.
  (d) Only if the population is normal
13. (a) Lower bound: 102.66; Upper bound: 113.34
  (b) Lower bound: 99.56; Upper bound: 116.44; the margin of error increases.
  (c) Lower bound: 103.96; Upper bound: 112.04; the margin of error decreases.   **(d)** No
  (e) The sample mean would increase, causing the interval to include larger values.
14. (a) Lower bound: 115.85; Upper bound: 130.15
  (b) Lower bound: 113.77; Upper bound: 132.23; the margin of error increases.
  (c) Lower bound: 117.53; Upper bound: 128.47; the margin of error decreases.   **(d)** No
  (e) The sample mean would increase, causing the interval to include larger values
15. (a) $542.25   **(b)** Yes
  (c) Lower bound: $326.65; Upper bound: $757.85. The Insurance Institute is 95% confident that the mean cost of repair to a Chevy Cavalier crashed at 5 miles per hour is between $326.65 and $757.85.
  (d) Lower bound: $361.32; Upper bound: $723.18. The Insurance Institute is 90% confident that the mean cost of repair to a Chevy Cavalier crashed at 5 miles per hour is between $361.65 and $723.18.
16. (a) 103.4 minutes   **(b)** Yes
  (c) Lower bound: 98.22 minutes; Upper bound: 108.67 minutes. The researcher is 95% confident that the flight time between the two cities on an American Airlines plane is between 98.22 minutes and 108.67 minutes.
  (d) Lower bound: 99.06 minutes; Upper bound: 107.83 minutes. The researcher is 90% confident that the flight time between the two cities on an American Airlines plane is between 99.06 minutes and 107.83 minutes.
17. (a) 50.67   **(b)** Yes
  (c) Lower bound: 43.89; Upper bound: 57.45; Dr. Oswiecmiski is 95% confident that the HDL cholesterol of his 20–29-year-old female patients is between 43.89 and 57.45.
  (d) No, because the population mean is contained within the interval.

18. (a) 48.33   **(b)** Yes

(c) Lower bound: 42.01; Upper bound: 54.66; Dr. Oswiecmiski is 95% confident that the HDL cholesterol of his 20–29-year-old male patients is between 42.01 and 54.66.

(d) No, because the population mean is contained within the interval.

19. (a) 22.95   **(b)** Yes

(c) Lower bound: 20.99; Upper bound: 24.91. Mrs. Gibson is 92% confident that the mean ACT Math score for students in District 204 is between 20.99 and 24.91.

(d) Yes, it appears that District 204 students score higher, because the lower bound of the confidence interval is greater than the population mean, 20.7.

20. (a) 23.55   **(b)** Yes

(c) Lower bound: 21.66; Upper bound: 25.44. Mr. Gibson is 94% confident that the mean ACT Science score for students in District 204 is between 21.66 and 25.44.

(d) Yes, it appears that District 204 students score higher because the lower bound of the confidence interval is greater than the population mean, 21.

21. (a) 258.8 days

(b)

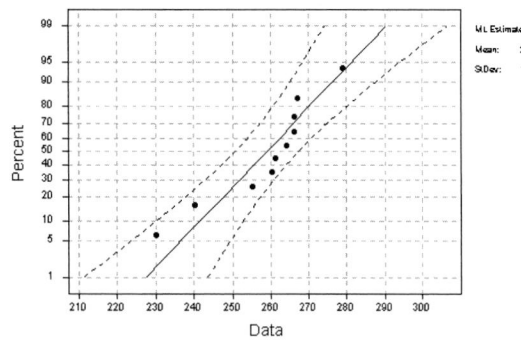

Normal Probability Plot for Gestation

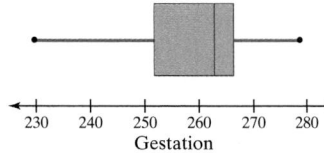

Gestation Period

(c) Lower bound: 250.5 days; Upper bound: 267.1 days. Dr. Oswiecmiski is 90% confident that the mean gestation period of her patients is between 250.5 days and 267.1 days.

(d) It is not likely, because 266 days is contained within the 90% confidence interval.

22. (a) 80.0° F

(b)

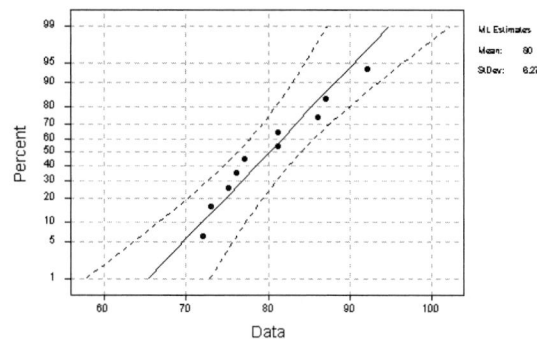

Normal Probability Plot for Temperature

High Temperature

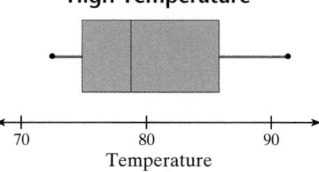

(c) Lower bound: 75.04° F; Upper bound: 84.96° F. We are 95% confident that the mean high temperature was between 75.04° F and 84.96° F.

(d) Yes, because 80° F is in the interval.

23. (a) 11.19 million shares

(b) Lower bound: 9.84 million shares; Upper bound: 12.54 million shares. We are 90% confident that the mean number of shares traded is between 9.84 million and 12.54 million.

(c) Lower bound: 7.28 million shares; Upper bound: 9.97 million shares. We are 90% confident that the mean number of shares traded is between 7.28 million and 9.97 million.

(d) Different samples lead to different sample means, which result in different intervals.

24. (a) 0.77 million shares

(b) Lower bound: 0.48 million shares; Upper bound: 1.06 million shares. We are 95% confident that the mean number of shares traded is between 0.48 million and 1.06 million.

(c) Lower bound: 0.55 million shares; Upper bound: 1.13 million shares. We are 95% confident that the mean number of shares traded is between 0.55 million and 1.13 million.

(d) Different samples lead to different sample means, which result in different intervals.

25. (a) 49,477.7 miles

(b) Lower bound: 40,644 miles; Upper bound: 58,311 miles. The researcher is 99% confident that the mean number of miles on all four-year-old Saturn SC1s in the Chicagoland area is between 40,644 and 58,311.

(c) Lower bound: 42,756 miles; Upper bound: 56,199 miles. The researcher is 95% confident that the mean number of miles on all four-year-old Saturn SC1s in the Chicagoland area is between 42,756 and 56,199.

(d) The margin of error decreases when the level of confidence decreases.

(e) No, since we cannot be sure that the driving habits of people living in the Chicagoland area are similar to those of the entire United States.

26. (a) 40,520.2 miles

(b) Lower bound: 33,510 miles; Upper bound: 47,530 miles. The researcher is 99% confident that the mean number of miles on all three-year-old Cavaliers in the Orlando area is between 33,510 and 47,530.

(c) Lower bound: 35,186 miles; Upper bound: 45,854 miles. The researcher is 95% confident that the mean number of miles on all three-year-old Cavaliers in the Orlando area is between 35,186 and 45,854.

(d) The margin of error decreases when the level of confidence decreases.

(e) No, since we cannot be sure that the driving habits of people living in Orlando are similar to those of the entire United States population.

27. 298; 173; decreases the sample size required

28. 188; 378; increases the sample size required

29. 130   **30.** 50

31. (a) 1051   **(b)** 4201   **(c)** Quadruples

32. (a) 352   **(b)** 1408   **(c)** Quadruples

36. (a) Lower bound: 44.59; Upper bound: 55.91

(b)

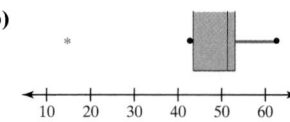

(c) Lower bound: 42.43; Upper bound: 53.66

(d) $\bar{x} = 48.1$

(e) Lower bound: 44.82; Upper bound: 51.35; width of interval decreases.

(f)

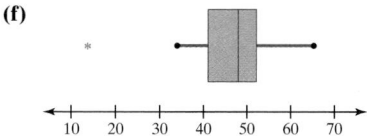

(g) Lower bound: 44.07; Upper bound: 50.60; not much effect.

37. 4 times   **38.** 4 times

8.2 Exercises (page 483)

1. (a) 1.316   **(b)** 1.697
   (c) −2.552   **(d)** 1.725

2. (a) 2.205   **(b)** 1.309
   (c) −1.943   **(d)** 2.120

3. (a) Lower bound: 103.7; Upper bound: 112.3
   (b) Lower bound: 100.4; Upper bound: 115.6; the margin of error increases.
   (c) Lower bound: 104.6; Upper bound: 111.4; the margin of error decreases.
   (d) No

4. (a) Lower bound: 45.5; Upper bound: 54.5
   (b) Lower bound: 44.6; Upper bound: 55.4; the margin of error increases.
   (c) Lower bound: 46.3; Upper bound: 53.7; the margin of error decreases.
   (d) No

5. (a) Lower bound: 16.85; Upper bound: 19.95
   (b) Lower bound: 17.12; Upper bound: 19.70; the margin of error decreases.
   (c) Lower bound: 16.33; Upper bound: 20.48; the margin of error increases.
   (d) Population must be normal

6. (a) Lower bound: 32.78; Upper bound: 37.42
   (b) Lower bound: 33.66; Upper bound: 36.55; the margin of error decreases.
   (c) Lower bound: 31.76; Upper bound: 38.44; the margin of error increases.
   (d) Population must be normal

7. Lower bound: 6.68 times; Upper bound: 7.13 times. The Gallup Organization is 99% confident that the mean number of times Americans bathed each week in 1999 is between 6.68 and 7.13.

8. (a) Lower bound: 3.52 times; Upper bound: 3.88. The Gallup Organization is 99% confident that the mean number of times Americans bathed each week in 1950 is between 3.52 and 3.88.
   (b) It appears that Americans bathed more in 1999 than in 1950.

9. Lower bound: 3.29 hours; Upper bound: 3.51 hours. The Gallup Organization is 95% confident that the mean number of hours Americans watched television in 1999 is between 3.29 and 3.51.

10. Lower bound: 3.079 inches; Upper bound: 4.182 inches; We are 95% confident that the mean amount of rainfall in Chicago during the month of April is between 3.079 and 4.182 inches.

11. Lower bound: 12.40 mg/l; Upper bound: 19.44 mg/l. The researcher is 99% confident that the mean concentration is between 12.40 and 19.44 mg/l.

12. (a) Lower bound: 8.078 mg/l; Upper bound: 11.982 mg/l. The researcher is 99% confident that the mean concentration is between 8.078 and 11.982 mg/l.
   (b) There does appear to be a difference between the two soil types, since the confidence intervals do not overlap.

13. (a) Yes
   (b) Lower bound: 3.017 grams; Upper bound: 3.055 grams. The researcher is 90% confident that the mean weight of a "wheat" penny is between 3.017 and 3.055 grams.
   (c) Increase the sample size.

14. (a) Yes
   (b) Lower bound: 37,855 miles; Upper bound: 49,543 miles. The researcher is 90% confident that the mean number of miles on four-year-old Camaros is between 37,855 and 49,543.
   (c) Increase the sample size.

15. (a) Yes
   (b) Lower bound: 196.37 thousand psi; Upper bound: 211.49 thousand psi. The researchers are 95% confident that the mean tensile strength of the composite material is between 196.37 thousand and 211.49 thousand psi.

16. (a) Yes
   (b) Lower bound: 238.2 yards; Upper bound: 270.4 yards. Dan is 95% confident that his mean driving distance is between 238.2 and 270.4 yards.

17. (a)

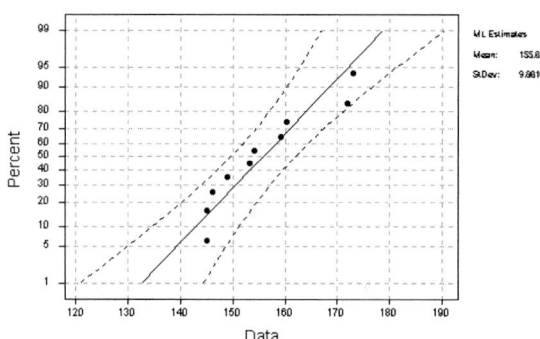

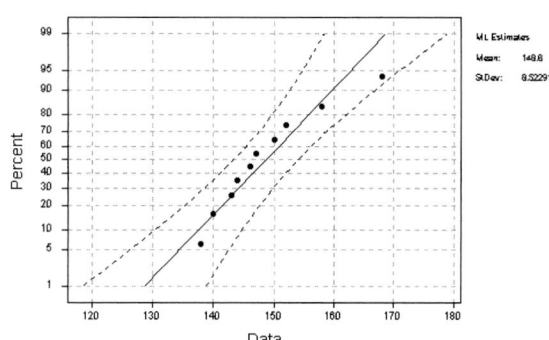

(b) American: Lower bound, 148.2 minutes; Upper bound, 163.0 minutes; United: Lower bound, 142.2 minutes; Upper bound, 155.0 minutes
   (c) No, because the confidence intervals overlap.

18. (a)

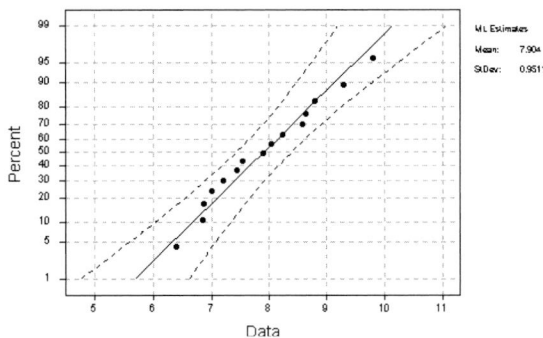

Normal Probability Plot for Flight

ML Estimates
Mean: 7.904
StDev: 0.951194

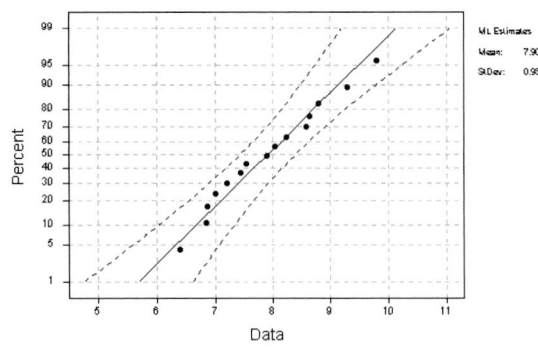

Normal Probability Plot for Control

ML Estimates
Mean: 7.904
StDev: 0.951194

(b) Flight: Lower bound, 7.359 mm; Upper bound, 8.449 mm; Control: Lower bound, 7.934 mm; Upper bound, 9.373 mm
(c) No, because the confidence intervals overlap.

19. z-interval: Lower bound: 68.39 inches; Upper bound: 71.32 inches
20. z-interval: Lower bound: 258.7 days; Upper bound: 276.8 days
21. Neither; the data do not appear to come from a normal population, and the sample size is small.
22. t-interval: Lower bound, 23.56%; Upper bound, 32.39%
23. t-interval: Lower bound, 101.4 minutes; Upper bound, 117.3 minutes
24. Neither; the data do not appear to come from a normal population, and the sample size is small.

25. (a)

Asking Price of Homes in Houston, TX

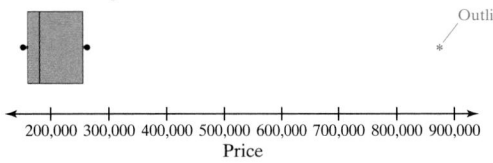

Outlier
*

200,000 300,000 400,000 500,000 600,000 700,000 800,000 900,000
Price

(b) Lower bound: $73,258; Upper bound: $434,209
(c) Lower bound: $149,802; Upper bound: $244,707
(d) The interval has a much smaller margin of error with the outlier removed.

26. (a)

Age of Death

*

20 30 40 50 60 70 80 90 100
Age

(b) Lower bound: 59.1 years; Upper bound: 78.7 years
(c) Lower bound: 65.3 years; Upper bound: 80.4 years

(d) The interval has a much smaller margin of error with the outlier removed.

8.3 Exercises (page 495)

1. Lower bound: 0.146; Upper bound: 0.254
2. Lower bound: 0.319; Upper bound: 0.481
3. Lower bound: 0.191; Upper bound: 0.289
4. Lower bound: 0.307; Upper bound: 0.360
5. Lower bound: 0.758; Upper bound: 0.805
6. Lower bound: 0.566; Upper bound: 0.634
7. (a) 0.054
 (b) $n\hat{p}(1 - \hat{p}) = 44.44 \geq 10$, and the sample is less than 5% of the population.
 (c) Lower bound: 0.042; Upper bound: 0.067
 (d) We are 90% confident that the proportion of Lipitor users who will experience a headache as a side effect is between 0.042 and 0.067.
8. (a) 0.784
 (b) $n\hat{p}(1 - \hat{p}) = 12.54 \geq 10$, and the sample is less than 5% of the population.
 (c) Lower bound: 0.661; Upper bound: 0.907
 (d) The researchers are 99% confident that the proportion of ulcer patients who receive Pepcid and then have their ulcers heal is between 0.661 and 0.907.
9. (a) 0.230
 (b) $n\hat{p}(1 - \hat{p}) = 177.1 \geq 10$, and the sample is less than 5% of the population.
 (c) Lower bound: 0.199; Upper bound: 0.261
 (d) The Gallup Organization is 98% confident that the proportion of adults 18 years or older who know someone who is capable of an act of violence in the workplace is between 0.199 and 0.261.
10. (a) 0.630
 (b) $n\hat{p}(1 - \hat{p}) = 236.32 \geq 10$, and the sample is less than 5% of the population.
 (c) Lower bound: 0.600; Upper bound: 0.660
 (d) The Gallup Organization is 95% confident that the proportion of adults 18 years or older who support a law that would make it illegal to perform "partial-birth abortions" except in cases necessary to save the life of the mother is between 0.600 and 0.660.
11. (a) $n\hat{p}(1 - \hat{p}) = 2682.37 \geq 10$, and the sample is less than 5% of the population.
 (b) Lower bound: 0.544; Upper bound: 0.560. The Centers for Disease Control are 99% confident that the proportion of mothers who breastfed their babies between 1990 and 1993 is between 0.540 and 0.564.
 (c) Lower bound: 0.540; Upper bound: 0.564. The Centers for Disease Control are 99% confident that the proportion of mothers who breastfed their babies between 1990 and 1993 is between 0.540 and 0.564.
 (d) The width of the interval increases.
12. (a) $n\hat{p}(1 - \hat{p}) = 542.74 \geq 10$, and the sample is less than 5% of the population.
 (b) Lower bound: 0.546; Upper bound: 0.583. The Harris Poll is 92% confident that the proportion of Americans who judge that state laws governing child safety restraints in vehicles should be strengthened is between 0.546 and 0.583.
 (c) Lower bound: 0.543; Upper bound: 0.586. The Harris Poll is 96% confident that the proportion of Americans who judge that state laws governing child safety restraints in vehicles should be strengthened is between 0.543 and 0.586.
 (d) The width of the interval increases.
13. (a) Lower bound: 0.179; Upper bound: 0.193. The Centers for Disease Control are 95% confident that the proportion of 30–39-year-old Americans who were found to be obese in 1999 is between 0.179 and 0.193.
 (b) Lower bound: 0.162; Upper bound: 0.176. The Centers for Disease Control are 95% confident that the proportion of

30–39-year-old Americans who were found to be obese in 1998 is between 0.162 and 0.176.
  (c) Yes
14. (a) Lower bound: 0.200; Upper bound: 0.212. The Centers for Disease Control are 95% confident that the proportion of Americans with high school diplomas who are obese is between 0.200 and 0.212.
  (b) Lower bound: 0.137; Upper bound: 0.149. The Centers for Disease Control are 95% confident that the proportion of Americans with four or more years of college who are obese is between 0.137 and 0.149.
  (c) Yes
15. (a) 1111 **(b)** 1842 **16. (a)** 1485 **(b)** 1692
17. (a) 683 **(b)** 1068 **18. (a)** 395 **(b)** 423
19. (a) 1566 **(b)** 6012 **20. (a)** 1269 **(b)** 1414
21. 984 **22.** 1016
24. Based on the survey results, George Bush was expected to receive between 46% and 50% of the votes, while Al Gore was expected to receive between 44% and 46% of the votes. Because the intervals overlap, the race was considered too close to call.
25. (a) 0.82 **(b)** 0.017
  (c) Lower bound: 0.787; Upper bound: 0.853. The student council is 95% confident that the proportion of students in favor of establishing a student union is between 0.787 and 0.853.

8.4 Exercises (page 503)

1. 10.117; 30.144 **2.** 12.401; 39.364
3. 9.542; 40.289 **4.** 3.565; 29.819
5. (a) Lower bound: 7.95; Upper bound: 23.66
  (b) Lower bound: 8.59; Upper bound: 20.63. The width of the interval decreases.
  (c) Lower bound: 6.61; Upper bound: 31.36. The width of the interval increases.
6. (a) Lower bound: 9.37; Upper bound: 66.00.
  (b) Lower bound: 12.07; Upper bound: 38.32. The width of the interval decreases.
  (c) Lower bound: 7.55; Upper bound: 102.7. The width of the interval increases.
7. Lower bound: 0.0303 gram; Upper bound: 0.0653 gram. We are 95% confident that the standard deviation weight of wheat pennies is between 0.0303 gram and 0.0653 gram.
8. Lower bound: 6934.09 miles; Upper bound: 20,929.74 miles. We are 95% confident that the standard deviation mileage on four-year-old Camaros is between 6934.09 and 20,929.74 miles.
9. Lower bound: 13.297 thousand psi; Upper bound: 28.545 thousand psi. We are 99% confident that the standard deviation tensile strength is between 13.297 thousand and 28.545 thousand psi.
10. Lower bound: 16.2 yards; Upper bound: 52.0 yards. Dan is 99% confident that the standard deviation driving distance is between 16.2 and 52.0 yards.

11. (a)

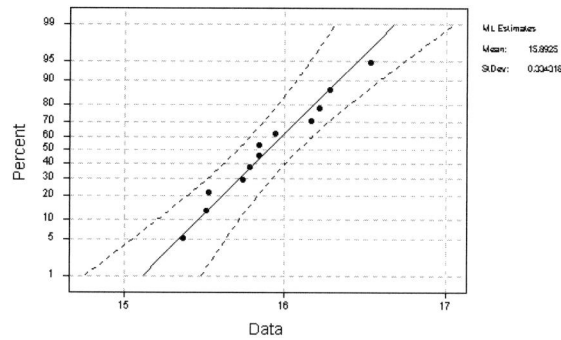

Normal Probability Plot for Ounces

(b) 0.349 oz
(c) Lower bound: 0.261 oz; Upper bound: 0.541 oz
(d) No

12. (a)

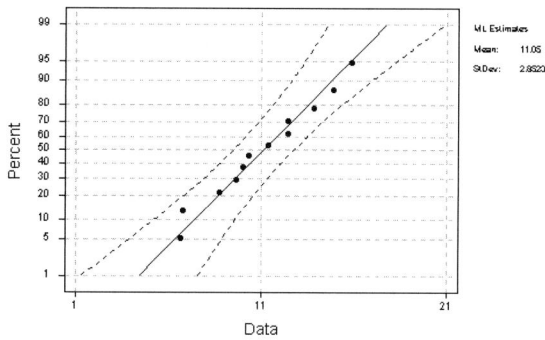

Normal Probability Plot for Return

(b) 2.98 percent
(c) Lower bound: 2.11 percent; Upper bound: 5.06 percent
(d) Yes
13. (a) AA: Lower bound: 7.2 minutes; Upper bound: 19.0 minutes; UA: Lower bound: 6.2 minutes; Upper bound: 16.4 minutes.
  (b) No
14. (a) Flight: Lower bound: 0.757 mm; Upper bound: 1.437 mm; Control: Lower bound: 0.999 mm; Upper bound: 1.896 mm
  (b) No
15. 73.772; 129.070

Chapter Review Exercises (page 507)

1. 2.898
2. 1.706
3. 10.283; 35.479
4. 2.603; 26.757
5. (a) Lower bound: 50.94; Upper bound: 58.66
  (b) Lower bound: 51.65; Upper bound: 57.95. The width of the interval increases.
  (c) Lower bound: 48.75; Upper bound: 60.85. The width of the interval increases.
6. (a) Lower bound: 97.07; Upper bound: 111.53
  (b) Lower bound: 98.86; Upper bound: 109.74. The width of the interval decreases.
  (c) Lower bound: 95.50; Upper bound: 113.11. The width of the interval increases.
  (d) Lower bound: 12.22; Upper bound: 23.21
7. (a) The sample size is large.
  (b) Lower bound: 61,227 miles; Upper bound: 63,673 miles. Dunlop is 90% confident that the mean distance its SP4000 tires will last is between 61,227 and 63,673 miles.
  (c) Lower bound: 60,992 miles; Upper bound: 63,908 miles. Dunlop is 95% confident that the mean distance its SP4000 tires will last is between 60,992 and 63,908 miles.
  (d) 15
8. (a) The sample size is large.
  (b) Lower bound: 307.9 minutes; Upper bound: 322.1 minutes. Motorola is 94% confident that the mean talk time on its Timeport P8160 digital phone is between 307.9 and 322.1 minutes.
  (c) Lower bound: 306.2 minutes; Upper bound: 323.8 minutes. Motorola is 98% confident that the mean talk time on its Timeport P8160 digital phone is between 306.2 and 323.8 minutes.
  (d) 23

9. (a)

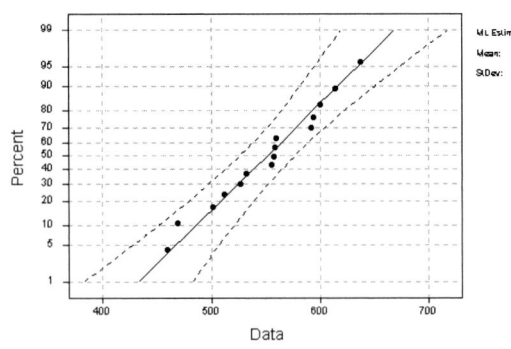

Normal Probability Plot for Canada

Normal Probability Plot for United State

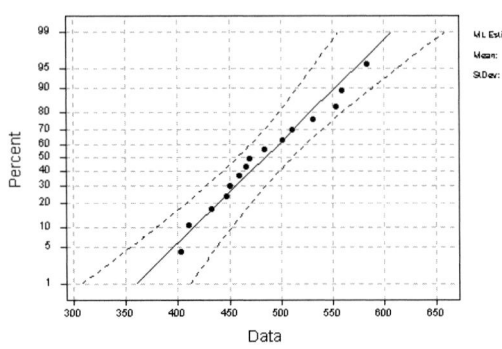

(b) Canada: 550.4; United States: 483.5
(c) Lower bound: 508.8; Upper bound: 592.0
(d) Lower bound: 435.9; Upper bound: 531.0
(e) No, the confidence intervals overlap.

10. (a)

Normal Probability Plot for Male

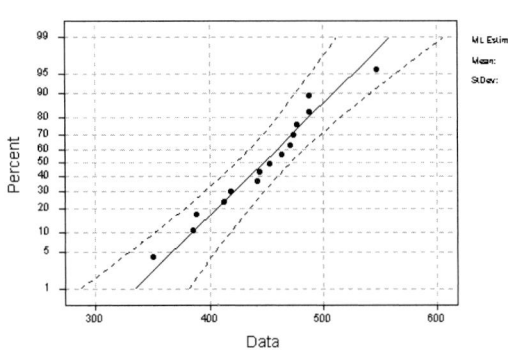

Normal Probability Plot for Female

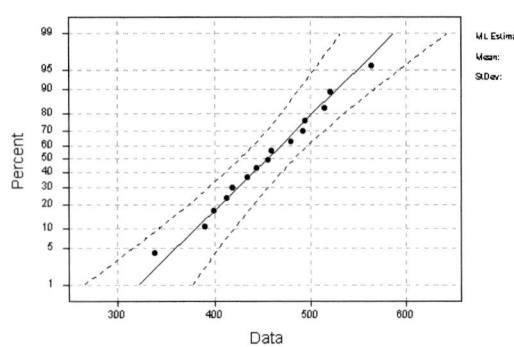

(b) Males: 446.5; Females: 453.5
(c) Lower bound: 413.7; Upper bound: 479.3
(d) Lower bound: 424.7; Upper bound: 482.3
(e) No

11. (a) Approximately normal; $\mu_{\bar{x}} = 2.27$; $\sigma_{\bar{x}} = \dfrac{1.22}{\sqrt{60}}$

(b) Lower bound: 1.95 children; Upper bound: 2.58 children. We are 95% confident that the mean number of children for couples who have been married for seven years is between 1.95 and 2.58.
(c) Lower bound: 1.85 children; Upper bound: 2.69 children. We are 99% confident that the mean number of children for couples who have been married for seven years is between 1.85 and 2.69.

12. (a) Approximately normal; $\mu_{\bar{x}} = 4.08$; $\sigma_{\bar{x}} = \dfrac{2.12}{\sqrt{50}}$

(b) Lower bound: 3.58 cars; Upper bound: 4.58 cars. We are 90% confident that the mean number of cars waiting at the McDonald's drive-through line between 11:50 A.M. and 12:00 noon is between 3.58 and 4.58.
(c) Lower bound: 3.48 cars; Upper bound: 4.68 cars. We are 95% confident that the mean number of cars waiting at the McDonald's drive-through line between 11:50 A.M. and 12:00 noon is between 3.48 and 4.68.

13. (a) $\bar{x} = 3.243$ liters; $s = 0.487$ liters
(b) Yes
(c) Lower bound: 2.934 liters; Upper bound: 3.553 liters. The researchers are 95% confident that the mean blood plasma volume of women is between 2.934 and 3.553 liters.
(d) Lower bound: 2.807 liters; Upper bound: 3.680 liters. The researchers are 99% confident that the mean blood plasma volume of women is between 2.807 and 3.680 liters.
(e) Lower bound: 0.312 liters; Upper bound: 1.001 liters. The researchers are 99% confident that the standard deviation blood plasma volume of women is between 0.312 liters and 1.001 liters.

14. (a) $\bar{x} = 57.8$ inches; $s = 15.4$ inches
(b) Yes
(c) Lower bound: 47.9 inches; Upper bound: 67.6 inches. The researcher is 95% confident that the mean depth of the Secchi dish is between 47.9 inches and 67.6 inches.
(d) Lower bound: 43.9 inches; Upper bound: 71.6 inches. The researcher is 99% confident that the mean depth of the Secchi dish is between 43.9 inches and 71.6 inches.
(e) Lower bound: 10.9 inches; Upper bound: 26.2 inches. The researcher is 95% confident that the standard-deviation depth of the Secchi dish is between 10.9 inches and 26.2 inches.

15. (a) Canada: Lower bound: 510.3; Upper bound: 590.5
(b) USA: Lower bound: 441.3; Upper bound: 525.6
(c) No

16. (a) Males: Lower bound: 418.9; Upper bound: 474.0
(b) Females: Lower bound: 420.9; Upper bound: 486.0
(c) No

17. (a) 0.086
(b) Lower bound: 0.064; Upper bound: 0.107. The Centers for Disease Control are 95% confident that the proportion of adult males 20–34 years old who have hypertension is between 0.064 and 0.107.
(c) 336   **(d)** 1068

18. (a) 0.948
(b) Lower bound: 0.932; Upper bound: 0.965. The EPA is 99% confident that the proportion of Americans who live in neighborhoods with acceptable levels of carbon monoxide is between 0.932 and 0.965.
(c) 593   **(d)** 3007

19. (a) Lower bound: 38.2; Upper bound: 82.4
(b) Lower bound: 40.1; Upper bound: 86.4
(c) No

20. (a) Lower bound: 36.4; Upper bound: 78.5
   (b) Lower bound: 43.0; Upper bound: 92.6
   (c) No

21. 0.0681   **22.** *t*-distribution

CHAPTER 9   Hypothesis Testing

9.1 Exercises (page 525)

1. Right tailed, μ **2.** Left tailed, p **3.** Two tailed, σ
4. Right tailed, p **5.** Left tailed, μ **6.** Two tailed, σ

7. (a) $H_o: \mu = 89$ vs $H_1: \mu < 89$
   (b) The researcher would reject the null hypothesis that the mean farm rent is $89 per acre when, in fact, the mean farm rent is $89 per acre.
   (c) The researcher would not reject the null hypothesis that the mean farm rent is $89 per acre when, in fact, the mean farm rent is less than $89 per acre.

8. (a) $H_o: \mu = 5.01$ vs $H_1: \mu < 5.01$
   (b) The researcher would reject the null hypothesis that the mean pH of the rain is 5.01 when, in fact, the mean pH of the rain is 5.01.
   (c) The researcher would not reject the null hypothesis that the mean pH of the rain is 5.01 when, in fact, the mean pH of the rain is less than 5.01.

9. (a) $H_o: p = 0.163$ vs $H_1: p < 0.163$
   (b) The politician would reject the null hypothesis that the proportion of Americans who do not have health insurance is 0.163 when, in fact, the proportion of Americans who do not have health insurance is 0.163.
   (c) The politician would not reject the null hypothesis that the proportion of Americans who do not have health insurance is 0.163 when, in fact, the proportion of Americans who do not have health insurance is less than 0.163.

10. (a) $H_o: p = 0.782$ vs $H_1: p > 0.782$
   (b) The nutritionist would reject the null hypothesis that the proportion of 12–19-year-old females who do not get the USDA's recommended daily allowance of protein is 0.782 when, in fact, the proportion of 12–19-year-old females who do not get the USDA's recommended daily allowance of protein is 0.782.
   (c) The nutritionist would not reject the null hypothesis that the proportion of 12–19-year-old females who do not get the USDA's recommended daily allowance of protein is 0.782 when, in fact, the proportion of 12–19 year-old females who do not get the USDA's recommended daily allowance of protein is more than 0.782.

11. (a) $H_o: \mu = 1338$ vs $H_1: \mu \neq 1338$
   (b) The economist would reject the null hypothesis that the mean energy expenditures are $1338 when, in fact, the mean energy expenditures are $1338.
   (c) The economist would not reject the null hypothesis that the mean energy expenditures are $1338 when, in fact, the mean energy expenditures are not $1338.

12. (a) $H_o: \mu = 36.7$ vs $H_1: \mu \neq 36.7$
   (b) The district attorney would reject the null hypothesis that the mean age of a death row inmate is 36.7 years when, in fact, the mean age of a death row inmate is 36.7 years.
   (c) The district attorney would not reject the null hypothesis that the mean age of a death row inmate is 36.7 years when, in fact, the mean age of a death row inmate is not 36.7 years.

13. (a) $H_o: \sigma = 4.2$ vs $H_1: \sigma > 4.2$
   (b) The analyst would reject the null hypothesis that the standard deviation rate of return is 4.2 percent when, in fact, the standard deviation rate of return is 4.2 percent.
   (c) The analyst would not reject the null hypothesis that the standard deviation rate of return is 4.2 percent when, in fact, the standard deviation rate of return is more than 4.2 percent.

14. (a) $H_o: \sigma = 111$ vs $H_1: \sigma < 111$
   (b) The teacher would reject the null hypothesis that the standard deviation SAT Verbal score is 111 when, in fact, the standard deviation SAT Verbal score is 111.
   (c) The teacher would not reject the null hypothesis that the standard deviation SAT Verbal score is 111 when, in fact, the standard deviation SAT Verbal score is less than 111.

15. There is sufficient evidence to support the claim that the mean farm rent in Indiana has decreased from $89 per acre.

16. There is not sufficient evidence to support the claim that the mean pH level has decreased from its 2000 level of 5.01.

17. There is not sufficient evidence to support the claim that the proportion of Americans who do not have health insurance has decreased from its 1998 level of 0.163.

18. There is sufficient evidence to support the claim that the proportion of 12–19-year-old females at the boarding school who get the USDA's recommended daily allowance of protein is greater than 0.782.

19. There is not sufficient evidence to support the claim that the mean energy expenditure today is different from $1338.

20. There is not sufficient evidence to support the claim that the mean age of a death row inmate is different from 36.7 years.

21. There is sufficient evidence to support the claim that the standard deviation rate of return is greater than 4.2 percent.

22. There is not sufficient evidence to support the claim that the standard deviation SAT Verbal score is less than 111.

23. There is not sufficient evidence to support the claim that the mean farm rent in Indiana is less than $89 per acre.

24. There is sufficient evidence to support the claim that the mean pH level of rain in Gunnison County, CO has decreased (which means that acidity has increased).

25. There is sufficient evidence to support the claim that the proportion of Americans who do not have health insurance has decreased from 0.163.

26. There is not sufficient evidence to support the claim that the proportion of 12–19-year-old females at a boarding school get the USDA's recommended daily allowance of protein.

27. (a) $H_o: \mu = 48.3$ vs $H_1: \mu > 48.3$
   (b) There is sufficient evidence to support the claim that the mean potato consumption in the United States is greater than 48.3 pounds per year.
   (c) Type I error; 0.05
   (d) Increase α

28. (a) $H_o: \mu = 505$ vs $H_1: \mu > 505$
   (b) There is not sufficient evidence to support the claim that the mean SAT Math score for students taking the prep course is greater than 505.
   (c) Type II error; 0.01
   (d) Increase α

29. (a) $H_o: p = 0.38$ vs $H_1: p < 0.38$
   (b) There is not sufficient evidence to support the claim that the proportion of traffic fatalities in which the driver had a BAC of 0.08 or higher decreased after the advertising campaign.
   (c) Type II error

30. (a) $H_o: p = 0.107$ vs $H_1: p > 0.107$
   (b) There is sufficient evidence to support the claim that the proportion of Americans who utilize the Internet is greater than 0.107.
   (c) Type I error

31. Let μ represent the mean population increase in mpg.
   $H_o: \mu = 0$ vs $H_1: \mu > 0$

32. (a) $H_o: \mu = 4$ vs $H_1: \mu < 4$
   (b) Prolong's claim is not true.

9.2 Exercises (page 539)

1. (a) $Z = -1.18$ **(b)** $-z_{0.05} = -1.645$

(c)

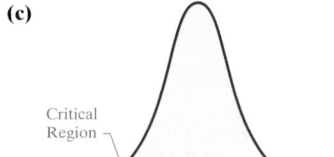

(d) No, the test statistic does not lie in the critical region.

2. (a) $Z = 1.92$ **(b)** $z_{0.01} = 1.28$

(c)

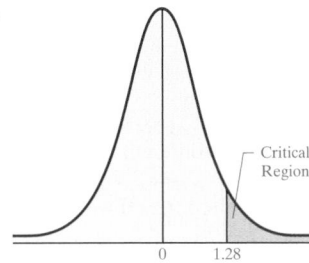

(d) Yes, the test statistic lies in the critical region.

3. (a) $Z = 3.29$ **(b)** $-z_{0.005} = -2.575$; $z_{0.005} = 2.575$

(c)

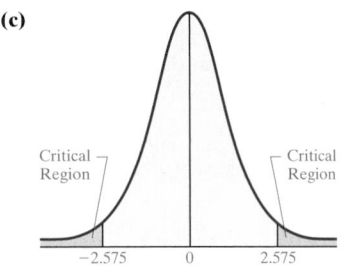

(d) Yes, the test statistic lies in the critical region.

4. (a) $Z = -1.32$ **(b)** $-z_{0.02} = -2.05$

(c)

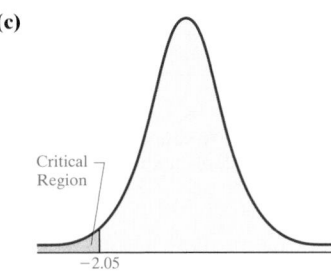

(d) No, the test statistic does not lie in the critical region.

5. (a) 0.0081   **(b)** Yes; P-value $< \alpha$

6. (a) 0.1147   **(b)** No; P-value $> \alpha$

7. (a) No   **(b)** 0.0610   **(c)** No; P-value $> \alpha$

8. (a) No   **(b)** 0.0091   **(c)** Yes; P-value $< \alpha$

9. Step 1: $H_o: \mu = 26.4$ vs $H_1: \mu > 26.4$
Step 2: $z_{0.05} = 1.645$
Step 3: $Z = 0.69$
Step 4: Do not reject H_o, because $Z < z_{0.05}$.
Step 5: There is not sufficient evidence at the $\alpha = 0.05$ level of significance to support the researcher's claim that the average age of a woman before she has her first child is greater than 26.4 years.

10. Step 1: $H_o: \mu = 25.1$ vs $H_1: \mu > 25.1$
Step 2: $z_{0.05} = 1.645$
Step 3: $Z = 2.58$
Step 4: Reject H_o, because $Z > z_{0.05}$.
Step 5: There is sufficient evidence at the $\alpha = 0.05$ level of significance to support the researcher's claim that the mean gas mileage is greater than 25.1 with the additive.

11. (a) The sample size is small.
(b) Step 1: $H_o: \mu = 516$ vs $H_1: \mu < 516$
Step 2: $-z_{0.1} = -1.28$
Step 3: $Z = -2.18$
Step 4: Reject H_o, because $Z < -z_{0.05}$.
Step 5: There is sufficient evidence at the $\alpha = 0.1$ level of significance to support the administrator's claim that the mean SAT Verbal score is less than 516.

12. (a) The sample size is small.
(b) Step 1: $H_o: \mu = 516$ vs $H_1: \mu \neq 516$
Step 2: $-z_{0.05} = 1.645$; $z_{0.05} = 1.645$
Step 3: $Z = 0.08$
Step 4: Do not reject H_o, because $-z_{0.05} < Z < z_{0.05}$.
Step 5: There is not sufficient evidence at the $\alpha = 0.1$ level of significance to support the researcher's claim that students whose first language is not English score differently from students whose first language is English.

13. (a) Yes
(b) Step 1: $H_o: \mu = 5.03$ vs. $H_1: \mu < 5.03$
Step 2: $Z = -4.78$
Step 3: $-z_{0.01} = -2.33$; P-value < 0.0001
Step 4: Reject H_o.
Step 5: There is sufficient evidence at the $\alpha = 0.01$ level of significance to support the claim that the mean acidity in Pierce County, WA has increased (the pH level has decreased).

14. (a) Yes
(b) Step 1: $H_o: \mu = 25$ vs. $H_1: \mu > 25$
Step 2: $Z = 3.61$
Step 3: $z_{0.05} = 1.645$; P-value $= 0.0002$
Step 4: Reject H_o.
Step 5: There is sufficient evidence at the $\alpha = 0.05$ level of significance to support the claim that the mean age of a bride in Memphis, Tennessee, is greater than the mean age of a bride in the United States.

15. (a) Yes
(b) Step 1: $H_o: \mu = 64$ vs. $H_1: \mu \neq 64$
Step 2: $Z = -3.30$
Step 3: $-z_{0.05} = -1.645$; $Z_{0.05} = 1.645$; P-value $= 0.0010$
Step 4: Reject H_o.
Step 5: There is sufficient evidence at the $\alpha = 0.1$ level of significance to support the claim that the mean amount of juice in the bottle is different from 64 ounces.

16. (a) Yes
(b) Step 1: $H_o: \mu = 1.56$ vs. $H_1: \mu \neq 1.56$
Step 2: $Z = 1.48$
Step 3: $-z_{0.05} = -1.645$; $Z_{0.05} = 1.645$; P-value $= 0.14$
Step 4: Do not reject H_o.
Step 5: There is not sufficient evidence at the $\alpha = 0.1$ level of significance to support the claim that the mean price of a gallon of gasoline is different from \$1.56.

17. (a) Yes
(b) Step 1: $H_o: \mu = 8.33$ vs. $H_1: \mu < 8.33$
Step 2: $Z = -0.86$
Step 3: $-z_{0.1} = -1.28$; P-value $= 0.19$
Step 4: Do not reject H_o.
Step 5: There is not sufficient evidence at the $\alpha = 0.1$ level of significance to support the claim that the mean period of time for which people own their cars has decreased from 8.33 years.

18. (a) Yes
   (b) Step 1: $H_o: \mu = 0$ vs. $H_1: \mu > 0$
   Step 2: $Z = 1.92$
   Step 3: $z_{0.05} = 1.645$; P-value $= 0.027$
   Step 4: Reject H_o.
   Step 5: There is sufficient evidence at the $\alpha = 0.05$ level of significance to support the claim that the mean temperature in the summer of 2000 was higher than normal.

19. Step 1: $H_o: \mu = 694$ vs. $H_1: \mu > 694$
   Step 2: $Z = 1.10$
   Step 3: P-value $= 0.1348$
   Step 4: Do not reject H_o.
   Step 5: There is not sufficient evidence at the $\alpha = 0.05$ level of significance to support the claim that the mean size of a farm in Kansas is greater than 694 acres.

20. Step 1: $H_o: \mu = 11.1$ vs. $H_1: \mu < 11.1$
   Step 2: $Z = -2.18$
   Step 3: P-value $= 0.0148$
   Step 4: Reject H_o.
   Step 5: There is sufficient evidence at the $\alpha = 0.05$ level of significance to support the claim that the output per well in the United States has decreased from its 1998 level of 11.1 barrels per day.

21. Step 1: $H_o: \mu = 40.24$ vs. $H_1: \mu > 40.24$
   Step 2: $Z = 1.62$
   Step 3: P-value $= 0.0525$
   Step 4: Reject H_o.
   Step 5: There is sufficient evidence at the $\alpha = 0.1$ level of significance to support the claim that the mean cellular telephone bill has increased from its 1999 level of $40.24.

22. Step 1: $H_o: \mu = 2.38$ vs. $H_1: \mu > 2.38$
   Step 2: $Z = 0.39$
   Step 3: P-value $= 0.3487$
   Step 4: Do not reject H_o.
   Step 5: There is not sufficient evidence at the $\alpha = 0.05$ level of significance to support the claim that the mean length of a cellular telephone call has increased.

23. Step 1: $H_o: \mu = 31.8$ vs. $H_1: \mu \neq 31.8$
   Step 2: $Z = 2.96$
   Step 3: P-value $= 0.0031$
   Step 4: Reject H_o.
   Step 5: There is sufficient evidence at the $\alpha = 0.05$ level of significance to support the claim that the mean daily volume of Dell stock is different this year from its 2000 level.

24. Step 1: $H_o: \mu = 11.4$ vs. $H_1: \mu \neq 11.4$
   Step 2: $Z = 2.57$
   Step 3: P-value $= 0.0103$
   Step 4: Reject H_o.
   Step 5: There is sufficient evidence at the $\alpha = 0.05$ level of significance to support the claim that the mean daily volume of Motorola stock is different this year from its 2000 level.

25. Lower bound: 63.93 ounces; Upper bound: 63.98 ounces. Because the confidence interval does not contain $\mu = 64$ ounces, we reject H_o.

26. Lower bound: $1.555; Upper bound: $1.598. Because the confidence interval contains $\mu = \$1.56$, we do not reject H_o.

27. Lower bound: 35.1 million shares; Upper bound: 43.3 million shares. Because the confidence interval does not contain $\mu = 31.8$ million shares, we reject H_o.

28. Lower bound: 12.69 million shares; Upper bound: 17.31 million shares. Because the confidence interval does not contain $\mu = 11.4$ million shares, we reject H_o.

29. (a) $H_o: \mu = 514$ versus $H_1: \mu > 514$
   (b) P-value $= 0.0666$. Since P-value $< \alpha$, we reject H_o. There is significant evidence at the $\alpha = 0.1$ level of significance to reject H_o.
   (c) There is no real practical difference between scores of 514 and 518.
   (d) P-value $= 0.2395$; Do not reject H_o.

32. (a) $H_o: \mu = 150$ versus $H_1: \mu < 150$
   (b) There is a 0.02 probability of obtaining a sample mean as extreme as or more extreme than the one obtained from a population whose mean is 150.

9.3 Exercises (page 551)

1. (a) $t = -1.379$ **(b)** $-t_{0.05} = -1.714$

(c)

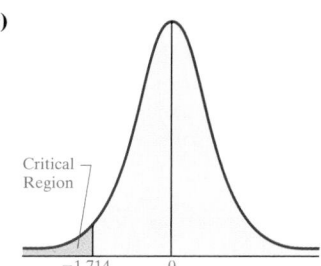

(d) No

2. (a) $t = 2.674$ **(b)** $t_{0.1} = 1.318$

(c)

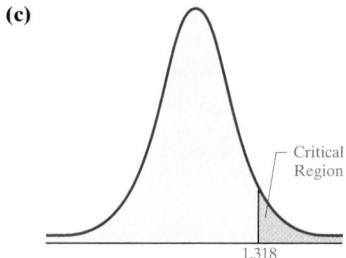

(d) Yes

3. (a) $t = 2.502$ **(b)** $-t_{0.005} = -2.819$; $t_{0.005} = 2.819$

(c)

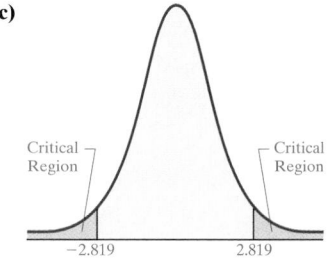

(d) No

4. (a) $t = -1.711$ **(b)** $-t_{0.02} = -2.189$

(c)

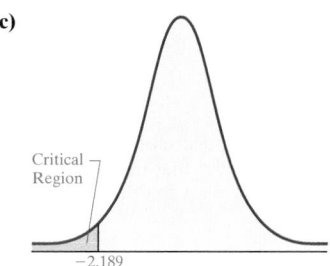

(d) No

5. (a) $t = -1.677$

(b)

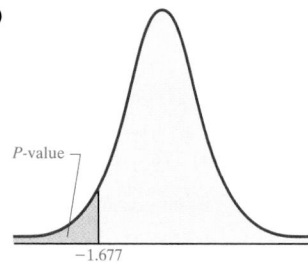

(c) P-value $= 0.0559$ **(d)** No

6. (a) $t = 1.109$

(b)

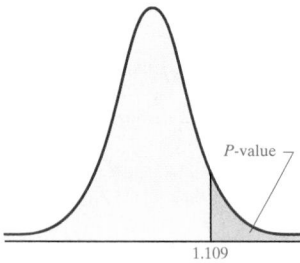

(c) P-value $= 0.1445$ **(d)** No

7. (a) No, $n \geq 30$ **(b)** $t = -3.108$

(c)

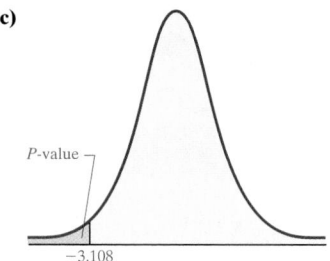

(d) P-value $= 0.0038$ **(e)** Yes

8. (a) No, $n \geq 30$ **(b)** $t = 2.455$

(c)

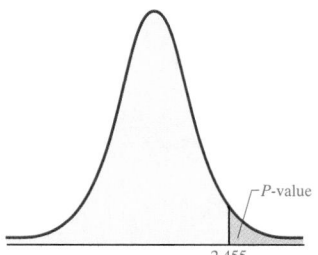

(d) P-value $= 0.0186$ **(e)** No

9. (a) Step 1: $H_0: \mu = 9.02$ vs $H_1: \mu < 9.02$
    Step 2: $-t_{0.01} = -2.718$
    Step 3: $t = -4.553$
    Step 4: Reject H_0.
    Step 5: There is sufficient evidence at the $\alpha = 0.01$ level of significance to support the claim that the hippocampal volume in alcoholic adolescents is smaller than 9.02 cm³.
  (b) P-value $= 0.0004$

10. (a) Large sample size
  (b) Step 1: $H_0: \mu = 12.88$ vs $H_1: \mu > 12.88$
    Step 2: $t_{0.01} = 2.390$ (using 60 df)
    Step 3: $t = 15.534$

Step 4: Reject H_0.
Step 5: There is sufficient evidence at the $\alpha = 0.01$ level of significance to support the claim that the serum retinol level of infants given the Vitamin A supplement is greater than 12.88 micrograms/dl.
  (c) P-value < 0.0001

11. (a) Step 1: $H_0: \mu = 20$ vs $H_1: \mu < 20$
    Step 2: $-t_{0.01} = -2.364$ (using 100 df)
    Step 3: $t = -2.114$
    Step 4: Do not reject H_0.
    Step 5: There is not sufficient evidence at the $\alpha = 0.01$ level of significance to support the claim that the mean daily consumption of fiber in 20–39-year-old males is less than 20 grams.
  (b) P-value $= 0.0175$

12. (a) Step 1: $H_0: \mu = 2750$ vs $H_1: \mu > 2750$
    Step 2: $t_{0.05} = 1.646$ (using 1000 df)
    Step 3: $t = 2.771$
    Step 4: Reject H_0.
    Step 5: There is sufficient evidence at the $\alpha = 0.05$ level of significance to support the claim that the mean daily consumption of sodium for 20–39-year-old females is more than 2750 mg..
  (b) P-value $= 0.0029$

13. (a) Step 1: $H_0: \mu = 98.6$ vs $H_1: \mu < 98.6$
    Step 2: $-t_{0.01} = -2.330$ (using 100 df)
    Step 3: $t = -15.119$
    Step 4: Reject H_0.
    Step 5: There is sufficient evidence at the $\alpha = 0.01$ level of significance to support the claim that the mean temperature of humans is less than 98.6°F.
  (b) P-value < 0.0001

14. (a) Step 1: $H_0: \mu = 98.6$ vs $H_1: \mu < 98.6$
    Step 2: $-t_{0.01} = -2.330$ (using 100 df)
    Step 3: $t = -3.169$
    Step 4: Reject H_0.
    Step 5: There is sufficient evidence at the $\alpha = 0.01$ level of significance to support the claim that the mean temperature of females is less than 98.6° F.
  (b) P-value $= 0.0001$

15. (a) Step 1: $H_0: \mu = 36.2$ vs $H_1: \mu \neq 36.2$
    Step 2: $-t_{0.025} = -2.040; t_{0.025} = 2.040$
    Step 3: $t = 1.591$
    Step 4: Do not reject H_0.
    Step 5: There is not sufficient evidence at the $\alpha = 0.05$ level of significance to support the claim that the mean age of a death-row inmate is greater than 36.2 years.
  (b) P-value $= 0.1218$

16. (a) Step 1: $H_0: \mu = 1338$ vs $H_1: \mu \neq 1338$
    Step 2: $-t_{0.025} = -2.032; t_{0.025} = 2.032$
    Step 3: $t = 1.567$
    Step 4: Do not reject H_0.
    Step 5: There is not sufficient evidence at the $\alpha = 0.05$ level of significance to support the claim that the mean energy expenditure for the most recent year is different from $1338.
  (b) P-value $= 0.1265$

17. (a) Step 1: $H_0: \mu = 200$ vs $H_1: \mu > 200$
    Step 2: $t_{0.05} = 1.685$
    Step 3: $t = 1.775$
    Step 4: Reject H_0.
    Step 5: There is sufficient evidence at the $\alpha = 0.05$ level of significance to support the claim that the mean cholesterol of males between 40 and 49 is above 200.
  (b) P-value $= 0.0419$

18. (a) Step 1: $H_0: \mu = 130$ vs $H_1: \mu > 130$
    Step 2: $t_{0.01} = 2.441$
    Step 3: $t = 3.153$

Step 4: Reject H_o.
Step 5: There is sufficient evidence at the $\alpha = 0.01$ level of significance to support the claim that the mean LDL cholesterol of 40–49-year-old females is above 130.

(b) P-value $= 0.0017$

19. (a) Yes

(b) **Step 1:** $H_o: \mu = 1.68$ vs $H_1: \mu \neq 1.68$
Step 2: $-t_{0.025} = -2.201$; $t_{0.025} = 2.201$
Step 3: $t = 0.78$
Step 4: Do not reject H_o.
Step 5: There is not sufficient evidence at the $\alpha = 0.05$ level of significance to support the claim that the mean diameter of the golf ball is different from 1.68 inches.

(c) P-value $= 0.45$

20. (a) Yes

(b) **Step 1:** $H_o: \mu = 1.62$ vs $H_1: \mu < 1.62$
Step 2: $-t_{0.1} = -1.363$
Step 3: $t = -3.84$
Step 4: Reject H_o.
Step 5: There is sufficient evidence at the $\alpha = 0.05$ level of significance to support the claim that the mean weight of the golf ball is less than 1.62 ounces.

(c) P-value $= 0.0014$

21. (a) Yes

(b) **Step 1:** $H_o: \mu = 7.0$ vs $H_1: \mu \neq 7.0$
Step 2: $-t_{0.025} = -2.160$; $t_{0.025} = 2.160$
Step 3: $t = 1.18$
Step 4: Do not reject H_o.
Step 5: There is not sufficient evidence at the $\alpha = 0.05$ level of significance to support the claim that the pH meter is calibrated incorrectly.

(c) P-value $= 0.26$

22. (a) Yes

(b) **Step 1:** $H_o: \mu = 220$ vs $H_1: \mu \neq 220$
Step 2: $-t_{0.025} = -2.921$; $t_{0.025} = 2.921$
Step 3: $t = 2.03$
Step 4: Do not reject H_o.
Step 5: There is not sufficient evidence at the $\alpha = 0.01$ level of significance to support the claim that the amount of Naproxen Sodium is different from 220 mg.

(c) P-value $= 0.059$

23. (a)

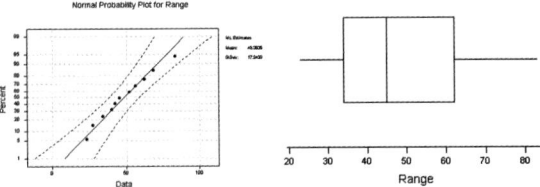

(b) **Step 1:** $H_o: \mu = 35$ vs $H_1: \mu > 35$
Step 2: $t_{0.05} = 1.812$
Step 3: $t = 2.451$
Step 4: Reject H_o.
Step 5: There is sufficient evidence at the $\alpha = 0.05$ level of significance to support the claim that the bat's range is more than 35 cm.

(c) P-value $= 0.017$

24. (a)

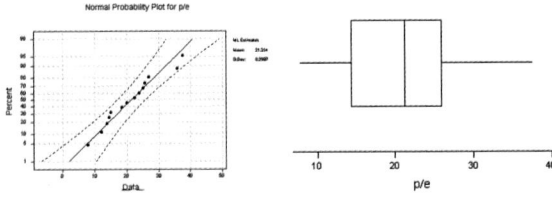

(b) **Step 1:** $H_o: \mu = 22.0$ vs $H_1: \mu < 22.0$
Step 2: $-t_{0.05} = -1.771$
Step 3: $t = -0.30$
Step 4: Do not reject H_o.
Step 5: There is not sufficient evidence at the $\alpha = 0.05$ level of significance to support the claim that the P/E ratio is below 22.0

(c) P-value $= 0.39$

25. $H_o: \mu = 0$ vs $H_1: \mu > 0$. There is less than a 0.01 probability of obtaining a sample mean of 0.8 mL/sec or larger from a population mean whose mean is 0.

26. (a) Yes

(b) $H_o: \mu = 130$ vs. $H_1: \mu < 130$. Because the P-value (0.098) is greater than the significance level ($\alpha = 0.05$), we do not reject the null hypothesis. There is not sufficient evidence to support the claim that the mean systolic blood pressure of the surgical patients is below 130 mm Hg.

27. (a) $H_o: \mu = 98.2$ vs. $H_1: \mu > 98.2$

(b) P-value $= 0.23$. Since the P-value is large, we do not reject the null hypothesis. There is not sufficient evidence to support the claim that the mean temperature of surgical patients is greater than $98.2°$ F.

28. The experiment was not conducted in an area that is representative of the entire state of Iowa. There are too many confounding variables.

9.4 Exercises (page 565)

1. $np_o(1 - p_o) > 10$
Step 1: $H_o: p = 0.3$ vs $H_1: p > 0.3$
Step 2: $z_{0.05} = 1.645$
Step 3: $Z = 2.31$; P-value $= 0.0103$
Step 4: Reject H_o.
Step 5: There is sufficient evidence at the $\alpha = 0.05$ level of significance to reject the null hypothesis. Conclude that $p > 0.3$.

2. $np_o(1 - p_o) > 10$
Step 1: $H_o: p = 0.6$ vs $H_1: p < 0.6$
Step 2: $-z_{0.01} = -2.33$
Step 3: $Z = -3.36$; P-value $= 0.0004$
Step 4: Reject H_o.
Step 5: There is sufficient evidence at the $\alpha = 0.01$ level of significance to reject the null hypothesis. Conclude that $p < 0.6$.

3. $np_o(1 - p_o) > 10$
Step 1: $H_o: p = 0.55$ vs $H_1: p < 0.55$
Step 2: $-z_{0.1} = -1.28$
Step 3: $Z = -0.74$; P-value $= 0.2301$
Step 4: Do not reject H_o.
Step 5: There is not sufficient evidence at the $\alpha = 0.1$ level of significance to reject the null hypothesis.

4. $np_o(1 - p_o) > 10$
Step 1: $H_o: p = 0.25$ vs $H_1: p < 0.25$
Step 2: $-z_{0.1} = -1.28$
Step 3: $Z = -0.46$; P-value $= 0.3221$
Step 4: Do not reject H_o.
Step 5: There is not sufficient evidence at the $\alpha = 0.1$ level of significance to reject the null hypothesis.

5. $np_o(1 - p_o) > 10$
Step 1: $H_o: p = 0.9$ vs $H_1: p \neq 0.9$
Step 2: $-z_{0.025} = -1.96$; $z_{0.025} = 1.96$
Step 3: $Z = -1.49$; P-value $= 0.1360$
Step 4: Do not reject H_o.
Step 5: There is not sufficient evidence at the $\alpha = 0.05$ level of significance to reject the null hypothesis.

6. $np_o(1 - p_o) > 10$
Step 1: $H_o: p = 0.4$ vs $H_1: p \neq 0.4$
Step 2: $-z_{0.005} = -2.575$; $z_{0.005} = 2.575$
Step 3: $Z = 1.29$; P-value $= 0.1967$

Step 4: Do not reject H_o.
Step 5: There is not sufficient evidence at the $\alpha = 0.01$ level of significance to reject the null hypothesis.

7. $np_o(1 - p_o) > 10$, and the sample size is less than 5% of the population size.

   (a) Step 1: $H_o: p = 0.47$ vs $H_1: p < 0.47$
     Step 2: $-z_{0.05} = -1.645$
     Step 3: $Z = -5.08$
     Step 4: Reject H_o.
     Step 5: There is sufficient evidence at the $\alpha = 0.05$ level of significance to support the claim that the proportion of households that have a gun has decreased since 1990.

   (b) P-value < 0.0001

8. $np_o(1 - p_o) > 10$ and the sample size is less than 5% of the population size.

   (a) Step 1: $H_o: p = 0.47$ vs $H_1: p > 0.47$
     Step 2: $z_{0.1} = 1.28$
     Step 3: $Z = 7.62$
     Step 4: Reject H_o.
     Step 5: There is sufficient evidence at the $\alpha = 0.05$ level of significance to support the claim that the proportion of 13–17-year-olds who favor life imprisonment without the possibility of parole for convicted murderers rather than the death penalty is greater than 0.47.

   (b) P-value < 0.0001

9. $np_o(1 - p_o) > 10$, and the sample size is less than 5% of the population size.

   (a) Step 1: $H_o: p = 0.019$ vs $H_1: p > 0.019$
     Step 2: $z_{0.01} = 2.33$
     Step 3: $Z = 0.65$
     Step 4: Do not reject H_o.
     Step 5: There is not sufficient evidence at the $\alpha = 0.01$ level of significance to support the claim that the proportion of Lipitor users who experience flulike symptoms is greater than 0.019.

   (b) P-value $= 0.2582$

10. $np_o(1 - p_o) > 10$, and the sample size is less than 5% of the population size.

   (a) Step 1: $H_o: p = 0.8$ vs $H_1: p > 0.8$
     Step 2: $z_{0.01} = 2.33$
     Step 3: $Z = 1.05$
     Step 4: Do not reject H_o.
     Step 5: There is not sufficient evidence at the $\alpha = 0.01$ level of significance to support the claim that the proportion of patients who are healed is greater than 0.8.

   (b) P-value $= 0.1470$

11. $np_o(1 - p_o) > 10$, and the sample size is less than 5% of the population size.

   (a) Step 1: $H_o: p = 0.071$ vs $H_1: p > 0.071$
     Step 2: $z_{0.01} = 2.33$
     Step 3: $Z = 1.25$
     Step 4: Do not reject H_o.
     Step 5: There is not sufficient evidence at the $\alpha = 0.01$ level of significance to support the claim that the proportion of 35–39-year-old mothers that give birth to low-birth-weight babies is more than 0.071

   (b) P-value $= 0.1063$

12. $np_o(1 - p_o) > 10$, and the sample size is less than 5% of the population size.

   (a) Step 1: $H_o: p = 0.249$ vs $H_1: p < 0.249$
     Step 2: $-z_{0.05} = -1.645$
     Step 3: $Z = -1.77$
     Step 4: Reject H_o.
     Step 5: There is sufficient evidence at the $\alpha = 0.05$ level of significance to support the claim that the proportion of 30-to-44-year-old males who exercise has decreased.

   (b) P-value $= 0.0387$

13. $np_o(1 - p_o) > 10$, and the sample size is less than 5% of the population size.

   (a) Step 1: $H_o: p = 0.33$ vs $H_1: p > 0.33$
     Step 2: $z_{0.05} = 1.645$
     Step 3: $Z = 5.41$
     Step 4: Reject H_o.
     Step 5: There is sufficient evidence at the $\alpha = 0.05$ level of significance to support the claim that the proportion of American adults 18 years of age or older who believe that at least one parent should stay at home to raise the children has increased.

   (b) P-value < 0.0001

14. $np_o(1 - p_o) > 10$, and the sample size is less than 5% of the population size.

   (a) Step 1: $H_o: p = 0.421$ vs $H_1: p \neq 0.421$
     Step 2: $-z_{0.05} = -1.645$; $z_{0.05} = 1.645$
     Step 3: $Z = 2.18$
     Step 4: Reject H_o.
     Step 5: There is sufficient evidence at the $\alpha = 0.1$ level of significance to support the claim that the proportion of households that own a personal computer has changed significantly since 1998.

   (b) P-value $= 0.0290$

15. $np_o(1 - p_o) > 10$, and the sample size is less than 5% of the population size.

   (a) Step 1: $H_o: p = 0.438$ vs $H_1: p > 0.438$
     Step 2: $z_{0.05} = 1.645$
     Step 3: $Z = 0.89$
     Step 4: Do not reject H_o.
     Step 5: There is not sufficient evidence at the $\alpha = 0.05$ level of significance to support the claim that the proportion of free throws made by Shaq is higher than 0.438.

   (b) P-value $= 0.1861$

16. $np_o(1 - p_o) > 10$, and the sample size is less than 5% of the population size.

   (a) Step 1: $H_o: p = 0.39$ vs $H_1: p \neq 0.39$
     Step 2: $-z_{0.05} = -1.645$; $z_{0.05} = 1.645$
     Step 3: $Z = 0.82$
     Step 4: Do not reject H_o.
     Step 5: There is not sufficient evidence at the $\alpha = 0.1$ level of significance to support the claim that the proportion of males 15 years of age or older living at home is different from 0.39.

   (b) P-value $= 0.4122$

17. $np_o(1 - p_o) > 10$, and the sample size is less than 5% of the population size.

   (a) Step 1: $H_o: p = 0.58$ vs $H_1: p \neq 0.58$
     Step 2: $-z_{0.025} = -1.96$; $z_{0.025} = 1.96$
     Step 3: $Z = 0.6190$
     Step 4: Do not reject H_o.
     Step 5: There is not sufficient evidence at the $\alpha = 0.05$ level of significance to support the claim that the proportion of Americans 18 years of age or older who have a great deal of concern regarding air pollution is different from 0.58.

   (b) P-value $= 0.5359$

18. $np_o(1 - p_o) > 10$, and the sample size is less than 5% of the population size.

   (a) Step 1: $H_o: p = 0.01$ vs $H_1: p > 0.01$
     Step 2: $z_{0.05} = 1.645$
     Step 3: $Z = 2.21$
     Step 4: Reject H_o.
     Step 5: There is not sufficient evidence at the $\alpha = 0.05$ level of significance to support the claim that the proportion of adults who are pathological gamblers is greater than 0.01.

   (b) P-value $= 0.0134$

19. $np_o(1 - p_o) > 10$, and the sample size is less than 5% of the population size.

(a) Step 1: H_o: $p = 0.85$ vs H_1: $p > 0.85$
Step 2: $z_{0.1} = 1.28$
Step 3: $Z = 1.97$
Step 4: Reject H_o.
Step 5: There is not sufficient evidence at the $\alpha = 0.1$ level of significance to support the claim that the proportion of teachers who use the Internet is greater than 0.85.

(b) P-value $= 0.0242$

20. $np_o(1 - p_o) > 10$, and the sample size is less than 5% of the population size.

(a) Step 1: H_o: $p = 0.578$ vs H_1: $p < 0.578$
Step 2: $-z_{0.1} = -1.28$
Step 3: $Z = -1.10$
Step 4: Do not reject H_o.
Step 5: There is not sufficient evidence at the $\alpha = 0.1$ level of significance to support the claim that the proportion of television and Internet households who have the television on during prime time is less than 0.578.

(b) P-value $= 0.1349$

21. $np_o(1 - p_o) > 10$, and the sample size is less than 5% of the population size.

(a) Step 1: H_o: $p = 0.37$ vs H_1: $p < 0.37$
Step 2: $-z_{0.05} = -1.645$
Step 3: $Z = -0.25$
Step 4: Do not reject H_o.
Step 5: There is not sufficient evidence at the $\alpha = 0.05$ level of significance to support the claim that the proportion of pet owners who talk to their animals on the answering machine or telephone is less than 0.37.

(b) P-value $= 0.3999$

22. $np_o(1 - p_o) > 10$, and the sample size is less than 5% of the population size.

(a) Step 1: H_o: $p = 0.85$ vs H_1: $p > 0.85$
Step 2: $z_{0.1} = 1.28$
Step 3: $Z = 0.198$
Step 4: Do not reject H_o.
Step 5: There is not sufficient evidence at the $\alpha = 0.1$ level of significance to support the claim that the proportion of Americans who eat a salad at least once a week is greater than 0.85.

(b) P-value $= 0.4215$

23. Step 1: H_o: $p = 0.04$ vs H_1: $p < 0.04$
Step 2: $np_o(1 - p_o) < 10$
Step 3: P-value $= 0.2887$
Step 4: Do not reject H_o. There is not sufficient evidence at the $\alpha = 0.05$ level of significance to support the claim that the proportion of mothers who smoke 21 or more cigarettes during their pregnancy is less than 0.04.

24. Step 1: H_o: $p = 0.032$ vs H_1: $p > 0.032$
Step 2: $np_o(1 - p_o) < 10$
Step 3: P-value $= 0.1099$
Step 4: Do not reject H_o. There is not sufficient evidence at the $\alpha = 0.05$ level of significance to support the claim that the proportion of Americans who work at home is greater than 0.032.

25. Step 1: H_o: $p = 0.096$ vs H_1: $p > 0.096$
Step 2: $np_o(1 - p_o) < 10$
Step 3: P-value $= 0.0410$
Step 4: Reject H_o. There is sufficient evidence at the $\alpha = 0.1$ level of significance to support the claim that the proportion of Californians who have a commute time of more than 60 minutes is greater than 0.096.

26. Step 1: H_o: $p = 0.015$ vs H_1: $p < 0.015$
Step 2: $np_o(1 - p_o) < 10$
Step 3: P-value $= 0.0578$
Step 4: Reject H_o. There is sufficient evidence at the $\alpha = 0.1$ level of significance to support the claim that the proportion of males living in Colorado who are teachers is less than 0.015.

9.5 Exercises (page 573)

1. (a) $\chi^2 = 20.496$ **(b)** $\chi^2_{0.95} = 13.091$

(c)
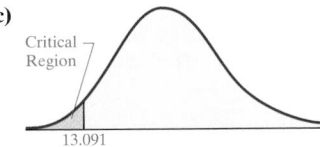

(d) Do not reject H_o, because $\chi^2 > \chi^2_{0.95}$.

2. (a) $\chi^2 = 15.986$ **(b)** $\chi^2_{0.01} = 29.141$

(c)
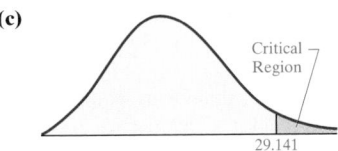

(d) Do not reject H_o, because $\chi^2 < \chi^2_{0.01}$.

3. (a) $\chi^2 = 30.222$ **(b)** $\chi^2_{0.1} = 24.769$

(c)
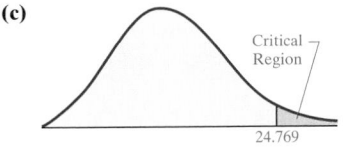

(d) Reject H_o, because $\chi^2 > \chi^2_{0.1}$.

4. (a) $\chi^2 = 17.273$ **(b)** $\chi^2_{0.99} = 22.164$

(c)
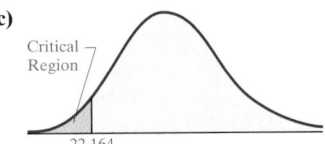

(d) Reject H_o, because $\chi^2 < \chi^2_{0.99}$.

5. (a) $\chi^2 = 13.707$ **(b)** $\chi^2_{0.975} = 3.816$; $\chi^2_{0.025} = 21.920$

(c)
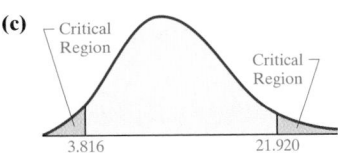

(d) Do not reject H_o, because $\chi^2_{0.975} < \chi^2 < \chi^2_{0.025}$.

6. (a) $\chi^2 = 9.333$ **(b)** $\chi^2_{0.95} = 11.591$; $\chi^2_{0.05} = 32.671$

(c)
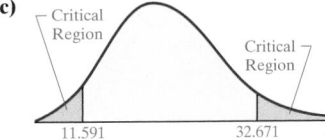

(d) Reject H_o, because $\chi^2 < \chi^2_{0.95}$.

7. Step 1: H_o: $\sigma = 4$ vs H_1: $\sigma < 4$
Step 2: $\chi^2_{0.95} = 13.848$
Step 3: $\chi^2 = 13.590$
Step 4: Reject H_o, because $\chi^2 < \chi^2_{0.95}$.
Step 5: There is sufficient evidence to support the manager's claim at the $\alpha = 0.05$ level of significance.

8. Step 1: $H_o: \sigma = 0.42$ vs $H_1: \sigma < 0.42$
Step 2: $\chi_{0.99}^2 = 7.015$
Step 3: $\chi^2 = 14.735$
Step 4: Do not reject H_o, because $\chi^2 > \chi_{0.99}^2$.
Step 5: There is not sufficient evidence to support the engineer's claim at the $\alpha = 0.01$ level of significance.

9. Step 1: $H_o: \sigma = 0.2$ vs $H_1: \sigma \neq 0.2$
Step 2: $\chi_{0.975}^2 = 8.231$; $\chi_{0.025}^2 = 31.526$
Step 3: $\chi^2 = 13.128$
Step 4: Do not reject H_o, because $\chi_{0.975}^2 < \chi^2 < \chi_{0.025}^2$.
Step 5: There is not sufficient evidence to support the claim that $\sigma \neq 0.2$ at the $\alpha = 0.05$ level of significance.

10. Step 1: $H_o: \sigma = 6.2$ vs $H_1: \sigma \neq 6.2$
Step 2: $\chi_{0.975}^2 = 8.907$; $\chi_{0.025}^2 = 32.852$
Step 3: $\chi^2 = 21.225$
Step 4: Do not reject H_o, because $\chi_{0.975}^2 < \chi^2 < \chi_{0.025}^2$.
Step 5: There is not sufficient evidence to support the claim that $\sigma \neq 6.2$ at the $\alpha = 0.05$ level of significance.

11. Step 1: $H_o: \sigma = 0.004$ vs $H_1: \sigma > 0.004$
Step 2: $\chi_{0.01}^2 = 24.725$
Step 3: $\chi^2 = 13.922$
Step 4: Do not reject H_o, because $\chi^2 < \chi_{0.01}^2$.
Step 5: There is not sufficient evidence to support the claim that $\sigma > 0.004$ at the $\alpha = 0.01$ level of significance.

12. Step 1: $H_o: \sigma = 0.005$ vs $H_1: \sigma > 0.005$
Step 2: $\chi_{0.01}^2 = 24.725$
Step 3: $\chi^2 = 12.360$
Step 4: Do not reject H_o, because $\chi^2 < \chi_{0.01}^2$.
Step 5: There is not sufficient evidence to support the claim that $\sigma > 0.005$ at the $\alpha = 0.01$ level of significance.

13. Step 1: $H_o: \sigma = 8.3$ vs $H_1: \sigma < 8.3$
Step 2: $\chi_{0.9}^2 = 15.659$
Step 3: $\chi^2 = 15.639$
Step 4: Reject H_o, because $\chi^2 < \chi_{0.9}^2$.
Step 5: There is sufficient evidence to support the claim that Allen Iverson is more consistent than other shooting guards in the NBA at the $\alpha = 0.1$ level of significance.

14. Step 1: $H_o: \sigma = 1.2$ vs $H_1: \sigma < 1.2$
Step 2: $\chi_{0.95}^2 = 34.764$ (using 50 df)
Step 3: $\chi^2 = 24.01$
Step 4: Reject H_o, because $\chi^2 < \chi_{0.95}^2$.
Step 5: There is sufficient evidence to support the claim that $\sigma < 1.2$ minutes at the $\alpha = 0.05$ level of significance.

15. (a)

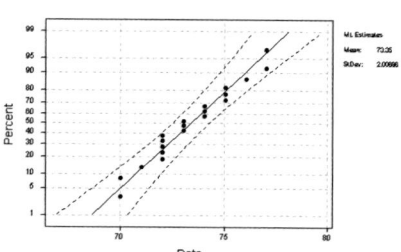

Normal Probability Plot for Height

(b) $s = 2.059$ inches
(c) Step 1: $H_o: \sigma = 2.9$ vs $H_1: \sigma < 2.9$
Step 2: $\chi_{0.99}^2 = 7.633$
Step 3: $\chi^2 = 9.578$
Step 4: Do not reject H_o, because $\chi^2 > \chi_{0.99}^2$.
Step 5: There is not sufficient evidence to support the claim that $\sigma < 2.9$ inches at the $\alpha = 0.01$ level of significance.

16. P-value $= 0.3199$
17. P-value $= 0.0446$

9.6 Exercises (page 579)

1. (a) Do not reject the null hypothesis when the alternative hypothesis is true.
(b) $0.7964; 0.2036$ **(c)** $0.9064; 0.0936$

2. (a) Do not reject the null hypothesis when the alternative hypothesis is true.
(b) $0.4914; 0.5086$ **(c)** $0.8739; 0.1261$

3. (a) Do not reject the null hypothesis when the alternative hypothesis is true.
(b) $0.6987; 0.3013$ **(c)** $0.9468; 0.0532$

4. (a) Do not reject the null hypothesis when the alternative hypothesis is true.
(b) $0.9714; 0.0286$ **(c)** $0.8966; 0.1034$

5. (a) Do not reject the null hypothesis when the alternative hypothesis is true.
(b) $0.0209; 0.9791$ **(c)** $0.6947; 0.3053$

6. (a) Do not reject the null hypothesis when the alternative hypothesis is true.
(b) $0.8535; 0.1465$ **(c)** $0.1465; 0.8535$

7. (a) Do not reject the null hypothesis when the alternative hypothesis is true.
(b) $0.5269; 0.4731$ **(c)** $0.7562; 0.2438$

8. (a) Do not reject the null hypothesis when the alternative hypothesis is true.
(b) $0.7519; 0.2481$ **(c)** $0.1674; 0.8326$

9. (a) Do not reject the null hypothesis that the mean age of a woman before she has her first child is 26.4 years when, in fact, the mean age is greater than 26.4 years.
(b) $0.8742; 0.1258$ **(c)** $0.7100; 0.2900$

10. (a) Do not reject the null hypothesis that the mean gas mileage with the additive is 25.1 when, in fact, the mean gas mileage is greater than 25.1.
(b) $0.6421; 0.3579$ **(c)** $0.2427; 0.7573$

11. (a) Do not reject the null hypothesis that the mean SAT Verbal score is 516 when, in fact, the mean SAT Verbal score is less than 516.
(b) $0.9581; 0.0419$ **(c)** $0.8357; 0.1643$

12. (a) Do not reject the null hypothesis that the mean SAT Math score is 516 when, in fact, the mean SAT Math score is less than 516.
(b) $0.9264; 0.0736$ **(c)** $0.6093; 0.3907$

13. $0.9351; 0.0649$. By lowering α, we increase the probability of making a Type II error, so the power of the test is lower.

14. $0.3495; 0.6505$. By increasing α, we lower the probability of making a Type II error, so the power of the test is higher.

15. (a) 0.1899 **(b)** 0.8101
16. (a) 0.2938 **(b)** 0.7062

Chapter Review Exercises (page 583)

1. (a) $H_o: \mu = 1100$ vs $H_1: \mu > 1100$
(b) We would reject the null hypothesis that the mean charitable contribution is $1100 when, in fact, the mean charitable contribution is $1100.
(c) We would not reject the null hypothesis that the mean charitable contribution is $1100 when, in fact, the mean charitable contribution is more than $1100.
(d) There is not sufficient evidence to support the claim that the mean charitable contribution is more than $1100.
(e) There is sufficient evidence to support the claim that the mean charitable contribution is more than $1100.

2. (a) $H_o: p = 0.176$ vs $H_1: p > 0.176$
(b) We would reject the null hypothesis that the proportion of purchases made on-line is 0.176 when, in fact, the proportion of purchases made on-line is 0.176.

(c) We would not reject the null hypothesis that the proportion of purchases made on-line is 0.176 when, in fact, the proportion of purchases made on-line is more than 0.176.

(d) There is not sufficient evidence to support the claim that the proportion of purchases made on-line is more than 0.176.

(e) There is sufficient evidence to support the claim that the proportion of purchases made on-line is more than 0.176.

3. 0.05

4. 0.113; 0.887; It is the probability of correctly rejecting the null hypothesis.

5. (a) $Z = -1.08$ **(b)** $-z_{0.05} = -1.645$

(c)

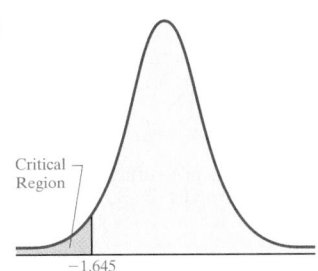

(d) No, because $Z > -z_{0.05}$ **(e)** 0.1406

6. (a) $Z = 2.18$ **(b)** $-z_{0.05} = -1.645$; $z_{0.05} = 1.645$

(c)

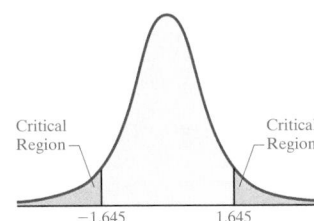

(d) Yes, because the test statistic lies in the critical region.

(e) 0.0290

(f) Lower bound: 66.38; Upper bound: 74.82. We reject the null hypothesis because the confidence interval does not contain $\mu = 65$.

7. (a) $t = -1.506$ **(b)** $-t_{0.01} = -2.624$; $t_{0.01} = 2.624$

(c)

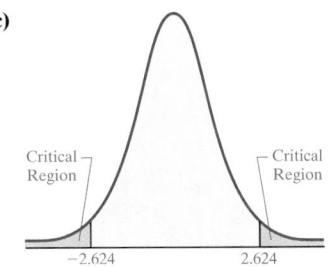

(d) No   **(e)** P-value $= 0.1543$

8. (a) $t = -2.222$ **(b)** $-t_{0.05} = -1.711$

(c)

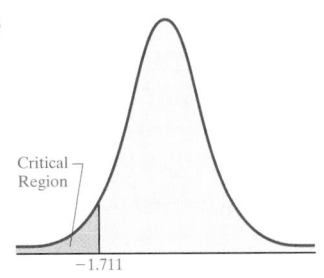

(d) Yes, because the test statistic lies in the critical region.

(e) P-value $= 0.0180$

9. $np_0(1 - p_0) > 10$, and the sample size is less than 5% of the population size.

(a) Step 1: $H_0: p = 0.6$ vs $H_1: p > 0.6$
   Step 2: $z_{0.05} = 1.645$
   Step 3: $Z = 1.94$
   Step 4: Reject H_0.
   Step 5: There is sufficient evidence at the $\alpha = 0.05$ level of significance to support the claim that $p > 0.6$.

(b) P-value $= 0.0264$

10. $np_0(1 - p_0) > 10$, and the sample size is less than 5% of the population size.

(a) Step 1: $H_0: p = 0.35$ vs $H_1: p \neq 0.35$
   Step 2: $-z_{0.005} = -2.575$; $z_{0.005} = 2.575$
   Step 3: $Z = -0.92$
   Step 4: Do not reject H_0.
   Step 5: There is not sufficient evidence at the $\alpha = 0.01$ level of significance to support the claim that $p \neq 0.35$.

(b) P-value $= 0.3572$

11. (a) $\chi^2 = 15.095$ **(b)** $\chi^2_{0.975} = 7.564$; $\chi^2_{0.025} = 30.191$

(c)

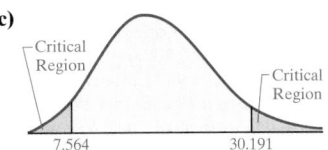

(d) Do not reject H_0, because $\chi^2_{0.975} < \chi^2 < \chi^2_{0.025}$.

12. (a) $\chi^2 = 26.508$ **(b)** $\chi^2_{0.1} = 33.196$

(c)

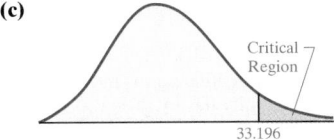

(d) Do not reject H_0 because $\chi^2 < \chi^2_{0.1}$

13. Step 1: $H_0: \mu = 78.62$ vs. $H_1: \mu \neq 78.62$
Step 2: $t = 0.927$
Step 3: $-t_{0.025} = -2.009$; $t_{0.025} = 2.009$; P-value $= 0.3584$
Step 4: Do not reject H_0.
Step 5: There is not sufficient evidence at the $\alpha = 0.05$ level of significance to support the claim that the mean price of a room has changed from $78.62.

14. Step 1: $H_0: \mu = 157.8$ vs. $H_1: \mu > 157.8$
Step 2: $t = 1.717$
Step 3: $t_{0.05} = 1.660$(using 100 df); P-value $= 0.0446$
Step 4: Reject H_0.
Step 5: There is sufficient evidence at the $\alpha = 0.05$ level of significance to support the claim that the mean household net worth where the head of household has a high school diploma has increased.

15. Step 1: $H_0: \mu = 474$ vs. $H_1: \mu > 474$
Step 2: $Z = 4.46$
Step 3: $z_{0.01} = 2.33$; P-value < 0.0001
Step 4: Reject H_0.
Step 5: There is sufficient evidence at the $\alpha = 0.01$ level of significance to support the claim that the mean SAT Math score for students who use their calculator frequently is higher than 474.

16. Step 1: $H_0: \mu = 7.53$ vs. $H_1: \mu > 7.53$
Step 2: $Z = 1.60$
Step 3: $z_{0.01} = 2.33$; P-value $= 0.0549$
Step 4: Do not reject H_0.
Step 5: There is not sufficient evidence at the $\alpha = 0.01$ level of significance to support the claim that the mean birth weight of a baby whose mother is on the special diet increases.

17. (a) Step 1: $H_o: \mu = 300$ vs. $H_1: \mu > 300$
Step 2: $t = 1.528$
Step 3: $t_{0.05} = 1.646$ (using 1000 df); P-value $= 0.0636$
Step 4: Do not reject H_o.
Step 5: There is not sufficient evidence at the $\alpha = 0.05$ level of significance to support the claim that the mean cholesterol consumption is greater than 300.

(b) Type I error: The nutritionist would reject the null hypothesis that the mean cholesterol consumption is 300 mg when, in fact, the mean consumption is 300 mg. Type II error: The nutritionist would not reject the null hypothesis that the mean cholesterol consumption is 300 mg when, in fact, the mean consumption is more than 300 mg.

(c) 0.05

18. (a) Step 1: $H_o: \mu = 2400$ vs. $H_1: \mu > 2400$
Step 2: $t = 9.183$
Step 3: $t_{0.1} = 1.290$ (using 100 df); P-value < 0.0001
Step 4: Reject H_o.
Step 5: There is sufficient evidence at the $\alpha = 0.1$ level of significance to support the claim that the mean sodium intake of females 20–39 years of age is above 2400 mg.

(b) Type I error: The nutritionist would reject the null hypothesis that the mean sodium intake is 2400 mg when, in fact, the mean consumption is 2400 mg. Type II error: The nutritionist would not reject the null hypothesis that the mean sodium intake is 2400 mg when, in fact, the mean sodium intake is more than 2400 mg.

(c) 0.1

19. (a) Yes
(b) Step 1: $H_o: \mu = 4.61$ vs. $H_1: \mu < 4.61$
Step 2: $Z = -2.48$
Step 3: $-z_{0.01} = -2.33$
Step 4: Do not reject H_o.
Step 5: There is not sufficient evidence at the $\alpha = 0.01$ level of significance to support the claim that the mean pH level has decreased (the acidity has increased).

(c) P-value $= 0.0065$. There is a 0.0065 probability of obtaining a sample mean of 4.32 or lower from a population whose mean is 4.61.

20. (a) Yes
(b) Step 1: $H_o: \mu = 14.0$ vs. $H_1: \mu \neq 14.0$
Step 2: $Z = -3.68$
Step 3: $-z_{0.005} = -2.575$; $z_{0.005} = 2.575$
Step 4: Reject H_o.
Step 5: There is sufficient evidence at the $\alpha = 0.01$ level of significance to support the claim that the mean hemoglobin reading is different from 14.0 grams per deciliter.

(c) P-value $= 0.0002$

21. $np_o(1 - p_o) > 10$, and the sample size is less than 5% of the population size.
(a) Step 1: $H_o: p = 0.56$ vs $H_1: p > 0.56$
Step 2: $z_{0.01} = 2.33$
Step 3: $Z = 0.23$
Step 4: Do not reject H_o.
Step 5: There is not sufficient evidence at the $\alpha = 0.1$ level of significance to support the claim that the proportion of tuberculosis cases that were of foreign-born residents is more than 0.56.

(b) P-value $= 0.4080$

22. $np_o(1 - p_o) > 10$, and the sample size is less than 5% of the population size.
(a) Step 1: $H_o: p = 0.394$ vs $H_1: p < 0.394$
Step 2: $-z_{0.1} = -1.28$
Step 3: $Z = -0.55$
Step 4: Do not reject H_o.
Step 5: There is not sufficient evidence at the $\alpha = 0.1$ level of significance to support the claim that the proportion of females who ordered merchandise or services by phone has decreased.

(b) P-value $= 0.2915$

23. Step 1: $H_o: \sigma = 104$ vs $H_1: \sigma > 104$
Step 2: $\chi^2_{0.1} = 30.813$
Step 3: $\chi^2 = 25.515$
Step 4: Do not reject H_o, because $\chi^2 < \chi^2_{0.1}$.
Step 5: There is not sufficient evidence to support the researcher's claim at the $\alpha = 0.1$ level of significance.

24. Step 1: $H_o: \sigma = 505.6$ vs $H_1: \sigma > 505.6$
Step 2: $\chi^2_{0.01} = 63.691$
Step 3: $\chi^2 = 110.41$
Step 4: Reject H_o, because $\chi^2 > \chi^2_{0.01}$.
Step 5: There is sufficient evidence to support the engineer's claim at the $\alpha = 0.01$ level of significance.

25. (a) 0.4438 **(b)** 0.5562
26. (a) 0.9754 **(b)** 0.0246
27. Step 1: $H_o: p = 0.49$ vs $H_1: p > 0.49$
Step 2: $np_o(1 - p_o) < 10$
Step 3: P-value $= 0.2740$
Step 4: Do not reject H_o. There is not sufficient evidence at the $\alpha = 0.05$ level of significance to support the claim that the proportion of Americans who believe that being a teacher is a prestigious occupation has increased.

28. Step 1: $H_o: p = 0.27$ vs $H_1: p < 0.27$
Step 2: $np_o(1 - p_o) < 10$
Step 3: P-value $= 0.0231$
Step 4: Reject H_o. There is sufficient evidence at the $\alpha = 0.1$ level of significance to support the claim that the proportion of Americans who consider reading to be their favorite pastime has declined.

CHAPTER 10 Comparing Two Population Parameters

10.1 Exercises (p. 601)

1. Dependent **2.** Independent **3.** Independent
4. Dependent **5.** Independent **6.** Independent

7. (a)

Observation	1	2	3	4	5	6	7
X_1	7.6	7.6	7.4	5.7	8.3	6.6	5.6
X_2	8.1	6.6	10.7	9.4	7.8	9	8.5
d_i	−0.5	1	−3.3	−3.7	0.5	−2.4	−2.9

(b) $\bar{d} = -1.614$; $s_d = 1.915$
(c) Step 1: $H_o: \mu_d = 0$ vs $H_1: \mu_d < 0$
Step 2: $-t_{0.05} = -1.943$
Step 3: $t = -2.230$
Step 4: Reject H_o, since $t < -t_{0.05}$.
Step 5: There is sufficient evidence to support the claim that the mean difference is less than zero.
(d) Lower bound: −3.39; Upper bound: 0.16

8. (a)

Observation	1	2	3	4	5	6	7	8
X_1	19.4	18.3	22.1	20.7	19.2	11.8	20.1	18.6
X_2	19.8	16.8	21.1	22	21.5	18.7	15	23.9
d_i	−0.4	1.5	1	−1.3	−2.3	−6.9	5.1	−5.3

(b) $\bar{d} = -1.075$; $s_d = 3.833$
(c) Step 1: $H_o: \mu_d = 0$ vs $H_1: \mu_d \neq 0$
Step 2: $-t_{0.005} = -3.499$; $t_{0.005} = 3.499$
Step 3: $t = -0.793$
Step 4: Do not reject H_o, since $-t_{0.005} < t < t_{0.005}$.
Step 5: There is not sufficient evidence to support the claim that the mean difference is different from zero.
(d) Lower bound: −5.82; Upper bound: 3.67

9. **(a)** This is matched-pairs data because two measurements (A and B) are taken on the same round.

 (b) **Step 1:** H_o: $\mu_d = 0$ vs H_1: $\mu_d \neq 0$
 Step 2: $-t_{0.005} = -3.106$; $t_{0.005} = 3.106$
 Step 3: $t = 0.85$; P-value $= 0.41$ (The differenced data were computed as A–B)
 Step 4: Do not reject H_o, since $-t_{0.005} < t < t_{0.005}$ (or P-value $> \alpha$).
 Step 5: There is not sufficient evidence at the $\alpha = 0.01$ level of significance to support the claim that the value for measurement A is different from the value for measurement B.

 (c) Lower bound: -0.309; Upper bound: 0.542. We are 99% confident that the mean difference in measurement is between -0.309 and 0.542 feet per second.

 (d)

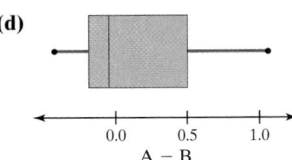

A − B

10. **(a)** This is matched-pairs data because the flexibility is measured on the same subject before and after the treatment.

 (b) **Step 1:** H_o: $\mu_d = 0$ vs H_1: $\mu_d > 0$ (The differenced data are computed as After–Before)
 Step 2: $t_{0.02} = 2.328$
 Step 3: $t = 1.04$; P-value $= 0.16$
 Step 4: Do not reject H_o, since $t < t_{0.02}$ (or P-value $> \alpha$).
 Step 5: There is not sufficient evidence at the $\alpha = 0.02$ level of significance to support the claim that the flexibility after exercise is greater than the flexibility before exercise. In other words, there is no evidence to support the belief that the exercise program increases flexibility.

 (c) Lower bound: -0.419; Upper bound: 1.169. We are 95% confident that the mean difference in flexibility is between -0.419 and 1.169 inches.

 (d)

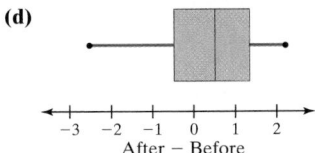

After − Before

11. **(a)** **Step 1:** H_o: $\mu_d = 0$ vs H_1: $\mu_d \neq 0$ (The differenced data are computed as Red–Blue)
 Step 2: $-t_{0.005} = -4.032$; $t_{0.005} = 4.032$
 Step 3: $t = -1.31$; P-value $= 0.25$
 Step 4: Do not reject H_o, since $-t_{0.005} < t < t_{0.005}$ (or P-value $> \alpha$).
 Step 5: There is not sufficient evidence at the $\alpha = 0.01$ level of significance to support the claim that the reaction time to blue is different from the reaction time to red.

 (b) Lower bound: -0.3316; Upper bound: 0.1456. We are 98% confident that the mean difference in reaction time to blue from that to red is between -0.3316 and 0.1456 second.

 (c)

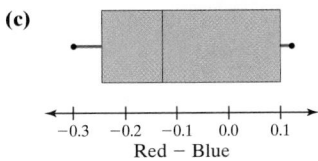

Red − Blue

12. **(a)** **Step 1:** H_o: $\mu_d = 0$ vs H_1: $\mu_d > 0$ (The differenced data are computed as R0–L3)
 Step 2: $t_{0.05} = 1.796$
 Step 3: $t = 2.61$; P-value $= 0.012$

Step 4: Reject H_o, since $t > t_{0.05}$ (or P-value $< \alpha$).
 Step 5: There is sufficient evidence at the $\alpha = 0.05$ level of significance to support the claim that the hemoglobin levels at lift-off minus three days are less than the hemoglobin levels upon return.

 (b) Lower bound: 0.27; Upper bound: 1.48. We are 90% confident that the mean difference in hemoglobin readings is between 0.27 grams per deciliter and 1.48 grams per deciliter.

 (c)

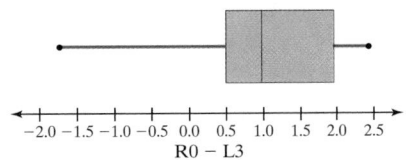

R0 − L3

13. **(a)** **Step 1:** H_o: $\mu_d = 0$ vs H_1: $\mu_d > 0$ (The differenced data are computed as Five-Year–Initial)
 Step 2: $t_{0.05} = 1.895$
 Step 3: $t = 2.38$; P-value $= 0.024$
 Step 4: Reject H_o, since $t > t_{0.05}$ (or P-value $< \alpha$).
 Step 5: There is sufficient evidence at the $\alpha = 0.05$ level of significance to support the claim that the clarity of the lake is improving.

 (b) Lower bound: 0.04; Upper bound: 10.21. We are 95% confident that the mean difference in the depth of the Secchi disk is between 0.04 inch and 10.21 inches.

14. **(a)** **Step 1:** H_o: $\mu_d = 0$ vs H_1: $\mu_d \neq 0$ (The differenced data are computed as Without–With)
 Step 2: $-t_{0.025} = -2.201$; $t_{0.025} = 2.201$
 Step 3: $t = -0.74$; P-value $= 0.47$
 Step 4: Do not reject H_o, since $-t_{0.025} < t < t_{0.025}$ (or P-value $> \alpha$).
 Step 5: There is not sufficient evidence at the $\alpha = 0.05$ level of significance to support the claim that aspirin affects the time it takes for blood to clot.

 (b) Lower bound: -0.37; Upper bound: 0.16. We are 90% confident that the mean difference in the time it takes for a clot to form is between -0.37 and 0.16 second.

15. **(a)** **Step 1:** H_o: $\mu_d = 0$ vs H_1: $\mu_d \neq 0$ (The differenced data are computed as Civic–Neon)
 Step 2: $-t_{0.025} = -3.182$; $t_{0.025} = 3.182$
 Step 3: $t = -0.437$; P-value $= 0.69$
 Step 4: Do not reject H_o, since $-t_{0.025} < t < t_{0.025}$ (or P-value $> \alpha$).
 Step 5: There is not sufficient evidence at the $\alpha = 0.05$ level of significance to support the claim that the repair costs differ.

 (b) Lower bound: -759; Upper bound: 521. We are 90% confident that the mean difference in repair costs is between $-\$759$ and \$521.

16. **(a)** **Step 1:** H_o: $\mu_d = 0$ vs H_1: $\mu_d > 0$ (The differenced data are computed as After–Before)
 Step 2: $t_{0.1} = 1.363$
 Step 3: $t = 2.70$; P-value $= 0.01$
 Step 4: Reject H_o, since $t > t_{0.1}$ (or P-value $< \alpha$).
 Step 5: There is sufficient evidence at the $\alpha = 0.1$ level of significance to support the claim that the preparatory course is effective.

 (b) Lower bound: 2.28; Upper bound: 22.56. We are 95% confident that the mean improvement in the test score is between 2.28 and 22.56 points.

17. **(a)** **Step 1:** H_o: $\mu_d = 0$ vs H_1: $\mu_d < 0$ (The differenced data are computed as Thrifty–Hertz)
 Step 2: $-t_{0.1} = -1.383$
 Step 3: $t = 0.089$; P-value $= 0.534$
 Step 4: Do not reject H_o, since $t > -t_{0.1}$ (or P-value $> \alpha$).
 Step 5: There is not sufficient evidence at the $\alpha = 0.1$ level of significance to support the claim that Thrifty is less expensive than Hertz.

(b) Lower bound: -5.08; Upper bound: 5.59. We are 90% confident that the mean difference in car-rental charges between Thrifty and Hertz is between $-\$5.08$ and $\$5.59$.

18. (a) Step 1: H_o: $\mu_d = 0$ vs H_1: $\mu_d \neq 0$ (The differenced data are computed as Therm1–Therm2)
Step 2: $-t_{0.025} = -2.306$; $t_{0.025} = 2.306$
Step 3: $t = 7.00$; P-value < 0.0001
Step 4: Reject H_o, since $t > t_{0.025}$ (or P-value $< \alpha$).
Step 5: There is sufficient evidence at the $\alpha = 0.1$ level of significance to support the claim that there is a difference between the mean temperatures recorded by thermocouple 1 and thermocouple 2.

(b) Lower bound: 0.017; Upper bound: 0.030. We are 90% confident that the mean difference in the temperature is between $0.017°$ C and $0.030°$ C.

19. (a) H_o: $\mu_d = 0$ vs H_1: $\mu_d \neq 0$
(b) The differences must be at least approximately normal, with no outliers.
(c) Yes, it seems that spaceflight does affect red-blood-cell count, because the P-value is 0.001.

20. (a) H_o: $\mu_d = 0$ vs H_1: $\mu_d < 0$ (the differenced data are computed as Simple–Go/No-Go)
(b) The differences must be at least approximately normal, with no outliers.
(c) Yes, it seems that the reaction time to the simple stimulus is quicker than the reaction time to the go/no-go stimulus, because the P-value is less than 0.001.

10.2 Exercises (p. 615)

1. (a) Step 1: H_o: $\mu_1 = \mu_2$ vs H_1: $\mu_1 \neq \mu_2$
Step 2: $-t_{0.025} = -2.145$; $t_{0.025} = 2.145$ (using 14 df)
Step 3: $t = 0.898$; P-value $= 0.38$
Step 4: Do not reject H_o, because $-t_{0.025} < t < t_{0.025}$ (or P-value $> \alpha$).
Step 5: There is not sufficient evidence at the $\alpha = 0.05$ level of significance to support the claim that $\mu_1 \neq \mu_2$.
(b) Lower bound: -1.53; Upper bound: 3.73

2. (a) Step 1: H_o: $\mu_1 = \mu_2$ vs H_1: $\mu_1 \neq \mu_2$
Step 2: $-t_{0.025} = -2.093$; $t_{0.005} = 2.093$ (using 19 df)
Step 3: $t = 2.486$; P-value $= 0.017$
Step 4: Reject H_o, because $t > t_{0.025}$ (or P-value $< \alpha$).
Step 5: There is sufficient evidence at the $\alpha = 0.05$ level of significance to support the claim that $\mu_1 \neq \mu_2$.
(b) Lower bound: 1.1; Upper bound: 12.9

3. (a) Step 1: H_o: $\mu_1 = \mu_2$ vs H_1: $\mu_1 > \mu_2$
Step 2: $t_{0.1} = 1.333$ (using 17 df)
Step 3: $t = 3.081$; P-value $= 0.002$
Step 4: Reject H_o, because $t > t_{0.1}$ (or P-value $< \alpha$).
Step 5: There is sufficient evidence at the $\alpha = 0.1$ level of significance to support the claim that $\mu_1 > \mu_2$.
(b) Lower bound: 3.57; Upper bound: 12.83

4. (a) Step 1: H_o: $\mu_1 = \mu_2$ vs H_1: $\mu_1 < \mu_2$
Step 2: $-t_{0.05} = -1.696$ (using 31 df)
Step 3: $t = -4.393$; P-value < 0.0001
Step 4: Reject H_o, because $t < -t_{0.05}$ (or P-value $< \alpha$).
Step 5: There is sufficient evidence at the $\alpha = 0.05$ level of significance to support the claim that $\mu_1 < \mu_2$.
(b) Lower bound: -30.75; Upper bound: -11.25

5. (a) Step 1: H_o: $\mu_1 = \mu_2$ vs H_1: $\mu_1 < \mu_2$
Step 2: $-t_{0.02} = -2.172$ (using 24 df)
Step 3: $t = -3.158$; P-value $= 0.0013$
Step 4: Reject H_o, because $t < -t_{0.02}$ (or P-value $< \alpha$).
Step 5: There is sufficient evidence at the $\alpha = 0.02$ level of significance to support the claim that $\mu_1 < \mu_2$.
(b) Lower bound: -16.65; Upper bound: -4.95

6. (a) Step 1: H_o: $\mu_1 = \mu_2$ vs H_1: $\mu_1 > \mu_2$
Step 2: $t_{0.05} = 1.782$ (using 12 df)
Step 3: $t = 1.237$; P-value $= 0.114$
Step 4: Do not reject H_o, because $t < t_{0.05}$ (or P-value $> \alpha$).
Step 5: There is not sufficient evidence at the $\alpha = 0.05$ level of significance to support the claim that $\mu_1 > \mu_2$.
(b) Lower bound: -1.60; Upper bound: 5.80

7. (a) Step 1: H_o: $\mu_{\text{treat}} = \mu_{\text{control}}$ vs H_1: $\mu_{\text{treat}} > \mu_{\text{control}}$
Step 2: $t_{0.01} = 2.403$ (using 50 df)
Step 3: $t = 2.849$; P-value $= 0.0026$
Step 4: Reject H_o, because $t > t_{0.01}$ (or P-value $< \alpha$).
Step 5: There is sufficient evidence at the $\alpha = 0.01$ level of significance to support the claim that mean improvement in the treatment group was greater than the mean improvement in the control group. The drug appears to be effective in improving the Young–Mania Rating Scale score.
(b) Lower bound: 1.98; Upper bound: 11.42. The researchers are 95% confident that the mean Young–Mania Rating Scale score for the treatment group is between 1.98 and 11.42 points higher than that of the control group.

8. (a) Step 1: H_o: $\mu_{\text{treat}} = \mu_{\text{control}}$ vs H_1: $\mu_{\text{treat}} > \mu_{\text{control}}$
Step 2: $t_{0.05} = 1.660$ (using 100 df)
Step 3: $t = 4.359$; P-value < 0.0001
Step 4: Reject H_o, because $t > t_{0.05}$ (or P-value $< \alpha$).
Step 5: There is sufficient evidence at the $\alpha = 0.05$ level of significance to support the claim that the mean reduction in the symptom-assessment score of the treatment group was greater than the mean score of the control group. The drug appears to be effective in treating the discomfort associated with the common cold.
(b) Lower bound: 0.202; Upper bound: 0.538. The researchers are 95% confident that the mean symptom-assessment score of the treatment group is between 0.202 and 0.538 points higher than the mean score of the control group.

9. (a) Yes, we can treat each sample as a simple random sample of all mixtures of each type. The samples were obtained independently. We are told that a normal probability plot indicates that the data could come from a population that is normal, with no outliers.
(b) Step 1: H_o: $\mu_{67\text{-}0\text{-}301} = \mu_{67\text{-}0\text{-}400}$ vs H_1: $\mu_{67\text{-}0\text{-}301} < \mu_{67\text{-}0\text{-}400}$
Step 2: $-t_{0.05} = -1.860$ (using 8 df)
Step 3: $t = -3.804$; P-value $= 0.0008$
Step 4: Reject H_o, because $t < -t_{0.05}$ (or P-value $< \alpha$).
Step 5: There is sufficient evidence at the $\alpha = 0.05$ level of significance to support the claim that the mean strength in Mixture 67-0-301 is less than the mean strength in Mixture 67-0-400.
(c) Lower bound: 416; Upper bound: 1212. We are 90% confident that the mean strength of Mixture 67-0-400 is between 416 and 1212 psi stronger than the mean strength of Mixture 67-0-301.
(d)

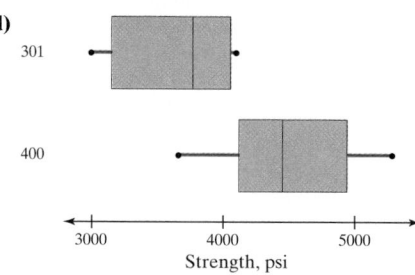

10. (a) Yes, each sample is a simple random sample. The samples were obtained independently. We are told that a normal probability plot indicates that the data could come from a population that is normal, with no outliers.

(b) Step 1: $H_o: \mu_{\text{females}} = \mu_{\text{males}}$ vs $H_1: \mu_{\text{females}} \neq \mu_{\text{males}}$
Step 2: $-t_{0.025} = -2.145$; $t_{0.025} = 2.145$ (using 14 df)
Step 3: $t = 0.62$; P-value $= 0.54$
Step 4: Do not reject H_o, because $-t_{0.025} < t < t_{0.025}$ (or P-value $> \alpha$).
Step 5: There is not sufficient evidence at the $\alpha = 0.05$ level of significance to support the claim that there is a difference in reaction time between females and males.

(c) Lower bound: -0.0483; Upper bound: 0.1006. We are 90% confident that the mean difference in reaction time for females and males is between -0.0483 and 0.1006 second.

(d)

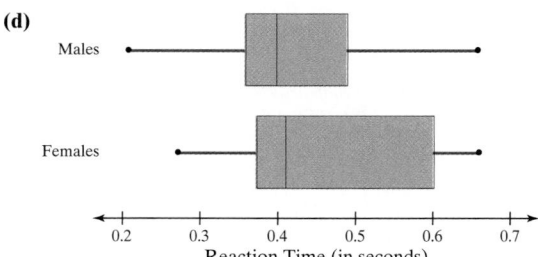

11. (a)

Normal Probability Plot for Carpet

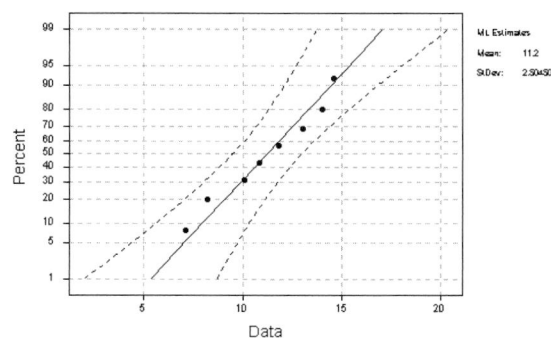

Normal Probability Plot for No Carpet

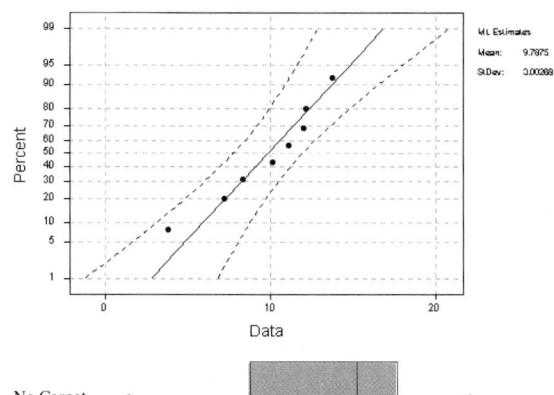

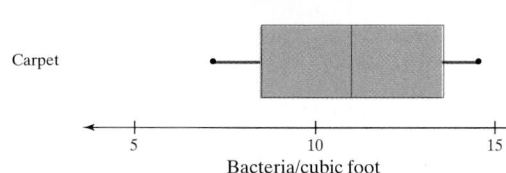

(b) Step 1: $H_o: \mu_{\text{carpet}} = \mu_{\text{nocarpet}}$ vs $H_1: \mu_{\text{carpet}} > \mu_{\text{nocarpet}}$
Step 2: $t_{0.05} = 1.895$ (using 7 df)
Step 3: $t = 0.96$; P-value $= 0.18$

Step 4: Do not reject H_o, because $t < t_{0.05}$ (or P-value $> \alpha$).
Step 5: There is not sufficient evidence at the $\alpha = 0.05$ level of significance to support the claim that carpeted rooms have more bacteria than uncarpeted rooms.

(c) Lower bound: -2.09; Upper bound: 4.91. We are 95% confident that the mean difference in the number of bacteria per cubic foot in a carpeted room versus that in an uncarpeted room is between -2.09 and 4.91.

12. (a)

Normal Probability Plot for Visual

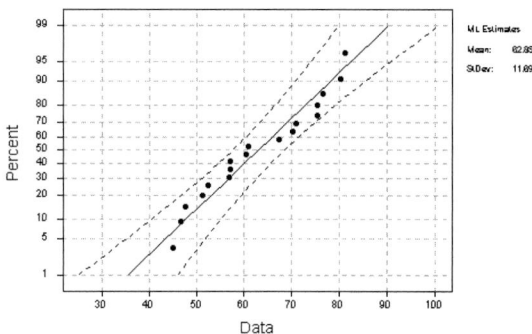

Normal Probability Plot for Textual

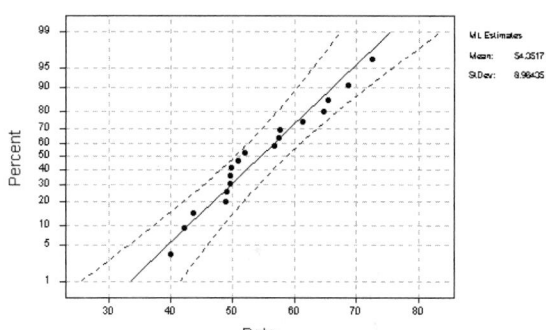

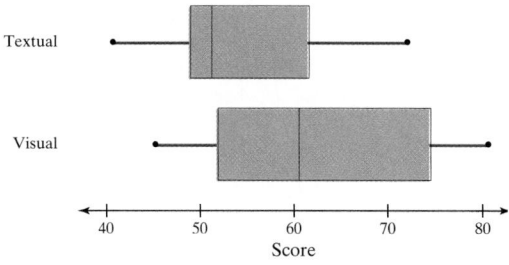

(b) Step 1: $H_o: \mu_{\text{visual}} = \mu_{\text{textual}}$ vs $H_1: \mu_{\text{visual}} \neq \mu_{\text{textual}}$
Step 2: $-t_{0.025} = -2.110$; $t_{0.025} = 2.110$ (using 17 df)
Step 3: $t = 2.38$; P-value $= 0.024$
Step 4: Reject H_o, because $t > t_{0.025}$ (or P-value $< \alpha$).
Step 5: There is sufficient evidence at the $\alpha = 0.05$ level of significance to support the claim that there is a difference in the test scores of people who use the visual manual and those who use the textual manual.

(c) Lower bound: 0.959; Upper bound: 16.038. We are 95% confident that the mean difference between the test scores of visual manual users versus those of textual manual users is between 0.959 points and 16.038 points. Because the interval does not contain zero, we take this as evidence against the null hypothesis.

13. (a) **Step 1:** $H_o: \mu_{Lemont} = \mu_{Naperville}$ vs $H_1: \mu_{Lemont} < \mu_{Naperville}$
Step 2: $-t_{0.05} = -1.696$ (using 31 df)
Step 3: $t = -1.793$; P-value $= 0.0394$
Step 4: Reject H_o, because $t < -t_{0.05}$ (or P-value $< \alpha$).
Step 5: There is sufficient evidence at the $\alpha = 0.05$ level of significance to support the claim that the mean price of a home in Lemont is less than the mean price of a home in Naperville.

(b) Lower bound: -110.33; Upper bound: -3.07. We are 90% confident that the mean price of a home in Lemont is between \$3.07 thousand and \$110.33 thousand less than the mean price of a home in Naperville.

(c) Sale prices of homes are typically skewed right, so we need large sample sizes in order to employ the Central Limit Theorem.

14. (a) **Step 1:** $H_o: \mu_{women} = \mu_{men}$ vs $H_1: \mu_{women} > \mu_{men}$
Step 2: $t_{0.05} = 1.696$ (using 31 df)
Step 3: $t = 1.111$; P-value $= 0.1358$
Step 4: Do not reject H_o, because $t < t_{0.05}$ (or P-value $> \alpha$).
Step 5: There is not sufficient evidence at the $\alpha = 0.05$ level of significance to support the claim that college women have more credit card debt than college men.

(b) Lower bound: $-\$182.2$; Upper bound: \$874.2. We are 90% confident that the mean difference in credit-card debt of college women and college men is between $-\$182.2$ and \$874.2.

15. (a) This is a completely randomized design. The treatment is the drug. It has two levels: 0.625 mg per day of conjugated estrogens, plus trimonthly medroxyprogesterone acetate or a placebo.

(b) **Step 1:** $H_o: \mu_{treatment} = \mu_{control}$ vs $H_1: \mu_{treatment} > \mu_{control}$
Step 2: $t_{0.01} = 2.467$ (using 28 df)
Step 3: $t = 2.745$; P-value $= 0.0046$
Step 4: Reject H_o, because $t > t_{0.01}$ (or P-value $< \alpha$).
Step 5: There is sufficient evidence at the $\alpha = 0.01$ level of significance to support the claim that the mean increase in serum HDL levels of women in the treatment group is greater than the mean increase in serum HDL levels of women in the control group.

(c) Lower bound: 1.45; Upper bound: 9.95. We are 95% confident that the mean difference in the increase in serum HDL levels in the treatment group over that of the control group is between 1.45 and 9.95 mg/dL.

16. (a) **Step 1:** $H_o: \mu_{do\,not} = \mu_{do}$ vs $H_1: \mu_{do\,not} > \mu_{do}$
Step 2: $t_{0.01} = 2.441$ (using 34 df)
Step 3: $t = 1.741$; P-value $= 0.0430$
Step 4: Do not reject H_o, because $t < t_{0.01}$ (or P-value $> \alpha$).
Step 5: There is not sufficient evidence at the $\alpha = 0.05$ level of significance to support the claim that the SAT Math test scores of students who do not plan on applying for financial aid are greater than the SAT Math test scores of students who do plan on applying for financial aid.

(b) Lower bound: -20.44; Upper bound: 119.44. We are 98% confident that the mean difference in test scores is between -20.44 and 119.44.

17. (a) $H_o: \mu_{men} = \mu_{women}$ vs $H_1: \mu_{men} < \mu_{women}$
(b) P-value $= 0.0051$. Because P-value $< \alpha$, we reject the null hypothesis. There is sufficient evidence at the $\alpha = 0.01$ level of significance to support the claim that the mean step pulse of men is less than the mean step pulse of women.
(c) Lower bound: -10.7; Upper bound: -1.5. We are 95% confident that the mean step pulse of men is between 1.5 beats per minute and 10.7 beats per minute lower than the mean step pulse of women.

18. (a) $H_o: \mu_{men} = \mu_{women}$ vs $H_1: \mu_{men} < \mu_{women}$
(b) P-value $= 0.0001$. Because P-value $< \alpha$, we reject the null hypothesis. There is sufficient evidence at the $\alpha = 0.01$ level of significance to support the claim that the women are more flexible than the men.

(c) Lower bound: -3.58; Upper bound: -1.12. We are 95% confident that the mean flexibility of women is between 1.12 inches and 3.58 inches higher than the mean flexibility of men.

10.3 Exercises (p. 628)

1. (a) $H_o: p_1 = p_2$ vs $H_1: p_1 > p_2$
(b) $Z = 3.08$
(c) $z_{0.05} = 1.645$
(d) P-value $= 0.0010$
Because $Z > z_{0.05}$ (or P-value $< \alpha$), we reject the null hypothesis. There is sufficient evidence to support the claim that $p_1 > p_2$.

2. (a) $H_o: p_1 = p_2$ vs $H_1: p_1 < p_2$
(b) $Z = -0.35$ **(c)** $-z_{0.05} = -1.645$
(d) P-value $= 0.3649$
Because $Z > -z_{0.05}$ (or P-value $> \alpha$), we do not reject the null hypothesis. There is not sufficient evidence to support the claim that $p_1 < p_2$.

3. (a) $H_o: p_1 = p_2$ vs $H_1: p_1 \neq p_2$
(b) $Z = -0.34$
(c) $-z_{0.025} = -1.96$; $z_{0.025} = 1.96$
(d) P-value $= 0.7307$
Because $-z_{0.025} < Z < z_{0.05}$ (or P-value $> \alpha$), we do not reject the null hypothesis. There is not sufficient evidence to support the claim that $p_1 \neq p_2$.

4. (a) $H_o: p_1 = p_2$ vs $H_1: p_1 \neq p_2$
(b) $Z = -2.19$ **(c)** $-z_{0.025} = -1.96$; $z_{0.025} = 1.96$
(d) P-value $= 0.0286$
Because $Z < -z_{0.05}$ (or P-value $< \alpha$), we reject the null hypothesis. There is sufficient evidence to support the claim that $p_1 \neq p_2$.

5. Lower bound: -0.04; Upper bound: 0.014
6. Lower bound: -0.09; Upper bound: 0.07
7. Lower bound: -0.06; Upper bound: 0.04
8. Lower bound: -0.04; Upper bound: 0.01
9. (a) Each sample can be thought of as a simple random sample; $n_1\hat{p}_1(1 - \hat{p}_1) \geq 10$ and $n_2\hat{p}_2(1 - \hat{p}_2) \geq 10$; and each sample is less than 5% of the population size.
Step 1: $H_o: p_1 = p_2$ vs $H_1: p_1 > p_2$
Step 2: $z_{0.05} = 1.645$
Step 3: $Z = 2.20$ (P-value $= 0.0139$)
Step 4: Reject H_o, since $Z > z_{0.05}$ (or P-value $< \alpha$).
Step 5: There is sufficient evidence at the $\alpha = 0.05$ level of significance to support the claim that a higher proportion of subjects in the treatment group (taking Prevnar) experienced fever as a side effect than in the control (placebo) group.

(b) Lower bound: 0.01; Upper bound: 0.07. We are 90% confident that the difference in the proportion of subjects who experience a fever as a side effect between the experimental and control groups is between 0.01 and 0.07.

10. (a) Each sample can be thought of as a simple random sample; $n_1\hat{p}_1(1 - \hat{p}_1) \geq 10$ and $n_2\hat{p}_2(1 - \hat{p}_2) \geq 10$; and each sample is less than 5% of the population size.
Step 1: $H_o: p_1 = p_2$ vs $H_1: p_1 \neq p_2$
Step 2: $-z_{0.025} = -1.96$; $z_{0.025} = 1.96$
Step 3: $Z = -0.20$ (P-value $= 0.8443$)
Step 4: Do not reject H_o, since $-z_{0.025} < Z < z_{0.025}$ (or P-value $> \alpha$).
Step 5: There is not sufficient evidence at the $\alpha = 0.05$ level of significance to support the claim that a different proportion of subjects taking Prevnar experienced drowsiness as a side effect than in the control (placebo) group.

(b) Lower bound: -0.14; Upper bound: 0.12. We are 99% confident that the difference in the proportion of subjects who experienced drowsiness as a side effect between the experiment and control group is between -0.14 and 0.12.

11. (a) Each sample is a simple random sample; $n_1\hat{p}_1(1 - \hat{p}_1) \geq 10$ and $n_2\hat{p}_2(1 - \hat{p}_2) \geq 10$; and each sample is less than 5% of the population size.

Step 1: $H_o: p_8 = p_c$ vs $H_1: p_8 > p_c$
Step 2: $z_{0.1} = 1.28$
Step 3: $Z = 0.99$ (P-value $= 0.1608$)
Step 4: Do not reject H_o, since $Z < z_{0.1}$ (or P-value $> \alpha$).
Step 5: There is not sufficient evidence at the $\alpha = 0.1$ level of significance to support the claim that a higher proportion of individuals with at most an 8th-grade education consume too much cholesterol than those with some college education.

(b) Lower bound: -0.04; Upper bound: 0.11. We are 95% confident that the difference in the proportion of individuals with at most an 8th-grade education and individuals with some college education who consume too much cholesterol is between -0.04 and 0.11.

12. (a) Each sample is a simple random sample; $n_1\hat{p}_1(1 - \hat{p}_1) \geq 10$ and $n_2\hat{p}_2(1 - \hat{p}_2) \geq 10$; and each sample is less than 5% of the population size.

Step 1: $H_o: p_f = p_m$ vs $H_1: p_f < p_m$
Step 2: $-z_{0.05} = -1.645$
Step 3: $Z = -3.71$ (P-value $= 0.0001$)
Step 4: Reject H_o, since $Z > z_{0.05}$ (or P-value $< \alpha$).
Step 5: There is sufficient evidence at the $\alpha = 0.05$ level of significance to support the claim that a lower proportion of females consumes too much saturated fat than males.

(b) Lower bound: -0.17; Upper bound: -0.05. We are 95% confident that the difference in the proportion of females and males who consume too much saturated fat is between 0.05 and 0.17 and that a lower proportion of females consumes too much saturated fat.

13. (a) Each sample is a simple random sample; $n_1\hat{p}_1(1 - \hat{p}_1) \geq 10$ and $n_2\hat{p}_2(1 - \hat{p}_2) \geq 10$; and each sample is less than 5% of the population size.

Step 1: $H_o: p_{2000} = p_{1990}$ vs $H_1: p_{2000} < p_{1990}$
Step 2: $-z_{0.1} = -1.28$
Step 3: $Z = -1.06$ (P-value $= 0.1456$)
Step 4: Do not reject H_o, since $Z > -z_{0.1}$ (or P-value $> \alpha$).
Step 5: There is not sufficient evidence at the $\alpha = 0.1$ level of significance to support the claim that the proportion of adults who have smoked at least one cigarette in the past week has decreased.

(b) Lower bound: -0.05; Upper bound: 0.01. We are 90% confident that the difference in the proportion of adults who have smoked at least one cigarette in the past week from 1990 to 2000 is between -0.05 and 0.01.

14. (a) Each sample is a simple random sample; $n_1\hat{p}_1(1 - \hat{p}_1) \geq 10$ and $n_2\hat{p}_2(1 - \hat{p}_2) \geq 10$; and each sample is less than 5% of the population size.

Step 1: $H_o: p_{1999} = p_{1996}$ vs $H_1: p_{1999} < p_{1996}$
Step 2: $-z_{0.1} = -1.28$
Step 3: $Z = -3.82$ (P-value $= 0.0001$)
Step 4: Reject H_o, since $Z < -z_{0.1}$ (or P-value $< \alpha$).
Step 5: There is sufficient evidence at the $\alpha = 0.1$ level of significance to support the claim that the proportion of adults who believe there is life of some form on other planets in the universe has decreased.

(b) Lower bound: -0.16; Upper bound: -0.06. We are 90% confident that the difference in the proportion of adults who believe there is life on other planets from 1996 to 1999 is between 0.06 and 0.16 and that a higher proportion believed that there is life on other planets in 1996.

15. (a) Each sample is a simple random sample; $n_1\hat{p}_1(1 - \hat{p}_1) \geq 10$ and $n_2\hat{p}_2(1 - \hat{p}_2) \geq 10$; and each sample is less than 5% of the population size.

Step 1: $H_o: p_{exp} = p_{control}$ vs $H_1: p_{exp} < p_{control}$
Step 2: $-z_{0.1} = -2.33$
Step 3: $Z = -6.74$ (P-value < 0.0001)

Step 4: Reject H_o, since $Z < -z_{0.1}$ (or P-value $< \alpha$).
Step 5: There is sufficient evidence at the $\alpha = 0.01$ level of significance to support the claim that the proportion of children in the experimental group who contracted polio is less than the proportion of children in the control group who contracted polio.

(b) Lower bound: -0.0005; Upper bound: -0.0003. We are 90% confident that the difference in the proportion of children who contract polio with the vaccine versus without the vaccine is between 0.0005 and 0.0003 and that a smaller percentage of children contracted polio in the experimental group.

16. (a) Each sample is a simple random sample; $n_1\hat{p}_1(1 - \hat{p}_1) \geq 10$ and $n_2\hat{p}_2(1 - \hat{p}_2) \geq 10$; and each sample is less than 5% of the population size.

Step 1: $H_o: p_{2001} = p_{1977}$ vs $H_1: p_{2001} > p_{1977}$
Step 2: $z_{0.05} = 1.645$
Step 3: $Z = 2.09$ (P-value $= 0.0183$)
Step 4: Reject H_o, since $Z > z_{0.05}$ (or P-value $< \alpha$).
Step 5: There is sufficient evidence at the $\alpha = 0.05$ level of significance to support the claim that the proportion of parents who fear for their oldest child's safety while at school has increased since 1977.

(b) Lower bound: 0.01; Upper bound: 0.15. We are 95% confident that the difference in the proportion of parents who fear for their oldest child's safety while at school from 2001 to 1977 is 0.02 to 0.14.

17. (a) $n = n_1 = n_2 = 1406$ **(b)** $n = n_1 = n_2 = 2135$

18. (a) $n = n_1 = n_2 = 2551$ **(b)** $n = n_1 = n_2 = 3383$

19. It doesn't seem to matter whether an individual takes a single dose of Pepcid in the evening or two doses during the course of the day.

20. There is some evidence to indicate that dizziness is a side effect of Accupril, as indicated by the fairly low P-value (0.072).

21. The researchers were testing a claim that the proportion of apnea episodes with the drug combination is less than the proportion of apnea episodes with a placebo. That is, they tested $H_o: p_{drug} = p_{placebo}$ versus $H_1: p_{drug} > p_{placebo}$. With a P-value less than 0.05, we have evidence against the null hypothesis, so there is sufficient evidence at the $\alpha = 0.05$ level of significance to support the claim that the drug combination is effective in treating apnea.

10.4 Exercises (p. 640)

1. 3.02   **2.** 2.70   **3.** 0.18; 4.65   **4.** 0.10; 7.46

5. 0.58   **6.** 0.30   **7.** 2.19   **8.** 1.93

9. Step 1: $H_o: \sigma_1 = \sigma_2$ vs $H_1: \sigma_1 \neq \sigma_2$
Step 2: $F_{0.975,15,15} = 0.35$; $F_{0.025,15,15} = 2.86$
Step 3: $F = 0.84$
Step 4: Do not reject H_o, since $F_{0.975,15,15} < F < F_{0.025,15,15}$.
Step 5: There is not sufficient evidence at the $\alpha = 0.05$ level of significance to support the claim that $\sigma_1 \neq \sigma_2$.

10. Step 1: $H_o: \sigma_1 = \sigma_2$ vs $H_1: \sigma_1 \neq \sigma_2$
Step 2: $F_{0.95,20,20} = 0.47$; $F_{0.05,20,20} = 2.12$
Step 3: $F = 0.87$
Step 4: Do not reject H_o, since $F_{0.95,20,20} < F < F_{0.05,20,20}$.
Step 5: There is not sufficient evidence at the $\alpha = 0.1$ level of significance to support the claim that $\sigma_1 \neq \sigma_2$.

11. Step 1: $H_o: \sigma_1 = \sigma_2$ vs $H_1: \sigma_1 > \sigma_2$
Step 2: $F_{0.01,18,26} = 2.86$
Step 3: $F = 2.39$
Step 4: Do not reject H_o, since $F < F_{0.01,15,15}$.
Step 5: There is not sufficient evidence at the $\alpha = 0.05$ level of significance to support the claim that $\sigma_1 > \sigma_2$.

12. Step 1: $H_o: \sigma_1 = \sigma_2$ vs $H_1: \sigma_1 < \sigma_2$
Step 2: $F_{0.95,20,25} = 0.50$
Step 3: $F = 0.48$

Step 4: Reject H_o, since $F < F_{0.95,20,25}$.
Step 5: There is sufficient evidence at the $\alpha = 0.05$ level of significance to support the claim that $\sigma_1 < \sigma_2$.

13. Step 1: $H_o: \sigma_1 = \sigma_2$ vs $H_1: \sigma_1 < \sigma_2$
Step 2: $F_{0.9,50,25} = 0.65$
Step 3: $F = 0.40$
Step 4: Reject H_o, since $F < F_{0.9,50,25}$.
Step 5: There is sufficient evidence at the $\alpha = 0.05$ level of significance to support the claim that $\sigma_1 < \sigma_2$.

14. Step 1: $H_o: \sigma_1 = \sigma_2$ vs $H_1: \sigma_1 > \sigma_2$
Step 2: $F_{0.05,22,12} \approx 2.54$
Step 3: $F = 2.16$
Step 4: Do not reject H_o, since $F < F_{0.05,22,12}$.
Step 5: There is not sufficient evidence at the $\alpha = 0.05$ level of significance to support the claim that $\sigma_1 > \sigma_2$.

15. Step 1: $H_o: \sigma_1 = \sigma_2$ vs $H_1: \sigma_1 \neq \sigma_2$
Step 2: $F_{0.975,54,59} \approx 0.58$; $F_{0.025,54,59} \approx 1.59$
Step 3: $F = 0.97$
Step 4: Do not reject H_o, since $F_{0.975,54,59} < F < F_{0.025,54,59}$.
Step 5: There is not sufficient evidence at the $\alpha = 0.05$ level of significance to support the claim that the standard deviation in the treatment group is different from the standard deviation in the control group.

16. Step 1: $H_o: \sigma_1 = \sigma_2$ vs $H_1: \sigma_1 \neq \sigma_2$
Step 2: $F_{0.975,215,213} \approx 0.73$; $F_{0.025,215,213} \approx 1.37$
Step 3: $F = 1$
Step 4: Do not reject H_o, since $F_{0.975,215,213} < F < F_{0.025,215,213}$.
Step 5: There is not sufficient evidence at the $\alpha = 0.05$ level of significance to support the claim that the standard deviation in the treatment group is different from the standard deviation in the control group.

17. Step 1: $H_o: \sigma_1 = \sigma_2$ vs $H_1: \sigma_1 > \sigma_2$
Step 2: $F_{0.01,64,64} \approx 1.91$
Step 3: $F = 6.94$
Step 4: Reject H_o, since $F > F_{0.01,64,64}$.
Step 5: There is sufficient evidence at the $\alpha = 0.01$ level of significance to reject the claim that the standard deviation in the treatment group is greater than the standard deviation in the control group.

18. Step 1: $H_o: \sigma_1 = \sigma_2$ vs $H_1: \sigma_1 > \sigma_2$
Step 2: $F_{0.01,34,37} \approx 2.10$
Step 3: $F = 1.06$
Step 4: Do not reject H_o since $F > F_{0.01,34,37}$.
Step 5: There is not sufficient evidence at the $\alpha = 0.01$ level of significance to support the claim that students applying for financial aid have more variability in their test scores than those who do not apply for financial aid.

19. (a) Step 1: $H_o: \sigma_{\text{single}} = \sigma_{\text{multiple}}$ vs $H_1: \sigma_{\text{single}} < \sigma_{\text{multiple}}$
Step 2: $F_{0.95,19,19} \approx 0.47$
Step 3: $F = 0.32$
Step 4: Reject H_o since $F < F_{0.95,19,19}$.
Step 5: There is sufficient evidence at the $\alpha = 0.05$ level of significance to support the claim that the standard deviation wait time in a single line is less than the standard deviation wait time in multiple lines.

(b)

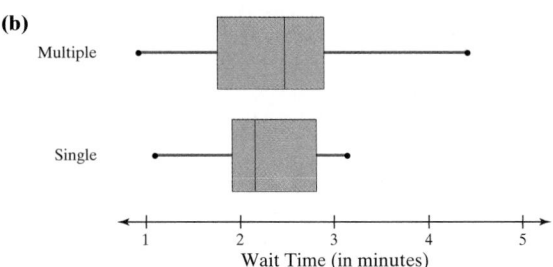

20. Step 1 $H_o: \sigma_{\text{old}} = \sigma_{\text{new}}$ vs $H_1: \sigma_{\text{old}} > \sigma_{\text{lnew}}$
Step 2: $F_{0.05,14,14} \approx 2.40$
Step 3: $F = 2.73$
Step 4: Reject H_o, since $F > F_{0.05,14,14}$.
Step 5: There is sufficient evidence at the $\alpha = 0.05$ level of significance to support the claim that the standard deviation fill in the new machine is less than the standard deviation fill in the old machine.

21. (a) Use of the procedures for conducting an F-test are satisfied because the normal probability plots indicate that it is reasonable to conclude that the sample data come from a population that is normal.
(b) Since the P-value is rather high, the nursing student should conclude that the standard deviation systolic blood pressure of men is not more variable than the standard deviation systolic blood pressure of women.

22. (a) P-value $> \alpha$, so we do not reject the null hypothesis. There is not sufficient evidence to support the claim that $\sigma_1 \neq \sigma_2$.

(b)

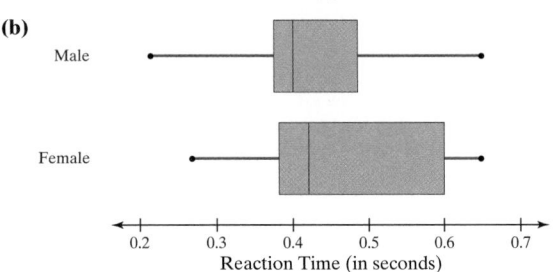

Chapter Review Exercises (p. 646)

1. Dependent   **2.** Independent
3. Independent   **4.** Dependent
5. (a) 3.23   **(b)** 0.24; 6.62   **6. (a)** 2.06   **(b)** 0.49

7. (a)

Observation	1	2	3	4	5	6
X_1	34.2	32.1	39.5	41.8	45.1	38.4
X_2	34.9	31.5	39.5	41.9	45.5	38.8
d_i	−0.7	0.6	0	−0.1	−0.4	−0.4

(b) $\bar{d} = -0.167$; $s_d = 0.450$
(c) Step 1: $H_o: \mu_d = 0$ vs $H_1: \mu_d < 0$
Step 2: $-t_{0.05} = -2.015$
Step 3: $t = -0.907$
Step 4: Do not reject H_o, since $t > -t_{0.05}$.
Step 5: There is not sufficient evidence to support the claim that the mean difference is less than zero.
(d) Lower bound: -0.79; Upper bound: 0.45

8. (a)

Observation	1	2	3	4	5	6	7
X_1	18.5	21.8	19.4	22.9	18.3	20.2	23.1
X_2	18.3	22.3	19.2	22.3	18.9	20.7	23.9
d_i	0.2	−0.5	0.2	0.6	−0.6	−0.5	−0.8

(b) $\bar{d} = -0.2$; $s_d = 0.526$
(c) Step 1: $H_o: \mu_d = 0$ vs $H_1: \mu_d \neq 0$
Step 2: $-t_{0.005} = -3.707$; $t_{0.005} = 3.707$
Step 3: $t = -1.006$
Step 4: Do not reject H_o, since $-t_{0.005} < t < t_{0.005}$.
Step 5: There is not sufficient evidence to support the claim that the mean difference is different from zero.
(d) Lower bound: -0.69; Upper bound: 0.29

9. (a) **Step 1:** $H_o: \mu_1 = \mu_2$ vs $H_1: \mu_1 \neq \mu_2$
   Step 2: $-t_{0.05} = -1.895$; $t_{0.05} = 1.895$ (using 7 df)
   Step 3: $t = 2.29$ (P-value $= 0.035$)
   Step 4: Reject H_o, since $t > t_{0.05}$ (or P-value $< \alpha$).
   Step 5: There is sufficient evidence at the $\alpha = 0.1$ level of significance to support the claim that $\mu_1 \neq \mu_2$.
   (b) Lower bound: 0.73; Upper bound: 7.67
   (c) **Step 1:** $H_o: \sigma_1 = \sigma_2$ vs $H_1: \sigma_1 \neq \sigma_2$
   Step 2: $F_{0.975,12,7} = 0.28$; $F_{0.025,12,7} \approx 4.76$
   Step 3: $F = 1.40$
   Step 4: Do not reject H_o, since $F_{0.975,12,7} < F < F_{0.025,12,7}$.
   Step 5: There is not sufficient evidence at the $\alpha = 0.05$ level of significance to support the claim that $\sigma_1 \neq \sigma_2$.

10. (a) **Step 1:** $H_o: \mu_1 = \mu_2$ vs $H_1: \mu_1 \neq \mu_2$
   Step 2: $-t_{0.025} = -2.069$; $t_{0.025} = 2.069$ (using 23 df)
   Step 3: $t = -2.054$ (P-value $= 0.0464$)
   Step 4: Reject H_o, since $t < -t_{0.025}$ (or P-value $< \alpha$).
   Step 5: There is sufficient evidence at the $\alpha = 0.05$ level of significance to support the claim that $\mu_1 \neq \mu_2$.
   (b) Lower bound: -12.44; Upper bound: 0.04
   (c) **Step 1:** $H_o: \sigma_1 = \sigma_2$ vs $H_1: \sigma_1 > \sigma_2$
   Step 2: $F_{0.05,23,26} \approx 1.93$
   Step 3: $F = 2.00$
   Step 4: Reject H_o, since $F > F_{0.05,23,26}$.
   Step 5: There is sufficient evidence at the $\alpha = 0.05$ level of significance to support the claim that $\sigma_1 > \sigma_2$.

11. (a) **Step 1:** $H_o: \mu_1 = \mu_2$ vs $H_1: \mu_1 > \mu_2$
   Step 2: $t_{0.01} = 2.423$ (using 40 df)
   Step 3: $t = 1.472$ (P-value $= 0.0726$)
   Step 4: Do not reject H_o, since $t > t_{0.01}$ (or P-value $> \alpha$).
   Step 5: There is not sufficient evidence at the $\alpha = 0.01$ level of significance to support the claim that $\mu_1 > \mu_2$.
   (b) Lower bound: -0.43; Upper bound: 6.43
   (c) **Step 1:** $H_o: \sigma_1 = \sigma_2$ vs $H_1: \sigma_1 < \sigma_2$
   Step 2: $F_{0.99,44,40} \approx 0.50$
   Step 3: $F = 0.67$
   Step 4: Do not reject H_o, since $F > F_{0.99,44,40}$.
   Step 5: There is not sufficient evidence at the $\alpha = 0.01$ level of significance to support the claim that $\sigma_1 < \sigma_2$.

12. (a) **Step 1:** $H_o: \mu_1 = \mu_2$ vs $H_1: \mu_1 < \mu_2$
   Step 2: $-t_{0.05} = -1.895$ (using 7 df)
   Step 3: $t = -1.357$ (P-value $= 0.0959$)
   Step 4: Do not reject H_o, since $t > -t_{0.05}$ (or P-value $> \alpha$).
   Step 5: There is not sufficient evidence at the $\alpha = 0.05$ level of significance to support the claim that $\mu_1 < \mu_2$.
   (b) Lower bound: -6.08; Upper bound: 2.68
   (c) **Step 1:** $H_o: \sigma_1 = \sigma_2$ vs $H_1: \sigma_1 \neq \sigma_2$
   Step 2: $F_{0.975,12,7} = 0.28$; $F_{0.025,12,7} \approx 4.76$
   Step 3: $F = 1.64$
   Step 4: Do not reject H_o, since $F_{0.975,12,7} < F < F_{0.025,12,7}$.
   Step 5: There is not sufficient evidence at the $\alpha = 0.05$ level of significance to support the claim that $\sigma_1 \neq \sigma_2$.

13. (a) $H_o: p_1 = p_2$ vs $H_1: p_1 \neq p_2$
   (b) $Z = -1.70$
   (c) $-z_{0.025} = -1.96$; $z_{0.025} = 1.96$
   (d) P-value $= 0.0895$
   Do not reject H_0. There is not sufficient evidence at the $\alpha = 0.05$ level of significance to support the claim that $p_1 \neq p_2$ (because $-z_{0.025} < Z < z_{0.025}$ or P-value $> \alpha$).

14. (a) $H_o: p_1 = p_2$ vs $H_1: p_1 < p_2$
   (b) $Z = -0.62$
   (c) $-z_{0.05} = -1.645$
   (d) P-value $= 0.2678$
   Do not reject H_0. There is not sufficient evidence at the $\alpha = 0.05$ level of significance to support the claim that $p_1 < p_2$ (because $Z > -z_{0.025}$ or P-value $> \alpha$).

15. (a) Yes, each sample is a simple random sample. The samples were obtained independently. We are told that a normal probability plot indicates that the data could come from a population that is normal, with no outliers.
   (b) **Step 1:** $H_o: \mu_{\text{females}} = \mu_{\text{males}}$ vs $H_1: \mu_{\text{females}} \neq \mu_{\text{males}}$
   Step 2: $-t_{0.025} = -2.201$; $t_{0.025} = 2.201$ (using 11 df)
   Step 3: $t = -0.80$; P-value $= 0.43$
   Step 4: Do not reject H_o, because $-t_{0.025} < t < t_{0.025}$ (or P-value $> \alpha$).
   Step 5: There is not sufficient evidence at the $\alpha = 0.05$ level of significance to support the claim that there is a difference between reaction times of females and males.
   (c) Lower bound: -0.21; Upper bound: 0.09. We are 95% confident that the difference in the mean reaction time to the "choice" stimulus is between -0.21 and 0.09 seconds. Because the interval contains 0, we do not reject the null hypothesis.
   (d)

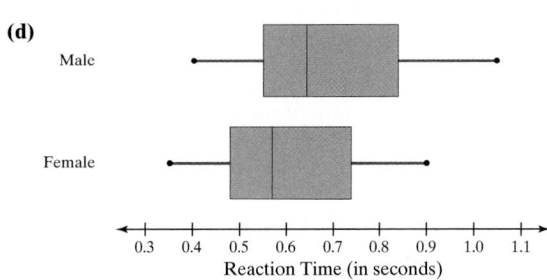

16. (a) Yes, each sample is a simple random sample. The samples were obtained independently. We are told that a normal probability plot indicates that the data could come from a population that is normal, with no outliers.
   (b) **Step 1:** $H_o: \mu_{\text{Texas}} = \mu_{\text{Illinois}}$ vs $H_1: \mu_{\text{Texas}} \neq \mu_{\text{Illinois}}$
   Step 2: $-t_{0.025} = -2.201$; $t_{0.025} = 2.201$ (using 11 df)
   Step 3: $t = 2.28$; P-value $= 0.039$
   Step 4: Reject H_o, because $t > t_{0.025}$ (or P-value $< \alpha$).
   Step 5: There is sufficient evidence at the $\alpha = 0.05$ level of significance to support the claim that the acidity of the rain near Houston is different from its acidity near Chicago.
   (c) Lower bound: 0.009; Upper bound: 0.513. We are 95% confident that the mean difference between the acidity of rain near Houston and the acidity of rain near Chicago is between 0.009 and 0.513. Because the interval does not contain 0, we reject the null hypothesis.
   (d)

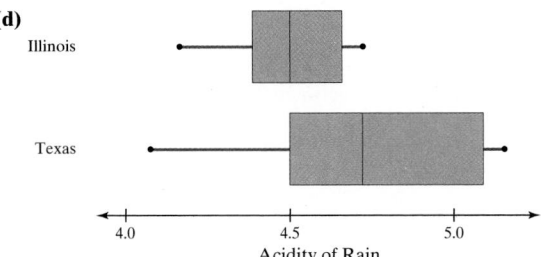

17. (a) Independent sampling, because the individuals selected are not related in any way.
   (b) **Step 1:** $H_o: \mu_{\text{wheat}} = \mu_{\text{modern}}$ vs $H_1: \mu_{\text{wheat}} < \mu_{\text{modern}}$
   Step 2: $-t_{0.05} = -1.734$ (using 18 df)
   Step 3: $t = -3.01$; P-value $= 0.0024$
   Step 4: Reject H_o, because $t < -t_{0.05}$ (or P-value $< \alpha$).
   Step 5: There is sufficient evidence at the $\alpha = 0.05$ level of significance to support the claim that the weight of wheat pennies is less than the weight of modern pennies.

(c) Lower bound: 0.009; Upper bound: 0.050. We are 95% confident that modern pennies have a mean weight that is between 0.009 grams and 0.050 grams higher than that of wheat pennies.

(d) It is likely that pennies "lose weight" over time.

18. (a) Dependent sampling, because the individuals selected are related.

(b) Step 1: $H_o: \mu_d = 0$ vs $H_1: \mu_d > 0$ (The differenced data are computed as Before–After)
Step 2: $t_{0.05} = 1.833$ (using 9 df)
Step 3: $t = 1.55$; P-value $= 0.077$
Step 4: Do not reject H_o because $t < t_{0.05}$ (or P-value $> \alpha$).
Step 5: There is not sufficient evidence at the $\alpha = 0.05$ level of significance to support the claim that the exercise program is effective in reducing pulse.

(c) Lower bound: -5.02; Upper bound: 14.22. We are 99% confident that the mean change in pulse rates due to exercise is between -5.02 and 14.22 beats per minute.

19. (a) Each sample is a simple random sample; $n_1\hat{p}_1(1 - \hat{p}_1) \geq 10$ and $n_2\hat{p}_2(1 - \hat{p}_2) \geq 10$; and each sample is less than 5% of the population size.
Step 1: $H_o: p_{exp} = p_{control}$ vs $H_1: p_{exp} < p_{control}$
Step 2: $-z_{0.01} = -2.33$
Step 3: $Z = -2.71$ (P-value $= 0.0033$)
Step 4: Reject H_o, since $Z < -z_{0.01}$ (or P-value $< \alpha$).
Step 5: There is sufficient evidence at the $\alpha = 0.01$ level of significance to support the claim that a lower proportion of women in the experimental group experienced a bone fracture than in the control group.

(b) Lower bound: -0.06; Upper bound: -0.01. We are 95% confident that the difference in the proportion of women who experienced a bone fracture between the experimental and control group is between -0.06 and -0.01.

(c) This is a completely randomized design. The treatment is drug. It has two levels: 5 mg of Actonel versus a placebo.

20. (a) Each sample is a simple random sample; $n_1\hat{p}_1(1 - \hat{p}_1) \geq 10$ and $n_2\hat{p}_2(1 - \hat{p}_2) \geq 10$; and each sample is less than 5% of the population size.
Step 1: $H_o: p_{exp} = p_{control}$ vs $H_1: p_{exp} > p_{control}$
Step 2: $z_{0.05} = 1.645$
Step 3: $Z = 2.21$ (P-value $= 0.0136$)
Step 4: Reject H_o, since $Z > z_{0.05}$ (or P-value $< \alpha$).
Step 5: There is sufficient evidence at the $\alpha = 0.05$ level of significance to support the claim that a higher proportion of subjects in the experimental group experienced a dry mouth than in the control group.

(b) Lower bound: 0.01; Upper bound: 0.08. We are 95% confident that the difference in the proportion of subjects who experienced a dry mouth between the experimental and control group is between 0.01 and 0.08.

21. (a) 2136   **(b)** 3383

22. (a) 762   **(b)** 1201

23. Step 1: $H_o: \sigma_{male} = \sigma_{female}$ vs $H_1: \sigma_{male} > \sigma_{female}$
Step 2: $F_{0.05,11,14} \approx 2.51$
Step 3: $F = 1.17$
Step 4: Do not reject H_o, since $F < F_{0.05,11,14}$.
Step 5: There is not sufficient evidence at the $\alpha = 0.05$ level of significance to support the claim that the standard deviation in the reaction time of male students is greater than the standard-deviation reaction time in female students.

24. Step 1: $H_o: \sigma_{Texas} = \sigma_{Illinois}$ vs $H_1: \sigma_{Texas} \neq \sigma_{Illinois}$
Step 2: $F_{0.975,11,14} \approx 0.30$; $F_{0.025,11,14} \approx 3.01$
Step 3: $F = 5.625$
Step 4: Reject H_o, since $F > F_{0.025,11,14}$.
Step 5: There is sufficient evidence at the $\alpha = 0.05$ level of significance to support the claim that the standard deviation in the acidity of rain near Houston is different from the standard deviation in the acidity of rain near Chicago.

CHAPTER 11   Chi-Square Procedures

11.1 Exercises (p. 664)

1.

p_i	0.2	0.1	0.45	0.25
Expected Counts	100	50	225	125

2.

p_i	0.15	0.3	0.35	0.20
Expected Counts	105	210	245	140

3. (a) $\chi^2 = 2.72$ **(b)** df $= 3$ **(c)** $\chi^2_{0.05} = 7.815$
(d) Do not reject H_o, since $\chi^2 < \chi^2_{0.05}$

4. (a) $\chi^2 = 2.2$ **(b)** df $= 4$ **(c)** $\chi^2_{0.05} = 9.488$
(d) Do not reject H_o, since $\chi^2 < \chi^2_{0.05}$

5. (a) $\chi^2 = 12.56$ **(b)** df $= 4$ **(c)** $\chi^2_{0.05} = 9.488$
(d) Reject H_o, since $\chi^2 > \chi^2_{0.05}$. There is sufficient evidence at the $\alpha = 0.05$ level of significance to reject the claim that the random variable X is binomial, with $n = 4$, $p = 0.8$.

6. (a) $\chi^2 = 11.987$ **(b)** df $= 4$ **(c)** $\chi^2_{0.05} = 9.488$
(d) Reject H_o, since $\chi^2 > \chi^2_{0.05}$. There is sufficient evidence at the $\alpha = 0.05$ level of significance to reject the claim that the random variable X is binomial, with $n = 4$, $p = 0.3$.

7. Step 1: H_o: The distribution of plain M&Ms is 30% brown, 20% yellow, 20% red, 10% orange, 10% blue, and 10% green
H_1: The distribution of plain M&Ms is not 30% brown, 20% yellow, 20% red, 10% orange, 10% blue, and 10% green

Step 2:

Color	Brown	Yellow	Red	Orange	Blue	Green
Frequency	125	77	90	42	31	35
Expected	120	80	80	40	40	40

Step 3: (1) All expected frequencies are greater than or equal to 1. (2) No more than 20% of the expected frequencies are less than 5.
Step 4: $\chi^2_{0.05} = 11.071$
Step 5: $\chi^2 = 4.321$
Step 6: Do not reject H_o, because $\chi^2 < \chi^2_{0.05}$.
Step 7: There is not sufficient evidence at the $\alpha = 0.05$ level of significance to reject the null hypothesis. There is no reason for us not to believe the claim made by M&M-Mars.

8. Step 1: H_o: The distribution of peanut M&Ms is 20% brown, 20% yellow, 20% red, 20% blue, 10% orange, and 10% green
H_1: The distribution of plain M&Ms is not 20% brown, 20% yellow, 20% red, 20% blue, 10% orange, and 10% green

Step 2:

Color	Brown	Yellow	Red	Blue	Orange	Green
Frequency	67	84	85	85	40	39
Expected	80	80	80	80	40	40

Step 3: (1) All expected frequencies are greater than or equal to 1. (2) No more than 20% of the expected frequencies are less than 5.
Step 4: $\chi^2_{0.05} = 11.071$
Step 5: $\chi^2 = 2.9625$
Step 6: Do not reject H_o, because $\chi^2 < \chi^2_{0.05}$.
Step 7: There is not sufficient evidence at the $\alpha = 0.05$ level of significance to reject the null hypothesis. There is no reason for us not to believe the claim made by M&M-Mars.

9. Step 1: H_o: The distribution of bicycle deaths is the same as the distribution of pedestrian deaths.
H_1: The distribution of bicycle deaths is not the same as the distribution of pedestrian deaths.

Step 2:

Time of Day	Midnight–3 A.M.	3 A.M.–6 A.M.	6 A.M.–9 A.M.	9 A.M.–Noon	Noon–3 P.M.	3 P.M.–6 P.M.	6 P.M.–9 P.M.	9 P.M.–Midnight
Frequency	19	20	42	34	39	98	101	47
Expected	44.8	28.4	36.8	24.4	24.4	49.2	102	90

Step 3: (1) All expected frequencies are greater than or equal to 1. (2) No more than 20% of the expected frequencies are less than 5.
Step 4: $\chi^2_{0.05} = 14.067$
Step 5: $\chi^2 = 99.548$
Step 6: Reject H_o, because $\chi^2 > \chi^2_{0.05}$.
Step 7: There is sufficient evidence at the $\alpha = 0.05$ level of significance to reject the null hypothesis. It is likely the case that the distributions of pedestrian deaths and bicycle deaths are not the same.

10. Step 1: H_o: The distribution of the age of mothers is the same as it was in 1990.
H_1: The distribution of the age of mothers is not the same as it was in 1990.
Step 2:

Age of Mother	15–19	20–24	25–29	30–34	35–39	40–44
Frequency	58	105	128	131	69	9
Observed	43	132.5	152.5	114	48	10

Step 3: (1) All expected frequencies are greater than or equal to 1. (2) No more than 20% of the expected frequencies are less than 5.
Step 4: $\chi^2_{0.05} = 11.071$
Step 5: $\chi^2 = 26.69876$
Step 6: Reject H_o, because $\chi^2 > \chi^2_{0.05}$.
Step 7: There is sufficient evidence at the $\alpha = 0.05$ level of significance to reject the null hypothesis. It is likely the case that the distribution of the age of mothers is different from what it was in 1990.

11. Step 1: H_o: $p_{Jan} = p_{Feb} = \cdots = p_{Dec}$
H_1: At least one of the proportions is different from the others.
Step 2:

Month	Jan	Feb	March	April	May	June
Frequency	52	35	44	42	42	36
Expected	41.66667	41.66667	41.66667	41.66667	41.66667	41.66667
Month	July	Aug	Sep	Oct	Nov	Dec
Frequency	44	34	36	46	48	41
Expected	41.66667	41.66667	41.66667	41.66667	41.66667	41.66667

Step 3: (1) All expected frequencies are greater than or equal to 1. (2) No more than 20% of the expected frequencies are less than 5.
Step 4: $\chi^2_{0.05} = 19.675$
Step 5: $\chi^2 = 8.272$
Step 6: Do not reject H_o, because $\chi^2 < \chi^2_{0.05}$.
Step 7: There is not sufficient evidence at the $\alpha = 0.05$ level of significance to reject the null hypothesis. The results of the test indicate that the distribution of birth month may be uniform.

12. Step 1: H_o: $p_{Sun} = p_{Mon} = \cdots = p_{Sat}$
H_1: At least one of the proportions is different from the others.
Step 2:

Day of the Week	Sunday	Monday	Tuesday	Wednesday	Thursday	Friday	Saturday
Frequency	16	35	16	28	34	41	30
Expected	200/7	200/7	200/7	200/7	200/7	200/7	200/7

Step 3: (1) All expected frequencies are greater than or equal to 1. (2) No more than 20% of the expected frequencies are less than 5.
Step 4: $\chi^2_{0.05} = 12.592$
Step 5: $\chi^2 = 19.03$
Step 6: Reject H_o, because $\chi^2 > \chi^2_{0.05}$.
Step 7: There is sufficient evidence at the $\alpha = 0.05$ level of significance to reject the null hypothesis. The results of the test indicate that the distribution of bicycle deaths is likely not uniform.

13. Step 1: H_o: $p_{Sun} = p_{Mon} = \cdots = p_{Sat}$
H_1: At least one of the proportions is different from the others.
Step 2:

Day of the Week	Sunday	Monday	Tuesday	Wednesday	Thursday	Friday	Saturday
Frequency	39	40	30	40	41	49	61
Expected	300/7	300/7	300/7	300/7	300/7	300/7	300/7

Step 3: (1) All expected frequencies are greater than or equal to 1. (2) No more than 20% of the expected frequencies are less than 5.
Step 4: $\chi^2_{0.05} = 12.592$
Step 5: $\chi^2 = 13.22667$
Step 6: Reject H_o, because $\chi^2 > \chi^2_{0.05}$.
Step 7: There is sufficient evidence at the $\alpha = 0.05$ level of significance to reject the null hypothesis. The results of the test indicate that the distribution of pedestrian deaths is likely not uniform.

14. Step 1: H_o: $p_1 = p_2 = \cdots = p_6 = 1/6$
H_1: At least one of the proportions is different from the others.
Step 2:

Outcome	One	Two	Three	Four	Five	Six
Frequency	62	76	76	62	57	67
Expected	66.67	66.67	66.67	66.67	66.67	66.67

Step 3: (1) All expected frequencies are greater than or equal to 1. (2) No more than 20% of the expected frequencies are less than 5.
Step 4: $\chi^2_{0.01} = 15.086$
Step 5: $\chi^2 = 4.669768$
Step 6: Do not reject H_o, because $\chi^2 < \chi^2_{0.01}$.
Step 7: There is not sufficient evidence at the $\alpha = 0.01$ level of significance to reject the null hypothesis. The results of the test indicate that it is reasonable to believe the die is fair.

17. (a) Expected number low birth weight: 8.52; Expected number without low birth weight: 111.48.
(b) H_o: $p = 0.071$ vs H_1: $p > 0.071$. $\chi^2 = 1.229$; $\chi^2_{0.05} = 3.841$. Do not reject H_o, because $\chi^2 < \chi^2_{0.05}$.
(c) Do not reject, because $Z < z_{0.05}(0.88 < 1.645)$.

18. (a) Expected number living at home: 156; Expected number not living at home: 244.
(b) H_o: $p = 0.39$ vs H_1: $p > 0.39$. $\chi^2 = 0.673$; $\chi^2_{0.05} = 3.841$. Do not reject H_o, because $\chi^2 < \chi^2_{0.05}$.
(c) Do not reject, because $Z < z_{0.05}(0.82 < 1.645)$.

19. $\Sigma(O - E) = 0$

11.2 Exercises (p. 674)

1. (a)

	<18	18–44	45–64	>65	Totals
Below Poverty Level	8550	4356	1520	958	15,384
Above Poverty Level	5884	3741	1756	1943	13,324
Totals	14,434	8097	3276	2901	28,708

(b)

	<18	18–44	45–64	>65	Totals
Below Poverty Level	8550	4356	1520	958	0.536
Above Poverty Level	5884	3741	1756	1943	0.464
Totals	0.503	0.282	0.114	0.101	1.00

(c) 53.6%   **(d)** 50.3%
(e)

	<18	18–44	45–64	>65
Below Poverty Level	0.556	0.283	0.099	0.062
Above Poverty Level	0.442	0.281	0.132	0.146

(f)

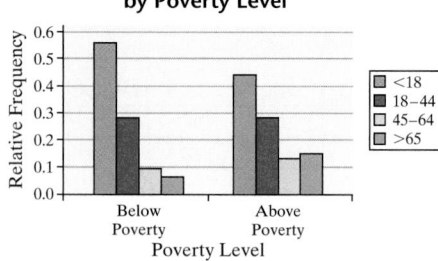

Medicaid Recipients by Poverty Level

Legend: <18, 18–44, 45–64, >65

(g) For younger individuals, a higher proportion of Medicaid recipients are below the poverty level, but as the individuals age, a higher proportion of Medicaid recipients are above the poverty level.

2. (a)

	Male	Female	Totals
200–299	16,349	18,328	34,677
300–399	75,672	90,197	165,869
400–499	177,265	213,756	391,021
500–599	186,947	216,564	403,511
600–699	98,407	108,358	206,765
700–800	28,691	29,744	58,435
Totals	583,331	676,947	1,260,278

(b)

	Male	Female	Totals
200–299	16,349	18,328	0.028
300–399	75,672	90,197	0.132
400–499	177,265	213,756	0.310
500–599	186,947	216,564	0.320
600–699	98,407	108,358	0.164
700–800	28,691	29,744	0.046
	0.463	0.537	1

(c) 32.0%   **(d)** 53.7%

(e)

	Male	Female
200–299	0.028	0.027
300–399	0.130	0.133
400–499	0.304	0.316
500–599	0.320	0.320
600–699	0.169	0.160
700–800	0.049	0.044

(f)

SAT Scores by Gender

Legend: 200–299, 300–399, 400–499, 500–599, 600–699, 700–800

(g) No association is apparent between SAT score and gender.

3. (a)

	Male	Female	Totals
16–24	4736	1461	6197
25–34	4112	1244	5356
35–44	3180	1089	4269
45–54	2028	738	2766
55–64	1321	530	1851
65–74	1212	626	1838
75–84	1028	553	1581
85 or older	329	146	475
Totals	17,946	6387	24,333

(b)

	Male	Female	Totals
16–24	4736	1461	0.255
25–34	4112	1244	0.220
35–44	3180	1089	0.175
45–54	2028	738	0.114
55–64	1321	530	0.076
65–74	1212	626	0.076
75–84	1028	553	0.065
85 or older	329	146	0.020
Totals	0.738	0.262	1

(c) 25.5%   **(d)** 26.2%

(e)

Age	Male	Female	Age	Male	Female
16–24	0.264	0.229	55–64	0.074	0.083
25–34	0.229	0.195	65–74	0.068	0.098
35–44	0.177	0.171	75–84	0.057	0.087
45–54	0.113	0.116	85 or older	0.018	0.023

(f)

Fatalities by Gender

Legend: 16–24, 25–34, 35–44, 45–54, 55–64, 65–74, 75–84, 85 or older

(g) It seems that the younger fatalities are more likely to be male, while older fatalities are more likely to be female.

4. (a)

	Did Not Graduate High School	High School Graduate	Some College	College Graduate	Totals
Never Married	4012	7790	6565	7685	26,052
Married, Spouse Present	15,122	36,076	27,003	29,811	108,012
Married, Spouse Absent	1877	2006	1435	1489	6807
Separated	1094	1515	1214	598	4421
Widowed	5000	4757	2264	1456	13,477
Divorced	2951	7047	5649	3766	19,413
Totals	30,056	59,191	44,130	44,805	178,182

(b)

	Did Not Graduate High School	High School Graduate	Some College	College Graduate	Totals
Never Married	4012	7790	6565	7685	**0.146**
Married, Spouse Present	15,122	36,076	27,003	29,811	**0.606**
Married, Spouse Absent	1877	2006	1435	1489	**0.038**
Separated	1094	1515	1214	598	**0.025**
Widowed	5000	4757	2264	1456	**0.076**
Divorced	2951	7047	5649	3766	**0.109**
Totals	**0.169**	**0.332**	**0.248**	**0.251**	**1.000**

(c) 14.6%
(d) 33.2%

(e)

	Did Not Graduate High School	High School Graduate	Some College	College Graduate
Never Married	0.133	0.132	0.149	0.172
Married, Spouse Present	0.503	0.609	0.612	0.665
Married, Spouse Absent	0.062	0.034	0.033	0.033
Separated	0.036	0.026	0.028	0.013
Widowed	0.166	0.080	0.051	0.032
Divorced	0.098	0.119	0.128	0.084

(f)

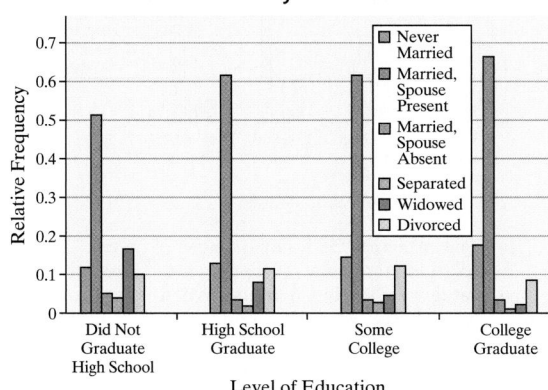

Marital Status by Level of Education

(g) It seems that college graduates are the most likely to be married with the spouse present. We notice a high proportion of widowed for the "did not graduate high school" group. This could be due to the fact that older individuals are likely to be widowed and also not to have finished high school.

5. (a)

	1980	1990	1995	Totals
≤19 years old	378,901	320,225	243,387	**942,513**
20–24 years old	460,650	474,620	393,537	**1,328,807**
≥25 years old	458,055	634,732	573,959	**1,666,746**
Totals	**1,297,606**	**1,429,577**	**1,210,883**	**3,938,066**

5. (b)

	1980	1990	1995	Totals
≤19 years old	378,901	320,225	243,387	**0.239**
20–24 years old	460,650	474,620	393,537	**0.337**
≥25 years old	458,055	634,732	573,959	**0.423**
Totals	**0.330**	**0.363**	**0.307**	**1**

(c) 33.0%
(d) 23.9%

(e)

	1980	1990	1995
≤19 years old	0.292	0.224	0.201
20–24 years old	0.355	0.332	0.325
≥25 years old	0.353	0.444	0.474

(f)

Abortions by Year

(g) It seems that in more recent years, a higher proportion of abortions are performed on individuals who are older than 25 years of age, while the proportion of individuals having abortions who are younger than 19 years of age is declining.

6. (a)

	Accidents and Adverse Effects	Malignant Neoplasms	Diseases of Heart	Cerebrovascular Diseases	Totals
1–4 years	1935	365	214	57	**2571**
5–14 years	3254	1386	326	82	**5048**
15–24 years	13,349	1699	1057	178	**16,283**
25–44 years	27,172	13,077	16,800	3320	**60,369**
45–64 years	18,286	132,771	100,124	15,362	**266,543**
65 years and older	32,975	384,186	605,673	139,144	**1,161,978**
Totals	**96,971**	**533,484**	**724,194**	**158,143**	**1,512,792**

6. (b)

	Accidents and Adverse Effects	Malignant Neoplasms	Diseases of Heart	Cerebrovascular Diseases	Totals
1–4 years	1935	365	214	57	0.002
5–14 years	3254	1386	326	82	0.003
15–24 years	13,349	1699	1057	178	0.011
25–44 years	27,172	13,077	16,800	3320	0.040
45–64 years	18,286	132,771	100,124	15,362	0.176
65 years and older	32,975	384,186	605,673	139,144	0.768
Totals	0.064	0.353	0.479	0.105	1.000

(c) 6.4%   **(d)** 1.1%

(e)

	Accidents and Adverse Effects	Malignant Neoplasms	Diseases of Heart	Cerebrovascular Diseases
1–4 years	0.0200	0.0007	0.0003	0.0004
5–14 years	0.0336	0.0026	0.0005	0.0005
15–24 years	0.1377	0.0032	0.0015	0.0011
25–44 years	0.2802	0.0245	0.0232	0.0210
45–64 years	0.1886	0.2489	0.1383	0.0971
65 years and older	0.3401	0.7201	0.8363	0.8799

(f)

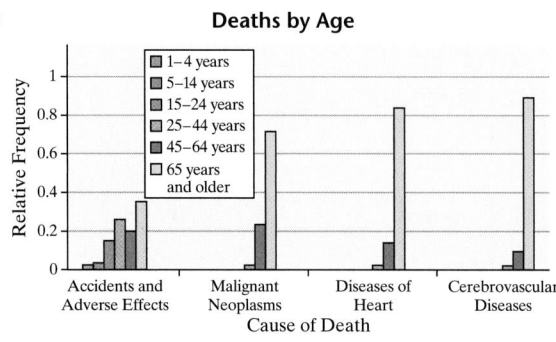

Deaths by Age

(g) Accidents and adverse effects are the most likely causes of death for individuals under the age of 44.

7. (a)

	In Relative Care	In Nonrelative Care	In Center-Based Program	Parental Arrangement	Totals
35 hours or more per week	2343	2272	2769	852	8236
Less than 35 hours per week	1210	1049	1412	1009	4680
Looking for Work	262	65	409	948	1684
Not in the Labor Force	585	501	1838	5681	8605
Totals	4400	3887	6428	8490	23,205

7. (b)

	In Relative Care	In Nonrelative Care	In Center-Based Program	Parental Arrangement	Totals
35 hours or more per week	2343	2272	2769	852	0.355
Less than 35 hours per week	1210	1049	1412	1009	0.202
Looking for Work	262	65	409	948	0.073
Not in the Labor Force	585	501	1838	5681	0.371
Totals	0.190	0.168	0.277	0.366	1

(c) 35.5%   **(d)** 19.0%

(e)

	In Relative Care	In Nonrelative Care	In Center-Based Program	Parental Arrangement
35 hours or more per week	0.284	0.276	0.336	0.103
Less than 35 hours per week	0.259	0.224	0.302	0.216
Looking for Work	0.156	0.039	0.243	0.563
Not in the Labor Force	0.068	0.058	0.214	0.660

(f)

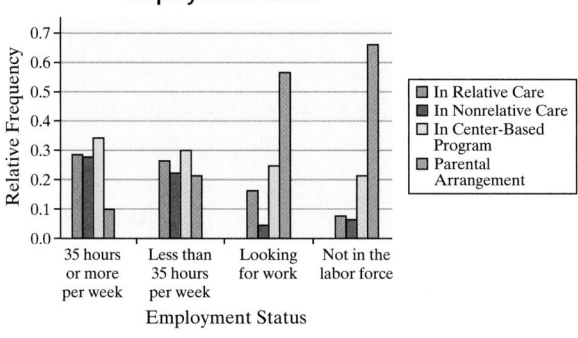

Child Care by Employment Status

(g) The category "35 hours or more per week" has the highest relative frequency, except in the "parental arrangement" category. Clearly, if a mother is neither in the labor force nor looking for work, the child is most likely in a parental arrangement.

8. (a)

	Full Owner	Part Owner	Tenant	Totals
Under 50 acres	460	57	48	565
50–179 acres	409	131	53	593
180–499 acres	189	169	45	403
500–999 acres	50	103	23	176
1000 acres or more	40	114	22	176
Totals	1148	574	191	1913

(b)

	Full Owner	Part Owner	Tenant	Totals
Under 50 acres	460	57	48	0.295
50–179 acres	409	131	53	0.310
180–499 acres	189	169	45	0.211
500–999 acres	50	103	23	0.092
1000 acres or more	40	114	22	0.092
Totals	0.600	0.300	0.100	1

(c) 31.0%   **(d)** 60.0%

(e)

	Full Owner	Part Owner	Tenant
Under 50 acres	0.814	0.101	0.085
50–179 acres	0.690	0.221	0.089
180–499 acres	0.469	0.419	0.112
500–999 acres	0.284	0.585	0.131
1000 acres or more	0.227	0.648	0.125

(f)

Size of a Farm by Tenure of Operator

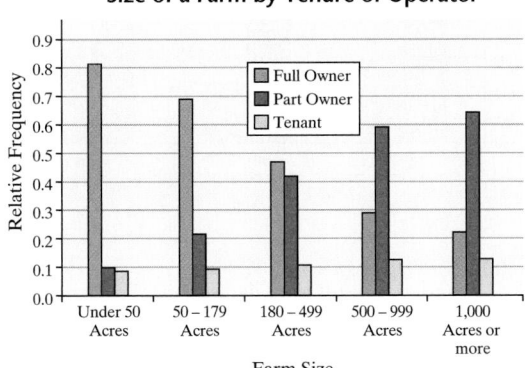

(g) As the size of the farm increases, the likelihood of it being a full-owner farm decreases. Likewise, as the size of the farm increases, a higher proportion of the operators are either part owners or tenants.

11.3 Exercises (p. 687)

1. (a) $\chi^2 = 1.701$
  (b) $\chi^2_{0.05} = 5.991$. Since $\chi^2 < \chi^2_{0.05}$, do not reject H_o. There is evidence at the $\alpha = 0.05$ level of significance to support the belief that X and Y are independent. It appears that X and Y are not related.
  (c) P-value = 0.427
2. (a) $\chi^2 = 13.053$
  (b) $\chi^2_{0.05} = 5.991$. Since $\chi^2 > \chi^2_{0.05}$, reject H_o. There is sufficient evidence at the $\alpha = 0.05$ level of significance to support the belief that X and Y are not independent. There is a relation between X and Y.
  (c) P-value = 0.001
3. $\chi^2 = 1.989$; $\chi^2_{0.05} = 5.991$. Since $\chi^2 < \chi^2_{0.05}$, do not reject H_o. There is evidence at the $\alpha = 0.05$ level of significance to support the claim that the proportions are equal. We don't have enough evidence to conclude that at least one of the proportions is different from the others. P-value = 0.370
4. $\chi^2 = 3.533$; $\chi^2_{0.05} = 5.991$. Since $\chi^2 < \chi^2_{0.05}$, do not reject H_o. There is evidence at the $\alpha = 0.05$ level of significance to support the claim that the proportions are equal. We don't have enough evidence to conclude that at least one of the proportions is different from the others. P-value = 0.171
5. (a)

	Both Biological/Adoptive parents	Single Parent	Parent and Step-Parent	Nonparental Guardian
Had Sexual Intercourse	78.553	52.368	41.895	26.184
Did Not Have Sexual Intercourse	71.447	47.632	38.105	23.816

(b) (1) all expected frequencies are greater than or equal to one and (2) no more than 20% of the expected frequencies are less than five.

(c) $\chi^2 = 10.357$
(d) $\chi^2_{0.05} = 7.815$. Since $\chi^2 > \chi^2_{0.05}$, reject H_o. There is sufficient evidence at the $\alpha = 0.05$ level of significance to conclude that sexual activity and family structure are associated.
(e) The biggest difference between observed and expected occurs under the family structure in which both parents are present. Fewer females were sexually active than was expected when both parents were present. This means that having both parents present seems to have an impact on whether the child is sexually active.

(f)

	Both Biological/Adoptive parents	Single Parent	Parent and Step-Parent	Nonparental Guardian
Had Sexual Intercourse	0.427	0.59	0.55	0.64
Did Not Have Sexual Intercourse	0.573	0.41	0.45	0.36

Family Structure and Sexual Activity

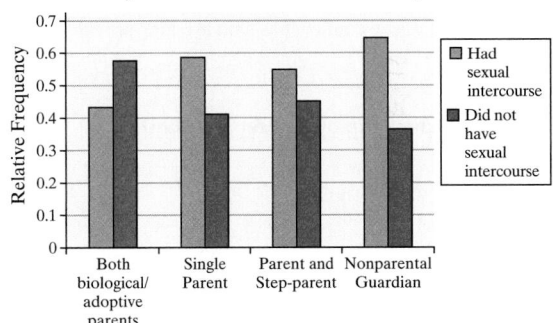

(g) P-value = 0.016

6. (a)

	Less than 3 months	3–5 months	More than 5 months (or never)
Intended	573.54	36.80	41.66
Unintended	73.01	4.68	5.3
Mistimed	179.45	11.51	13.04

(b) (1) all expected frequencies are greater than or equal to 1 and (2) no more than 20% of the expected frequencies are less than 5.
(c) $\chi^2 = 21.357$
(d) $\chi^2_{0.05} = 9.488$. Since $\chi^2 > \chi^2_{0.05}$, reject H_o. There is sufficient evidence at the $\alpha = 0.05$ level of significance to conclude that "wantedness of pregnancy" and "months pregnant before prenatal care" are associated.
(e) The biggest difference between observed and expected occurs between "intended" and "less than 3 months." The observed is greater than the expected, which implies that intended pregnancies are likely to have early prenatal care.

(f)

	Less than 3 months	3–5 months	More than 5 months (or never)
Intended	0.910	0.040	0.051
Unintended	0.771	0.096	0.133
Mistimed	0.828	0.093	0.078

Prenatal Care by Wantedness of the Pregnancy

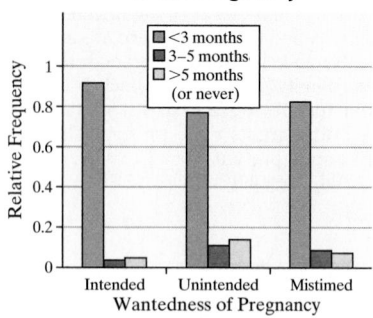

7. (a) $\chi^2 = 32.926$; $\chi^2_{0.05} = 16.919$. Since $\chi^2 > \chi^2_{0.05}$, reject H_o. There is sufficient evidence at the $\alpha = 0.05$ level of significance to conclude that "level of education" and "area of country" are associated.

(b) The cell corresponding to "Midwest" and "not a high-school graduate" contributed most to the test statistic. The expected was more than the observed, which means that the Midwest appears to have a lower proportion of residents than the rest of the country has who are high school graduates or higher.

(c)

Education by Region of Country

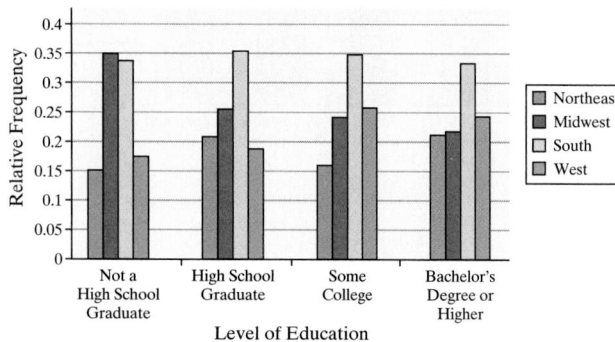

8. (a) $\chi^2 = 7.803$; $\chi^2_{0.05} = 12.592$. Since $\chi^2 < \chi^2_{0.05}$, do not reject H_o. There is sufficient evidence at the $\alpha = 0.05$ level of significance to support the belief that smoking status and number of years of education are not associated. It does not appear to be the case that number of years of education plays a role in determining smoking status.

(b) P-value $= 0.253$

(c)

Smoking Status vs. Level of Education

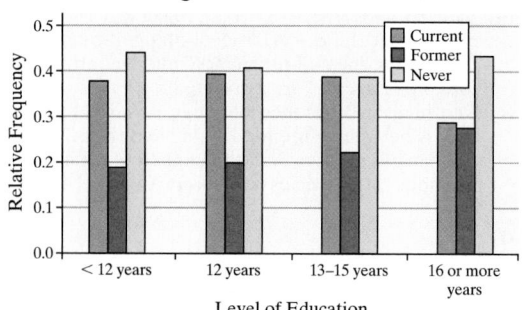

9. (a) $\chi^2 = 6.681$; $\chi^2_{0.05} = 5.991$. Since $\chi^2 > \chi^2_{0.05}$, reject H_o. There is sufficient evidence at the $\alpha = 0.05$ level of significance to support the belief that "age" and "opinion" are associated. It appears to be the case that age plays a role in

determining one's opinion regarding the legalization of marijuana. The "50 or older" group is less likely to be in favor of the legalization of marijuana.

(b) P-value $= 0.035$

(c)

Legalization of Marijuana

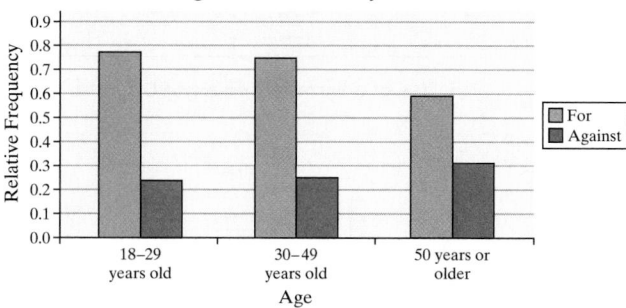

10. (a) $\chi^2 = 0.036$; $\chi^2_{0.1} = 2.706$. Since $\chi^2 < \chi^2_{0.1}$, do not reject H_o. There is not sufficient evidence at the $\alpha = 0.1$ level of significance to support the belief that "gender" and "opinion" are associated. It appears to be the case that gender is not associated with one's opinion regarding choice.

(b) P-value $= 0.849$

(c)

Abortion

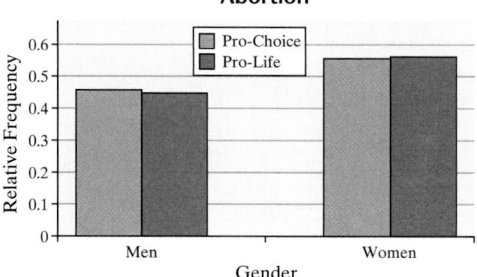

11. (a) $\chi^2 = 0.946$; $\chi^2_{0.1} = 7.815$. Since $\chi^2 < \chi^2_{0.05}$, do not reject H_o. There is not sufficient evidence at the $\alpha = 0.05$ level of significance to support the belief that "gender" and "delinquencies" are associated.

(b) P-value $= 0.814$

(c)

Delinquencies by Type

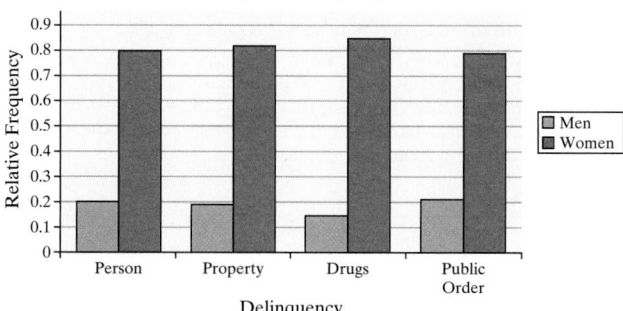

12. (a) $\chi^2 = 12.291$; $\chi^2_{0.1} = 9.236$. Since $\chi^2 > \chi^2_{0.1}$, reject H_o. There is sufficient evidence at the $\alpha = 0.1$ level of significance to support the belief that "gender" and "age" are associated when it comes to visits to the emergency room. In the "75 and older" age group, fewer males than expected visited, while more females than expected visited.

(b) P-value $= 0.031$

12. (c)

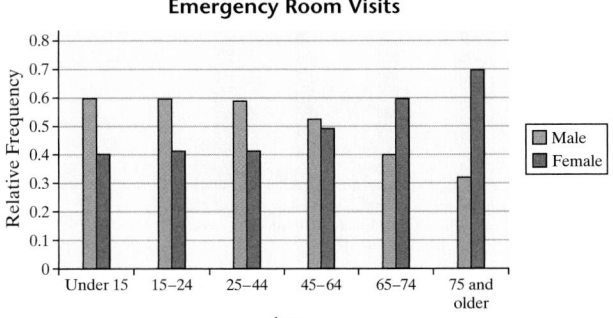

Emergency Room Visits

13. (a) H_0: $p_{18-29} = p_{30-49} = p_{50-64} = p_{65 \text{ and older}}$ vs H_1: at least one of the proportions is not equal to the rest. $\chi^2 = 6.000$; $\chi^2_{0.05} = 7.815$. Since $\chi^2 < \chi^2_{0.05}$, do not reject H_0. There is not sufficient evidence at the $\alpha = 0.05$ level of significance to support the claim that at least one proportion is different from the others. The evidence suggests that the proportion of individuals in each age group who smoked at least one cigarette in the past week is the same.
(b) P-value $= 0.112$

(c)

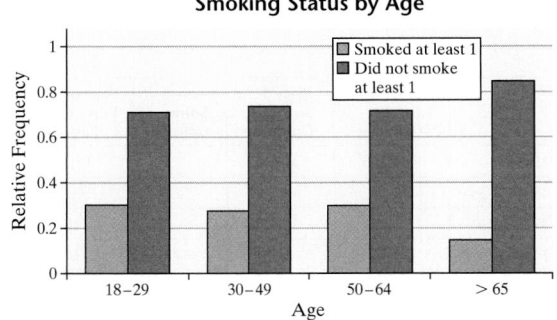

Smoking Status by Age

14. (a) H_0: $p_{\text{east}} = p_{\text{south}} = p_{\text{midwest}} = p_{\text{west}}$ vs H_1: at least one of the proportions is not equal to the rest. $\chi^2 = 3.541$; $\chi^2_{0.1} = 6.251$. Since $\chi^2 < \chi^2_{0.1}$, do not reject H_0. There is not sufficient evidence at the $\alpha = 0.1$ level of significance to support the claim that at least one proportion is different from the others. The evidence suggests that the proportion of individuals in each region that is satisfied with the way things are going in the United States is the same.
(b) P-value $= 0.316$

(c)

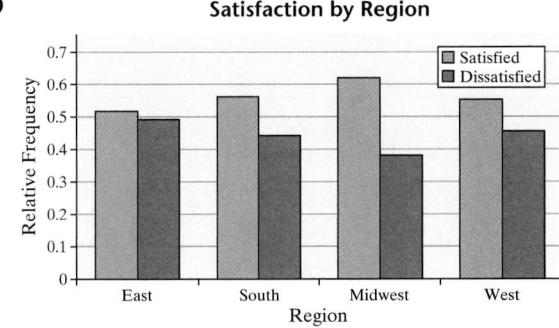

Satisfaction by Region

15. (a) H_0: $p_{\text{placebo}} = p_{50} = p_{100} = p_{200} = p_{\text{naproxen}}$ vs H_1: at least one of the proportions is not equal to the rest. $\chi^2 = 49.703$; $\chi^2_{0.01} = 13.277$. Since $\chi^2 > \chi^2_{0.01}$, reject H_0. There is sufficient evidence at the $\alpha = 0.01$ level of significance to support the belief that at least one proportion is different from the others. The evidence suggests that the subjects taking

Naproxen experienced a higher incidence rate of gastroduodenal ulcers than the other treatment groups.
(b) P-value < 0.001

(c)

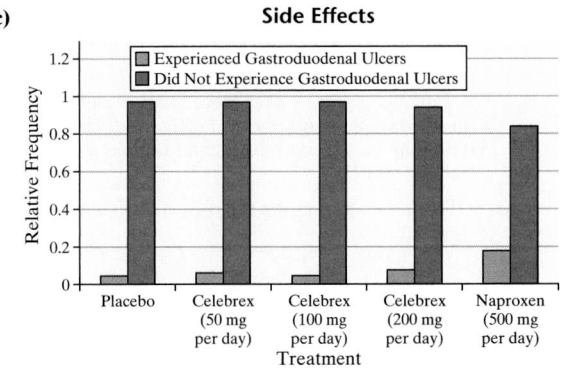

Side Effects

16. (a) H_0: $p_{\text{celebrex}} = p_{\text{placebo}} = p_{\text{naproxen}} = p_{\text{diclofenac}} = p_{\text{ibuprofen}}$ vs H_1: at least one of the proportions is not equal to the rest. $\chi^2 = 4.673$; $\chi^2_{0.01} = 13.277$. Since $\chi^2 < \chi^2_{0.01}$, do not reject H_0. There is not sufficient evidence at the $\alpha = 0.01$ level of significance to support the claim that at least one proportion is different from the others. The evidence suggests that the proportion of individuals in each treatment group who experienced dizziness as a side effect is the same.
(b) P-value $= 0.323$

(c)

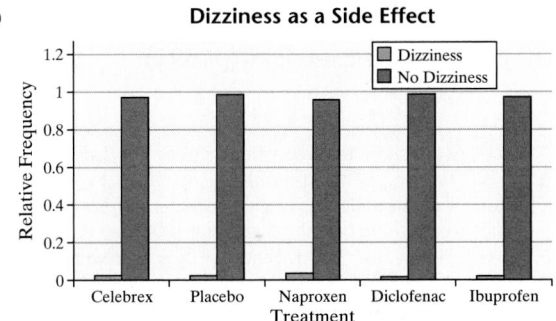

Dizziness as a Side Effect

17. (a)

	Course	Personal	Work
Female	13	5	3
Male	10	6	13

(b) $\chi^2 = 5.595$; $\chi^2_{0.1} = 4.605$. Since $\chi^2 > \chi^2_{0.1}$, reject H_0. The evidence suggests that there is some relation between gender and drop reason. Females are more likely to drop because of the course, while males are more likely to drop because of work.
(c) P-value $= 0.061$
(d)

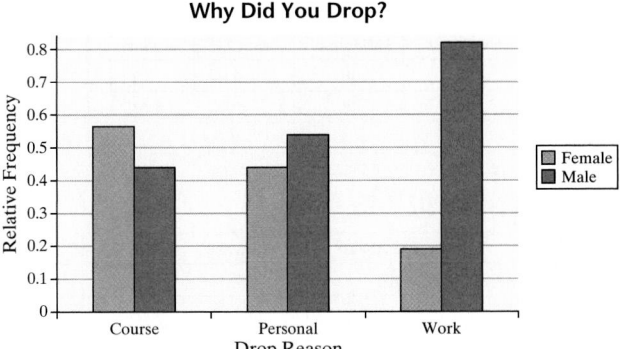

Why Did You Drop?

18. (a)

	Democrat	Republican
Grade School	7	2
High School	10	6
College	9	12

(b) $\chi^2 = 3.483$; $\chi^2_{0.1} = 4.605$. Since $\chi^2 < \chi^2_{0.1}$, do not reject H_o. The evidence suggests that there is no association between level of education and political affiliation. The lack of association may be a result of the small sample size.
(c) P-value $= 0.175$
(d)

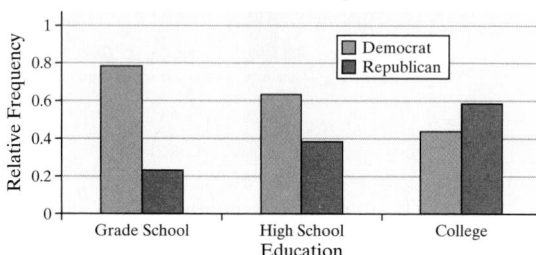

Political Affiliation by Education

19. (a) 267.5; 760.5   **(b)** $\chi^2 = 1.114$
(c) $\chi^2_{0.05} = 3.841$; Since $\chi^2 < \chi^2_{0.05}$, do not reject H_o. There is not significant evidence at the $\alpha = 0.05$ level of significance to support the claim that the proportion is different today from what it was in 1990.
(d) $z = -1.055576$; $z^2 = 1.114$

Chapter Review Exercises (p. 695)

1. $\chi^2 = 0.578$; $\chi^2_{0.05} = 5.991$; Since $\chi^2 < \chi^2_{0.05}$, do not reject H_o. There is not sufficient evidence at the $\alpha = 0.05$ level of significance to conclude that the wheel is out of balance.
2. $\chi^2 = 4.94$; $\chi^2_{0.05} = 23.21$; Since $\chi^2 < \chi^2_{0.05}$, do not reject H_o. There is not sufficient evidence at the $\alpha = 0.05$ level of significance to conclude that the dice are not fair.
3. $\chi^2 = 9.709$; $\chi^2_{0.1} = 9.236$; Since $\chi^2 > \chi^2_{0.1}$, reject H_o. There is sufficient evidence at the $\alpha = 0.05$ level of significance to conclude that the distribution of educational attainment is different today than it was in 1994.
4. $\chi^2 = 29.223$; $\chi^2_{0.05} = 5.991$; Since $\chi^2 > \chi^2_{0.05}$, reject H_o. There is sufficient evidence at the $\alpha = 0.05$ level of significance to conclude that the distribution of school crime is different today than it was in 1992.

5. (a)

	Northeast	Midwest	South	West	Totals
Handgun	58	76	197	82	413
Rifle	6	28	42	33	109
Shotgun	4	5	18	5	32
Totals	68	109	257	120	554

(b)

	Northeast	Midwest	South	West	Totals
Handgun	58	76	197	82	0.745487
Rifle	6	28	42	33	0.196751
Shotgun	4	5	18	5	0.057762
Totals	0.1227437	0.196751	0.463899	0.216606	1

(c) 74.5%   **(d)** 12.3%

(e)

	Northeast	Midwest	South	West
Handgun	0.853	0.697	0.767	0.683
Rifle	0.088	0.257	0.163	0.275
Shotgun	0.059	0.046	0.070	0.042

(f)

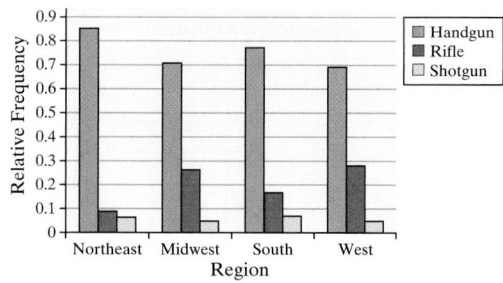

Law Enforcement Officers Killed

(g) Not much association.

6. (a)

	Not a High School Graduate	High School Graduate	Some College	Four or More Years of College	Totals
25–34 years	4683	12,554	11,216	10,822	39,275
35–44 years	5335	15,117	12,272	11,694	44,418
45–54 years	4428	10,933	8957	9809	34,127
55–64 years	4562	8301	4496	4941	22,300
At least 65 years	10,565	11,223	5537	4743	32,068
Totals	29,573	58,128	42,478	42,009	172,188

(b)

	Not a High School Graduate	High School Graduate	Some College	Four or More Years of College	Totals
25–34 years	4683	12,554	11,216	10,822	0.2281
35–44 years	5335	15,117	12,272	11,694	0.2580
45–54 years	4428	10,933	8957	9809	0.1982
55–64 years	4562	8301	4496	4941	0.1295
At least 65 years	10,565	11,223	5537	4743	0.1862
Totals	0.1717	0.3376	0.2467	0.2440	1

(c) 33.76%   **(d)** 18.62%
(e)

	Not a High School Graduate	High School Graduate	Some College	Four or More Years of College
25–34 years	0.1584	0.2160	0.2640	0.2576
35–44 years	0.1804	0.2601	0.2889	0.2784
45–54 years	0.1497	0.1881	0.2109	0.2335
55–64 years	0.1543	0.1428	0.1058	0.1176
At least 65 years	0.3573	0.1931	0.1303	0.1129

(f)

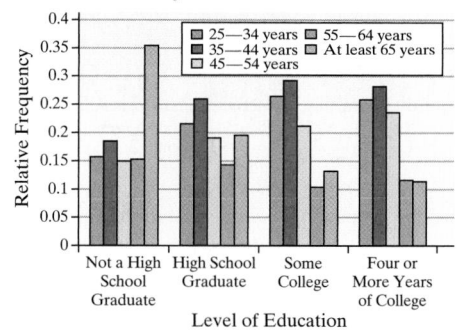

Education Attainment by Level of Education

6. (g) Individuals who are at least 65 years of age are most likely to not be high-school graduates. The older an individual is, the less likely he or she is to have four or more years of college.

7. (a)

	Male	Female	Totals
Passenger in Vehicle	677	632	**1309**
Pedestrian	277	169	**446**
Bicycle	109	32	**141**
Totals	**1063**	**833**	**1896**

(b)

	Male	Female	Totals
Passenger in Vehicle	677	632	**0.6904**
Pedestrian	277	169	**0.2352**
Bicycle	109	32	**0.0744**
Totals	**0.5607**	**0.4393**	

(c) 56.07%   **(d)** 7.44%

(e)

	Male	Female
Passenger in Vehicle	0.6369	0.7587
Pedestrian	0.2606	0.2029
Bicycle	0.1025	0.0384

(f)

Fatalities Involving a Motor Vehicle

[Bar chart: Relative Frequency (y-axis, 0 to 0.8) vs Gender (Male, Female). Legend: Passenger in Vehicle, Pedestrian, Bicycle.]

(g) There is not much association between gender and cause of fatality.

8. (a)

	0–4	5–14	15–24	25–34	35–44	Totals
Male	36	153	4070	2830	1695	**8784**
Female	27	101	489	499	466	**1582**
Totals	**63**	**254**	**4559**	**3329**	**2161**	**10,366**

(b)

	0–4	5–14	15–24	25–34	35–44	Totals
Male	36	153	4070	2830	1695	**0.8474**
Female	27	101	489	499	466	**0.1526**
Totals	**0.0061**	**0.0245**	**0.4398**	**0.3211**	**0.2085**	**1**

(c) 2.45%   **(d)** 15.26%

(e)

	0–4	5–14	15–24	25–34	35–44
Male	0.0041	0.0174	0.4633	0.3222	0.1930
Female	0.0171	0.0638	0.3091	0.3154	0.2946

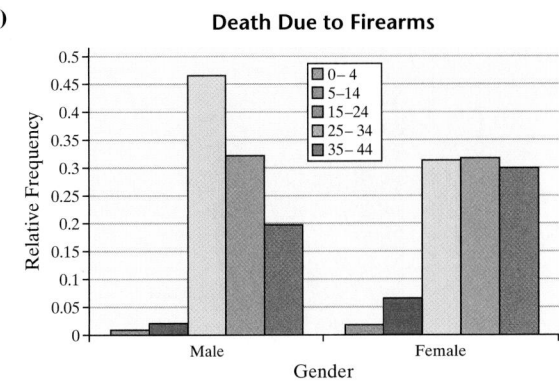

(f)

Death Due to Firearms

[Bar chart: Relative Frequency (y-axis, 0 to 0.5) vs Gender (Male, Female). Legend: 0–4, 5–14, 15–24, 25–34, 35–44.]

(g) There is some association between age and gender. If the victim is male, then he is most likely 15–24 years of age.

9. (a)

	Humans Developed, with God Guiding	Humans Developed, but God Had no Part in Process	God Created Humans in Present Form	Other/No Opinion
February 2001	365.82	116.94	467.27	65.97
June 1993	366.18	117.06	467.73	66.03

(b) All expected values are greater than 5.
(c) $\chi^2 = 2.203$
(d) $\chi^2_{0.05} = 7.815$; Do not reject H_o. The evidence indicates that it is reasonable to conclude that "belief" is independent of "date".
(e) "No opinion" contributed the most, but it still wasn't much.

(f)

Evolution or Creation

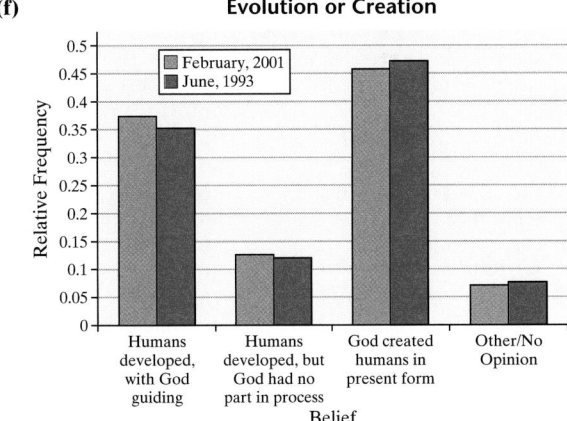

[Bar chart: Relative Frequency (y-axis, 0 to 0.5) vs Belief (Humans developed, with God guiding; Humans developed, but God had no part in process; God created humans in present form; Other/No Opinion). Legend: February, 2001; June, 1993.]

(g) P-value $= 0.531$

10. (a)

	Vaginal	Caesarean
White	241.49	63.51
Black	47.51	12.49

(b) All expected counts are greater than 5.
(c) $\chi^2 = 0.031$
(d) $\chi^2_{0.05} = 3.841$; Do not reject H_o. The evidence indicates that it is reasonable to conclude that race is independent of delivery method.
(e) None of the cells contributed very much to the test statistic.

10. (f)

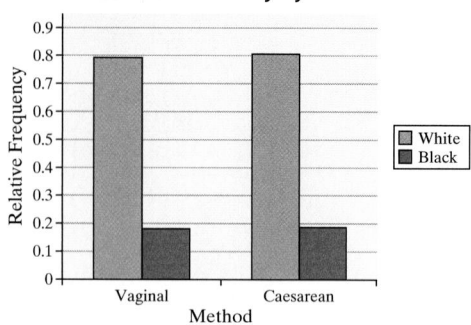

Method of Delivery by Race

White / Black

(g) P-value $= 0.860$

11. $\chi^2 = 242.829$; $\chi^2_{0.01} = 30.578$; Reject H_o. The evidence indicates that it is reasonable to conclude that race is not independent of region.

12. $\chi^2 = 4.875$; $\chi^2_{0.05} = 7.815$; Do not reject H_o. The evidence indicates that it is reasonable to conclude that marital status is independent of gender.

13. $\chi^2 = 3.877$; $\chi^2_{0.05} = 7.815$; Do not reject H_o. The evidence indicates that it is reasonable to conclude that the proportion of Americans who had a common cold is the same for each region of the country.

14. $\chi^2 = 3.093$; $\chi^2_{0.05} = 5.991$; Do not reject H_o. The evidence indicates that it is reasonable to conclude that the proportion of Americans in the different age groups who believe Americans are willing to work hard is the same.

CHAPTER 12   Inference on the Least-Squares Regression Model; ANOVA

12.1 Exercises (p.718)

1. (a) $b_o = -2.3256$; $b_1 = 2.0233$ **(b)** 0.5134
 (c) 0.1238 **(d)** $t = 16.34$; Reject H_o
2. (a) $b_o = -3.7$; $b_1 = 1.1$ **(b)** 0.7303
 (c) 0.1155 **(d)** $t = 9.53$; Reject H_o
3. (a) $b_o = 1.2$; $b_1 = 2.2$ **(b)** 0.8944
 (c) 0.2828 **(d)** $t = 7.78$; Reject H_o
4. (a) $b_o = 3.6$; $b_1 = -1.8$ **(b)** 0.5164
 (c) 0.1633 **(d)** $t = -11.02$; Reject H_o
5. (a) $b_o = 116.6$; $b_1 = -0.72$ **(b)** 3.286
 (c) 0.1039 **(d)** $t = -6.93$; Reject H_o
6. (a) $b_o = -3.3$; $b_1 = 0.78$ **(b)** 1.742
 (c) 0.1102 **(d)** $t = 7.08$; Reject H_o
7. (a) $b_o = 12.4932$; $b_1 = 0.1827$ **(b)** 0.0954
 (c) The residuals are normally distributed based on a normal probability plot.
 (d) 0.02756
 (e) $t = 6.63$; P-value < 0.001; Reject H_o: $\beta_1 = 0$.
 (f) Lower bound: 0.1204; Upper bound: 0.2450.
 (g) 17.3 inches
8. (a) $b_o = 2675.6$; $b_1 = 0.6764$ **(b)** 271.0
 (c) The residuals are normally distributed based on a normal probability plot.
 (d) 0.2055
 (e) $t = 3.29$; P-value $= 0.011$; Reject H_o: $\beta_1 = 0$.
 (f) Lower bound: 0.2025; Upper bound: 1.1503.
 (g) 4705 psi
9. (a) $b_o = 1.114$; $b_1 = 1.3902$ **(b)** 0.4944
 (c) The residuals are normally distributed based on a normal probability plot.
 (d) 0.1501
 (e) $t = 9.26$; P-value < 0.001; Reject H_o: $\beta_1 = 0$.

(f) Lower bound: 0.902; Upper bound: 1.878
(g) 37.16 inches
10. (a) $b_o = 0.2088$; $b_1 = 0.0575$ **(b)** 0.1121
 (c) The residuals are normally distributed based on a normal probability plot.
 (d) 0.0046
 (e) $t = 12.50$; P-value < 0.001. Reject H_o: $\beta_1 = 0$.
 (f) Lower bound: 0.0492; Upper bound: 0.0658
 (g) 0.899 mg
11. (a) $b_o = 2.034$; $b_1 = 1.6363$ **(b)** 10.66
 (c) The residuals are normally distributed based on a normal probability plot.
 (d) 0.6265
 (e) $t = 2.61$; P-value $= 0.024$. Reject H_o: $\beta_1 = 0$.
 (f) Lower bound: -0.31; Upper bound: 3.58
 (g) 8.91 percent
12. (a) $b_o = 607.7$; $b_1 = 25.012$ **(b)** 64.85
 (c) The residuals are normally distributed based on a normal probability plot.
 (d) 2.189
 (e) $t = 11.43$; P-value < 0.001. Reject H_o: $\beta_1 = 0$.
 (f) Lower bound: 16.186; Upper bound: 33.838
 (g) 2040.9 Kcal

13. (a)

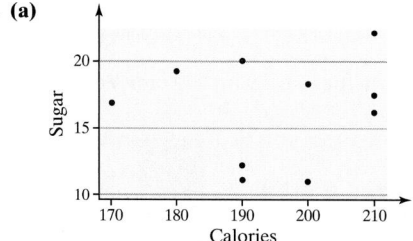

(b) $\hat{y} = 0.93 + 0.0821x$ **(c)** 4.151
(d) The residuals are normally distributed based on a normal probability plot.
(e) 0.0961
(f) $t = 0.85$; P-value $= 0.413$; Do not reject H_o: $\beta_1 = 0$.
(g) Lower bound: -0.13; Upper bound: 0.30
(h) No; $\overline{y} = 17.1$ grams

14. (a)

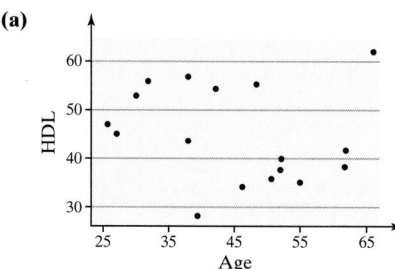

(b) HDL $= 50.784 - 0.1298$ (Age)

(c)

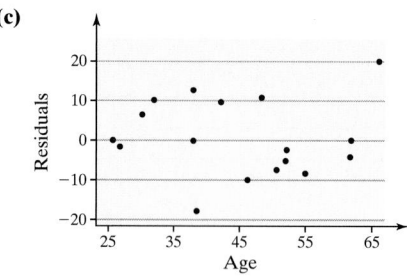

The linear model seems appropriate, based on the residual plot. The point corresponding to the 66-year-old may be an outlier.

(d) A boxplot does not indicate that the 66-year-old is an out-lier; however, Minitab does say that it is an outlier.
(e) 9.953
(f) The residuals are normally distributed based on a normal probability plot.
(g) 0.2021   (h) Do not reject H_o: $B_1 = 0$.
(i) Lower bound: -0.56; Upper bound: 0.30
(j) No, the mean HDL cholesterol of the individuals in the study is 44.94.

15. (a) $\hat{y} = -3,771,542,830 + 2,018,994x$
(b) $t = 21.81$; P-value < 0.001; Reject H_o: $B_1 = 0$.

(c)
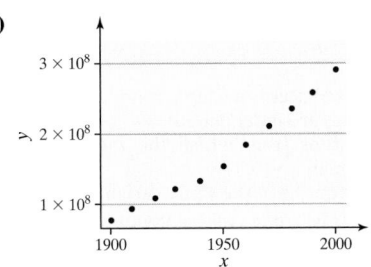

(d)
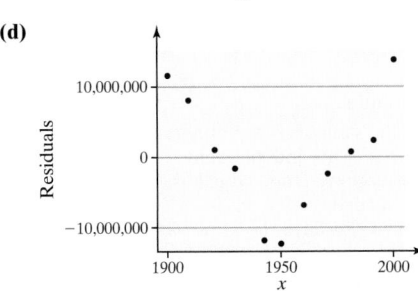

(e) Linear model is not appropriate.
(f) The moral is that the inferential procedures may lead us to believe that a linear relation between the two variables ex-ists; however, the simple diagnostic tools (such as residual plots) indicate that a linear model is inappropriate.

16. (a) $\hat{y} = -12.497 + 0.0657x$
(b) $t = 17.61$; P-value < 0.001; Reject H_o: $B_1 = 0$.

(c)
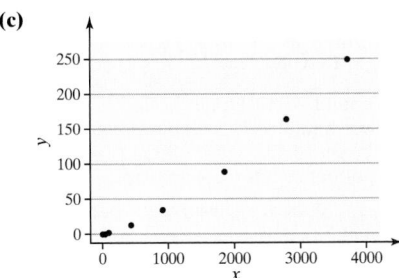

(d)
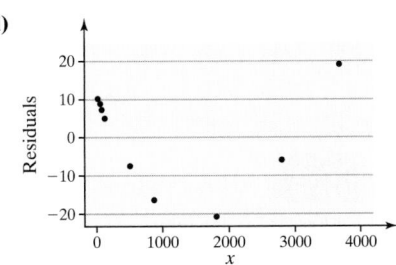

(e) Linear model is not appropriate.
(f) The moral is that the inferential procedures may lead us to believe that a linear relation between the two variables ex-ists; however, the simple diagnostic tools (such as residual plots) indicate that a linear model is inappropriate.

17. (a)

(b) Weight $= -36.8 + 3.284$ (Height); $t = 2.41$; P-value $= 0.033$; Reject H_o: $\beta_1 = 0$.
(c) Weight $= -85.3 + 3.948$ (Height); $t = 1.58$; P-value $= 0.144$; Do not reject H_o: $\beta_1 = 0$.

18. (a) 26.36   (b) 26.36   (c) 2.167
(d) Normal with mean 26.36 and standard deviation 2.167.

12.2 Exercises (p. 727)

1. (a) 11.84
(b) Lower bound: 10.87; Upper bound: 12.80
(c) 11.84
(d) Lower bound: 9.94; Upper bound: 13.74
(e) The confidence interval is an interval estimate for the mean value of y at $x = 7$, while the prediction interval is an inter-val estimate for a single value of y at $x = 7$.

2. (a) 5.1
(b) Lower bound: 4.0; Upper bound: 6.2
(c) 5.1
(d) Lower bound: 2.5; Upper bound: 7.7
(e) The confidence interval is an interval estimate for the mean value of y at $x = 8$, while the prediction interval is an inter-val estimate for a single value of y at $x = 8$.

3. (a) 4.28
(b) Lower bound: 2.49; Upper bound: 6.07
(c) 4.28
(d) Lower bound: 0.92; Upper bound: 7.64
(e) The confidence interval is an interval estimate for the mean value of y at $x = 1.4$, while the prediction interval is an in-terval estimate for a single value of y at $x = 1.4$.

4. (a) 0.36
(b) Lower bound: -0.52; Upper bound: 1.24
(c) 0.36
(d) Lower bound: -1.14; Upper bound: 1.86
(e) The confidence interval is an interval estimate for the mean value of y at $x = 1.8$, while the prediction interval is an in-terval estimate for a single value of y at $x = 1.8$.

5. (a) 17.20 inches
(b) Lower bound: 17.12 inches; Upper bound: 17.28 inches
(c) 17.20 inches
(d) Lower bound: 16.97 inches; Upper bound: 17.43 inches
(e) The confidence interval is an interval estimate for the mean head circumference of all children who are 25.75 inches tall. The prediction interval is an interval estimate for the head circumference of a single child who is 25.75 inches tall.

6. (a) 4400.4 psi
(b) Lower bound: 4147.8 psi; Upper bound: 4653.1 psi
(c) 4400.4 psi
(d) Lower bound: 3726.3 psi; Upper bound: 5074.6 psi
(e) The confidence interval is an interval estimate for the mean 28-day strength of all concrete cylinders that have a 7-day strength of 2550 psi. The prediction interval is an in-terval estimate for the 28-day strength of a single cylinder whose 7-day strength is 2550 psi.

7. (a) 37.02 inches
(b) Lower bound: 36.65 inches; Upper bound: 37.40 inches
(c) 37.02 inches

7. (d) Lower bound: 35.84 inches; Upper bound: 38.20 inches
 (e) The confidence interval is an interval estimate for the mean right tibia length of all space rats that have a right humerus length of 25.83 mm. The prediction interval is an interval estimate for the right tibia length of a single space rat whose right humerus length is 25.83 mm.

8. (a) 0.899 mg
 (b) Lower bound: 0.827 mg; Upper bound: 0.971 mg
 (c) 0.899 mg
 (d) Lower bound: 0.642 mg; Upper bound: 1.156 mg
 (e) The confidence interval is an interval estimate for the mean nicotine content of all cigarettes that have a tar content of 12 mg. The prediction interval is an interval estimate for the nicotine content of a single cigarette whose tar content is 12 mg.

9. (a) 8.91 percent
 (b) Lower bound: 2.34 percent; Upper bound: 15.47 percent
 (c) 8.91 percent
 (d) Lower bound: −11.34 percent; Upper bound: 29.15 percent
 (e) The confidence interval is an interval estimate for the mean rate of return for all months in which the rate of return of the S&P 500 is 4.2 percent. The prediction interval is an interval estimate for the rate of return of Cisco if the rate of return of the S&P 500 is 4.2 percent.

10. (a) 2040.9 Kcal
 (b) Lower bound: 1932.3 Kcal; Upper bound: 2149.5 Kcal
 (c) 2040.9 Kcal
 (d) Lower bound: 1757.8 Kcal; Upper bound: 2324.0 Kcal
 (e) The confidence interval is an interval estimate for the mean Kcal for all people whose fat-free mass is 57.3 kg. The prediction interval is an interval estimate for the Kcal of an individual whose fat-free mass is 57.3 kg.

11. (a) Because we did not reject the null hypothesis that there is no linear relation between calories and sugar content.
 (b) Construct a 95% confidence interval about sugar content using the methods presented in Section 8.2. Lower bound: 14.5 g; Upper bound: 19.7 g.

12. (a) Because we did not reject the null hypothesis that there is no linear relation between age and HDL cholesterol.
 (b) Construct a 95% confidence interval about HDL cholesterol using the methods presented in Section 8.2. Lower bound: 39.9; Upper bound: 50.0.

12.3 Exercises (p. 738)

1. (a) $H_0: \mu_{sp} = \mu_{sd} = \mu_{nt} = \mu_{sc} = \mu_{gl}$ vs. H_1: At least one of the means is not equal.
 (b) (1) Each of the samples is a simple random sample.
   (2) The k samples are independent.
   (3) The populations from which the samples are drawn must be normal.
   (4) The populations have the same variance.
 (c) P-value = 0.009, which is less than $\alpha = 0.05$, so we reject the null hypothesis.
 (d) Yes, it appears that the Spring disk method of tilling results in the highest yield.
 (f) Spring disk
 (g) Recommend the Spring disk method.

2. (a) $H_0: \mu_L = \mu_{FP} = \mu_{NT} = \mu_{CP} = \mu_{RR}$ vs H_1: At least one of the means is not equal.
 (b) (1) Each of the samples is a simple random sample.
   (2) The k samples are independent.
   (3) The populations from which the samples are drawn must be normal.
   (4) The populations have the same variance.
 (c) P-value = 0.013, which is less than $\alpha = 0.05$, so we reject the null hypothesis.
 (d) Yes
 (f) It seems that Liberty is significantly different from Fall plowed.
 (g) Probably go with Liberty or No-Till

3. (a) $H_0: \mu_M = \mu_T = \mu_W = \mu_R = \mu_F$ vs H_1: At least one of the means is not equal.
 (b) (1) Each of the samples is a simple random sample.
   (2) The k samples are independent.
   (3) The populations from which the samples are drawn must be normal.
   (4) The populations have the same variance.
 (c) P-value = 0.000, which is less than $\alpha = 0.01$, so we reject the null hypothesis.
 (d) Yes
 (e) Monday appears to have significantly fewer births than the other four days.

4. (a) $H_0: \mu_{JM} = \mu_{AJ} = \mu_{JS} = \mu_{OD}$ vs H_1: At least one of the means is not equal.
 (b) (1) Each of the samples is a simple random sample.
   (2) The k samples are independent.
   (3) The populations from which the samples are drawn must be normal.
   (4) The populations have the same variance.
 (c) P-value = 0.084, which is greater than $\alpha = 0.01$, so we reject the null hypothesis.
 (d) Yes
 (f) No period has a significantly different number of births from the others.

5. (a) $H_0: \mu_{simple} = \mu_{go/nogo} = \mu_{choice}$ vs H_1: At least one of the means is not equal.
 (b) (1) Each of the samples is a simple random sample.
   (2) The k samples are independent.
   (3) The populations from which the samples are drawn must be normal.
   (4) The populations have the same variance.
 (c) $F = 3.23$; $F_{0.05,2,15} = 3.68$; P-value = 0.068. Do not reject the null hypothesis.
 (d)

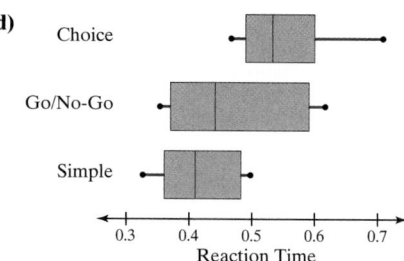

 (e) Simple: Lower bound: 0.340; Upper bound: 0.498
   Go/No-Go: Lower bound: 0.391; Upper bound: 0.549
   Choice: Lower bound: 0.472; Upper bound: 0.630
   Yes, since the confidence intervals overlap.

6. (a) $H_0: \mu_{Canada} = \mu_{Denmark} = \mu_{USA}$ vs H_1: At least one of the means is not equal.
 (b) (1) Each of the samples is a simple random sample.
   (2) The k samples are independent.
   (3) The populations from which the samples are drawn must be normal.
   (4) The populations have the same variance.
 (c) $F = 13.68$; $F_{0.05,2,16} \approx 3.49$; P-value < 0.001. Reject the null hypothesis.
 (d)

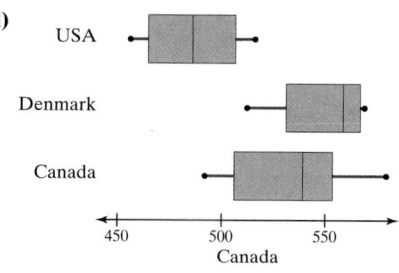

(e) Canada: Lower bound: 515.96; Upper bound: 552.54
Denmark: Lower bound: 532.96; Upper bound: 569.54
USA: Lower bound: 470.08; Upper bound: 506.66
Yes, it appears that the United States scores lower than each
of the other two countries.

7. (a) H_o: $\mu_{Large} = \mu_{Pass} = \mu_{Midsize}$ vs H_1: At least one of the
means is not equal.
(b) (1) Each of the samples is a simple random sample.
(2) The k samples are independent.
(3) The populations from which the samples are drawn
must be normal.
(4) The populations have the same variance.
(c) $F = 2.50$; $F_{0.05,2,18} \approx 3.49$; P-value $= 0.111$. Do not reject
the null hypothesis.

(d)

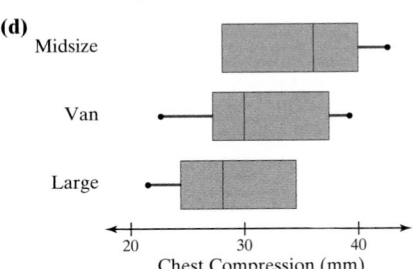

8. (a) H_o: $\mu_{Large} = \mu_{Pass} = \mu_{Midsize}$ vs H_1: At least one of the
means is not equal.
(b) (1) Each of the samples is a simple random sample.
(2) The k samples are independent.
(3) The populations from which the samples are drawn
must be normal.
(4) The populations have the same variance.
(c) $F = 0.96$; $F_{0.05,2,18} \approx 3.49$; P-value $= 0.403$. Do not reject
the null hypothesis.

(d)

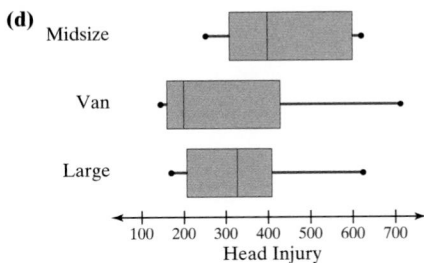

9. (a) H_o: $\mu_{301} = \mu_{400} = \mu_{353}$ vs H_1: At least one of the means is
not equal.
(b) The standard deviation for Mixture 67-0-400 is more than two
times larger than the standard deviation for Mixture 67-0-301.

10. (a) The researchers wanted to be sure that any differences in
the groups were due to the treatment, rather than to other
factors that may have not been identified prior to the study.
In addition, the researchers wanted to verify that the patients are similar in uncontrolled factors.
(b) This is the randomization required for a well-designed experiment. When researchers randomize the individuals to
the treatment groups, uncontrolled factors tend to even
themselves out.
(c) Neither the experimental units nor the researchers knew
which group each experimental unit belonged to. This design helps to remove any potential bias that may slip into
the study.
(d) There is a probability of less than 0.001 of obtaining the sample statistics obtained if the null hypothesis is true. Because
this probability is small, we are inclined to believe that the
null hypothesis is not true, so we reject the null and conclude
that at least one of the means differs from the others.

Chapter Review Exercises (p. 747)

1. (a) $b_o = 32.12$; $b_1 = -3.5339$; 18.7 mpg
(b) 1.848
(c) The residuals are normal.
(d) 0.5528
(e) $t = -6.39$; P-value < 0.001; Reject H_o: $\beta_1 = 0$.
(f) Lower bound: -4.7279; Upper bound: -2.3399
(g) Lower bound: 17.6 mpg; Upper bound: 19.8 mpg
(h) 18.7 mpg
(i) Lower bound: 15.3 mpg; Upper bound: 22.1 mpg
(j) The predicted value is the mean value of the response for
any given value of the predictor. Since the mean is the expected value, we conclude that the predicted value is the
best guess for an individual car. The confidence interval is
an interval estimate for the mean mpg of all cars that have a
3.8-liter engine. The prediction interval is an interval estimate for the mpg of a single car that has a 3.8-liter engine.

2. (a) $b_o = -0.309$; $b_1 = 0.2119$; 16.69 chirps per second
(b) 0.9715
(c) The residuals are normal.
(d) 0.0387
(e) $t = 5.47$; P-value < 0.001; Reject H_o: $\beta_1 = 0$.
(f) Lower bound: 0.1283; Upper bound: 0.2955
(g) Lower bound: 16.24 chirps per second; Upper bound: 17.13
chirps per second
(h) 16.69 chirps per second
(i) Lower bound: 14.91 chirps per second; Upper bound: 18.46
chirps per second
(j) The predicted value is the mean value of the response for
any given value of the predictor. Since the mean is the expected value, we conclude that the predicted value is the
best guess for an individual cricket. The confidence interval
is an interval estimate for the mean chirps per second of all
crickets when the temperature is 80.2° F. The prediction interval is an interval estimate for the chirps per second of a
single cricket when the temperature is 80.2° F.

3. (a) $b_o = -132.6$; $b_1 = 1.1702$; $920.60   **(b)** 85.95
(c) The residuals are normal.   **(d)** 0.2636
(e) $t = 4.44$; P-value $= 0.002$; Reject H_o: $\beta_1 = 0$.
(f) Lower bound: 0.5739; Upper bound: 1.7665
(g) Lower bound: $864.00; Upper bound: $977.10
(h) $920.60
(i) Lower bound: $753.20; Upper bound: $1088.00
(j) The predicted value is the mean value of the response for
any given value of the predictor. Since the mean is the expected value, we conclude that the predicted value is the best
guess for an individual apartment. The confidence interval is
an interval estimate for the mean rent of all 900-square-foot
apartments. The prediction interval is an interval estimate
for the rent of a single 900-square-foot apartment.

4. (a) $b_o = 29.705$; $b_1 = 2.6351$; 48.2 inches   **(b)** 2.450
(c) The residuals are normal.   **(d)** 0.2067
(e) $t = 12.75$; P-value < 0.001; Reject H_o: $\beta_1 = 0$.
(f) Lower bound: 2.2008; Upper bound: 3.0694
(g) Lower bound: 47.1 inches; Upper bound: 49.2 inches
(h) 48.2
(i) Lower bound: 43.8 inches; Upper bound: 52.5 inches
(j) The predicted value is the mean value of the response for
any given value of the predictor. Since the mean is the expected value, we conclude that the predicted value is the
best guess for an individual child. The confidence interval is
an interval estimate for the mean height of all seven-year-
old boys. The prediction interval is an interval estimate for
the height of a single seven-year-old boy.

5. (a) $b_o = 67.388$; $b_1 = -0.2632$ **(b)** 11.19
(c) The residuals are normal.   **(d)** 0.1680
(e) $t = -1.57$; P-value $= 0.138$; Do not reject H_o: $\beta_1 = 0$.
(f) 57 psi

6. (a) Price $= 20976.2 - 2054.6$ Age
(b) $t = -10.11$; P-value < 0.001; Reject H_o: $\beta_1 = 0$.

6. (c)

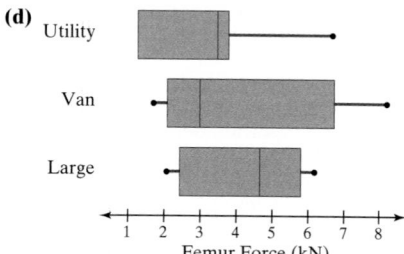

(d) The residual plot shows a discernible pattern, so a linear model is not appropriate. The moral is that we should always perform graphical diagnostic tests along with inferential procedures before drawing any conclusions regarding the model.

7. (a) H_o: $\mu_{organic} = \mu_{mineral} = \mu_{surface}$ vs H_1: at least one of the means is not equal

(b) (1) each of the samples is a simple random sample
(2) the 3 samples are independent
(3) the populations from which the samples are drawn must be normal
(4) the populations have the same variance

(c) Since P-value < 0.001, we reject the null hypothesis. There is sufficient evidence to conclude that at least one of the means is different from the others.

(d) Yes

(e) From the confidence intervals, it appears that mean concentration of dissolved organic carbon (in mg/l) in organic soil is greater than mineral.

8. (a) H_o: $\mu_{large} = \mu_{van} = \mu_{utility}$ vs H_1: at least one of the means is not equal

(b) (1) Each of the samples is a simple random sample.
(2) The k samples are independent.
(3) The populations from which the samples are drawn must be normal.
(4) The populations have the same variance.

(c) $F = 0.81$; P-value $= 0.461$. Do not reject the null hypothesis.

(d)

Utility

Van

Large

Femur Force (kN)

9. (a) H_o: $\mu_1 = \mu_2 = \mu_3$ vs H_1: At least one of the means is not equal.

(b) (1) Each of the samples is a simple random sample.
(2) The k samples are independent.
(3) The populations from which the samples are drawn must be normal.
(4) The populations have the same variance.

(c) $F = 8567.46$; P-value < 0.001; Reject the null hypothesis.

(d)

Thermo3

Thermo2

Thermo1

Temperature

10. The least-squares regression model is given by $y_i = \beta_0 + \beta_1 x_i + \varepsilon_i$, where y_i is the value of the response variable for the ith individual, β_0 and β_1 are the parameters to be estimated based upon sample data, x_i is the value of the predictor variable for the ith individual, and ε_i is a random error term with mean 0 and variance $\sigma_{\varepsilon_i}^2 = \sigma^2$. The error terms are independent.
$i = 1 \ldots n$ where n is the sample size (number of ordered pairs in the data set).

To conduct inference on a least-squares regression line,

(1) the sample is obtained using random sampling.
(2) the residuals are normally distributed with constant error variance.

CHAPTER 13   Nonparametric Statistics

13.2 Exercises (p. 765)

1. (a) $n = 14$; $n_M = 6$; $n_F = 8$; $r = 6$
(b) Lower: 3; Upper: 12
(c) Do not reject H_o. The sequence of data is random.

2. (a) $n = 15$; $n_M = 5$; $n_F = 10$; $r = 4$
(b) Lower: 3; Upper: 12
(c) Do not reject H_o. The sequence of data is random.

3. (a) $n = 19$; $n_Y = 9$; $n_N = 10$; $r = 5$
(b) Lower: 5; Upper: 16
(c) Reject H_o. The sequence of data is not random.

4. (a) $n = 21$; $n_Y = 11$; $n_N = 10$; $r = 10$
(b) Lower: 6; Upper: 17
(c) Do not reject H_o. The sequence of data is random.

5. $n = 18$; $n_F = 11$; $n_C = 7$; $r = 8$; Lower critical value $= 5$; Upper critical value $= 14$. Do not reject H_o. The sequence of data is random.

6. $n = 15$; $n_R = 9$; $n_P = 6$; $r = 9$; Lower critical value $= 4$; Upper critical value $= 13$. Do not reject H_o. The sequence of data is random.

7. $n = 14$; $n_O = 8$; $n_L = 6$; $r = 8$; Lower critical value $= 3$; Upper critical value $= 12$. Do not reject H_o. The sequence of data is random.

8. $n = 15$; $n_O = 9$; $n_L = 6$; $r = 11$; Lower critical value $= 4$; Upper critical value $= 13$. Do not reject H_o. The sequence of data is random.

9. $n = 20$; $n_A = 14$; $n_R = 6$; $r = 4$; Lower critical value $= 5$; Upper critical value $= 14$. Reject H_o. The sequence of data is not random.

10. $n = 18$; $n_A = 15$; $n_R = 3$; $r = 3$; Lower critical value $= 3$; Upper critical value $= 8$. Reject H_o. The sequence of data is not random.

11. $n = 45$; $n_P = 26$; $n_N = 19$; $r = 26$; $Z = 0.94$. Do not reject H_o. The sequence of data is random. We have reason to believe that the stock price fluctuates randomly from day to day.

12. $n = 41$; $n_P = 31$; $n_N = 10$; $r = 14$; $Z = -0.92$. Do not reject H_o. The sequence of data is random. We have reason to believe that the stock prices fluctuate randomly from quarter to quarter.

13. (a) A A A A A B B B B A A
(b) $n = 11$; $n_A = 7$; $n_B = 4$; $r = 3$; Lower critical value $= 2$; Upper critical value $= 10$. Do not reject H_o. The sequence of data is random.

14. (a) B B A A A B B B B A A
(b) $n = 11$; $n_A = 5$; $n_B = 6$; $r = 4$; Lower critical value $= 3$; Upper critical value $= 10$. Do not reject H_o. The sequence of data is random.

13.3 Exercises (p. 774)

1. H_o: $M = 8$ vs H_1: $M < 8$; $k = 8$; Critical value: 6. Do not reject H_o.

2. H_o $M = 50$ vs H_1 $M > 50$; $k = 7$; Critical value: 5. Do not reject H_o.

3. H_o: $M = 100$ vs H_1: $M \neq 100$; $z = -0.86$; $z_{0.025} = -1.96$. Do not reject H_o.

4. H_o: $M = 68$ vs $>H_1$: $M \neq 68$; $z = -2.00$; $z_{0.025} = -1.96$. Reject H_o.

5. H_o: $M = 12$ vs H_1: $M > 12$; $k = 3$; Critical value: 3. Reject H_o.

6. H_o: $M = 15$ vs H_1: $M < 15$; $k = 7$; Critical value: 3. Do not reject H_o.

7. H_o: $M = 4.9$ vs H_1: $M < 4.9$; $k = 6$; Critical value: 5. Do not reject H_o. There is not sufficient evidence to support the claim that the median pH level is less than 4.9.

8. H_o: $M = 26.7$ vs H_1: $M < 26.7$; $k = 8$; Critical value: 5. Do not reject H_o. There is not sufficient evidence to support the claim that the median age at which women marry in Cook County is less than 26.7 years.

9. H_o: $M = 62{,}000$ vs H_1: $M > 62{,}000$; $k = 2$; Critical value: 2. Reject H_o. There is sufficient evidence to support the claim that the median salary of lawyers who recently graduated from law school is more than \$62,000.

10. H_o: $M = 225{,}000$ vs H_1: $M > 225{,}000$; $k = 7$; Critical value: 4. Do not reject H_o. There is not sufficient evidence to support the claim that the median price of a home in Lemont is more than \$225,000.

11. H_o: $M = 1000$ vs H_1: $M > 1000$; $k = 5$; Critical value: 3. Do not reject H_o. There is not sufficient evidence to support the claim that the median salary is more than \$1 million.

12. H_o: $M = 36{,}300$ vs H_1: $M < 36{,}300$; $k = 5$; Critical value: 5. Reject H_o. There is sufficient evidence to support the claim that the median number of miles on three-year-old Cavaliers is less than 36,300.

13. 0.0835   **14.** 0.2517

15. 0.0327   **16.** 0.4018

13.4 Exercises (p. 782)

1. Critical value: 17; Reject H_o.

2. Critical value: 60; Do not reject H_o.

3. Critical value: 30; Do not reject H_o.

4. Critical value: 100; Do not reject H_o.

5. Critical value: 40; Do not reject H_o.

6. Critical value: 21; Do not reject H_o.

7. $Z = -1.45$; $-z_{0.05} = -1.645$; Do not reject H_o.

8. $Z = -1.72$; $-z_{0.05} = -1.645$; Reject H_o.

9. H_o: $M_D = 0$ vs H_1: $M_D > 0$ (compute before–after); $T = 12$; Critical value: 8. Do not reject H_o. There is not sufficient evidence to support the claim that the exercise program is effective in reducing waistline.

10. H_o: $M_D = 0$ vs H_1: $M_D < 0$ (compute before–after); $T = 19.5$; Critical value: 13. Do not reject H_o. There is not sufficient evidence to support the claim that the exercise program is effective in increasing flexibility

11. H_o: $M_D = 0$ vs H_1: $M_D \neq 0$ (compute blue–red); $T = 5$; Critical value: 2. Do not reject H_o. There is not sufficient evidence to support the claim that there is a difference in reaction time to blue versus to red.

12. H_o: $M_D = 0$ vs H_1: $M_D < 0$ (compute HL3–HR0); $T = 12.5$; Critical value: 17. Reject H_o. There is sufficient evidence to support the claim that the median hemoglobin at lift-off minus three days is less than the median hemoglobin upon return.

13. H_o: $M_D = 0$ vs H_1: $M_D > 0$ (compute five-year depth–initial depth); $T = 5$; Critical value: 5. Do no reject H_o. There is not

sufficient evidence to support the claim that the clarity of the lake is improving.

14. H_o: $M_D = 0$ vs H_1: $M_D < 0$ (compute after–before); $T = 13.5$; Critical value: 5. Do not reject H_o. There is not sufficient evidence to support the claim that aspirin affects the median time it takes for a clot to form.

15. H_o: $M_D = 0$ vs H_1: $M_D > 0$ (compute Hertz–Thrifty); $T = 29$; Critical Value: 10. Do not reject H_o. There is not sufficient evidence to support the claim that Thrifty is less expensive than Hertz.

16. H_o: $M_D = 0$ vs H_1: $M_D > 0$ (compute 92 octane–87 octane); $T = 23$; Critical Value: 10. Do not reject H_o. There is not sufficient evidence to support the claim that the gas mileage obtained from 92 octane is greater than the gas mileage obtained from 87 octane.

17. (a) H_o: $M_D = 0$ vs H_1: $M_D \neq 0$
(b) Yes, because the P-value is 0.000.

18. (a) H_o: $M_D = 0$ vs H_1: $M_D > 0$
(b) Yes, because the P-value is 0.000.

13.5 Exercises (p. 794)

1. $T = 92$; Critical values $= 50, 130$; Do not reject H_o

2. $T = 45$; Critical values $= 18, 62$; Do not reject H_o

3. $T = 39$; Critical value $= 96$; Reject H_o

4. $T = 89$; Critical value $= 71$; Do not reject H_o

5. $T = 130$; Critical value $= 152$; Do not reject H_o

6. $T = 142$; Critical value $= 124$; Reject H_o

7. $T = 337$; $Z = 1.32$; $-z_{0.025} = -1.96$; $z_{0.025} = 1.96$; Do not reject H_o

8. $T = 715$; $Z = 2.76$; $z_{0.05} = 1.645$; Reject H_o

9. H_o: $M_{\text{Denver}} = M_{\text{Chicago}}$ vs H_1: $M_{\text{Denver}} \neq M_{\text{Chicago}}$ $T = 147$; Critical values $= 70, 168$; Do not reject H_o. There is not sufficient evidence to conclude that the price of housing in Denver is different from the price of housing in Chicago.

10. H_o: $M_{\text{Off}} = M_{\text{Def}}$ vs H_1: $M_{\text{Off}} > M_{\text{Def}}$; $T = 62.5$; Critical value $= 59$; Reject H_o. There is sufficient evidence to conclude that the median weight of an offensive tackle is greater than that of a defensive tackle.

11. H_o: $M_{\text{Carpet}} = M_{\text{No Carpet}}$ vs H_1: $M_{\text{Carpet}} > M_{\text{No Carpet}}$; $T = 38.5$; Critical value $= 48$; Do not reject H_o. There is not sufficient evidence to conclude that the median amount of bacteria in carpeted rooms is more than that in uncarpeted rooms.

12. H_o: $M_{\text{exp}} = M_{\text{control}}$ vs H_1: $M_{\text{exp}} > M_{\text{control}}$; $T = 25.5$; Critical value $= 26$; Do not reject H_o. There is not sufficient evidence to conclude that the median tibia length in the experimental group is greater than that in the control group.

13. H_o: $M_{\text{Lincoln}} = M_{\text{Clarendon}}$ vs H_1: $M_{\text{Lincoln}} \neq M_{\text{Clarendon}}$; $Z = 3.43$; Critical values: $-z_{0.025} = -1.96$; $z_{0.025} = 1.96$; Reject H_o. There is sufficient evidence to conclude that the median calcium level in Lincoln County is different from that in Clarendon County.

14. H_o: $M_{\text{Lincoln}} = M_{\text{Clarendon}}$ vs H_1: $M_{\text{Lincoln}} \neq M_{\text{Clarendon}}$; $Z = 0.79$; Critical values: $-z_{0.025} = -1.96$; $z_{0.025} = 1.96$; Do not reject H_o. There is not sufficient evidence to conclude that the median potassium level in Lincoln County is different from that in Clarendon County.

15. H_o: $M_A = M_B$ vs H_1: $M_A \neq M_B$; $T = 83$; Critical values: 65, 160; Do not reject H_o. There is not sufficient evidence to conclude that there is a difference in the grades earned in the two classes.

16. H_o: $M_A = M_B$ vs H_1: $M_A \neq M_B$; $T = 124.5$; Critical values: 65, 160; Do not reject H_o. There is not sufficient evidence to conclude that there is a difference in the opinions of the two critics.

13.6 Exercises (p. 802)

1. (a)

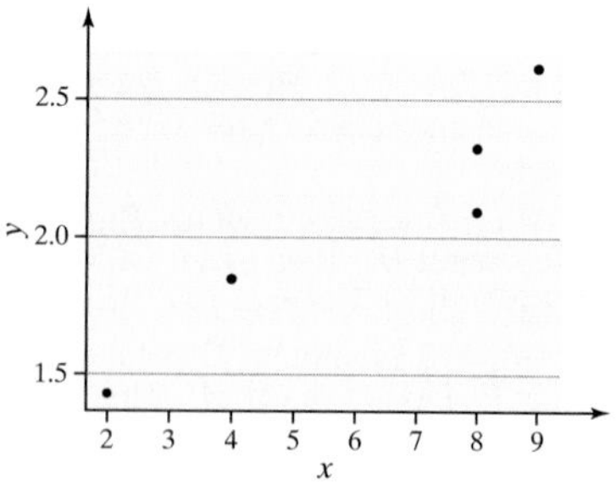

(graph showing scattered points with x-axis from 2 to 9 and y-axis from 1.5 to 2.5)

(b) 0.975   **(c)** Reject H_o.

2. (a)

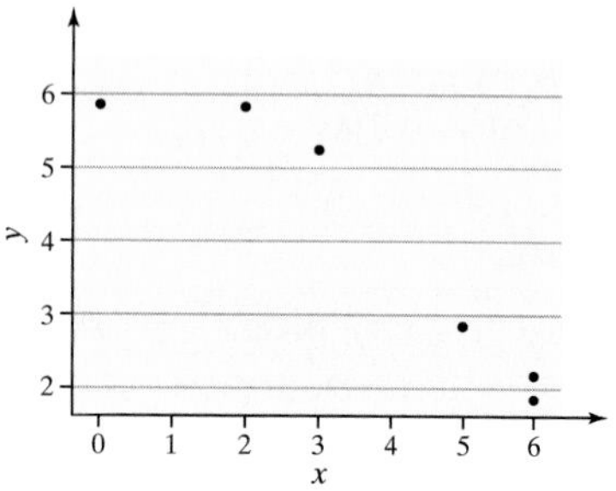

(graph showing scattered points with x-axis from 0 to 6 and y-axis from 2 to 6)

(b) −0.986   **(c)** Reject H_o.

3. (a)

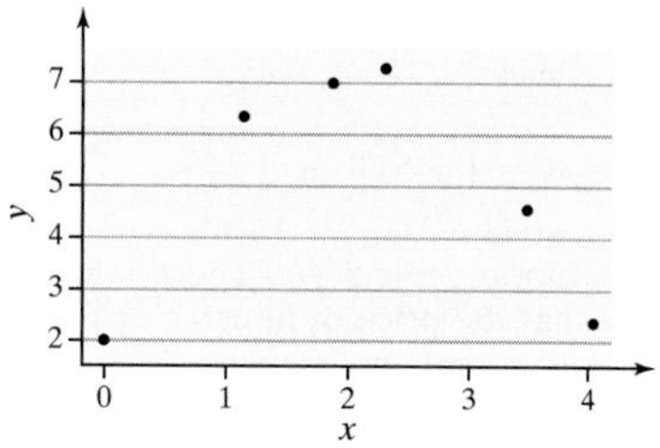

(graph showing scattered points with x-axis from 0 to 4 and y-axis from 2 to 7)

(b) 1   **(c)** Reject H_o

4. (a)

(graph showing scattered points with x-axis from 0 to 5 and y-axis from 0 to 6)

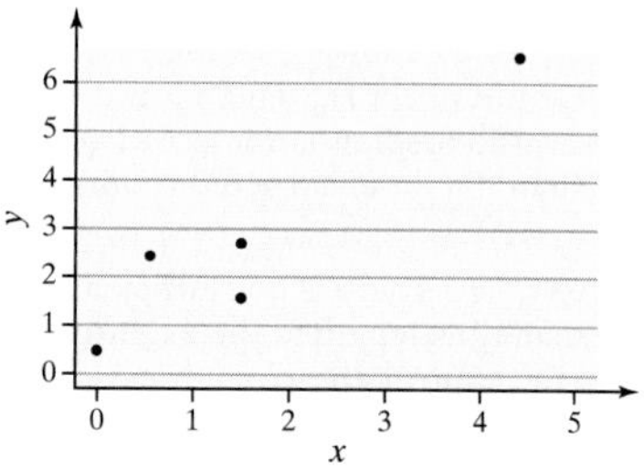

(b) 1   **(c)** Do not reject H_o

5. (a) $r_s = 0.778$; Reject H_o. There is sufficient evidence to conclude that there is a positive association between percentage of population with at least a bachelor's degree and per capita personal income.

(b)

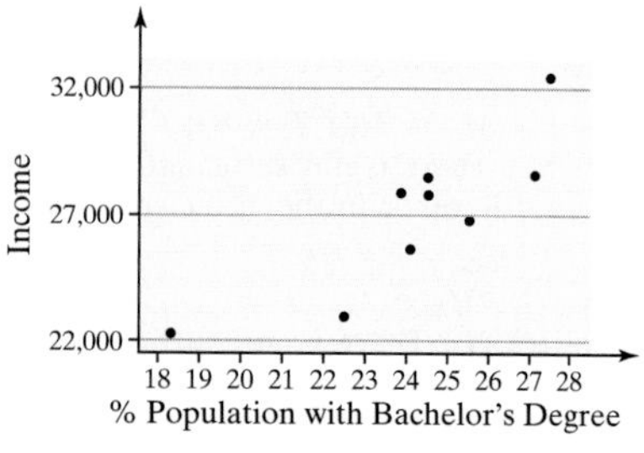

(graph with x-axis "% Population with Bachelor's Degree" from 18 to 28 and y-axis "Income" from 22,000 to 32,000)

6. (a) $r_s = 0.524$; Do not reject H_o. There is not sufficient evidence to conclude that there is a positive association between population and crime rate.

(b)

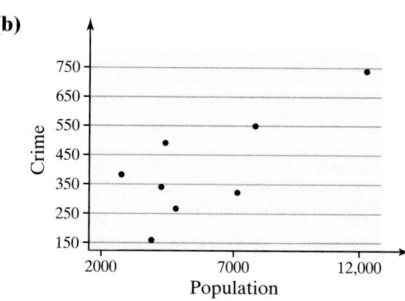

(c) With Illinois included, we reject the null hypothesis, but with Illinois excluded, we do not reject the null hypothesis.

7. (a) $r_s = 0.200$; Do not reject H_o. There is not sufficient evidence to conclude that there is a positive association between income and birthrate.

(b)

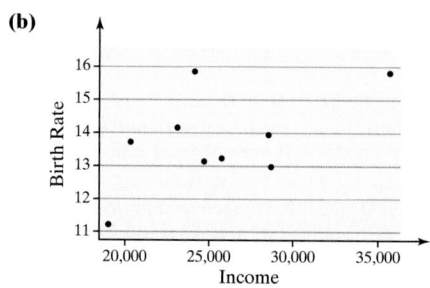

8. (a) $r_s = 0.179$; Do not reject H_o. There is not sufficient evidence to conclude that there is a positive association between final standings and total yards.

(b)

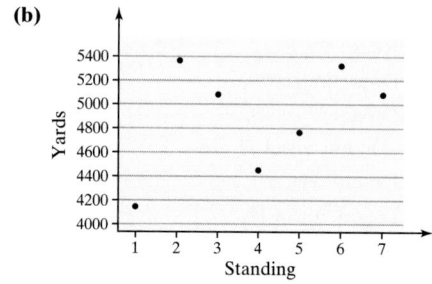

9. (a) $r_s = 0.986$; Reject H_o. There is sufficient evidence to conclude that there is a positive association between housing cost and commute time.

(b)

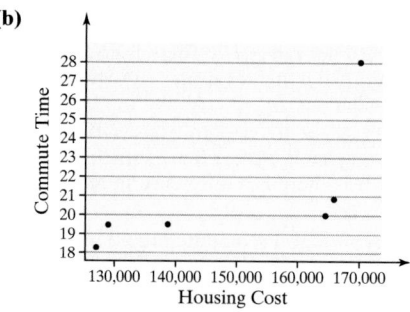

10. (a) $r_s = 0.026$; Do not reject H_o. There is not sufficient evidence to conclude that there is any association between compensation and stock return.

(b)

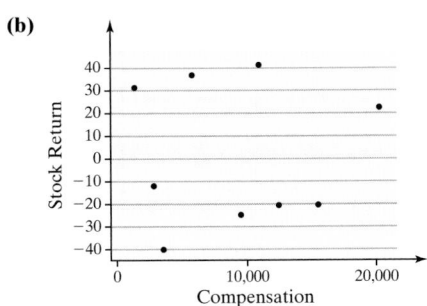

11. $r_s = 1$

12. $r_s = -1$

13.7 Exercises (p. 810)

1. (a) $H = 0.88$
(b) 5.6923
(c) Do not reject H_o

2. (a) $H = 1.22$
(b) 5.5985
(c) Do not reject H_o

3. (a) H_o: the distributions of the populations are the same.
H_1: the distributions of the populations are not the same.
(b) $H = 18.77$
(c) $\chi^2_{0.05} = 9.488$
(d) Reject H_o. The distributions of births by day of the week are not the same.

(e)

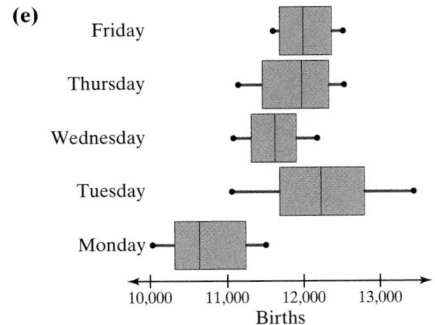

4. (a) H_o: the distributions of the populations are the same.
H_1: the distributions of the populations are not the same.
(b) $H = 5.16$
(c) $\chi^2_{0.05} = 7.815$
(d) Do not reject H_o. There is evidence that supports the belief that the distributions of births by season are the same.

(e)

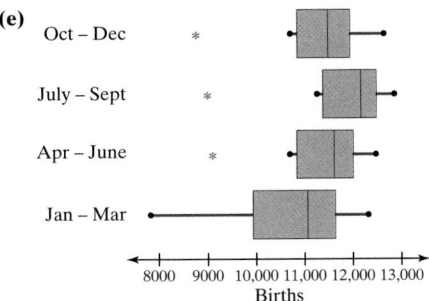

5. $H = 10.97$; $\chi^2_{0.05} = 9.488$. Reject H_o. There is sufficient evidence to conclude that the distribution of number of plants is not the same for each plot type.

6. $H = 11.16$; $\chi^2_{0.05} = 9.488$. Reject H_o. There is sufficient evidence to conclude that the distribution of number of plants is not the same for each plot type.

7. $H = 5.24$; $\chi^2_{0.01} = 9.210$. Do not reject H_o. There is not sufficient evidence to conclude that the distribution of reaction time is the same for each stimulus.

8. $H = 13.08$; $\chi^2_{0.01} = 9.210$. Reject H_o. There is sufficient evidence to conclude that the distribution of math scores is not the same for each country.

9. $H = 4.71$; $\chi^2_{0.01} = 9.210$. Do not reject H_o. There is not sufficient evidence to conclude that the distribution of chest compression for each car type is the different.

10. $H = 2.59$; $\chi^2_{0.01} = 9.210$. Do not reject H_o. There is not sufficient evidence to conclude that the distribution of head injury for each car type is the different.

Chapter Review Exercises (p. 816)

1. $n = 23$; $n_E = 12$; $n_W = 11$; $r = 8$; Lower critical value: 7; Upper critical value: 18. Do not reject H_o. The sequence of data is random.

2. $n = 22$; $n_E = 12$; $n_W = 10$; $r = 10$; Lower critical value: 7; Upper critical value: 17. Do not reject H_o. The sequence of data is random.

3. H_o: $M = 15$ vs H_1: $M > 15$; $k = 7$; Critical value: 5. Do not reject H_o. There is not sufficient evidence to support the claim that the median number of hours students talk on the phone each week is more than 15.

4. H_o: $M = 15$ vs H_1: $M < 15$; $k = 4$; Critical value: 5. Reject H_o. There is sufficient evidence to support the claim that the median number of hours students spend studying is less than 15.

5. H_o: $M_D = 0$ vs H_1: $M_D > 0$ (compute 2000–1996); $T = 32.5$; Critical value: 100. Reject H_o. There is sufficient evidence to support the claim that the number of errors has increased.

6. H_o: $M_D = 0$ vs H_1: $M_D > 0$ (compute Before–After); $T = 14.5$; Critical value: 8. Do not reject H_o. There is not sufficient evidence to support the claim that the exercise program is effective.

7. H_o: $M_F = M_M$ vs H_o: $M_F \neq M_M$; $T = 80$; Critical values: 54, 116; Do not reject H_o. There is significant evidence to conclude that the reaction time of females is different from the reaction time of males.

8. H_o: $M_T = M_I$ vs H_1: $M_T > M_I$; $T = 127$; Critical value $= 116$; Reject H_o. There is significant evidence to conclude that the pH of rain in Houston is higher than that of rain in Illinois.

9. $r_s = -0.872$; Reject H_o; There is sufficient evidence to conclude that there is a negative association between engine displacement and miles per gallon.

10. $r_s = 0.850$; Reject H_o; There is sufficient evidence to conclude that there is a positive association between temperature and chirps per second.

11. (a) H_o: the distributions of the populations are the same.
H_1: the distributions of the populations are not the same.
(b) $H = 17.20$ **(c)** $\chi^2_{0.05} = 5.991$
(d) Reject H_o. There is evidence that supports the belief that the distributions of concentration of dissolved organic carbon are not the same.

(e)

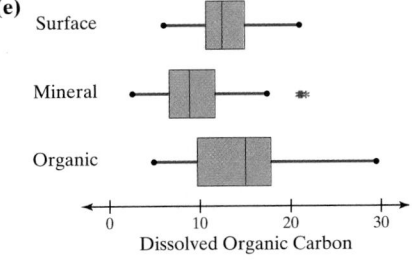

12. (a) H_o: the distributions of the populations are the same.
H_1: the distributions of the populations are not the same.
(b) $H = 1.28$ **(c)** $\chi^2_{0.05} = 5.991$
(d) Do not reject H_o. There is evidence which supports the belief that the distributions of femur force are the same for all three types of car.

(e)

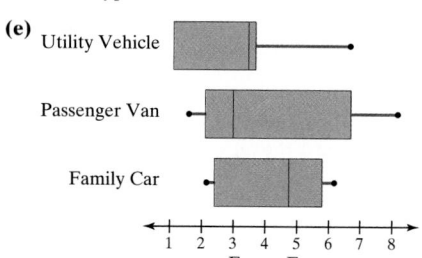

Femur Force

APPENDIX B   Lines

Appendix B Exercises (p. A-26)

1. (a) $\frac{1}{2}$
(b) For every 2-unit increase in x, y will increase by 1 unit.
2. (a) $-\frac{1}{2}$
(b) For every 2-unit increase in x, y will decrease by 1 unit.
3. (a) $-\frac{1}{3}$
(b) For every 3-unit increase in x, y will decrease by 1 unit.
4. (a) $\frac{1}{3}$
(b) For every 3-unit increase in x, y will increase by 1 unit.
5. Slope $= -\frac{3}{2}$ **6.** Slope $= -2$

7. Slope $= -\frac{1}{2}$ **8.** Slope $= \frac{2}{3}$

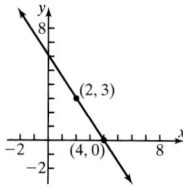   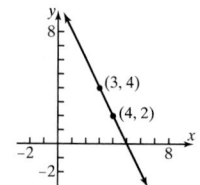

9. Slope $= 0$ **10.** Slope $= 0$

11. Slope undefined   **12.** Slope undefined

13.

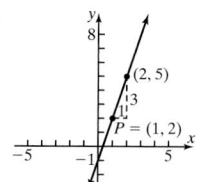

14.

15.

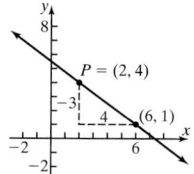

16.

17.

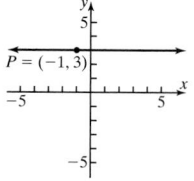

18.

19.

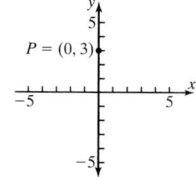

20.

21. $(2, 6)$; $(3, 10)$; $(4, 14)$ **22.** $(-1, 5)$; $(0, 7)$, $(1, 9)$
23. $(4, -7)$; $(6, -10)$; $(8, -13)$ **24.** $(0, 6)$; $(3, 10)$; $(6, 14)$
25. $(-1, -5)$; $(0, -7)$; $(1, -9)$ **26.** $(5, 0)$; $(6, -1)$; $(7, -2)$
27. $x - 2y = 0$ or $y = \frac{1}{2}x$ **28.** $x + 2y = 0$ or $y = -\frac{1}{2}x$
29. $x + y = 2$ or $y = -x + 2$
30. $x - 3y = -4$ or $y = \frac{1}{3}x + \frac{4}{3}$
31. Slope $= 2$; y-intercept $= 3$ **32.** Slope $= -3$; y-intercept $= 4$

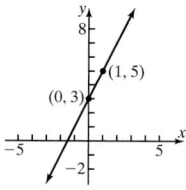

33. $y = 2x - 2$;
Slope $= 2$; y-intercept $= -2$

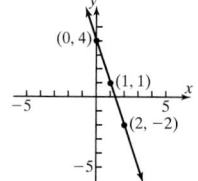

34. $y = -\frac{1}{3}x + 2$;
Slope $= -\frac{1}{3}$;
y-intercept $= 2$

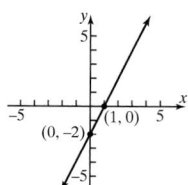

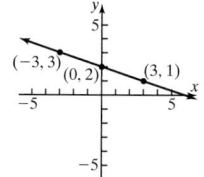

35. Slope $= \frac{1}{2}$;
y-intercept $= 2$

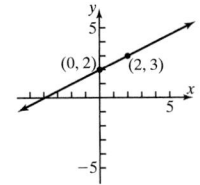

36. Slope $= 2$;
y-intercept $= \frac{1}{2}$

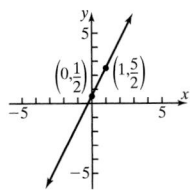

37. $y = -\frac{1}{2}x + 2$; Slope $= -\frac{1}{2}$;
y-intercept $= 2$

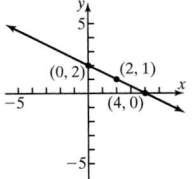

38. $y = \frac{1}{3}x + 2$; Slope $= \frac{1}{3}$;
y-intercept $= 2$

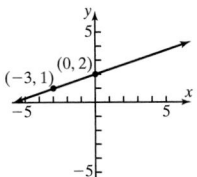

39. $y = \frac{2}{3}x - 2$; Slope $= \frac{2}{3}$;
y-intercept $= -2$

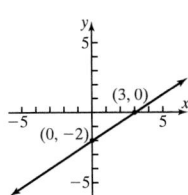

40. $y = -\frac{3}{2}x + 3$; Slope $= -\frac{3}{2}$;
y-intercept $= 3$

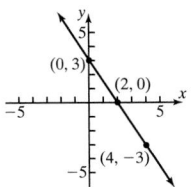

41. $y = -x + 1$; Slope $= -1$;
y-intercept $= 1$

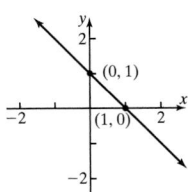

42. $y = x - 2$; Slope $= 1$;
y-intercept $= -2$

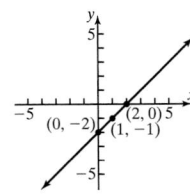

43. Slope undefined;
no y-intercept

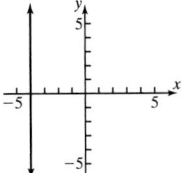

44. Slope $= 0$; y-intercept $= -1$

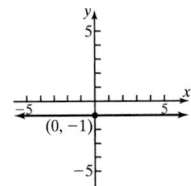

45. Slope $= 0$; y-intercept $= 5$

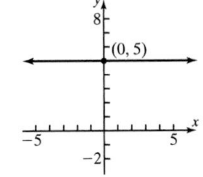

46. Slope undefined;
no y-intercept

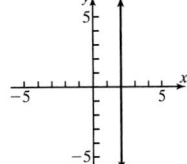

47. $y = x$; Slope $= 1$;
y-intercept $= 0$

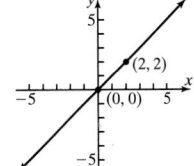

48. $y = -x$; Slope $= -1$;
y-intercept $= 0$

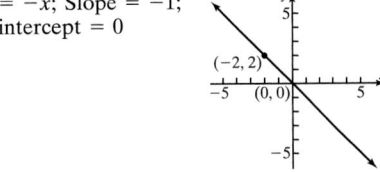

49. $y = \frac{3}{2}x$; Slope $= \frac{3}{2}$;
y-intercept $= 0$

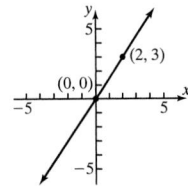

50. $y = -\frac{3}{2}x$; Slope $= -\frac{3}{2}$;
y-intercept $= 0$

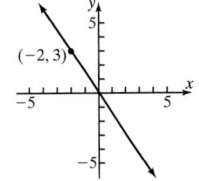

INDEX